TABLE VI Cumulative *t*-distribution $F(t)$

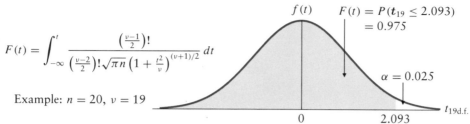

$$F(t) = \int_{-\infty}^{t} \frac{\left(\frac{\nu-1}{2}\right)!}{\left(\frac{\nu-2}{2}\right)!\sqrt{\pi n}\left(1 + \frac{t^2}{\nu}\right)^{(\nu+1)/2}} \, dt$$

Example: $n = 20$, $\nu = 19$

$f(t)$

$F(t) = P(t_{19} \leq 2.093)$ $= 0.975$

$\alpha = 0.025$

$t_{19\text{d.f.}}$

0   2.093

$F(t)$	.75	.90	.95	.975	.99	.995	.9995
ν (α)	(.25)	(.10)	(.05)	(.025)	(.01)	(.005)	(.0005)
1	1.000	3.078	6.314	12.706	31.821	63.657	636.619
2	.816	1.886	2.920	4.303	6.965	9.925	31.598
3	.765	1.638	2.353	3.182	4.541	5.841	12.941
4	.741	1.533	2.132	2.776	3.747	4.604	8.610
5	.727	1.476	2.015	2.571	3.365	4.032	6.859
6	.718	1.440	1.943	2.447	3.143	3.707	5.959
7	.711	1.415	1.895	2.365	2.998	3.499	5.405
8	.706	1.397	1.860	2.306	2.896	3.355	5.041
9	.703	1.383	1.833	2.262	2.821	3.250	4.781
10	.700	1.372	1.812	2.228	2.764	3.169	4.587
11	.697	1.363	1.796	2.201	2.718	3.106	4.437
12	.695	1.356	1.782	2.179	2.681	3.055	4.318
13	.694	1.350	1.771	2.160	2.650	3.012	4.221
14	.692	1.345	1.761	2.145	2.624	2.977	4.140
15	.691	1.341	1.753	2.131	2.602	2.947	4.073
16	.690	1.337	1.746	2.120	2.583	2.921	4.015
17	.689	1.333	1.740	2.110	2.567	2.898	3.965
18	.688	1.330	1.734	2.101	2.552	2.878	3.922
19	.688	1.328	1.729	2.093	2.539	2.861	3.883
20	.687	1.325	1.725	2.086	2.528	2.845	3.850
21	.686	1.323	1.721	2.080	2.518	2.831	3.819
22	.686	1.321	1.717	2.074	2.508	2.819	3.792
23	.685	1.319	1.714	2.069	2.500	2.807	3.767
24	.685	1.318	1.711	2.064	2.492	2.797	3.745
25	.684	1.316	1.708	2.060	2.485	2.787	3.725
26	.684	1.315	1.706	2.056	2.479	2.779	3.707
27	.684	1.314	1.703	2.052	2.473	2.771	3.690
28	.683	1.313	1.701	2.048	2.467	2.763	3.674
29	.683	1.311	1.699	2.045	2.462	2.756	3.659
30	.683	1.310	1.697	2.042	2.457	2.750	3.646
40	.681	1.303	1.684	2.021	2.423	2.704	3.551
60	.679	1.296	1.671	2.000	2.390	2.660	3.460
120	.677	1.289	1.658	1.980	2.358	2.617	3.373
$\infty(z_\alpha)$	.674	1.282	1.645	1.960	2.326	2.576	3.291

* This table is abridged from the "Statistical Tables" of R. A. Fisher and Frank Yates published by Oliver & Boyd, Ltd., Edinburgh and London, 1938. It is here published with the kind permission of the authors and their publishers.

Statistical Analysis
FOR BUSINESS AND ECONOMICS

FIRST CANADIAN EDITION

DONALD L. HARNETT
INDIANA UNIVERSITY

JAMES L. MURPHY
UNIVERSITY OF NORTH CAROLINA AT CHAPEL HILL

WITH CONTRIBUTIONS BY
KEN MACKENZIE
CONCORDIA UNIVERSITY

ADDISON-WESLEY PUBLISHERS

DON MILLS, ONTARIO • READING, MASSACHUSETTS
MENLO PARK, CALIFORNIA • NEW YORK
WOKINGHAM, ENGLAND • AMSTERDAM • BONN
SYDNEY • SINGAPORE • TOKYO • MADRID • SAN JUAN

Publisher: Ron Doleman
Coordinating Editor: Kateri Lanthier
Copy Editor: Bonnie Di Malta
Designer: Gord Pronk
Desktop Formatting: Golda D. Wiseman, Don McCahill, Robert A. Adams
Technical Art: Robert A. Adams

SPSS is a registered trademark of SPSS, Inc.
SAS is the registered trademark of SAS Institute Inc.,
Cary, N.C., 27522, U.S.A.

Canadian Cataloguing in Publication Data

Harnett, Donald L.
      Statistical Analysis for business and economics

1st Canadian ed.
Includes bibliographical references and index.
ISBN 0--201--60178--8

1. Economics---Statistical methods. 2. Commercial
statistics. 3. Statistics.   I. Murphy, James L.,
1939-- . II. Title.

HB137.H37 1993   519.5'024658   C93--093262--5

ISBN 0--201--60178--8

    C D E --- VH --- 97 96 95

To Pam and Linda

Contents

Preface

Purpose and Approach

Readability, understanding, and organization have been our major concerns throughout the writing, classroom testing, and revisions of this textbook. Designed for use in teaching the concepts and methods of statistics to practicing managers, as well as to beginning students, it provides a mixture of intuitive explanation, relevant examples, and computer usage. Our approach avoids the verbiage of many texts in attempting to explain basic concepts. We present the single best way in which we can explain the material, and then enhance each point with numerous examples.

Although some texts include many diverse and specialized examples that distract the reader from the statistical concept and methodology being presented, we have selected examples that are realistic without being overly complex. Our expectation is that the reader needs to learn how to use statistics in her or his major field. Furthermore, we keep the numerical busywork to a minimum in examples (and in problems, too). Examples and problems were chosen to illustrate realistic and practical uses of the topics and thereby maintain a high level of motivation for the reader.

Throughout the presentation we have tried to avoid compromising the basic concepts, and to provide sufficient depth for a worthwhile understanding of them. Still, our presentation is truly designed for the beginning student, and is less mathematically demanding than that of many texts with the same prescribed background of algebra. The material in Appendix B provides a review of these fundamentals. It is not assumed the reader has studied calculus, although there are some occasions when the explanation indicates how calculus could be used. In some instances, complementary explanations or derivations that involve calculus or other nonelementary mathematics, are presented in a footnote. Many tables, figures and printouts complement the text.

We are pleased that our depth of coverage in many topics---such as explanation of random variables, statistical inference, decision theory, and econometric analysis in regression---exceed that found in many texts designed for beginning students. The text may be covered consecutively, chapter-by-chapter, if it is used in a full-year course. For shorter courses, selection of chapters, or sections within chapters quite easily allows for the design of a course with less breadth.

First Canadian Edition

This edition represents a complete revision of our text. All chapters have been reviewed and revised. While we have attempted to maintain the strengths of previous versions of the text, many new and exciting changes have been made.

- A major change is the extensive use of Canadian data and examples throughout the text. Appendix A now contains eight data sets, including a variety of time series and cross-sectional information from Canada. The examples and study questions throughout the text frequently illustrate concepts from a Canadian perspective.

- Numerous statistical problems used in past CGA examinations have been added. These problems are designated by the symbol ◆.
- An appendix reviewing the algebra of statistics has been added, as have new chapters on quality control and linear programming.
- Where needed, the writing has been revised to update and simplify methods, thereby making concepts easier to understand.
- Additional emphasis has been placed on using computers for statistical analysis. In this regard we have provided a large number of additional computer outputs to illustrate many of the popular statistical packages in use today, such as Lotus 123, Minitab, Execustat, SAS,* and SPSS.† The analysis of larger data sets is emphasized, including graphical methods for data presentation.
- For those courses that follow the CGA curriculum, we have added an optional chapter that introduces linear programming. The emphasis in the chapter is on formulation and computer solutions, but for better comprehension of the computer printout, sections on graphical solutions and sensitivity analysis have been included. A novel feature is the review of linear functions and inequalities, together with the relevant properties of their graphs. The numerous examples include two case studies to be completed using a computer.

The new open layout is designed to make reading the text easier, emphasizing the important concepts and formulas. Study questions provide an "example" of the type of analysis expected of the reader; these questions are presented periodically with full solutions, based on prior exposition and examples. There are many numbered examples within each chapter. The most important definitions and formulas are set off in boxes, or in boldface type. At the end of each chapter a list of key terms and definitions is provided.

Since problem solving is essential to learning statistical analysis, we have included problems at various levels. Each chapter has both *Problems* and a set of *Exercises*. The former depend quite heavily on the text presentation. As many of these as possible should be worked by the reader. The Exercises include more challenging questions, usually because they require some extra step, mathematical expertise, or combination of concepts that were not directly illustrated in the text. Many chapters have at least one *Case Problem* as well. These longer problems, requiring more interpretation and formulation than end-of-chapter problems, represent situations that the student may face in later courses or in the job world.

Most chapters also have a problem section headed *Using the Computer*. The instructor will need to select the computer problems that are most convenient given the type of computer services available and the software knowledge of the students. In general, we encourage students to use statistical packages whenever possible to solve the problems in this book.

Acknowledgments

Special gratitude is due instructors who have used the previous three editions of this text and have made suggestions for improvements and additions for this edition, especially those instructors at the University of Illinois. The authors also express thanks to the several reviewers who carefully read the manuscript version and aided us in working toward consistency and accuracy in our presentation: Michael Sklar, University of Georgia; H. F. Williamson, University of Illinois, Urbana;

---

* SAS is the registered trademark of SAS Institute, Inc., Gary, N.C. 27522, U.S.A.

† SPSS is a registered trademark of SPSS, Inc.

Jackie Redder, Virginia Polytechnic Institute; Joseph Nordstrom, University of Houston, Central Campus; Stanley Steinkemp, University of Illinois, Urbana; Edgar Hickman, University of South Carolina; Nicholas Farnum, California State University, Fullerton; Ronald Koot, Pennsylvania State University; Paul Berger, Boston University; Terry Seaks, University of North Carolina, Greensboro; Mary Sue Younger, University of Tennessee, Knoxville; Don Robinson, Illinois State University; Jeffery Green, Ball State University; Timothy Wittig, Oklahoma State University; Nancy Carter, California State University, Chico; Jack Suyderhoud, University of Hawaii; David Closs, Michigan State University; and J. White.

Some of the exercises in this text represent actual or modified questions from old CPA exams. These exercises are the only multiple-choice questions in the book. Material from the CPA Examinations and Unofficial Answers, copyright 1971--1978 by the American Institute of Certified Public Accountants, Inc., is used with permission. Figures, tables, or data drawn from other copyrighted sources are reprinted with the permission of those sources.

Special thanks must be given to Lynda Carson and David Harrison of CGA Canada, who provided direction in the revising of this book for Canadian students. Material from the CGA examination is used with permission of the Certified General Accountants Association of Canada.

We are grateful to the Literary Executor of the late Sir Ronald A. Fisher, R.F.S., to Dr. Frank Yates, F.R.S., and to Longman Group Ltd., London for permission to reprint tables from their book *Statistical Tables for Biological, Agricultural and Medical Research* (6th Edition, 1974).

We have been most fortunate to have, at Addison-Wesley Publishers, a caring editor, Ron Doleman, and a very thorough and patient coordinating editor, Kateri Lanthier. Ken MacKenzie and Bob Adams also made valuable contributions.

Finally, we express our thanks for the understanding and help-in-kind received from our wives and children during this endeavour.

Bloomington, Indiana   D.L.H.
Chapel Hill, North Carolina   J.L.M.

For the Reader

As you begin to study statistics, you should note the special features of this book designed to help you use it and learn from it. Appendix A contains eight data sets that are frequently used in the examples or problems denoted by bold type such as **Data Set**. Appendix B provides a review of some basic concepts and notation from algebra. Appendix C contains many useful statistical tables. If you find you wish to consult additional sources, we have included a selected bibliography following the Answers to Odd-Numbered Problems. Two of the most commonly used statistical tables are also reproduced inside the front cover for handy reference. Inside the back cover is a partial glossary of symbols.

Throughout the text, important features and definitions have been set off in boxes or in boldface type. Terms and formulas that you probably need to know are included at the end of each chapter. Study Questions appear periodically in the text, with complete solutions. Answers to selected odd-numbered problems follow Appendix C at the back of the book. End-of-section or end-of-chapter problems are similar to the text examples and are designed to test your knowledge of the basic concepts. We urge you to work as many of the problems as possible as a study aid.

The end-of-chapter exercises involve independent work or may include some extra challenge. There are a few multiple choice exercises modified from past CPA examinations (from the U.S.), and a number of special problems, designated by the symbol ♦, representing previous CGA examination questions (from Canada). We hope these will encourage and prepare you to make use of statistics outside of the statistics course itself---especially in your career or business.

Statistics is a difficult course for many students---therefore, we also wish you "good luck."

CHAPTER 1

Introduction and Descriptive Statistics

Introduction

Statistical techniques are put to use in one form or another in almost all branches of modern science and in many other fields of human activity as well. As Soloman Fabricant said, "The whole world now seems to hold that statistics can be useful in understanding, assessing, and controlling the operations of society." Progress in our society can be measured by a variety of numerical indices. Statistics are used to describe, manipulate, and interpret these numbers.

One of our objectives in this chapter is to distinguish between statistics used for descriptive purposes and statistics used for making predictions and testing theories about what is called the *population*. We will also begin to learn the notation and the process of relating a sample to a population. Finally, we will study various methods for describing and summarizing the information contained in either a population or a sample.

Statistics and Statistical Analysis

Although the origins of statistics can be traced to studies of games of chance in the 1700s, it is only in the past 70 years that applications of statistical methods have been developed for use in almost all fields of science — social, behavioural, and physical. Most early applications of statistics consisted primarily of data presented in the form of tables and charts. This field, known as **descriptive statistics,** soon grew to include a large variety of methods for arranging, summarizing, or somehow conveying the characteristics of a set of numbers. Today, these techniques account for what is certainly the most visible application of statistics — the mass of quantitative information that is collected and published in our society every day. Crime rates, births and deaths, divorce rates, price indices, the Dow-Jones average, and batting averages are but a few of the many familiar *statistics*.

In addition to conveying the characteristics of quantifiable information, descriptive measures provide an important basis for analysis in almost all academic disciplines — especially in the social and behavioural sciences, where human behaviour generally cannot be described with the precision possible in the physical sciences. Statistical measures of satisfaction, intelligence, job aptitude, and leadership, for example, serve to expand our knowledge of human motivation and performance. In the same fashion, indices of prices, productivity, gross national product, employment, free reserves, and net exports serve as the tools of management and government in considering policies directed toward promoting long-term growth and economic stability.

The Use of Statistics in Decision-making

Despite the enlarging scope and increasing importance of descriptive methods over the past two hundred years, these methods now represent only a minor, relatively unimportant portion of the body of statistical literature. The phenomenal growth in statistics since the turn of the century has taken place mainly in the field called **statistical inference** or **inductive statistics**. This field is concerned with the formulation and testing of generalizations, as well as the prediction and estimation of relationships between two or more variables. The terms *inferential* and *inductive analysis* are used here because this aspect of statistics involves drawing conclusions (or inferences) about the unknown characteristics of certain phenomena on the basis of only limited or imperfect information. Generally, this involves drawing conclusions about a set of data (called a population) based on values observed in a sample drawn from that population. From this sample information, statistical inference can often derive the quantitative information necessary for deciding among alternative courses of action when it is impossible to predict exactly what the consequence of each of these will be.

The process of drawing conclusions from limited information is one familiar to all of us, for almost every decision we face must be made without knowing the consequences with certainty. For example, in deciding to watch television tomorrow rather than study, you may, at least subconsciously, be inferring that your grades will not suffer as a result of this decision. Also, you probably have given considerable time and thought to your choice of a job after college, but here again your decision must be made on the basis of the limited amount of information that can be provided by aptitude tests, guidance counselors, and the advice of your family and friends. If you make a poor choice, you may suffer the loss of considerable time and money. Similar problems are faced in business. Should a new product be introduced? What about plant expansion? How much should be spent on advertising? The economic adviser to government policy-makers must choose among various alternative recommendations for preventing unemployment, improving the trade balance, dampening inflationary spirals, and increasing production and income. In general the best choices can only be *inferred* from less-than-perfect information about future events. As a result, such decisions often are made under conditions that expose the decision-maker to considerable risk. The process of making decisions under these circumstances is usually referred to as **decision-making under uncertainty**.

Statistics as a decision-making tool plays an important role in the areas of research and development and in prediction and control in a wide variety of fields. Both government and industry, for instance, participate in the development, testing, and certification of new drugs and medicines, a process that often requires a large number of statistical tests and decisions concerning the safety and effectiveness of these drugs for public use. Similarly, the psychologist, the lawyer, and any person who makes decisions involving uncertain factors such as human behaviour often will base decisions on data of a statistical nature. Since complex decision situations almost always call for some type of statistical analysis, formal or informal, explicit or implicit, it is difficult to overemphasize the importance of inferential statistics to the decision-maker. In fact, *statistics is often defined as the set of methods for making decisions under uncertainty*.

Definition of the Statistical Population

In statistical inference problems, the set of all values under consideration, all pertinent data, is customarily referred to as a **population** or **universe**.

> In general, any set of quantifiable data can be referred to as a population if that set of data consists of *all values of interest*.

For example, in deciding on the choice of a job, you may want to estimate the salaries being earned by people with degrees in the field. Similarly, a business manager may want to know how many customers might buy a new product considered for possible production or the increase in sales to expect from the implementation of a particular advertising campaign. A government policy-maker may want to estimate the changes in demand for food that would result from increased welfare payments to the handicapped or a relaxation of restrictions on imported products. A legislator may need to infer the level of state revenue available from a special excise tax on tobacco products or a sales tax so that a reliable budget can be prepared. In each of these cases, the set of *all relevant values* constitutes a population. The incomes of all accountants in Quebec could represent a population, or, the income of these people could represent a sample of all accountants in Canada. Other examples of populations might include the price/earnings ratio of all companies in Canada's Fortune 500, the amount of tax dollars paid by Canadian companies with sales greater than 100,000 million dollars, or the monthly level of energy consumed by households with incomes less than $30,000.

When we make decisions we naturally would prefer to have access to as much information as possible about the relevant population or populations. One can avoid the possibility of making an incorrect inference only when all the information about a population is available. Unfortunately, it is usually impossible and much too costly to collect all the information concerning the population associated with a practical problem. Consequently, inferences and the resulting decisions must be made on the basis of limited or imperfect information about the population. The function of statistics as an aid to the decision-maker is to help him or her decide:

1. the information about a population needed for a particular type of decision;
2. how this information can best be collected and analyzed for use in making decisions

In trying to decide what information about a population is necessary for making a decision, we shall be referring to certain numerical characteristics that distinguish that population. These numerical characteristics, called **parameters**, describe specific properties of the population.

> Numerical characteristics of populations are referred to as population parameters, or simply parameters.

For instance, one parameter of the population, *executive salaries in the steel industry* is the average salary in that industry, since this measure describes the *central tendency* of all salaries in that population. The personnel director of any firm in that industry would certainly like to know the value of this parameter because such information would be valuable in setting salaries for new executives and for determining raises from one year to the next. Another population parameter involves *proportions*. For example, a number of recent court cases have centred on the proportion of workers in a company or industry who belong to a minority group. Discrimination has been charged in some situations because of the low proportion of minority workers.

section 1.3

Describing a Population

☐ **EXAMPLE 1.1**   Assume that you are the mayor of Chatham, Ontario, a city of 43,900 according to 1991 data. You have decided on a nationwide advertising campaign to try to attract new business and industry to your city. In order to advertise the relative advantages of Chatham, you decide to collect economic information for all cities in Canada whose size is roughly comparable to that of Chatham. Such data are readily available from numerous sources such as the *Canadian Economic Observer, Handbook of Consumer Markets,* and *Statistics Canada.* The data in Table 1.1 are a subset of the data in **Data Set 1** in Appendix A. These data are for the 60 Canadian cities with between 25,000 and 100,000 people. Note that Chatham, which is one of these cities, has 43,900 people. Also shown in Table 1.1 is the total personal income for each city and its total retail sales in millions of dollars.

TABLE 1.1 Cities with Between 25,000–100,000 People

City	Number of People (thousands)	Income (millions)	Sales (millions)	City	Number of People (thousands)	Income (millions)	Sales (millions)
1. Alma	30.3	$449.7	$218.7	31. New Glasgow	38.6	$527.9	$258.8
2. Baie-Comeau	32.9	596.3	306.1	32. North Bay	57.2	976.9	375.1
3. Barrie	88.1	1,666.3	703.9	33. Orillia	32.3	247.0	206.0
4. Bathurst	35.7	473.7	249.3	34. Owen Sound	28.2	489.4	172.3
5. Belleville	92.3	1,683.4	654.8	35. Penticton	40.8	627.4	260.2
6. Brandon	42.0	669.8	585.6	36. Peterborough	90.5	1,641.3	627.7
7. Brantford	93.6	1,622.4	622.2	37. Port Alberni	25.0	423.2	188.4
8. Brockville	39.9	770.5	303.0	38. Prince Albert	42.7	612.8	305.8
9. Campbell River	28.3	493.6	227.4	39. Prince George	69.4	1,204.3	576.5
10. Charlottetown	58.9	854.7	427.9	40. Red Deer	61.2	1,060.8	439.8
11. Chatham	43.9	814.4	317.8	41. Rimouski	47.9	780.3	378.4
12. Chilliwack	52.0	771.1	336.4	42. Rouyn	37.9	586.7	269.3
13. Corner Brook	34.5	444.7	233.3	43. Saint Jerome	46.5	712.5	321.8
14. Cornwall	52.9	893.2	337.5	44. Saint-Hyacinthe	50.2	800.2	369.2
15. Courtney	40.5	615.8	239.1	45. Saint-Jean-sur-Richelieu	63.3	986.7	454.6
16. Drummondville	59.0	849.8	379.0	46. Salaberry-de-Valleyfield	39.0	601.5	268.8
17. Fort McMurray	52.8	1,165.2	554.1	47. Sarnia	95.8	2,051.9	847.3
18. Fredericton	68.4	1,192.3	639.4	48. Sault Ste. Marie	83.7	1,510.7	582.2
19. Granby	55.2	872.1	402.8	49. Sept-Iles	25.0	386.4	180.0
20. Grand Falls	26.3	327.6	177.5	50. Shawinigan	62.3	902.9	395.6
21. Grande Prairie	28.7	503.1	214.9	51. Sorel	46.4	721.4	342.7
22. Joliette	36.2	554.0	254.7	52. Stratford	27.5	529.8	200.2
23. Kamloops	61.1	1,020.5	461.3	53. Thetford Mines	30.9	446.0	203.8
24. Kelowna	95.6	1,525.4	672.0	54. Timmins	47.7	835.7	328.0
25. Lethbridge	61.5	1,045.4	415.4	55. Truro	42.4	612.6	295.5
26. Lunenburg	25.8	349.7	168.5	56. Val-d'Or	29.0	475.0	223.6
27. Medicine Hat	51.2	825.1	323.4	57. Vernon	44.6	681.6	299.9
28. Midland	36.9	606.7	228.6	58. Victoriaville	40.3	595.4	277.1
29. Moose Jaw	38.0	586.5	276.4	59. Williams Lake	33.5	533.9	250.3
30. Nanaimo	64.8	1,028.7	440.1	60. Woodstock	26.9	491.2	186.0

We first note that you have made a decision about the relevant population when you selected data for all cities with 25,000–100,000 people. You might have considered the relevant population to be all cities in Canada, or perhaps all cities with fewer than 250,000 people. For the present, we also assume you have decided to focus only on the number of people in each city , rather than the income and sales data.

The first step in working with any set of data is to present it in some sort of summarized form, to get a feel for it. There are numerous ways of summarizing and presenting data, some of which will be presented later in this chapter, and some in Chapter 2. One important emphasis in Chapter 2 will be on graphical measures. A few graphical measures are presented in this chapter, along with the concept of a frequency distribution, and that of a population parameter.

One way to summarize data is to construct a **frequency distribution**. To do this, we group the data into classes, and then count the number of observations (the frequency) falling in each class. For example, Table 1.2 represents the Lotus 1-2-3 output for data on city size in Table 1.1. Consider the first line in Table 1.2. The number on the left is the upper limit on city size, the number on the right is the frequency. Thus the first line of Table 1.2 indicates there are 15 cities with fewer than 35,000 people. The next line indicates that there are 17 cities with more than 35,000 and at most 45,000 people. If we let x represent the number of people , and f represent frequency, then the second line of Table 1.2 has a frequency of $f = 17$ for the following class:

$$35,000 < x \le 45,000$$

TABLE 1.2   Lotus 1-2-3 Output for Table 1.1

Number of People Upper Limit (in 000's)	Number of Cities Frequency
35	15
45	17
55	9
65	10
75	2
85	1
95	4
105	2

(Note: For those familiar with Lotus, this table was generated from a file containing the 60 cities, and then using the Lotus commands /DD.)

Similarly, $f = 9$ for the next class, which is as follows:

$$45,000 < x \le 55,000$$

Table 1.2 is a **frequency distribution**. The sum of the frequencies in Table 1.2 is 60, the total number of cities.   ■

Calculating population parameters. *Generally, population parameters are designated by Greek letters.* In this section we demonstrate the calculation of two population parameters: (1) the mean of a population, and (2) the population proportion. The Greek letter μ (mu) is used to represent the mean of a population; similarly the Greek letter π (pi) is used to designate the population proportion.

Suppose you want to summarize the data in Table 1.1 by finding the average income for the 60 cities. This average is called the arithmetic mean, or sometimes just the mean. To determine a population mean, you need to add all values in the population, and then divide by the number of observations. The number of observations in a population is designated by the letter N. In Table 1.1, $N = 60$.

Formula 1.1 is used to calculate the mean of a population. In this formula, the first value in the population is denoted as x_1, the second as x_2, and so forth, with the last value x_N.

Formula for μ, the population mean:

$$\mu = \frac{1}{N}(x_1 + x_2 + \cdots + x_N) = \frac{1}{N}\sum_{i=1}^{N} x_i \qquad (1.1)$$

Suppose we use Formula 1.1 to find the mean μ (mu) for the *income* data in Table 1.1. Note that the income for the first city (Alma) is $x_1 = 449.7$, the income for the second city (Baie-Comeau) is $x_2 = 596.3$, and the income of the last city (Woodstock) is $x_{60} = x_N = 491.2$. Thus, the population mean is:

$$\mu = \frac{1}{60}(449.7 + 596.3 + \cdots + 491.2) = \frac{1}{60}(48{,}325.1) = 805.41833$$

The average total personal income for cities in this population is 805.42 million dollars. Notice that the income for Chatham, 814.4 million dollars, is slightly higher than the population mean, a fact that you, as mayor, may wish to emphasize should you consider income in your advertising for business.

Proportions are also used to describe populations, and often there are many different proportions one could calculate from the same population. Suppose, for example, you wish to determine the proportion of the 60 cities in Table 1.1 having sales over 300 million dollars. A count indicates that 33 of the cities in Table 1.1 have sales over 300 million dollars. Thus the proportion of cities with sales over 300 million dollars is:

$$\pi = \frac{33}{60} = 0.55$$

Multiplying by 100, we say that 55 percent of the cities in this population have sales over 300 million dollars.

Population proportion:

$$\pi = \frac{x}{N} \qquad (1.2)$$

Let's use the definition in Formula 1.2 to calculate the proportion of cities in Table 1.1 that have more than 65,000 people. This can be done using the frequencies in Table 1.2. Starting with the row for 75,000, and adding the subsequent frequencies, we find that there are $2 + 1 + 4 + 2 = 9$ cities with greater than 65,000 people. Thus, for Formula (1.2), $x = 9$ and $N = 60$, the proportion is as follows:

$$\pi = \frac{9}{60} = 0.15$$

This means that 15% of the cities have more than 65,000 people.

There are numerous population parameters other than μ and π that can be used to describe a population. We will discuss some of these parameters in subsequent chapters.

It is important to note that the task of determining the exact value of a population parameter may be quite difficult. This may be due to the inconvenience or impracticality of collecting the necessary data. If we are interested in the parameter *average executive salary*, it may not be possible even to identify all the executives in a given industry, much less their salaries. Similarly, the proportion of minority workers in an industry may be difficult to determine because of a reluctance of companies to provide such information, even if they keep records on it.

Use of Samples Drawn from a Population

Since it is often impossible or impractical to determine the exact value of the parameters of a population, the characteristics of a given population are commonly judged by observing a **sample** drawn from all possible values.

> A sample is a subset of a population.

The individual values contained in a sample are often referred to as *observations*, and the population from which they come is sometimes called the *parent population*. We may, for example, take a sample of 100 executives, determine their current salaries, and on the basis of these observations, make statements about different characteristics (parameters) of the population of all executive salaries such as the average salary, or the variability of salaries in a certain industry, or perhaps the average salary in that industry a year from now.

As another example, suppose a quality-control engineer is responsible for ensuring the reliability of electrical components produced in some production process. Testing each and every item may be prohibitively expensive. Or it may be impossible if the inspection process destroys the components. Consider the problem of producing a computer disk designed to last 1,000 hours. An inspector might test each disk for 1,000 hours or until it becomes defective; but then what would be left for the manufacturer to sell? The solution to this problem lies in determining the reliability of all items produced (a population parameter) by inspecting only a subset (a sample) of the items. In order to make decisions about a population on the basis of a sample, we will calculate certain numerical characteristics of a sample called **sample statistics**.

> Numerical characteristics of samples are referred to as *sample statistics* or simply *statistics*.

The mean of a sample is a sample statistic. A proportion calculated from a sample is a sample statistic.

Thus, when a numerical characteristic applies to a population, it is called a parameter. A numerical characteristic describing a sample is called a *statistic*. The usefulness of such measures is obvious if one considers the difficulty of making a logical presentation of the meaning and interpretation of a given data set. Simple intuitive or naked-eye analysis of the values can be misleading and may easily miss some important implications. Furthermore, presenting such analysis of large data sets is tedious for the presenter and boring for the listener or reader. If the important and most useful information in a data set can be condensed into a few summary measures, then comprehension and comparison of different populations or samples becomes much easier. In decision-making problems (for example, in statistical analysis of pollution-abatement systems or of a welfare program), summary presentation of this nature is called *data reduction*. All the information in a data set that is useful for a particular purpose is reduced into a single measure such as a reliability measure or an average payment.

☐ **EXAMPLE 1.2**   Assume again that you are mayor of Chatham, but that you do not have access to the population data in Table 1.1. Typically, census figures are not available for most populations. Furthermore, let us assume that it would be quite expensive for you to collect data on the 60 cities in the population, so you have decided to take a sample. You decide to take a *random* sample of ten cities, where random means that all the cities have the same chance of being included in the sample. In general, a sample larger than ten would be taken. Using one of the sampling methods presented in Chapter 7, the sample of ten cities shown in Table 1.3. might have been selected.

Calculating a sample mean. The mean of a sample is found by adding all of the numbers in the sample and dividing the sum by the number of values in the sample. Generally, we let the letter n denote the number of sample values and let $\bar{x}$ (read as *x-bar*) denote **the sample mean**. Thus, if $x_1, x_2, \ldots, x_n$ represent the values in a sample, then $\bar{x}$ is calculated as follows:

Mean of a sample:

$$\bar{x} = \frac{1}{n} \sum_{i=1}^{n} x_i \qquad (1.3)$$

TABLE 1.3   Random Sample of Ten Cities from a Population of Sixty Cities

City	Number of People (thousands)	Income (millions)	Sales (millions)
Campbell River	28.3	$493.6	$227.4
Courtney	40.5	615.8	239.1
Joliette	36.2	554.0	254.7
Nanaimo	64.8	1,028.7	440.1
Owen Sound	28.2	489.4	172.3
Prince Albert	42.7	612.8	305.8
Rouyn	37.9	586.7	269.3
Sarnia	95.8	2,051.9	847.3
Sept-Iles	25.0	386.4	180.0
Stratford	27.5	529.8	200.2

To calculate the mean income for the sample data in Table 1.3, we let $x_1 = \$493.6$, $x_2 = \$615.8, \ldots, x_n = x_{10} = 529.8$. Adding these ten numbers together and then dividing the sum by ten gives the sample mean:

$$\bar{x} = \frac{1}{10}(7,349.1) = 734.91$$

Thus, if we had only this sample to use, we might estimate the average income for all 60 cities (the population mean) to be 734.91 million dollars. Recall from our calculations earlier that the actual population mean is 805.42 million dollars. The sample estimate is about 70.5 million dollars too low. This result emphasizes the fact that sample statistics represent only *estimates* of a population parameter. Sometimes the estimate will be quite good, at other times it may not be very good. Unfortunately, since the actual population parameter is never known, we do not know for certain when our estimate is good and when it is not so good. ■

Now let us use the sample in Table 1.3 to estimate π, the proportion of cities with more than 65,000 people. The **sample proportion** will be denoted by the symbol p, where p is defined as follows:

Sample proportion:

$$p = \frac{x}{n} \tag{1.4}$$

In this formula, x is the number of items in the sample satisfying the characteristic to be determined, and n is the sample size. Looking at our sample in Table 1.3 of ten cities, we see that only one city has over 65,000 people. Hence, an estimate of π based on this sample would be:

$$p = \frac{1}{10} = 0.10$$

Since $\pi = 0.15$, this sample estimate is lower than the population value. The reason that sample estimates differ from population values is that a sample does not provide full information. A sample is only a part of the whole and thus provides only partial information. Also, samples generally differ from one another because each one depends on the particular part of the population selected for that sample. This introduces what statisticians call **sampling error**.

Sampling errors are the differences between sample estimates and population parameters caused by the fact that samples are merely a part of the population.

Large samples are preferred because we want to keep the sampling error small so that we can have more confidence in the reliability of the estimate. Of course, larger samples cost more money, so there is a trade-off between more reliability and more expense. Perfect accuracy is obtained only when $n = N$, which means that we sample the whole population. However this is a **census** and not really a sample. Sample statistics are used most often to:

1. make estimates about certain population parameters
2. test hypotheses (or assumptions) about certain population parameters
3. determine the optimal decision in a situation of uncertainty

Figure 1.1 illustrates the relationships between population parameters and sample statistics. In it the upper arrow represents the process of estimating population parameters. The lower arrow represents hypothesis testing.

The methods for relating populations and samples will be described in greater detail beginning in Chapter 7. For now, we merely wish to establish the major purpose for which these concepts will be used.

> Samples are used to aid in drawing inferences, testing hypotheses about population parameters, and for making decisions. Since samples give only partial information about a population, any decisions or conclusions based on a sample should be accompanied by a knowledge of the reliability of the sample estimates.

Chapter 2 discusses additional summary measures useful in describing populations. The study of probability in Chapters 3–6 develops skills and techniques for assessing the reliability of sample information. Beginning in Chapter 7, we present sample measures that are useful in drawing inferences and testing hypotheses about population parameters.

	Population (all pertinent data)	Sample (subset of data)
Characteristics	Parameters	Statistics
Examples	Population average (μ) Population proportion (π)	Sample average ($\bar{x}$) Sample proportion (p)
Inferences about the population based on observations from a sample	Estimation	
Assumed population parameters tested by using sample statistics	Hypothesis testing	
Using inferences and knowledge of the uncertainty of these inferences to make decisions	Decision making under uncertainty	

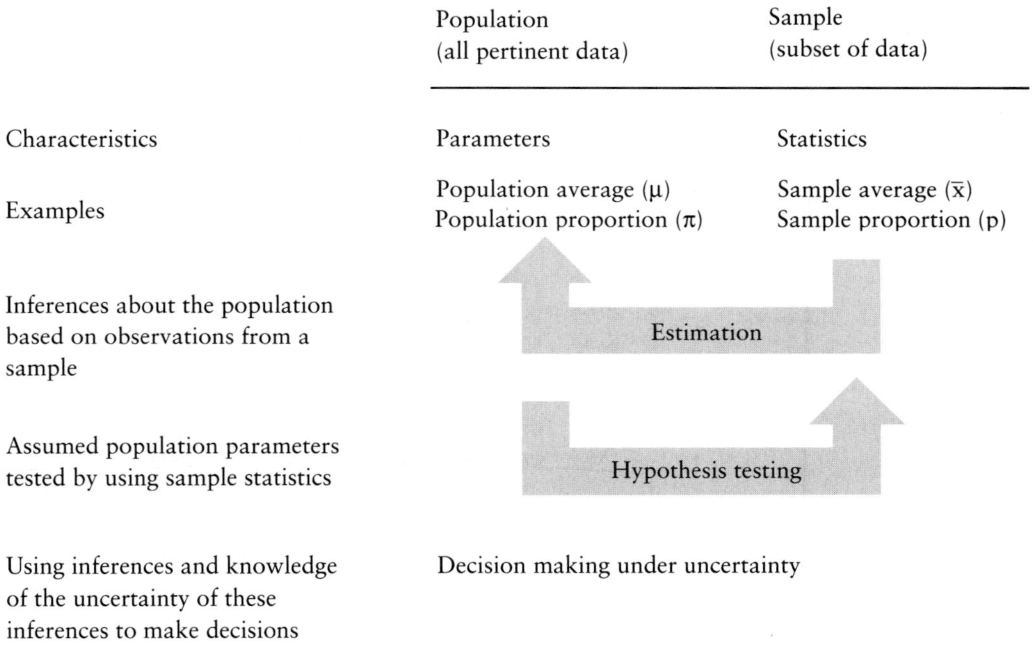

FIGURE 1.1   Statistical terms

Types of Data and Data Presentation

section 1.5

Business and government have many, many sources for data. Some of these data are historical information, perhaps kept in computer files. This is *internal information*. At other times, an organization may generate new information, by taking a sample or even a census. We will call this *generated data*. Finally, there are many, many outside sources of information, which we will call *external data*.

Internal data. Most businesses and governmental agencies keep a wide variety of information on computers. Some of this information includes employee data (personal information, payroll accounts, tax records, et cetera), marketing information (sales, advertising, consumer preferences), and of course a lot of information relevant to finance, accounting, and operations.

Generated data. Data may be gathered by a company or a government agency using a wide variety of techniques, such as surveys, personal interviews, focus groups, or panel studies. For example, information may be gathered on a proposed new product, testing for safety, durability, and efficiency/effectiveness. Consumers may be asked for their opinion on a new advertising campaign, or for their preference among political candidates.

Sometimes generated data is collected by the company or agency itself. Other times, the information is gathered by an outside source, such as a marketing research firm, or a university.

External data. The availability of external sources of information seems almost overwhelming. In the U.S., the Bureau of the Census and the Bureau of Labor Statistics are convenient sources. In Canada, a comparable source is Statistics Canada, reporting on the census data taken every five years. The *Canadian Economic Observer* provides monthly data of interest to business. The Conference Board of Canada publishes market data generated by the government on a regular basis.

There are many commercial organizations gathering data. The Nielsen company collects data in both the U.S. and Canada on consumer preferences and viewing patterns for television and radio. Other sources include Dun and Bradstreet (for credit-worthiness). Many universities and local governments gather data that is available to the public. The Wharton (University of Pennsylvania) econometric model is a forecasting tool used in many industries.

It will be convenient for us to distinguish two types of data throughout this text. They are cross-sectional data and time series data. Cross-sectional data is information gathered at a single point in time — a "snapshot." Thus, the listing of the salaries of the top executives in the Fortune 500 companies for the last year represents cross-sectional data. On the other hand, if we track one or more of these salaries over a period of years, we get time-series data.

Charts and Graphs

Once we have all the population values, or the information from a sample, it is important to be able to present these data in an efficient manner. Graphs and charts, the most popular and most convenient means for such presentations, are usually employed when a visual representation is desired. Although there are many alternative methods for presenting data in this form, only a few will be discussed here. The *pie chart*, for example, is a familiar device for describing how a given quantity is subdivided. In Figure 1.2, the relevant quantity is the fees for an office visit charged by the 40 doctors in **Data Set 4**. These are cross-sectional data. This chart indicates, for example, that 20 percent of the fees were less than $40 ($< 40$), 30 percent were between $40–$50, and so forth. The output in Figure 1.2 was drawn using a Lotus 1-2-3 spreadsheet. Notice that a category that has 20 percent of the values in the data set (such as < 40) comprises 20 percent of the 360 degrees of the circle.

A popular descriptive device for presenting time series data is a line graph, such as shown in Fig 1.3. These data are taken from **Data Set 5**, and represent the consumer price index (CPI) for Canada from 1950 to 1990. This output was generated by the Execustat program.

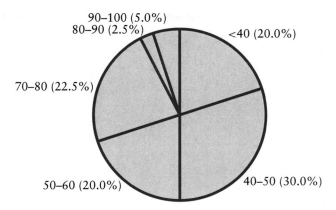

FIGURE 1.2   Fees for 40 doctors

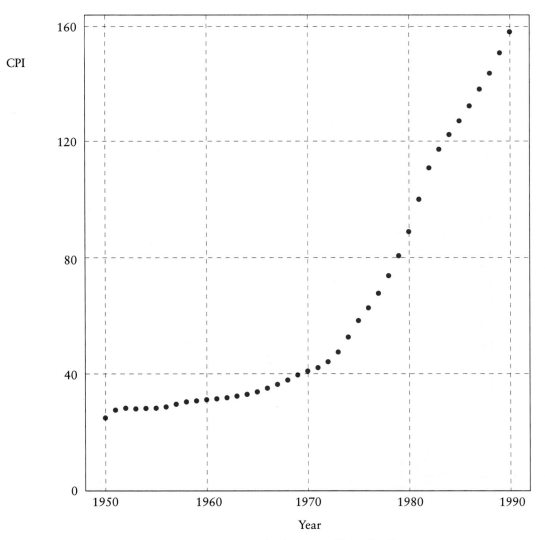

FIGURE 1.3   Scatterplot for CPI in Data Set 5

Our final illustration of a graphical form (Figure 1.4) is derived from an example in Darrell Huff's delightful book *How To Lie With Statistics* (Norton, 1954). This example depicts the increase in the number of cows between 1860 (eight million) and 1936 (24 million). In drawing pictures of cows to represent this growth, one naturally would be inclined to draw the 1936 cow three times as long as the 1860 cow. Of course, a cow three times as long looks rather peculiar unless it is also three times as high. But if the 1936 cow is three times as high and three times as wide, it is *nine* times as large as the 1860 cow in terms of area. Such a figure would seriously misrepresent the true growth.

1860

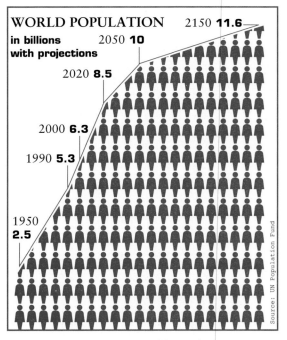

1936

FIGURE 1.4   A threefold increase

FIGURE 1.5   World Population

Business journals and news magazines often adopt a somewhat whimsical device to avoid this difficulty. Interested primarily in presenting information in a form understandable to the layman (not the statistician), such journals would depict growth in the number of cows by showing one cow to represent 1860 and three cows to represent 1936 — thus, each would represent eight million animals.

Similarly, growth in auto production from, let's say, 10 million to 27 million cars could be indicated by lopping off the motor and front wheels of the third car. This truncation is less gruesome in the case of the car than in the case of the cow. Figure 1.5 is an illustration of such a graph, from *TIME* magazine.

Frequency Distributions

Although graphs and charts such as those shown in Figures 1.2 and 1.3 often serve a very useful function, they are not appropriate for most purposes of statistical analysis and decision-making because they provide only a representation of the information and not the actual data themselves. Statistical purposes usually require that the data be presented in a form that gives a more precise indication of the information at hand. Some method is needed that will summarize or describe large masses of data without loss or distortion of the essential characteristics of the information and will also make the data easier to interpret. One such method is the arrangement of data into what is called a *frequency distribution* or *frequency table*. In constructing a frequency distribution, it is first necessary to divide the data into a limited number of different categories or classes and then to record the number of times (the frequency) an observation falls (or is distributed) into each class. Table 1.4 is an illustration of a frequency distribution. This table represents the amount of state income tax (x) paid by a population of 78 adults from the state of Indiana.

The first column in Table 1.4 presents the eight classes, each of which is $400 in width. The first class, $0 < x \leq$ $400 has a frequency of 16, which indicated that 16 of the 78 taxpayers paid between $0 and $400. A **relative frequency**, as shown in Table 1.4, is the frequency in each class *relative* to the total number of observations.

> Relative frequency is determined by dividing the frequency of each class by the total number of observations and expressing the result as a decimal.

TABLE 1.4 Frequency Distribution for Taxes

Class	Frequency Distribution	Relative Frequency
$0 < x \leq$ $400	16	0.205
$400 < x \leq$ $800	18	0.231
$800 < x \leq$ $1,200	20	0.256
$1,200 < x \leq$ $1,600	8	0.103
$1,600 < x \leq$ $2,000	9	0.115
$2,000 < x \leq$ $2,400	4	0.051
$2,400 < x \leq$ $2,800	2	0.026
$2,800 < x \leq$ $3,200	1	0.013
	$N = 78$	1.000

Thus, the first relative frequency in Table 1.4 is $f_1/N = 16/78 = 0.205$, where f denotes frequency and the subscript 1 indicates that this is the first frequency in the sample. The second relative frequency is $f_2/N = 18/78 = 0.231$, and so forth. Note that the sum of all relative frequencies must equal 1.00 since $\sum f_i = N$ and

$N/N = 1.0$. Calculation and tabulation of these measures makes it clear that taxes between $800 and $1,200 occurred with the greatest frequency.

Statisticians have developed certain guidelines for the constructions of frequency distributions.

1. Classes are generally chosen so that the width of each class, called the *class interval*, is the same for all categories. Otherwise, interpretation of the frequency distribution may be difficult. For example, grouping the tax values in Table 1.4 into unequal classes such as $0 < x \le 200, $200 < x \le $1,000$, $2,000 < x \le $4,000$ is ill-advised. Comparisons between the number of people in each category would then be misleading, since the size of the categories is not consistent.

2. The number of classes should probably be *fewer than 15* for ease of handling and to ensure sufficient compacting of the information and *at least 6* to avoid loss of information due to grouping together widely diverse data.

3. *Open-ended intervals* should be avoided. Too much information is lost if categories such as "$\le $15,000$" are used. If a few extreme values do not conveniently fit into frequency categories, they should be listed separately.

4. Categories should be defined so that no single observation could fall into more than one *overlapping* category. For example, categories such as $17,000–$21,000 and $21,000–$25,000 are ambiguous, since it is not clear in which category to place a value of exactly $21,000. If we use our convention for denoting the categories, $17,000 < x \le $21,000$, and $21,000 < x \le $25,000$, there is no overlap, and it is clear that $21,000 falls in the first category.

5. The *midpoint* of each category should be made to be representative of the values assigned to that category. This is important because these midpoints are often used as proxies for all the values in their respective classes. Such proxies or representative values are called **class marks**.

☐ **EXAMPLE 1.3**   Consider a group of sales items in a clothing store where many such items are priced as $9.98, $14.99, $19.95, et cetera. To set up classes such as $5.00 < x \le 10.00, $10.00 < x \le 15.00, $15.00 < x \le 20.00 would betray poor judgment, since most of the data fall near the end of each class. A better choice might be to use the classes $7.50 < x \le 12.50, $12.50 < x \le 17.50, $17.50, < x \le 22.50. For these classes, the midpoints are $10.00, $15.00, and $20.00, which more closely represent the typical values within the classes.   ■

While it is often useful to arrange the values in a data set into a frequency distribution (as in Table 1.4), many analysts prefer a pictorial presentation. Perhaps the most common type is the graph in which the classes are plotted on the horizontal axis and the frequency of each class is plotted on the vertical axis. This type of graph is called a **histogram** or *bar graph*. Figure 1.6 represents the histogram for the frequency distribution in Table 1.4.

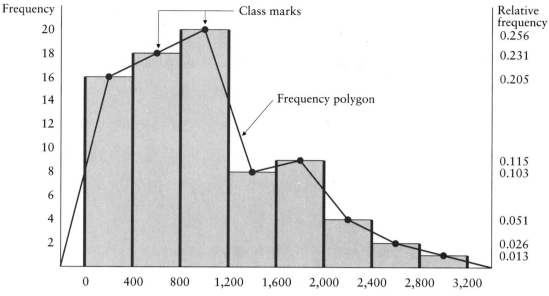

FIGURE 1.6   Histogram and frequency polygon for data in Table 1.4

A helpful addition to the histogram is a **frequency polygon,** which is constructed by drawing a straight line between the midpoints (class marks) of adjacent class intervals. The frequency polygon for the data in Figure 1.6, indicated by the line through the class marks, serves to smooth a set of values. The reader should verify at this point that in Figure 1.6 the graph of the *relative* frequencies is the same as that of the *absolute* frequencies except that the values for the vertical scale are different (relative frequencies are shown on the right-hand side of Figure 1.6).

TABLE 1.5   Cumulative Frequency and Cumulative Relative Frequency for the Distribution of Taxes in Table 1.4

Class	Frequency	Cumulative Frequency	Cumulative Relative Frequency
$\$0 < x \le \$400$	16	16	0.205
$\$400 < x \le \$800$	18	34	0.436
$\$800 < x \le \$1,200$	20	54	0.692
$\$1,200 < x \le \$1,600$	8	62	0.795
$\$1,600 < x \le \$2,000$	9	71	0.910
$\$2,000 < x \le \$2,400$	4	75	0.962
$\$2,400 < x \le \$2,800$	2	77	0.987
$\$2,800 < x \le \$3,200$	1	78	1.000

Another important method of presenting a data set is the table of *cumulative frequencies,* or table of *cumulative relative frequencies.* Table 1.5 applies this method to the tax data in Table 1.4. A **cumulative frequency** is the *sum* of the *absolute* frequencies, from the lowest class to the highest class considered:

$$\sum_{i=1}^{k} f_i = \text{cumulative frequency of } k\text{th class}$$

For example, by the end of the second class in Table 1.5 (at $800) the cumulative frequency for taxes is $16 + 18 = 34$. Similarly, by $1,200 the cumulative frequency is 54 (the sum of $16 + 18 + 20$). A **cumulative relative frequency** is the *sum* of the *relative* frequencies from the lowest class to the highest class considered:

$$\text{Cumulative relative frequency at class } k = \sum_{i=1}^{k} \frac{f_i}{N}$$

At the value $1,200 for the end of the third class, the cumulative relative frequency is:

$$\sum_{i=1}^{3} \frac{f_i}{N} = \frac{54}{78} = 0.692$$

This value indicates that 69.2% of the taxes for this population were less than or equal to $1,200. Note that the cumulative frequency for the highest class ($2,800 < x \leq \$3,200$ in this case) must equal 1.00, since

$$\sum_{\text{all}} \frac{f_i}{N} = \frac{N}{N}$$

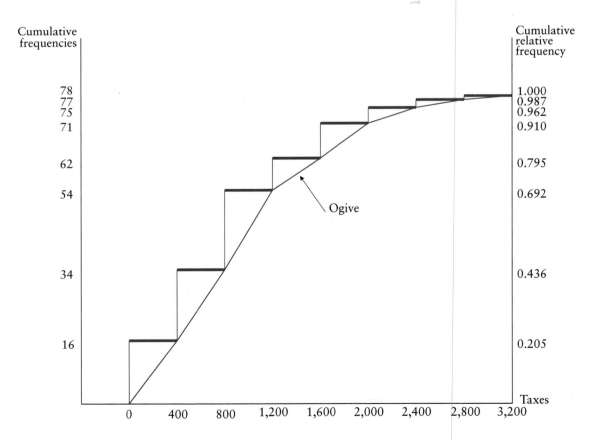

FIGURE 1.7   Cumulative frequencies and cumulative relative frequencies

Just as a graph of the frequencies of a set of values provides a visual description of the original data, so a graph of the cumulative relative frequencies provides visual information about cumulative values. Note in Figure 1.7 that cumulative relative frequencies can be plotted in the same fashion as relative frequencies and that this **cumulative histogram** can be smoothed by a line similar to the frequency polygon used in Figure 1.6. In this case, the smoothing line is called an **ogive**, and the ogive connects the corner points of the cumulative histogram.

The distributions in Tables 1.4 and 1.5 might lead the governor of Indiana to ask other questions requiring further statistical analysis. For example, what proportion of states have lower taxes than Indiana? Would more business and industry be attracted to the state if taxes were lower? Although these questions concerning Indiana do not call for earth-shattering decisions, it is evident that statistical analysis of available data can be useful in finding answers. However, if the data represent compound portfolio yields by the 40 largest insurance companies, similar kinds of questions could be very important to the financial management of a single company or to stockbrokers, bankers, and brokers in general. The same kind of statistical analysis developed in this text using simple examples also applies to a wide range of very important managerial and governmental decision-making problems.

☐ STUDY QUESTION 1.1   **Grocery Bills at Kroger's**

A study for the marketing department of the Kroger grocery chain was designed to determine the average grocery bill paid by Kroger shoppers. The study recorded the amount paid by every tenth shopper in checkout lane number 5 over a period of five consecutive days in September. Assume that the first 20 customers in this study had the following bills rounded to the nearest dollar:

$$\begin{array}{ccccccc}
\$102 & \$58 & \$14 & \$89 & \$44 & \$123 & \$63 \\
\$75 & \$90 & \$97 & \$52 & \$84 & \$114 & \$77 \\
\$110 & \$99 & \$61 & \$88 & \$49 & \$63 &
\end{array}$$

1. What is the population in this study? Does it appear that this study will provide a sample that is representative of the population? Comment on any difficulties with the sample design. From a statistical point of view, do you see any problems in using bills that are rounded to the nearest dollar?
2. On the basis of the first 20 customers, what value would you estimate for μ? What value would you estimate for π, the population proportion of shoppers with bills over $100?
3. Construct the frequency distribution and the histograms of relative frequencies and cumulative relative frequencies. Add the frequency polygon and the ogive to your histograms.

● ANSWER

1. The population is the grocery bills for all shoppers at Kroger. There could be many problems with the study. First, the study involves only five consecutive days, and the store is probably open seven days a week. There is thus a possible bias in omitting two days. Also, the study was conducted in September, which may or may not be representative of the rest of the year. It is not clear whether a grocery bill includes other items – for example, if a shopper buys mailing envelopes, does this count as groceries? And should only checkout lane 5 be used? This lane may have different characteristics from other lanes, such as being

closer to the entrance, having more efficient, friendly workers, or not catering to people with only one or two items. From a statistical viewpoint, rounding to the nearest dollar should not cause any problems because it is probably safe to assume the cents portion of a bill will be less than $0.50 half the time and greater than $0.50 half the time.

2. The best estimate of μ is:

$$\bar{x} = (102 + 58 + \cdots + 63)/20 = 1552/20 = \$77.60$$

The best estimate of π is:

$$p = (\text{number of bills} > 100)/20 = 4/20 = 0.20$$

3. Let's pick classes of $10 in width, starting with $40 and considering the $14 bill to be an **outlier** (see Figure 1.8).

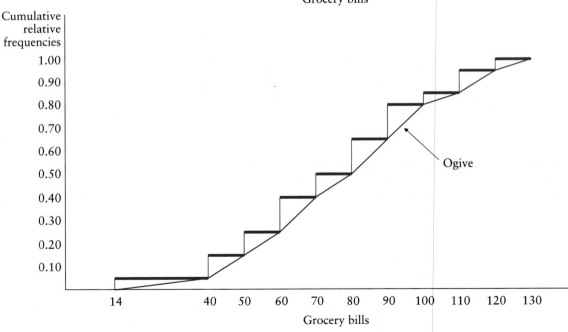

FIGURE 1.8   The frequency distribution

TABLE 1.6 Relative Frequencies for Grocery Bills at Kroger's

Class Limits	Frequency	Percent
14	1	0.05
$40 < x \le 50$	2	0.10
$50 < x \le 60$	2	0.10
$60 < x \le 70$	3	0.15
$70 < x \le 80$	2	0.10
$80 < x \le 90$	4	0.20
$90 < x \le 100$	2	0.10
$100 < x \le 110$	2	0.10
$110 < x \le 120$	1	0.05
$120 < x \le 130$	1	0.05

PROBLEMS

1.1 If you are given a set of numbers, how can you tell whether these numbers represent a population or a sample? If you are given a mean or a proportion, how can you tell whether the value is a sample estimate or a population parameter?

1.2 Use Table 1.1 for the following:

a) Devise your own plan for taking a random sample of 10 from the incomes in Table 1.1. Take the sample.

b) Is your sample mean fairly close to the population mean?

c) Take a random sample of 30 from the incomes in Table 1.1. Is your sample mean of 30 closer to μ than the mean of your sample of 10? Did you expect it to be? Explain why.

d) Would you guess that the mean of a sample of 30 will always be closer to μ than the mean of a sample of 10? Explain.

1.3 Take a random sample of size 15 from the 179 cities in **Data Set 1**. What proportion of the cities in your sample have sales that exceed $500 (in millions)? How close an estimate is your sample proportion to the population value of π?

1.4 Answer the following questions:

a) What is the population proportion of cities in Table 1.1 having incomes greater than 800 million dollars? Would this be a good population parameter for the mayor of Chatham to advertise?

b) If you are the mayor of Red Deer, what population parameter from Table 1.1 would you advertise? Explain.

1.5 **Data Set 2** includes the sales and debt/equity ratio of 100 Canadian companies from *Fortune* magazine.

a) Find the mean sales for the 100 companies. What proportion of the 100 companies had a debt/equity ratio greater than 1.0?

b) By using a computer, the following numbers were generated randomly from numbers between 1 and 50: 29, 43, 49, 11, 35, 15, 30, 3, 22, 19, 41, 8. Use the companies corresponding to these 12 numbers to form a random sample of the sales of the first 50 companies. How close is the sample mean to the population mean of sales of these 50 companies?

c) Generate your own randomly selected numbers to take a sample of $n = 15$. Answer the same question as in part (b).

1.6 Answer the following questions:

a) A classmate of yours has suggested that the first ten cities in **Data Set 1** would constitute a perfectly reasonable random sample of size $n = 10$. Another classmate suggests picking every fifth city until you have a sample of 10 (starting at a randomly selected place in the table). What do you think of these two methods for taking a random sample? Is one plan better than the other? Explain.

b) Repeat the questions in part (a) using **Data Set 2** and picking companies rather than cities.

1.7 Use Table 1.1 to answer the following:

a) Construct the frequency distribution, the histogram, and the frequency polygon using the data in Table 1.1 (the city size values) using classes of width 10 (initially) and then 20. Which width seems better to you? Explain.

b) Construct the cumulative frequency distribution and the cumulative histogram for the city size data in Table 1.1 using the class intervals in part (a). Add the ogive to your cumulative histogram.

1.8 Construct a frequency distribution similar to Table 1.5 for the first 50 companies, using the sales column in **Data Set 2.** Use the following classes:
$2,000,000 < x \le 4,000,000$,
$4,000,000 < x \le 6,000,000$, et cetera. Use your table to determine the population proportion of companies with sales less than $14,000,000.

1.9 For Problem 1.8, construct the histogram and the cumulative histogram. Add the frequency polygon and the ogive.

1.10 The following annual starting salaries were offered to 16 accounting majors about to receive their college degrees:

$37,500	$34,900	$36,200	$36,500
36,400	35,400	35,800	35,500
34,600	37,600	36,800	36,000
35,600	36,400	34,400	34,100

a) Is this data set a population or a sample? How do you know?

b) Find the mean of the 16 starting salaries.

c) Use classes of $34,000 < x \le 34,500$, $34,500 < x \le 35,000$, et cetera. to construct a frequency distribution similar to Table 1.4.

d) What percent of these accounting majors will earn more than $35,000? What percent will earn $36,000 or less?

1.11 Construct a pie chart using **Data Set 7** and the variable called *Class*.

1.12 Write a brief report concerning earning power in 1950 compared with 1990, using Figure 1.3.

1.13 Using the data in **Data Set 1**, construct a pie chart showing the percent of cities with sales falling in each of the following five categories: $0 < x \le 200$, $200 < x \le 400$, $400 < x \le 600$, $600 < x \le 800$, and $x > 800$ (in millions of dollars).

1.14 What is statistical inference? Why is statistical inference important in business and the social and behavioural sciences? Give several examples of the use of statistical inference in an area of interest to you.

1.15 Find an example (from a newspaper, magazine, et cetera) of a data set used to report business or economic data. Is the data set a population or a sample? Explain how this data set can be or was used in decision-making.

CHAPTER SUMMARY

KEY TERMS AND EXPRESSIONS

Descriptive statistics: Methods concerned with arranging, summarizing, or somehow conveying the characteristics of a set of numbers.

Statistical inference: Making generalizations, predictions, or conclusions about characteristics of a population based on the characteristics of a sample assumed to have been drawn from that population.

Decision-making under uncertainty (or risk): A decision-making process in which there is uncertainty about what outcome will result from a particular action.

Population: All relevant values of interest in a particular context.

Parameters: Certain numerical characteristics of a population such as its mean or a particular proportion.

Frequency distribution: The arranging of a data set into classes and the recording of the number (frequency) of values in each class.

Population mean: The average of a population of N values:
$$\mu = \frac{1}{N} \sum_{i=1}^{N} x_i$$

Population proportion: The proportion of values in the population meeting some specified condition:
$$\pi = \frac{x}{N}$$

Sample: A subset of a population.

Sample statistics: Numerical characteristics of a sample.

Sample mean: The average of a sample of n values:

$$\bar{x} = \frac{1}{n} \sum_{i=1}^{n} x_i$$

Sample proportion: The proportion of values in the sample meeting some specified condition or characteristic:

$$p = \frac{x}{n}$$

Sampling errors: The differences between sample estimates and the actual values of the population parameter, which occur because a sample is only a part of the population.

Census: An enumeration or listing of the entire set of values in the population.

Relative frequency: The frequency of a class divided by the total number of observations and expressed as a decimal.

Class marks: The representative values for the classes in a frequency distribution — often the midpoint of the class interval.

Histogram: A graph or bar chart showing the classes on the horizontal axis and the frequency or relative frequency of each class on the vertical axis.

Frequency polygon: A series of straight lines connecting the midpoints (class marks) of adjacent classes on a histogram.

Cumulative frequency: The sum of the number of occurrences of all values in a specified class plus the frequencies in all preceding classes.

Cumulative relative frequency: The sum of the relative frequency in a specified class plus the relative frequencies in all preceding classes.

Cumulative histogram: A histogram showing cumulative frequencies (or cumulative relative frequencies) on the vertical axis.

Ogive: A series of straight lines connecting the lower corner points of a cumulative histogram.

Outlier: A value in a population that is not representative of the population.

USING THE COMPUTER

1.16 Use a computer package at your university such as MINITAB, Execustat, Interactive Data Analysis [IDA], Statistical Package for the Social Sciences [SPSS], or Statistical Analysis System [SAS] to calculate the mean and the frequency distribution for the ten year return information in **Data Set 7**. If possible, use this program to generate the histogram and the cumulative histogram. Add your own frequency polygon and ogive.

1.17 Use a computer package at your university to calculate the mean and the frequency distribution for the General Motors returns in **Data Set 8**.

1.18 Using a computer package, present a graph of the R123 variable in **Data Set 5**.

1.19 Solve parts (b) and (c) of Problem 1.10 using a computer package.

1.20 Answer Problem 1.7 using a computer package.

1.21 **Data Set 6** represents data from a survey on food consumption for the elderly (55 or over).

a) Construct a histogram for monthly income, using the data in column 5 and noting one outlier.

b) Summarize all the data presented in some convenient manner.

CASE PROBLEM

1.22 A student union recently completed a large survey designed to study usage of the union building. This study surveyed the student population of approximately 30,000, plus approximately 6,000 faculty and staff. Primarily, the university union wanted to know who was using the union, how often they used it, and what parts of the union they used. They were willing to send out 1,000 sample questionnaires to obtain these data. Design a procedure for distributing, collecting and analyzing the sample questionnaires for this particular situation (or your own union, if appropriate). Be as specific as possible as to whom the questionnaires will be sent and any problems you would anticipate. [*Note:* We will return to this same case in Chapter 7.]

Summary Measures for Populations

Introduction

In Chapter 1, the concepts of a population and a sample were introduced. Also, some descriptive measures were presented for a population and for a sample, as were some types of charts and graphs that are useful for describing the numbers in a data set. In this chapter, the emphasis is less on the comparison between populations and samples and more on the important descriptive measures that summarize the data in quantitative form. In particular, the topics of this chapter include the meaning, the calculation techniques, and the use of summary measures for a *population*. As was mentioned before, these summary measures are called *parameters*.

The most commonly used parameters for interpreting and understanding the meaning of the values in a population are the measures of *central location* (or central tendency) and of *variability*. Their use in summarizing the information in a data set is invaluable for giving a logical presentation or for making an argument based on the set of facts implied by the data set.

☐ **EXAMPLE 2.1**   Think of the task of presenting information on the local price of new 27″ TV sets. Assume that you have a listing of all the retail prices for each TV set now in stock. Your first statements would probably be something like: "The typical price of TV sets is about $430," or "TV prices vary from a low of $350 to a high of $750." In the first statement, you are trying to present the central tendency of the price of a 27″ TV set, and in the second you are groping for a way to describe the variability in individual prices.   ■

☐ **EXAMPLE 2.2**   A friend collects data on the monthly changes in sales of durable goods for each of the past 30 months. When asked to summarize what the data show, the friend may say: "The average change in sales is 0.8%, but in 17 of the months, the change has been greater than 1%." The first part of the statement gives information on the central location, and the second part helps to interpret the degree of consistency or the variability of the data.   ■

TABLE 2.1   Common Summary Measures — Parameters

Central location: Arithmetic mean	Variability: Standard deviation
Median	Variance
Mode	Range
Geometric mean	Percentiles

Summary measures permit us to do more than merely duplicate the entire set of observations (preferably in some convenient format, such as a chart or diagram). The two types of summary measures most often used in statistical inference and decision-making are the central location and the variability of the data. There are a number of different ways of measuring these two characteristics, as shown in Table 2.1. Some of these terms are perhaps already familiar to you, while others may be new, technical terms. Although each is useful for certain purposes, this text will emphasize the two most common and useful measures in statistical inference, namely, the *arithmetic mean* and the *standard deviation*.

Central Location

The single most important measure describing numerical information is the location of the centre of the data. The term *central location* may refer to any one of a number of different measures including the *mean*, the *median*, and the *mode*. As the examples in this section will illustrate, each of these measures is appropriate for certain descriptive purposes, but not for others.

☐ **EXAMPLE 2.3**   A city transportation office hires a survey company to do traffic counts on some specific streets during the summer. A monitoring device counts the number of times a vehicle rolls over a trip wire. However, a breakdown is also desired of vehicles in terms of cars, trucks, buses and any kind of trailer, including those pulled by a truck cab. Over a randomly selected set of ten hours, the company records 14,000 vehicles, including 9,200 cars, 2,840 trucks, 510 buses, and 1,450 trailers. What is the central location of this data set? All that can be reported is that the vehicle type most frequently observed was cars. Clearly, there is no such thing as the *average* vehicle across these categories.   ∎

☐ **EXAMPLE 2.4**   Suppose that all of the 2,840 trucks in Example 2.3 had to pass through a weighing station and the listing of all the gross vehicle weights is available. All 2,840 weights in this population might have been different, but let us assume that nine of them were the same (to the nearest ten pounds). If this weight is the most frequently occurring weight, would it be the best measure of central location for this data set? Not necessarily! This most frequently occurring weight might be near the extremes of the distribution of weights, not near the centre at all.   ∎

The Mode

> The **mode** is defined as the value that occurs most often or, in a frequency distribution, the point (or class mark) corresponding to the value with the highest frequency.

Note that the mode may be a poor measure of central location, since the most frequently occurring value may not appear near the centre of the data. Furthermore, the mode need not even be unique. Consider the frequency distributions shown in Figure 2.1.

The first distribution in Figure 2.1 shows the age of persons purchasing compact disks from an electronic equipment store during a sale. The ages are recorded to the nearest five years. The mode of this distribution is located at the lowest age level, 25 years. However, this mode certainly cannot be considered representative of the central location of this distribution of ages. The second distribution classifies sales at a fast food outlet into dollar intervals. This distribution has two modes, one at sales between $1 and $2 (perhaps for a soft drink, and small order of fries) and one at sales between $4 and $5 (perhaps for a double cheeseburger, large fries, and milk shake). Neither of these modes is especially useful for decision-making applications, since neither appears to be representative of the central location.

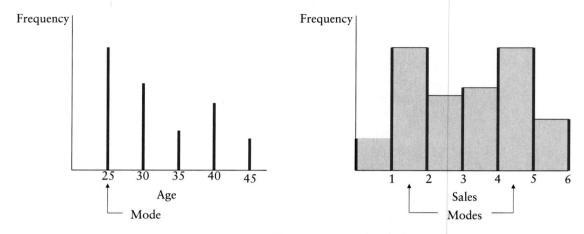

FIGURE 2.1   Examples of the mode for two distributions

For purely descriptive purposes, the mode can be useful in representing the most frequently occurring value. Consider the distributions in Figure 2.2, which are the same distributions shown in Figure 2.1, except that they now represent different data.

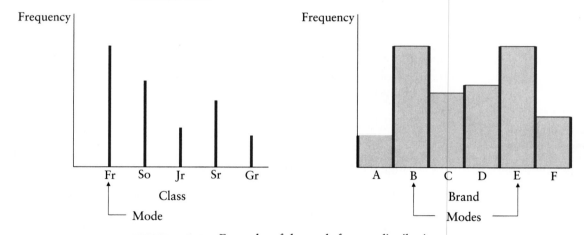

FIGURE 2.2   Examples of the mode for two distributions

The first distribution now describes the class distribution of students at a certain university. The modal class is the freshman class. There are more freshman than students of any other class. In the second distribution, the groups indicate the brands of television that consumers selected as best in a recent survey. Two brands, B and E, tied for being selected most often as the best television. In such cases, the mode is the appropriate measure, since the data measure only frequencies and it is not possible to find the average of these values as we could with the ages or dollars in Figure 2.1.

The Median

Another measure of the central tendency of a data set is the **median**.

> The median is the middle value in a set of numbers arranged in order of magnitude.

When it is desirable to divide the data into two groups, each group containing exactly the same number of values, the median is the appropriate point of division. Finding the median of a set of numbers is not difficult when these numbers are arranged in ascending or descending order. If the number of values in the data set (N) is odd, the middle value can be determined by counting off, from either the highest or lowest value, $(N + 1)/2$ numbers: the resulting number divides the data into the two desired groups and thus represents the median. For example, in a list of five values the median is found by counting down (or up) three values, $(5 + 1)/2 = 3$. In a list of seven values, the median is found by counting down (or up) $(7 + 1)/2 = 4$ values, so the median is the fourth value from either end.

When N is even, there are two middle values, $N/2$ and $(N/2) + 1$, and the median is usually defined as the number halfway between these two values. The median of six values is thus halfway between the third and fourth numbers.

Consider the populations with values listed in Table 2.2. Each data set gives the number of each type of small business that is located in the suburban districts of a city. The types of businesses reported are:

A taxi companies
B swimming pool contractors/service dealers
C home-computer sales stores
D food supermarkets

TABLE 2.2 Central Location Measures

	Data Set **A**	Data Set **B**	Data Set **C**	Data Set **D**
Observations	2,2,3,7,8,9,11	5,7,8,10,10,14	2,3,4,4,4,7	11,9,26,11,10,11
Median	7	9	4	11
Mode	2	10	4	11
Mean	6	9	4	13

Note that in these cases (and for any data set), no matter how many items there are, the median always has a value such that the *number of values* on each side of the median *is equal* when all the values are arranged in numerical order. The only time this rule causes some confusion (but, technically, still holds) is when there are several values equal to the median, as in Data Sets C and D in Table 2.2. In Data Set D, we have not arranged the data in numerical order, to emphasize that the data do not always come in order.

For population A with an odd number of values, the median number of taxi companies is the middle value of the seven values. It is the fourth value in the ordering. For the other populations with an even number of values, the median is the average of the third and fourth ordered values, as these are the two middle values.

Also, Table 2.2 gives the mode for each of these populations. The mode may be lower, higher, or the same as the median. No general rule applies, since the median and the mode depend on the particular population studied.

A third summary measure shown in the table is the simple *arithmetic mean*, commonly referred to as the *average*. The mean of a data set may be thought of as the *point of balance* of the data, analogous to the centre of gravity for a distribution of mass in physics.

As presented in Chapter 1, this average is designated by the symbol μ for a population mean and by the symbol $\bar{x}$ for the sample mean. Note, from the data sets in Table 2.2, that the mean may be less than, greater than, or equal to the median. For the populations A, B, C, and D, the **population mean** is calculated by using Formula 2.1, which repeats Formula 1.1.

Population mean:

$$\mu = \frac{x_1 + x_2 + \cdots + x_N}{N} = \frac{1}{N}\sum_{i=1}^{N} x_i \tag{2.1}$$

Comparison of the Mode, Median, and Mean

The arithmetic mean is the most widely used measure of central location. Its disadvantage, for descriptive purposes, is that it is affected more by extreme values than the median or the mode because it takes into account the differences among all values, not merely their rank order (as does the median) or their frequency (as does the mode). A recent cartoon illustrated this problem quite well by depicting a small-town worker commenting to a reporter that "the average yearly income in this town is $200,000 — there's one person making two million dollars, and ten of us workers making $20,000."

Use of the median requires knowledge not only of the frequency of the values in a data set, as in determining the mode, but also of their ranking, so that these values can be ordered and the middle value obtained.

☐ **EXAMPLE 2.5**   Consider **Data Set 7**, which presents information on the performance of 48 Canadian mutual funds. For each fund, a measure of the fund's size is given as follows: VS = very small, S = small, M = medium, L = large, and VL = very large. The table below gives the frequencies for the funds in these categories.

TABLE 2.3   Size of 48 Canadian Mutual Funds from Data Set 7

Size	Frequency
VS	8
S	12
M	14
L	11
VL	3
Total	48

The mode for these data is the *M* rating; the median also occurs at the *M* rating (since the 24th and 25th values both lie in this class). It would be inappropriate to calculate a mean, since the measurement of size is categorical, and the differences between the size categories are not equal.   ■

In contrast to this example, economic and business problems generally involve data in which the differences among values are known – income measures, output quantities, retained profits, prices, and interest rates. The same factor that makes the mean inappropriate for frequency data and ranked data is its special advantage in these cases; it is a more reliable measure of central location because it requires more knowledge about the population, namely, the difference between each value in the data set.

It should be pointed out that the mean, median, and mode are *not* the only measures of central location. Another type of mean, the *geometric mean*, is especially useful in certain types of problems in business and economics. It is a particularly appropriate measure of the central location of data expressed in relative terms, such as rates of change or ratios (change in the price indices or in yields on stocks and bonds). The geometric mean gives equal weight to changes of equal relative importance. For example, if an index is doubled in value, this change is weighted equally to a change that halves the value of this index. One primary difficulty with the use of the geometric mean generally is that it cannot be used if any value in the data set is zero (no change). We will not present this measure or other special cases of means, since we wish to emphasize the use of the arithmetic mean.

Weighted Average

In some applications, the form of the arithmetic mean presented in Formula 2.1 is not appropriate, since it weights each given value equally. For situations in which some values are more important than others, a weighted average should be used.

☐ **EXAMPLE 2.6**   A couple has three types of savings: an annuity A, some long term treasury bonds B, and a savings certificate C. The principal and yield in each type of investment are as follows:

TABLE 2.4   Three Types of Savings

	Annuity A	Bonds B	Savings Certificate C
Principal	$15,000	30,000	5,000
Yield	9%	13%	8%

If this couple wishes to determine its average percentage yield, the use of the arithmetic mean given by Formula 2.1 would be inappropriate. Adding the three yields and dividing by 3 would give $(9 + 13 + 8)/3 = 30/3 = 10$ percent. A yield of 10% on this total savings of $50,000 would mean $5,000 per year return. Obviously, the couple is doing better than this. The actual return on the annuity is $(\$15,000)(0.09) = \$1,350$. For the bonds, it is $(\$30,000)(0.13) = \$3,900$ and for the certificate it is $(\$5,000)(0.08) = \$400$.

The total return is $\$1,350 + \$3,900 + \$400 = \$5,650$

The correct average yield is $(\$5,650/\$50,000)(100) = 11.3\%$ ■

In the above example and in many applications, a *weighted average* provides the correct mean value. If the values $x_1, x_2, \ldots, x_k$ have weights $w_1, w_2, \ldots, w_k$, a weighted average is defined as follows:

Weighted average:

$$\mu = \frac{\sum_{i=1}^{k}(w_i x_i)}{\sum_{i=1}^{k} w_i} \tag{2.2}$$

Each value of x_i is weighted by how often it occurs or by how important it is, and this product is divided by the sum of the weights. In Example 2.6, the x_i values are the three yields 9%, 13%, and 8%. The weights are the number of dollars invested (the principal amount) at each yield. Using the weighted average formula, the mean yield is:

$$\mu = \frac{\sum_{i=1}^{3}(\text{principal})_i (\text{yield})_i}{\sum_{i=1}^{3}(\text{principal})_i}$$

$$= \frac{15,000(9) + 30,000(13) + 5,000(8)}{15,000 + 30,000 + 5,000}$$

$$\mu = \frac{565,000}{50,000} = 11.3\%$$

The simple arithmetic average given in Formula 2.1 is a special case of the weighted average given in Formula 2.2 in which all the weights are equal to 1, since each value in the population is listed separately. If each $w_i = 1.0$ in Formula 2.2, then the following is true:

$$\mu = \frac{\sum_{i=1}^{k}[(1)x_i]}{\sum_{i=1}^{k=N}(1)} = \sum_{i=1}^{N} \frac{x_i}{N}$$

In other cases that we will consider, the weights in Formula 2.2 may be frequencies, probabilities, or other measures. We return now to the use of the weighted average in finding a measure of central location for a population.

The Mean of a Frequency Distribution

The formula presented for the mean (Formula 2.1) is based on the assumption that each value of the data set is given separately. Often, however, it is much easier to manipulate large amounts of data by grouping them into a *frequency distribution*. Columns 1 and 2 of Table 2.5 give an example of such a distribution: the monthly salaries (reported to the nearest 100 dollars) of the population of nonmedical staff in a hospital.

One way to find the mean of this population would be to sum all 250 values separately. To do this we sum 8 values of $\$1,700 + 23$ values of $\$1,800 + \cdots + 11$ values of $\$2,200$, and then divide by 250. This is the procedure presented earlier in Formula 2.1. But most of us learned long ago that multiplication is easier than repeated addition; hence, we should take advantage of the fact that there are only six *different* salary values in Table 2.5, not 250. In other words, instead of adding $1,700 eight times, we can use the product 8($1,700). Similar products are used for every value of x_i, as shown in column (3) of Table 2.3. The sum of these products for all six values divided by 250 yields μ:

$$\mu = \frac{492,000}{250} = \$1,968$$

The mean or average salary is thus $1,968.

TABLE 2.5   Calculating the Mean for a Frequency of Monthly Salaries

(1) Salary (x_i)	(2) Frequency (f_i)	(3) $x_i f_i$	(4) Relative Frequency $\left(\frac{f_i}{N}\right)$	(5) $x_i \left(\frac{f_i}{N}\right)$
$1,700	8	13,600	0.032	54.4
1,800	23	41,400	0.092	165.6
1,900	75	142,500	0.300	570.0
2,000	90	180,000	0.360	720.0
2,100	43	90,300	0.172	361.2
2,200	11	24,200	0.044	96.8
Sum	250	492,000	1.000	1,968.0

In this case, a weighted average is used for $k = 6$ classes of values: $x_1 = 1,700$, $x_2 = 1,800, \ldots, x_6 = 2,200$. The weights are the frequency f_i of occurrence of each x_i. Thus, the mean is as follows:

Population mean for frequency distribution:

$$\mu = \frac{1}{N} \sum_{i=1}^{k} x_i f_i \qquad (2.3)$$

Formula 2.3 is a special case of a weighted average for which the weights are the *frequencies*. It is sometimes convenient to rewrite Formula 2.3 in a slightly different (but equivalent) form, placing N inside the sum sign. In this application of a weighted average, the values are again x_i, but the weights are now *relative frequencies*, $w_i = (f_i/N)$. These are shown in column 4 of Table 2.5 and (as always) these relative frequencies sum to unity. Thus, another formula for finding the mean of a frequency distribution using relative frequencies is as follows:

Population mean for frequency distribution:

$$\mu = \sum_{i=1}^{k} x_i \left(\frac{f_i}{N}\right) \qquad (2.4)$$

The use of Formula 2.4 is demonstrated by column 5 of Table 2.5. Note that the sum of this column yields $\mu = 1{,}968$, the same value we calculated above by using Formula 2.3.

We must point out here that it is quite common in frequency tables for the values of x to be given as class intervals rather than as specific numbers. In such cases, the mean can still be calculated by using either Formula 2.3 or Formula 2.4. The value of x_i that should be used in the formula is the *class mark* for the ith interval. The usual class mark is the midpoint of the class interval. This selection is based on the assumption that the midpoint is the average of all occurrences of values of x within the interval. Since this assumption may not be exactly true, it is usually not worthwhile to determine exact midvalues. A rounded-off value may be used because the calculation of summary measures for a data set given in class interval form always involves a *grouping error*. This error tends to be small if the number of observations in each class is large. If several classes have frequencies of less than 5, it is desirable to combine some of the categories. The best strategy for small data sets (or if a computer is to be used for calculations) is to avoid grouping errors and to list all the separate values.

◻ STUDY QUESTION 2.1   Average Number of City Swimming Pools

In a selected area, there are 20 cities with approximately 50,000 people. A phone call was made to the government offices in each of these towns to determine the number of public swimming pools in the town. Table 2.6 presents the values reported for this population.

a) Find the mean of this population.

b) Arrange the population values into a frequency distribution and find the mean.

TABLE 2.6   Public Pools in Cities with Approximately 50,000 People

City	Number of Pools	City	Number of Pools
1	3	11	3
2	3	12	2
3	1	13	1
4	0	14	2
5	2	15	2
6	2	16	4
7	4	17	1
8	0	18	2
9	1	19	2
10	4	20	1

(Source: City Parks and Recreation Departments.)

● **ANSWER**

a)
$$\mu = \frac{1}{N} \sum_{i=1}^{N} x_i$$

$$= \frac{1}{20} \sum_{i=1}^{20} x_i$$

$$= \frac{1}{20}(3 + 3 + 1 + 0 + \cdots + 2 + 2 + 1) = \frac{40}{20} = 2.0$$

b)

Value x	0	1	2	3	4	Sum
Frequency f	2	5	7	3	3	20

$$\mu = \sum_{i=1}^{k} f_i x_i \bigg/ \sum_{i=1}^{k} f_i = \sum_{i=1}^{5} \frac{f_i x_i}{N}$$

$$= [2(0) + 5(1) + 7(2) + 3(3) + 3(4)]/20$$

$$= \frac{40}{20} = 2.0$$

The average number of public swimming pools in these cities is 2. ■

☐ STUDY QUESTION 2.2   Mean of Motor Assembly Times

Each of 30 trainees learning to repair small electric motors was given a test to complete an assembly of a 28-piece model of a motor. The number of minutes to complete the task was recorded for each trainee. This population of values is given in Table 2.7. Find the mean number of minutes to complete the assembly, using frequencies as weights as shown in Formula 2.3.

TABLE 2.7   Minutes to Complete Motor Assembly for 30 Trainees

Minutes	Frequency
$3.5 < x \le 4.5$	5
$4.5 < x \le 5.5$	4
$5.5 < x \le 6.5$	6
$6.5 < x \le 7.5$	9
$7.5 < x \le 8.5$	1
$8.5 < x \le 9.5$	3
$9.5 < x \le 10.5$	1
$10.5 < x \le 11.5$	1

● **ANSWER**   A representative value (class mark) must be selected for each interval of minutes. Choose the rounded-off values of the midpoints of each interval, $x_i = 4, 5, 6, \ldots, 11$.

$$\mu = \sum_{i=1}^{8} f_i x_i / N$$

$$= [5(4) + 4(5) + 6(6) + 9(7) + 1(8) + 3(9) + 1(10) + 1(11)]/30$$

$$= 195/30$$

$$= 6.5$$

The average number of minutes for trainees to complete assembly of the model of the motor is 6.5. ■

Two items are worth attention from these study questions. First, after you have found the answer to a statistical problem, the solution and final interpretation should always be clearly stated in a sentence. Second, the methodology and formula used should be made clear.

PROBLEMS

2.1 Explain what is meant by a measure of central location. Give an example from a recent newspaper or magazine of some use of a central location measure.

2.2 Refer to **Data Set 2** and find the median debt/equity for all 100 companies. [*Note:* There are missing data.]

2.3 Five $45 sweaters are on sale for $35, and three $85 coats are on sale for $60. Find the average percent decrease in price for these sale items.

2.4 The number of customers in a rural post office for 16 working days was: 68, 83, 47, 51, 91, 89, 99, 73, 62, 58, 91, 66, 75, 84, 77, 69.

a) Find the mean and the median.

b) Does this population have a unique mode? If so, is this mode a good measure of central location?

2.5 The owner of a local movie theatre showing art films has tabulated the ages of customers attending the last two showings:

TABLE 2.8   Art Film Theatre Attendance

Age Group	Number
18–22	60
23–27	80
28–32	50
33–37	40
38–42	30
43–47	20
48–52	20

a) In which class does the median fall? Would the midpoint of this class be a good guess for the median? If not, what age would you use as an approximation to the median?

b) What is the mode of this distribution?

c) Calculate the mean for this population. Use the midpoints $20, 25, \ldots, 50$ to represent all values in a class.

2.6 On the basis of Figure 2.3, find the mean unemployment rate for the seven months indicated. What must you assume in order for this measure to have a meaningful interpretation?

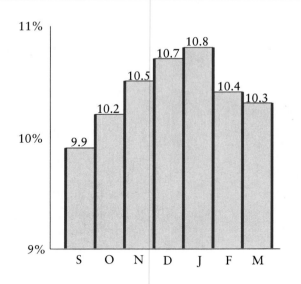

FIGURE 2.3   Unemployment rate

2.7 The distribution of the number of out-of-province phone calls made in a month by 100 residents of a small town is indicated by the following frequencies:

TABLE 2.9   Out-of-Province Telephone Calls

Number of calls per resident	0	1	2	3	4
Frequency	47	33	14	5	1

a) What are the median and the mode of this population?

b) Find the mean of this population.

2.8 Suppose that a certain gasoline producer sponsors a mileage economy test involving a population of 30 cars. The frequencies of the number of miles per gallon, x, recorded to the nearest gallon, are given in Table 2.10.

TABLE 2.10   Gasoline Mileage Economy Results

Mileage x	Number of Cars f
25	8
26	9
28	7
30	6

Find the average miles per gallon for this population using Formula 2.3.

2.9 Twenty communities provide information on the vacancy rate in local apartments. Find the mean of the following population of vacancy rates, using Formula 2.4. [*Hint*: Use the middle value for each vacancy rate.]

TABLE 2.11   Apartment Vacancy Rates

Relative Frequency	Vacancy Rate
0.5	3–7%
0.3	8–12%
0.2	13–17%

2.10 Refer to **Data Set 4** and consider the values for *net incomes of doctors*, as a population.

a) Find the median and the mean for income. Explain the difference between these two measures of central location.

b) Group the values of income into class intervals of $10,000 in width, beginning with the following interval:

$$\$90,000 < \text{income} \le \$100,000$$

Use Formula 2.3 to find μ. Explain the difference between this outcome and the mean found in part (a).

2.11 Repeat Problem 2.10 using the values for *expenses*. In part (b), use intervals of $10,000, beginning at $50,000.

2.12 Using the information in Figure 2.4, find the mean price of gas on Easter for the six years represented.

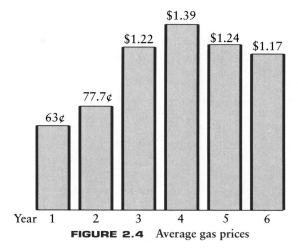

FIGURE 2.4   Average gas prices

Measures of Dispersion

Measures of central location usually do not give enough information to provide an adequate description of the data because variability or spread is ignored. An individual who bases a judgment on the mean alone may be compared to the person whose head is in a freezer and whose feet are in an oven declaring, "On the average, I feel fine." Another measure is needed, one that indicates how spread out or *dispersed* the data are.

◻ **EXAMPLE 2.7**   A broker suggests two different stocks to a client. One is for a microelectronics firm that has an average annual rate of growth over the past five years of 16%. The other is for an electric utility firm that has a growth rate of 8%. Which one would the client choose? Is the mean growth rate sufficient information to make an intelligent choice? It may be if all other characteristics are similar. However, suppose that it is also true that the first firm has had growth in one year as large as 30% and as low as −50% (a decline). The growth rate of the utility firm has always been between 7.5% and 8.5% over this period. How does this new information on variability affect the client's choice? It might be used as an indication of the risk of the two stocks. The client must choose between stocks with a relatively sure 8% growth rate and a riskier 16% growth rate.   ■

Since there are a number of ways to measure variability, let us consider some of the properties that a good measure should have. A good index of spread should be independent of the central location of the observations, that is, independent of the mean of the data. This property implies, in effect, that if a constant were added to or subtracted from each value in a set of observations, this transformation would not influence the measure of spread. In addition, to be most useful, a measure of spread should take into account *all* observations in its calculation, rather than just a few selected values such as the highest and lowest. Finally, a good measure should reflect the typical spread of the data, and it should be convenient to manipulate mathematically.

The Range

One simple example of a measure of spread is the **range**.

> The range is the *absolute difference* between the highest and lowest values in the data set.

The ranges of the four data sets in Table 2.2 are

$$|11 - 2| = 9 \quad |14 - 5| = 9 \quad |7 - 2| = 5 \quad \text{and} \quad |26 - 9| = 17$$

The range has the advantages of being independent of the measure of central location and being easy to calculate. It has the *disadvantages* of ignoring all but two values of the data set and not necessarily giving a *typical* measure of the dispersion, since a single extreme value changes the range radically.

The Mid-range

One way to help reduce the disadvantage of the range being highly sensitive to one extreme value is to throw out the outliers or extreme values by calculating a measure of the spread of the innermost concentrated portion of the data. Such a measure is called a **mid-range** and is obtained by excluding a specified proportion of the extreme values at both ends of the ordered values in the data set. Some common mid-ranges used are the 80% mid-range and the 50% mid-range.

☐ **EXAMPLE 2.8** **Data Set 2** includes the values of the retail sales of the top 50 Canadian companies listed in order. The range of the sales is the largest value minus the smallest. Remember, these data are in thousands of dollars.

$$R = (\text{maximum sales}) - (\text{minimum sales})$$
$$= 18,458,171 - 2,433,726 = \$16,024,445 \ (000\text{'s})$$

For this same population, the 80% mid-range would exclude the top 10% and the bottom 10% of the values of sales. The difference between the largest and the smallest of the remaining 80% of the values is found. Since the number of items in this population is 50, the top 10% of the values is the set of the largest five values. Excluding these and excluding the smallest five values gives the middle 40 values, those ranked 6th through 45th in sales:

$$80\% \text{ midrange} = (\text{sales of 6th firm}) - (\text{sales of 45th firm})$$
$$= 10,499,700 - 2,563,522 = \$7,936,178 \ (000\text{'s})$$

A mid-range uses more information than the range, since it involves the number of cases (N), the ranking of the values, the exclusion of a set percentage of the values, and the maximum and minimum of the remaining values. Because it is still quite easy to calculate, a mid-range is somewhat more desirable than the range in having good properties for a measure of spread or variability. ■

Deviations   There is an even better measure of variability that meets all the desirable properties. First, recall that we want our measure to be independent of the mean of the data. In other words, the value of μ should have no influence on the value of our measure of variability. This objective is accomplished by working always with data sets that have the *same* mean. That is, if all the populations that we wish to describe have the same mean, then the value of μ cannot influence our measure of variability. It is obvious, of course, that not all data sets have the same mean to begin with. We have to *transform* the values in each set in such a way that the transformed means are all equal.

The transformation used in statistics is designed to yield a data set always having $\mu = 0$. To make $\mu = 0$ is quite simple: merely subtract the mean of the original data set from each value in that set. Each resulting number, called a *deviation* and denoted $(x - \mu)$, indicates how far and in which direction the original number lies from the mean. For example, the deviation $(x - \mu) = 5$ reflects a value of x five units above the mean, and the deviation $(x - \mu) = -7$ indicates a value of x seven units below the mean.

The sum of the deviations will always equal zero; and so the average of the deviations will always equal zero. Consider, for example, a data set consisting of the five values of x shown in Table 2.12, which gives the number of cars towed per day (Monday–Friday) for illegal parking in a university permit-only lot.

TABLE 2.12   Observations and Deviations

Number of Cars Towed (x)	Deviations ($x - \mu$)
4	−6
8	−2
50	0
13	+3
15	+5
Sum 50	0
Mean 10	0

If we subtract the mean of these five numbers (which is $\mu = 10$) from each value of x, the mean of the new set of values, labeled $x - \mu$, must equal zero. Any set of numbers can be transformed in this fashion into a set of deviations with a mean of zero.

To formalize the above process, consider a population with N values x_i, $i = 1, 2, \ldots, N$, and mean μ. When these N values are transformed into deviations from the mean, the new values are $x_i - \mu$ for $i = 1, 2, \ldots, N$, and the sum of these deviations must be zero:

$$\sum_{i=1}^{N}(x_i - \mu) = 0$$

Since the transformation $(x_i - \mu)$ gives all sets of data a common central location, all have means of zero, measures of dispersion defined in terms of deviations about the mean have the desirable property of being independent of central location.

While the sum of the deviations about μ is advantageous because it takes into account *all* the observations and is independent of the mean, this sum clearly cannot be our measure of variability, since its value always equals zero. We will see in the following section that if we *square* each deviation before we sum, the resulting measure no longer equals zero and is relatively easy to manipulate mathematically. If we take the *average* of these squared deviations by dividing their sum by N, our measure also will reflect the typical spread of the data.[1]

Variance

Consider the *average squared deviations* about the mean. Squaring the deviations avoids the problem inherent in ordinary deviations about the mean (namely, that their sum always equals zero). Indeed, as we indicated above, this index meets all the properties of a good measure of spread; *thus the average squared deviation is the traditional basis for measuring the variability of a data set.* Since it uses the deviations about the mean, it is independent of central location. It uses every value in the data set and is reasonably easy to compute mathematically. Furthermore, it is very sensitive to any change in the values; even a single change of one value in a set of 100 would result in a different measure of variability.

This *average squared deviation* measure is called the *variance* and is denoted for a population by the symbol σ^2, which is the square of the lower case Greek letter *sigma*. The **population variance** (σ^2) is defined as follows:

Population variance:

$$\sigma^2 = \frac{1}{N} \sum_{i=1}^{N} (x_i - \mu)^2 \tag{2.5}$$

To calculate a variance using Formula 2.5, one first calculates each deviation; these deviations are squared, the squared deviations are then summed, and finally the sum is divided by N.

□ **EXAMPLE 2.9** We calculate a population variance using the values of x in Table 2.13 representing the number of refrigerators assembled by ten different workers on an assembly line. That is, worker 1 assembled 115 refrigerators, worker 2 assembled 122 refrigerators, et cetera. The mean number of refrigerators assembled is shown at the bottom of the first column:

$$\mu = \frac{1,200}{10} = 120$$

The deviations about the mean are shown in the second column. Note that the sum of these deviations equals zero, as it must. The third column of values gives the

---

[1] Another possibility for measuring variability is to average the sum of the absolute deviations about the mean, as follows:

$$\frac{1}{N} \sum |x_i - \mu| = \text{mean absolute deviation} = \text{MAD}$$

This MAD measure has all the desirable properties described above, except for the fact that it is not convenient to manipulate mathematically.

squared deviations about the mean, the sum of which is 436. Hence, the *average squared deviation* (the variance) of this population is:

$$\sigma^2 = \frac{1}{N}\sum_{i=1}^{N}(x_i - \mu)^2 = \frac{436}{10}$$

$$= 43.6 \text{ (refrigerators)}^2$$

Since we have squared the values of x in this process, the units for x have also been squared. That is, the units are now refrigerators squared. ∎

TABLE 2.13 Calculation of the Population Variance for Refrigerators

Worker	Number of refrigerators x	Deviation from the mean $(x - \mu)$	Deviation squared $(x - \mu)^2$
1	115	−5	25
2	122	+2	4
3	129	+9	81
4	113	−7	49
5	119	−1	1
6	124	+4	16
7	132	+12	144
8	120	0	0
9	110	−10	100
10	116	−4	16
	1200	0	436
	$\mu = 120$	0	$43.6 = \sigma^2$

From these calculations, it is probably apparent that finding the variance is a tedious process, yet one that can easily be adapted for solution by a computer. The only precaution is that when a computer package is used it must be clear as to whether the program is calculating a population variation or a sample variance. In Chapter 7, we will calculate a sample variance; for now, we are calculating population variances. Figure 2.5 shows the computer calculation for the income variable in **Data Set 2**.[2] We used the Lotus 1-2-3 functions to find the mean, variance, and range for this variable. Lotus calculates population variances.

```
Lotus 1-2-3 output for income variable in Data Set 2

Mean        88664.1
Variance    4E+10
Range       1826200
```

FIGURE 2.5 Summary measures for income variable in Data Set 2

---

[2] Income is stored in column D, rows 13 to 112 of our **Data Set 2** file. The Lotus command for the mean is @AVG(D13..D112), @VAR(D13..D112) for the variance, and @MAX(D13..D112)–@MIN(D13..D112) for the range.

There are several interesting features in the output above. Note that the mean is presented in decimal form ($88,664.10), while the variance and range are in integer form. Actually, with numbers this large, the decimal part of the values are quite meaningless, hence whole numbers are preferable here. The value of the variance is given in scientific notation (4E+10), which is, 4 followed by 10 zeros, or 40,000,000,000 (dollars squared). For **Data Set 2** there are some companies with income not reported. In such cases, the program treats these observations as missing data, and hence the population size is less than the original number of companies, which was $N = 100$. It is especially important to have a program which treats blank spaces as missing data and *not* as zeros. Lotus 1-2-3 does this correctly.

☐ STUDY QUESTION 2.3   Variance of Canoe Rentals

The data in Table 2.14 show the weekly number of canoes rented at the New River Camp Station for 40 weeks. Find the variance of this population, using Formula 2.5.

TABLE 2.14   Weekly Canoe Rentals over 40 weeks

63	68	71	74	76	78	81	84	85	89
66	70	73	75	76	79	82	84	85	90
67	71	73	75	76	79	82	85	86	92
68	71	74	75	77	79	84	85	86	94

● **ANSWER**   Using Formula 2.5 and the mean value of 78.2:

$$\sigma^2 = \frac{1}{40}\sum_{i=1}^{40}(x_i - 78.2)^2$$

$$= \frac{1}{40}[(63 - 78.2)^2 + (66 - 78.2)^2 + \cdots + (94 - 78.2)^2]$$

$$= \frac{1}{40}(231.04 + 148.84 + \cdots + 249.64)$$

$$= \frac{1}{40}(2{,}214.40) = 55.36(\text{canoes})^2$$

A computer printout of the variance and other measures for the population in Table 2.14 is shown in Figure 2.6. The arithmetic average is the mean, 78.200. The variance shown is 55.360.

This comparison of the computer output in Figure 2.6 with our hand calculations illustrates one *disadvantage* of using preprogrammed statistical computer packages. *They do not always calculate only the exact statistic that is desired.* Their *advantage* is clear: the user does not have to write the entire computer program. Remember that whenever you use someone else's computer program, you must know how the output measures are defined and calculated, or you might use them inappropriately. For example, look at Figure 2.6 for the computer printout for percentage frequency (ADJ PCT) and cumulative frequency (CUM PCT). The printing format of the program used only integer values, so these frequencies are rounded off and could be misunderstood. The first value of 63 occurs once and should have a percentage frequency of $(1/40)(100) = 2.5$, rather than 2. In the second line, for the value 66, the percentage frequency should again be 2.5. Note that the cumulative frequency is now $5(2.5 + 2.5)$, although it appears that the computer has obtained 5 by adding $2 + 2$. ∎

```
CANOE                      WEEKLY CANOE RENTALS

              ADJ   CUM                ADJ   CUM                ADJ   CUM
   CODE  FREQ PCT   PCT    CODE  FREQ  PCT   PCT   CODE  FREQ   PCT   PCT

   63    1    2     2      75    3     7     40    85    4      10    85
   66    1    2     5      76    3     7     47    86    2      5     90
   67    1    2     7      77    1     2     50    89    1      2     92
   68    2    5     13     78    1     2     52    90    1      2     95
   70    1    2     15     79    3     7     60    92    1      2     97
   71    3    7     22     81    1     2     63    94    1      2     100
   73    2    5     27     82    2     5     67
   74    2    5     32     84    3     7     75


   MEAN       78.200    MEDIAN      77.500    MODE    85.000
   STD DEV     7.535    VARIANCE    55.360    RANGE   31.000
   MINIMUM    63.000    MAXIMUM     94.000

   VALID CASES    40    MISSING CASES    0
```

FIGURE 2.6   Frequency distribution and summary measures for the data in Table 2.14

The Standard Deviation

Very often, the positive square root of the variance, denoted σ and called the **population standard deviation**, is used in place of (or in conjunction with) the population variance to describe variability. The standard deviation is usually more convenient than the variance for *interpreting* the variability of a data set, since σ^2 is in squared units while σ is in the same units as the original data. The population standard deviation is defined as follows:

Population standard deviation:

$$\sigma = +\sqrt{\frac{1}{N}\sum_{i=1}^{N}(x_i - \mu)^2} \qquad (2.6)$$

For the data in Table 2.13, the standard deviation for refrigerators is:

$$\sigma = \sqrt{\text{Variance}} = \sqrt{43.6} = 6.60 \text{ refrigerators}$$

In general, a precise interpretation of values of σ and σ^2 is difficult because variability depends so highly on the unit of measurement. For instance, variability of family income in Canada is certainly larger when measured in dollars than when measured in thousands of dollars. Nevertheless, these variability measures are very useful. In all cases, as the spread of a population increases, the values of σ^2 and σ will also increase. On the other hand, if $\sigma^2 = \sigma = 0$, there is no variability at all to the data. This means that all x-values are the same and equal to their mean or that x is a constant.

One **rule of thumb** that often provides a good *approximation* to the spread of a set of observations states the following:

> *About 68 percent* of all values in a population will fall within *one* standard deviation to either side of the mean, and *about 95 percent* of all values will fall within *two* standard deviations to either side of the mean.

In other words, the interval from $(\mu - 1\sigma)$ to $(\mu + 1\sigma)$, which we will write as $(\mu \pm 1\sigma)$, often will contain about 68 percent (or about $\frac{2}{3}$) of all population values. Similarly, the interval $(\mu - 2\sigma)$ to $(\mu + 2\sigma)$, that is $(\mu \pm 2\sigma)$, often will contain about 95% of all the population values. We must emphasize that these rules are only approximations and do not necessarily hold for any one discrete example. It is not difficult, for example, to show for the data on refrigerators (Table 2.13) that 60% of the population (six of the ten values) fall in the interval $(\mu \pm 1\sigma)$ and 100 percent of the data fall in the interval $(\mu \pm 2\sigma)$. These intervals are shown in Table 2.15. Recall that $\mu = 120.0$ and $\sigma = 6.60$.

TABLE 2.15   Use of the Rule of Thumb for Interpreting Variability

Interval	Values within Interval	Actual Percent of Population within Interval	Rule of Thumb
$\mu \pm 1\sigma = 120 \pm 6.60$ $= \begin{cases} 113.4 \text{ to} \\ 126.6 \end{cases}$	115,116,119,120,122,124	60%	68%
$\mu \pm 2\sigma = 120 \pm 2(6.60)$ $= \begin{cases} 106.80 \text{ to} \\ 133.20 \end{cases}$	110,113,115,116,119 120,122,124,129,132	100%	95%

The rule of thumb described above is based on a symmetrical bell-shaped curve called the normal, presented in Chapter 6.

☐ **EXAMPLE 2.10**   Consider once again the canoe rental data in Table 2.14. In Study Question 2.3, we determined that the mean of this population is $\mu = 78.2$ canoes and that the variance is $\sigma^2 = 55.36$ (canoes)^2. Because the variance is in squared units, it is often more appropriate to use the value of the standard deviation:

$$\sigma = \sqrt{55.36} = 7.44 \text{ canoes}$$

If the rule of thumb described earlier holds, then $\mu \pm 1\sigma$ should contain about 68% of the canoe rental data values, and $\mu \pm 2\sigma$ should contain about 95% of all these values. Checking these intervals against the values in Table 2.14 (without rounding) gives the following results:

TABLE 2.16   The Degree of Variability for the Canoe Data in Table 2.14

Interval	Number of Values	Percent of Values
$\mu \pm 1\sigma = 78.20 \pm 7.44 = 70.76$ to 85.64	28	70%
$\mu \pm 2\sigma = 78.20 \pm 2(7.44) = 63.32$ to 93.08	38	95%

The percent of values within the specified intervals are consistent with the rule of thumb. Such comparisons serve as a check on the reasonableness of the calculated values for μ and σ. If we had found that the interval $\mu \pm 1\sigma$ included more than 90% of the values of the population (too many), or that it included only 30% (too few), we would have known to recheck the calculations or re-examine the population for unusual values.

Also, understanding this rule of thumb helps to give us a mental picture of the distribution of the population. The mean μ gives the central location. The standard deviation σ gives a *standard* unit of spread around the mean that includes about $\frac{2}{3}$ of the values of the population. Hence, had we known only that $\sigma = 7.44$ and $\mu = 78.20$ canoes, and had we never seen the list of values for the population, we still could have given a good description of this particular set of values. ■

Considering all the measures of central location and dispersion that we have presented, the two measures most often useful in statistical inference and decision-making are the *mean* and the *standard deviation*. These are common everyday terms to any statistician, as they are used daily in helping to make decisions based on statistical analysis of data sets. The mean is precisely the balance point of all the values. The standard deviation is the typical (or standard) size of the difference (deviation) between the individual values of the population and the mean of the population. As such, it provides a good insight into the extent of variability in the data set, especially when the rule of thumb applies. The reader should keep in mind that the variance and the standard deviation do *not* represent two different ways of measuring the variability of a population. Since σ is merely the positive square root of σ^2, these two measures reflect the *same information* about variability but are expressed in different units. The standard deviation is easier to interpret because it is *not* in squared units, but it is more difficult than the variance to manipulate mathematically because of the square-root sign.

Population Variance for a Frequency Distribution

In Formula 2.5, we calculated the variance of a population, assuming that all frequency values were equal to 1 ($f_i = 1$). This formula can be generalized to take into account frequencies other than 1 in exactly the same manner in which the formula for the mean μ was generalized. Again, we assume that there are k different values of x. A squared deviation $(x_i - \mu)^2$ is calculated for every observation. Each squared deviation is then weighted by its frequency. Dividing the sum of the products by N we obtain the following:

Population variance for a frequency distribution:

$$\sigma^2 = \frac{1}{N} \sum_{i=1}^{k} (x_i - \mu)^2 f_i \qquad (2.7)$$

Formula 2.7 is illustrated by the first four columns of Table 2.17 for our salary example, which originated in Table 2.5. The mean salary was found to be $\mu =$

$1,968. Using Formula 2.7 and the sum in column 4, we find:

$$\sigma^2 = \frac{1}{250}(3,004,000) = 12,016(\text{dollars})^2$$

Notice that the sum in column 6 results in this same variance. Thus, summing column 6 is equivalent to Formula 2.7. ∎

TABLE 2.17   Calculating the Variance for a Frequency Distribution of Monthly Salaries[3]

(1)	(2)	(3)	(4)	(5)	(6)
	Frequency			Relative Frequency	$(x_i - \mu)^2\left(\dfrac{f_i}{N}\right)$
Salary (x_i)	(f)	($x_i - \mu$)	$(x_i - \mu)^2 f_i$	(f_i/N)	
$1,700	8	−268	574,592	0.032	2,298.368
1,800	23	−168	649,152	0.092	2,596.608
1,900	75	−68	346,800	0.300	1,387.200
2,000	90	32	92,160	0.360	368.640
2,100	43	132	749,232	0.172	2,996.928
2,200	11	232	592,064	0.044	2,368.256
Sum	250 = N		3,004,000	1.000	12,016.000

☐ STUDY QUESTION 2.4   Dispersion of the Number of City Swimming Pools

a) Find the variance and standard deviation for the frequency distribution of the swimming pool data in Study Question 2.1.
b) What percentage of the population values lie within one standard deviation of the mean?

• ANSWER

a) The calculations are easily organized by using a tabular format. If we remember that the mean is an integer, $\mu = 2$, Formula 2.7 is easy to apply.

TABLE 2.18   Dispersion of the Number of City Swimming Pools

x_i	f_i	$x_i - \mu$	$(x_i - \mu)^2$	$(x_i - \mu)^2 f_i$
0	2	−2	4	8
1	5	−1	1	5
2	7	0	0	0
3	3	+1	1	3
4	3	+2	4	12
	N = 20			Sum = 28

---

[3] The inquisitive reader may wonder why the sum of column 3 [$(x_i - \mu)$] in Table 2.17 does not equal zero. The reason is that each deviation occurs according to the frequencies in column 2. If each deviation is multiplied by its frequency and the products are summed, their total will be zero.

The variance in the number of city swimming pools is:

$$\sigma^2 = \frac{1}{N} \sum_{i=1}^{k} (x_j - \mu)^2 f_i = \frac{1}{20}(28) = 1.4(\text{pools})^2$$

The standard deviation in the number of pools is:

$$\sigma = \sqrt{1.4} = 1.18 \text{ pools}$$

b) $\mu \pm 1\sigma = 2 \pm 1.18$ is the interval [0.82, 3.18], which includes the population values, 1, 2, and 3. These occur with frequencies 5, 7, and 3, respectively. Thus, $5 + 7 + 3 = 15$ of the 20 population values are in this interval $\mu \pm 1\sigma$. The percentage within the interval $\mu \pm 1\sigma$ is $(15/20) \times 100 = 75\%$. ■

☐ STUDY QUESTION 2.5   Dispersion of Motor Assembly Times

For the data on minutes to complete the assembly of a model of a motor as given in Study Question 2.2, see Table 2.7. Find the variance, the standard deviation, and the percentage of population values within the interval $\mu \pm 1\sigma$.

● **ANSWER**   The data on minutes is given by a grouped frequency distribution. Class marks are used to represent the values within each group. A tabular arrangement is convenient for organizing the computations, remembering that $\mu = 6.5$.

TABLE 2.19   Dispersion of Motor Assembly Times

Class Mark x_i	f_i	$x_i - \mu$	$(x_i - \mu)^2 f_i$
4	5	-2.5	31.25
5	4	-1.5	9.00
6	6	-0.5	1.50
7	9	+0.5	2.25
8	1	+1.5	2.25
9	3	+2.5	18.75
10	1	+3.5	12.25
11	1	+4.5	20.25
$N = 30$			Sum = 97.50

The variance for complete motor assembly time is:

$$\sigma^2 = \frac{1}{N} \sum (x_i - \mu)^2 f_i$$

$$= \frac{1}{30}(97.50)$$

$$= 3.25(\text{minutes})^2$$

The standard deviation is $\sigma = \sqrt{3.25} = 1.80$ minutes.

The interval $\mu \pm 1\sigma$ includes values from $(6.5 - 1.80)$ to $(6.5 + 1.80)$. That is, the interval is [4.7, 8.3]. This interval includes the class marks of 5, 6, 7, and 8, and the frequencies of these class marks are 4, 6, 9, and 1, respectively. Thus, the approximate (due to the grouping error and the use of the class marks) percentage of population values within the interval [4.7, 8.3] is $100[(4+6+9+1)/30] = 66.7\%$. ■

Three Important Measures of a Data Set

Before we present some other descriptive and summary measures of populations, it is important to recognize that we have already discussed the three most important measures of data sets. These are *size, central location*, and *variability*. For further study in statistics and for use in decision problems, it is necessary to master the calculation of these measures and to understand their meaning.

Size, determined by counting the number of items in the population, is denoted by N. The mean (denoted by μ) is often the best measure of central location, especially for most business and economics applications. When each separate value of the population is listed, the mean is determined by using Formula 2.1. If the population values are given in a frequency listing, Formula 2.3 is most often used. If the values are grouped in class intervals, the class mark is substituted for x_i in this formula. Variability is best measured by the variance or the standard deviation. Formula 2.5 is appropriate when the individual values are available. Formula 2.7 is appropriate when a frequency listing of values is available.

Why are these three measures so important? They are the summary measures to which most persons refer when presenting results of a study or when using quantitative data to support some argument. They are the measures to use in writing a report based on data collected or found in a reference. They are the measures that will command our attention throughout this text. It must be noted that, many times, one or the other of these measures is used alone by a spokesperson, whether he or she is a politician, manager, teacher, or scientist. Look in a newspaper to find some examples of the use of size, mean, or standard deviation of a data set without reference to one of the others. However, be wary in making conclusions or decisions based on fewer than all three of these measures. Data may be misrepresented for the sake of an argument by using one or two of these measures while omitting the third.

Inadequacy of Central Location Measures Alone

Consider the case in which a person must choose between two sales jobs, each having potential earnings of $50,000 a year. One company representative says that their salespeople earning $50,000 work an average of 30 hours per week. The other prospective employer says the average for similar employees is 50 hours. One might decide on this basis to work for the first company with the *average* work week of 30 hours. Be careful! The average hours worked per week to earn $50,000 in the first company may be as low as 30 because the company president has hired some relatives who hardly work at all each week while the typical salesperson is working 65 hours per week. Or, the first company may have only two such salespeople who share all the mail orders. A third new person would split the total pot significantly or, perhaps, not share at all. In the other company, the average may be based on 800 salespeople. The measures for the second company would give a much more reliable value for the time and salary expected to occur for the 801st person. It is necessary to know more about the distribution of the data than merely the mean before this measure can be used intelligently in making a decision.

Inadequacy of Variability Measures Alone

Consider the decision process when you ask a special friend out to dinner to celebrate your A-grade in statistical analysis. Two restaurants are suggested as very suitable, and you are told that the variability in the price of a dinner is $10 in the first and $3 in the second. Is this enough information to make a sound decision? Suppose that the mean price for a dinner in the first restaurant is $12, while in the second it is $30. Or, suppose that the first restaurant has only three dinner selections — squid, shark, and eel — while the data for the second restaurant are based on 20 different specialties of the house, including meat, fish, and fowl. Again, it is obvious that while the variability is an important consideration, this measure by itself (without knowledge of the mean and the number of cases) is often insufficient for decision-making and may even be misleading.

The same consideration would apply to an investment decision between two managed funds. Information on the variability in the annual rate of return for each fund would be important to know but not sufficient. You should want to know the average as well; and you should want to know the number of years on which these measures are based.

☐ STUDY QUESTION 2.6   Analyzing Advertising Programs of Competitors

A marketing consultant for a beverage producer reviews the advertising programs of its competitors and notes that two of these competitors are preparing for a new promotional program during which the average price of a six-pack will be dropped 20%. Should the consultant try to devise a new marketing strategy that would be equally effective in offsetting the price reduction of each competitor?

● **ANSWER**   The summary measure given is a central location measure. The consultant should try to learn something about the standard deviation as well. One competitor may be planning to drop the price 5–30%, depending on the location of the market throughout the country. The other competitor may be planning a 20% drop nationwide with no variability. Two different reactions may be appropriate. Also, the total market share or the number of cases of beverage sold by each of these competitors may be relevant. One may be a very small and specialized beverage producer distributing only 1000 cases per week. The other may be one of the largest producers, distributing millions of cases per day. Obviously, the beverage producer might have different levels of concern over the two planned advertising programs. In summary, the single measure of 20% does not provide enough information, although it may be a very good summary measure for indicating central location.   ■

In the discussion above, we emphasized that the mean and the variance (or standard deviation) alone are insufficient measures for summarizing a data set. Often, the standard deviation (σ) increases proportionally to the mean. A measure designed to indicate the size of σ relative to μ is the **coefficient of variation (CV)**. This measure indicates what proportion the standard deviation is of the mean as follows:

$$CV = \frac{\sigma}{\mu} \, 100$$

Thus, if $\mu = 200$, and $\sigma = 20$, then $CV = (20/200)(100) = 10$ indicates that the average variability (measured by $\sigma = 20$) is 10 percent of the mean. Recall the data on assembly times for a motor, in Study Question 2.5, where $\mu = 6.5$ minutes and $\sigma = 1.80$ minutes. For this example

$$CV = \frac{1.8}{6.5} \, 100 = 27.7$$

The coefficient of variation indicates that the standard deviation is 27.7% of the mean. In many statistics problems (such as forecasting), we would like the CV to be less than 10%. Thus, 27.7% represents a fairly high value for a coefficient of variation.

PROBLEMS

2.13 A recruiter for a certain company claims that advancement opportunities are great in the company because present salaries of five-year employees range from 20% to 200% more than their corresponding beginning salaries. Explain why this statistical information might be inadequate for a prospective employee who is trying to decide whether or not to take a job with this company.

2.14 Find the variance for the population described in Problem 2.4.

2.15 Find the variance for the population described in Problem 2.5.

2.16 Use the information in Problem 2.7 to do the following:

a) Find the variance of the number of calls per student using Formula 2.7.

b) What percent of the population falls within the interval $\mu \pm 1\sigma$. Within the interval $\mu \pm 2\sigma$?

c) What is the coefficient of variation?

2.17 Use the information in Problem 2.8 to do the following:

a) Find the standard deviation for the population.

b) Find the percent of the population that falls within the $\mu \pm 1\sigma$ and $\mu \pm 2\sigma$ intervals.

c) Find the coefficient of variation.

2.18 Consider the following frequency distribution:

TABLE 2.20

Class	Frequency	Class Mark	xf	$(x - \mu)^2 f$
1–5	4	3	12	210.2500
6–10	8			
11–15	3			
16–20	5		90	

a) Find the mean of this population by completing the table above.

b) Find the variance.

2.19 Find the variance for the population in Problem 2.9 using Formula 2.7. Use (f/N) as weights rather than f, as was the procedure in column 6 of Table 2.17.

2.20 A bank has 156 branch offices. The age (x) of the branch managers is given in the frequency distribution of Table 2.21.

TABLE 2.21

Age	Frequency
$30 \leq x \leq 34$	8
$35 \leq x \leq 39$	21
$40 \leq x \leq 44$	24
$45 \leq x \leq 49$	32
$50 \leq x \leq 54$	40
$55 \leq x \leq 59$	23
$60 \leq x \leq 64$	8

Find the mean and standard deviation of the ages of the branch managers.

2.21 Use the information in Problem 2.12 to do the following:

a) Find the variance of the gas prices.

b) What proportion of the observed years have gas prices within one standard deviation of the mean?

c) What proportion of μ is σ?

2.22 Use the information in Problem 2.6 to do the following:

a) Find the standard deviation of the unemployment rates.

b) What proportion of the months have unemployment rates within one standard deviation of the mean?

c) What is the coefficient of variation?

<table>
<tr><td>section 2.4</td></tr>
</table>

Other Descriptive Measures

While the mean and the standard deviation are the most common descriptive measures, there are a number of other measures that give additional information about the characteristics of a data set. This section is devoted to describing, rather briefly, a few of these measures.

Percentiles, Deciles, and Quartiles

The summary measures described thus far all use just a single number to describe certain characteristics of a population. In some circumstances, it may be helpful to use *more* than one number to describe a data set. For example, a company recruiter visiting a college campus may be interested in learning more than just the mean or median grade point average for all graduating seniors. This person may want to know the average of those members of the graduating class who form the upper 10%, the upper 20%, and so forth. Percentiles, deciles, and quartiles are useful in this circumstance in that they divide a data set into a specified number of groups, each containing the same number of values. **Percentiles** divide the data into 100 equal parts, each representing one percent of all values. The 90th percentile, for example, is that value which has 90% of all values below it and 10% above it. Thus, a student scoring higher than 95% and lower than 5% of all students on the college board exams is said to have scored in the 95th percentile. Percentiles can be *determined exactly* from a table of cumulative relative frequencies of ungrouped data and *approximated* from a table of grouped data.

Quartiles and deciles are defined in much the same fashion as percentiles: **quartiles** divide the data into four equal parts, while **deciles** divide the data into ten equal parts. The *first* quartile value is that point which exceeds one-fourth and is exceeded by three-fourths of the observations. Only three quartile values are necessary to divide the data into four parts. Likewise, nine decile values divide a set of observations into ten equal parts. The *fifth decile* and the *second quartile* values are equivalent to the *median*.

Some other percentile or quartile measures are already familiar to us in terms of other measures. The 50% mid-range is equivalent to the range between the first and third quartiles, called the **interquartile range**. The range between the first and ninth decile is the 80% mid-range. The range between the 16th and the 84th percentile would include the middle 68% of the values of the population. Therefore, in accord with our rule of thumb, one-half of this 68% mid-range could be used to approximate the size of the standard deviation, especially if the distribution is symmetric and has a single mode.

Shapes of Distributions

Having a method for describing the *shape* of a frequency distribution is often more helpful than just being able to describe the central location or spread of a set of values. Most of the distributions representing real-world problems are called *unimodal* distributions, implying that they have only one peak, or *mode*. A distribution with two peaks is called a **bimodal distribution**. Often, distributions with more than one mode actually reflect the merging of two or more *separate* kinds of data into a single set of values.

Consider, for example, the frequency distribution shown in Figure 2.7 representing the frequency of sales of Chevrolet automobiles for a large dealership, in thousands of dollars (e.g., 11 = $11,000). What Figure 2.7 actually represents is *two* unimodal distributions: one reflecting the sales of the so called "economy" or compact Chevrolets, and the other representing the sales of intermediate cars. If we make this distinction and plot the resulting frequency distributions, the two distributions in Figure 2.8 are obtained. Note that the distribution in Figure 2.8(a) has a fairly long *tail* to the right, a characteristic common to many distributions representing data in the behavioural and social sciences, especially income distributions.

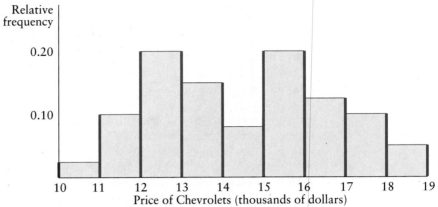

FIGURE 2.7   Combined sales of Chevrolets

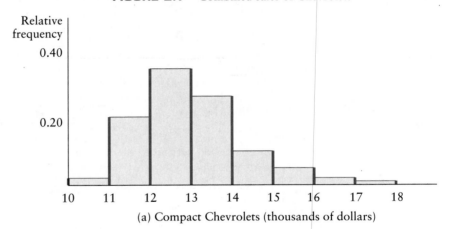

(a) Compact Chevrolets (thousands of dollars)

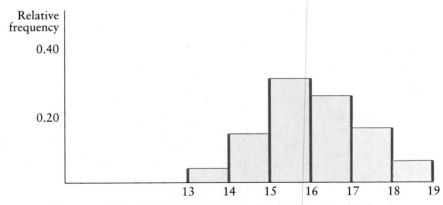

(b) Intermediate-sized Chevrolets (thousands of dollars)

FIGURE 2.8   Chevrolet sales

A distribution is a **symmetric distribution** if it has the same shape on both sides of its median. Imagine folding the picture of a distribution in half at its median. To be symmetric, the two halves must match perfectly — they must be *mirror images* of one another. For all symmetric distributions, the median equals the mean. The mode will also equal the median if the distribution is unimodal. Figure 2.9 shows three symmetric distributions.

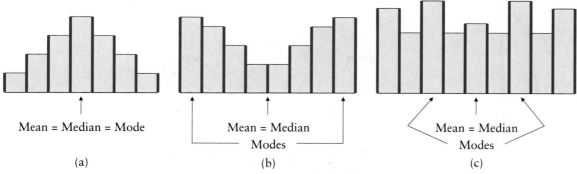

Mean = Median = Mode

(a)

Mean = Median

Modes

(b)

Mean = Median

Modes

(c)

FIGURE 2.9   Symmetric distributions

A distribution that is not symmetric, but rather has most of its values either to the right or to the left of the mode, is said to be a **skewed distribution**. If most of the values of a distribution fall to the *right* of the mode, as in Figure 2.8(a), this distribution is said to be skewed to the right or *skewed positively*. A distribution with the opposite shape, with most values to the *left* of the mode, is said to be skewed to the left, or *skewed negatively*. Note in Figure 2.10 how the lack of symmetry in a distribution affects the relationship between the mean, the median, and the mode. For a completely symmetrical unimodal distribution, such as Figure 2.9(a), these three values must all be equal. As the distribution becomes skewed positively, the mode remains at the value representing the highest frequency, but the median and the mean move to the right.

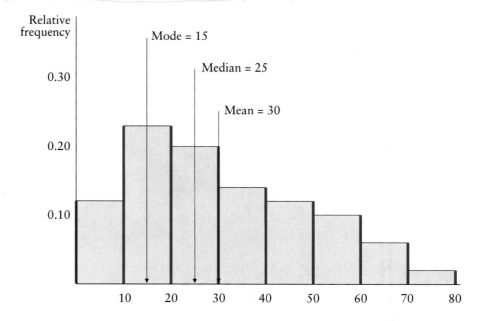

FIGURE 2.10   The relationship between the mean, the median, and the mode for a distribution with positive skewness

Various memory aids make it easy to remember the direction and the effect of skewness on the measures of central location in a unimodal distribution. Two useful ones are the following:

1. The order of magnitude of the central location measures is *alphabetical* in a *negatively-skewed* distribution (mean, median, mode) and *reversed* in a *positively-skewed* distribution such as Figure 2.10.

2. If a distribution is stretched sideways, the direction of stretch is the direction of skewness. A distribution with its right-hand side stretched out in the positive (increasing numerical value) direction has positive skewness. A distribution with its left tail stretched out in the negative (decreasing numerical value) direction is negatively skewed.

Kurtosis

Another descriptive measure of the shape of a distribution relates to its flatness or peakedness. The term applied to this characteristic of shape is **kurtosis**. The flat distribution with short broad tails illustrated in Figure 2.11 is called *platykurtic*. A very peaked distribution with long thin tails is called *leptokurtic*. Measures of kurtosis (and skewness) are important to mathematical statisticians in their study of the theoretical properties of distributions. Although summary measures for kurtosis exist, we will not present them in this text, since measures of kurtosis are of relatively little use in elementary applications of statistics.

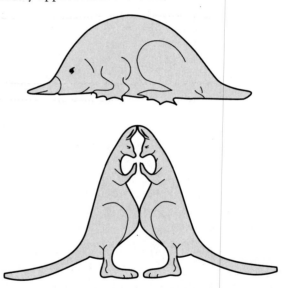

FIGURE 2.11   Platykurtic curves have short tails like a platypus, while leptokurtic curves have long tails like kangaroos, noted for "lepping" (after W. S. Gosset)

section 2.5

Data Presentation — Using the Computer

We have indicated that most statistical computations today involve using a statistical package for the computer. Indeed, any serious work cannot (practically) be accomplished using hand calculations, for numerous reasons, a few of which are presented here:

1. Often, the data set is so large that hand calculation of even relatively simple statistics would take much too long to complete.

2. Some analyses are so involved that without a computer they are not practical for hand calculations.

3. Calculations without a computer are subject to many human errors, such as merely adding a column of numbers incorrectly.

4. Graphical presentation summarizing a data set are convenient and relatively straightforward using a computer; they are tedious and often impractical by hand.

A large number of computer packages are available for statistical analysis. We will mention and describe how to use a few of these packages, recognizing that the reader may be using a different package. Fortunately, the output of many packages contains much of the same information, so that if one learns to interpret one output, there will be considerable carryover to other outputs.

There are packages for mainframe computers, and packages for personal computers. Sometimes a version of a mainframe package is available for a PC. Often, the PC packages are not as powerful, or cannot handle as much data as mainframe programs, although this is less and less of a problem as PCs become more powerful. The student versions of some programs offer fewer options, and/or are restricted in the amount of data that can be handled.

There are a few packages that have been around for many years. These include SPSS (Statistical Package for the Social Sciences), BMDP (Biomedical Package), SAS (Statistical Analysis System) and IDA (Interactive Data Analysis). Among the many other packages are: Minitab, Statpak, Execustat, BSTAT, Mystat, Systat, Statistix, and Doane's package, Exploring Statistics with the IBM P.C. Many spreadsheets (such as Lotus 1-2-3) and database programs will perform routine statistical analysis. Finally, there are specialized packages for graphical presentations. Perhaps the best known of these graphical packages is *Harvard Graphics*. Many word-processing programs will do fine graphs; for example, Draw Perfect is the graphical package accompanying Word Perfect.

In this section, we demonstrate the use of several statistical packages to show how data can be summarized and presented. The methods presented represent only a small subset of the techniques available.

☐ **EXAMPLE 2.11**   We used the Minitab program to generate, for **Data Set 4,** the descriptive summary and the dot plot presented in Figure 2.12. [*Note:* we omit in Figure 2.12 several statistical measures which have not yet been covered in this text. The Q1 and Q3 values are the first and third quartiles. The dotplot shows all 40 observations as dots. For those who know Minitab, the commands **Describe C4** and **Dotplot C4** were used at the MTB prompt because the variable FEE was stored in column 4 (C4) of our Minitab file, which was imported from Lotus.]

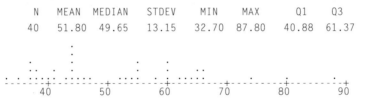

```
  N   MEAN  MEDIAN  STDEV   MIN    MAX    Q1     Q3
 40  51.80   49.65  13.15  32.70  87.80  40.88  61.37
```

FIGURE 2.12   Minitab output for fees, in Data Set 4

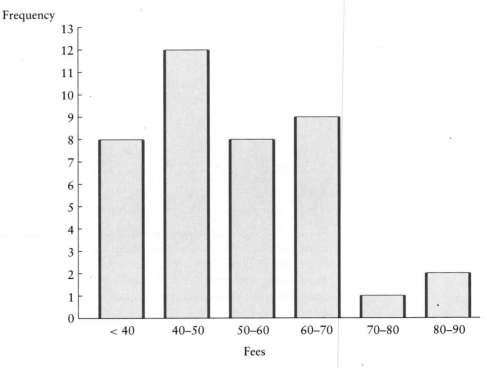

FIGURE 2.13 The fee data from Data Set 4

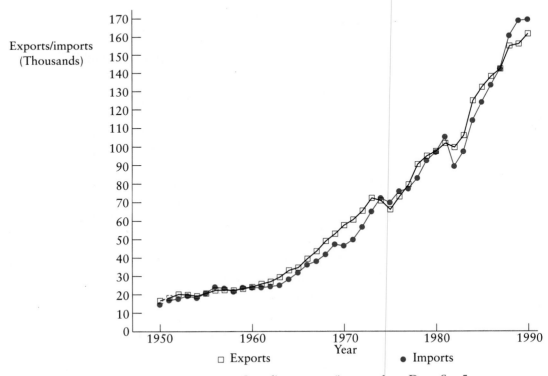

FIGURE 2.14 Canadian exports/imports from Data Set 5

Lotus 1-2-3 does an excellent job of presenting data in graphical form. Figure 2.13 presents the doctor fees in **Data Set 4** in histogram form. For those familiar with Lotus, we used the /DD comands to construct a frequency distribution, with categories < $40, $40--$50, $50--$60, $60--$70, $70--$80, and > $80. The graph function was then used to create a title and the legends.

The second Lotus graph, in Figure 2.14, presents the Canadian export/ import data (1950--1990), from **Data Set 5**, in time series form. This output looks particularly nice if your computer has a colour monitor, or you have a colour printer.   ■

❑ EXAMPLE 2.12   Some computer programs do especially good graphics, and Execustat is one of the better ones. To demonstrate the 3-dimensional capability of such packages, we have generated two graphs from **Data Set 4**, using Execustat. The first of these graphs, Figure 2.15, is a 3-dimensional histogram, showing physician fees on one axis and hours worked on another. The vertical axis is frequency. This type of graph is useful in visualizing how hours and fees are related. Notice in this case that fees were divided into just three categories (< $50, $50--$80, and > $80), and hours were divided into two categories (< 50 and > 50). Other categories could have been used, and might have been more useful depending on the circumstances.

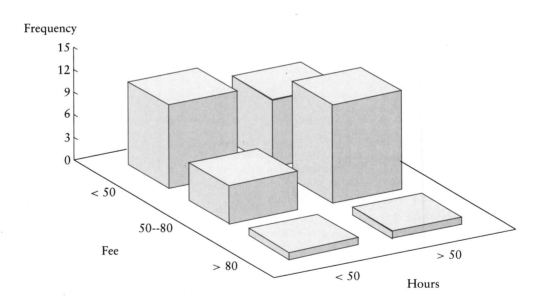

FIGURE 2.15   Histogram for Data Set 4

Our second Execustat output (Figure 2.16) is a 3-dimensional scatterplot relating physician fees, income, and hours worked, all from **Data Set 4**. While such 3-dimensional graphs frequently appear impressive, interpreting them is often difficult.

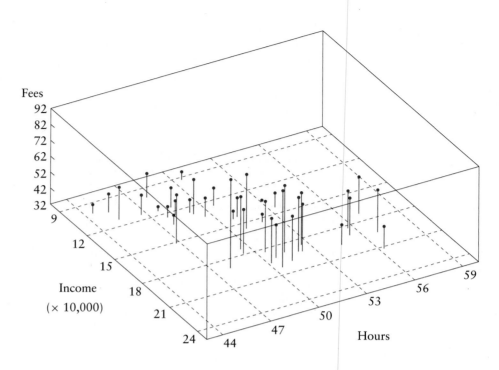

FIGURE 2.16   Scatterplot relating income, fees, and hours

PROBLEMS

2.23 Answer parts (a), (b), and (c).

a) A financial management company operates ten mutual funds. For each of the past five months, the numbers of their funds that have increased in value per share have been 3, 5, 1, 8, and 3. Show that the mean and standard deviation for this population of five numbers are 4.0 and 2.37, respectively.

b) Suppose that in the next two months the numbers of managed funds that increase in value per share are 2 and 6. Include these observations with those in part (a) and find the mean of this population of seven numbers. Show that it has a smaller standard deviation than in part (a).

c) Suppose that a different company also manages ten funds and had the same experience as the company in part (a). However, in the next two months, the numbers of its funds that increase in value per share are zero and 8. Find the mean and explain why the standard deviation is larger in this population than in part (a).

2.24 One hundred families are registered in a regional welfare office for financial assistance under the Aid for Dependent Children program. The number of children per family is given as follows:

Number of children:	0	1	2	3	4	5	6—10
Number of families:	2	3	15	35	20	15	10

a) What is the median number of children per family? What is the modal number? Find the mean number of children.

b) What is the 60% mid-range for the number of children per family? What is the standard deviation?

c) What proportion of the families have a number of children within one standard deviation of the mean?

2.25 Given the following values for the number of rooms reserved in a population of ten motels, find the mean, mode, median, 60% mid-range, and standard deviation:

35   14   6   18   14
27   19   7   12   14

2.26 The population *kitchen employees in seven local restaurants* is 2, 9, 1, 3, 10, 3, and 2.

  a) Find the mean, median, and mode.

  b) Calculate σ^2 for these values.

  c) Is this population symmetric, or is it skewed positively or negatively?

2.27 Answer the following questions about percentiles, quartiles, and deciles.

  a) What does it mean if a math score is reported as being in the *85th percentile*?

  b) If your college grades are in the third quartile, what does this mean?

  c) If the sales growth of a franchise is in the eighth decile among all outlets in its region, what does this mean?

2.28 Discuss the difference between the interquartile range and $\mu \pm 1\sigma$. Which one would be easier for the layperson to understand?

2.29 Given the following distribution of the rate (x) of capacity utilized by a population of 32 steel-producing plants, find the mean and variance of x. Use the midvalue of each class (the class mark) as the value of x.

TABLE 2.22 Rate of Capacity Used by Steel-Producing Plants

Utilization Rate	Frequency	Class Mark
96–100	4	98
91–95	5	93
86–90	6	
81–85	5	
76–80	1	
71–75	4	
66–70	2	
61–65	5	

2.30 The frequency distribution in Table 2.23 shows the weekly sales of a pizza restaurant for its first year of operation.

TABLE 2.23

Sales	Number of Weeks
0–$5,999	4
$6,000–11,999	6
12,000–17,999	10
18,000–23,999	16
24,000–29,999	12
30,000–35,999	4
Total	52

  a) Compute the mean and the mode.

  b) Compute the variance.

  c) Present these data in a graphical form.

2.31 Return to Problem 1.10, which gives the starting salaries for 16 accounting majors after receiving their college degrees.

  a) Find the median and the mode.

  b) Using the classes suggested in Problem 1.10(c), find the mean of these data. Explain any difference between this mean and the one calculated in Problem 1.10(b).

2.32 Assume that the data listed in Problem 1.10 are for a population and compute the following:

  a) range, and the interquartile range

  b) variance and the standard deviation

  c) percent of the observations falling within one standard deviation from the mean and the percent falling within two standard deviations from the mean.

  d) Repeat part (b) using the grouped data in Problem 1.10(c).

2.33 The ten households in Oldberry, North Carolina, report the following incomes:

$30,500	$24,150	$22,505	$26,245	$25,570
$26,600	$34,800	$31,325	$29,170	$39,000

  a) Find the mean, standard deviation, and median of these data.

  b) Compare the variability and skewness of this distribution with a regional income distribution that reports a mean of $30,000, standard deviation of $3,000, and median of $28,000.

  c) Use a computer graphics package to describe these data.

2.34 How are the mean, the median, and the mode related in a completely symmetrical and unimodal frequency distribution? How are they related in positively-skewed and in negatively-skewed unimodal distributions? Sketch several distributions to illustrate your answer.

CHAPTER SUMMARY

In this chapter we have focused on describing the central location and variability of populations as aids to decision-making. The two measures that are of greatest importance are the mean and the standard deviation. The population mean μ is the most important measure of central location, and the standard deviation σ is the most important measure of variability. The primary formula for calculating the mean is:

$$\mu = \frac{1}{N} \sum_{i=1}^{k} x_i f_i$$

When all the values are listed separately and each is given equal weight, each value of f_i is 1, and $k = N$. When the data are arranged in a grouped distribution, the values of x_i are the class marks for each class.

The standard deviation is calculated as the *square root* of the variance. The variance formula is:

$$\sigma^2 = \frac{1}{N} \sum_{i=1}^{k} (x_i - \mu)^2 f_i$$

Again, f_i are the frequencies, and x_i are the values or the class marks of specified groups of values.

KEY TERMS AND EXPRESSIONS

Mode: The value that occurs most frequently.

Median: The middle value in a set of values (population or a sample).

Population mean: The average of a set of N values:

$$\mu = \frac{1}{N} \sum_{i=1}^{N} x_i \quad \text{or} \quad \mu = \frac{1}{N} \sum_{i=1}^{k} x_i f_i$$

Range: The absolute value of the difference between the maximum and minimum values in a data set.

A% mid-range: The absolute value of the difference between the highest and lowest of the middle A% of the values in the data set, excluding $[(100 - A)/2]$% of the extreme values at each end of the distribution.

Population variance (σ^2): The average of the squared deviations of values of x from their mean:

$$\sigma^2 = \frac{1}{N} \sum_{i=1}^{N} (x_i - \mu)^2$$

or

$$\sigma^2 = \frac{1}{N} \sum_{i=1}^{k} (x_i - \mu)^2 f_i$$

Population standard deviation (σ): The square root of the variance:

$$\sigma = \sqrt{\sigma^2}$$

Rule of thumb: $\mu \pm 1\sigma$ includes about 68% of the population values; $\mu \pm 2\sigma$ includes about 95% of the values.

Coefficient of variation: A measure designed to indicate the proportion the standard deviation is of the mean:

$$CV = \left(\frac{\sigma}{\mu} \right) 100$$

Percentiles: Those values that separate a data set into 100 equal parts.

Quartiles: Three values that separate a data set into four equal parts.

Deciles: Nine values that separate a data set into ten equal parts.

Interquartile range: The absolute value of the difference between the third quartile value and the first quartile value, equivalent to the 50% mid-range.

Bimodal distribution: A distribution with two distinct modes.

Symmetric distribution: A distribution with the same shape on both sides of the median.

Skewed distribution: Any distribution that is not symmetric. Skewed to the right (positively) means that the mean is to the right of the median. Skewed negatively is the opposite.

Kurtosis: A measure of the shape of a distribution, depicting its degree of flatness or peakedness.

EXERCISES

(Use the computer for these problems whenever possible.)

2.35 Find an example from a newspaper, magazine, et cetera, of using only *means* to draw some conclusion. Examine the argument closely and explain the need to know the *size* or *variability* of the populations and how this could strengthen or weaken the argument.

2.36 Find an example from a newspaper, magazine, et cetera, of using only *variability* to draw some conclusions. Examine the argument closely and explain the inadequacy of it, or explain how knowledge of a *size* or *average* measure could strengthen or change the argument.

2.37 Acquire 50 observations on a variable of interest to you such as wage rates or apartment rental rates. Find the mean and the standard deviation of your data. Use these to present a summary statement of the information provided by your data.

2.38 Make up two sets of eight values each, with the following characteristics:

a) same average but different variability

b) same range but different averages

c) same average and same range, but different 50% mid-range

2.39 A movie producer holds a preview of a new movie and asks viewers for their reaction. By age groups the following results are obtained.

TABLE 2.24 Viewer Reaction to a New Movie by Age Group

	< 20	20–39	40–49	≥ 50
Liked the movie	140	75	50	10
Disliked the movie	60	50	50	20

Summarize these results using means and standard deviations of ages.

2.40 T. M. Jones, manager of Shark Loan, Inc., has kept a record of the frequency of the *time between arrivals* of customers at his loan office. These data, shown below, indicate that the time interval between consecutive arrivals was between zero and 20 minutes on 50 occasions, between 20 and 40 minutes on 33 different occasions, et cetera. Since there were 150 customers during this period, there are 150 interarrival times (the time to the first customer is counted as one interarrival time).

TABLE 2.25 Time Interval Between Customers

Minutes between Customers (t)	Frequency (f)
$0 < t \le 20$	50
$20 < t \le 40$	33
$40 < t \le 60$	22
$60 < t \le 80$	15
$80 < t \le 100$	11
$100 < t \le 120$	8
$120 < t \le 140$	5
$140 < t \le 160$	3
$160 < t \le 180$	2
$180 < t \le 200$	1
	150

a) Construct a histogram of relative frequencies and a cumulative relative frequency distribution for the interarrival times. Draw the polygon for these distributions.

b) Find the mode, the median, the mean, and the standard deviation. (Use class marks of 10, 30, 50, ...).

c) What percent of the observations fall within $\mu \pm 1\sigma$? What percent fall within $\mu \pm 2\sigma$?

d) Based on these data, how many customers would you estimate for Shark Loan next week, if the office is open five days a week, ten hours a day?

2.41 Assume that you are responsible for auditing last month's accounts receivable for the 10,000 credit accounts on the Easy Charge Company. The company has furnished you with the following summary data for this population. This is a slight abstraction of 12,223 actual credit balances.

TABLE 2.26

Balance Due	Frequency	Balance Due	Frequency
$0–99.99	3,123	$600–699.99	180
100–199.99	2,085	700–799.99	90
200–299.99	1,927	800–899.99	53
300–399.99	1,355	900–999.99	25
400–499.99	743	> $1000	19
500–599.99	400		

a) Draw the histogram of relative frequencies and the polygon for these data.

b) As an auditor, are you satisfied with the manner in which the company summarized the data?

c) Use the midpoint of each class and the associated frequencies to calculate the mean of this population. Assume that the 19 values in the eleventh class average $1,050.

d) Calculate σ and σ^2 for this population. What percent of the population lies within $\mu \pm 1\sigma$ and $\mu \pm 2\sigma$?

e) Is this distribution skewed to the right or the left?

♦ **2.42** To assist in scheduling future cases in the local small claims court, the court clerk collects data on the length of time required to hear recent cases. The 25 cases heard by the judge in 1993 took the following times (in minutes). Assume the data are a population.

TABLE 2.27 Hearing Time for 25 Small Claims Cases

Trial Number	Time (minutes)	Trial Number	Time (minutes)
1.	68	14.	55
2.	99	15.	32
3.	126	16.	74
4.	45	17.	98
5.	87	18.	54
6.	106	19.	128
7.	112	20.	62
8.	38	21.	30
9.	66	22.	53
10.	57	23.	69
11.	83	24.	106
12.	145	25.	44
13.	77		

a) Construct a frequency distribution and relative frequency, using five classes of width 25 each. Make the lower limit of the first class equal to 25.

b) Calculate the coefficient of variation for this population.

♦ **2.43** In a statistical process-control method for a manufacturing operation, items from the output of the process are selected and their dimensions carefully measured. A machine is producing axles which have a specified diameter of 100 cm. A sample of eight axles is found to have the following diameters in centimetres

101	106	97	102
103	96	98	98

a) Calculate the mean, variance, standard deviation, and mode of the diameters of the axles being produced. Treat the eight values as a population.

b) Find the median and the 50% mid-range of the eight values.

2.44 The frequency distribution of employee years of service for Henry Enterprises is positively skewed (not symmetrical). If a CA wishes to describe the years of service of the typical Henry employee in a special report, the measure of central tendency that the CA should use is the:

a) standard deviation

b) arithmetic mean

c) mode

d) median

USING THE COMPUTER

2.45 Refer to **Data Set 4** in Appendix C and find the variance and standard deviation of a doctor's fees. Also, determine the percentage of the population values that lie within one standard deviation of the mean.

2.46 Refer to **Data Set 8** and find the variance and standard deviation of the returns for IBM. Determine the proportion of the returns within the intervals $\mu \pm 1\sigma$ and $\mu \pm 2\sigma$. Present the data in a time series graph.

2.47 The weekly wages in September 1993 of 105 employees in a textile mill are given in Table 2.28. Find the mean and standard deviation of the weekly wages.

2.48 Use **Data Set 1** to answer the following.

a) Find the mean and standard deviation of *per capita* income. Then determine the percentage of the population values in the intervals $\mu \pm 1\sigma$ and $\mu \pm 2\sigma$. Use a computer package, if possible.

b) Use a computer graphics program to present the per capita incomes in **Data Set 1** in several formats. For example, you might give a pie chart, or a frequency distribution, or even a 3-dimensional plot relating population to income.

TABLE 2.28 Weekly Wages of a Textile Mill's Employees

Weekly Wages (x)	Employees
$360 < x \leq 370$	4
$370 < x \leq 380$	14
$380 < x \leq 390$	18
$390 < x \leq 400$	28
$400 < x \leq 410$	20
$410 < x \leq 420$	12
$420 < x \leq 430$	9

CASE PROBLEM

2.49 A number of investment services and brokerage houses regularly publish recommendations on which common stocks to purchase for various investment goals. Based on these opinions, a list is compiled of the 300 stocks that were most recommended for purchase one year ago. The subsequent total return on these stocks over a 12-month period is given below. Using summary measures, describe the total return for this population.

TABLE 2.29 The 300 Most Recommended Stocks for Purchase

Total Return	f	Total Return	f
$-3 < x \leq -2$	3	$17 < x \leq 18$	13
$-2 < x \leq 1$	1	$18 < x \leq 19$	12
$-1 < x \leq 0$	1	$19 < x \leq 20$	10
$0 < x \leq 1$	1	$20 < x \leq 21$	8
$1 < x \leq 2$	2	$21 < x \leq 22$	6
$2 < x \leq 3$	6	$22 < x \leq 23$	3
$3 < x \leq 4$	10	$23 < x \leq 24$	2
$4 < x \leq 5$	2	$24 < x \leq 25$	7
$5 < x \leq 6$	6	$25 < x \leq 26$	2
$6 < x \leq 7$	16	$26 < x \leq 27$	8
$7 < x \leq 8$	11	$27 < x \leq 28$	2
$8 < x \leq 9$	8	$28 < x \leq 29$	2
$9 < x \leq 10$	18	$29 < x \leq 30$	1
$10 < x \leq 11$	22	$30 < x \leq 31$	1
$11 < x \leq 12$	23	$31 < x \leq 32$	1
$12 < x \leq 13$	22	$32 < x \leq 33$	0
$13 < x \leq 14$	19	$33 < x \leq 34$	1
$14 < x \leq 15$	21	$34 < x \leq 35$	1
$15 < x \leq 16$	16	$35 < x \leq 36$	0
$16 < x \leq 17$	11	$36 < x \leq 37$	1

CHAPTER 3

Probability Theory: Discrete Sample Spaces

Before we can progress further in our discussion of the use of statistics to make decisions or to reach conclusions, it is important to present some of the fundamental concepts necessary for statistical analysis, particularly those relating to probability. Chapters 3–6 are devoted to probability. Then, in Chapter 7, we will begin to combine these probability concepts with the summary measures of Chapters 1 and 2 in order to develop methods for estimation, hypothesis-testing, and decision-making.

Introduction

section 3.1

Any analytical approach to statistical problems involves evaluations of just how likely it is that certain events have occurred or will occur.

> An event is defined as some subset of the possible outcomes in a decision-making situation under conditions of uncertainty.

☐ **EXAMPLE 3.1** Suppose you are the owner of a large Chevrolet dealership. You are currently faced with the annual problem of placing the January/February order for new cars, a time when new car sales are usually quite slow. If you order too many, the cars sit on the lot, you pay interest on the money borrowed, and you may have to pay property tax on the unsold cars. An order for too few, however, may lead to lost sales for customers who want to buy from inventory. You are wondering what the probability is that you will run out of stock of the new four-door Chevrolet sedans if you only order ten cars. ■

> A probability is a number between 0 and 1 that indicates how likely it is that an event will occur. If an event is impossible, then its probability is zero. If an event is certain, then its probability is 1.0.

A fundamental part of almost all types of statistical analysis includes finding the value between 0 and 1 that represents how likely to occur an event is, and probability theory provides the foundation for the methods of this analysis.

The origins of probability theory date back to the 1600s when mathematicians Blaise Pascal and Pierre Fermat became interested in games of chance. Although Pascal and Fermat corresponded regularly about problems involving elements of chance, not until over 100 years later did this new branch of mathematics find many applications beyond the French gambling houses of the seventeenth century. The work of Karl Gauss and Pierre Laplace was instrumental during the later 1700s in extending probability theory to problems of the social sciences and actuarial mathematics. Laplace commented, "It is remarkable that a science that began with the consideration of games of chance could have become the most important object of human knowledge." Despite the contributions made in the seventeenth through the nineteenth centuries, the bulk of modern statistics has developed in the past 60 years. R. A. Fisher, J. Neyman, E. S. Pearson, and A. Wald are among the more prominent researchers who have contributed to the phenomenal growth of statistics.

The Probability Model

In statistics, we often wish to specify the probability of some event. For example, we may wish to determine the probability that a computer chip will be defective, or the probability that the price of dairy products will decrease, or that an error will be discovered in an inventory audit. To specify the probability associated with a given situation, it is extremely important to define what *experiment* underlies this situation and what outcomes can result from this experiment. As we will demonstrate in this chapter and in Chapter 4, making probability assessments is simplified by using a *probability model* as a framework for the mental construction of the problem. Such a probability model provides the foundation for using certain probability laws and formulas.

The Experiment

The first component in a probability model is the definition of the **experiment**.

> An experiment is any situation capable of replication under essentially stable conditions.

A replication is a repeat of the experiment. Replications need not actually be performed but must be at least theoretically conceivable. For example, auditing a company's inventory could be an experiment, even though the auditor intends to do it only once this year. We can imagine repeating such an audit many times and theoretically consider the probability of finding many different outcomes.

☐ **EXAMPLE 3.2** For an experiment that would be repeated over and over, consider a manufacturing process making child-proof lids for plastic jars containing medicine. If the lids are too loose, a child may be able to open the jar. If the lid is too tight, some people (particularly the elderly) may have difficulty opening it. Given a production process that does not always produce lids with exactly the same interior dimensions, what is the probability that a lid will be too loose or too tight? ■

Testing a computer program for errors might be an experiment. You might be interested in the theoretical chances that the program will run perfectly. Clearly, an experiment is defined very broadly to correspond to *any situation involving uncertainty*, whether it actually recurs many times or whether the replications are hypothetical.

When an experiment is defined, it is necessary to specify *all* the procedures associated with the experiment. For example, in Chapter 1 we drew a random sample from the cities in **Data Set 1**. Such an experiment (it *is* an experiment!) can be conducted either with replacement or without replacement. Think of picking the cities to be included in the sample one at a time. If sampling is with replacement, after a city is picked it is put back on the list, and this same city can be picked again. Thus, the same city could appear more than once in a given sample. For sampling without replacement, a city picked is not replaced on the list; hence a given city can occur at most once in the sample. Although most samples are taken without replacement, the probability analysis is easier if replacement occurs, or if we assume that it does.

Sample Spaces

Once an experiment is defined, it becomes obvious that not all replications of the experiment will result in the same outcomes. For instance, suppose the experiment is to count the number of defective child-proof lids. The lids and jars are packed in boxes, where each box contains 100 child-proof jars and lids. Each time a box is inspected, this can be thought of as a replication of the experiment. The number of defective lids in each box can be any number from 0 to 100.

The different outcomes of an experiment are often referred to as *sample points*, and the set of all possible outcomes is called the **sample space**. In the case of child-proof lids, the sample points are *discrete and finite*, where discrete means that the outcomes can be separated from one another and finite means that the number of outcomes is limited. If the experiment had been *count the number of lids until you find the first defective*, then the sample space would be discrete and infinite since there is no limit to the number of lids before the first defective, assuming production continues indefinitely. Other examples of a discrete sample space include the number of errors in a computer program and the dollar amount an investor could lose in the stock market.

In contrast to a discrete sample space is the concept of a continuous sample space. A sample space is continuous if the number of possible outcomes is infinite and uncountable. The number of hours it takes a certain light bulb to burn out represents a continuous sample space because the outcome of this experiment could be *any* real number from zero up to some upper bound, say, 10,000 hours. There is obviously an infinite number of outcomes possible here and no way to separate and count them. The net weight of a box of packaged cereal, the length of fish caught in a trout stream, and the distance a car can travel on a tank of gas are all examples of outcomes in a continuous sample space.

> Generally, the sample space is continuous if the data are obtained by measurement and discrete if the data are obtained by counting.

We must hasten to add that it is not always clear from the statement of an experiment exactly what outcomes are relevant. For example, the outcome of a $1,000 investment in the stock market might be classified in any number of ways, including any one of the following:

1. Investment earns money, loses money, or breaks even.
2. Investment earns some specific rate of return.
3. Investment earns a yield (x) of either $0 < x \leq 2\%$, $-2\% < x \leq 0$, $2\% < x \leq 4\%$, $-4\% < x \leq -2\%$, et cetera.

> In defining the sample space of an experiment, one must be sure that the outcomes are mutually exclusive and exhaustive.

Mutually exclusive outcomes are those that have no overlap. Thus, we could not define the outcomes of an investment in the stock market as 0–2%, 2%–4%, 4%–6%, et cetera because these categories overlap at 2%, 4%, and so forth. **Exhaustive outcomes** mean that no possible outcome is left off the list. For example, we could not define the possible outcomes of a $1,000 investment as *earns money* or *loses money* because this sample space omits the outcome *breaks even*.

Any subset of the outcomes of an experiment is called an **event**. For example, the set of outcomes $-10\% < x \leq 10\%$ could be considered an event in our investment example, as could the set of outcomes *do not lose money*. Events may or may not be mutually exclusive and exhaustive.

To summarize briefly, we have defined the following terms and their role in every probability model.

1. An experiment: Situation capable of replication under stable conditions.
2. Outcome of an experiment (sample space):
   a. Discrete (separable): The number of outcomes is countable.
      • Finite (an upper limit on number)
      • Infinite (no upper limit on number)
   b. Continuous (nonseparable): The number of outcomes is infinite.
3. Event: Some subset of the outcomes of an experiment.
4. Mutually exclusive and exhaustive outcomes: Outcomes that do not overlap (are mutually exclusive) and account for (exhaust) all possible results of the experiment.

There are two additional components of every probability model: (1) a random variable and (2) a probability function. These two additional components of the model are important in describing the probability of the entire set of events of interest in a given experiment. They will be discussed in detail in Chapter 4.

Subjective and Objective Probability

section 3.3

There is some disagreement, even among authorities, about the definition of the **probability of an event**. The first and more traditional viewpoint uses the following definition.

> **Probability** is the relative frequency with which an event occurs over time.

Under this definition, a probability is usually referred to as a *frequency probability* or an **objective probability** since it is determined by objective evidence and would have the same value regardless of who did the interpretation.

The second interpretation of probability assigns probabilities based on the decision-maker's subjective estimates, using prior knowledge, information, and experience as a guide. This approach, in which a probability is referred to as a **subjective probability**, has gained considerable importance in statistical theory, largely because of the influence of such statisticians as L. J. Savage, R. Schlaifer, and H. Raiffa.

Suppose you estimate the probability to be 0.25 that General Motors sells more than 80,000 cars this week, or you estimate that there is a 0.90 chance the local grocery store will sell more than 300 loaves of bread today. These are subjective evaluations in which your personal opinion about the probability of these events need not agree with that of the President of GM or the manager of the grocery store, or anyone else.

The problem with the *frequency approach* to estimating probabilities is that in many real-world settings there may be little or no historical data available on which to base an estimate of the probability of an event. In such cases, only a *subjective* probability can be determined, and this probability may differ even among experts who have similar technical knowledge and identical information. For example, various scientists in 1960 gave different estimates of the probability that humans would walk on the moon within that decade. Similarly, investment brokers differ substantially in their opinion on how the stock market will behave over the next several months.

Much of the historical development of probability can be traced to an analysis of problems in which only a finite number of outcomes may take place and in which each of these outcomes is assumed to have the same chance of occurring. In such situations, if any one of the N *equally likely* outcomes can take place, then the probability of any one outcome occurring is $1/N$.

☐ **EXAMPLE 3.3**   Suppose that *Reader's Digest* mails out announcements of a contest to 50,000 different people, stating that the grand-prize winner will be selected *at random* from the list of 50,000 people. Random selection, in this context, means that each person is equally likely to be selected; the probability of being the grand-prize winner is thus P(grand-prize winner) $= 1/50,000 = 0.00002$.[1]   ■

When the number of equally likely outcomes in a given problem is relatively small, it is often possible to determine the probability of each outcome by counting the total number of outcomes (N), and then calculating $1/N$.

In Section 3.4 we will discuss several rules that aid in this counting process. Before doing so, we can now present a rule for finding the probability of an event when this event is composed of a number of equally likely outcomes. The probability of an event is the ratio of the number of outcomes comprising this event to the total number of equally likely outcomes in the sample space.

Probability of an event:

$$P(\text{event}) = \frac{\text{Number of outcomes comprising the event}}{\text{Total number of equally likely outcomes in the sample space}}$$
$$(3.1)$$

We give numerous examples of this rule throughout the chapter.

☐ **EXAMPLE 3.4**   Assume that you are randomly going to pick one company from the first 50 companies shown in **Data Set 2**. You want to know the probability of picking a company with sales greater than $5,000,000,000. In this case, the total number of equally likely outcomes is 50. There are 19 companies with sales over $5 billion; hence:

$$P(\text{event}) = \frac{\text{Number of companies with sales} > \$5 \text{ billion}}{\text{Number of equally likely outcomes}}$$
$$= \frac{19}{50} = 0.38$$

---

[1] Probability values can be stated as either fractions or decimals. For the most part, in this chapter the fractional form will be more convenient.

Therefore, a company with sales greater than 5 billion dollars will be picked almost 40% of the time. ∎

Before continuing, we must formally present the two basic properties necessary for defining the probability of an event. If an event E_i is a subset of a discrete sample space denoted by S, and $P(E_i)$ is the probability of that event, then the following **two basic properties** must hold:

> Property 1. $0 \leq P(E_i) \leq 1.0$ for every subset E_i of S
>
> Property 2. $P(S) = \Sigma P(E_i) = 1.0$ for mutually exclusive and exhaustive events

It is easy to recognize that these properties are consistent with our previous examples. The first one says that the probability of an event can never be less than zero (which represents an impossibility) nor greater than one (which represents a certainty). The second property applies to a set of mutually exclusive events, and says that the events E_i comprising the sample space must be *exhaustive* — it must be a certainty that one of the mutually exclusive events in the sample space will take place in each replication of the experiment.

We have emphasized, in this section, that one often wants to know the total number of possible outcomes in an experiment. Since, in many situations, it is not immediately obvious how many different outcomes there are for a given experiment, various rules have been developed for calculating this number. These rules, called *counting rules*, are discussed in Section 3.4.

Counting Rules

Many probability experiments involve two or more steps, each of which can result in one of a number of different outcomes. To calculate probabilities in such experiments, we often first determine the total number of possible outcomes.

□ **EXAMPLE 3.5**   Three people are asked whether or not they own stock. There are three steps (interviewing three people), and each step has two outcomes, stock owner (S) or not a stock owner (NS). There are eight different outcomes to this experiment, as shown in Figure 3.1. ∎

Basic Counting Rules

In the stock ownership example above, there are only three steps (people), and each step has two possible outcomes (S or NS). The total number of outcomes (N) in this experiment is:

$$N = (2)(2)(2) = 8$$

To generalize this type of calculation, suppose we denote the number of outcomes in the first step of an experiment as n_1, the number of outcomes in the second step as n_2, and so forth, with n_k denoting the number of outcomes in the last (or kth) step. The **basic counting rule** states that the total number of outcomes (N) equals the product of the number of outcomes in each step.

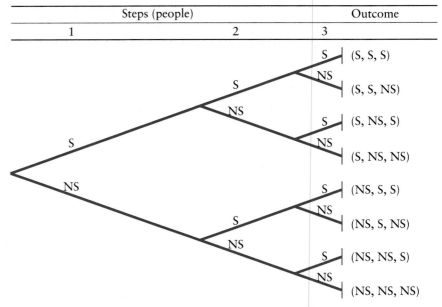

FIGURE 3.1   Tree diagram for stock ownership experiment

Basic counting rule:

$$\text{Total number of sample points } N = n_1(n_2)\ldots(n_k) \qquad (3.2)$$

In our stock-ownership example, $n_1 = 2$, $n_2 = 2$, and $n_3 = 2$; hence, $N = n_1 \cdot n_2 \cdot n_3 = 2 \cdot 2 \cdot 2 = 8$.

☐ **EXAMPLE 3.6**   To illustrate Formula 3.2, consider a company that is going to select one of four different pricing policies and then select one of three different advertising packages. In this example, $n_1 = 4$ (pricing) and $n_2 = 3$ (advertising). The total number of outcomes of this experiment by Formula 3.2 is:

$$N = n_1 \cdot n_2 = 4 \cdot 3 = 12$$

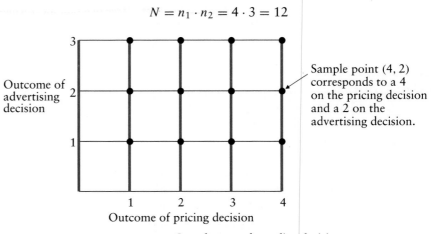

FIGURE 3.2   Sample space for policy decisions

The twelve different sample points (outcomes) in the sample space for this experiment are shown in the grid in Figure 3.2. If all 12 sample points are assumed to be equally likely (which they may not be), then the probability of any one occurring is $1/N = \frac{1}{12}$.

As with our stock-ownership example, the sample space can be described by the use of a tree diagram (Figure 3.3). Note that, as before, the order of outcomes is important [outcome (2, 3) differs from outcome (3, 2)]. ■

Step 1 – Pricing decision	Step 2 – Advertising

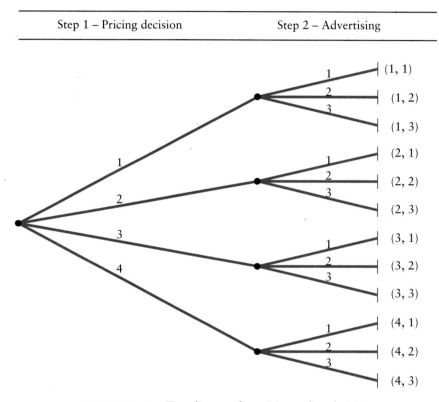

FIGURE 3.3   Tree diagram for pricing-policy decisions

More Basic Probability

Up to this point, we have focused on determining the total number of sample points in the sample space and using this information to calculate the probability of each equally likely sample point. We now turn to the situation that occurs in most practical problems, where the event of interest includes more than one sample point. In these circumstances, the *probability of an event* can be determined by *adding* the probabilities of each of the sample points that are a part of the event of interest. Since, in this chapter, all of the sample points we will illustrate can be assumed to be equally likely, the equivalent of adding their probabilities can be expressed by a multiplication as in the following equation.

Probability of an event:

$$P(\text{event}) = P(\text{one sample point}) \times \left(\begin{array}{c} \text{Number of relevant} \\ \text{sample points} \end{array} \right) \qquad (3.3)$$

To illustrate this rule, we return to our marketing-policy decisions of Figure 3.2 and assume that someone is interested in the probability that *either* the pricing strategy equals 1 *or* the advertising strategy is 2 or larger. From Figure 3.3, we know that there are 12 different sample points; if they are all assumed to be equally likely, then:

$$P(\text{one sample point}) = \frac{1}{12}$$

The tree diagram in Figure 3.3 can be used to determine how many different sample points have a 1 in the first position (pricing) or a 2 or more in the second position (advertising). The following nine points have those characteristics:

$$(1,1), \ (1,2), \ (1,3), \ (2,2), \ (2,3), \ (3,2), \ (3,3), \ (4,2), \ (4,3)$$

Hence, the number of relevant sample points equals 9, and we find the following probability:

$$P(\text{price} = 1 \text{ or advertising} \geq 2) = \left(\frac{1}{12} \right) \left(9 \right) = \frac{9}{12} = \frac{3}{4}$$

In other words, we would expect, assuming equally likely outcomes, three of every four such decisions would either have price = 1 or have 2 or more for advertising (or both).

☐ **EXAMPLE 3.7**   As another illustration of Formula 3.3, suppose that in our stock-ownership survey of three people we want to determine the probability of the outcome *two owners, one non-owner*. Recall from Figure 3.1 that the probability of each sample point, assuming equally likely outcomes, is $\frac{1}{8}$. Hence:

$$P(\text{one sample point}) = \frac{1}{8}$$

The relevant sample points in this example are the three outcomes (S, S, NS), (S, NS, S), and (NS, S, S). Thus, the number of relevant sample points is 3. The probability of the event (2 stock owners, 1 non-owner) is therefore:

$$P(2 \text{ S}, 1 \text{ NS}) = \left(\frac{1}{8} \right) \left(3 \right) = \frac{3}{8} \qquad \blacksquare$$

Using the same approach as used in Example 3.7, the reader should verify each of the probabilities below and note that they satisfy the two basic properties of all probabilities.

$$P(3 \text{ stock owners}) = \frac{1}{8}$$

$$P(2 \text{ stock owners, 1 non-owner}) = \frac{3}{8}$$

$$P(1 \text{ stock owner, 2 non-owners}) = \frac{3}{8}$$

$$P(3 \text{ non-owners}) = \frac{1}{8}$$

$$\text{Sum} = \frac{8}{8}$$

The above examples involved such a small number of outcomes that we could readily list the entire sample space and count the number of relevant sample points. In problems with larger sample spaces, this approach is impractical, if not impossible. The remaining sections in this chapter are devoted to presenting rules and formulas designed to help calculate probabilities without going through a cumbersome enumeration process. As we progress through these rules, however, the reader should bear in mind that, at least for finite sample spaces, the formulas still represent what are essentially counting rules.

☐ STUDY QUESTION 3.1 Assignment of OSHA Inspectors

An important task of certain business and governmental agencies involves assigning workers to specific tasks (or machines). For example, the United States Department of Labor assigns OSHA (Occupational Safety and Health Act) specialists to inspect employer locations for safety. Suppose a city has three inspectors (A, B, and C) and two first-priority locations (where a catastrophe or fatality has occurred), and must now assign one inspector to one of the two locations. Draw the tree diagram for this problem and find the probability that A is given the assignment or that the location is number 2. Use the counting rule to determine the total number of outcomes.

• **ANSWER**   As shown in Figure 3.4, there are (3)(2) = 6 outcomes, each with probability $\frac{1}{6}$.

$$P(A \text{ or } 2) = \left(\frac{1}{6}\right)\left(4\right) = \frac{2}{3}$$ ■

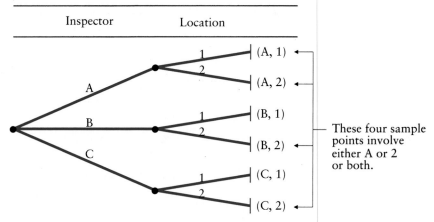

FIGURE 3.4   Tree diagram for Study Question 3.1

<table>
<tr><td>section 3.5</td></tr>
</table>

Permutations and Combinations

In some probability problems, one has a set of objects, all distinguishable from one another, and wants to know how many different ways there are of ordering these objects. This may happen, for example, when a number of different jobs are waiting to be finished in a business which handles customizing orders, or when we might want to know the number of different cities a sales representative could visit in one week.

❏ **EXAMPLE 3.8**   Suppose we want to determine the number of different ways the top three candidates for the new dean of a business school can be ranked by the search and screen committee. Suppose, for example, we label the three candidates for the dean's position as A, B, and C. In this case, it is quite simple to list all six different ways that the three candidates can be ordered:

$$\begin{array}{ccc} A\,B\,C & B\,A\,C & C\,A\,B \\ A\,C\,B & B\,C\,A & C\,B\,A \end{array}$$

We might think of these six orderings as all possible points in a sample space. If all six points are equally likely to occur in an experiment, then the probability of any *one* ordering is $\frac{1}{6}$. ■

The number of ways of ordering n objects (where n is any number) can be determined by using Formula 3.2.

❏ **EXAMPLE 3.9**   Suppose that a job-shop foreman has eight jobs in line and they can be completed only one at a time. Step 1 can be thought of as completing one of the jobs, step 2 as completing a second job, and so forth, step 8 being the last job to be completed. In this experiment, $n_1 = 8$ (eight different jobs can go first), $n_2 = 7$ (there are only seven jobs left after one job is taken first), $n_3 = 6, \cdots, n_8 = 1$, so that the total number of possible outcomes (orderings) is, by Formula 3.2:

$$8(7)(6)(5)(4)(3)(2)(1) = 40,320$$

The product of the numbers on the left-hand side is usually written in a shorthand notation as 8!, which is read as *eight factorial*.   ■

In general, if the number of objects to be ranked or ordered is n (where n is a positive integer), then the symbol $n!$ (read **n factorial**) represents the number of possible arrangements (orderings) of these n objects. Thus, the special case of Formula 3.2 appropriate for determining the number of ways of ordering n objects is:

Number of orderings of n objects:

$$n \text{ factorial:} \quad n! = n(n-1)(n-2)\cdots(3)(2)(1) \qquad (3.4)$$

Formula 3.4 is used to determine the number of possible orderings of n different objects.[2] In such cases, the experiment will consist of n steps, and each step will have one fewer possible outcomes than the prior step.

□ EXAMPLE 3.10   Consider the number of ways a corporate vice-president in charge of systems might rank four different brands of computers (A, B, C, D) being considered for purchase. In this situation, the number of objects to be arranged is $n = 4$. Hence, the number of orderings is

$$n! = 4! = 4(3)(2)(1) = 24$$

If these 24 orderings are all equally likely, then the probability that any one will occur is $\frac{1}{24}$.   ■

Permutations

Each different ordering of a set of objects is called a permutation. Thus, Formula 3.4 is one way of determining the number of permutations of n objects. In many probability problems, we are not interested in the number of permutations of *all n* objects, but rather of some *subset* of these objects.

□ EXAMPLE 3.11   The job-shop foreman in Example 3.9 has eight jobs waiting to be finished, but only three of these jobs can be placed on tomorrow's schedule. The foreman wants to know how many orderings there are if three jobs are picked out of the eight. In this experiment, there are three steps: The first step has eight possible outcomes (eight different jobs can be the one to be scheduled first), the second step has seven possible outcomes, and the third step has six possible outcomes. By the basic counting rule (Formula 3.2), the number of permutations is:

$$n_1(n_2)(n_3) = 8(7)(6) = 336$$

The number 336 gives the number of permutations of 8 objects taken 3 at a time, which is denoted by the symbol $_8P_3$.   ■

In general, we will denote the number of objects in the subset by the letter x, and the total number of objects by the letter n (where $x \leq n$). Thus, $_nP_x$ denotes the number of **permutations of n objects taken x at a time**.

By the basic counting rule, the value of $_nP_x$ is the product of the number of outcomes of step 1 (n) times the number of outcomes of step 2 ($n - 1$), and so forth, until all x steps are included. This product is as follows:

---

[2] The value of 0! is defined as 1.

Value of $_nP_x$:

$$_nP_x = n(n-1)(n-2)\cdots(n-x+1) \qquad (3.5)$$

This formula for $_nP_x$ is equivalent to Formula 3.6.[3]

Permutations of n objects taken x at a time:

$$_nP_x = \frac{n!}{(n-x)!} \qquad (3.6)$$

A good exercise for the reader is to verify that $_8P_3 = 336$, using Formula 3.5.

To illustrate the use of Formula 3.6, suppose a list of four investments (A, B, C, D) for a business firm is presented to the board of directors, and the board is asked to rank the two projects they consider to be the best opportunities. To answer the question, "How many different orderings are possible of two investment opportunities out of a total of four?", we need to calculate the number of permutations of $n = 4$ objects taken $x = 2$ at a time, or $_4P_2$:

$$_4P_2 = \frac{4!}{(4-2)!} = \frac{4!}{2!} = \frac{4 \cdot 3 \cdot 2 \cdot 1}{2 \cdot 1} = 12$$

The 12 permutations are shown in Table 3.1. If all 12 of these permutations are equally likely, then the probability of any one occurring is $\frac{1}{12}$.

TABLE 3.1   Permutations of Investment Possibilities

Rank	1	2	3	4	5	6	7	8	9	10	11	12
1	A	A	A	B	B	B	C	C	C	D	D	D
2	B	C	D	A	C	D	A	B	D	A	B	C

Combinations

The number of permutations of a set of objects represents the number of ways the objects can be ordered. But in many circumstances, one cannot or does not want to be concerned with order. For instance, the order in which voters are surveyed on public issues generally is assumed to be unimportant, as is the order in which cards are received in a bridge hand, or the order in which bids are received in a sealed-bid

---

[3] To prove this relationship, we first rewrite Formula 3.4 as follows:

$$n! = n(n-1)(n-2)\cdots(n-x+1)(n-x)!$$

Dividing both sides of this expression by $(n-x)!$ yields

$$n(n-1)(n-2)\cdots(n-x+1),$$

which is identical to Formula 3.6.

competition. In these cases, interest usually centres on the number of *combinations* of objects that can occur, where two sets of objects are considered to be identical if they contain exactly the same elements, no matter how these objects are arranged. *A combination is thus a set of objects where order is unimportant.* The symbol $_nC_x$ is used to denote the number of **combinations of n objects taken x at a time.**

There are always *fewer* combinations than permutations for a given n and x, since different orderings do not count as combinations, but do count as permutations. Thus, $_nP_x$ will always be larger than $_nC_x$ by a factor of $x!$:

$$_nC_x = \frac{_nP_x}{x!}$$

By substituting for $_nP_x$ from Formula 3.6, we can write the following formula:

> Combinations of n objects taken x at a time:
>
> $$_nC_x = \frac{n!}{x!(n-x)!} \qquad (3.7)$$

☐ **EXAMPLE 3.12**   To illustrate Formula 3.7, suppose the Air Force has decided to award software contracts for $500 million worth of new computer equipment to two of the six companies submitting bids. The number of different ways that two winning firms ($x = 2$) can be selected out of $n = 6$ is as follows:

$$_6C_2 = \frac{6!}{2!(6-2)!} = \frac{6 \cdot 5 \cdot 4 \cdot 3 \cdot 2 \cdot 1}{(2 \cdot 1)(4 \cdot 3 \cdot 2 \cdot 1)} = 15$$

If these 15 combinations are all equally likely, then the probability that any one combination occurs is $\frac{1}{15}$. ■

As n becomes larger, the number of combinations can become very large. For example, suppose a bridge player wants to determine how many different bridge hands are possible. The number of hands in this case is the number of combinations of $n = 52$ objects (cards) taken $x = 13$ at a time (13 cards to a hand):

$$_{52}C_{13} = \frac{52!}{13!(52-13)!}$$

Even with an electronic calculator, these factorials are not much fun to evaluate; hence, they are often merely left in the factorial form shown above. Our bridge player, however, was determined enough to calculate that 635013559600 different bridge hands are possible and they are all equally likely.

PROBLEMS

3.1 Consider this experiment: General Motors picks a new president out of candidates A, B, C, and D.

a) Describe the outcomes of the experiment. Is this sample space finite or infinite, discrete or continuous?

b) Your present thoughts are that candidates A, B, and C are equally likely, and candidate D is three times as likely as A. What probability values should you assign to A, B, C, and D? Are these values subjective or objective probabilities?

c) Show that the probabilities you determined in part (b) meet the two basic probability properties.

3.2 Describe an experiment for each of the following situations. Use business-oriented examples not mentioned in the text.

a) The sample space is discrete and finite.

b) The sample space is discrete and infinite.

c) The sample space is continuous.

3.3 Indicate whether the sample space is finite or infinite, discrete or continuous, if the experiment involves the following.

a) The amount of money General Motors earns this year.

b) The number of years before a woman is first elected President of the United States.

c) The percent by which the price of a stock might decrease, if percents are restricted to integer values.

d) The percent by which the price of a stock might decrease, if percents can be any decimal value.

e) The kilometres per litre a new car achieves.

3.4 Indicate whether the following events are (1) mutually exclusive and/or (2) exhaustive.

a) the events *stock market goes up* and *stock market does not go up*

b) the events *Federal Government reduces taxes* and *consumer prices decline*

c) the events *pass next test* and *earn an A in statistics*

3.5 Suppose the *Reader's Digest* contest mentioned in Section 3.3 is giving out one grand prize, 500 second prizes, and 1,000 third prizes. There are 50,000 people who might win, and no one can win more than one prize. What is the probability that you will win if you are one of the 50,000 people?

3.6 NASA is testing four new space suits for future shuttle flights. For this test, each suit will be classified as either *pass* or *fail*.

a) Describe the sample space for this experiment. Draw the tree diagram.

b) How many different outcomes are there? How many outcomes are there if one is interested only in the number of passes and failures?

c) If *pass* and *fail* are considered equally likely, what are $P(0$ pass$)$, $P(1$ pass$)$, $P(2$ pass$)$, $P(3$ pass$)$, and $P(4$ pass$)$? Do these values sum to one?

3.7 Use the information in **Data Set 1** to determine the probability that a randomly selected city will have more than 30,000 households and retail sales greater than $800 million.

3.8 Suppose you are planning on taking a survey of two out of five local retail establishments.

a) Describe the sample space for the experiment *select two establishments without replacement*. [*Hint*: Label the establishments 1, 2, 3, 4, 5, and list all pairs — note that order is *not* important here.]

b) What is the probability that establishment 1 will be included in the survey?

c) What is the probability that either establishment 1 or establishment 2 will be included in the survey?

3.9 The following data describe certain characteristics of the assembly-line workers for a General Electric plant.

TABLE 3.2 Assembly Line Data

	Men	Women	Over 50
White	120	140	75
Black	40	30	10
Asian	10	20	10

a) How many people are employed on this assembly line?

b) If a worker is selected randomly, what is the probability that this person will be black?

c) What is the probability that a person selected at random will be over 50?

3.10 The common stocks listed by a certain investing service are rated 1–5 according to return and 1–3 according to risk.

a) Draw the tree diagram representing the different ways a given stock can be classified.

b) If each stock is equally likely to be classified into each point in the sample space, what is the probability of each sample point?

c) How many sample points have either a return rating of < 3 or a risk rating of < 2? Use Formula 3.3 to determine P(return < 3 or risk < 2).

d) Use your tree diagram to determine the probability that both return < 3 and risk < 2.

3.11 A company making garage-door openers advertises that the customer can select one of the possible frequency codes by selecting nine switches in one of two positions (+ or −).

a) How many different codes might a person who has forgotten the code have to try before being assured of finding the correct one. (The answer *all of them* is not sufficient.) What is the probability that this person will be right on one randomly selected try?

b) Suppose the person knows that eight of the nine switches are set on + and one on −. What is the probability that the person will be correct on one randomly selected try?

3.12 A job-shop operation has seven possible jobs it should complete today. Unfortunately, on any one day, only four jobs can be completed.

a) If the order in which the jobs are completed is not important, how many different schedules might the shop have today?

b) Assume that the order is important today. How many different schedules are there now?

c) Job 1 is for the owner of the job shop. How many of the schedules in part (a) include job 1? How many of the schedules in part (b) include job 1?

3.13 Wendy's fast food chain advertises that you can order a hamburger with none or any one or more of eight toppings such as a tomato. As the manager of Wendy's, you want to advertise the number of different combinations of toppings that are possible. What is this number including no toppings?

3.14 The president of ARVO Industries is scheduled to visit the company plants located in Ontario.

a) In how many different orders can three plants be visited? Draw the tree diagram.

b) In how many different orders can the ARVO president visit three plants if there are ten possible plants that could be visited?

c) How many different combinations of three plants could be visited if there are ten plants?

3.15 A computer program has failed to work in the middle of an important production-scheduling operation. The head of the systems department has decided that one of three possible programming errors has caused the problem. If the three possible errors are labeled as A, B, and C, how many different orders (permutations) are there for examining the possible errors, one at a time?

3.16 Five candidates remain for the position of vice-president of finance for Datacomp Company. The personnel committee has been asked to submit three names to the company president.

a) How many different combinations of three people are possible? (Assume that the president wants the names unranked.)

b) How many different orderings are possible? (Assume that the president wants the names ranked.)

c) If the candidates are listed alphabetically and three are picked randomly, what is the probability that the first three names will be picked?

3.17 The EPA (Environmental Protection Agency) director has to decide on the priorities among U.S. cities for the spending of Federal money for pollution cleanup. Ten areas are under consideration for money.

a) How many different ways can the ten areas be ranked if ties are not permitted?

b) How many different combinations are possible if only three areas will receive money for cleanups?

3.18 A CPA certification committee has announced a list of five essay questions, two of which will be selected randomly to be on the next CPA exam. Assume that, in studying for the CPA exam, you find time to prepare for only two of the five. You know you will pass this portion of the exam if at least one of the two questions you select to study is on the exam.

a) List the sample space for the experiment *CPA committee picks two questions without replacement.*

b) What is the probability that you will pass?

USING THE COMPUTER

3.19 Use a computer package to calculate the following.

a) The number of different ways 50 cities could be ranked, for example, 1, 2, ..., 50 in terms of the

amount spent on education per capita, before you know the dollar amounts.

b) The number of different combinations if a portfolio

is to be composed of 25 stocks selected out of 100 possible stocks.

c) The number of permutations of 12 candidates for the new CFO of a company when there are 82 applicants.

3.20 Many business firms are reluctant to transmit internal data from one computer terminal to another without proper security procedures. One method for securing data has been to code the data at its entry point, the decoding method being known only to receiving personnel. Suppose a coding scheme is suggested in which the customer can select different codes by specifying each of 56 transmittable characters as either on or off. As president of this company, would you consider this enough codes, knowing that a spy could use a computer program capable of trying (randomly) 1,000 codes a second in an effort to break your code?

section 3.6

Probability Rules

One can often determine the probability of an event from knowledge about the probability of one or more other events in the sample space. In this section, we will discuss rules for finding the probability of complementary and conditional events, the probability of the union of two events, and the joint probability of two events.

Basic Definitions. Before describing these rules, we present a few definitions. If we designate A and B as two events of interest in a particular experiment, then the following definitions hold:

1. $P(\bar{A})$ = Probability that A does *not* occur in one trial of the experiment.
   $P(\bar{A})$ is called the probability of the *complement* of A.
2. $P(A \mid B)$ = Probability that A occurs *given that* B has taken place (or will take place).
   $P(A \mid B)$ is called the *conditional probability* of A given B.
3. $P(A \cap B)$ = Probability that *both A and B* occur in one trial of the experiment.
   $P(A \cap B)$ is called the probability of the *intersection* of A and B or the *joint* probability of A and B.
4. $P(A \cup B)$ = Probability that *either A or B or both* occur in one trial of the experiment.
   $P(A \cup B)$ is called the probability of the *union* of A and B.

Elaboration of these definitions follows.

Probability of the Complement

Perhaps the simplest way to form a new event from a given event is to take the *complement* of that event. For example, the *complement* of the sample space A, which is denoted by $\bar{A}$ (read A-bar), contains all the points in the sample space that are *not part* of A. If S denotes the total sample space, then:

$$\bar{A} = S - A \quad \text{or} \quad \bar{A} = \{\text{All sample points } not \text{ in } A\}$$

Suppose that the sample space S is the set of all students in a given university and A is the subset containing sophomores; then the event $\bar{A}$ includes all students in that university who are *not* sophomores. As another example, if we define set A to represent companies with sales less than or equal to 300,000 units, which we write as follows:

$$A = \{\text{Companies with sales} \leq 300,000 \text{ units}\}$$

then

$$\bar{A} = \{\text{Companies with sales} > 300,000 \text{ units}\}$$

Using the basic properties of a probability model, from the probability of an event we can determine the probability of the complement of that event. Suppose a sample space contains N sample points and some event A contains a of these points; that is, $P(A) = a/N$. Then $\bar{A}$ must contain $(N - a)$ sample points. We can write the **probability of the complement** of the event $P(\bar{A})$ as follows:

$$P(\bar{A}) = \frac{(N - a)}{N} = \frac{N}{N} - \frac{a}{N} = 1 - \frac{a}{N}$$

Probability rule for complements:

$$P(\bar{A}) = 1 - P(A) \qquad (3.8)$$

Let us apply this rule to our marketing-policy decision example of Section 3.4. Suppose that we label $P(A)$ as follows:

$$P(A) = P(\text{price} = 1 \text{ or advertising} \geq 2)$$

From Section 3.4, we know that this probability equals $\frac{3}{4}$. The probability of the complement of (A) is the probability that price exceeds 1 and advertising equals 1:

$$P(\bar{A}) = P(\text{price} > 1 \text{ and advertising} = 1)$$
$$= 1 - P(\text{price} = 1 \text{ or advertising} \geq 2)$$
$$= 1 - \frac{3}{4} = \frac{1}{4}$$

As a further illustration of the probability rule for complements, if the probability that long-term interest rates will fall below 8% in the next year is 0.25, then the probability that rates will *not* fall below 8% is:

$$1 - 0.25 = 0.75$$

Two complementary events must be *exhaustive* because they take into account (or exhaust) all possible events. In addition, complementary events must always be *mutually exclusive* because none of the sample points in A can be a sample point in the complement of A.

Conditional Probability

In some probability problems, we are interested in determining whether some event A occurs *given that* or *on the condition that* some other event B has already taken place (or will take place in the future). Such a conditional event is read as "A given B" and is usually written as $(A \mid B)$, where the vertical line is read as given. Consider the following example.

◻ **EXAMPLE 3.13**   McMaster University recently conducted a survey of undergraduate students in order to gather information about usage of the Student Union Building. The population for this study included all 30,000 undergraduate students enrolled in the university. The Union Building is interested in increasing usage, particularly among females and seniors at the university. The survey was sent to a random sample of the 30,000 students. The Venn diagram[4] (Figure 3.5) can be useful in illustrating probabilities. Assume that the sample space under consideration is all 30,000 undergraduate students at McMaster, event A represents the $a = 6,000$ students who are seniors, and event B represents the $b = 13,500$ students who are females. Suppose also that 2,500 of the 13,500 females are seniors.

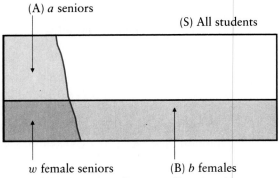

FIGURE 3.5   Venn diagram of overlapping events

The conditional event $A \mid B$ represents those students who are seniors selected from those who satisfy the condition of being *female*. The probability of conditional events of this nature is often of interest in specific sampling problems. For example, if a student is selected at random, and given that the selected student is female, what is the probability that the student is also a senior? We denote this probability by $P(A \mid B)$ and determine its value by calculating the frequency (w) of students who are female and seniors relative to the total number of females (b). This relative frequency is:

$$P(A \mid B) = \frac{w}{b} = \frac{2,500}{13,500} = 0.185$$

Similarly, $P(B \mid A)$ can be expressed as the question, "given that a selected student is a senior, what is the probability that the student is female?" The answer is,

$$P(B \mid A) = \frac{w}{a} = \frac{2,500}{6,000} = 0.417$$

Let us now write $P(A \mid B)$ in a round-about, but more convenient form. By dividing w and b by N (the total number of sample points) we obtain:

$$P(A \mid B) = \frac{w}{b} = \frac{w/N}{b/N}$$

---

[4] Named after logician J. Venn (1834–1923).

Another way of writing b/N is $P(B)$. Similarly, w/N can be written as $P(W)$. Recall from our earlier definition that an event W, which represents the occurrence of both a senior (A) and a female (B), is the *intersection of A and B*; thus, $P(W) = P(A \cap B)$. Putting these facts together, the probability that a randomly selected student is a senior, *given that* this person is a female, is:

$$P(A \mid B) = P(\text{Senior} \mid \text{Female}) = \frac{P(A \cap B)}{P(B)} = \frac{w/N}{b/N} = \frac{w}{b} = \frac{2{,}500}{13{,}500} = 0.185$$

Similarly, the probability that a randomly selected student is a female *given that* this person is a senior is:

$$P(B \mid A) = \frac{P(A \cap B)}{P(A)} = \frac{w/N}{a/N} = \frac{2{,}500}{6{,}000} = \frac{w}{b} = 0.417 \qquad \blacksquare$$

We can now formalize the definition of a **conditional probability**.

Conditional probability of A, given B:

$$P(A \mid B) = \frac{P(A \cap B)}{P(B)}$$

Conditional probability of B, given A:

$$P(B \mid A) = \frac{P(A \cap B)}{P(A)} \qquad (3.9)$$

To illustrate Formula 3.9, let us reconsider the marketing-policy example of Figure 3.2 and define the following two events:

$$A = \text{ad decision is} \geq 2 \qquad B = \text{price decision is } 1$$

From the tree diagram for this example (Figure 3.3), we know that $N = 12$ and $P(\text{price is } 1) = \frac{1}{4}$. There are two sample points for which the price = 1 and the ad decision is ≥ 2 [that is, $(1, 2)$ and $(1, 3)$]; hence $P(A \cap B) = \frac{1}{6}$. The conditional probability $P(A \mid B)$ is thus:

$$P(\text{ad} \geq 2 \mid \text{price is } 1) = \frac{P(\text{ad} \geq 2 \cap \text{price is } 1)}{P(\text{price is } 1)}$$

$$= \frac{\frac{1}{6}}{\frac{1}{4}} = \frac{2}{3}$$

This result is easily verified by the tree diagram in Figure 3.3, as we can follow the price = 1 branch and see that two-thirds of the endpoints on this branch yield ad ≥ 2.

In our next example of conditional probabilities, we emphasize that it is necessary to know the total number of sample points (N) in order to use Formula 3.9, and the given condition need not occur first. Indeed, it is possible for the conditional event to occur later. For example, it is legitimate to determine the probability $P(\text{stock market goes up today} \mid \text{prime interest rate will be raised tomorrow})$, even though the given condition (prime interest rate will be raised tomorrow) does not occur first.

☐ **EXAMPLE 3.14**   Suppose that two parts of a particular product are produced simultaneously in a production process. Let D_1 denote the fact that the first part is defective and D_2 denote the fact that the second part is defective. From past production records, it is known that the probability that part 1 is defective is $P(D_1) = 0.15$. Also, it is known from these records that the probability that *both* parts are defective is as follows:

$$P(D_1 \cap D_2) = 0.05$$

The conditional probability that part 2 is defective, *given that* the first part is defective, can be determined by using Formula 3.9:

$$P(D_2 \mid D_1) = \frac{P(D_1 \cap D_2)}{P(D_1)} = \frac{0.05}{0.15} = \frac{1}{3}$$

$P(D_1 \mid D_2)$ cannot be calculated in this example unless we know the value of $P(D_2)$.

■

Probability of an Intersection

In studying conditional probabilities in the last section, we indicated that $P(A \cap B)$ represents the probability of the intersection of A and B — that is, the probability that both A and B take place in one trial of an experiment. For example, the crosshatched area in Figure 3.5 represents the probability that a student is both a senior and a female. Since there are 2,500 female seniors, $P(\text{senior} \cap \text{female}) = 2,500/30,000 = 0.083$. Several additional intersections were presented in the last section, namely:

$$P(D_1 \cap D_2) = 0.05 \quad \text{and} \quad P(\text{ad} \geq 2 \cap \text{price} = 1) = \frac{1}{6}$$

We now want to develop a formula for the probability of an intersection. To do so, one merely has to solve Formula 3.9 for $P(A \cap B)$. The resulting formula is called the *general rule of multiplication* and provides a method for finding the probability of an intersection.

General rule of multiplication:

$$P(A \cap B) = P(A)P(B \mid A) = P(B)P(A \mid B) \qquad (3.10)$$

The first part of Formula 3.10 can be interpreted as follows: The probability that *both* A and B take place is given by two occurrences — event A takes place, with probability $P(A)$, and event B takes place on the condition that A occurs, with probability $P(B \mid A)$. The probability that both occurrences take place is the *product* of these two probabilities, or $P(A)P(B \mid A)$. For example, let us again consider the production problem previously presented, where we assumed that the probability of the first component being defective is $P(D_1) = 0.15$. Suppose that we also know from past records (Example 3.14) that the conditional probability $P(D_2 \mid D_1) = \frac{1}{3}$. These two probabilities can be used to determine $P(D_2 \cap D_1)$, as follows:[5]

$$P(D_2 \cap D_1) = P(D_1)P(D_2 \mid D_1) = \left(0.15\right)\left(\frac{1}{3}\right) = 0.05$$

The probability that the intersection of two (or more) events occurs in a given experiment is often referred to as the **joint probability** of these events. The term *joint probability* implies that the events under consideration take place in the same trial of an experiment. Depending on the nature of the experiment, events that occur jointly do not necessarily take place at identical points in calendar or clock time. For example, in our marketing policy problem, the result of the pricing and advertising decision may be considered a joint occurrence even though the two decisions are not made simultaneously.

Because the expressions $P(E_1 \cap E_2)$ and $P(E_2 \cap E_1)$ for any events E_1 and E_2 do not imply any ordering over time, the following is true:

$$P(E_1 \cap E_2) = P(E_2 \cap E_1)$$

To illustrate the intersection of two events graphically, we let A and B in the Venn diagram, shown in Figure 3.6, represent events within some sample space S. The intersection of A and B is represented by the shaded portion of these two events, labeled $A \cap B$.

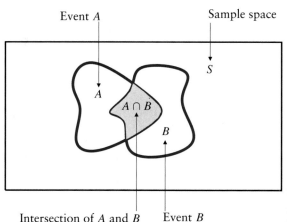

FIGURE 3.6 The intersection of A and B (shaded portion)

Probability of a Union

The **additive probability**, or probability of the union of two events A and B, written $P(A \cup B)$, is the probability that either A occurs, or B occurs, or both A and B occur. The union of events A and B is illustrated by Figure 3.7. The probability $P(A \cup B)$ is found by identifying the proportion of sample points that are included either in A or in B, or in the intersection of A and B.

---

[5] If the values of $P(D_2)$ and $P(D_1 \mid D_2)$ are known, then we calculate $P(D_2 \cap D_1)$ as follows:

$$P(D_2 \cap D_1) = P(D_2)P(D_1 \mid D_2)$$

This approach must also yield $P(D_2 \cap D_1) = 0.05$.

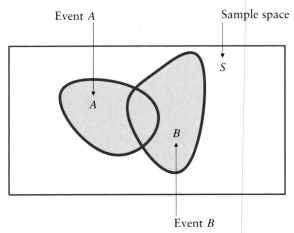

FIGURE 3.7   The union of A and B (shaded portion)

The entire shaded area in Figure 3.5 also represents a union — in this case, the union of the events *senior* and *female*. Recall from that example that there were $a = 6,000$ seniors, $b = 13,500$ females, $w = 2,500$ female seniors, and $N = 30,000$ students. To determine the probability that a randomly selected student is either a senior or a female (or both), we cannot merely add because this sum *double-counts* the females who are seniors.

$$\frac{a}{N} + \frac{b}{N} = \frac{6,000}{30,000} + \frac{13,500}{30,000}$$

In other words, that sum is too large by the following amount:

$$\frac{w}{N} = \frac{2,500}{30,000}$$

Therefore, the correct probability is as follows:

$$P(\text{senior} \cup \text{female}) = P(\text{senior}) + P(\text{female}) - P(\text{senior} \cap \text{female})$$

$$= \frac{a}{N} + \frac{b}{N} - \frac{w}{N}$$

$$= \frac{6,000}{30,000} + \frac{13,500}{30,000} - \frac{2,500}{30,000}$$

$$= 0.200 + 0.450 - 0.083$$

$$= 0.567$$

This example demonstrates the *general rule of addition*. If we substitute the letter A for senior and the letter B for female in the formulation above, then the general rule of addition can be written as follows:

General rule of addition:

$$P(A \cup B) = P(A) + P(B) - P(A \cap B) \tag{3.11}$$

Formula 3.11 can be used to find the probability of the union of A and B in our marketing policy problem, where $A = (\text{ad} \geq 2)$ and $B = (\text{price} = 1)$.

$$P(A \cup B) = P(A) + P(B) - P(A \cap B)$$

$$P(\text{ad} \geq 2 \cup \text{price} = 1) = P(\text{ad} \geq 2) + P(\text{price} = 1) - P(\text{ad} \geq 2 \cap \text{price} = 1)$$

In this example, we assumed four equally likely prices and three equally likely ad decisions, and so $P(\text{ad} \geq 2) = \frac{8}{12} = \frac{2}{3}$ and $P(\text{price} = 1) = \frac{3}{12} = \frac{1}{4}$; also, we calculated $P(\text{ad} \geq 2 \cap \text{price} = 1) = \frac{1}{6}$. Thus

$$
\begin{aligned}
P(\text{ad} \geq 2 \cup \text{price} = 1) &= \frac{8}{12} + \frac{3}{12} - \frac{2}{12} \\
&= \frac{9}{12} \\
&= \frac{3}{4}
\end{aligned}
$$

This agrees with the result that we calculated (less formally) in Section 3.4. You should be able to count the nine sample points in Figure 3.3 where either price = 1 or ad $\geq$ 2, or both.

In our production process example, we now assume that $P(D_2) = 0.10$, in addition to the values we previously assumed, namely $P(D_1 \cap D_2) = 0.05$ and $P(D_1) = 0.15$. These values can be used to calculate $P(D_1 \cup D_2)$:

$$
\begin{aligned}
P(D_1 \cup D_2) &= P(D_1) + P(D_2) - P(D_1 \cap D_2) \\
&= 0.15 + 0.10 - 0.05 = 0.20
\end{aligned}
$$

section 3.7 Special Cases of Probability Rules

Formulas 3.10 and 3.11 are *general* formulas that are appropriate for all types of events. There are, however, special cases of these formulas that can make calculating certain probabilities easier. We will examine these special rules for the case of mutually exclusive events and for independent events.

Mutually Exclusive Events

When the events A and B are mutually exclusive, the danger of double-counting is eliminated. That is, if A and B are mutually exclusive events, then there is *no overlap* of sample points in A and B that can be counted twice. The intersection $A \cap B$ in this special case has probability zero, $P(A \cap B) = 0$. We can thus rewrite Formula 3.11 as shown next.

Special case of addition rule (given mutually exclusive events):

$$P(A \cup B) = P(A) + P(B) \tag{3.12}$$

The Venn diagram in Figure 3.8 illustrates the relationship between the sets A and B when these sets are mutually exclusive.

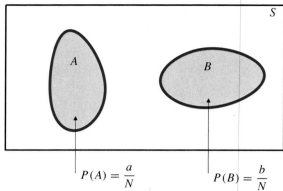

FIGURE 3.8   Illustration of the special rule of addition for mutually exclusive events: $P(A \cap B) = 0$, so $P(A \cup B) = P(A) + P(B)$

☐ **EXAMPLE 3.15**   Determining the probability that either the Expos or the Cubs win the National League pennant this year is an example of the type of problem that involves Formula 3.12. These events are mutually exclusive. It is not possible for both teams to win, hence:

$$P(\text{Expos win} \cup \text{Cubs win}) = P(\text{Expos win}) + P(\text{Cubs win})$$

(Some people would say the probability *either* would win is too low to worry about, but that is only their subjective opinion.)   ■

Special Case of Independence. Two events are said to be **independent** if what happens with one event does not influence (or is not influenced by) what happens with some other event. Suppose the two events are A and B. To be independent, the probability that A occurs cannot influence, or be influenced by, any knowledge of the event B. Dependence implies just the opposite — that the occurrence of one event *is* influenced by the occurrence of some other event.

Probability Rules for Independent Events

The most important effect of assuming independence is that it simplifies the calculation of joint probabilities; the result is a special case of the multiplication rule. If A and B are independent, then the joint probability of A and B can be determined by using the following formula:

> Special case of multiplication rule when A and B are independent:
>
> $$P(A \cap B) = P(A)P(B) = P(B)P(A) \qquad (3.13)$$

Most airlines use two separate computer systems to handle reservations, one system acting as a backup for the other. Let A = the event that the first system fails and B = the event that the second system fails. If A and B are independent, then the probability that the second system fails, $P(B)$, cannot be influenced by the fact that the first system has failed (event A). Medical scientists are continually conducting research to determine whether certain diseases are independent of, or dependent on, a variety of factors. The probability of becoming ill with cancer, for instance, has been reported to be related to (dependent on) whether one smokes, the quality of the air one breathes, and the food one eats.

In many problems, it may be difficult to determine whether two events are independent or dependent. Note, for example, the controversy generated by the question of whether or not the presence of the artificial sweetener saccharine in soft drinks is independent of the occurrence of cancer in humans. In many statistical problems, it may not be clear whether the events of interest are independent or dependent. In such cases, either: (1) it is not important or it is impossible to determine whether the events are independent or dependent, (2) one is trying to *prove* whether the events are independent or dependent, or (3) the experimenter can assume that the events are independent because of the way the experiment is defined. These three situations are considered below.

1. When it is not important or it is impossible to determine whether the events are independent or dependent, then the formulas derived thus far — Formulas 3.9, 3.10, and 3.11 — should be used. *These formulas hold for both independent and dependent events.*

2. In some problems, it is important to attempt to *prove* whether events are independent or dependent. In real-world problems, this occurs when one is trying to establish the relationship between events such as cigarette smoking and cancer. From a statistical point of view, it is more convenient to work with events that are independent, because we can use simplified versions of Formulas 3.9, 3.10, and 3.11. If A and B are independent, then $P(A)$ must be unaffected by whether or not B occurs, and $P(B)$ must be unaffected by whether or not A occurs. The rule for proving the independence of two events A and B is as follows:

A and B are independent if either one of the following two relationships holds true:
$$P(A \mid B) = P(A) \qquad \text{or} \qquad P(B \mid A) = P(B) \qquad (3.14)$$

If $P(A \mid B) = P(A)$ then it must be true that $P(B \mid A) = P(B)$, and conversely. [6] Since independence is the complement of dependence, to verify that two events are dependent, we need only show that one of the two relationships in Formula 3.14 does *not* hold true as follows:

A and B are dependent if either one of the following two relationships holds true:
$$P(A \mid B) \neq P(A) \qquad \text{or} \qquad P(B \mid A) \neq P(B) \qquad (3.15)$$

Suppose we use the rules described above to determine whether or not independence exists in our production-process example. To determine whether D_1 and D_2 are independent or dependent, we must look at one or both of the following relationships:

$$P(D_1 \mid D_2) \text{ versus } P(D_1) \qquad \text{and/or} \qquad P(D_2 \mid D_1) \text{ versus } P(D_2)$$

---

[6] Proof of this is left for the reader in Exercise 3.51.

If *either* relationship can be shown to be an equality, then D_1 and D_2 are independent. Similarly, if either relationship can be shown *not* to be an equality, then D_1 and D_2 must be dependent. Remember from page 89 that the value of $P(D_2)$ was 0.10. Also remember that in Example 3.14 we found the conditional probability, $P(D_2 \mid D_1) = \frac{1}{3}$. Since

$$P(D_2 \mid D_1) = \frac{1}{3} \text{ does not equal } P(D_2) = 0.10,$$

the events D_1 and D_2 cannot be independent; in other words, they must be dependent.

3. In some experiments, the events are *assumed* to be independent. For instance, a bank might safely assume that the amount of loan requested is independent among loan applicants. In Chapter 7, we will discuss a procedure that assures that sample observations are taken *randomly* (independently), meaning that the outcome of one sample observation cannot influence the outcome of any other sample observation.

☐ **EXAMPLE 3.16**   Let's assume that one of the airlines mentioned previously, with a computer reservation system and an independent backup computer, would like to determine the probability that both systems fail. Assume that the probability that the first computer fails on any given day is 0.01 and the probability that the backup computer fails is also 0.01. Then the probability that they both fail is as follows:

$$P(\text{1st fails} \cap \text{2nd fails}) = P(\text{1st fails})\,P(\text{2nd fails})$$
$$= (0.01)(0.01) = 0.0001 \qquad ■$$

☐ **EXAMPLE 3.17**   Suppose a soft-drink manufacturer uses two machines in its capping process. Defective caps result from one machine with probability $P(M_1) = 0.001$, and defective caps result from the second machine with probability $P(M_2) = 0.003$. Assuming independence, the probability of a defective cap being found on both of two randomly selected bottles, each from a different machine, is:

$$P(M_1 \cap M_2) = P(M_1)P(M_2) = (0.001)(0.003) = 0.000003$$

There are thus three chances in a million that both selected bottles have defective caps.   ■

The Distinction between Mutually Exclusive Events and Independence

Beginning students of statistics often confuse the concepts of independence and mutually exclusive events. It is important that the reader understand the difference between these concepts and the implications of each in probability theory. Thus, we present the following two general statements.

1. Events that are mutually exclusive must be dependent, but dependent events need not be mutually exclusive.
2. Events that are not mutually exclusive may be either independent or dependent. However, events that are independent cannot be mutually exclusive.

☐ **EXAMPLE 3.18** To illustrate these two statements, we will consider the following four events:

A = interest rates decline in the next month
B = interest rates do not decline in the next month
C = the sale of homes increases in the next month
D = the weather next year is very mild

The events A and B are clearly mutually exclusive — if one occurs, the other cannot. Because the occurrence of either A or B influences the occurrence of the other (it *precludes* the other from taking place), A and B are dependent. Events A and C are also dependent (the sales of homes depends on the interest rate), but they are certainly not mutually exclusive (they can both happen). Thus, we have illustrated statement 1.

Events A and C are not mutually exclusive and are dependent. Events A and D are not mutually exclusive and are independent. This illustrates the first part of statement 2.

Events A and D also illustrate the second part of statement 2. These two events are independent, but they are not (and cannot be) mutually exclusive. To summarize:

> Mutually exclusive implies dependence, and independence implies not mutually exclusive, but no other simple implications among these conditions hold true.

■

PROBLEMS

3.21 As an exercise to test your understanding of the concepts discussed in this chapter, answer the following questions about your perception of how prices on the New York Stock Exchange (use the Dow-Jones average) will change over the next month.

a) Estimate the probability that the Dow-Jones average will increase over the next month. Denote this as $P(\text{DJ up})$.

b) What is the probability of the complement of (DJ up)?

c) Estimate the probability that the unemployment rate will decline next month, denoted as $P(\text{UR down})$.

d) Estimate $P(\text{DJ up} \mid \text{UR down})$. Are the two events independent or dependent? Explain.

e) Estimate $P(\text{UR down} \mid \text{DJ up})$. Must this probability be the same as $P(\text{DJ up} \mid \text{UR down})$? Explain.

f) Determine $P(\text{DJ up} \cap \text{UR down})$ and $P(\text{DJ up} \cup \text{UR down})$ based on your answers to parts (a) through (e).

g) Draw a Venn diagram representing the events (DJ up) and (UR down).

3.22 The Easy-Charge Company is being audited. The company comptroller presents the following table, showing the amount owed by each customer and whether or not a cash advance has been made.

TABLE 3.3 Easy Charge's Audit Data

Amount Owed (x) By Customers	Customers Receiving Cash Advance	Customers Not Receiving Cash Advance
$0 < x \leq 100$	229	2,894
$100 < x \leq 200$	378	1,707
$200 < x \leq 300$	501	1,426
$300 < x \leq 400$	416	939
$400 < x \leq 500$	260	483
$500 < x \leq 600$	289	478
Total customers	2,073	7,927

a) Find $P(\text{cash advance})$ and $P(\overline{\text{cash advance}})$.

b) Find $P(\text{cash advance} \mid \text{amount owed} < \$100)$.

c) Find $P(\text{amount owned} < \$100 \mid \text{cash advance})$.

d) Are the events *amount owed < $100* and *cash advance* independent or dependent?

e) Find $P(\$100 < x \leq \$200 \cap \text{cash advance})$.

f) Find $P(\$100 < x \leq \$200 \cup \text{cash advance})$.

3.23 The personnel manager for General Electric has kept careful records on the age (either age ≤ 30, or $30 < \text{age} \leq 50$, or age > 50) and sex of the people applying for jobs at their Bloomington (IN) plant. Half of the applicants were 30 years old or younger, and half of these people were females.

a) Find the probability that a randomly selected applicant is 30 or under and is a female. $P(A \cap B) = \frac{P(A)P(B)}{\frac{1}{2} \times \frac{1}{2}}$

b) If $P(\text{female} \mid \text{age} \leq 30) = \frac{1}{2}$, and $P(\text{female}) = \frac{7}{16}$, does this indicate independence or dependence of the events *female* and *age ≤ 30*?

c) Use Table 3.4 to find $P(\text{female} \cap \text{age} \leq 30)$, $P(\text{age} \leq 50)$, and $P(\text{age} \leq 30 \mid \text{female})$.

TABLE 3.4 Age and Sex of Job Applicants

	Age ≤ 30	$30 < \text{age} \leq 50$	Age > 50	
Female	$\frac{1}{4}$	$\frac{1}{16}$	$\frac{1}{8}$	$\frac{7}{16}$
Male	$\frac{1}{4}$	$\frac{3}{16}$	$\frac{1}{8}$	$\frac{9}{16}$
	$\frac{1}{2}$	$\frac{1}{4}$	$\frac{1}{4}$	

d) Find $P(\text{female} \cup \text{age} > 50)$ using $P(\text{age} > 50) = \frac{1}{4}$.

3.24 The following data describe certain characteristics of the students enrolled at a university.

TABLE 3.5 Certain Characteristics of University Students

	Men	Women	Over 21
Freshmen	1,325	1,100	125
Sophomores	1,200	900	175
Juniors	900	850	325
Seniors	725	775	950
Graduates	1,350	875	2,225

Calculate the following:

a) $P(\text{sophomore} \cap \text{male})$ and $P(\text{sophomore} \mid \text{male})$

b) the probability that a randomly selected student is over 21

c) the probability that a randomly selected male is over 21, if age and sex are assumed to be independent

3.25 A group of investors is about to build an indoor tennis facility in Toronto. Their choice of heat for the facility will be gas or electricity. The investors' assessment as to the probability of which method will be best depends on the winter weather over the next three years, as follows:

TABLE 3.6 Probability of Type of Winter Weather

Heat	P	Mild (M)	Normal (N)	Cold (C)
Gas (G)	0.60	$P(G \cap M)$ =?	$P(G \cap N)$ =?	$P(G \cup C)$ =?
Electricity (E)	0.40	$P(E \cap M)$ = 0.18	$P(E \cap N)$ =?	$P(E \cap C)$ =?
	1.00	$P(M)$ =?	$P(N)$ =?	$P(C) = 0.30$

a) If $P(M \mid G) = 0.20$, find $P(G \cap M)$. $= P(M \mid G)\, P(G)$

b) Find $P(G \cup M)$.

c) Using your prior results and assuming $P(N \mid G) = 0.50$, complete the table shown above.

d) Determine whether or not M and G are independent.

3.26 You have decided to conduct an in-depth study of one of ten accounting firms. Three of the firms (1, 2, and 3) are located in the Montreal area (event A). Six of the firms (2, 3, 4, 5, 6, and 7) have over 200 employees (event B), and five of the firms (2, 4, 6, 8, and 10) had revenues over one million dollars last year (event C). You decide to pick at random from among the ten firms.

a) Find $P(A)$ and $P(A \cup B)$.

b) Find $P(B \mid C)$ and $P(C \mid B)$.

c) Are the events A, B, and C mutually exclusive? Are they exhaustive? Explain.

d) Are the events A and B independent or dependent?

3.27 You have 12 employees, six males and six females, who had perfect attendance records over the past year. One of the males and one of the females are to be picked, at random, and each one wins a free trip to Hawaii. The males are numbered 1–6, and the females are also numbered 1–6.

a) What is the probability that the male and the female whose numbers are 6 will be selected?

b) What is the probability that one or both persons with the number 6 will be selected?

c) What is the probability that the two numbers selected will be different? [*Hint*: Use the rule of complements.]

3.28 Assume that the U.S. Senate is composed of 48 Republicans and 52 Democrats. Twelve of the Republicans are women, and 13 of the Democrats are women. You decide to pick senators, at random, and interview them. Selection is without replacement.

a) What is the probability that the first person you interview is a Republican and the second is a Democrat?

b) What is the probability of a Republican on either the first or second interview, or on both interviews?

c) What is the probability of interviewing a Republican on the first interview or a woman on the second interview or both?

d) Are the events *Republican on the first interview* and *woman on the second interview* independent or dependent?

e) Repeat each of the questions above, assuming that the senators are picked with replacement (a person could be interviewed twice).

3.29 A company is trying to design new chairs for the 250 employees who sit in front of a machine all day. One hundred of these employees are females, and 130 weigh over 150 pounds. Also, 30 women and 140 men are taller than 67 inches. If one of these employees is selected at random to test a new chair, what is the probability that the person:

a) is a male.

b) weighs over 150 pounds.

c) is taller than 67 inches.

d) is a male not taller than 67 inches.

e) is a female, given that the person is taller than 67 inches.

Marginal Probability

In a number of circumstances, it is convenient to assume that a single event always occurs jointly with other events. For instance, it may be helpful not only to identify defective items resulting from a production process, but also to specify exactly *which* machines (or which workers) produced these defectives. Insurance companies are interested not only in the amount of damage associated with each automobile accident but, among other things, the city in which the accident took place and the age and sex of the driver. Similarly, students in a university are classified not only as males and females, but also according to class standing and major. An applicant for a loan may be classified not only by the dollar amount requested, but also by how long this person has been employed, the person's income, the amount of other debts, et cetera. In such situations, the probability of the event in question (the probability of producing a defective item across all machines and all workers or the probability of an accident involving at least $1,000 of damage across all cities and all drivers) may not be known directly but can be calculated by summing its chance of occurrence in combination with the other relevant factors identified in the problem.

Consider the problem of producing a certain type of battery in three different plants with different equipment and employees. Suppose the weekly average number of batteries produced in these three plants, denoted by E_1, E_2, and E_3, is 500, 2,000, and 1,500, respectively. Further, let's assume that the probabilities that a defective (D) is produced in *each* of the three plants are as follows:

$$P(D \mid E_1) = 0.020 \qquad P(D \mid E_2) = 0.015 \qquad P(D \mid E_3) = 0.030$$

Suppose that the batteries produced by the three plants supply one automaker. The automaker receives 4,000 batteries weekly and the probabilities that randomly selected batteries originated in each plant are:

$$P(E_1) = \frac{500}{4,000} \qquad P(E_2) = \frac{2,000}{4,000} \qquad P(E_3) = \frac{1,500}{4,000}$$

What is the probability that the battery used by the automaker in a randomly selected car is defective? This probability, $P(D)$, is a *marginal probability*, and its value can be determined by the special rules for marginal probabilities. It may clarify the concept of a marginal probability if we express the values for this example in the form of a table (Table 3.7). Note that the values in Table 3.7 can be used to calculate the three conditional probabilities given previously, $P(D \mid E_1)$ = $\frac{10}{500}$ = 0.020, $P(D \mid E_2)$ = $\frac{30}{2,000}$ = 0.015, and $P(D \mid E_3)$ = $\frac{45}{1,500}$ = 0.030.

TABLE 3.7 Good and Defective Batteries Produced in Three Different Plants

	Plants			Total
	E_1	E_2	E_3	
Good (G)	490	1,970	1,455	3,915
Defective (D)	10	30	45	85
Total	500	2,000	1,500	4,000

The probability of a defective in this context is called a **marginal probability** since its value can be read directly from the right-hand margin of Table 3.7; $P(D)$ = $\frac{85}{4,000}$ = 0.02125. Slightly more than 2% of the batteries are defective.

Rather than find $P(D)$ via the frequencies in Table 3.7, we often calculate such values from a list of the corresponding joint probabilities, as shown in Table 3.8. The proportion of defectives in this problem is illustrated in Figure 3.9.

TABLE 3.8 Joint Probabilities for Good and Defective Batteries

	Plants			Total
	E_1	E_2	E_3	
Good (G)	$\frac{490}{4,000}$	$\frac{1970}{4,000}$	$\frac{1,455}{4,000}$	$\frac{3,915}{4,000}$
Defective (D)	$\frac{10}{4,000}$	$\frac{30}{4,000}$	$\frac{45}{4,000}$	$\frac{85}{4,000}$
Total	$\frac{500}{4,000}$	$\frac{2,000}{4,000}$	$\frac{1,500}{4,000}$	$\frac{4,000}{4,000} = 1.00$

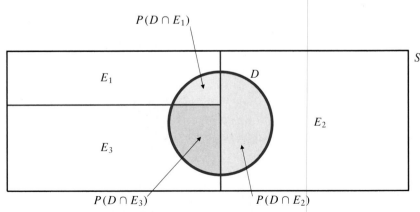

Marginal probability: $P(D) = \sum P(D \cap E_i)$

FIGURE 3.9 Illustration of a marginal probability

The circle labeled D in Figure 3.9 represents the proportion of defectives in the sample space S. There are three shaded areas in this circle, representing the intersection of D with E_1, E_2, and E_3. The probabilities that a given battery will be in one of these three intersections are $P(D \cap E_1)$, $P(D \cap E_2)$, and $P(D \cap E_3)$. Finally, since there is no overlap among the three intersections, the probability $P(D) = \frac{85}{4,000}$ is now easily seen to be the sum of three joint probabilities:

$$P(D) = P(D \cap E_1) + P(D \cap E_2) + P(D \cap E_3)$$

$$= \frac{10}{4,000} + \frac{30}{4,000} + \frac{45}{4,000} = 0.02125$$

By now it should be fairly clear that if one has a table of joint probabilities such as Table 3.8, then calculating marginal probabilities is not very difficult. Constructing a joint-probability table, however, usually involves considerably more effort than it takes to calculate the marginal probability directly by using a formula.

Let us develop our formula for a marginal probability in the context of calculating $P(D)$ for the battery example. Recall that $P(D)$ was written as the sum of three joint probabilities:

$$P(D) = P(D \cap E_1) + P(D \cap E_2) + P(D \cap E_3)$$

We know from Formula 3.10 that a *joint probability* can always be written as the *product of two probabilities*, one of which is a conditional probability. Using Formula 3.10 to rewrite our expression for $P(D)$, we obtain:

$$P(D) = P(E_1)P(D \mid E_1) + P(E_2)P(D \mid E_2) + P(E_3)P(D \mid E_3)$$

The probabilities on the right-hand side are known values and can be substituted to find $P(D)$:

$$P(D) = \frac{500}{4,000}(0.020) + \frac{2,000}{4,000}(0.015) + \frac{1,500}{4,000}(0.030) = 0.02125$$

This result agrees with that calculated previously. The generalization of this example leads to the following definition of $P(D)$.

> If D represents an event such that one of the mutually exclusive events E_1, E_2, $\cdots$, E_k always must occur jointly with any occurrence of D, then the probability of D is called a marginal (or unconditional) probability.

Its value may be determined by the following rule:

$$P(D) = \sum_{i=1}^{k} P(D \cap E_i) = P(D \cap E_1) + P(D \cap E_2) + \cdots + P(D \cap E_k)$$

From the general rule of multiplication, Formula 3.10, we know that the following is true:

$$P(D \cap E_i) = P(E_i)P(D \mid E_i)$$

Thus, the formula for a marginal probability can be written as shown here:

Marginal probability:

$$P(D) = \sum_{i=1}^{k} P(D \cap E_i) = \sum_{i=1}^{k} P(E_i)P(D \mid E_i)$$

$$= P(E_1)P(D \mid E_1) + P(E_2)P(D \mid E_2) + \cdots + P(E_k)P(D \mid E_k)$$

$$(3.16)$$

☐ **EXAMPLE 3.19**   Consider the problem of estimating the probability that Carl Yastrzemski (former Boston Red Sox great) got a hit on a randomly selected turn at bat, if it is known that his relative frequency of hits was 0.315 when the pitcher was right-handed and 0.262 when the pitcher was left-handed.[7] If 0.315 is taken as the probability of a hit given a right-handed pitcher, $P(H_R) = 0.315$, and 0.262 as the probability of a hit given a left-handed pitcher, $P(H_L) = 0.262$), and if we assume that the probabilities that Yastrzemski faced right-handed and left-handed pitchers were $P(R) = 0.75$ and $P(L) = 0.25$, respectively, then:

$$P(\text{Hit}) = P(R)P(H \mid R) + P(L)P(H \mid L)$$

$$= 0.75(0.315) + 0.25(0.262) = 0.302$$

■

section 3.9

Bayes' Rule

One of the most interesting (and controversial) applications of the rules of probability theory involves estimating unknown probabilities and making decisions on the basis of new (sample) information. Statistical decision theory is a new field of study that has its foundations in just such problems. Chapter 17 investigates the area of statistical decision theory in some detail; this section describes one of the basic formulas of the area, **Bayes' rule.**

An English philosopher, the Reverend Thomas Bayes (1702–1761), was one of the first to work with rules for revising probabilities in the light of sample information. Bayes' research, published in 1763, went largely unnoticed for over a century and only recently has attracted a great deal of attention. His contribution consists primarily of a unique method for calculating conditional probabilities. The so-called *Bayesian* approach to this problem addresses itself to the question of determining the probability of some event, E_i, *given that* another event, A, has been (or will be) observed; in other words, determining the value of $P(E_i \mid A)$. The event A is usually thought of as new information. Thus, Bayes' rule is concerned with determining the probability of an event given certain new information, such as that obtained from a sample, a survey, or a pilot study. For example, a sample output of three defectives in 20 trials (event A) might be used to estimate the probability that a machine is not working correctly (event E_i).

---

[7] Data based on Yastrzemski's major-league career record.

Probabilities prior to revision by Bayes' rule are called *a priori*, or simply *prior* probabilities, because they are determined before the new information is taken into account. Prior probabilities may be either objective or subjective values. A probability that has undergone revision in the light of new information (via Bayes' rule) is called a *posterior probability*, since it represents a probability calculated *after* this information is taken into account. Posterior probabilities are always conditional probabilities, the conditional event being the new information. Thus, by the use of Bayes' rule a prior probability, which is an unconditional probability, becomes a posterior probability, which is a conditional probability. In order to calculate such posterior probabilities, we will first derive Bayes' rule for the general problem of determining $P(E_i \mid A)$.

Recall that, earlier in this chapter, the order of events was shown to be immaterial in calculating joint probabilities. The implication is that $P(E_i \cap A)$ must be equivalent to $P(A \cap E_i)$; therefore, the following relationships must hold true (Formula 3.10):

$$P(E_i \cap A) = P(A)P(E_i \mid A)$$

$$P(E_i \cap A) = P(E_i)P(A \mid E_i)$$

If the above two formulas hold, then it must also be true that the two right-hand-side representations must be equal to each other:

$$P(A)P(E_i \mid A) = P(E_i)P(A \mid E_i)$$

We can now solve for $P(E_i \mid A)$ directly by dividing both sides by $P(A)$:

Calculation of a posterior probability:

$$P(E_i \mid A) = \frac{P(E_i)P(A \mid E_i)}{P(A)} \qquad (3.17)$$

The numerator of Formula 3.17 represents the probability that A and E_i both will occur, while the denominator is the probability that A alone will occur. If both these probabilities are calculable, then the conditional probability of the event E_i, given some new information A, can be determined.

The relationship that Bayes developed for calculating posterior probabilities uses Formula 3.17 as a substitute way to calculate the marginal probability in the denominator of Formula 3.17.

Bayes' rule:

$$P(E_i \mid A) = \frac{P(E_i)P(A \mid E_i)}{\sum_{j=1}^{k} P(E_j)P(A \mid E_j)} \qquad (3.18)$$

$$= \frac{P(E_i)P(A \mid E_i)}{P(E_1)P(A \mid E_1) + P(E_2)P(A \mid E_2) + \cdots + P(E_k)P(A \mid E_k)}$$

Just as in Formula 3.17, the numerator of Formula 3.18 represents the probability that both A and E_i will occur, while the denominator is the probability that A alone will occur.

☐ **EXAMPLE 3.20**   To illustrate Bayes' rule using our battery example, suppose we want to calculate the probability that a battery came from Plant 2 (E_2) *given that* the battery is defective (D). In this example, the event of interest is E_2 and the information is (D). By Bayes' rule we can write the following:

$$P(E_2 \mid D) = \frac{P(E_2)P(D \mid E_2)}{P(E_1)P(D \mid E_1) + P(E_2)P(D \mid E_2) + P(E_3)P(D \mid E_3)}$$

All the values necessary to calculate $P(E_2 \mid D)$ were given in our previous discussion of this problem. The substitutions are shown below:

$$P(E_2 \mid D) = \frac{\left(\frac{2,000}{4,000}\right)\left(0.015\right)}{\left(\frac{500}{4,000}\right)\left(0.020\right) + \left(\frac{2,000}{4,000}\right)\left(0.015\right) + \left(\frac{1,500}{4,000}\right)\left(0.030\right)} = 0.353$$

The posterior probability of E_2 after observing a defective battery is 0.353. This same value can be verified from Table 3.7 — the proportion of defectives in E_2 to the total number of defectives is $\frac{30}{85} = 0.353$. Bayes' rule allows us to calculate such probabilities without constructing such a table.   ■

☐ **EXAMPLE 3.21**   Suppose that a questionnaire is sent to rural households with probability $P(R) = 0.50$ and to urban households with probability $P(U) = 0.50$, where R stands for *rural* and U for *urban*. Households are divided into low-income (L) and high-income (H). Furthermore, the following conditional probabilities are known:

$$P(H \mid R) = 0.20, \quad P(L \mid R) = 0.80$$
$$P(H \mid U) = 0.40, \quad P(L \mid U) = 0.60$$

These probabilities are shown in the tree diagram of Figure 3.10. Now suppose that the location code has been omitted on one of the questionnaires received so that it is not known whether it is from a rural or an urban household. Our prior probabilities suggest that the probability is 0.50 that it comes from a rural household and 0.50 that it comes from an urban household. Suppose that analysis of the responses in the questionnaire shows that it was obviously completed by a high-income household. How does this new information affect our probabilistic knowledge of whether it came from a rural or an urban household?

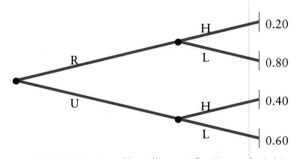

FIGURE 3.10   Tree diagram for Example 3.21

Formula 3.18 can be used to find the revised (posterior) probability that the questionnaire came from a rural household, given the information that it came from a high-income household, $P(R \mid H)$:

$$P(R \mid H) = \frac{P(R)P(H \mid R)}{P(R)P(H \mid R) + P(U)P(H \mid U)}$$

$$= \frac{(0.50)(0.20)}{(0.50)(0.20) + (0.50)(0.40)} = \frac{1}{3}$$

The posterior probability that a randomly selected household is rural, given that the family is known to have a high income, is $\frac{1}{3}$. This value is illustrated in Figure 3.11 as the ratio of the one heavily shaded rectangle to all three shaded (high-income) rectangles. ■

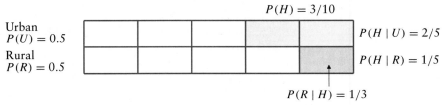

FIGURE 3.11 Illustration for Bayes' rule

We end this section by writing Bayes' rule in a slightly different form, one that will be especially convenient in Chapter 17 when we study the use of Bayes' rule in the context of statistical decision theory:

$$P(\text{event}_i \mid \text{sample information}) = \frac{P(\text{event}_i)\,P(\text{sample information} \mid \text{event}_i)}{\sum_j P(\text{event}_j)\,P(\text{sample information} \mid \text{event}_j)}$$

☐ **STUDY QUESTION 3.2   Probability of an IRS Audit**

An accounting article reported the data in Figure 3.12 showing the chances a taxpayer in the United States has of being audited by the IRS (Internal Revenue Service).

a) Rewrite these data as a 2×6 table, where the six categories are the incomes/forms and the two categories are the experiences of being audited and not being audited. In the body of the table, put the number of taxpayers (in millions). Label the six income categories C1–C6 and the two audit categories A and $\overline{A}$.

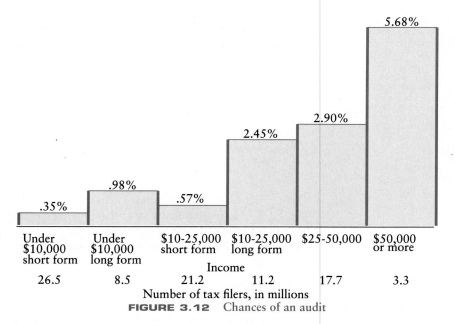

FIGURE 3.12 Chances of an audit

b) What is the probability a taxpayer will have an income in the range $25,000–$50,000?

c) What is the probability that a taxpayer with income of $25,000–$50,000 will be audited?

d) What is the probability that a randomly selected taxpayer will be audited?

e) Given that a person has been selected for an audit, what is the probability that this person had an income between $25,000 and $50,000? Use Bayes' rule.

f) Are the events *audited* and *income $25,000–$50,000* independent or dependent?

● **ANSWER**

a)

TABLE 3.9 Number of Taxpayers (Millions) Audited by the IRS

	Incomes/Forms						Totals
	C1	C2	C3	C4	C5	C6	
A	0.09	0.08	0.12	0.27	0.51	0.19	1.26
$\bar{A}$	26.41	8.42	21.08	10.93	17.19	3.11	87.14
Totals	26.50	8.50	21.20	11.20	17.70	3.30	88.40

b) P(income $25,000–50,000) = 17.70/88.40 = 0.2002$, where 88.40 is the total number of taxpayers.

c) P(audited | $25,000–$50,000) = 0.51/17.70 = 0.0288$.

d) $P(\text{audited}) = P(C1)P(A \mid C1) + P(C2)P(A \mid C2) + \cdots + P(C6)P(A \mid C6)$

$$= (0.0035)(26.50/88.40) + (0.0098)(8.50/88.40)$$

$$+ \cdots + (0.0568)(3.30/88.40) = 0.0144$$

e) $P(C5 \mid A) = \dfrac{P(C5)P(A \mid C5)}{P(C1)P(A \mid C1) + P(C2)P(A \mid C2) + \cdots + P(C6)P(A \mid C6)}$

$\qquad = \dfrac{(0.0288)(17.70/88.40)}{(0.0035)(26.50/88.40) + (0.0098)(8.50/88.40) + \cdots + (0.0568)(3.30/88.40)}$

$\qquad = \dfrac{0.0058}{0.0144} = 0.4028$

f) $P(C5 \mid A) = 0.4028$ and $P(C5) = 0.2002$. Since these two probabilities are not equal, the events are dependent. ∎

section 3.10

Application of Probability Theory: An Example

A contractor who produces delicate electronic components essential to the manufacturing of certain computer equipment cannot determine whether the component part produced has been assembled correctly without tearing the component apart and, in the process, destroying the usefulness of that component. It is possible, however, to purchase a machine that, according to its makers' claim, will help detect defective components. This machine, which indicates only that the component appears to be good (+) or that it appears to be defective (−), is not infallible — sometimes it will indicate positive when the component is defective or negative when the component is good. To determine the ability of the machine to distinguish between good and defective items, 400 randomly selected components were first tested by the machine and then torn apart to see whether they were good or defective. The results of this research are given in Table 3.10. In this case, the sample space is discrete and finite. The values in Table 3.10 can be used to calculate a number of probabilities concerning the machine's reliability and the quality state of the components.

TABLE 3.10 Computer Detection of Good and Defective Electronic Components

State of Component	Results of Test		Sum across Row
	Positive	Negative	
Good	342	18	360
Defective	8	32	40
Sum of column	350	50	400

Intersections

The joint probabilities of the two component states (good or defective) with the results of the test (positive or negative) are shown in Table 3.11.

TABLE 3.11 Joint Probabilities Associated with Table 3.10

State of Component	Results of Test		Sum across Row
	Positive	Negative	
Good	0.855	0.045	0.900
Defective	0.020	0.080	0.100
Sum of column	0.875	0.125	1.000

Marginals

The sums across rows or down columns in Table 3.11 are marginal probabilities. Although the marginal (unconditional) probability of a good item can be determined directly (from Table 3.10) to be:

$$P(\text{Good}) = \frac{360}{400} = 0.90$$

The probability P(Good) can also be determined via Formula 3.16 as follows:

$$P(\text{Good}) = P(\text{Good} \cap \text{Positive}) + P(\text{Good} \cap \text{Negative})$$
$$= 0.855 + 0.045 = 0.90$$

Similarly, the probability that the test reads positive is:

$$P(\text{Positive}) = P(\text{Good} \cap \text{Positive}) + P(\text{Defective} \cap \text{Positive})$$
$$= 0.855 + 0.020 = 0.875$$

Unions

The probability of the union of two events can be determined by using the general rule of addition, Formula 3.11. For example, the probability of *either* a good component *or* a positive test is as follows:

$$P(\text{Good} \cup \text{Positive}) = P(\text{Good}) + P(\text{Positive}) - P(\text{Good} \cap \text{Positive})$$
$$= 0.90 + 0.875 - 0.855 = 0.92$$

Conditionals

The manufacturer in our problem is primarily interested in the probability that a particular component is good given the condition that the machine indicates positive or negative. This can be determined from Table 3.10 by noting that out of 350 components that tested positive, 342 were good, and of the 50 that tested negative, 18 were good, therefore:

$$P(\text{Good} \mid \text{Positive}) = \frac{342}{350} = 0.977$$

$$P(\text{Good} \mid \text{Negative}) = \frac{18}{50} = 0.36$$

Note that these two probabilities do not add up to *one*, since they are based on different conditional events. However, the value of $P(\text{Defective} \mid \text{Negative})$ must equal the following since these events are complementary:

$$1 - P(\text{Good} \mid \text{Negative}) = 1 - 0.36 = 0.64$$

The conditional probability $P(\text{Good} \mid \text{Positive})$ is the type of probability that can be (and often is) calculated by using Bayes' rule. To use Bayes' rule in this example, we need to know the probabilities $P(\text{Positive} \mid \text{Good})$ and $P(\text{Positive} \mid \text{Defective})$, which from Table 3.10 are easily seen to be $P(\text{Positive} \mid \text{Good}) = \frac{342}{360} = 0.95$ and $P(\text{Positive} \mid \text{Defective}) = \frac{8}{40} = 0.20$. The Bayesian calculation of $P(\text{Good} \mid \text{Positive})$ is:

$$P(\text{Good} \mid \text{Positive})$$

$$= \frac{P(\text{Good})P(\text{Positive} \mid \text{Good})}{P(\text{Good})P(\text{Positive} \mid \text{Good}) + P(\text{Defective})P(\text{Positive} \mid \text{Defective})}$$

$$= \frac{(0.90)(0.95)}{(0.90)(0.95) + (0.10)(0.20)} = \frac{0.855}{0.875} = 0.977$$

The result agrees with the $\frac{342}{350} = 0.977$ calculated above.

The results of the machine test in this problem are obviously not independent of the state of the component. If they were independent, $P(\text{Good} \mid \text{Positive})$ would have to equal $P(\text{Good})$, and $P(\text{Defective} \mid \text{Negative})$ would have to equal $P(\text{Defective})$, which is not the case. But how much better off is the manufacturer by knowing the results of the test? The manufacturer is in good shape if the test is positive, as the guess can then be made that the component is good, and the guess will be correct 97.7% of the time. After a negative indication, however, by guessing the component to be defective, the manufacturer will be correct only 64% of the time. Fortunately, a positive test will occur most often (87.5%) and a negative test relatively infrequently (12.5%).

Multiplying 97.7 by 0.875 and 64.0 by 0.125 gives the total percent of the time a correct assessment may be made, assuming that the manufacturer always accepts the results of the machine test. This process is just a common-sense use of the formal rule for adding up all the joint occurrences of those events. Using the formal rule, we find that the test indicates the correct state of the component 93.5% of the time:

$$P(\text{Correct}) = P(\text{Good} \cap \text{Positive}) + P(\text{Defective} \cap \text{Negative})$$

$$= P(\text{Positive})P(\text{Good} \mid \text{Positive}) + P(\text{Negative})P(\text{Defective} \mid \text{Negative})$$

$$= 0.875(0.977) + 0.125(0.64)$$

$$= 0.855 + 0.080$$

$$= 0.935$$

Without this machine, if the manufacturer always presumes that all components are good, the percent of correct decisions will be 90%, since the prior probability is $P(\text{Good}) = \frac{360}{400} = 0.90$. If we knew how much this machine costs (to buy and operate) and how much the firm's revenue would increase as a result of the machine's superior ability to distinguish between good and defective components, then we could determine whether the machine is worth purchasing.

Table 3.12 provides a summary of many of the probability rules presented in this chapter and their relationships to the different conditions that may be present in statistics problems.

TABLE 3.12 Summary of Probability Rules

Rule Name	Formula	General Rule	Rule for Mutually Exclusive Events	Rule for Independence
Complements	(3.8)	$P(\bar{A}) = 1 - P(A)$		
Conditional probability	(3.9)	$P(A \mid B) = \dfrac{P(A \cap B)}{P(B)}$	$P(A \mid B) = 0$	$P(A \mid B) = P(A)$
Joint probability	(3.10)	$P(A \cap B) = P(B)P(A \mid B)$ $= P(A)P(B \mid A)$	$P(A \cap B) = 0$	$P(A \cap B) = P(A)P(B)$
Probability of a union	(3.11)	$P(A \cup B) = P(A) + P(B)$ $- P(A \cap B)$	$P(A \cup B)$ $= P(A) + P(B)$	$P(A \cup B) = P(A)$ $+ P(B) - P(A)P(B)$
Marginal probability	(3.16)	$P(D) = \Sigma P(D \cap E_i)$ $= \Sigma P(E_i)P(D \mid E_i)$		
Bayes' rule	(3.18)	$P(E_i \mid A) = \dfrac{P(E_i)P(A \mid E_i)}{\Sigma P(E_j)P(A \mid E_j)}$		

PROBLEMS

3.30 Two hundred marketing strategies were classified as very effective, moderately effective, or not effective in conjunction with three pricing strategies (I, II, III) shown in Table 3.13:

TABLE 3.13 Marketing/Pricing Strategies

Marketing Strategies	Pricing Strategies			
	I	II	III	Totals
Very effective	20	50	30	100
Moderately effective	20	20	20	60
Not effective	20	10	10	40
Totals	60	80	60	200

a) Convert these data into a table showing a joint probability in each cell.

b) Use Formula 3.16 to calculate the marginal probability P(Very effective).

c) Use Bayes' rule to calculate the posterior probability P(Pricing strategy II | Very effective).

3.31 Use Bayes' rule to calculate the following.

a) In Problem 3.25, find the probability that gas heat will be best given that the winters will be mild.

b) In Problem 3.23, calculate the probability that a randomly selected applicant is a female, given that this person is 30 years old or younger.

3.32 Suppose you are now the part owner of a ski resort in the midwest. Over the past several winters, January weather has been very unpredictable. Your biggest profit comes from the weekends. On some weekends, it was actually too cold for skiing. Other weekends have been relatively warm, or perhaps rainy. You determine the probability that you make a profit on a given weekend is $\frac{3}{4}$ if the weather is favourable. If the weather is unfavourable, the probability that you make a profit is $\frac{1}{8}$. Assume that the forecast is for a $\frac{2}{5}$ chance of favourable weather.

a) What is the probability that you will make a profit from the weekend operation?

b) Suppose on Monday you find that you have made a profit. What is the probability that the weather on the preceding weekend was favourable?

3.33 You have decided to invest in the stock market for the first time and are considering three investment strategies. You want to earn at least a 10% return on your money. The probability of a 10% return if you pick the best of the three strategies is $\frac{1}{3}$. If you do not pick the best of the three strategies, your chances of a 10% return are $\frac{1}{5}$.

a) What is the probability that you will earn a return of 10% if you pick randomly among the strategies?

b) Given that you find at the end of six months that you have earned a 10% return, what is the probability that you picked the best of the three strategies?

3.34 One-fourth of the customers entering a certain Radio Shack store are less than 25 years old. One percent of the customers less than 25 years old make a major purchase (over $100), and 5% of the customers 25 or older make a major purchase. What is the probability that if a major purchase is made, it was by a person 25 or older?

3.35 A candidate studying for the CA exam recognizes five potential essay questions that might be the one asked on the exam. Unfortunately, this person has time to study for only one of the essay questions. The candidate picks, at random, one of the questions to study. If the candidate studies the right question, the probability of passing the exam is 0.90. If one of the other four questions is on the exam, the probability of passing is 0.30. The exam does, in fact, contain one of the five questions.

a) What is the probability the candidate will pass the test?

b) Suppose the candidate passes. What is the probability that this person picked the correct question to study?

3.36 The Easy-Charge Company described in Problem 3.22 has released the following data on the number of customers who were given cash advances last month.

TABLE 3.14 Easy-Charge's Financial Data

Amounts Owed (x) by Customers	Customers Receiving a Cash Advance	Customers Not Receiving a Cash Advance
$0 < x ≤ 100	229	2,894
$100 < x ≤ 200	378	1,707
$200 < x ≤ 300	501	1,426
$300 < x ≤ 400	416	939
$400 < x ≤ 500	260	483
$500 < x ≤ 600	289	478
Total customers	2,073	7,927

a) Use Formula 3.16 to calculate the marginal probability P(Cash advance).

b) Use Bayes' rule to calculate the posterior probability P(Amount Owed ≤ $100 | Cash advance).

3.37 A Gallup survey in the *Wall Street Journal* reported on hours worked by chief executives as shown in Figure 3.13. Notice the values in Figure 3.13 are *percents* for each size of firm.

a) Among large firms, what is the probability that a randomly selected executive works more than 60 hours per week?

b) If an executive works 70 hours or more, what is the probability that this person is associated with a small firm? Use Bayes' rule. Assume 50% of the executives were from large firms, 25% from medium firms, and 25% from small firms.

c) Complete Table 3.15, showing in each cell the appropriate joint probability for a randomly selected executive.

TABLE 3.15 Hours Worked By Executives

Firm Size	Less Than 50	50–59	60–69	70 or more	Marginals
Large	0.030				0.500
Medium					
Small					
Marginals	0.115				

3.38 Answer the following given the survey information in Table 3.16 for two hundred people.

TABLE 3.16 Education and Salary

Salary	Some College	None
Low	30	50
Medium	50	40
High	20	10
	100	100

a) Illustrate the use of Bayes' rule by finding the probability of selecting a noncollege respondent, presuming that the one selected is in the highest salary bracket indicated.

b) Are salary and years of college independent in this problem?

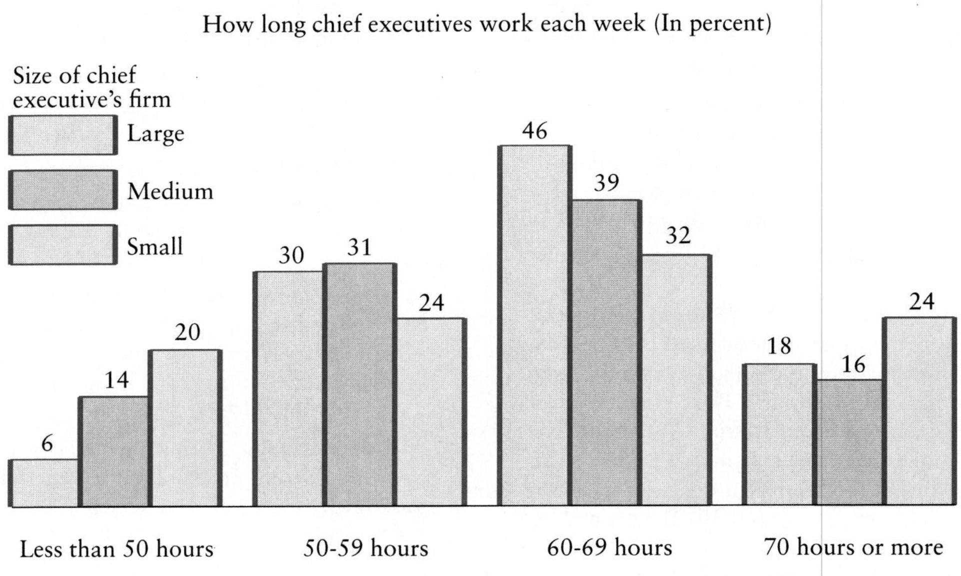

How long chief executives work each week (In percent)

FIGURE 3.13   Executive work week. (Reprinted by permission of the *Wall Street Journal*. ©Jones & Company, Inc. All rights reserved.)

3.39 Consider two types of economic stabilization policies – fiscal (controlled by Congress) and monetary policy (controlled by the Federal Reserve Board). Assume that the policy decisions made by these two institutions are independent of one another and that the action of either group is correct 80% of the time. Finally, assume that the probabilities that the economy follows a generally stable growth pattern due to (or in spite of) these policy actions are:

P(Stable growth | Neither acting correctly) = 0.40

P(Stable growth | Both acting correctly) = 0.99

P(Stable growth | Only 1 acting correctly) = 0.70

a) Use the independence assumption to calculate:

P(Neither acting correctly)

P(Both acting correctly)

P(Only 1 acting correctly)

b) You are given the sample information that growth is stable for a particular period. Use Bayes' rule to calculate:

P(Only 1 acting correctly | Stable growth)

P(Both acting correctly | Stable growth)

P(Neither acting correctly | Stable growth)

Check to see whether these three probabilities sum to 1.0.

CHAPTER SUMMARY

KEY TERMS AND EXPRESSIONS

Experiment: Any operation capable of replication under essentially stable circumstances. A situation involving uncertainty.

Sample space: Outcomes of an experiment — may be discrete and finite, discrete and infinite, or continuous and infinite.

Mutually exclusive outcomes: Two or more possible results of an experiment any one of which, if it occurs, rules out the occurrence of any other.

Exhaustive outcomes: Outcomes that account for (exhaust) the entire sample space.

Event: A subset of the outcomes of an experiment.

Probability of an event (using equally likely outcomes): Ratio of the number of outcomes comprising the event to the total number of outcomes in the sample space.

Probability: A number greater than or equal to 0 and less than or equal to 1 that indicates how likely an event is to occur.

Objective probability: A probability value determined by objective evidence, often relative frequencies.

Subjective probability: A probability value determined by an individual based on this person's knowledge, information, and experience.

Two basic properties:
1. $0 \leq P(E_i) \leq 1$ for every subset E_i of S
2. $P(S) = \sum_i P(E_i) = 1$ for mutually exclusive and exhaustive events.

Basic counting rule: Total number of sample points:

$$N = n_1(n_2)(n_3) \cdots (n_k)$$

n factorial: $n! = n(n-1)(n-2)\cdots(3)(2)(1)$

Permutations of n objects taken x at a time:

$$_nP_x = \frac{n!}{(n-x)!}$$

Combinations of n objects taken x at a time:

$$_nC_x = \frac{n!}{x!(n-x)!}$$

Probability of an event:

$$P(\text{event}) = P\left(\begin{array}{c}\text{one relevant} \\ \text{sample point}\end{array}\right)\left(\begin{array}{c}\text{number of relevant} \\ \text{sample points}\end{array}\right)$$

Probability of the complement: The probability that A will not take place in one replication of an experiment:

$$P(\bar{A}) = 1 - P(A)$$

Conditional probability of A given that B has taken (or will take) place:

$$P(A \mid B) = \frac{P(A \cap B)}{P(B)}$$

Joint probability (intersection): Both A and B occur in one replication of an experiment:

$$P(A \cap B) = P(B)P(A \mid B) = P(A)P(B \mid A)$$

Additive probability (union): Either A or B or both occur in one replication of an experiment:

$$P(A \cup B) = P(A) + P(B) - P(A \cap B)$$

Independence: One event does not influence the probability of another. If independent, $P(A \mid B) = P(A)$ and $P(A \cap B) = P(A)(P(B)$.

Marginal probability: $P(A) = \sum_i P(E_i)P(A \mid E_i)$

Bayes' rule:

$$P(E_i \mid A) = \frac{P(E_i)P(A \mid E_i)}{\sum_j P(E_j)P(A \mid E_j)}$$

$$= \frac{P(\text{event}_i)P(\text{sample information} \mid \text{event}_i)}{\sum_j P(\text{event}_j)P(\text{sample information} \mid \text{event}_j)}$$

EXERCISES

3.40 Answer the following questions about probability.

a) Distinguish between objective and subjective probability. Describe what you think to be the advantages and limitations of each of these interpretations of probabilities.

b) What is the probability that the real GDP growth in Canada this year will exceed 4%? Is this a subjective or an objective probability? At what odds would you be indifferent between the two sides of a $1 bet, one side saying growth will not exceed 4%, the other side saying growth will exceed 4%? Are these odds

consistent with your answer about the probability of more than a 4% growth in real GDP? Explain why they are or are not consistent.

3.41 In defining probability, what is meant by the terms *experiment* and *event*? How are these terms related to the limit of relative frequency? How does one go about determining the limit of relative frequency in practical problems?

3.42 A local business has been talked into buying a number of raffle tickets. The prize is a $500 colour television set. If 4,000 tickets are sold, how much is each ticket worth?

3.43 Four employees have been selected to take a written test for possible promotion to supervisor. Two of the employees are women. The maximum test score is 100 points. Three of the employees scored above 90 on the test, and every employee either exceeded 90, or is a woman, or both.

a) What is the probability that an employee exceeded 90 and is a woman?

b) Given that an employee is a woman, what is the probability that she scored above 90?

c) Given that an employee scored above 90, what is the probability that this person is a woman?

3.44 Suppose an instructor announces that the final exam will consist of five questions, which will be randomly selected from a list of ten questions handed out one week before the exam. In order to pass the exam, a student must be able to answer at least four of the exam questions selected. What is the probability that a student who can answer eight of the ten questions will pass the exam?

3.45 The following is a set of weekly wages in dollars for six employees: 372, 400, 288, 395, 389, 378. If two of these employees are to be selected at random to serve as labour representatives, what is the probability that at least one will have a wage lower than the average?

3.46 Two different types of questionnaires were used during the 1990 U.S. Census of Population, a short form (asking only names, ages, and incomes of each household) and a long form (asking for considerably more information). In Town A, 30% of the houses received the long form; in Town B, 20% received the long form; and in Town C, 10% received the long form. Town A has 50,000 houses, Town B has 100,000 houses, and Town C has 40,000 houses.

a) Considering all three towns as one group, what is the probability that a house will receive the long form?

b) Given that a house received the long form, what is the probability that the house is in Town A? What is this probability for B? For C?

c) Complete the following 2 × 3 table (two forms × three towns) by placing a joint probability in each cell and five marginal probabilities around the outside. Assume that one house is randomly selected.

TABLE 3.17 Joint and Marginal Probabilities

	Town A	Town B	Town C	Marginals
Long form				
Short form				
Marginals				

3.47 A bank has studied its chequing accounts and found that 1% of all cheques are returned for insufficient funds. For chequing accounts that have been open less than one year, the percent of returned cheques is 5%. Ninety-six percent of all accounts have been open for more than one year. Student accounts represent 6% of the bank's chequing accounts, and one-third of the student accounts have been open for less than one year.

a) What is the probability that a randomly selected account will be that of a student and will have been open for less than one year?

b) If a cheque is returned for insufficient funds, what is the probability that the account has been open for less than one year?

c) Is the event *cheque returned* independent of the event *open less than one year*? Is the event *open for less than one year* independent of the event *student*?

3.48 An automobile insurance company has examined its records and compiled the following probability table representing how likely it is that each one of their policyholders has an accident in a one-year period. The number of policyholders in each category is given in parentheses.

TABLE 3.18 Probability of a Car Accident by Age

Sex	Less than 25	25–65	More than 65
Female	0.10 (10,000)	0.04 (50,000)	0.08 (20,000)
Male	0.20 (8,000)	0.05 (60,000)	0.06 (20,000)

a) Explain the meaning of the probability 0.10 in the upper-left cell.

b) How many accidents should the company expect in a year?

c) If an accident occurs, what is the probability that it involved someone less than 25 years old? What is the probability that a male was the driver?

d) Are the events *male driver* and *age less than 25* independent?

3.49 The probability that an individual has Type O blood is 0.45, the probability of Type A blood is 0.40, the probability of Type B blood is 0.10, and the probability of Type AB blood is 0.05. Two randomly selected individuals agree to donate blood. What is the probability that both have the same blood type or that at least one of the two has Type O blood?

3.50 Credit-Wise loan company has recorded both the activity level of the local economy (either Hi, Med, or Low) and the mean interarrival times ($0 <$ time ≤ 20 min, $20 <$ time ≤ 60 min, $60 <$ time ≤ 200 min) for its customers over the past 150 weeks.

TABLE 3.19 Credit-Wise Company Records

Time Interval (t) Between Customers	State of Economy		
	Hi	Med	Low
A $\quad 0 < t \leq 20$	30	12	8
B $\quad 20 < t \leq 60$	30	21	4
C $\quad 60 < t \leq 200$	30	12	3

a) Find $P(\text{Hi})$, $P(\text{Med})$, $P(\text{Low})$, $P(A)$, $P(B)$, and $P(C)$.

b) Find $P(A \mid \text{Hi})$, $P(A \mid \text{Med})$, $P(A \mid \text{Low})$.

c) Use Formula 3.16 to find $P(A)$.

d) Are the events A, B, C independent of the state of the economy?

e) Suppose Credit-Wise would like to revise the probabilities $P(\text{Hi})$, $P(\text{Med})$, $P(\text{Low})$ in the light of the sample evidence S. Find $P(\text{Hi} \mid S)$, $P(\text{Med} \mid S)$, and $P(\text{Low} \mid S)$ given that $P(S \mid \text{Hi}) = 0.05$, $P(S \mid \text{Med}) = 0.10$, and $P(S \mid \text{Low}) = 0.40$.

3.51 Prove that if $P(A \mid B) = P(A)$, then $P(B \mid A) = P(B)$.

3.52 Table 3.20 provides unemployment percents for males and females during a recession.

a) According to this table, what is the probability that a randomly selected person who is unemployed will be both adult and white, $P(A \cap W)$? What is $P(A \cup W)$?

b) If the unemployed person is an adult, what is the probability that person is white? What is $P(W)$?

c) Is the event W independent of the event A? Explain, using your answer to part (b).

d) Find the value of $P(A)P(W)$. Use this value and your results from part (a) to determine whether A and W are independent.

e) Use Bayes' rule to determine the probability $P(A \mid W)$.

TABLE 3.20 Unemployment Percents During a Recession

	Males	Females
White Adult	36.0%	25.0%
White Teen-Age	9.5	8.0
Nonwhite Adult	9.5	8.0
Nonwhite Teen-Age	2.0	2.0

3.53 Consider the information in **Data Set 1** as a population. For a randomly selected city, answer the following.

a) Find the probability of an income exceeding $1000 (million) or exceeding 20.0 (thousand) households.

b) Find the probability of an income of exceeding $1000 (million) and exceeding 20.0 (thousand households.)

c) Find the probability of an income exceeding $1000 (million) given that the number of households exceeds 20.0 (thousand). (Solve by counting cities.)

d) Solve part (c) using Bayes' rule.

e) Determine whether a city's income exceeds $1000 is independent of the number of households exceeding 20.0.

3.54 Use **Data Set 2** to determine the probability that a company randomly selected (from this population of 100) will be above the median debt/equity ratio and have sales above $1,000,000. Omit all companies with missing debt/equity ratios.

CASE PROBLEM

3.55 Culver, Inc. has advertised in numerous Sunday papers that they will sell one million new push-button telephones for $10 each plus mailing costs. Suppose Culver has had these phones made in Taiwan for a net cost of $9 each and they expect to sell all one million. They guarantee that each customer must be satisfied or money will be refunded. Culver estimates the probability to be 0.05 that a customer will receive a defective phone. They do not test the phones in advance. The probability that a defective phone will be returned is estimated to be 0.50. Culver also estimates the probability to be 0.01

that a nondefective phone will be returned. A returned defective phone costs Culver an extra $200. (The defective phone is thrown away, and Culver replaces it with a phone purchased locally.) A returned phone that is not defective costs them an extra $3 (mailing and handling charges). What is the probability that a randomly selected phone is returned? If a phone is returned, what is the probability that it was defective? How much profit can Culver expect to make assuming that all one million phones are sold?

CHAPTER 4

Discrete Random Variables and Expectations

section 4.1

Introduction and Probability Models

In Chapter 3, we studied rules for associating a probability value with a single event or with a subset of events in an experiment. Now we are ready to expand the scope of our analysis and consider *all* possible events in an experiment. A slightly more formal notation will also be introduced. We begin by examining one of the most important concepts in probability, the *random variable*.

Random Variable

Given an experiment and a set of *mutually exclusive* and *exhaustive* outcomes, it is common to consider questions about the probability of the occurrence of any one or more of these outcomes by use of the **random variable** concept.

> A **random variable** is a well-defined rule for assigning a numerical value to all possible outcomes of an experiment.

This means that the symbols used in Chapter 3 to designate the outcomes of an experiment — *not defective* or *defective*, et cetera — are now going to be replaced with numbers. A random variable is a rule designating a number to be associated with each outcome of the experiment.

The outcomes of some experiments readily meet this definition of a random variable because they are already well-defined numbers. For example, the number of hours that a given light bulb might last is a well-defined number, the number of defectives that could occur in a lot of transistors is a well-defined number; and the potential yield on an investment of $1,000 is a well-defined number. In other cases the outcomes of an experiment may be qualitative. For example, the outcome of a single ballot on a bond election is *For* or *Against*, and the outcome of taking a course could be a grade of A, B, C, D, or F. In these instances, the probability model must specify exactly what numerical value corresponds to each qualitative outcome. Registrars at many colleges do this for grades by letting $A = 4$, $B = 3$, $C = 2$, $D = 1$, and $F = 0$. In the case of the ballot, one common way to define a random variable is to let *For* $= 1$ and *Against* $= 0$. There may be less agreement in attempting to define a random variable for the experiment *drive from Montreal to Edmonton*. In this case the sample space would need to be converted to some consistent measure, such as the *number of dollars* required for automobile repairs.

In working with *continuous* sample spaces, it is sometimes convenient to reduce the sample space to just a few discrete points. For example, the yield on a $1,000 investment might be classified as falling into one of just a small number of intervals such as 0 to 2.0, 2.1 to 4.0, et cetera; and the dollar amount of repairs on a trip to Edmonton could be classified as either less than $50, between $50 and $100, or over $100. In all these examples, we have a random variable only when numerical values are assigned to the outcomes of the experiment by a well-defined rule.

The rule is often expressed as a formula; it is the *general* statement defining the random variable relative to all conceivable outcomes of the experiment. When specific outcomes of the experiment are substituted into the formula, the result is a value of the random variable. The value is a *specific* result relating to a particular outcome.

In making the assignment of numerical values to the outcomes of an experiment, we will denote random variables by letters in *boldface* type, such as $\boldsymbol{x}, \boldsymbol{y}, \boldsymbol{z}$, or sometimes by subscripted boldface letters such as $\boldsymbol{x}_1, \boldsymbol{x}_2, \boldsymbol{x}_3$. *Specific* values of such random variables will be denoted by letters in lightface type, such as x, y, z, or perhaps x_1, x_2, x_3. Thus, the designation $\{\boldsymbol{x} = x\}$ is read as "the random variable $\boldsymbol{x}$ takes on the value x." The following examples will illustrate this notation.

☐ **EXAMPLE 4.1**   *Experiment*: Survey a wage earner and ask whether the person bought a new car during the previous year.

Outcomes: Two discrete outcomes: bought a car or not
Sample space: Discrete and finite
Random variable: Define $\boldsymbol{x} = 1$ if the person bought a car and $\boldsymbol{x} = 0$ if not

Although any values may be used to give numerical labels to the outcomes in an experiment such as this one, zero and one are especially convenient mathematically in many situations involving just two outcomes. Such a random variable may be called an **indicator variable**, since its value of 0 or 1 *indicates* whether or not a specific characteristic occurred. Since the variable $\boldsymbol{x}$ in this case gives a well-defined rule for assigning numerical values to the experiment, $\boldsymbol{x}$ is a random variable.   ■

☐ **EXAMPLE 4.2**   *Experiment*: Taking an exam.

Outcomes: Grades A, B, C, D, F
Sample space: Discrete and finite
Random variable: Define $\boldsymbol{y} = 4$ if the grade is A,
$\qquad\qquad\qquad\quad \boldsymbol{y} = 3$ if the grade is B,
$\qquad\qquad\qquad\quad \boldsymbol{y} = 2$ if the grade is C,
$\qquad\qquad\qquad\quad \boldsymbol{y} = 1$ if the grade is D, and
$\qquad\qquad\qquad\quad \boldsymbol{y} = 0$ if the grade is F.

The familiar four-point grade system is simply an assignment of numbers to a grade measure. Since the variable $\boldsymbol{y}$ gives a well-defined rule for assigning numbers to the outcomes of this experiment, $\boldsymbol{y}$ is a random variable.   ■

☐ **EXAMPLE 4.3**   *Experiment*: Driving a car from Montreal to Edmonton.

Outcomes: Various car troubles that might be encountered on trip
Sample space: Discrete (infinite but countable)
Random variable: Define $\boldsymbol{z} = $ nearest number of dollars paid for repairs, $\{z = 0, 1, 2, 3, \ldots\}$.

The random variable $\boldsymbol{z}$ in this case is discrete, and it is also infinite, since there is no limit on the amount of repairs. Realistically, however, there is some upper bound to the value of $\boldsymbol{z}$, perhaps equal to the cost of the car if it is a total loss due to an accident. Also, this probability model assumes no negative values for $\boldsymbol{z}$, since we doubt that anyone can find a *Tom Sawyer* mechanic willing to pay for the chance to do the needed repairs.   ■

◻ **EXAMPLE 4.4**   *Experiment:* Investing $1,000 in a common stock.

Outcomes: Values of yield or rate of return

Sample space: Continuous (always infinite)

Random variable: Define x = value of yield, $\{-\infty < x < +\infty\}$.

A *continuous random variable* is obtained from a continuous sample space whenever a single value of x is assigned to each outcome in the sample space. Thus, since a yield can be *any* positive or negative number, x must be continuous.   ∎

◻ **EXAMPLE 4.5**   *Experiment:* Investing $1,000 in a common stock.

In this example we simplify the experiment in Example 4.4 somewhat by grouping the various yields into different classes. For example, we might let one class represent all yields between 0 and 2%, another represent 2.1–4.0%, et cetera. This simplification results in the following probability model:

Outcomes: Class intervals of yields

Sample space: Discrete and infinite (no limit on the number of classes)

Random variable: Define x = the midpoint or some representative value (the class mark) of the yields in each class interval.   ∎

We should point out that the numerical value assigned to an outcome in an experiment need not be unique to that outcome. That is, several different outcomes may be assigned the same numerical value. This fact is easily seen in the experiment about driving to Edmonton, for in this case there are certainly many different outcomes (car troubles) that would lead to the same value of the random variable (same dollar value of cost).

Probability Distributions

Once an experiment and its outcomes have been clearly stated and the random variable of interest has been defined, then the probability of the occurrence of any value of the random variable can be specified. Let us present some new examples.

◻ **EXAMPLE 4.6**   Suppose 140 salespeople are assigned to a certain region and they are to be divided randomly into four sections of this region. The number of persons assigned to each section is determined by the population and area of the sections as follows:

TABLE 4.1   Assignment of 140 Salespeople into Four Sections of a Region

Section	Assignments
1	25
2	45
3	40
4	30
Total	140

If you are one of the salespersons involved in this assignment, you could view this process as an experiment with *four outcomes*. The sample space is discrete and finite; a random variable x may be defined to have values equal to the section number, $x = 1, 2, 3,$ or 4. The probability that you will be assigned to any one section can be determined and denoted by the symbol $P(x)$. For example, the probability of your being assigned to Section 1 is denoted $P(x = 1)$ or $P(1)$. The probability that you will be assigned to Section 1 is simply the proportion of assignments that are made to Section 1 relative to the total number of persons, which is:

$$P(1) = \frac{25}{140} = 0.179$$

This is the *least probable* outcome of the experiment. What value of x has the highest probability? That is, what section assignment is the most probable outcome? Clearly, you have the highest chance of being assigned to Section 2, since this section will have the most persons. Its probability is:

$$P(2) = \frac{45}{140} = 0.321$$

Continuing in this manner, we can find the probability of each possible value for the random variable x. When this is done, we have obtained the **probability distribution** for x. Table 4.2 and Figure 4.1 depict the probability distribution for the random variable in this assignment problem.

TABLE 4.2 Probability Distribution for x in the Section Assignment of Example 4.6

Outcome	Value of x	$P(x)$
Section 1	1	$(25/140) = 0.179$
Section 2	2	$(45/140) = 0.321$
Section 3	3	$(40/140) = 0.286$
Section 4	4	$(30/140) = 0.214$
Sum		1.000

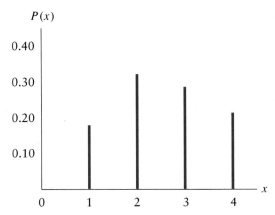

FIGURE 4.1 Graph of the discrete probability distribution for x given in Table 4.1

In this example, only four discrete values of x have a positive probability. All other values of x have a probability of occurring equal to zero, indicating that they are impossible. Also, the sum of the probabilities of all values of x is equal to 1, indicating that these four are the only possible outcomes; we know with certainty that one of them will occur in each assignment. ■

The construction of a probability distribution is not always as simple as in the previous example where the random variable had a unique value for each section. To illustrate a slightly more involved experiment in which the random variable is not as directly related to the outcomes, we present a somewhat simplified version of a two-car accident problem.

☐ **EXAMPLE 4.7**   Suppose a highway safety consultant studies the flow of cars on a particular stretch of roadway. For simplification, we will consider only two-car accidents. Also, assume that each car may contain from one to six persons and that each of these cases is equally likely. For this situation, we examine the total number of persons involved in a two-car accident.

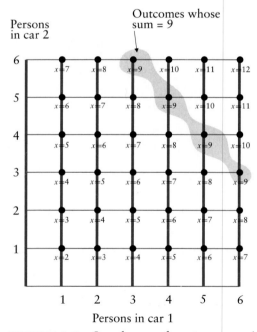

FIGURE 4.2   Sample space for a two-car accident

Since the number of persons in each car may be 1, 2, 3, 4, 5, or 6 (six outcomes), there are $6 \times 6 = 36$ possible outcomes if we count the number of people in two cars. The sample space of 36 outcomes is discrete and finite as illustrated in Figure 4.2. The random variable x is equal to the sum of the persons in two cars involved in an accident. That is, x can assume any integer value from 2 to 12, depending on the number of persons in each of the cars. Note that the number of different values for x is only 11, even though the number of possible outcomes in the experiment is 36. Some of the outcomes result in the same value for x. Since we have assumed that the number of persons per car, 1, 2, 3, 4, 5, or 6, are equally likely, the probability of any value of x is given by the number of sample points for which the number of persons equals x, divided by the *total number* of sample points. For example, let us find $P(x = 9)$, which is usually shortened to $P(9)$. In Figure 4.2, we can observe the number of sample points corresponding to this value of x. Out of all 36 outcomes, those satisfying the condition $\{x = 9\}$ are the four ordered pairs (3, 6), (4, 5), (5, 4), and (6, 3), where the first entry is the number of persons in car 1 and the second entry is the number of persons in car 2. Thus, $P(9) = \frac{4}{36}$. Similarly, we could find the probability that the value of x would be 3. The ordered pairs (1, 2) and (2, 1) are the only sample points satisfying $x = 3$, and so $P(3) = \frac{2}{36}$. Figure 4.3 is a graph of the probability distribution of the random variable $x =$ the number of persons involved in a two-car accident. ■

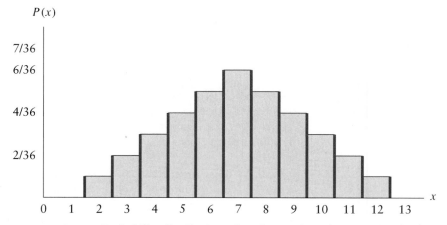

FIGURE 4.3   Probability distribution of x, the number of persons involved in a two-car accident

Once the probability distribution of a random variable is determined, it can be used to answer all types of questions about the outcomes of the experiment. From Figure 4.3, it is obvious that the most common occurrence would be seven persons involved in a two-car accident, given our simplifying conditions. The probability that the number of persons exceeds eight could be found by summing together the probabilities for the values of x above eight:

$$P(x > 8) = P(9) + P(10) + P(11) + P(12)$$

Once a probability distribution is obtained for a random variable, it can also be analyzed and used in decision-making or in presenting an argument. As with any distribution of values, two very important summary characteristics should be determined. These summary measures are the:

1. population mean to describe the central location
2. population variance to describe the spread of the distribution

After we have formalized the concept of a probability distribution a little more, we will return to the task of determining methods for calculating such measures. For now, what matters is the understanding of the relation between a specific experiment and the induced probability distribution resulting from it. Figure 4.4 illustrates this relationship and completes the process of describing the probability model. First, the experiment must be clearly stated so that all the conceivable outcomes can be understood. A random variable is then formulated to assign a value to each possible outcome of the experiment. By using probability rules, the probability of each value of the random variable can be determined. The probability distribution

$P(x)$ is a table, a formula, or a graph of the random variable x and the associated probabilities.

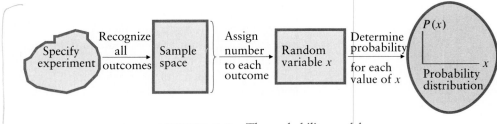

FIGURE 4.4 The probability model

section 4.2

Probability Mass Functions (p.m.f.)

> A probability distribution involving only discrete values of x is usually called a *probability mass function.*

A **probability mass function (p.m.f.)** is usually described in one of three ways: (**1**) by a graph, such as Figure 4.3, (**2**) by a table of values, such as Table 4.2, or (**3**) by a formula.[1] The name *mass function* derives from the fact that all outcomes associated with the value of a discrete random variable can be represented on a graph by a vertical line whose height (or *mass*) indicates the probability of that value.

To illustrate the concept of describing a mass function by graph, table, and formula, consider the problem of determining how long a certain grocery item might sit on the shelf before being sold. For a package of cheese, the estimate is that there is a 50 : 50 chance the cheese will be sold on any given day. Suppose we let $x =$ the day on which the item is sold. Since there is a 50 : 50 chance that the item is sold on the first day, $P(x = 1) = \frac{1}{2}$. If $\{x = 2\}$, this means the item was not sold on day one and *is* sold on day two. Thus, $P(x = 2) = \frac{1}{2} \cdot \frac{1}{2} = \frac{1}{4}$. Similarly, $P(x = 3) = \frac{1}{2} \cdot \frac{1}{2} \cdot \frac{1}{2} = \frac{1}{8}$. A graph of the p.m.f. for this experiment, and a table of its values are shown in Figure 4.5 and Table 4.3, respectively.

TABLE 4.3   The P.M.F. for Cheese Sales

x	$P(x)$
1	$1/2 = 0.500$
2	$1/4 = 0.250$
3	$1/8 = 0.125$
4	$1/16 = 0.063$
5	$1/32 = 0.031$
.	.
.	.
.	.

---

[1] The reader is referred to the review of functions in Appendix B.

Using a graph and/or a table in this problem is inconvenient because of the fact that although x is discrete, an infinite number of x values is possible. That is, the cheese might not be sold for a very large number of days. In reality, after a certain number of days, it should be removed from the shelf and not sold. Thus, Figure 4.5 and Table 4.3 are somewhat unsatisfactory because they present only a series of dots to indicate the values of x and their probability after five days. A formula, on the other hand, can be used to *explicitly* specify how $P(x)$ and x are related for *all* values of x. In this case, the relationship is easily found to be:

$$P(x) = \begin{cases} (\tfrac{1}{2})^x & \text{for } x = 1, 2, 3, \ldots, \infty \\ 0 & \text{otherwise} \end{cases}$$

By substituting $x = 1, x = 2, \ldots, x = 5$ into this formula, the reader can verify the values in Table 4.3 and Figure 4.5.

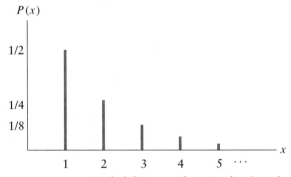

FIGURE 4.5   Probability mass function for day of sale of cheese

By now the reader should recognize the similarity between the concept of probabilities of events in Chapter 3 and probabilities for a random variable. The same properties defined in Chapter 3 for probabilities of events can now be specified in terms of a random variable. The first property is that all probabilities associated with values of the random variable x must be nonnegative and cannot exceed 1.0.

Property 1:
$$0 \leq P(\pmb{x} = x) \leq 1$$

Second, we know that the sum of the probabilities of all values of the random variable must equal 1.

Property 2:
$$\sum_{\text{All } x} P(x) = 1$$

These properties repeat the fundamental concepts about probability. For any value of a random variable, the probability measure is an index with a *minimum of zero* (representing impossibility) and a *maximum of one* (representing certainty). Also, since every outcome possible in an experiment must lead to some value of x according to a well-defined rule, Property 2 says that every time the experiment occurs, it is a certainty that some outcome and associated value of x occurs.

Cumulative Mass Function (c.m.f.)

The concept of *cumulative* relative frequency and the graphical representations thereof, which were introduced in Chapter 1, also have their counterparts in the study of probability. A **cumulative mass function (c.m.f.)** describes how probability accumulates in exactly the same fashion as column four in Table 1.5 describes how relative frequency accumulates — by *summing* all the relative frequency values. The value of the cumulative mass function at any given point x is usually denoted by the symbol $F(x)$, where $F(x)$ is the *sum of all values* of the probability mass function for all values of the random variable x that are *less than or equal* to x. That is,

Cumulative mass function at the point x_0:

$$F(x_0) = P(x \leq x_0) = \sum_{x \leq x_0} P(x) \tag{4.1}$$

For our cheese example, the value of $F(x)$ when $x = 1$ is $F(1) = 0.50$ because $P(x \leq 1) = 0.50$. Similarly, $F(2) = 0.75$ because $P(x \leq 2) = 0.50 + 0.25 = 0.75$. As with a probability mass function, a cumulative mass function must be defined for *all* values of the random variable. This is usually accomplished by means of either a graph, a table, or a formula. The table and graph for the cheese example are shown below in Table 4.4 and Figure 4.6. A c.m.f. graph will always look like a series of steps (a *step-function*) ascending from zero to one as the value of x increases.

TABLE 4.4   The C.M.F. for Cheese Sales

x	$F(x)$
1	0.500
2	0.750
3	0.875
4	0.938
5	0.969
.	.
.	.
.	.

Figure 4.6 is perhaps a better way to illustrate the c.m.f. than Table 4.4, for the former emphasizes the fact that $F(x)$ is defined for *all* values of x from negative infinity to positive infinity. That is, the cumulative mass function $F(x)$ is defined for *any* value of x, not just the integer values listed in Table 4.4. As should be clear from Figure 4.6, $F(x) = 0$ for all values of x from minus infinity up to $x = 1$. At $x = 1$, the value of $F(x)$ becomes 0.50. Similarly at $x = 2$, the value of the function becomes 0.75. Note that for *any* number between $x = 2$ and $x = 3$, $F(x) = 0.75$. Suppose that we arbitrarily pick a number, say $x = 2.45$. From Figure 4.6, $F(2.45)$ can easily be seen to be:

$$F(2.45) = 0.750$$

The value $F(3) = 0.875$ is interpreted as meaning that there is a probability of 0.875 that the cheese will be sold in three days or less.

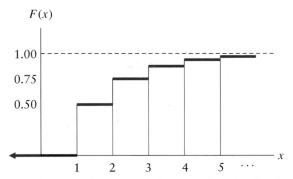

FIGURE 4.6   The cumulative mass function for day of sale of cheese

☐ **EXAMPLE 4.8**   Three college graduates (probably English and history majors) go into business in a little bakery shop near campus. From experience, they know that students love to receive a package of homemade brownies. They decide to specialize in homemade brownie squares, and they serve them in sizes from one-inch squares to a super-large foot square, which is their best bargain, since no special cutting and packaging is needed. Table 4.5 gives the sizes of brownie squares (x) in inches and the relative frequencies of their sales over the long run. The relative frequencies are interpreted as probabilities, $P(x)$. We see that for this discrete set of values, $0 \leq P(x) \leq 1$ for each x, and the following is true so that the two properties of a probability mass function are satisfied:

$$\sum_{\text{All } x} P(x) = 1$$

The cumulative relative frequencies are given by the values in the row designated $F(x)$. In this situation, the outcomes are discrete and finite. The graph of the cumulative probability distribution is shown in Figure 4.7. Either function, the p.m.f. $[P(x)]$ or the c.m.f. $[F(x)]$, may be used to determine the probability of any event defined in terms of the values of x. Also, there is often more than one correct approach to finding the probability using either the table or the graph.

For example, to find the probability of selling a brownie larger than two inches, $P(x > 2)$, we might use the p.m.f. directly:

$$P(x > 2) = P(4) + P(6) + P(12)$$
$$= 0.10 + 0.33 + 0.22$$
$$= 0.65.$$

TABLE 4.5   The P.M.F. and C.M.F. for Homemade Brownie Squares

Square size, x	1″	2″	4″	6″	12″
$P(x = x)$	0.08	0.27	0.10	0.33	0.22
$F(x) = P(x \leq x)$	0.08	0.35	0.45	0.78	1.00

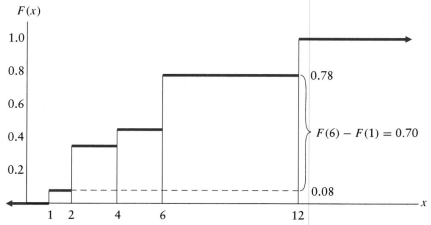

FIGURE 4.7   A c.m.f. sketch based on Table 4.5

This probability can also be easily determined by using the complementary law of probability:

$$P(x > 2) = 1 - P(x \leq 2)$$

With use of the p.m.f., the result is as follows:

$$P(x > 2) = 1 - P(1) - P(2)$$
$$= 1 - 0.08 - 0.27 = 0.65$$

Since $P(x \leq 2) = F(2)$, the solution could be quickly found by using the cumulative mass function:

$$P(x > 2) = 1 - F(2) = 1.0 - 0.35 = 0.65$$

To illustrate a slightly more difficult case, let us find the probability of selling a brownie that is neither the smallest nor the largest size. This event *excludes* sizes $x = 1$ and $x = 12$; and so the event could be written $1 < x \leq 6$. With use of the c.m.f., $F(x)$, as shown in Table 4.5:

$$P(x \leq 6) = F(6) = 0.78$$

But since $F(6)$ *includes* the probability $P(x \leq 1) = F(1)$, we must *subtract* this value from $F(6)$:

$$P(1 < x \leq 6) = F(6) - F(1) = 0.78 - 0.08 = 0.70$$

To check this logic, the same probability may be found by summing the appropriate values of the p.m.f.:

$$P(1 < x \leq 6) = P(2) + P(4) + P(6)$$
$$= 0.27 + 0.10 + 0.33 = 0.70$$

As seen from the above examples, the cumulative mass function is useful in determining probability values for various types of events. Since this function will be used frequently in problems of statistical inference, the student should thoroughly understand this concept and all of the above examples before proceeding.

☐ **STUDY QUESTION 4.1**   **Receipt of Registered Mail Items**

A self-employed accountant receives materials, forms, and signed documents from her clients in the mail. Each day the accountant must sign for a number of registered mail items. In the following probability mass function, x represents the number of registered mail items received per day.

a) Sketch the p.m.f. and the c.m.f.

b) Use each sketch to find the probability that the number of registered mail items received on a given day exceeds two but is not more than seven.

$$2 < x \leq 7$$

● **ANSWER**

TABLE 4.6   Daily Registered Mail Received by an Accountant

No. of items, x	0	1	2	3	4	5	6	7	8	9
$P(x)$	0.07	0.14	0.18	0.24	0.12	0.10	0.08	0.04	0.02	0.01

a) The p.m.f. and the c.m.f. are shown in Figure 4.8

b) Using the p.m.f. sketch:

$$P(2 < x \leq 7) = \sum_{x=3}^{7} P(x) = P(3) + P(4) + P(5) + P(6) + P(7)$$

$$= 0.24 + 0.12 + 0.10 + 0.08 + 0.04 = 0.58$$

Or, using the c.m.f. sketch:

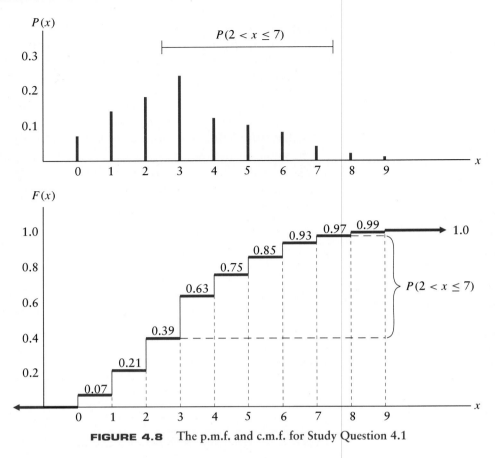

FIGURE 4.8 The p.m.f. and c.m.f. for Study Question 4.1

$$P(2 < x \le 7) = F(7) - F(2) = 0.97 - 0.39 = 0.58$$ ■

▢ STUDY QUESTION 4.2 Teacher Salary Supplements

All the public school teachers in a certain isolated school district receive an annual salary supplement from the local school funds depending on their experience, education, certification level, and teaching fields. There are six levels of supplements for all 970 teachers as shown in Table 4.7.

TABLE 4.7 Levels of Salary Supplements for Teachers in Isolated School Districts

Level	1	2	3	4	5	6
supplement, x	$200	$500	$1,000	$1,500	$2,000	$3,000
Number of teachers	109	204	324	186	102	45

a) If a teacher were selected at random, explain how x can be interpreted as a random variable.

b) Find the probability mass function and the cumulative mass function for x.

c) Use each of the functions in part (b) to determine the probability that a teacher selected at random has a local salary supplement larger than $750 and less than $3,000.

• ANSWER

a) Selecting a teacher at random is a situation involving uncertainty because we do not know which one would be selected from among the total of 970. This experiment could conceivably be replicated again and again, each time selecting a teacher at random, then replacing that person into the total pool and selecting one again, then replacing and selecting, replacing and selecting, et cetera. Thus, the long-run frequencies of the number of teachers with each supplement relative to the total number $N = 970$ can be interpreted as probabilities. Since the size of the supplement is the matter of interest and it is already a quantitative measure, its level of dollars can be defined as the values of a random variable x. The sample space is discrete and finite.

b) Each $P(x)$ is obtained as the long-run relative frequency, f_i/N, as shown in column 2 of Table 4.8. The C.M.F. is in column 3.

TABLE 4.8 The P.M.F. and C.M.F. for Salary Supplement (x)

x	$P(x) =$ P.M.F.	$F(x) =$ C.M.F.
200	$109/970 = 0.112$	0.112
500	$204/970 = 0.210$	$0.112 + 0.210 = 0.322$
1,000	0.334	$0.322 + 0.334 = 0.656$
1,500	0.192	$0.656 + 0.192 = 0.848$
2,000	0.105	$0.848 + 0.105 = 0.953$
3,000	0.047	$0.953 + 0.047 = 1.000$

c) Using the p.m.f. (column 2) in Table 4.8,

$$P(750 < x < 3,000) = P(1,000) + P(1,500) + P(2,000)$$

$$= 0.334 + 0.192 + 0.105 = 0.631$$

Using the c.m.f. (column 3):

$$P(750 < x < 3,000) = F(2,999) - F(750)$$

since the supplement of $3,000 is *not* to be included. The probability accumulated at $2,999 is the same as at $2,000, and the cumulative probability at $750 is the same as at $500:

$$P(750 < x < 3,000) = 0.953 - 0.322 = 0.631$$ ■

Some Further Considerations

We must next consider the parameters of a given probability distribution, such as those in the earlier examples for two-car accidents or salary supplements. Recall from Chapter 2 that the important features of *any* distribution (which we now know includes probability distributions) are the measures of *central location* and *dispersion*. Knowing the mean salary supplement per teacher, for example, would be of value in setting the school budget. A measure of the variability of supplements is also important when one is interested in deviations from the expected supplement. In the next section the measures of central location and dispersion for a probability distribution are presented. It is very important to be able to determine these measures for any probability distribution of interest.

section 4.3

Expected Values

Using the material presented thus far, we can now determine the probability of a single event of an experiment or describe the probability of the entire set of outcomes associated with a given random variable. This information, however, may not be concise enough for most decision-making contexts. Recall that we had the same problem in Chapter 2, when it was not sufficient merely to present all the data. In that situation, several characteristics of these data were also given, the most important of which were the *mean* and the *variance*. The same types of measures are also useful in describing probability distributions. However, in this case we must speak not of an *observed* mean or an *observed* variance, but of the mean or variance that would be *expected* to result (on the average) for the random variable under consideration. These summary measures are thus given the name *expectations* or *expected values*.

Expected Value

> The expected value of a discrete random variable x is found by multiplying each value of the random variable by its probability and then summing all these products.

The letter E usually denotes an expected value, and this symbol is followed by brackets enclosing the random variable of interest. Thus, the symbol $E[x]$ represents the expected value of the random variable x. The expected value of x is the *balancing point* for the probability mass function. It is simply a *weighted average* of the population of x-values where the weights are probabilities. Recall Formula 2.2 for a weighted average, $\mu = [\Sigma x_i w_i]/\Sigma w_i$. For the mean or expected value of a probability distribution, the probability $P(x)$ is the weight used to describe how often each value of x should be included in the summation. In the denominator, the sum of the weights is the sum of the probabilities, $\Sigma P(x)$. However, from Property 2, we know that the sum of the probabilities must always equal 1. Thus, the general formula for an **expected value** is:

> Expected value of x:
> $$\mu = E[x] = \sum_{\text{All } x} x P(x) \tag{4.2}$$

❏ **EXAMPLE 4.9**   School enrolments by age group are reported annually. From these reports the probability $P(x)$ that a student selected from the population of all students with ages from 5 to 34 is given in column 3 in Table 4.9.

We find the expected value of the age of a student by using Formula 4.2. Each age class is represented by a class mark (x). In the sum, each value of x is weighted by the probability of its occurrence, $P(x)$:

$$E[x] = 5.5(0.119) + 10(0.492) + \cdots + 29.5(0.025)$$
$$= 12.494 \text{ years}$$

■

class mark

TABLE 4.9   Calculating $E[x]$ for the Age (x) of Students

Age Class	x	$P(x)$	$xP(x)$
5–6	5.5	0.119	0.655
7–13	10.0	0.492	4.920
14–17	15.5	0.251	3.891
18–19	18.5	0.056	1.036
20–24	22.0	0.057	1.254
25–34	29.5	0.025	0.738
		Sum 1.000	12.494

□ **EXAMPLE 4.10**   A broker studies the possible return over the next year from a treasury bill fund. The interest rates fluctuate weekly, but predictions on the possible annual returns can be made. If the annual yield is 7%, then the value of an investment at the end of one year is 1.07 times its starting balance. Let the random variable x denote the investment return factor and let $P(x)$ be the (subjective) probabilities assigned by the broker as shown in Table 4.10. The broker wishes to know what value to expect for x, on the average, in this experiment. In other words, if we repeated this experiment many times, what would be the average of all the x values? What we want to determine is the *expected value* of x, or $E[x]$.

One method to *approximate* the mean value in any experiment is to replicate the experiment many times, add up the observed numbers, and divide by the number of observations; but such a procedure is often impractical, if not impossible, and gives only an approximation of the desired value.

TABLE 4.10   Investment Return Factors

x= factor	1.06	1.07	1.08	1.09	1.10	1.11	1.12
$P(x)$	0.04	0.15	0.20	0.25	0.22	0.11	0.03

Fortunately, there is no need to replicate an experiment if the probability mass function is known, for we then already have all the information needed. For instance, since $P(x = 1.08) = 0.20$, we would expect the factor of $x = 1.08$ to occur in 20% of all potential replications. The *weight* we assign to $x = 1.08$ is thus 0.20. Similarly, the weight for $x = 1.09$ is 0.25. By substituting the values from Table 4.10 into Formula 4.2, we can calculate the expected investment return factor next year as follows:

$$E[x] = \sum_{\text{All } x} xP(x)$$
$$= 1.06(0.04) + 1.07(0.15) + 1.08(0.20) + 1.09(0.25)$$
$$+ 1.10(0.22) + 1.11(0.11) + 1.12(0.03)$$
$$= 1.089$$

The expected factor is 1.089, or the expected yield is 8.9%.   ■

□ **STUDY QUESTION 4.3**   Expected Value of Product Size

Find the expected size of a brownie square sold to a given customer if the probability distribution is as given in Table 4.5.

• **ANSWER** By Formula 4.2, the expected size is:

$$E[x] = \sum_{\text{All } x} x P(x)$$
$$= 1(0.08) + 2(0.27) + 4(0.10) + 6(0.33) + 12(0.22)$$
$$= 5.64 \text{ inches}$$

∎

Expected Value of a Function of a Random Variable

The previous uses of Formula 4.2 were concerned with finding the expectation or expected value of a random variable. We can also find the expectation of *any function* of a random variable. For instance, instead of finding the mean of the random variable x, we might be interested in determining the expected value of x^2, or of log x, or of e^x. If x is a random variable, then these functions of x are also random variables, and their expected values can be determined. Suppose we let $g(x)$ represent the random variable whose value is $g(x)$ when the value of x is x. The expected value of $g(x)$ is defined as follows:

Expected value of $g(x)$:

$$E[g(x)] = \sum_{\text{All } x} g(x) P(x). \tag{4.3}$$

The only difference between Formulas 4.3 and 4.2 is that in 4.3, $P(x)$ are the weights of values of $g(x)$ rather than values of x.

One relatively straightforward expectation is the one in which $g(x) = x^2$; that is, $E[x^2]$. We use it to illustrate the application of Formula (4.3). Recalling Example 4.8 of the small student bakery making brownie squares, it would be necessary to find $E[x^2]$ if we wanted to determine the expected amount of square inches of brownies. This would help the managers decide on the quantity of raw ingredients needed for an *average* day. For this case, we let $g(x) = x^2$ and apply Formula 4.3 to the values in Table 4.11:

TABLE 4.11   Probability for Different Numbers of Square Inches of Brownies

x^2	1^2	2^2	4^2	6^2	12^2
$P(x)$	0.08	0.27	0.10	0.33	0.22

The expected amount of square inches of brownies required by the bakery is:

$$E[x^2] = \sum_{\text{All } x} x^2 P(x)$$
$$= (1^2)(0.08) + (2^2)(0.27) + (4^2)(0.10) + (6^2)(0.33) + (12^2)(0.22)$$
$$= 46.32 \text{ inches squared}$$

Note that this value of $E[x^2]$ differs from the square of $E[x]$, which is $\mu^2 = (5.64)^2 = 31.81$. In general, $E[x^2] \neq (E[x])^2$; *they have different meanings (the mean of the squares versus the square of the mean).*

□ STUDY QUESTION 4.4   Expected Return over Two Years

Suppose the broker in Example 4.10 had a two-year time horizon in mind. Then the broker would be interested in the compound return over two years. If the broker assumes that the same annual rates of return hold with the same probabilities, find the expected compound yield for two years.

• ANSWER   For this problem we let x^2 represent the return for two years, where x is the one-year factor. For example, if the return factor each year is (1.08), then the return for two years would be $(1.08)^2$. Using Table 4.10 and Formula 4.3, we obtain

$$E[x^2] = \sum_{\text{All } x} x^2 P(x)$$

$$= (1.06)^2(0.04) + (1.07)^2(0.15) + (1.08)^2(0.20)$$
$$+ (1.09)^2(0.25) + (1.10)^2(0.22) + (1.11)^2(0.11) + (1.12)^2(0.03)$$
$$= 1.186$$

The expected two-year factor is 1.186; the expected two-year return is 18.6%.

The Variance of a Random Variable

In the same way that the variance of a population is defined as the average squared deviation of the population values from their mean (μ), so the *variance* of a random variable can be defined in terms of the expected squared deviation of the values of x around their expected value $E[x]$. We denote this **variance of the random variable** x by the symbol $V[x]$, which is defined as follows:

$$V[x] = \sigma^2 = E[(x - \mu)^2]$$

Because the squared-deviation term within the brackets $[(x - \mu)^2]$ is a function of the random variable x, it can be written as $g(x) = (x - \mu)^2$. Since we know how to find $E[g(x)]$ from Formula 4.3, this means that we already know how to find $E[g(x)] = E[(x - \mu)^2]$. Making the substitution for $g(x) = [(x - \mu)^2]$ in Formula 4.3, we obtain:

Variance of x:

$$V[x] = \sigma^2 = E[(x - \mu)^2] = \sum_{\text{All } x}(x - \mu)^2 P(x) \qquad (4.4)$$

variance of discrete random variable

Again, the variance is simply the weighted average of the squared deviations, where the weights here are probabilities. Because the sum of the weights is $\Sigma P(x) = 1$, the denominator portion of the formula disappears (division by the value 1 is unnecessary). Formula 4.4 is the traditional way of defining the variance of a discrete random variable. It can also be used to compute a standard deviation, since the standard deviation, denoted by σ, is always the positive square root of the variance:

Standard deviation of x:

$$\sigma = +\sqrt{V[x]} \qquad (4.5)$$

◻ **EXAMPLE 4.11**   We use Formula 4.4 to find the variance of the number of registered mail items received per day by the accountant introduced in Study Question 4.1. The p.m.f. is repeated in Table 4.12.

TABLE 4.12   Daily Registered Mail Received by an Accountant

No. of items, x	0	1	2	3	4	5	6	7	8	9
$P(x)$	0.07	0.14	0.18	0.24	0.12	0.10	0.08	0.04	0.02	0.01

A tabular format is convenient for demonstrating the necessary calculations. In Table 4.13, column (3) shows the product terms from columns (1) and (2). These are used in Formula 4.2 to find the expected number of registered mail items:

$$\mu = E[x] = \sum_{\text{All } x} x P(x) = 3.21 \text{ mail items}$$

The variance using Formula 4.4 is:

$$V[x] = E[x - \mu]^2 = \sum_{\text{All } x} (x - 3.21)^2 P(x).$$

TABLE 4.13   Calculational Format to Find $E[x]$ and $V[x]$

(1) x	(2) $P(x)$	(3) $xP(x)$	(4) $x - \mu$	(5) $(x-\mu)^2 P(x)$
0	0.07	0.00	−3.21	0.7213
1	0.14	0.14	−2.21	0.6838
2	0.18	0.36	−1.21	0.2635
3	0.24	0.72	−0.21	0.0106
4	0.12	0.48	0.79	0.0749
5	0.10	0.50	1.79	0.3204
6	0.08	0.48	2.79	0.6227
7	0.04	0.28	3.79	0.5746
8	0.02	0.16	4.79	0.4589
9	0.01	0.09	5.79	0.3352
Sum	1.00	3.21		4.0659

These terms involve some tedious calculations, as shown in columns (4) and (5) of Table 4.13. The result of summing column (5) gives:

$$V[x] = 4.0659 \text{ mail items}^2$$

Since the variance is in squared units, the more easily interpreted measure is the standard deviation as follows:

$$\sigma = \sqrt{V[x]} = \sqrt{4.0659} = 2.016 \text{ mail items} \qquad ■$$

It is important to emphasize at this point that the reader should always check the reasonableness of calculations such as $E[x]$ and $V[x]$. For instance, if $E[x]$ is not near where you would expect the centre of gravity to be, then you should double-check your calculations. A good way to check the reasonableness of $V[x]$ is to use the rule of thumb for dispersion presented in Chapter 2. This rule says that if the probability distribution is fairly symmetrical and unimodal, then 68% and 95% represent good approximations to the percent of the distribution falling in the intervals $\mu \pm 1\sigma$ and $\mu \pm 2\sigma$, respectively. For probability distributions, these rules mean that approximately 68% and 95% of the *probability* should be within $\mu \pm 1\sigma$ and $\mu \pm 2\sigma$, respectively.

☐ **EXAMPLE 4.12**   For the data in Table 4.13 and $E[x]$ and $V[x]$ shown in Example 4.11, the interval $\mu \pm 1\sigma$ has a lower and upper limit as follows:

$$(\mu - 1\sigma) = 3.210 - 2.016 = 1.194$$

$$(\mu + 1\sigma) = 3.210 + 2.016 = 5.226$$

The interval $(1.194 < x < 5.226)$ includes values of x of 2, 3, 4, and 5 for which the sum of associated probabilities is:

$$P(2) + P(3) + P(4) + P(5) = 0.18 + 0.24 + 0.12 + 0.10 = 0.64$$

Thus, the interval $\mu \pm 1\sigma$ includes 64% of the probability distribution, which is close to the 68% approximation using our rule of thumb.

The interval $(\mu \pm 2\sigma)$ has endpoints $[3.210 - 4.032, 3.210 + 4.032]$, which can be simplified to $[-0.822, 7.242]$. Values of x included in this interval are all those shown in Table 4.13 *except* the bottom values, $x = 8$ and $x = 9$. Since $P(8) = 0.02$ and $P(9) = 0.01$, the rule of complements may be used to find:

$$P(x \le 7) = 1.00 - 0.02 - 0.01 = 0.97$$

Again, this result is reasonably close to the value suggested by our rule of thumb.

■

PROBLEMS

4.1 Sketch the probability and cumulative mass functions for the random variable x representing the size of salary supplement in Study Question 4.2. Explain their differences and the relationship between them.

4.2 Distinguish between the p.m.f. and the c.m.f. for a discrete random variable x.

4.3 Five different technologies are commonly used for preventing air pollution in coal-burning industries. The age of the technology is measured by the number of years since its introduction, denoted by x. The proportion of use of the technology is given by the fractions denoted by p.

TABLE 4.14   Five Different Air Pollution Technologies

			Years		
Age of Technology, x	2	7	8	16	17
p	1/6	1/3	1/12	1/6	1/4

a) Compute the expected value of the age of the technology currently in use.

b) Find $V[x]$.

4.4 Use Problem 4.3 to answer the following.

a) Sketch the probability mass function for this population.

b) Sketch the cumulative mass function. What probability corresponds to $F(2.0)$, $F(9.5)$, and $F(17.0)$?

c) Does the p.m.f. graphed in part (a) meet the two conditions required of all probability functions?

4.5 Five service repair technicians for an appliance dealer handle from one to five repair jobs per hour. Suppose that the number of jobs done per hour is equally likely to be any of these values: 1, 2, 3, 4, or 5. Also, each technician does a different number of jobs. A supervisor selects two of the five hourly repair records of the technicians and finds the value of x, the *sum* of the number of repairs on the two hourly reports.

a) Sketch the probability distribution of this random variable.

b) Find the expected value of x.

c) Find the standard deviation of x.

d) Suppose the above experiment is done without the assumption that each technician does a different number of jobs. Sketch the new probability distribution.

4.6 A statistics professor announces that final grades will consist of 20% A's, 30% B's, 30% C's, 10% D's, and 10% F's.

a) If x is a random variable that is 4 for an A, 3 for a B, et cetera, what would be the expected grade point in the class? $= 4(20\%) + 3(30\%) + 2(30\%) + 1(10\%) + 0(10\%)$

b) Calculate $V[x]$ for this class.

c) Calculate $\mu \pm 1\sigma$ and $\mu \pm 2\sigma$ for this problem. Is the percent of values of x within these intervals close to the rule of thumb?

4.7 Reconsider the cheese sale example using the probability distribution in Table 4.3 and limiting x to $x \le 6$.

a) Find $E[x]$.

b) Find $V[x]$ using Formula 4.4.

4.8 Hospital records indicate that the need for treatment of broken legs occurs from one to seven times per day. Assume that each of these values is equally likely to occur on a given day.

a) Suppose that you guess randomly the number of such cases that will occur next Thursday. What is the probability that you will be correct?

b) Construct the probability mass function for the number of broken-leg cases treated per day.

c) What is the mean of the random variable?

d) What is the variance? What percent of the days will have a number of such cases that lies within the intervals $\mu \pm 1\sigma$ and $\mu \pm 2\sigma$?

4.9 The dollar values of daily sales by a certain small store for the first ten days of the month are 175, 188, 196, 202, 194, 215, 188, 194, 196, 202.

a) Find the mean of this population. [Each value has probability $\frac{1}{10}$.]

b) Find σ^2 and σ.

c) What percent of the observations fall within $\mu \pm 1\sigma$ and $\mu \pm 2\sigma$?

4.10 Weekly sales of dogwood trees at a nursery are $x = 1, 2, 3$, or 4 according to the following function:

$$P(x) = \begin{cases} \dfrac{1}{10}x & \text{for } x = 1, 2, 3, 4 \\ 0 & \text{otherwise} \end{cases}$$

a) Sketch this function and show that it satisfies the two properties necessary if $P(x)$ is to be a p.m.f.

b) Find the expected number of sales.

c) Find the variance of sales.

d) Calculate the percent of x values falling within $\mu \pm 1\sigma$. Speculate on why this percent is not as close to 68% as in most problems thus far. Does $\mu \pm 2\sigma$ contain close to 95% of the values?

4.11 Suppose that the number of automatic checks built into an inventory analysis is unknown. However, the probability distribution is given by the following probability mass function:

$$P(x) = \begin{cases} \dfrac{1}{14}x^2 & \text{for } x = 1, 2, \text{ or } 3 \\ 0 & \text{otherwise} \end{cases}$$

a) Graph both the probability mass function and the cumulative mass function for this experiment.

b) Show that this p.m.f. satisfies the two properties described in Section 4.2.

c) Find the mean and the variance of this distribution.

4.12 A candy bar marketing promotion for a new 35¢ bar includes a coupon printed on the inside of the label, which gives the purchasers an immediate cash rebate. The coupons are distributed as follows:

40% have value of 5¢   20% have value of 25¢

30% have value of 10¢   10% have value of $1.

What is the expected value of the net returns on sales of 500 bars if all the coupons are redeemed?

4.13 A manufacturer can ship either 4,000 or 12,000 boxes of spark plugs to an automotive outlet in Germany. Suppose that we let x = sales of spark plugs, in units of 1,000 boxes. The manufacturer estimates that the following p.m.f. accurately describes sales:

$$P(x) = \begin{cases} \dfrac{3}{x}x & \text{for } x = 4, \text{ or } 12 \\ 0 & \text{otherwise} \end{cases}$$

a) Sketch this p.m.f., verifying that it meets the two necessary conditions for a mass function.

b) Find $E[x]$ and $V[x]$.

4.14 An oil company makes four brands of motor oil. Each is the same product marketed with a different label. For example, one is the label for the oil company brand and is sold at a higher price than another that uses the label of an auto parts distributor. The other two labels are marketed as Montgomery Ward oil and a generic No-Name. The prices are discounted lower and lower across these different labels so that the profits on these items are 50¢, 25¢, 10¢, and 5¢, respectively. The distribution of sales is 30% each for the brands of the oil company and auto parts distributor and 20% each for the Montgomery Ward and No-Name brands.

a) What is the probability that a randomly selected sale would earn exactly 10¢ profit?

b) What is the probability that two randomly selected sales will earn a total of 50¢ or more profit?

c) What is the average profit earned per quart of motor oil sales?

4.15 A publisher offers students a selling position to sell a series of "How To ... " books to predetermined potential customers. The offer is unusual, owing to the sales commission rule. The payment is $2 if no sale is made to the first contact, and the work day is over. The payment is $4 if a sale is made with the first customer but not with the second. It is $8 if the first two contacts result in sales but the third does not, $16 if three consecutive sales are made but the fourth contact results in no sale, et cetera. That is, the commission rule is a starting payment of $2, which is increased by a factor of 2 for each consecutive contact until the string of sales is broken.

The special arrangement is offered because the publisher provides the names (sequentially) of potential customers who have already purchased the first book in the series and have returned a card indicating an interest in buying the rest of the books. On the basis of the records of other sales representatives, assume that the probability of a sales contact with any potential customer is $\frac{1}{2}$. The publishing company protects its own interests by enlisting only dedicated salespeople by charging an initial fee for the privilege of selling its books.

a) How much would you be willing to pay for the opportunity to sell? [If you said less than $2, you do not understand the problem.]

b) If a student can do this as a summer job with a fresh start every day, what is the probability on a given day that $65 or less would be earned (about the same wages as an alternate eight-hour per day job at $8 per hour).

c) If it is agreed that a run of consecutive sales can be carried over day after day until broken, what is the expected value for a one-time opportunity to participate in this scheme? Would anyone be willing to pay a participation fee equal to this expected value?

4.16 A large computer equipment firm with 13,000 employees started ten years ago and enlarged its operation for the first time seven years ago. It more than doubled its size two years ago and doubled that again last year. As a result, the distribution of the completed years of employment of workers with this company is:

TABLE 4.15 Years of Employee Service

Years of employment	10	7	2	1	0
Number of employees	1000	2000	3250	6500	250

a) Find the probability distribution for x = years of employment, and find the expected value of x.

b) Find the standard deviation of the years of employment x.

4.17 An entrepreneur is faced with two investment opportunities that each require an initial outlay of $10,000. The estimated return on investment x will be either $40,000, $20,000, or $0, with probabilities of 0.25, 0.50, and 0.25, respectively. For investment y, the returns should be $30,000, $20,000, or $10,000, with probabilities of one third in each case.

a) Compute $E[x]$ and $E[y]$.

b) Check your calculations in (a) by first dividing all values by 10,000, determining $E[x]$ and $E[y]$, and then multiplying the results by 10,000.

c) Compute $V[x]$ and $V[y]$. Try to check your answer by again dividing by 10,000. What is the relationship between $V[x]$ and $V[x/10,000]$ and $V[x]/10,000$?

4.18 Use the p.m.f. on the age of students in Table 4.9.   Find the variance and the standard deviation of age (x).

USING THE COMPUTER

4.19 Complete the following:

a) Find or write a computer program to calculate the expected value and the standard deviation of a frequency distribution if the input data are class marks and probabilities.

b) Use your program to find the mean and standard deviation of income for families, given the distribution in Table 4.16. Note the problem of having an *open-ended* interval (over 60,000). Assume that the average income for all families in this group is $100,000.

TABLE 4.16 Distribution of Family Income

Income ($)	$P(x)$
$0 < x \le 10,000$	0.089
$10,000 < x \le 20,000$	0.103
$20,000 < x \le 30,000$	0.118
$30,000 < x \le 40,000$	0.199
$40,000 < x \le 50,000$	0.127
$50,000 < x \le 60,000$	0.141
Over $60,000$	0.223

CASE PROBLEM

4.20 The United States population according to the 1990 Census of Population was 257,173,981. The age distribution of the population is given in Table 4.17.

a) If you randomly selected a person from this population, what is the probability that the age of the person would exceed 59?

b) What is the median age?

c) Find the proportion of the population with their age within one standard deviation of the expected value. Assume that 90 is a representative value for the eldest age group.

TABLE 4.17 Age Distribution of U.S. Population

Age	$P(x)$	Age	$P(x)$
0–4	0.072	45–49	0.048
5–9	0.074	50–54	0.052
10–14	0.081	55–59	0.050
15–19	0.093	60–64	0.045
20–24	0.094	65–69	0.039
25–29	0.086	70–74	0.030
30–34	0.078	75–79	0.021
35–39	0.062	80–84	0.013
40–44	0.052	Over 84	0.010

section 4.4

Expectation Rules

The concept of mathematical expectation, or expected value, will prove so useful in the coming chapters that the consideration of a few of the important properties of expectations will be beneficial at this time. These rules will be presented without formal proof, and it is not necessary that they be memorized. They will, however, be referred to in subsequent sections and be useful in solving problems.

Rule 1. $E[k] = k$ — The expected value of a constant is the constant itself.

Rule 2. $V[k] = 0$ — The variance of a constant is zero.

Rule 3. $E[kx] = kE[x]$ — The expected value of the product of a constant times a variable is the product of the constant times the expected value of the variable.

Rule 4. $V[kx] = k^2 V[x]$ — The variance of the product of a constant times a variable is the product of the *square* of the constant times the variance of the variable.

Rule 5. $E[a \pm bx] = a \pm bE[x]$ — The expected value of the quantity $(a + bx)$ [or $(a - bx)$] is a plus (or minus) b times the expectation of x.

Rule 6. $V[a \pm bx] = b^2 V[x]$ — The variance of the quantity $(a+bx)$ [or $(a-bx)$] equals b^2 times the variance of x.

Note in Rules 4 and 6 that the constant is squared on the right-hand side. This result occurs because variances involve squared deviations, and any constant times x will itself be squared in calculating the variance. Also, the addition of a constant to a random term does not affect the variance of that term.

Let us discuss these rules briefly. Rules 1 and 2 give the expected value and variance of a constant. A constant by definition always has the same value, say, $k = 3$. Each time k is observed, $k = 3$. The average of a set of the same values, $3, 3, 3, \ldots, 3$ is, of course, the constant value 3. Also, since each observation of k equals the average value of k, then any measure of squared deviations between the observations and the average will be zero. To state the obvious, the variance of a constant is zero because a constant does not vary.

Rules 3 and 4 are simple derivations based on the definitions of expected values. Consider the function $g[x] = kx$; then $E[kx] = \Sigma(kx)P(x)$. Since k is constant, it may be removed from the sum as a common factor. This gives $E[kx] = k\Sigma x P(x)$. Since $\Sigma x P(x) = E[x]$ by definition, we obtain $E[kx] = kE[x]$. Rules 5 and 6 are combinations of the previous four rules. Let us practice using these rules.

❑ EXAMPLE 4.13 Suppose a time–work study shows that x, the quantity of chairs upholstered per day on a work line in a furniture factory, averages 24 with a variance of 9. If each chair requires five staples, then it is easy to find the summary measures for the total number of staples T by applying Rules 3 and 4 with $k = 5$.

$$E[T] = E[5x] = 5E[x] = 5 \times 24 = 120 = \mu_T$$
$$V[T] = V[5x] = 5^2 V[x] = 25 \times 9 = 225 = \sigma_T^2$$

The standard deviation for the total is $\sqrt{225} = 15 = \sigma_T$. Using our rule of thumb, we can guess that on approximately $\frac{2}{3}$ of all days, the total number of staples required will be between $\mu_T - 1\sigma_T$ and $\mu_T + 1\sigma_T$; that is, between $120 - 15 = 105$ and $120 + 15 = 135$. ◼

❑ EXAMPLE 4.14 Continuing Example 4.13, suppose management knows that the fixed cost of running the factory for a day is $2,000 and the variable cost for stapling is $28 per staple. Can we determine the important summary measures of the distribution of the daily cost when we are given the daily total number of staples T? One way would be to use the original definitions and recompute the probability distribution for costs (C). Alternatively, we can apply Rules 5 and 6 with $a = 2,000$ and $b = 28$.

$$\mu_C = E[C] = E[2,000 + 28T] = 2,000 + 28E[T]$$
$$= 2,000 + 28(120) = \$5,360.$$
$$\sigma_C{}^2 = V[C] = V[2,000 + 28T] = 0 + (28)^2 V[T]$$
$$= 784(225) = 176,400 \text{ dollars}^2.$$

To return to a measure of variability *not* in squared units, we find the standard deviation, $\sigma_C = \sqrt{V[C]} = \$420$. ∎

As mathematicians like to say after a long proof, "Q.E.D.", which stands for the Latin phrase, *quod erat demonstrandum*, meaning *which was to be demonstrated* and indicates completion. In our case, Q.E.D. might mean *Quite Easily Done*.

The reader can verify Rules 5 and 6 algebraically by completing Exercise 4.21 or arithmetically by working Exercise 4.31. It should be noted, from the above examples, that the standard deviations were obtained as multiples of the original ones:

$$\sigma_T = 5\sigma_x \quad \text{and} \quad \sigma_C = 140\sigma_T.$$

The standard deviation is not affected by adding or subtracting a constant. Such an operation has the effect only of moving the central location of a distribution but not changing its spread. Two widely used applications of Rules 1–6 are now presented for practice.

Expectations of Linear Transformations

The changing from one variable into another according to a formula as we did in Examples 4.13 and 4.14 is called a *transformation*. If the formula used is $y = a+bx$ (where a and b are constants), it is called a *linear transformation*. A graph of the relation $y = a+bx$ is a straight line (i.e., linear, as opposed to quadratic, exponential, logarithmic, etc.). When $y = a + bx$, it is not necessary to derive a new probability distribution for y if the one for x is already known. Similarly, it is not necessary to recompute the mean and variance from basic definitions. Remember to use Rules 5 and 6 to find

$$E[y] = a + bE[x] \quad \text{and} \quad V[y] = b^2 V[x].$$

Expectations of a Standardized Variable

Another common transformation is one that changes the central location and the scale of a variable to *standardized units*. The standardized variable is often used in scaling test scores and in making comparisons among measures with different units. In statistics, **standardization** is used extensively for simplifying distributions and variables so that solutions to problems are easier.

Standardized variable: For a random variable x with expected value μ and standard deviation σ, we denote the standardized variable as z and define it as follows:

$$z = \frac{x - \mu}{\sigma} \tag{4.6}$$

We can apply Rules 5 and 6 to find the expected value and variance of a standardized variable. Rewriting z as

$$z = \frac{1}{\sigma}x - \frac{1}{\sigma}\mu$$

and remembering that μ and σ are constants (parameters of the distribution of x), we can identify the values of a and b in Rules 5 and 6 as $a = (-1/\sigma)\mu$ and $b = (1/\sigma)$:

$$E[z] = E\left[-\frac{1}{\sigma}\mu + \frac{1}{\sigma}x\right] = -\frac{1}{\sigma}\mu + \frac{1}{\sigma}E[x]$$

Since $E[x] = \mu$, $E[z] = (-\mu/\sigma) + (\mu/\sigma) = 0$. *Thus, the mean of the standardized variable equals zero.* Now, let us consider the variance of a standardized variable:

$$V[z] = V\left[-\frac{1}{\sigma}\mu + \frac{1}{\sigma}x\right] = 0 + \frac{1}{\sigma^2}V[x]$$

Since $V[x] = \sigma^2$, then $V[z] = (\sigma^2/\sigma^2) = 1.0$. Thus, $\sigma_z = \sqrt{V[z]} = 1.0$ also. *Thus, the variance and the standard deviation of the standardized variable are both equal to one.*

The importance of this result is that any variable may be *standardized* by subtracting its mean (to move the central location to zero) and then dividing by its standard deviation (to adjust the variability of the distribution so that it always has a standard deviation of 1).

▢ EXAMPLE 4.15 Recall the distribution used earlier (Example 4.11) of x, the number of registered mail items requiring a signature by an accountant. The p.m.f. for this distribution (plus its previously calculated mean and standard deviation) are shown in Figure 4.9.

The first part of this standardization involves subtracting the mean $\mu = 3.21$ from each value of x. This moves the entire distribution of x in Figure 4.9 to one located at a mean of zero, since every value is reduced by 3.21. See the scale for $(x - \mu)$ in Figure 4.9. A previous value of $x = 4$ is changed to $(4 - 3.21) = 0.79$; the value of $x = 2$ is changed to $(2 - 3.21) = -1.21$, and so on. The shape or spread of the distribution is unchanged, but the distribution now has a central location (a mean) of zero.

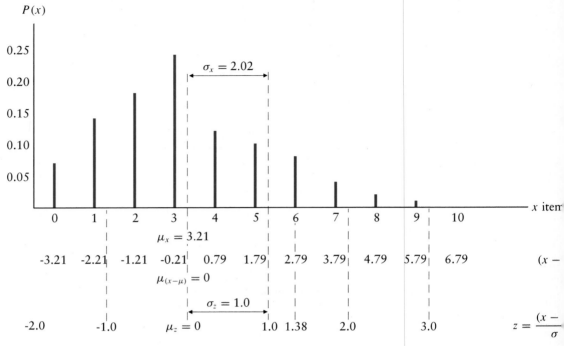

FIGURE 4.9 Effect of a standardization

The final step in a standardization is the conversion of the scale of the variable from one that had a standard deviation of σ to a new scale that has a standard deviation of 1. This is accomplished by dividing all values of $(x - \mu)$ by σ. The value of $x = 6$ now becomes $(6 - 3.21)/2.016 = 1.384$. This means that the value $x = 6$ is 1.384 standard deviations above the mean of $\mu = 3.21$. Any other values for x can be transformed similarly. The new scale for z has a mean of 0 at the same point that the original scale for x had a mean of 3.21. A one-unit change on the new scale for z is equivalent to a change of 2.016 units for x. The new scale is in dimensionless standard deviation units, not in units of the number of registered mail items. ∎

Bivariate Probability Functions[†]

section 4.5

In many practical situations, an experiment may involve outcomes that are related to two (or more) random variables. This section considers probability functions that involve more than one variable: such functions are called *multivariate* probability functions. In this section, only the case of *bivariate* (two variables) probability functions is presented. The distributions discussed so far in this text represent *univariate* probability functions, as only one random variable was involved.

A case of a univariate function might involve a manager who is interested in the productivity of a group of workers. Perhaps the workers' output varies per hour (or per week). If so, the long-run relative frequencies of these different productivities could be formulated as the probability distribution of a single random variable. The

---

[†] Sections 4.5 and 4.6 may be omitted without loss of continuity

expected value and standard deviation of this random variable could be determined and used in discussions about pay packages, working conditions, et cetera.

Now, let us assume that the manager goes a step further to determine why productivity differs among workers. The manager might consider differences among workers in size, skill, training, experience, education, hours of sleep, nutrition, and so on. These characteristics of the workers are also random variables. Each or any combination of these random variables might be important in affecting the productivity of the workers. To find out which ones are and which ones are not important, joint analysis (of two or more random variables) is necessary. Given such an analysis, it might be possible to formulate policies for rest breaks, retraining seminars, exercise periods, food service, et cetera, to improve the expected productivity or to reduce its standard deviation.

Another illustration might involve the owner of a taxi company (assuming a nonregulated market) who is trying to decide whether to increase rates. There is uncertainty in this situation as to what the owner's competitors intend to do and what the public will demand. The random variable x might be defined as the price changes of the competitors, and the random variable y might represent the demand levels for taxi services. If the owner can assign probabilities to the different potential price changes and demand levels, the owner will have a standard statistical decision problem involving **combined random variables**. The reader can probably begin to see some real potential for complexity in the application of combined random variables in real-life problems. In this beginning study of statistics, we limit our discussion to simpler examples in order to present the basic concepts.

The Joint Probability Function

When a sample space involves two or more random variables, the function describing their combined probability is called a *joint probability function*.

> The joint probability function for two discrete random variables x and y is denoted by the symbol $P(x, y)$, where $P(x, y) = P(x = x \text{ and } y = y)$. That is, $P(x, y)$ represents the probability that x assumes the value x and y assumes the value y.

As we will show, most of the probability rules discussed thus far have analogous rules for the case of two or more random variables. For example, the two properties of all probability functions presented in Section 4.2 have direct counterparts for joint probability functions, as shown below:

> Property 1:
> $$0 \leq P(x, y) \leq 1$$
>
> Property 2:
> $$\sum_{\text{All } y} \sum_{\text{All } x} P(x, y) = 1$$

☐ **EXAMPLE 4.16** Consider the results of a study investigating the relationship between the number of jobs a college graduate holds in the first five years after graduation (x) and the number of promotions (y). Based on the experience of a large number of recent college graduates, the joint probability distribution is shown in Table 4.18. The values in Table 4.18 are the joint probabilities that x, the number of jobs, occurs in conjunction with y, the number of promotions. For example, $P(x = 2 \text{ and } y = 3) = P(2, 3)$ is the probability that a randomly selected college graduate from this population had two jobs and been promoted three times in the first five years after graduation. From Table 4.18, $P(2, 3) = 0.10$. This is a relatively common occurrence based on this population, since it happens in one out of ten cases on the average. ∎

TABLE 4.18 Probabilities for Job-Promotion Study

		Number of promotions (y)				Marginal total
		1	2	3	4	
Number of jobs (x)	1	0.1	0.15	0.12	0.06	0.43
	2	0.05	0.07	0.10	0.05	0.27
	3	0.04	0.02	0.14	0.10	0.30
Marginal Total		0.19	0.24	0.36	0.21	$1.00 = \Sigma\Sigma P(x, y)$

Marginal Probability

Table 4.18 presents not only joint probabilities, but also the **marginal probabilities** for x and for y. The concept of marginal probability is the same as that used in Chapter 3. To find a marginal probability for a specific value of a combined random variable, it is necessary only to add together the probabilities of all the intersections involving that specific value. For example, the marginal probability for $x = 2$ jobs is the sum of all the joint probabilities involving $x = 2$. These are shown in Table 4.18 as the values in the second row. The sum across the columns is given in the right margin of the table, $P(x = 2) = 0.27$. Similarly, a *marginal probability* for any value of y may be found by summing all the joint probabilities involving that value of y. If you want to know the probability that a graduate will have had two promotions, then you sum all the values in the column for $y = 2$, obtaining $P(y = 2) = 0.24$. Thus, the values in the *margin* of a joint probability table give the values of the marginal probabilities for the corresponding values of x and y.[2]

Conditional Probability

A **conditional probability** is also defined for combined random variables in the same way that it was for events in Chapter 3. In words,

$$P(\text{event} \mid \text{condition}) = \frac{P(\text{intersection})}{P(\text{conditon})}$$

---

[2] The formulas for computing such marginal probabilities for combined random variables x and y are:

$$\text{Marginal probability of } x = \sum_{\text{All } y} P(x, y)$$

$$\text{Marginal probability of } y = \sum_{\text{All } x} P(x, y)$$

The relationship among the three types of probabilities — joint, marginal, and conditional — is the same as that first expressed in the multiplication law for intersections. The following is always true:

Joint probability = (marginal probability)(conditional probability)

Thus, the definition for a conditional probability is as follows:

$$\text{Conditional probability} = \frac{\text{joint probability}}{\text{marginal probability}}$$

For example, to find the **conditional probability** of a value x given a conditional value y for the two random variables x and y, one computes:

$$P(x \mid y) = \frac{P(x, y)}{P(y)}$$

In terms of Table 4.18, such computations are quite obvious and result in the correct common-sense solution. If we wish to determine the probability that a graduate will have had three jobs given that the graduate is one of those having had two promotions:

$$P(x = 3 \mid y = 2) = \frac{P(3, 2)}{P(y = 2)} = \frac{0.02}{0.24} = \frac{1}{12}$$

The denominator for this probability ratio does *not* pertain to all values that may occur in the original survey, but only that set of outcomes which satisfies the given condition (two promotions). One out of twelve such cases of two promotions, on the average, will also be a case in which the number of jobs is three.

It is also possible to find conditional probabilities for a particular number of promotions given the pool of cases for a certain number of jobs. To find the probability that the number of promotions is four from among all those cases in which the number of jobs is one:

$$P(y = 4 \mid x = 1) = \frac{P(1, 4)}{P(x = 1)} = \frac{0.06}{0.43} = 0.14.$$

Be sure to always use the probability of the given condition in the denominator.

Independence

Just as we were able in Chapter 3 to determine whether two events are independent, we can, in the present context, determine whether two random variables are independent. If the knowledge of a certain condition on one variable does not affect the probability of the occurrence of values of the other random variable, then the two variables are independent. That is, x and y are independent if the conditional probability of x given y is the same as the marginal probability of x. If x and y are independent, it also follows that the conditional probability is the same as the marginal probability. Thus, for two independent random variables, their joint probability values must equal the product of the two corresponding marginal probability values.

> If x and y are independent, then $P(x, y) = P(x)P(y)$

If the above relationship does *not* hold for *all* possible combinations of x and y, then these random variables are *dependent*. Only one violation of the condition is necessary to demonstrate dependence. For the data in Table 4.18 it is easily shown that *none* of the pairs of x and y satisfies the condition for independence. For example, the joint probability of one job and two promotions is $P(1, 2) = 0.15$, but this value is not equal to the product of the marginal probabilities,

$$P(x = 1)P(y = 2) = 0.43(0.24) = 0.1032$$

Alternatively, we could examine any or all comparisons between marginal probabilities and their corresponding conditional probabilities. For one example, $P(x = 3) = 0.30$, but we have seen that $P(x = 3 \mid y = 2) = (\frac{1}{12})$. Clearly, the given condition on the number of promotions ($y = 2$) does affect the probability of the number of jobs held ($x = 3$). Thus, we can conclude that the number of jobs and number of promotions are *not* independent, but *dependent* random variables.

◻ STUDY QUESTION 4.5   Size and Depth of Buried Utility Cable

A contracting firm is bidding on a project to repair some old cable conduits for a city. The cable size y is either 4 cm or 9 cm in diameter and is buried at a depth x of either 1, 2, or 4 feet below ground. Based on city records, the overall joint distribution of the size and depth of cable can be determined and is shown in Table 4.19.

a) Find the marginal probabilities for size of cable y and depth of cable x.
b) Find the conditional probability that a randomly selected section of cable needing repair will be buried two feet deep given that it is 9 cm cable.
c) Determine whether the size and depth of cable are independent or dependent.

TABLE 4.19   Joint Probability Distribution for Size and Depth of Cable

		Size (cm), y	
		4	9
	1	0.24	0.16
Depth (feet), x	2	0.12	0.08
	4	0.24	0.16

• ANSWER

a) The marginal probability of y, $P(y)$, equals $\sum_x P(x, y)$ for a given y:

$$P(y = 4) = \sum_x P(x, 4) = \begin{matrix} 0.24 \\ +0.12 \\ +0.24 \\ \hline 0.60 \end{matrix}$$

$$P(y = 9) = \sum_x P(x, 9) = \begin{matrix} 0.16 \\ +0.08 \\ +0.16 \\ \hline 0.40 \end{matrix}$$

The marginal probability of x, $P(x)$, equals $\sum\limits_{y} P(x, y)$ for a given x:

$$P(x = 1) = \sum_{y} P(1, y) = 0.24 + 0.16 = 0.40$$

$$P(x = 2) = \sum_{y} P(2, y) = 0.12 + 0.08 = 0.20$$

$$P(x = 4) = \sum_{y} P(4, y) = 0.24 + 0.16 = 0.40$$

b) The conditional probability, $P(\text{depth} = 2 | \text{size} = 9)$, is found by the definitional rule relating conditional, joint, and marginal probabilities:

$$P(x = 2 \mid y = 9) = \frac{P(2, 9)}{P(y = 9)} = \frac{0.08}{0.40} = \frac{1}{5}$$

c) If x and y are independent, $P(x, y) = P(x)P(y)$. Let's try some values of x and y:

$$P(1, 4) = 0.24; \quad P(x = 1)P(y = 4) = 0.40(0.60) = 0.24$$

$$P(2, 4) = 0.12; \quad P(x = 2)P(y = 4) = 0.20(0.60) = 0.12$$

$$P(4, 9) = 0.16; \quad P(x = 4)P(y = 9) = 0.40(0.40) = 0.16$$

So far they all satisfy the condition. To prove independence, *all* values must be checked. Let us try one more combination using the alternate rule for independence that *the conditional probability must equal the marginal probability*, $P(x \mid y) = P(x)$. From part (b) above, $P(x = 2 \mid y = 9) = \frac{1}{5}$. From part (a) the marginal probability is the same, $P(x = 2) = 0.20$, and so independence is indicated. If we continue checking, we would find no cases of dependence. Therefore, the depth and size of cable are independent.

Expectations for Combined Random Variables

As we have seen, there are three relevant probability distributions when we have situations involving more than one characteristic of interest. If we have a random variable x and another random variable y, the three relevant distributions are the *joint, marginal, and conditional* probability distributions. As with any distribution, it is important to find the summary measures of central location and variability for these distributions. The marginal and conditional distributions obtained for one of the combined random variables are simply distributions of one variable. The computation of expected values for marginal probability distributions is exactly the same as for a single random variable. For example, consider the marginal distribution of the depth of cable given in Study Question 4.5:

Depth of Cable (feet)	x	1	2	4
Marginal Probability	$P(x)$	0.4	0.2	0.4

The formulas for finding $E[x]$ and $V[x]$ are the same as those presented in Section 4.3.

When dealing with the *joint* probability distribution of x and y, the rule for finding expectations is very similar to Formula 4.3. Suppose that we write any function of the two random variables x and y as $g(x, y)$. Then, the direct extension of Formula 4.3 gives the following:

Expected value of $g(x, y)$:

$$E[g(x, y)] = \sum_{\text{All } y} \sum_{\text{All } x} g(x, y) P(x, y) \qquad (4.7)$$

For example, we may want to find the expected value of the product of x times y, in which case:

$$g(x, y) = x \cdot y \quad \text{and} \quad E[x \cdot y] = \sum_{y} \sum_{x} (x \cdot y) P(x, y)$$

Similarly, if $g(x, y) = x + y$, then:

$$E[x + y] = \sum_{y} \sum_{x} (x + y) P(x, y)$$

We investigate two specific cases of Formula (4.7) in Examples 4.17 and 4.18.

❑ **EXAMPLE 4.17**   As an illustration of Formula 4.7 when $g(x, y) = x \cdot y$, consider a lumberyard that sells plywood panelling in two lengths, 4 ft and 8 ft, and in three different widths, 2 ft, 4 ft, and 6 ft. The owners of the lumberyard are interested in determining the average amount of panelling sold, in terms of area (square feet). That is, they want to determine $E[x \cdot y]$, where x = length and y = width. By the basic counting rule of Section 3.2, there are $n_1 = 2$ times $n_2 = 3$, or $n_1 \cdot n_2 = 6$, different arrangements of widths and lengths sold. The distributions $P(x)$, $P(y)$, and $P(x, y)$ for the sale of these six combinations, based on company records, are given in Table 4.20.

TABLE 4.20   Joint Distribution for Length and Width of Plywood

		Width (feet), y			
		2	4	6	$P(x)$
Length (feet), x	4	0.05	0.05	0.10	0.20
	8	0.10	0.50	0.20	0.80
$P(y)$		0.15	0.55	0.30	$1.00 = \Sigma\Sigma P(x, y)$

The determination of $E[x \cdot y]$ for these data is conveniently arranged in the Table 4.21.

The second column gives the probability for each product of x times y shown in the third column. The multiplication of these two columns yields the products $[(x \cdot y) \cdot P(x, y)]$ in the far right column, whose sum is the expected number of square feet of panelling sold,

$$E[x \cdot y] = \sum_{\text{All } x} \sum_{\text{All } y} (x \cdot y) P(x \cdot y)$$

$$E[x \cdot y] = 30.80$$

■

TABLE 4.21   Calculation of $E[x \cdot y]$ using Table 4.20

(x, y)	$P(x, y)$	Area $x \cdot y$	$(x \cdot y)P(x, y)$
(4, 2)	0.05	8	0.40
(4, 4)	0.05	16	0.80
(4, 6)	0.10	24	2.40
(8, 2)	0.10	16	1.60
(8, 4)	0.50	32	16.00
(8, 6)	0.20	48	9.60
	Sum = 1.00		$E[x \cdot y] = 30.80$

Covariance of x and y

A very important function for which we will want to apply Formula 4.7 is the function of the *cross-product of deviations*, $g(x, y) = (x - \mu_x)(y - \mu_y)$. *The expected value of this function is called the* **covariance of x and y** and is denoted by $C[x, y]$. The covariance measures how much the two random variables vary with each other (how they *co-vary*).

Covariance of x and y:

$$C[x, y] = E[(x - \mu_x)(y - \mu_y)] \qquad (4.8)$$

If high values of x (relative to μ_x) tend to be associated with high values of y (relative to μ_y) and low x-values tend to be associated with low y-values, then $C[x, y]$ will be a large positive number.[3] If low values of one variable tend to be associated with high values of the other, and *vice-versa*, this makes $C[x, y]$ a large negative number. If the two variables have no systematic relation to each other, but move higher or lower independently, then $C[x, y] = 0$. This is a two-variable counterpart to the concept of a variance for one variable. If each y in Formula 4.8 is replaced by an x, the result is the expectation of deviations of x squared, which is the variance, $E[(x - \mu_x)(x - \mu_x)] = E[(x - \mu_x)^2] = V[x]$.

☐ **EXAMPLE 4.18**   We can illustrate Formula 4.9 for the case of the joint distribution of the size and depth of cable given in Table 4.19. Again, it is convenient to arrange the relevant computations in a tabular format as shown in Table 4.22. Recall that $\mu_x = 2.40$ and $\mu_y = 6$ for these data.

From the sum in column (4) we see that the covariance is

$$C[x, y] = 0$$

This result could have been anticipated, because we earlier found, using Table 4.19, that the variables x and y are independent. ∎

---

[3] This occurs because when $(x - \mu_x)$ is positive, $(y - \mu_y)$ is also positive, and when $(x - \mu_x)$ is negative, $(y - \mu_y)$ will also be negative; hence, the sign of $(x - \mu_x)(y - \mu_y)$ will be positive for such pairs of values of x and y. The sum of all these cross-products of deviations will then tend to be large and positive.

TABLE 4.22   Calculations for demonstrating Formula (4.9)

(1)	(2)	(3)		(4)
(x, y)	$P(x, y)$	$(x - \mu_x)(y - \mu_y)P(x, y)$	$=$	$E[(x - \mu_x)(y - \mu_y)]$
(1, 4)	0.24	$(1 - 2.40)(4 - 6)(0.24)$	$=$	0.672
(1, 9)	0.16	$(1 - 2.40)(9 - 6)(0.16)$	$=$	−0.672
(2, 4)	0.12	$(2 - 2.40)(4 - 6)(0.12)$	$=$	0.096
(2, 9)	0.08	$(2 - 2.40)(9 - 6)(0.08)$	$=$	−0.096
(4, 4)	0.24	$(4 - 2.40)(4 - 6)(0.24)$	$=$	−0.768
(4, 9)	0.16	$(4 - 2.40)(9 - 6)(0.16)$	$=$	0.768
Sum	1.00			0

Expectation of $ax + by$

Another special case of $E[g(x, y)]$ that has practical importance is when

$$g(x, y) = ax + by,$$

where a and b are constants. The important summary measures of this function are the **expectation of the weighted sum** $ax + by$ and the **variance of the weighted sum** $ax + by$.

Expected value of $(ax + by)$:

$$E[ax + by] = \sum_{\text{All } y}\sum_{\text{All } x}(ax + by)P(x, y)$$

$$= aE[x] + bE[y]$$

(4.10)

Variance of $(ax + by)$:

$$V[ax + by] = a^2 V[x] + b^2 V[y] + 2ab C[x, y]$$

(4.11)

The derivation and proof of these formulas follow directly from the definitions of expected values already presented. These formulas are very useful for finding the summary measures for distributions of random variables that are linear combinations of previously defined random variables. By using Formulas 4.10 and 4.11, the mean and standard deviation of the new variables can be found without excessive calculation.

☐ **EXAMPLE 4.19**   Consider the plywood panelling example with probability distribution for $x = $ width and $y = $ length of plywood as given in Table 4.20. Table 4.23 helps us to determine the means of x and y.

The expected values are $E[x] = 7.20$ and $E[y] = 4.30$. Using the rules developed thus far, it is not difficult to show that $V[x] = 2.56$, $V[y] = 1.71$ and the covariance of x and y is $C[x, y] = -0.16$.

TABLE 4.23 Calculation of Expected Values

(1)	(2)	(3)	(4)	(5)	(6)
x	$P(x)$	$xP(x)$	y	$P(y)$	$yP(y)$
4	0.20	0.80	2	0.15	0.30
8	0.80	6.40	4	0.55	2.20
			6	0.30	1.80
Sum	1.00	7.20		1.00	4.30

Now, since these plywood panels are sold with a protective tape all around to protect the edges from moisture or chipping, we might be interested in the amount of protective taping used. Let us denote this by $T = 2x + 2y$, since the amount of tape depends on the perimeter of a given panel. What are the expected value and variance for the distribution of the random variable T?

It would be very tedious to recompute all possible values of the perimeter, weight these values by the appropriate probabilities, and find $E[T]$ and $V[T]$ by use of the calculational formulas. Instead, Formulas 4.10 and 4.11 can be used directly, where a and b each equal 2.

$$E[T] = E[2x + 2y] = 2E[x] + 2[E[y]$$
$$= 2(7.20) + 2(4.30) = 23 \text{ feet}$$

The average amount of tape used per panel is 23 feet.

$$V[T] = V[2x + 2y] = 2^2V[x] + 2^2V[y] + 2(2)(2)C[x, y]$$
$$= 4(2.56) + 4(1.71) + 8(-0.16)$$
$$= 15.80 \text{ (feet)}^2$$

The standard deviation for the amount of tape used per panel is

$$\sigma_T = \sqrt{V[T]} = 3.97 \text{ feet} \qquad \blacksquare$$

A common problem in statistical applications involves finding the difference between two random variables. In this special case of Formulas 4.10 and 4.11, the values of the constants are $a = 1$ and $b = -1$. Again, if the variables x and y are independent, the expected value and the variance of the difference between x and y are given by:

$$E[x - y] = E[x] + (-1)E[y]$$
$$= E[x] - E[y]$$
$$V[x - y] = V[x] + (-1)^2V[y]$$
$$= V[x] + V[y]$$

Note that the variance of the *difference* between two random variables is the *sum* of their variances. The sum or difference of more than two independent random variables is merely an extension of the preceding examples for x and y. The formulas for this extension are presented below.

> Expectations of sums or differences of a finite number of combined random variables, $x_1, x_2, \cdots, x_n$:
>
> $$E[x_1 \pm x_2 \pm \cdots \pm x_n] = E[x_1] \pm E[x_2] \pm \cdots \pm E[x_n] \qquad (4.12)$$
>
> And if the x's are independent:
>
> $$V[x_1 \pm x_2 \pm \cdots \pm x_n] = V[x_1] + V[x_2] + \cdots + V[x_n]$$

The formula for the mean of sums (or differences) of random variables holds whether or not the variables are independent. The formula for variance holds only when the variables are independent so that all the covariance terms are zero. Finally, note that the variance *of a sum or of a difference* is always the *sum* of the variances. This follows because the value of $(+1)^2$ or of $(-1)^2$ is always $+1$.

□ **EXAMPLE 4.20** The number of orders written by a salesperson per week is described by a random variable x with expected value $\mu_x = 25$ and variance $V[x] = 9$. The number of these orders that are not shipped and not received within 10 days is described by a random variable y with expected value $\mu_y = 6$ and variance $V[y] = 4$. Let us find the expected value and variance of the number of *good* orders per week. Call this variable **G**, denoting a case in which an order is taken and then filled within 10 days so that the customer is satisfied and likely to reorder in the future. First, we assume that the number of orders is independent of the number of orders unfilled within 10 days. This assumption means that the unfilled orders are not systematically related to the actions of this one salesperson. Then, we assign $a = 1$ and $b = -1$ to find the difference $\mathbf{G} = x - y$, the number of successful orders, and to find its expected value and variance according to Formulas 4.10 and 4.11:

$$E[\mathbf{G}] = E[x] - E[y] = 25 - 6 = 19$$
$$V[\mathbf{G}] = V[x] + V[y] = 9 + 4 = 13$$

Again, note that the mean of a difference is the *difference* of the means, but the variance of a difference is the *sum* of the variances. ∎

A summary of the bivariate expectation formulas from this section is provided in Table 4.24.

TABLE 4.24 Bivariate Expectation Formulas

Function	Formulas
Mean of $(x \cdot y)$	$E[x \cdot y] = \sum_x \sum_y (x \cdot y) P(x, y)$
Covariance of $(x$ and $y)$	$C[x, y] = E[(x - \mu_x)(y - \mu_y)]$
Mean of $(ax \pm by)$	$E[ax \pm by] = aE[x] \pm bE[y]$
Variance of $(ax \pm by)$	$V[ax \pm by] = a^2 V[y] + b^2 V[y] \pm 2abC[x, y]$

PROBLEMS

4.21 Using the definitions for expected value and variance, show the following algebraically:

a) $E[a + bx] = a + bE[x]$

b) $V[a + bx] = b^2 V[x]$

4.22 Use the information about flight arrivals to answer the following.

a) The number of flight arrivals per hour at the Calgary airport is described by a random variable x with mean 10 and variance 9. Find the expected value and variance of the random variable y describing the number of airline workers employed per hour in this airport where $y = 12 + 2x$.

b) Let the number of flight arrivals per hour at the Edmonton airport be a random variable x and the number at the Montreal airport be a random variable y. Also, $E[x] = 5$, $V[x] = 9$, $E[y] = 10$, and $V[y] = 25$. The variables x and y are independent.

i) Find $E[x \cdot y]$, $E[x + 2y]$, and $E[13 - 2x]$.

ii) Find $V[x - y]$, $V[x + 2y]$, and $V[13 - 2x]$.

iii) What is the value of $C[x, y]$?

4.23 The data in the following table represent the sales of cars by one of the major automobile companies for each of four recent years.

TABLE 4.25 Car Sales Over Four Years

$P(x)$	x
0.250	2,483,000
0.250	2,519,000
0.250	2,511,000
0.250	2,495,000
1.000	$E[x] = ?$

a) Calculate the four values of $y = a + bx$, where $a = -2,500$ and $b = 0.001$. $E[y] \leftarrow$

b) Calculate $E[x]$ by calculating $E[y] = E[a + bx]$. The value of $E[x]$ is then derived by solving Rule 5 of Section 4.4 for $E[x]$:

$$E[x] = \frac{E[a + bx] - a}{b}$$

c) Calculate $V[x]$ by finding $V[a + bx]$ first and then by solving Rule 6 for $V[x]$:

$$V[x] = \frac{V[a + bx]}{b^2}$$

4.24 Managers of a television manufacturing firm believe that more errors can be corrected in the products of the company if the circuits of the televisions are tested several times. A study of the values of the tests is made where y = number of tests and x = number of errors found. The following joint probability table reflects the results.

TABLE 4.26 Number of Television Set Circuit Errors versus Number of Tests

		Errors, x			
		1	2	3	Sum
Tests, y	1	0.10	0.05	0.05	0.20
	2	0.10	0.20	0.10	0.40
	3	0.05	0.15	0.20	0.40
Sum		0.25	0.40	0.35	

a) Find $P(x = 2)$, $P(y = 2)$, $P(x = 3 \mid y = 2)$.

b) Would you conclude that x and y are independent or dependent from the data? Explain.

c) Find $E[x]$ and $E[y]$.

d) Find $E[x \cdot y]$ and $E[x + y]$.

e) Find $C[x, y]$.

f) Find $E[5x - 3y]$.

g) Find $V[5x - 3y]$.

4.25 Consider the joint probability distribution in Table 4.27.

TABLE 4.27 Joint Probability Distribution for x and y

		y	
		10	20
x	1	0.10	0.10
	6	0.50	0.30

a) Find $E[x]$ and $E[y]$.

b) Find $C[x, y]$.

c) Find $V[x]$ and $V[y]$.

d) Find $V[3x - 4y]$ using Formula 4.10.

4.26 Use the tabulated data to answer each of the following. Assume that the pairs of x and y shown in Table 4.28 occur with one-fourth probability.

TABLE 4.28

x	5	2	3	6
y	6	6	6	6

a) Find $E[x]$, $E[y]$, $V[x]$, and $V[y]$.

b) Find $E[x + y]$ and $E[x - y]$.

c) Are x and y independent or dependent? Explain.

d) Find $V[x + y]$ and $C[x, y]$.

4.27 For the data of Table 4.19, show that

a) $E[x + y] = 8.40 = E[x] + E[y]$.

b) $V[x - y] = 7.84 = V[x] + V[y]$.

4.28 It seems that a large number of high-tech positions are being filled by the younger employees. A study is done to determine the relation between the number of years of employment (x) and the number of high-tech-related job promotions (y) of those employees. The results are shown in this joint probability table.

TABLE 4.29 Joint Probability of Job Promotion versus Years of Employment

		Employment, x		
		1	5	10
Promotions, y	1	1/20	2/20	3/20
	2	4/20	0	3/20
	3	2/20	4/20	1/20

a) Find the marginal probability functions for x and y. What is the value of $P(y = 2)$?

b) Find $E[x]$ and $E[y]$.

c) Calculate $P(x = 10 \mid y = 1)$.

d) Determine whether x and y are independent.

4.29 Refer to the information in Problem 4.28. Salaries, fringe benefits, and other employee matters such as overtime opportunities are related to both the years of employment and the number of high-tech-related job promotions of the workers. In order to establish some workable rules, the managers need to know the characteristics of the distributions of some functions of these random variables. Find the following:

a) $E[x \cdot y]$

b) $E[x + y]$ and $E[x - y]$

c) $C[x, y]$

d) $V[x + y]$ and $V[x - y]$

CHAPTER SUMMARY

KEY TERMS AND EXPRESSIONS

Random variable: A well-defined rule for assigning a numerical value to all possible outcomes of an experiment.

Indicator variable: A variable that takes on the value one if a specific characteristic occurs and the value zero if it does not.

Probability distribution: A specification (usually by a graph, a table, or a function) of the probability associated with each value of a random variable.

Probability mass function (p.m.f.): A discrete probability distribution.

Cumulative mass function (c.m.f.): A summation of the values of a p.m.f., starting at the lower limit and going up to and including a specified value of the random variable. $F(x) = P(x \le x)$.

Expected value of x or $E[x]$: The weighted mean or average of the random variable x.

$$E[x] = \sum_{\text{All } x} x P(x)$$

Variance of x or $V[x]$: The expectation of the squared deviations of a random variable about its mean μ.

$$V[x] = E[(x - \mu)^2]$$

Standardization of x: The transformation

$$z = (x - \mu)/\sigma.$$

Combined random variables x **and** y: Variables having a joint probability distribution $P(x, y)$ for the probability of the intersection of specific values of x and y.

Marginal probability for one of the combined random variables, $P(x)$: The sum of all the joint probabilities for which the specific value x occurs.

Conditional probability for one of the combined random variables, $P(x \mid y)$: The ratio of the joint probability to the marginal probability of the given condition.

$$P(x \mid y) = \frac{P(x, y)}{P(y)}$$

Covariance of x **and** y: $C[x, y] = E[x \cdot y] - E[x]E[y]$

Independence: $E[x \cdot y] = E[x] \cdot E[y]; C[x, y] = 0, V[ax + by] = a^2 V[x] + b^2 V[y].$

Expectation of a weighted sum of combined random variables:

$$E[ax + by] = aE[x] + bE[y]$$

Variance of a weighted sum of combined random variables: $V[ax + by] = a^2 V[x] + b^2 V[y] + 2abC[x, y]$

EXERCISES

4.30 The table below shows the joint probability distribution for the length of want ads in a newspaper and the number of times the ad is repeated by the customer. Find the following

a) $V[x]$

b) $V[y]$

c) $C[x, y]$ using Formula 4.9

TABLE 4.30 Joint Probability of Number of Want Ad Repeats versus Ad Length

		Length (inches), x		
		1	2	3
	0	0.10	0.05	0.05
Number of repeats, y	1	0.20	0.25	0.15
	2	0.10	0.10	0.0

4.31 A firm has a toll-free phone service for inquiries about the status of orders, shipments, et cetera. The total phone cost is estimated to be $4. However, if the result of the inquiry is better customer relations and good will, the benefit is estimated to be $2. Assume that half of the inquiries result in this benefit and the others are neutral (benefit of zero). Each inquiry is independent of any other. Let x denote the number of inquiries out of the next four calls that result in this positive benefit, where $x = 0, 1, 2, 3,$ or 4. Let the value to the firm for these next four calls be $y = 2x - 4$.

a) Is y a random variable?

b) Find $E[x]$ and $V[x]$.

c) Using the probability distribution for y described in part (a), find $E[y]$ and $V[y]$.

d) Using the results in part (b) and the expectation rules, find $E[y]$ and $V[y]$. Compare your answers here to your results in part (c).

4.32 Prove that a random variable y and a constant k are always statistically independent.

4.33 Given: x is a discrete random variable with values chosen at random from the set 1, 2, 3, 4, 5, and 6; y is a random variable with values of integers at least as large as x and not greater than 6.

a) Determine the joint probability function of x and y.

b) Find the conditional probabilities $g(y \mid x = 3)$.

c) Find the expected value of y.

4.34 Refer to the p.m.f. for sales of brownies (x) in Table 4.5. The cost of a sale is determined to be 5¢ per transaction plus 10¢ per inch of brownie size; that is $c = 5 + 10x$.

a) Find the p.m.f. for cost c. Then find $E[c]$ and $V[c]$.

b) Substitute the values of $E[x]$ and $V[x]$ into the expectation Rules 5 and 6 of Section 4.4 to find $E[5 + 10x]$ and $V[5 + 10x]$.

4.35 Prove that $V[ax + by] = a^2 V[x] + b^2 V[y] + 2abC[x, y]$.

4.36 Prove the following.

a) Expectation Rule 5 in Section 4.4 is a special case of Formula 4.10.

b) Rule 6 is a special case of Formula 4.11.

4.37 Prove that $C[x, y] = E[x, y] - E[x]E[y]$.

4.38 For $P(x, y)$ on the length and width of plywood panels in Table 4.20, find $V[x]$ and $V[y]$. Use the fact that $C[x, y] = E[x, y] - E[x]E[y]$ to verify that $C[x, y] = -0.16$.

4.39 Refer to the ten observations in Problem 4.9. Subtract 175 from each observation. Find μ and σ^2 for the new set of values. Compare these to the values found in Problem 4.9, parts (a) and (b).

4.40 Refer to the ten observations in Problem 4.9. Subtract 195 from each observation and divide each of these differences by 10. Find μ and σ^2 for the transformed set of values. Explain your results by comparing them to the expected value and the variance of the standardized variable for these ten observations.

4.41 Consider the distribution for sales of brownie squares given in Table 4.5. Suppose the profit on these items is 3¢ per square inch of brownie. Find the expected profit per sale and the standard deviation of this profit.

4.42 Find the values for the mean and variance of the number of persons involved in two-car accidents as described in Example 4.7.

4.43 Referring to the two-car accident problem in Example 4.7, let us drop the simplifying assumption of equal probabilities for each value of x. A more realistic distribution of the number of persons per car can be determined from records of a Highway Safety Research Centre as shown in Table 4.31.

TABLE 4.31   Probability Distribution Number of Persons per Car

x	1	2	3	4	5	6
$P(x)$	0.35	0.30	0.10	0.15	0.08	0.02

Using this p.m.f., find the mean and standard deviation of the number of persons involved in a two-car accident.

4.44 Refer to Study Question 4.2 concerning salary supplements for teachers. Suppose that the p.m.f. determined in part (b) of that question also applies to a group of teachers in a more urban school district. However, their salary supplements y are always $100 higher than double the salary supplements x. That is, $y = 100 + 2x$.

a) Find the mean and standard deviation of the salary supplement x for teachers in the rural district.

b) Find the mean and standard deviation of the salary supplement y for teachers in the urban district.

4.45 Using the data on jobs x and promotions y in Table 4.29, find the following:

a) $V[x]$ and $V[y]$

b) $C[x, y]$, using the formula in Exercise 4.37.

c) whether or not jobs and promotions are independent random variables

4.46 With reference to Table 4.19 concerning the size x and depth y of cable, find $C[x, y]$. Use the formula in Exercise 4.37.

4.47 Refer to Problem 4.13 for the p.m.f. of sales of boxes of spark plugs. If the net profit per box sold is $10, find the total expected profit and the variance of total expected profit.

CASE PROBLEM

TABLE 4.32   Joint Probability Distribution of Weights and Distance Shipped

		Weight, y	
	2	5	10
500	0.02	0.18	0.17
Distance, x 1500	0.10	0.20	0.10
2500	0.03	0.12	0.08

4.48 Air-Overnight handles packet delivery for a large section of the country. We can simplify the description of their service by the joint probability distribution in Table 4.32. The distance that packets are shipped is categorized in three levels of x (kilometres). The weight of packets shipped is also categorized in three levels of y (kg).

a) Sketch the marginal p.m.f. for distance, x. Find its expected value and variance.

b) Find $V[y]$ and $C[x, y]$. Use the formula in Exercise 4.37.

c) Determine whether distance and weight are independent or dependent.

d) Suppose the rate schedule for packets is 30¢ per kilogram plus 1¢ per kilometre. Find the expected value and standard deviation of the revenue per packet shipped.

CHAPTER 5

Discrete Probability Distributions

<table>
<tr><td>section 5.1</td></tr>
</table>

Introduction

While it is often useful to determine probabilities for a specific discrete random variable or combined random variables, there are many situations in statistical inference and decision-making that involve the same type of probability functions. In such instances, it is useful to apply the theory of probability functions from the previous chapters to obtain *general* results about the mean, the variance, independence, and other characteristics of the random variables. Then it is not necessary to derive such results over and over again in each special case using different numbers. It would be quite discouraging to know all these concepts of probability and still have to go through the process of formulating a new probability function and deriving its characteristics every time we are concerned with a slightly different experiment. Fortunately, we can avoid this difficulty by recognizing the similarities between certain types, or families, of apparently unique experiments and then merely matching a given case to the general formulas. Some of these families of discrete probability distributions are discussed in this chapter.

<table>
<tr><td>section 5.2</td></tr>
</table>

The Binomial Distribution

Many experiments share the common trait that their outcomes can be classified into one of two events. For instance, a car salesperson talking to a customer might view the outcomes as either sale or no sale. Similarly, a bill could be classified as either paid or due, a production process may turn out items that are either good or defective, and stock market indices either go up or do not go up on a given day. In fact, it is often possible to describe the outcomes of many of life's ventures in this fashion merely by distinguishing only two events, which may for convenience be labeled *success* and *failure*. (These terms, however, imply neither good nor bad.) Experiments involving repeated independent trials, each with just *two* possible outcomes, form the basis for the most widely used discrete probability distribution, the **binomial distribution**.

Bernoulli Trials

Several generations of the Bernoulli family, Swiss mathematicians of the 1700s, usually receive credit as the originators of the early research on probability theory, especially on problems involving the binomial distribution. In fact, each repetition of an experiment involving only two outcomes is called a *Bernoulli trial*. For the purposes of probability theory, interest centres not on a single Bernoulli trial, but rather on a series of *independent, repeated* Bernoulli trials. That is, we are interested in more than one trial. The fact that these trials must be *independent* means that the results of any one trial cannot influence the results of any other trial. In addition, when a Bernoulli trial is repeated, it means that the conditions under which each trial is held should be an exact replication of the conditions underlying all other trials. This implies that the probabilities of the two possible outcomes cannot change from trial to trial.

☐ **EXAMPLE 5.1** Suppose four shoppers in a supermarket are randomly selected and asked whether they prefer brand A or brand B peanut butter. If the response of one shopper does not influence the response of any other, then the trials are independent. The trials are repeated if each shopper is asked the questions in exactly the same manner. When these conditions are met, the probability that the first shopper questioned will pick brand B will be the same as the probability that the second shopper will pick brand B or that a shopper questioned third or fourth picks it. This experiment involves four trials. Before we pick the four shoppers, we might assume, for example, that 0.70 is the probability of a success. Let's call the selection of brand B a success. The assumption of 0.70 might be reasonable if a previous study had found that 70% of the shoppers preferred brand B. Before we take the sample, a typical question might be to ask what the probability is of exactly three successes in the four trials given that $\pi = 0.70$. In other words, what is the probability that three of the four shoppers pick brand B and one picks brand A? ∎

The binomial distribution is completely characterized by n (the number of trials) and π (the probability of a success on one trial). The values of n and π are referred to as the *parameters* of this distribution. The word *parameter* in this context has the same meaning as it did in Chapter 1 — it refers to a characteristic of a population.[1] Given specific values of n and π, one can calculate the probability of any specified number of successes.

> In a binomial distribution, the probabilities of interest are those of receiving a certain number (x) of successes in n independent trials, each trial having the same probability (π) of success.

The Binomial Formula

The probability rules of Chapter 3 can be used to calculate binomial probabilities. To determine the probability of exactly x successes in n repeated Bernoulli trials, each with a constant probability of success equal to π, it is necessary to find the probability of *any one* ordering of outcomes where there are x successes. If there are x successes in n trials, there must, of course, be $(n - x)$ failures. This probability is then multiplied by the number of possible occurrences. This is exactly the same process we followed in Chapter 2 using the following formula:

$$P(\text{event}) = (\text{Number of relevant sample points})\,P(\text{one such sample point})$$

The number of relevant sample points is given by the combination formula from Chapter 3, for n objects taken x at a time.

$$\text{Number of relevant sample points:} \quad {}_nC_x = \frac{n!}{x!(n-x)!}$$

[1] Since it is common in discussing the binomial distribution to refer to the number of trials as the *sample size*, we will use a lowercase n to denote this number. Technically, however, the number of trials is a population parameter and hence could be denoted by capital N. We use the Greek letter pi (π) to denote the probability of a success on a single trial, and use $p = x/n$ to denote the *sample* proportion of successes. This follows our convention of using Roman letters for sample measures and Greek letters for population measures. In some statistical texts and papers, the symbol p is used to denote the probability of a success on a single trial.

The probability of one relevant sample point is:[2]

$$P(\text{one sample point}) = \pi^x (1 - \pi)^{n-x}$$

Putting these together gives the probability mass function (p.m.f.) for a random variable x from an experiment involving independent repeated Bernoulli trials, each having the same probability, π, of success. This p.m.f. is called the *binomial distribution*. The formula for the binomial distribution is given below.

Binomial formula:

$$P(\text{exactly } x \text{ successes in } n \text{ trials})$$

$$= \frac{n!}{x!(n-x)!}\pi^x (1 - \pi)^{n-x} \quad \text{for} \quad \begin{array}{l} x = 0, 1, 2, \dots, n \\ n = 1, 2, 3, \dots \end{array} \tag{5.1}$$

☐ EXAMPLE 5.2 We can illustrate Formula 5.1 via the stock owner–non-owner example from Chapter 3. In that example, there were $n = 3$ trials (three interviews), and for each trial (interview) the probability of interviewing a stock owner was 0.50. Now suppose that we are interested in determining the probability that, in three trials (interviews), we find two stock owners and one non-owner — that is, we want to calculate $P(x = 2)$, where there are 2 stock owners and $(n - x) = (3 - 2) = 1$ non-owner. Substituting $n = 3$, $x = 2$ and $\pi = 0.50$ into Formula 5.1, we find the following probability:

$$P(x = 2) = \frac{3!}{2!(3 - 2)!}(0.50)^2(0.50)^1 = \frac{6}{2(1)}(0.25)(0.50) = 0.375$$

This is the same result, $P(x = 2) = 3/8$, as shown on page 75. ■

as shown on page 75.

Determining Binomial Probabilities

section 5.3

The binomial probability distribution is a *discrete* distribution, since we can separately itemize the possible values of x. Each probability value must be nonnegative, and the sum of these probabilities over all values of x must equal 1 — that is, the properties of a probability mass function are satisfied.

---

[2] Assume that the x successes come first, followed by the $(n - x)$ failures, where π is the probability of success and $1 - \pi$ is the probability of failure.

$$\underbrace{\pi(\pi)(\pi)\cdots\pi}_{x \text{ successes}}\underbrace{(1 - \pi)(1 - \pi)(1 - \pi)\cdots(1 - \pi)}_{(n-x)\text{ failures}} = \pi^x (1 - \pi)^{n-x}$$

Recall from Chapter 3 that the joint probability of a series of independent events does not depend on the *order* in which they are arranged. Hence, the value of

$$\pi^x (1 - \pi)^{n-x}$$

represents the probability of *any* possible arrangement of x successes and $(n - x)$ failures.

TABLE 5.1   Finding Binomial Probabilities for $n = 4, \pi = 0.70$

x	$_nC_x$	$\pi^x(1 = \pi)^{n-x}$	$P(x) = {}_nC_x\pi^x(1-\pi)^{n-x}$
0	$\dfrac{4!}{0!4!} = 1$	$(0.70)^0(0.30)^4 = 0.0081$	$P(0) = 0.0081$
1	$\dfrac{4!}{1!3!} = 4$	$(0.70)^1(0.30)^3 = 0.0189$	$P(1) = 0.0756$
2	$\dfrac{4!}{2!2!} = 6$	$(0.70)^2(0.30)^2 = 0.0441$	$P(2) = 0.2646$
3	$\dfrac{4!}{3!1!} = 4$	$(0.70)^3(0.30)^1 = 0.1029$	$P(3) = 0.4116$
4	$\dfrac{4!}{4!0!} = 1$	$(0.70)^4(0.30)^0 = 0.2401$	$P(4) = 0.2401$
			Sum $= 1.0000$

To illustrate the use of the binomial distribution, let's use the peanut butter taste test presented earlier, where $n = 4$ and $\pi = 0.70$. Recall, in this case, that a success is defined to be someone who picks brand B (maybe the company is sponsoring the study). Earlier, we indicated that one might want to determine the probability that three shoppers will pick brand B and one will pick brand A. This is the probability of three successes and one failure in four trials and can be calculated from Formula 5.1 as follows:

$$P(x_{\text{binomial}} = 3) = \frac{4!}{3!(4-3)!}0.70^3(1-0.70)^1 = \frac{24}{6(1)}(0.1029) = 0.4116$$

The probability that there will be four successes in four trials is calculated in the same manner:

$$P(x_{\text{binomial}} = 4) = \frac{4!}{4!(4-4)!}0.70^4(1-0.70)^0 = \frac{24}{24}(0.2401)(1) = 0.2401$$

Indeed, the probability of any number of successes from 0 to 4 can be determined in the same way. Table 5.1 organizes the necessary calculations for all these values, and Figure 5.1 illustrates the resulting probability function. Notice in column (2) of Table 5.1 that the number of combinations, $_nC_x$, has a symmetrical pattern — both the smallest value of $x(x = 0)$ and the largest value of $x(x = n)$ give $_nC_x = 1$.

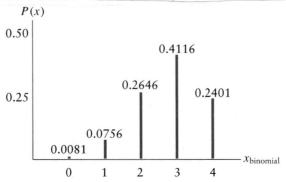

FIGURE 5.1   Binomial distribution for $n = 4, \pi = 0.70$

The largest values of $_nC_x$ are in the middle. This symmetry is a characteristic of $_nC_x$ no matter what values n and x assume.

Using a Binomial Table

Although calculating the binomial probabilities in Table 5.1 was not very complex, if n becomes much larger, the difficulty of making such calculations could become tedious. In such cases, we may wish to employ a binomial table.

☐ **EXAMPLE 5.3**   Assume that $n = 20$ items are sampled from a production process that produces either good or defective contact lenses. What is the probability of finding four defective lenses if $n = 20$ and $\pi = 0.10$? We label a defective lens as a success and use Formula 5.1:

$$P(x_{\text{binomial}} = 4) = {}_nC_x\pi^x(1 - \pi)^{n-x} = {}_{20}C_4(0.10)^4(0.90)^{20-4}$$

$$= \frac{20!}{(4!)(20 - 4)!}(0.10)(0.10)(0.10)(0.10)\overbrace{(0.90)(0.90)\cdots(0.90)}^{16 \text{ terms}}$$

Only the foolish would desire to calculate such a number more than once, and only those with a computer may wish to do it once. Fortunately, computers can be used to perform such tasks and tabulate the results. The answer to this problem and many others similar to it are readily available in tables similar to Table I in Appendix C at the end of the book. This table gives the probability of x successes for a number of the more commonly used values of n and for values of π from 0.01 to 0.99. Table 5.2 is an example of a binomial table — specifically, it is taken from Table I in Appendix C. This page gives the binomial probabilities for $n = 20$ and selected values of π.

To find the value of $P(x = 4)$ given that $n = 20$ and $\pi = 0.10$, look for the column whose heading is 10. This column represents 0.10, as all decimals have been omitted. Now look along the *left-hand* margin until you find $x = 4$. At the row and column intersection of $\pi = 0.10$ and $x = 4$ is the probability $P(x = 4) = 0.0898$. This value is boxed. If we had wanted the probability $P(x = 15)$ when $n = 20$ and $\pi = 0.44$, this number (also boxed) could be found in the same manner and is seen in Table 5.2 to be $P(x = 15) = 0.0038$. ■

The entire probability distribution for values of x when $n = 20$ and $\pi = 0.10$ can be read from Table I. *When the probability values become smaller than 0.00005, the table ends. Thus, if an event cannot be found in the binomial table, such as 18 defectives in 20 items when $\pi = 0.10$, it should be apparent from the table that this value is very small and, for most practical purposes (certainly for any use in this text), can be considered zero, even though theoretically it is not an impossibility.* If all the probabilities for $\pi = 0.10$ and $n = 20$ (or any other combination of n and π) are summed, the total must equal 1.0000. Some columns in Table I do not sum to 1.0000 because of rounding errors.

An important part of Table I is its symmetry. Values of π up to 0.50 (found across the top of each set of numbers) always use the x-values in the *left-hand* margin. The values of π that are greater than 0.50 are found across the *bottom* of each section of the table. When π is greater than 0.50, the appropriate x-values are read from the *right-hand* margin. In our example about defective lenses, we could have focused attention on good lenses rather than defective ones. That is, we might

TABLE 5.2   Binomial Probabilities for $n = 20$ (from Table I, Appendix C)

$n = 20$

x \ π	01	02	03	04	05	06	07	08	09	10	
0	8179	6676	5438	4420	3585	2901	2342	1887	1516	1216	20
1	1652	2725	3364	3683	3774	3703	3526	3282	3000	2702	19
2	0159	0528	0988	1458	1887	2246	2521	2711	2828	2852	18
3	0010	0065	0183	0364	0596	0860	1139	1414	1672	1901	17
4	0000	0006	0024	0065	0133	0233	0364	0523	0703	0898	16
5	0000	0000	0002	0009	0022	0048	0088	0145	0222	0319	15
6	0000	0000	0000	0001	0003	0008	0017	0032	0055	0089	14
7	0000	0000	0000	0000	0000	0001	0002	0005	0011	0020	13
8	0000	0000	0000	0000	0000	0000	0000	0001	0002	0004	12
9	0000	0000	0000	0000	0000	0000	0000	0000	0000	0001	11
	99	98	97	96	95	94	93	92	91	90	π \ x

x \ π	11	12	13	14	15	16	17	18	19	20	
0	0972	0776	0617	0490	0388	0306	0241	0189	0148	0115	20
1	2403	2115	1844	1595	1368	1165	0986	0829	0693	0576	19
2	2822	2740	2618	2466	2293	2109	1919	1730	1545	1369	18
3	2093	2242	2347	2409	2428	2410	2358	2278	2175	2054	17
4	1099	1299	1491	1666	1821	1951	2053	2125	2168	2182	16
5	0435	0567	0713	0868	1028	1189	1345	1493	1627	1746	15
6	0134	0193	0266	0353	0454	0566	0689	0819	0954	1091	14
7	0033	0053	0080	0115	0160	0216	0282	0360	0448	0545	13
8	0007	0012	0019	0030	0046	0067	0094	0128	0171	0222	12
9	0001	0002	0004	0007	0011	0017	0026	0038	0053	0074	11
10	0000	0000	0001	0001	0002	0004	0006	0009	0014	0020	10
11	0000	0000	0000	0000	0000	0001	0001	0002	0003	0005	9
12	0000	0000	0000	0000	0000	0000	0000	0000	0001	0001	8
	89	88	87	86	85	84	83	82	81	80	π \ x

x \ π	21	22	23	24	25	26	27	28	29	30	
0	0090	0069	0054	0041	0032	0024	0016	0014	0011	0008	20
1	0477	0392	0321	0261	0211	0170	0137	0109	0087	0068	19
2	1204	1050	0910	0783	0669	0568	0480	0403	0336	0278	18
3	1920	1777	1631	1484	1339	1199	1065	0940	0823	0716	17
4	2169	2131	2070	1991	1897	1790	1675	1553	1429	1394	16
5	1845	1923	1979	2012	2023	2013	1982	1933	1868	1879	15
6	1226	1356	1478	1589	1686	1768	1833	1879	1907	1916	14
7	0652	0765	0883	1003	1124	1242	1356	1462	1558	1643	13
8	0282	0351	0429	0515	0609	0709	0815	0924	1034	1144	12
9	0100	0132	0171	0217	0271	0332	0492	0479	0563	0654	11
10	0029	0041	0056	0075	0099	0128	0163	0205	0253	0308	10
11	0007	0010	0015	0022	0030	0041	0055	0072	0094	0120	9
12	0001	0002	0003	0005	0008	0011	0015	0021	0029	0039	8
13	0000	0000	0001	0001	0002	0002	0003	0005	0007	0010	7
14	0000	0000	0000	0000	0000	0000	0001	0001	0001	0002	6
	79	78	77	76	75	74	73	72	71	70	π \ x

TABLE 5.2   Binomial Probabilities for $n = 20$ (from Table I, Appendix C)

$n = 20$

x π	31	32	33	34	35	36	37	38	39	40	
0	0006	0004	0003	0002	0002	0001	0001	0001	0001	0000	20
1	0054	0042	0033	0025	0020	0015	0011	0009	0007	0005	19
2	0229	0188	0153	0124	0100	0080	0064	0050	0040	0031	17
3	0619	0513	0453	0383	0323	0270	0224	0185	0152	0123	17
4	1181	1062	0947	0839	0738	0645	0559	0483	0412	0350	16
5	1698	1599	1493	1384	1272	1161	1051	0945	0843	0746	15
6	1907	1881	1839	1782	1712	1632	1543	1447	1347	1244	14
7	1714	1770	1811	1836	1844	1836	1812	1774	1722	1659	13
8	1251	1354	1450	1537	1614	1678	1730	1767	1790	1797	12
9	0750	0849	0952	1056	1158	1259	1354	1444	1526	1597	11
10	0370	0440	0516	0598	0686	0779	0875	0974	1073	1171	10
11	0151	0188	0231	0280	0336	0398	0467	0542	0624	0710	9
12	0051	0066	0085	0108	0136	0168	0206	0248	0299	0355	8
13	0014	0019	0026	0034	0045	0058	0074	0094	0118	0146	7
14	0003	0005	0006	0009	0012	0016	0022	0029	0038	0049	6
15	0001	0001	0001	0002	0003	0004	0005	0007	0010	0013	5
16	0000	0000	0000	0000	0000	0001	0001	0001	0002	0003	4
	69	68	67	66	65	64	63	62	61	60	π x

x π	41	42	43	44	45	46	47	48	49	50	
1	0004	0003	0002	0001	0001	0001	0001	0000	0000	0000	19
2	0024	0018	0014	0011	0008	0006	0005	0003	0002	0002	18
3	0100	0080	0064	0051	0040	0031	0024	0019	0014	0011	17
4	0295	0247	0206	0170	0139	0113	0092	0074	0059	0046	16
5	0656	0573	0496	0427	0365	0309	0260	0217	0180	0148	15
6	1140	1037	0936	0839	0746	0658	0577	0501	0432	0370	14
7	1585	1502	1413	1318	1221	1122	1023	0925	0830	0739	13
8	1790	1768	1732	1683	1623	1553	1474	1388	1296	1201	12
9	1658	1707	1742	1763	1771	1763	1742	1708	1661	1602	11
10	1268	1358	1446	1524	1593	1652	1700	1734	1755	1762	10
11	0801	0895	0991	1089	1185	1280	1370	1455	1533	1602	9
12	0417	0486	0561	0642	0727	0818	0911	1007	1105	1201	8
13	0178	0217	0260	0310	0366	0429	0497	0572	0653	0739	7
14	0062	0078	0098	0122	0150	0183	0211	0264	0314	0370	6
15	0017	0023	0030	0038	0049	0062	0078	0098	0121	0148	5
16	0004	0005	0007	0009	0013	0017	0022	0028	0036	0046	4
17	0001	0001	0001	0002	0002	0003	0005	0006	0008	0011	3
18	0000	0000	0000	0000	0000	0000	0001	0001	0001	0002	2
	59	58	57	56	55	54	53	52	51	50	π x

have posed our question as: "What is the probability of 16 good lenses if $n = 20$ and $\pi = 0.90$?" The answer to this question is the same probability we determined above, 0.0898. Refer again to Table 5.2. In this case, the appropriate probability is found by looking for $\pi = 0.90$ across the bottom of each set of numbers, and then reading *up* the right-hand side of the table until reaching $x = 16$. Note that both methods end up at exactly the same (boxed) point in Table 5.2. This is because the event *16 good lenses* is the same as the event *4 bad lenses*. The reader should use Table I in Appendix C (for $n = 4$, $\pi = 0.70$) to verify the probabilities shown in Figure 5.1 in this chapter.

Cumulative probabilities can also be obtained from Table I by summing the probabilities of interest. For example, the probability that two or fewer defective lenses will appear in a sample of n items is written as $P(x \leq 2) = F(2)$. If $n = 20$ and $\pi = 0.10$, this value is:

$$F(2) = P(x \leq 2) = P(0) + P(1) + P(2)$$
$$= 0.1216 + 0.2702 + 0.2852$$
$$= 0.6770$$

section 5.4   Using the Computer for Binomial Problems

In Section 5.3, we showed how to determine binomial probabilities by using the binomial formula (5.1) or Table I in Appendix C. For anyone with access to a computer, the easiest way to determine binomial probabilities is to use a statistical package. A very large number of such packages exist, and all operate in essentially the same manner. Although the notation often differs from package to package, determining how to use each package is typically relatively easy. We will demonstrate the Doane package here, using the parameters from the last example above, namely $n = 20$ and $\pi = 0.10$.

For the Doane package, the user first accesses the program menu (select P), and chooses the binomial (binom) option. The program will then ask for the number of trials (n) and the probability of success on a single trial. This probability, which we call π, is labeled p in the Doane package. Thus, the sequence of questions and answers (in bold face) for our problem is:

How many trials (n)? **20**

What is the probability of success (p)? **0.10**

The Doane package gives exact binomial probabilities, as well as cumulative binomial probabilities. In the Doane notation, r is the number of successes; exact probabilities are labeled as $P(X = r)$ and cumulative probabilities as $P(X \geq r)$ and $P(X < r)$. Note that these two cumulative probabilities are complementary — they sum to one. The output below is for $n = 20$, $p = 0.10$. Probabilities less than 0.0001 have been omitted. The probability calculated at the end of Section 5.3 was

$$P(x \leq 2) = 0.6770$$

Because $P(x \leq 2) = P(x < 3)$, the comparable Doane probability is:

$$P(X < 3) = 0.6769$$

The values 0.6770 (on page 163) and 0.6769 differ because of rounding errors.

```
n = 20
p = 0.10
r = number of successes in 20 trials
```

r	Exact P(X = r)	Cumulative P(X ≥ r)	Cumulative P(X < r)
0	0.1216	1.0000	0.0000
1	0.2701	0.8784	0.1216
2	0.2852	0.6083	0.3917
3	0.1901	0.3231	0.6769
4	0.0898	0.1330	0.8670
5	0.0319	0.0432	0.9568
6	0.0089	0.0113	0.9887
7	0.0020	0.0024	0.9976
8	0.0004	0.0004	0.9996
9	0.0001	0.0001	0.9999

Characteristics and Use of the Binomial Distribution

The shape of the binomial distribution depends on both n and π. It will be useful to consider different combinations of n and π:

1. When n is small and π is less than 0.50.
2. When n is small and π is greater than 0.50.
3. When n is large and/or $\pi = 0.50$.

1. Small n and $\pi < 0.50$. Whenever $\pi < 0.50$, the binomial distribution is skewed to the right. The smaller the values of both n and π, the more pronounced will be the skewed appearance of the distribution. An illustration of a highly skewed (to the right) binomial distribution is given in Figure 5.2, where $n = 4$ and $\pi = 0.10$.

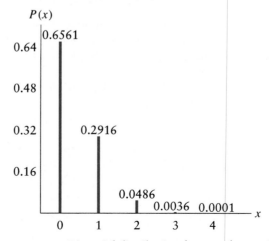

FIGURE 5.2 Binomial distribution for $n = 4$, $\pi = 0.10$

2. Small n and $\pi > 0.50$. Whenever $\pi > 0.50$, the binomial distribution is skewed to the left. The smaller the value of n and the larger the value of π, the more pronounced will be the skewness. Figure 5.1 illustrates the skewness to the left when $n = 4$ and $\pi = 0.70$.

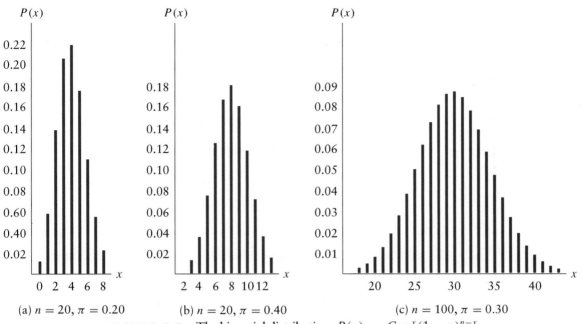

(a) $n = 20$, $\pi = 0.20$ (b) $n = 20$, $\pi = 0.40$ (c) $n = 100$, $\pi = 0.30$

FIGURE 5.3   The binomial distribution: $P(x) = {}_nC_x\pi^x(1-\pi)^{n-x}$

3. Large n and/or $\pi = 0.50$. When $\pi = 0.50$, the binomial distribution will always be symmetrical, no matter what size n assumes. The reader might try to sketch $n = 4, \pi = 0.50$ to verify that this distribution is, indeed, symmetrical. More important, however, is that when π is not equal to 0.50, the shape of the binomial becomes more and more symmetrical as the value of n increases. Figure 5.3 illustrates this fact. Note in parts (a) and (b) of this figure that even though n is as small as 20, the distributions for $\pi = 0.20$ and $\pi = 0.40$ are fairly symmetrical in appearance. For $n = 100$ and $\pi = 0.30$, as shown in part (c) of Figure 5.3, the distribution is very symmetrical and bell-shaped. One rule of thumb is that the distribution will be fairly symmetrical if $n\pi(1-\pi)$ is larger than 3.0. For Figure 5.3(a), $n\pi(1-\pi) = 20(0.20)(0.80) = 3.2$. For Figure 5.3(b), $n\pi(1-\pi) = 20(0.40)(0.60) = 4.8$, and for Figure 5.3(c), $n\pi(1-\pi) = 100(0.30)(0.70) = 21.0$. Thus, by the rule of thumb, all three of these distributions should be fairly symmetrical in appearance, especially part (c), and they are.

Mean of the Binomial Distribution

Since the binomial distribution is characterized by the value of the two parameters, n and π, one might anticipate that the summary measures of the mean and standard deviation also can be determined in terms of n and π. It should appear reasonable that the mean number of successes in any given experiment must equal the number of trials (n) times the probability of a success on each trial (π). If, for example, the probability that a process produces a defective item is $\pi = 0.10$, then the mean number of defectives in 20 trials is $20(0.10) = 2$; the mean number in 50 trials is

$50(0.10) = 5$, and the mean number in 100 trials is $100(0.10) = 10$. Thus, the mean number of successes in n trials is $n\pi$:

Binomial mean:

$$E[x_{\text{binomial}}] = \mu = n\pi \qquad (5.2)$$

expected value (or mean)

Variance and Standard Deviation of the Binomial Distribution

The variance and standard deviation of the binomial distribution are also quite easily derived and are as follows: [3]

Binominal variance and standard deviation:

Binomial variance: $V[x_{\text{binomial}}] = \sigma^2 = n\pi(1 - \pi)$

Binomial standard deviation: $\sigma = \sqrt{n\pi(1 - \pi)}$ (5.3)

The variance in 20 Bernoulli trials of a process with probability $\pi = 0.10$ of producing defectives is thus:

$$V[x] = n\pi(1 - \pi) = 20(0.10)(0.90)$$
$$= 1.80$$

The standard deviation is:

$$\sqrt{n\pi(1 - \pi)} = \sqrt{1.80}$$
$$= 1.34$$

Note from Table 5.3 that the intervals $(\mu \pm 1\sigma)$ and $(\mu \pm 2\sigma)$ for this problem contain slightly more of the total probability (obtained from Table I) than the rule of thumb given in Chapter 1 (68% and 95%) would indicate.

TABLE 5.3   The Percentage of Defectives Falling Within Two Standard Deviations from the Mean

Interval	Percent of Probability
$\mu \pm 1\sigma = 2.00 \pm 1.34 = 0.66$ to 3.34	$100\sum_{x=1}^{3} P(x) = 75\%$
$\mu \pm 2\sigma = 2.00 \pm 2(1.34) = 0$ to 4.68	$100\sum_{x=0}^{4} P(x) = 97\%$

---

[3] The explanation and derivation of these formulas is the same as for the counting variable in Section 4.7.

The mean and standard deviation of the binomial distribution in Figures 5.1 and 5.3 can also be found by using Formulas 5.2 and 5.3. For the former example, where $n = 4$ and $\pi = 0.70$, the mean is

$$n\pi = 4(0.70) = 2.8$$

The variance is:

$$n\pi(1 - \pi) = 4(0.70)(0.30)$$
$$= 0.84$$

The standard deviation is:

$$\sqrt{V[x]} = \sqrt{0.84} = 0.92$$

For the latter case of $n = 4$ and $\pi = 0.10$, the mean is $n\pi = 4(0.10) = 0.4$, the variance is $n\pi(1 - \pi) = 4(0.10)(0.90) = 0.36$, and the standard deviation is $\sqrt{V[x]} = \sqrt{0.36} = 0.60$.

Application of the Binomial Distribution

The binomial distribution is useful for investigating a number of special decision problems. One particular problem is that of determining whether the outcomes resulting from repeated trials form a sequence that has a systematic pattern, or whether the different outcomes occur randomly in an unpredictable pattern. For example, stockbrokers have various theories about whether fluctuations in the stock market occur in a random sequence. As another illustration, concern often exists about whether defectives in a production process are random or follow a systematic pattern. One popular belief is that defectives from assembly-line production occur more often on Mondays and Fridays and immediately before and after rest breaks. One test for randomness in a sequence of outcomes, called a *runs test*, is based on the binomial distribution. The runs test is presented in Chapter 18. We now present other examples of the use of the binomial distribution.

☐ EXAMPLE 5.4   Concern about Inflation/Unemployment

Assume that the Prime Minister of Canada is concerned with both inflation and unemployment. The Prime Minister is undecided as to which problem is viewed as more serious by the voting public. One group of advisers claims that 90% of the public views unemployment as more serious. Another group of advisers suggests that the two problems are viewed as equally serious. Obviously, the Prime Minister cannot learn the preferences of the entire population of Canadian voters; but suppose a decision is made to sample households at random, asking voters which problem is more serious. To illustrate the process, we will assume that a sample of $n = 20$ is taken, knowing that a much larger sample would be reasonable in this situation. The results are:

Unemployment more serious	Inflation/unemployment equally serious	Total
14	6	20

Which of the advisers would appear to be more correct on the basis of this sample? The view of the unemployment group is that $\pi = 0.90$, while the view of the other group is that $\pi = 0.50$. On the basis of $n = 20$, the number of presumably independent trials, we can calculate the expected value (or mean) by using Formula 5.2.

$$\text{If } \pi = 0.90: E[x] = n\pi = 20(0.90) = 18$$
$$\text{If } \pi = 0.50: E[x] = n\pi = 20(0.50) = 10$$

These values do not help the Prime Minister a lot, because the observed number of voters answering *unemployment* (14) is exactly halfway between these two means. But now let's calculate the *probability* that 14 answer *inflation* when $n = 20$ and π is either 0.90 or 0.50. Using Table I in Appendix C or Figure 5.2, we find:

1. When $\pi = 0.90$: $P(x = 14) = 0.0089$
2. When $\pi = 0.50$: $P(x = 14) = 0.0370$

The probability of 14 voters answering *unemployment* when $\pi = 0.50$ is more than four times as large as when $\pi = 0.90$. On the basis of this survey, we would thus tend to agree more with the advisers who say that unemployment and inflation are viewed as equally serious. ∎

When examining the reasonableness of a hypothesis (such as $\pi = 0.90$) in the light of a sample result (such as $x = 14$), the usual procedure is to calculate the probability of the observed outcome *or* any more extreme outcomes. To find this type of union of outcomes, the *more extreme* outcomes are included by using the appropriate inequality (either $\leq$ or $\geq$). That is, we use $P(x \leq 14)$ or $P(x \geq 14)$ rather than the probability that x exactly equals 14. The direction of the inequality is chosen to include the *more extreme* values, meaning those further away from the mean of the distribution. Thus, for $\pi = 0.90$, we wish to find the probability that $x \leq 14$, since the observed result ($x = 14$) is less than the expected value, which is $n\pi = 20(0.90) = 18$. If the hypothesis is $\pi = 0.50$, then the procedure is to calculate the probability of 14 *or more* because the observed result (14) exceeds the expected value, which is $n\pi = 20(0.50) = 10$. These two probabilities are:

1. When $\pi = 0.90$: $P(x \leq 14) = 0.0114$
2. When $\pi = 0.50$: $P(x \geq 14) = 0.0577$

The higher probability for $\pi = 0.50$ supports the second group of advisers who suggest that voters believe the problems are equally serious. The following procedure is appropriate in determining probabilities for decision-making.

If the observed value is less than the expected value, calculate the probability that x is *less than or equal to* the observed value:

$$P(x \leq \text{ observed value})$$

If the observed value exceeds the expected value, calculate the probability that x is *greater than or equal to* the observed value:

$$P(x \geq \text{ observed value})$$

☐ **EXAMPLE 5.5**   Another way of using a binomial probability distribution is to reverse the sense of the question and ask what value of π would be most compatible with the survey result. This process of examining a sample to make a statement about a population parameter is the basis of *statistical inference*. If we examine Table 5.2 for $n = 20$, we see that the probability of $x = 14$ is the greatest when $\pi = 0.70$. That is, when $\pi = 0.70$ and $n = 20$, $P(x = 14) = 0.1916$, and no other value of $P(x)$ is larger than 0.1916. Thus, we might conclude that a true value of $\pi = 0.70$ for the population seems most reasonable or likely. If the survey had resulted in 15 voters answering *unemployment*, then the most likely value for π would have been $\pi = 0.75$. ■

Using probabilities in decision-making or statistical inference can be better understood if we can determine the degree of sensitivity, or more precisely, the chances of error, in our conclusion. Such errors are discussed in detail in Chapters 10 and 11. At this point, we hope merely to give some illustrations and thus a motivation for studying probability distributions. The following example is an illustration of the use of the binomial distribution in a decision process where the chances of making errors are determined.

▢ EXAMPLE 5.6 Assume that a production process for making an automobile part is malfunctioning and will require a minor or a major adjustment. If the defective rate is 10% ($\pi = 0.10$), then only a minor adjustment is necessary; if the rate of defectives has jumped to 25% ($\pi = 0.25$), then a major adjustment is necessary. The problem at this point is how to decide, on the basis of a random sample of size $n = 20$, whether the process requires a minor or a major adjustment. This decision is not without risks, however, for we assume it to be costly to make the wrong decision — in other words, to make a minor adjustment to a process needing a major adjustment or to make a major adjustment to a process needing only minor adjustments.

In this circumstance, we need to know how probable it is that x defectives will occur in a sample of $n = 20$ when $\pi = 0.10$ and how probable x defectives are when $\pi = 0.25$. Table 5.4 provides these values taken from the columns in Table 5.2 for $\pi = 0.10$ and $\pi = 0.25$.

Suppose, for the moment, that four defectives is established as the decision point between a major and minor adjustment. If there are four or more defectives, then major adjustments are made. If there are three or fewer defectives in the sample, minor repairs are made. This decision rule will lead to an *incorrect* decision if x (the number of defectives sampled) is greater than or equal to 4 when $\pi = 0.10$; that is, the correct decision would be a minor adjustment since the true π still equals 0.10, but our decision rule leads us to make a major adjustment (since $x \geq 4$). Similarly, if $x < 4$ when the true π has really changed to 0.25, then an incorrect decision is also made. We would make a minor adjustment (since $x < 4$) when a major adjustment is really needed (since $\pi = 0.25$). From Table 5.2, we see that the probabilities of making these two types of error are as follows:

1. Making a major adjustment when only a minor adjustment is necessary:

$$P(x \geq 4 \mid \pi = 0.10) = 0.1331$$

2. Making a minor adjustment when a major adjustment is necessary:

$$P(x < 4 \mid \pi = 0.25) = 0.2251$$

The analysis thus far has been based on using $x = 4$ as a decision point. The probabilities in the analysis will, of course, change if a decision point other than $x = 4$ is used. Suppose the choice between a major and a minor adjustment is set to depend on the critical value of $x = 3$ defectives; then the probability of the two types of error can be calculated from Table 5.4 to be as follows:

1. $\quad P(x \geq 3 \mid \pi = 0.10) = 0.3232$

2. $\quad P(x < 3 \mid \pi = 0.25) = 0.0912$

TABLE 5.4   Using the Binomial Distribution in Decision-Making

x	Decision		$\pi = 0.10$		$\pi = 0.25$	
0			⎰ 0.1216		⎰ 0.0032	
1	Minor	Correct	0.2702		0.0211	
2	adjustment	decision	0.2852	Error	0.0669	0.2251
3	↓		⎱ 0.1901		⎱ 0.1339	
			Decision value			
4	↑		0.0898		0.1897	
5			0.0319		0.2023	
6			0.0089		0.1686	
7			0.0020		0.1124	
8			0.0004		0.0609	
9	Major	Error	⎰ 0.0001 ⎱ 0.1331		Correct ⎰ 0.0271	
10	adjustment		0.0000		decision 0.0099	
11			0.0000		0.0030	
12			0.0000		0.0008	
13			0.0000		0.0002	
14–20	↓		0.0000		0.0000	
Sum			1.0000		1.0000	

For a given value of n, one of these types of errors such as making a major adjustment when a minor adjustment is necessary, or vice versa, can be made smaller only if the other is allowed to become larger. Just what decision rule (such as using $x = 3$ or $x = 4$ as the critical value) is *best* in a given circumstance depends largely on the costs associated with making these errors. We shall examine this subject in more detail in Chapters 10 and 17. ∎

Binomial Proportions

section 5.6

All the binomial problems studied thus far involved the random variable x, where x represents the *number* of successes in n Bernoulli trials. In this section, we will show that any one of these problems could have been solved by using the variable x/n, where x/n represents the *proportion* of successes in n Bernoulli trials. For simplicity of notation, the sample proportion will be called p. For all practical purposes, *it makes no difference in solving a problem whether x is used, or $x/n = p$ is used.*

To illustrate the statement above, suppose we redo Figure 5.1, which shows the binomial distribution for $n = 4, \pi = 0.70$. Instead of using x on our horizontal axis, this time (Figure 5.4) we use p on the horizontal axis.

The important aspect of Figure 5.5 is that it looks identical to Figure 5.1 except for the values on the horizontal axis. In other words, dividing each value of x by n does not change any of the probability values. The mean and variance of $p = x/n$ will be different from $E[x] = n\pi$ and $V[x] = n\pi(1 - \pi)$, but we can

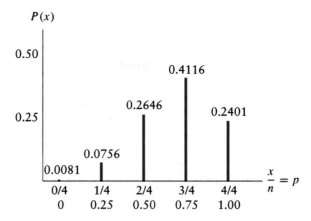

FIGURE 5.4   Binomial distribution for $n = 4$, $\pi = 0.70$, using p as the variable

easily derive the new values using the algebra of expectations.[4] The **expectations of a binomial proportion** are:

Binomial proportion expectations:

$$\text{Mean of } p = E[p] = \pi$$

$$\text{Variance of } p = V[p] = \frac{\pi(1 - \pi)}{n}$$

(5.4)

□ EXAMPLE 5.7   A newspaper article has suggested that only 40% of the small businesses in Toronto follow accepted auditing procedures. To test this assertion, an accountant takes a random sample of 50 small businesses in Toronto. Should the accountant doubt the article's suggestion if 54% of these 50 small businesses are following accepted auditing procedures?

---

[4] The proofs are:

$$E[p] = E[x/n] = \frac{1}{n}E[x] \qquad \text{(Rule 3 of Section 4.4)}$$

$$= \frac{1}{n}(n\pi) \qquad \text{(since } E[x] = n\pi)$$

$$= \pi$$

$$V[p] = V[x/n] = \frac{1}{n^2}V[x] \qquad \text{(Rule 4 of Section 4.4)}$$

$$= \frac{1}{n^2}n\pi(1 - \pi) \qquad \text{(since } V[x] = n\pi(1 - \pi))$$

$$= \frac{\pi(1 - \pi)}{n}$$

> Since Table I is presented in terms of the *number* of successes (x), rather than the *proportion* of successes (x/n), a problem involving x/n is usually solved by transforming it to the comparable problem involving x.

Remember from Section 5.3 that we generally do not calculate the probability of one specific value in problems of this nature, but rather the probability that x is greater than or equal to the observed value when the observed value exceeds the expected value. In this example, we want to calculate the proportion

$$P(p \geq 0.54)$$

because the observed value of 54% exceeds the expected value of 40%. Since $n = 50$, $p \geq 0.54$ is equivalent to $x \geq 50\,(0.54)$, or $x \geq 27$. Thus:

$$P(p \geq 0.54) = P(x \geq 27).$$

This problem is easily solved by using Table I for $n = 50$, $\pi = 0.40$, and $x \geq 27$. Be sure to recognize that π in this problem is 0.40 (and not 0.54), because 0.40 is the population proportion (π) that we are considering. From Table I:

$$P(x \geq 27) = 0.0154 + \cdots + 0.0001 = 0.0314$$

Thus, in random samples of this nature, only a little over 3% of the time would one expect 27 or more successes in 50 trials. The accountant would appear to have good reason to doubt the newspaper's assertion and to believe that the true population proportion is larger than 0.40.

Would the newspaper's assertion still be in doubt if, say, 48% of 50 businesses used accepted auditing procedures? In this case,

$$P(p \geq 0.48) = P(x \geq 24) = 0.1562,$$

which means there is almost a 16% chance that this result (48%) could occur if the newspaper is correct. Perhaps 0.16 is too high a probability for the accountant to risk criticizing the newspaper for its 40% assertion. In Chapter 10, we will study the process of trying to decide how low a probability has to be before one can reject the assertion on which this probability was calculated. *One quite arbitrary rule often used is that the probability must be less than 0.05 in order to reject the assertion.*

In our Toronto example, the result could have been in the *opposite* direction — perhaps only 22% of the businesses sampled use accepted auditing procedures. The appropriate calculation now is for the probability that p will be 0.22 *or less* because 0.22 is less than the expected value of $\pi = 0.40$. From Table I, $n = 50$ and $\pi = 0.40$:

$$P(p \leq 0.22) = P(x \leq 11) = 0.0056$$

There is less than a 1% chance of having 11 or fewer businesses using accepted practices in a sample of 50 when the true population proportion is 0.40. Since this probability is quite low (much less than the 5% rule mentioned above), a sample result of 22% would again give the accountant cause to doubt the newspaper's assertion and to worry that the true percentage of businesses using accepted procedures in the population may even be less than 40%. ∎

PROBLEMS

5.1 Six Chevy vans are being tested by *Consumer Reports* for quality control. In the past, 40% of the vans tested have had some safety problems on delivery such as a headlight out or a seatbelt not working.

a) Construct a sketch of the binomial distribution for $n = 6$, $\pi = 0.40$. Is this distribution skewed right or left?

b) What is the expected number of defectives for the distribution in part (a)? What are the variance and standard deviation?

c) What is the probability of four or more defectives in part (a)?

5.2 A company produces dynamic RAM memory chips for computers. Suppose that, in the past, about 55% of the RAM chips have been defective. Fifty new chips are being tested.

a) How many chips would you expect to be defective out of 50?

b) Draw a rough sketch of the binomial distribution. Is the distribution skewed right, skewed left, or approximately symmetrical?

c) Would you be surprised if only 20 of the chips were defective? [*Hint*: Calculate $P(x \leq 20 \mid n = 50$, $\pi = 0.55)$.]

5.3 A contractor submits bids on construction projects and there are always other contractors bidding on the same projects. Assume that the long-run chances of this contractor's bid being the one selected are one of five. What is the probability that this contractor's bid will be selected in exactly two of the next four projects? Explain.

5.4 Thirty percent of the applicants for a certain job are from minority groups. What is the probability that five applicants, selected at random, will include exactly two people from a minority group?

5.5 Use Table I in Appendix C for the following:

a) Sketch the binomial p.m.f. and the binomial c.m.f. for $n = 8$ and $\pi = 0.40$.

b) What is the probability $P(x = 7)$ for the parameters in part (a)? What is the probability $P(x \geq 7)$?

c) Find the mean and the variance of this distribution.

5.6 Use Formula 5.1 to determine the binomial mass function for the parameters $n = 5$, $\pi = 0.50$. Check your answer with Table I. Sketch both the mass function and the cumulative function for these parameters.

5.7 An audit was conducted of 22,395 invoices belonging to Anco Industries, Inc. The audit looked at Anco invoices to determine whether the correct excise tax had been paid on a new product, for the period 1990–1992. A sample of 165 invoices indicated that Anco had underpaid on 28 of the invoices and had overpaid on 15.

a) How many of the population of 22,395 would you estimate were underpaid? How many would you estimate were overpaid?

b) If the average underpayment was $10.20 and the average overpayment was $1.81, what does Anco owe in back excise taxes (excluding interest and penalties)?

5.8 A direct-mailing marketing approach has, in the past, resulted in sales to 1% of the customers receiving the mailing.

a) If 99,000 ads are mailed, how many sales would be expected?

b) What is the lowest number and highest number of sales you would expect? (*Hint*: Use $\mu \pm 2\sigma$.)

5.9 Use the binomial distribution program contained in a computer statistical package to answer the following questions.

a) Find $P(x = 25)$ when $n = 37$ and $p = 0.60$.

b) Find $P(x \geq 25)$ and $P(x < 25)$ when $n = 37$ and $p = 0.60$.

c) Find $P(x \geq 133)$ when $n = 400$ and $p = 0.30$.

d) Find $P(x = 10) + P(x < 5)$ when $n = 19$ and $p = 0.40$.

5.10 Five products are selected from a very large group of a certain kind. If 40% of the products are defective, what is the probability that fewer than two or more than three of the five selected will be defective?

5.11 A bank estimates that one customer in four who visits the main office will require services lasting more than four minutes. A line at the main office has six customers. What is the probability, for this line, that

a) exactly three customers will take longer than four minutes?

b) at least three customers will take longer than four minutes?

c) at most three customers will take longer than four minutes?

d) two, three, or four customers take longer?

e) What is the expected number of customers taking longer than four minutes? What is the variance?

5.12 If a manufacturing process is working properly, only 10% of the items produced will be defective.

a) You take a random sample of five items. What is the probability that exactly two of these will be defective?

b) Suppose you select 25 items at random. What is the expected number of defectives?

5.13 A certain corporation claims that, on the basis of past trends, four of every five of their new employees will remain with the company at least five years. Would you dispute this claim if only 13 of 20 new employees last five years or longer? [*Hint:* Calculate $P(x \leq 13 \mid \pi = 0.80)$ using Table I, or using a computer package.]

5.14 As a restaurant owner, you are trying to decide how much seating to allocate to nonsmokers versus smokers. Your estimate is that, on the average, 40% of your customers will request the smoking section. You decide to check on 100 randomly selected customers tonight.

a) What is the probability that the percentage of smokers will be at least 35% and no more than 45%, assuming your 40% guess is correct?

b) Would you doubt the 40% guess if the percentage of smokers is 50% in your sample tonight? [*Hint:* Calculate $P(x \geq 50)$.]

c) Explain why the binomial assumptions might be violated when randomly selecting customers on a given night.

5.15 A bakery was fined for distributing consistently underweight loaves of bread. Suppose that this bakery claims that the authorities just took a *bad sample* and that in reality 50% of their loaves are either of exactly the correct weight or slightly overweight.

a) If, in a random sample of 100 loaves, 67 are underweight, would you support the bakery's claim? Explain.

b) Suppose y is the number of loaves that are underweight in a sample of 100. How large does y have to be before *you* start disbelieving the bakery's claim?

5.16 A Burger King TV ad says that people prefer broiling to frying by a 3:1 ratio. In other words, the probability of preferring broiling is $\pi = \frac{3}{4} = 0.75$. A critic of this ad campaign says that people are equally divided ($\pi = 0.50$). A sample of 50 people resulted in 30 who say they prefer broiling. Do these results tend to support Burger King or the critic? [*Hint:* Calculate $P(x \geq 30 \mid \pi = 0.50)$ and $P(x \leq 30 \mid \pi = 0.75)$.]

5.17 The manager of a new grocery store is giving out a prize to each customer who enters between noon and 1 p.m. Each customer draws from a box of coupons. Seventy-five percent of the coupons are for a free medium-sized soft drink, and 25% are for a free pizza. Four customers enter, and each one draws one coupon. The number of customers drawing a free pizza will be designated x.

a) Find the probability distribution of x and sketch its cumulative mass function.

b) Find the probability that at least two pizzas will be drawn from among the four customers.

5.18 During May, the probability that a certain realtor sells a house on any given day is 0.40. Only one house can be sold each day. What is the probability, on three randomly selected days in May, that this realtor will sell exactly two houses?

5.19 Last year, two out of every three customers who made telephone orders from a mail-order company called during the day. The phone lines are open 24 hours per day.

a) Would you conclude that this year the percentage is different if a random sample of 20 customers revealed that eight phone orders were *not* made during the day?

b) Would you be surprised if only eight of the 20 customers in part (a) *had* called during the day?

section 5.7 # The Hypergeometric Distribution

As we have indicated, the binomial distribution has widespread applications in many different areas, particularly in problems concerned with sampling. For such applications, use of the binomial distribution usually requires the assumption that one is sampling *with replacement*, because π must remain constant from trial to trial. However, many practical sampling problems involve sampling *without replacement*. Fortunately, if n is not too large in relation to the population size, the binomial can still be used because it provides a good approximation to the correct answer. However, in cases where *sampling is without replacement and the sample size exceeds 5% of the population size*, this approximation is not sufficiently accurate, and it is necessary to use the **hypergeometric distribution** to determine the correct probability. The hypergeometric distribution applies to problems in which there are two or more different kinds of elements in a finite population. Let us consider the case in which there are two different types of elements, N_1 of the first type and N_2 of the second type. The probability of drawing a sample of x_1 of this first type of element and x_2 of the second type is given by the **hypergeometric p.m.f.:**

Hypergeometric p.m.f.:

$$P(x_1 \text{ out of } N_1 \text{ and } x_2 \text{ out of } N_2) = \frac{(_{N_1}C_{x_1}) \cdot (_{N_2}C_{x_2})}{_{(N_1+N_2)}C_{(x_1+x_2)}} \qquad (5.5)$$

Formula 5.5 is a direct result of applying the counting and probability rules from Chapter 3. The first term in the numerator is the number of combinations of N_1 objects taken x_1 at a time, while the second term is the number of combinations of N_2 objects taken x_2 at a time. By the basic counting rule, we multiply

$$(_{N_1}C_{x_1}) \cdot (_{N_2}C_{x_2})$$

to find the total number of combinations of *both* x_1 out of N_1 *and* x_2 out of N_2. The denominator is the total number of combinations of $(N_1 + N_2)$ objects taken $(x_1 + x_2)$ at a time.

Example of the Hypergeometric Distribution

❑ **EXAMPLE 5.8**   Let's apply the hypergeometric distribution to a production process in which electrical components are produced in lots of 50. If this process is working correctly, there will be no defective items among the 50 produced. Let us assume, however, that at random intervals the process begins to malfunction, so that some of the components produced thereafter are defective. Since inspecting each and every one of the 50 items in a lot is relatively expensive, the hypergeometric distribution can be used to assess the probability that a random sample will detect defective components. Suppose, for example, that the process has, in fact, been malfunctioning, and exactly five components in a particular lot are defective. What is the probability that exactly one of these five defectives will appear in a sample of four randomly selected components? That is, what is the probability that a sample of four contains exactly one defective and three good components? This probability, that the sample contains $x_1 = 1$ of the $N_1 = 5$ defective components and $x_2 = 3$ of the $N_2 = 45$ good components, is given by the hypergeometric p.m.f.:

$$P(1 \text{ defective and 3 good}) = \frac{(_5C_1) \cdot (_{45}C_3)}{_{(5+45)}C_{(1+3)}} = \frac{(_5C_1) \cdot (_{45}C_3)}{_{50}C_4}$$

$$= \frac{(5!/1!4!) \times (45!/3!42!)}{50!/4!46!} = 0.308$$

Similarly, one might want to calculate the probability of encountering two or fewer defectives in a random sample of four components:

$P(2 \text{ or fewer defectives})$

$= P(0 \text{ defectives}) + P(1 \text{ defective}) + P(2 \text{ defectives})$

$= \dfrac{(_5C_0) \cdot (_{45}C_4)}{_{50}C_4} + \dfrac{(_5C_1) \cdot (_{45}C_3)}{_{50}C_4} + \dfrac{(_5C_2) \cdot (_{45}C_2)}{_{50}C_4}$

$= \dfrac{(5!/0!5!) \cdot (45!/4!41!) + (5!/1!4!) \cdot (45!3!42!) + (5!/2!3!) \cdot (45!/2!43!)}{50!/4!46!}$

$= 0.998$

This probability indicates that two or fewer defectives is highly likely (99.8% chance). ∎

Similarities of the Hypergeometric and the Binomial Distributions

We should emphasize once more that the critical assumption implied by the way probabilities are calculated in the hypergeometric distribution is that *sampling takes place from a finite population, without replacement.* In terms of the present example, this means that the probability of finding a defective *changes* after each one of the four items is inspected. For instance, the probability that the first item selected is defective, assuming a random sample, is 5/50, or 0.10. If this item is, in fact, defective, then there are only four defectives remaining, so that on the second draw the probability of receiving a defective is 4/49, or 0.082. In this way, the experimental situation differs from the binomial situation, where the trials are independent — that is, where the probabilities π and $1 - \pi$ do not change during the trials.

Since calculating hypergeometric probabilities involves tedious arithmetic, sampling experiments are generally devised, whenever possible, so that the binomial distribution can be used instead. That is, experiments involve either infinite populations, or sampling with replacement, or sample sizes of 5% or less of the population. In the latter case, it makes little difference whether the binomial or hypergeometric distribution is used, although the hypergeometric always gives the exact answer. Table 5.5 summarizes these differences.

TABLE 5.5   Summary of Hypergeometric vs. Binomial Distribution

Distribution	Assumptions	Formula
Binomial	Sampling with replacement or from an infinite population (for practical purposes, $n \leq 5\%$ of N). π is a constant.	$_nC_x\pi^x(1 - \pi)^{n-x}$
Hypergeometric	Sampling without replacement from a finite population. π changes with each sample observation.	$\dfrac{(_{N_1}C_{x_1}) \cdot (_{N_2}C_{x_2})}{_{(N_1+N_2)}C_{(x_1+x_2)}}$

PROBLEMS

5.20 The dean of the business school at Concordia University has been asked to select three students for a certain committee. Twenty juniors volunteer to be on this committee, as do 30 seniors. If the dean selects the three students randomly from the total group of 50 volunteers, what is the probability that one junior and two senior students will be selected?

5.21 In Las Vegas, gambling is big business. One of the popular games is poker, in which it is possible to calculate certain probabilities when the number of decks being used is known. Assuming that only a single deck is used, calculate the following probabilities.

a) A full house consisting of three aces and two kings

b) Four of a kind consisting of four aces and one king

c) Four of a kind consisting of four aces and any other card

5.22 A university department has three assistant professors, two associate professors, and four full professors. The student newspaper randomly picks five of these professors to interview. What is the probability that they will select two assistant professors, one associate professor, and two full professors? [*Hint*: Use an extension of the hypergeometric Formula 5.5 to three categories.]

5.23 Suppose a committee of six is to be chosen from ten people, five of whom are Conservatives and five of whom are NDP.

a) If the committee is to be chosen by random selection, what is the probability that there will be three NDP and three Conservatives on the committee?

b) What is the probability that a majority of the committee members will be NDP?

5.24 Brand B Aspirin Company decides to randomly select 10 out of 100 doctors working in a large hospital. If 50% of the 100 doctors actually prefer brand B, what is the probability that the results of the sample will find that 9 out of 10 doctors surveyed prefer brand B?

5.25 Some computer programs exist for calculating hypergeometric probabilities. Solve problem 5.23 (a) by finding and then using such a statistical program.

5.26 A company selling magazine subscriptions has offered numerous prizes to people who return a special envelope, with either a yes sticker (indicating they want to subscribe) or a no sticker. Thirty percent of several thousand respondents use the yes sticker. In a list of the ten top prizes, you later find that eight of these people had returned the yes sticker. Does it appear that the selection of winners was random? [*Hint*: Determine the probability of eight *or more* yes stickers among 10 winners.]

5.27 How does the hypergeometric distribution differ from the binomial distribution? Under what circumstances is the hypergeometric appropriate? Under what circumstances is the binomial appropriate?

5.28 Suppose that in a production run of ten home air-conditioning units, three are defective. A sample of three units is to be randomly drawn from the ten. What is the probability of receiving *at least* one defective if the samples are drawn:

a) with replacement

b) without replacement

5.29 Redo Problem 5.20 using a binomial approximation. In this case, let the probability that a junior will be selected be $\pi = 20/50$, and let $1 - \pi = 30/50$ represent the probability that a senior is selected. There are $n = 3$ trials, and you need to calculate $P(x = 1)$. Compare this value with your answer to Problem 5.20.

5.30 Redo Problem 5.24 using a binomial approximation. Let the probability that a doctor prefers brand B be $\pi = 0.50$, and calculate $P(x = 9)$ assuming $n = 10$.

5.31 Redo Problem 5.23(a) using the binomial distribution. Why is this approximation not a good one?

5.32 Assume that 2,073 of the 10,000 customers of the Easy Charge Company from Problem 3.22 received a cash advance during September. You take a random sample of 100 of their 10,000 customers.

a) Write down the hypergeometric expression representing the probability that 21% of the sample will be customers who received a cash advance.

b) Find the binomial probability that best approximates the hypergeometric probability presented in part (a).

section 5.8 — The Poisson Distribution

Another important discrete distribution, the **Poisson distribution,** has recently been found to have a fairly wide range of applications, especially in the area of operations research. This distribution was named for its originator, the French mathematician S. D. Poisson (1781–1840), who described its use in a paper written in 1837. Its rather morbid first applications indicated that the Poisson distribution quite accurately described the probability of deaths in the Prussian army resulting from the kick of a horse, as well as the number of suicides among women and children. More recent and useful applications involve the rates of arrivals at a service facility or requests for service at that facility, as well as the rate at which this service is provided. Examples of such successful applications of the Poisson distribution include problems concerning the number of arrivals or requests for service per unit time at tollbooths on an expressway, checkout counters in a supermarket, teller windows in a bank, and runways in an airport.

In examples of the above nature, the Poisson distribution can be used to determine the probability of x occurrences (arrivals or service completions) per unit time if four basic assumptions are met. First, it must be possible to divide the time interval being used into a large number of small subintervals in such a manner that the probability of an occurrence in each of these subintervals is very small. Second, the probability of an occurrence in each of the subintervals must remain constant throughout the time period being considered. Third, the probability of two or more occurrences in each subinterval must be small enough to be ignored. Fourth, an occurrence or nonoccurrence in one subinterval must not affect the occurrence or nonoccurrence in any other subinterval — the occurrences must be independent.

Of these four assumptions, numbers (1) and (3) are general enough to apply to almost any setting involving arrivals over time. However, the assumptions that occurrences are constant over time and independent are much less likely to be met in potential applications of the Poisson distribution. Nevertheless, the Poisson distribution does seem to apply in a surprisingly large variety of different situations.

◘ EXAMPLE 5.9 Consider the number of arrivals per hour at a bank, and assume that we divide a given hour into intervals of one second. Assume also that the *probability* that a customer will arrive during any given second is very small and remains constant throughout the one-hour period. Furthermore, assume that only one customer can arrive in a given second and that the number of arrivals in a given time period is independent of the number of arrivals in any *other* time period (customers do not turn away because of long lines). Under these circumstances, the number of arrivals in the one-hour period follows the Poisson distribution. These four assumptions and how they fit the bank example are summarized below.

■

Parameters of the Poisson Distribution

Examples of the Poisson distribution such as those given above pertain to the probability of x occurrences (arrivals or service completions) *per unit of time*.[5] The only parameter necessary to characterize a population described by the Poisson distribution is the *mean rate* at which events occur. We shall use the Greek letter

---

[5] The Poisson distribution can also be applied to problems involving the number of occurrences of a random variable for a given unit of *area*, such as the number of typographical errors on a page, the number of white blood cells in a blood suspension, the number of flaws in a fabric, or the number of imperfections in a surface of wood, metal, or paint. The Poisson distribution can be derived from the binomial distribution by letting the number of trials (n) go to infinity and holding $n \cdot \pi$ constant. When π is small, the Poisson distribution often provides a good approximation to the binomial.

TABLE 5.6   An Application of the Poisson Distribution

Assumption	Bank Example
1. Possible to divide time interval of interest into many small subintervals.	1. Can divide the hour into subintervals of one second each.
2. Probability of an occurrence remains constant throughout the time intervals.	2. The hour is one in which the most reasonable anticipation is a steady flow of customers.
3. Probability of two or more occurrences in a subinterval is small enough to be ignored.	3. Impossible for two people to enter the bank simultaneously, for example, in the same second.
4. Independence of occurrences.	4. Arrivals at the bank are not influenced by the length of the lines.

---

lambda, λ, for this parameter. Lambda can be defined as the mean rate of occurrence for any convenient unit of time — one minute, ten minutes, an hour, a day, or even a year. A value of $\lambda = 2.3$, for example, could indicate that there are, on the average, 2.3 requests for service in a particular bank every minute, or 2.3 customers arriving at a restaurant every 10 minutes. For practical applications, the mean rate at which events occur must be determined empirically. That is, λ must be known in advance, perhaps on the basis of a previous study of the situation. Once λ is known, the **probability mass function for the Poisson distribution** can be used to determine the probability that exactly x occurrences, or events, take place in the specified time interval. The value of λ must be positive, and x can assume any integer value from 0 to infinity.

Poisson p.m.f.:

$$P(x = x) = \begin{cases} \frac{e^{-\lambda}\lambda^x}{x!} & \text{for } x = 0, 1, 2, \ldots, \infty, \ \lambda > 0 \\ 0 & \text{otherwise} \end{cases} \qquad (5.6)$$

☐ **EXAMPLE 5.10**   Assume that the bank discussed previously knows from past experience that between 10 and 11 a.m. of each day, the mean arrival rate is $\lambda = 60$ customers per hour. Suppose that the bank wants to determine the probability that exactly two customers will arrive in a given one-minute time interval between 10 and 11 a.m. Because arrivals are assumed to be constant over a given time interval, the rate of 60 per hour is equivalent to an arrival rate of $\lambda = 1$ customer per minute. Substituting $\lambda = 1$ and $x = 2$ into Formula 5.6 yields:

$$P(2 \text{ arrivals}) = \frac{e^{-1}(1)^2}{2!} = \frac{1}{2e}$$

Since e equals (approximately) 2.71828, we obtain the following probability:

$$P(2 \text{ arrivals}) = \frac{1}{2(2.71828)} = 0.1839$$

Similarly, the bank might want to calculate $P(2 \text{ or fewer arrivals})$:

$$P(2 \text{ or fewer arrivals}) = P(0) + P(1) + P(2)$$

$$= \frac{e^{-1}(1)^0}{0!} + \frac{e^{-1}(1)^1}{1!} + \frac{e^{-1}(1)^2}{2!}$$
$$= 0.3679 + 0.3679 + 0.1839 = 0.9197 \qquad \blacksquare$$

As was the case for the binomial, Poisson probabilities have been extensively tabulated, so that the task of calculating probabilities using Formula 5.6 can be avoided. Table II gives the probabilities for selected values of λ from $\lambda = 0.01$ to $\lambda = 20.0$. The probability values for the above example are shown in Table II under the heading $\lambda = 1.0$. These values are graphed in part (a) of Figure 5.5.

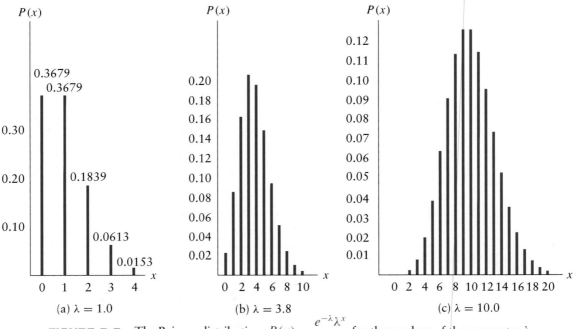

FIGURE 5.5 The Poisson distribution: $P(x) = \dfrac{e^{-\lambda}\lambda^x}{x!}$ for three values of the parameter λ

Each value of the parameter λ represents a different member of the family of Poisson distributions. In a supermarket, for example, the mean number of arrivals per minute may be $\lambda = 3.8$. In this case, the probability of observing exactly one arrival in a randomly selected minute would be 0.0850, determined from Table II, using $x = 1$ and $\lambda = 3.8$ as shown in Figure 5.6(b). As a final example, the mean number of arrivals per minute might be $\lambda = 10$ at a city subway station during rush hour. The probability of observing two or fewer arrivals in a randomly selected minute during this period would be found by summing the values for $x = 0, 1$, and 2 in Table II under $\lambda = 10$. This probability is 0.0028, indicating quite a rare event [see part (c) of Figure 5.5].

Note that in Figure 5.5 all probabilities are nonzero, and only a discrete number of values of x have positive probabilities. Thus, x_{Poisson} is an example of a discrete random variable having an infinite number of outcomes. As for all discrete mass functions, the sum of the probabilities over all values of x must be 1.0. The graphs in Figure 5.5 demonstrate that this distribution has positive skewness, since x cannot be lower than zero but may be any positive integer. However, Figure 5.5(c) also indicates that when λ is not too close to zero, the shape of the Poisson distribution appears to be fairly symmetrical.

Mean and Variance of the Poisson Distribution

The Poisson distribution has only one parameter (λ), so the mean and variance of the distribution must be functions of this parameter. Indeed, λ is defined as the *mean* number of occurrences of the particular event per time or space unit. Therefore, the **mean of the Poisson distribution** is λ. What is not obvious at all, but is proven in many statistics books, is that **the variance of the Poisson distribution** *is also identically equal to* λ.

Mean and variance of the Poisson distribution

$$\text{Poisson mean: } \mu = \lambda$$
$$\text{Poisson variance: } \sigma^2 = V(x_{\text{Poisson}}) = \lambda$$

(5.7)

Thus, if a value of $\lambda = 1.0$ indicates that customers are arriving at a bank according to a Poisson probability distribution at an average rate of 1.0 customer every minute, then the variance of these arrivals is also 1.0.

Determining a Poisson Distribution in a Practical Situation

Suppose that it has been suggested to the manager of a large supermarket that arrivals at the checkout counters might follow a Poisson distribution during certain periods of time. The manager investigates this probability by checking the reasonableness of the four basic assumptions listed earlier, especially assumptions number 2 (constant probability) and 4 (independence). After careful consideration, the time interval 4–6 p.m., Monday–Friday, is selected as an appropriate period during which all four assumptions seem reasonable.

The next step this manager might take is the collection of observations concerning the number of arrivals within the two hours from 4–6 p.m. Rather than count the number of customers arriving for many different *two-hour* time periods, arrivals are recorded in each of 100 *one-minute* periods, randomly selected over several days, between 4 and 6 p.m. This procedure is reasonable, since arrivals are assumed to be constant over the two-hour period; hence it makes no difference, theoretically at least, what time unit is used. The number (x) of customers arriving per minute in this study ranged from 0 to 10, as shown in Table 5.7. For example, the third line of Table 5.7 indicates that on 19 different occasions there were exactly two arrivals in the one-minute period. The fourth row indicates that there were exactly three arrivals on 23 different occasions.

Recall that, for the Poisson distribution, both μ and σ^2 are equal. Hence, in checking to see if the data in Table 5.7 follow a Poisson distribution, the manager might first wish to see if $\mu = \sigma^2$. Column (4) in this table gives the appropriate values for calculating μ. Using Formula 2.4, the calculated value of μ is as follows:

$$\mu = \sum_{i=1}^{k} x_i \left(\frac{f_i}{N}\right) = 3.79$$

The variance of the data in Table 5.7 can be calculated by using Formula 4.4. This formula applied to the data in Table 5.7 gives the following results:

$$V[x] = \sigma^2 = 3.91$$

TABLE 5.7   Arrivals at a Supermarket Counter

(1) Arrivals x	(2) Observed Frequency	(3) $\dfrac{f}{N}$	(4) $x\left(\dfrac{f}{N}\right)$
0	1	0.01	0.00
1	8	0.08	0.08
2	19	0.19	0.38
3	23	0.23	0.69
4	17	0.17	0.68
5	15	0.15	0.75
6	8	0.08	0.48
7	3	0.03	0.21
8	3	0.03	0.24
9	2	0.02	0.18
10	1	0.01	0.10
Sum	100	1.00	3.79

We see that for these data, μ and σ^2 are very nearly equal in value (3.79 vs. 3.91). Theoretically, they are supposed to be *exactly* equal, but in a sample of just 100 time periods we would not expect the observed value of either μ or σ^2 to *exactly* equal the population parameter λ. The closeness of μ to σ^2 in this case is encouraging enough for the store manager to make the most important test, namely, to see whether the observed relative frequencies correspond to the theoretical frequencies for the Poisson distribution. To make this comparison, suppose we assume that $\lambda = 3.8$. Note that it is not known from the data in Table 5.7 whether $\lambda = 3.79$ or 3.91, or some other value, and so the choice of $\lambda = 3.8$ is somewhat arbitrary. Now, if the number of arrivals in these 100 one-minute periods does follow a Poisson distribution with $\lambda = 3.8$, we would expect the observed frequencies in column (3) of Table 5.7 to correspond closely to the probabilities of the following Poisson distribution:

$$P(x) = \frac{e^{-3.8}(3.8)^x}{x!}$$

These values, from Table II under the heading $\lambda = 3.8$, are reproduced in Table 5.8. We see in Table 5.8 that the observed relative frequencies correspond quite well to the Poisson values for $\lambda = 3.8$. A good exercise for the reader at this point would be to verify, for the probabilities shown in the last column of Table 5.8, that the mean and variance are equal — in other words, that $\mu = \sigma^2 = 3.8$. To determine the probability within intervals about the mean, we need the standard deviation. The standard deviation of the Poisson distribution when $\lambda = 3.8$ is:

$$\sigma = \sqrt{3.8} = 1.95$$

Using Table 5.8, column (3), the intervals

$$\mu \pm 1\sigma = 3.8 \pm 1.95 \quad \text{and} \quad \mu \pm 2\sigma = 3.8 \pm 2(1.95)$$

are shown in Table 5.9 to contain 71% and 96% of the probability, respectively. These are again close to our rule of thumb values of 0.68 and 0.95 for interpreting the meaning of the standard deviation.

TABLE 5.8 Comparison of Observed Relative Frequencies with the Theoretical Frequencies of the Poisson Distribution

(1) Arrivals	(2) Relative Frequency	(3) Poisson Value $P(x) = e^{-3.8}(3.8)^x/x!$
0	0.010	0.0224
1	0.080	0.0850
2	0.190	0.1615
3	0.230	0.2046
4	0.170	0.1944
5	0.150	0.1477
6	0.080	0.0936
7	0.030	0.0508
8	0.030	0.0241
9	0.020	0.0102
10	0.010	0.0039
11	0.000	0.0013
12	0.000	0.0004
13	0.000	0.0001
Sum	1.000	1.0000

TABLE 5.9 The Probability Contained within One Standard Deviation from the Mean

Interval	Probability Included
$\mu \pm 1\sigma = 3.80 \pm (1.95) = 1.85$ to 5.75	$\sum_{x=2}^{5} P(x) = 0.7082$
$\mu \pm 2\sigma = 3.80 \pm 2(1.95) = 0$ to 7.70	$\sum_{x=0}^{7} P(x) = 0.9600$

section 5.9

Using the Computer for Poisson Problems

In this section, we demonstrate use of the Doane statistical package to determine Poisson probabilities. Specifically, we reproduce Table 5.8, where $\mu = 3.8$.

First access the program menu, then select the menu number of the Poisson distribution (Pois). The program will then ask: "What is the mean (Mu)?" Our response is 3.8, which gives the following table of exact and cumulative probabilities. Probabilities less than 0.0001 have been omitted. Note that the probabilities in the second column are the same as those in Table 5.8.

r	Exact $P(X=r)$	Cumulative $P(X \geq r)$	Cumulative $P(X < r)$
0	0.0224	1.0000	0.0000
1	0.0850	0.9776	0.0224
2	0.1615	0.8926	0.1074
3	0.2046	0.7311	0.2689
4	0.1944	0.5265	0.4735
5	0.1477	0.3322	0.6678
6	0.0936	0.1844	0.8156
7	0.0508	0.0909	0.9091
8	0.0241	0.0401	0.9599
9	0.0102	0.0160	0.9840
10	0.0039	0.0058	0.9942
11	0.0013	0.0019	0.9981
12	0.0004	0.0006	0.9994
13	0.0001	0.0002	0.9998

PROBLEMS

5.33 In an airport, an average of 8.5 pieces of baggage per minute are handled, in accordance with a Poisson distribution. Find the probability that ten pieces of baggage are handled in a selected minute of time.

5.34 Suppose that in a textile manufacturing process, an average of two flaws per ten running yards of material have appeared. What is the probability that a given ten-yard segment will have 0 or 1 defects, if the number of flaws follows a Poisson distribution?

5.35 On the average, 2.3 telephone calls per minute are made through a central switchboard, following a Poisson distribution. What is the probability that during a given minute exactly two calls will be made?

5.36 Use Formula 5.6 to determine the probabilities associated with the Poisson distribution for $\lambda = 2.0$. Sketch both the mass and the cumulative distributions. Check your answers by using Table II of Appendix C. What are the mean and variance of this distribution?

5.37 For the Poisson distribution:

a) Find what percent lies within $\mu \pm 1\sigma$ and $\mu \pm 2\sigma$ when $\lambda = 1$. How do these values compare with the rule of thumb given in Chapter 1?

b) Repeat part (a) for $\lambda = 4$ and $\lambda = 9$, and comment on why you think the percents are getting closer to the rule of thumb.

5.38 A barbershop has, on the average, ten customers between 8:00 and 9:00 each morning that it is open. Customers arrive according to a Poisson distribution. Use a computer and/or Table II to answer the following questions:

a) What is the probability that the barbershop will have exactly ten customers between these times on a given morning?

b) What is the probability that the barbershop will have more than 12 customers in this time period?

c) What is the probability that the barbershop will have fewer than six customers?

5.39 Airplanes arrive at a small airport at the rate of three per hour, according to a Poisson distribution. Use a computer and/or Table II to answer the following questions:

a) What is the probability that there will be exactly three arrivals in a given one-hour period?

b) What is the probability that there will be exactly six arrivals in a *two-hour* period?

c) Explain, in words, why it is more probable to have exactly three arrivals in one hour than it is to have exactly six arrivals in two hours.

5.40 Consider the values of $P(x)$ for $\lambda = 1$ in Table II.

a) Show for these values that $E[x] = \lambda = 1$.

b) Show that $V[x] = \lambda = 1$.

CHAPTER SUMMARY

KEY TERMS AND EXPRESSIONS

Binomial distribution: Discrete probability mass function (p.m.f.) involving independent, repeated, Bernoulli trials. A Bernoulli trial is a replication of an experiment in which one of two mutually exclusive and exhaustive outcomes must take place.

Binomial formula: $P(x) = {}_nC_x\pi^x(1-\pi)^{n-x}$

Binomial parameters:

$$\mu = E[x] = n\pi$$
$$\sigma^2 = V[x] = n\pi(1-\pi)$$

Expectations for a binomial proportion:

$$p = \frac{x}{n}; \quad E[p] = \pi; \quad V[p] = \frac{\pi(1-\pi)}{n}$$

Hypergeometric distribution: Discrete probability mass function (p.m.f.) involving sampling without replacement from a finite population. Involved with calculating probabilities such as x_1 out of N_1 and x_2 out of N_2.

Hypergeometric p.m.f.:

$$P(x_1 \text{ out of } N_1 \text{ and } x_2 \text{ out of } N_2) = \frac{({}_{N_1}C_{x_1})\cdot({}_{N_2}C_{x_2})}{{}_{(N_1+N_2)}C_{(x_1+x_2)}}$$

Poisson distribution: Discrete p.m.f. involving events which take place relatively infrequently when only a small subinterval of time is being considered.

Poisson p.m.f.:

$$P(x) = \begin{cases} \frac{e^{-\lambda}\lambda^x}{x!} & x = 0, 1, 2, \ldots \\ 0 & \text{otherwise} \end{cases}$$

Mean and variance of the Poisson distribution:

$$\mu = E[x] = \lambda$$
$$\sigma^2 = V[x] = \lambda$$

EXERCISES

♦ **5.41** The airline industry has determined, through extensive studies, that the proportion of passengers who make reservations but do not claim or cancel them is 0.25. Flight 505, with a capacity of 300 passengers, has 380 persons on reservation.

a) What is the expected number of seats claimed against reservations for this flight?

b) What is the probability that the proportion of reservations claimed will be more than 0.75?

c) What is the probability that the flight will be able to accommodate everyone who shows up with a reservation?

♦ **5.42** The manager of an insurance company has determined that in a typical day an agent can sell insurance, on the average, to 10% of the customers she visits. Assume that the agent will visit 20 customers on Monday and 20 on Tuesday.

a) Determine the probability that the agent will be able to sell insurance to at most one customer per day.

b) Determine the probability that she is able to sell insurance to at least four and at most six customers on Tuesday.

c) Determine the probability that she is not able to sell any insurance on either of the two days.

5.43 It is possible to generalize the binomial distribution to include the class of problems where there are more than just two outcomes. Suppose that there are k different (distinguishable) outcomes, and the probabilities of occurrence of these outcomes are $\pi_1, \pi_2, \ldots, \pi_k$. Assuming these k outcomes to be mutually exclusive and exhaustive, it must be true that $\pi_1 + \pi_2 + \cdots + \pi_k = 1$. Now, assume that we want to determine the (joint) probability of n_1 outcomes of the first kind, n_2 outcomes of the second kind, up to n_k outcomes of the kth kind, where $n = n_1 + n_2 + \cdots + n_k$. An extension of Formula 3.6 for combinations (${}_nC_x$) gives the number of ways these objects could occur in n trials, where $n = n_1 + n_2 + \cdots + n_k$. Multiplying this formula by the appropriate probabilities results in a probability distribution called the *multinomial distribution*.

Multinomial distribution:

$$P(n_1, n_2, \ldots, n_k) = \frac{n!}{n_1!n_2!\cdots n_k!}\pi_1^{n_1}\pi_2^{n_2}\cdots\pi_k^{n_k}$$

a) Use the multinomial distribution to determine the probability of receiving, in seven random draws (with replacement) from a hardware bin of bolts, two bolts of size A, four bolts of size B, and one bolt of size C. Inventory consists of 20 bolts of size A, 10 bolts of size B, and 5 bolts of size C.

b) Suppose the probability that an individual has type O blood is 0.45, the probability of type A is ˙0, the probability of type B is 0.10, and the probab ˙cy of type AB is 0.05. For six randomly selected donors at a blood bank, what is the probability that three people will have type O, two will have type A, and one will have type AB blood?

5.44 The Pascal (or negative binomial) distribution is appropriate when one is interested in determining the probability that n Bernoulli trials will be required to produce r successes. This probability is as follows:

$$P(n) = \frac{(n-1)!}{(r-1)!(n-r)!}\pi^r(1-\pi)^{n-r} \text{ for } n \geq r$$

For example, suppose an advertising agency is trying to evaluate the effects of a television commercial advertising swimming pool chlorine. A caller is assigned to contact, at random, residential dwellings in Phoenix, where 40% of the homes have pools.

a) What is the probability that it will take ten or fewer calls to find exactly five homes with pools? [Assume that all calls are answered politely.]

b) What is the average number of calls required in order to have five successes if $E[n] = r/\pi$?

c) What is the variance of the number of calls required in part (a) if $V[n] = r(1-\pi)/\pi^2$?

5.45 A company hiring systems analysts has found that, on the average, they hire one person out of every 12 who come for a second interview. On the basis of these data, what is the probability that they will hire at least one of the next four people who come for a second interview? Are the assumptions of the binomial reasonable for this application? Explain.

5.46 Assume the two baseball teams playing in the World Series are exactly evenly matched for each game in the series.

a) What is the most likely number of games to be played in a best-out-of-seven series?

b) What is the most likely number of games if one team is always a 3:1 favorite?

5.47 The expected value of x in a series of repeated Bernoulli trials is defined as follows:

$$E[x] = \sum_{x=0}^{n} x(_nC_x)\pi^x(1-\pi)^{n-x}$$

a) Use the above relationship to prove that the mean of the binomial distribution equals $n\pi$.

b) In the same manner, prove that the variance of the binomial distribution equals $n\pi(1-\pi)$.

5.48 A classical example of the Poisson distribution resulted from a study of the number of deaths from horse kicks in the Prussian Army from 1875 to 1894. The data for this example are shown in Table 5.10.

TABLE 5.10 Prussian Army (1875–1894) Death Rate Due to Horse Kicks

Deaths per Corps (per year)	Observed Frequency
0	144
1	91
2	32
3	11
4	2
5 and over	0
Total	280

a) Fit a Poisson distribution to this data. [*Hint:* Note that there were 196 deaths from the 280 observations; hence the mean death rate was $196/280 = 0.700$.] How good does the Poisson approximation appear to be?

b) Do the assumptions of the Poisson distribution seem reasonable in this problem? Explain.

5.49 Use Table I to determine the binomial probabilities for $n = 10$ and $\pi = 0.20$, and then use Table II to find the Poisson approximation to these probabilities. Comment on how good the Poisson approximation is in this case. Graph both distributions on the same sheet of paper.

5.50 Using the Poisson distribution in the third column of Table 5.8, show by calculation that its mean and variance are both equal to 3.8.

5.51 Assume that the customers of the Shark Loan Company (Exercise 2.40) arrive at the loan office at a rate of $\lambda = 12$ customers per day.

a) Graph the probability mass function for all values of x between 5 and 18, inclusive.

b) Suppose the people at Shark have noticed that approximately 50 people walk by their office each day. If we assume [from part (a)] that there is a constant probability that each of these people will enter, the binomial distribution can be used to describe the arrival rate.

  i) What is the appropriate value of π if we assume an average of 12 of the 50 people enter? What will μ and σ^2 be for this binomial distribution?

ii) Superimpose on your graph from part (a) the probability mass function of the binomial for values of x between 5 and 18.

5.52 Out of 10 salespeople, seven (call them group A) make sales on 20% of their calls. The other three (call them group B) make sales on 50% of their calls.

a) What is the average percentage of sales to calls for all ten salespeople?

b) Suppose the sales manager selects three of these salespeople at random to assign to a new territory. What is the probability that exactly two of them will be from group A?

c) Suppose we follow one of the salespeople in group A on the next five calls, each of which is considered independent of any of the others. What is the probability that this person makes more than one but fewer than four sales in those five calls?

5.53 Sears has tested ten Die Hard batteries, each five years old, to see whether each battery will start a car after sitting out in zero degree weather for 24 hours. On the basis of past experience, Sears estimates the probability to be 0.08 that a battery will not start the car. Find the binomial probability that five of the ten will fail. Use a Poisson approximation to solve this problem. Compare the variance of the binomial distribution for this problem with the variance of the Poisson distribution.

5.54 The following bridge hand almost broke up the 1955 world championship tournament because it occurred twice in the space of a few hours.

| Spades: | A, K, 9, 5 | Hearts: | Q, 8, 4 |
| Diamonds: | J, 7, 3 | Clubs: | 10, 6, 2 |

a) Write down an expression representing the probability of the occurrence of this hand, assuming the cards are dealt randomly.

b) Determine a nonprobabilistic explanation as to why such a bridge hand might have occurred twice in the 1955 world championship.

5.55 The following proofs are not easy. The reader interested in them may wish to consult a more mathematically oriented text.

a) Prove the following for the Poisson distribution.

$$E[x] = \sum_{x=0}^{\infty} x \frac{e^{-\lambda}\lambda^x}{x!} = \lambda$$

b) Prove the following for the Poisson distribution.

$$V[x] = \lambda$$

c) Prove the following for $\lambda = n\pi$ a constant.

$$\lim_{n\to\infty} {}_nC_x \pi^x (1-\pi)^{n-x} = \frac{e^{-\lambda}\lambda^x}{x!}$$

d) Prove the following for the binomial distribution.

$$\sum_{\text{all } x} P(x) = 1$$

5.56 A Certified Public Accountant has been asked by a client, a department store, to assist in determining the effects on customer service of eliminating a clerk in one department. The probability of a customer's arriving for service is the same at all moments in time regardless of what has happened in previous moments. If the Certified Public Accountant analyzes this queueing (waiting-line) problem mathematically, the frequency distribution generally used would be which of the following?

a) normal

b) binomial

c) hypergeometric

d) Poisson

USING THE COMPUTER

5.57 A university library has 2,000 fluorescent lights that fail at random times, independently of one another. The library custodian estimates the probability that each light fails on any given day to be 0.001. It takes the custodian 30 minutes to change a light. What is the probability that it will take the custodian longer than 2 hours to change all the lights that fail on any given day? Use the binomial distribution.

5.58 Repeat Problem 5.57 using a Poisson approximation.

5.59 The marketing department of Procter and Gamble mailed 1,000 questionnaires, one half to randomly selected low-income households, and one half to middle-income households. Out of the first 100 questionnaires returned, 65 were from the middle-income households, and 35 were from the low-income households. What is the probability of 65 or more questionnaires returned from the middle-income families if the two types of households have the same response rate?

CASE PROBLEM

5.60 The First National Bank is deciding on the amount of money to place in their MONEY MOVER machine each weekend. They obviously do not want to run short and have unhappy customers. On the other hand, they do not want to have too much, as they earn a considerable amount of interest each day by investing their *float* (uncommitted money). Customers of the bank can withdraw either $25 or $50 once during the weekend. The bank's vice president estimates that for each of their 15,200 customers, the probability is 0.01 that the customer will use the machine. About half of the customers withdraw $25, and half withdraw $50. The money is placed in the machine in packets of $25, so that a customer who wants $50 gets two packets of $25. The bank vice president decides to place enough money in the machine so that the probability of running short is less than 0.001. How much should be placed in the machine?

CHAPTER 6

Probability Theory: Continuous Random Variables

Introduction

Thus far, we have examined experiments involving only a discrete set of outcomes and limited ourselves to discrete probability values. As we indicated earlier, however, an outcome set can be continuous as well as discrete, which implies that the random variable in an experiment must be able to assume a continuous form. Fortunately, most probability theory is basically the same for discrete and continuous random variables, and the formulas presented in Chapters 3 and 4 hold for both cases.

Probability functions defined in terms of a continuous random variable are usually referred to as **probability density functions** (abbreviated **p.d.f.**), or *density functions*. In this chapter, we will discuss the similarities and differences between density functions for continuous random variables and the probability mass functions described in Chapters 4 and 5. Some of the more useful density functions, those used in applications dealing with a wide range of experimental situations and decision problems, will then be introduced.

Probability Density Functions

If an experiment can result in an infinite, noncountable number of outcomes, then the random variable defined must be continuous. Typically, whenever the value of a random variable is *measured* rather than *counted*, a continuous random variable is defined. Examples in which outcomes are measured rather than counted include the water level in a lake, the pressure in a steam boiler, the distance between two points, and the number of ounces in a cereal box. The values of the random variables in these examples can be any of an infinite number of values within a defined interval, $[a, b]$. If we redefine these examples as the *errors* (deviations from the mean) in measuring water level, pressure, distances, or ounces, then such a random variable could be any number from minus a to plus b (b could be infinity in some cases).

When we say a random variable can be *any* number between two limits, we mean any value is at least *theoretically* possible. For practical purposes, we usually cannot measure such variables with very great accuracy. For example, the length of long-distance business phone calls can, theoretically, be any number from zero to infinity. However, the time is usually recorded in minutes or in minutes and seconds. With electronic timing devices, the length of a long-distance call might be recorded to the nearest millisecond, but this degree of accuracy is usually not warranted. Hence, while such a variable is theoretically continuous, for measurement purposes it is more nearly discrete. We will see in this chapter that in such applications, continuous variables are often more convenient to manipulate than discrete variables.

Recall that, for a probability mass function, the value of $P(x = x)$ was represented by the *height* of the spike at the point $x = x$. One of the major differences between discrete and continuous probability distributions is that this representation no longer holds. As we will elaborate more thoroughly in this chapter, *probability for a continuous p.d.f. is represented by the area between the x-axis and the density function*.

To better understand the concept of a probability density function, consider the case of a business person who is trying to estimate the probabilities of various levels of sales for a new product to be marketed. In order to estimate the probability of sales as high as 7,000 units, this person decides to assess probabilities using seven different intervals of 1,000 units each. Let us assume that Table 6.1 shows this probability assessment, where x = number of possible sales of the new product.

This probability distribution can be represented in a histogram, just as was done in Chapter 1, and smoothed with a frequency polygon by connecting the class marks of the intervals. The resulting histogram is shown in Fig. 6.1.

TABLE 6.1   Probabilities of Sales

Interval [a,b]	Midpoint (Class Mark)	Probability
$0 < x \leq 1{,}000$	500	0.00
$1{,}000 < x \leq 2{,}000$	1,500	0.05
$2{,}000 < x \leq 3{,}000$	2,500	0.25
$3{,}000 < x \leq 4{,}000$	3,500	0.30
$4{,}000 < x \leq 5{,}000$	4,500	0.25
$5{,}000 < x \leq 6{,}000$	5,500	0.10
$6{,}000 < x \leq 7{,}000$	6,500	0.05
		Sum = 1.00

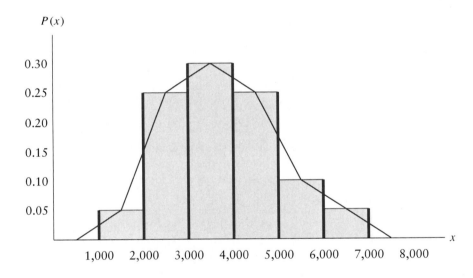

FIGURE 6.1   Frequency polygon and histogram based on Table 6.1

The choice of a class interval of size 1,000 for this problem was quite arbitrary. Almost any size interval could have been used. For example, suppose that we now decrease the width of the classes to an interval of, say, 500 or 250, or even to a class interval of 1. Figure 6.2 illustrates how the frequency polygon for these data changes as the width of the interval decreases (and, correspondingly, as the *number* of intervals increases). Let us denote the width of the class interval in a histogram as Δx (read "delta-x"), where $\Delta x = 1{,}000$ for Figure 6.1, $\Delta x = 500$ for Figure 6.2(a), and $\Delta x = 250$ for Figure 6.2(b). In these three figures, *the height of the histogram indicates the probability that x falls in the interval.* Thus, we can determine a probability such as $P(a \leq x \leq b)$ by summing the heights corresponding to each of the events that satisfy $\{a \leq x \leq b\}$.

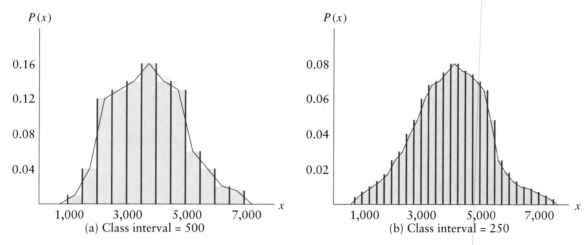

FIGURE 6.2 The frequency polygon for two different class sizes

Probability as an Area

Note what happens as $\Delta x \to 0$ in Figures 6.1, 6.2, and 6.3. As the size of the intervals becomes smaller and smaller, the frequency polygon begins to look more and more like a continuous function. Note particularly in Figure 6.2 that the sum of the *heights* of the histograms begins to closely approximate the *area* under the frequency polygon. Using calculus, it can be shown that at the limit, as $\Delta x \to 0$ (when the variable becomes continuous) the following is true:[1]

> The probability that the random variable x falls between the two values a and b, $P(a \leq x \leq b)$, exactly equals the area under the frequency polygon between a and b.

Figure 6.3 illustrates the transition from a discrete p.m.f. to a continuous probability density function (p.d.f.). In order to maintain a clear distinction between them, we will label the vertical axis for the mass function $P(x)$ and label the vertical axis for the density function $f(x)$. The value of $f(x)$ is thus the height of the continuous function at a specific point $x = x$.

As the width of the class interval decreases and becomes closer and closer to zero, the number of classes (or events) under consideration must increase until, at the limit (that is, when the interval size $\to$ zero) there are an *infinite* number of classes between any two values of x. The histogram, in this case, becomes an *infinite* number of infinitesimally narrow spikes set side by side. According to the rules of

---

[1] More formally, at the limit, as $\Delta x \to 0$, the width of the class interval is denoted by the symbol dx instead of Δx. The frequency polygon is now called a density function, and the height of the density function at $x = x$ is denoted as $f(x)$. Finally, the summation sign becomes an integral sign, $\int_a^b$, where this integral sign is interpreted to mean *the limit of summation as* $\Delta x \to 0$. Putting all this together, we obtain the following result for continous random variables:

$$P(a \leq x \leq b) = \lim_{\Delta x \to 0} \sum_a^b P(x)\Delta x = \int_b^a f(x)dx$$

$$= \text{Area under the curve from } a \text{ to } b$$

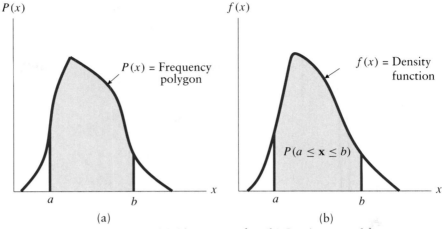

FIGURE 6.3   (a) Discrete p.m.f.   (b) Continuous p.d.f.

probability, the probability that any one of these spikes will occur is $(1/\infty)$, which is zero. Thus, an important fundamental rule of continuous random variables is the following rule:

> When the random variable is continuous, the probability that any one specific value takes place is zero.

Because the probability of a single point is now zero, we can determine probability values only for intervals, such as $P(a \leq x \leq b)$.

Note in Figure 6.3(b) that the frequency polygon is called a *density function* when the variable x is continuous. As we have indicated, the probability that x falls in the interval $a \leq x \leq b$ is given by the **area under the density function**, and not by the height of the density function. It is very important *not* to make the mistake of thinking that $f(x)$ represents probability. The value of $f(x)$ merely represents how high or dense the function is at any specified value of x. It cannot represent probability, for we already pointed out that $P(x = x) = 0$ in the continuous case.

> For continuous random variables:
>
> $$P(a \leq x \leq b) = \text{Area under } f(x) \text{ from } a \text{ to } b \qquad (6.1)$$

For a continuous random variable it makes no difference whether the endpoints a and b are included in the interval or not, since the probability of observing any one specific point, such as exactly a or exactly b, equals zero. Thus, for a continuous random variable:

$$P(a < x < b) = P(a \leq x < b) = P(a < x \leq b) = P(a \leq x \leq b)$$

A probability density function (p.d.f.) is thus the description of a population (an experiment) when the variable x is continuous just as a probability mass function is the description when x is discrete. The description of the population in the case of a p.d.f. must indicate the value of $f(x)$ for all possible values of x. Since there are an infinite number of values of x, a p.d.f. is usually not described by a table, but either by a graph such as Figure 6.3(b) or by a formula. Let us give an example of a function representing a p.d.f. Then, we specify the two properties that all probability density functions must satisfy.

□ EXAMPLE 6.1   The number of tons of crushed stone used by a state highway department each week varies between 50 tons and 300 tons, depending on the type of road projects underway and the weather during that week. Figure 6.4 shows a probability density function for the tons of crushed stone used per week, x, in units of 1,000 tons. Thus, $x = 0.20$ represents $0.20(1,000) = 200$ tons.

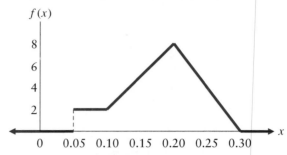

FIGURE 6.4   Probability density function for Example 6.1

The probability that values of x will occur is measured by the area under the probability density function, $f(x)$. The probability that x equals a specific value, say, $P(x = 0.15)$, is zero. Since a single point has no mathematical width, the area (height × width) above it is zero regardless of the height. Thus, the probability that the highway department will use exactly $0.15(1,000) = 150$ tons in a given week is zero.

Also, it is obvious in Figure 6.4 that probability is not measured by the height of $f(x)$ alone. At the point $x = 0.20$ (200 tons), the height of $f(x)$ is 8.0. This cannot measure probability, since a probability value must always lie between zero and one.   ■

A probability density function must satisfy two basic properties that are similar to those for a probability mass function. The major difference between the two is that, while neither $f(x)$ nor $P(x)$ can be negative, the values of $f(x)$ do not necessarily have to be less than or equal to 1. On the other hand, it must be true that the total area under $f(x)$, from $-\infty$ to $+\infty$, has to equal 1 for the same reason that $\Sigma P(x) = 1$ in the case of a discrete random variable.

Properties of all probability density functions:

1. $f(x) \geq 0$ The density function is never negative.
2. $P(-\infty \leq x \leq \infty) = 1$ The total area under the density
                                           function always equals 1.[2]

---

[2] This property can be expressed, using calculus, as follows:

$$\int_{-\infty}^{\infty} f(x)\,dx = 1$$

Let us examine Figure 6.5 to show how these properties hold for the probability density function of Example 6.1. First, the function $f(x)$ is always positive. It never drops below the x-axis. Next, using geometry to find the area under the function, we see that the sum is 1 for the areas of the subdivided rectangles and triangles. For example, the area under $f(x)$ between the values $x = 0.10$ and $x = 0.20$ is subdivided into a rectangle and a triangle with the following areas:

$$\text{Rectangle area} = (\text{height} \times \text{width}) = (2 \times 0.10) = 0.20$$

$$\text{Triangle area} = \frac{1}{2}(\text{base} \times \text{height}) = \frac{1}{2}(0.10 \times 6) = 0.30$$

The same type of calculation gives all the other subdivided areas under the probability density function $f(x)$ in Figure 6.5. The sum of these areas is 1.0. Note that the function $f(x)$ equals zero for $x < 0.05$ and $x > 0.30$. There can be no area under the curve beyond these bounds.

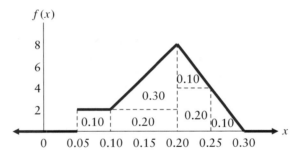

FIGURE 6.5 Probability measures based on Figure 6.4

Also, we can apply Formula 6.1 to find the probability of any *interval* of values for x. Referring to Figure 6.5, we find:

$$P(0.10 < x < 0.20) = 0.20 + 0.30 = 0.50$$
$$P(0.20 \leq x \leq 0.25) = 0.20 + 0.10 = 0.30$$

For a *continuous* random variable, *it does not matter whether the endpoint is included in the interval or not.* The addition of the endpoint changes the probability only by the value of $\frac{1}{\infty} = 0$; and so it has no effect.

☐ **EXAMPLE 6.2** Consider a mail-order book club that is interested in the pattern of its subscribers' payments for the books they order. At the time when their order is filled, the members of this club are sent a bill which states that payment is due within five weeks of the shipping date. In analyzing recent records of this book club, it was found that only about 16% of all customers remit their payment within the first two weeks; most people wait until week four or five to send in their money. Column (2) of Table 6.2 shows the number of payments received in each of the five weeks for the past 100,000 orders; the relative frequency of each value of x is shown in column (3).

TABLE 6.2   Example Distribution of Book Club Payments

(1) Week Payment was Received x	(2) Number of Payments Received f	(3) Relative Frequency $\frac{f}{N} = P(x)$	(4) Cumulative Relative Frequency $F(x)$	(5) $f(x) = 0.08x - 0.04$
1	3,940	0.039	0.039	0.040
2	12,012	0.120	0.159	0.120
3	20,133	0.201	0.360	0.200
4	27,852	0.279	0.639	0.280
5	36,063	0.361	1.000	0.360
Sum	100,000	1.000		1.000

Discrete case. Suppose we now plot the mass and cumulative functions describing the probability, for each of the five weeks, that a randomly selected customer will pay his or her bill. Figure 6.6 shows the graph of these functions. The tops of the probability lines in Fig. 6.6(a) form a fairly straight line that has a slope of 0.08 and a vertical intercept of −0.04. This relation is shown by the dotted line in the figure. An equation for $P(x)$ represented by a curve connecting the tops of the probability values can thus be written as $f(x) = 0.08x - 0.04$. The fact that this equation quite accurately describes $P(x)$ for the discrete values $x = 1, 2, 3, 4,$ and 5 is shown by comparing columns (3) and (5) in Table 6.2. ■

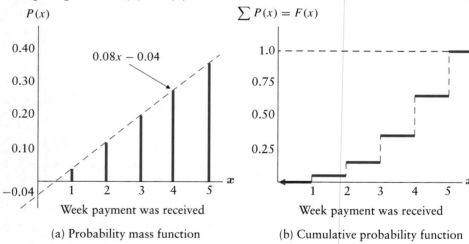

FIGURE 6.6   Probability functions representing mail-order payments from Table 6.2, columns (3) and (4)

Continuous Case   The probabilities shown in Table 6.2 assume that the book club can distinguish only which week ($x = 1, 2, 3, 4, or 5$) a customer's payment was received. But suppose we want a continuous approximation based on the assumption that a payment can be received at *any* value of x between 0 and 5, that is, x need not be an integer.

To find this approximation, we need a function that yields a probability of $P(0 \le x \le 1) = 0.039$ (or 0.04 when rounded) that the payment was received *between* the shipping date and the end of the first week, a probability of $P(1 \leq x \leq 2) = 0.12$ that the payment was received in the second week, and so forth, with the last probability $[P(4 \leq x \leq 5)]$ equal to 0.361 (or 0.36 when rounded). Although we will not present the process, it is not hard to determine that the function that yields these probabilities is $0.08x$. All values of x that do not fall between 0 and 5 must have a probability of zero since payments are received only between $x = 0$ and $x = 5$. Hence, our formal definition of the probability density function for this example is the following:

$$f(x) = \begin{cases} 0.08x & 0 \leq x \leq 5 \\ 0 & \text{otherwise} \end{cases}$$

This continuous approximation is graphed in Figure 6.7.

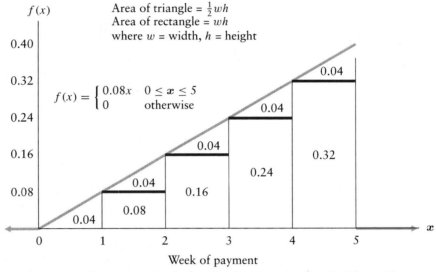

FIGURE 6.7   Continuous density function for example of book-club weekly payments

In the discrete case, the probability $P(x = 1) = 0.039$ represents the probability that a payment was received *during* the first week, meaning from 0 to 1 week. In the continuous case, we approximate this value by $P(0 \leq x \leq 1)$. Because *area* is interpreted as probability in the continuous case, $P(0 \leq x \leq 1)$ is given by the area of the small triangle in the lower left-hand corner of Figure 6.7. This triangle has a width of $w = 1$ and a height of $h = 0.08$. Since the area of a triangle is $A = \frac{1}{2}wh$, this area is $\frac{1}{2}(1)(0.08) = 0.04$. That is, $P(0 \leq x \leq 1) = 0.04$, which agrees very closely with the probability for the discrete case 0.039. To take another example, consider $P(2 \leq x \leq 3)$. The total area in this case consists of a triangle with area $\frac{1}{2}wh = \frac{1}{2}(1)(0.08) = 0.04$, plus a rectangle with area $wh = (1)(0.16) = 0.160$. The sum of these two areas is $P(2 \leq x \leq 3) = 0.200$, which again agrees very closely with the discrete case, $P(x = 3) = 0.201$. The remaining probabilities can be determined similarly.

Now, let us see if this density function satisfies the two properties of all probability density functions. First, as shown by Figure 6.7, the function never goes below the x-axis; hence, the condition $f(x) \geq 0$ is satisfied. Second, we can show that the total area under the function and above the x-axis equals 1 by summing the areas of the individual triangles and rectangles in Figure 6.7. Or we can find the area under the large triangle; this triangle has width $w = 5$ and height $h = 0.40$; hence, the total area is $\frac{1}{2}(5)(0.40) = 1$

Although we have limited ourselves to integer values in assessing probabilities in this example, it is not necessary to do so. The probability $P(1.7 \leq x \leq 3.5)$, for instance, can be determined by the same methods of geometry applied above. The reader should realize that using geometry is possible in our book-club example because the function $f(x)$ is a simple one (a straight line), for which we know how to find areas. For other more complex density functions, geometry cannot be used. In such cases, the methods of integral calculus can sometimes be used to find the appropriate area under $f(x)$, although this approach usually is not very convenient. Fortunately, such areas (probabilities) for commonly used density functions have been calculated and have been listed in tables or the computation can be programmed to be determined by a computer. Hence, one seldom needs to use integral calculus in solving practical problems.

Examples of Other p.d.f.'s

A number of frequently used probability density functions will be investigated later in this chapter. For now, the diagrams in Figure 6.8 should suffice to give you some insight into different types of density functions. In the first diagram, the density function is seen to be a constant, equal to 2.0 for values between $x = 1.0$ and $x = 1.5$ and equal to zero for all other values of x. In this case, the random variable x might represent the number of bushels (in millions) of wheat the USSR buys from the U.S.A. in a given year. Perhaps the U.S.A. will not sell less than 1.0 million or more than 1.5 million; hence, $\{1.0 \leq x \leq 1.5\}$.

In the second diagram, the function $f(x)$ is the straight line $\frac{1}{4} + \frac{1}{8}x$ for values between $x = -2$ and $x = 2$ (and zero otherwise). The reader should verify that the area under this function is 1. This function emphasizes that the values of x need not be positive. For instance, a value of $x = -1$ in our book-club example might mean that the customer prepaid one week before the bill went out. Finally, in the third diagram, $f(x)$ is a decreasing function for x between zero and infinity.[3] This type of function is often used in situations where x represents the *time between* certain events. A classic example is the instance in which x represents the time interval between the beginning and the end of a service, such as a checkout at a supermarket, or the waiting time for a customer before a service begins, such as waiting in a doctor's office, or waiting in line at a toll booth. Analysis of such probability density functions is important for improving customer services and for hiring the appropriate number of employees during different periods of the work week.

section 6.3

Similarities Between Probability Concepts for Discrete and Continuous Random Variables

As we have indicated, the basic difference between a probability mass function and a probability density function is that in the former case probabilities are measured by the *height* of the function, while in the latter case probabilities are measured by *areas* under the function. Most of the probability concepts developed in Chapter 4 are similar for both discrete and continuous random variables. Formal representations of many of the formulas will *look* different, but will not be different in

---

[3] In Figure 6.8(c), the symbol e denotes the same nonrepeating, nonterminating decimal we encountered in Section 5.8, $e \approx 2.71828$.

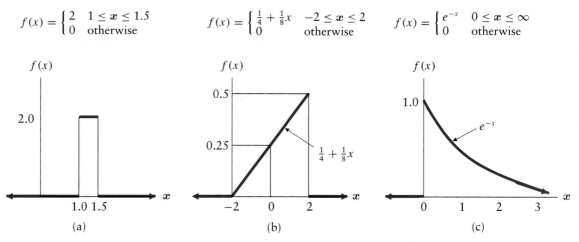

$$f(x) = \begin{cases} 2 & 1 \le x \le 1.5 \\ 0 & \text{otherwise} \end{cases} \qquad f(x) = \begin{cases} \frac{1}{4} + \frac{1}{8}x & -2 \le x \le 2 \\ 0 & \text{otherwise} \end{cases} \qquad f(x) = \begin{cases} e^{-x} & 0 \le x \le \infty \\ 0 & \text{otherwise} \end{cases}$$

FIGURE 6.8   Continuous probability density functions

meaning. They look different because wherever a summation occurs in a formula involving probabilities of a discrete random variable, it is replaced in the continuous case by an integral. That is, rather than summing the values representing the heights of a probability mass function, we calculate probabilities by integrating a probability density function. Although we will present the concept of a cumulative distribution function (c.d.f.) for continuous random variables, as well as their mean and variance, we will not present the formulas for a joint distribution, marginal distribution, conditional distribution, independence, and covariance. These formulas, however, can be derived directly from the comparable concepts in Chapter 4.

Cumulative Distribution Function

As before, the function $F(x)$ represents the probability that the random variable x assumes a value less than or equal to some specified value, say, b. To calculate $F(b)$ in the continuous case, it is necessary to *integrate* $f(x)$ over the relevant range, rather than to sum discrete probabilities. Since integrating $f(x)$ is equivalent to finding the area under $f(x)$, the **cumulative distribution function** $F(x)$ at the value b is defined as follows. See Figure 6.9, which follows.

Cumulative distribution function[4]:

$$F(b) = P(x \le b) = \text{all area under } f(x) \text{ for } x \le b \qquad (6.2)$$

It is important to keep in mind that while the values of $F(x)$ represent probabilities, the values of $f(x)$ do not represent probabilities. We will not extensively illustrate how to calculate cumulative functions, but rather present a table of values of $F(x)$ derived by summing the probabilities in column 5 of Table 6.2.

---

[4] Using calculus, $F(b) = \int_{-\infty}^{b} f(x)\,dx$. Exercise 6.37 asks the reader to verify the formula for $F(x)$ for the three density functions graphed in Figure 6.8.

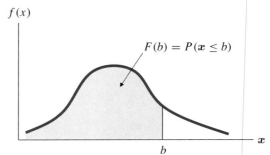

FIGURE 6.9 $F(x)$ for continuous random variable if $x = b$

Once a cumulative distribution function has been tabled (as in Table 6.3), it can be used to find the probabilities of many events of interest. The following formulas, which will prove especially useful, have been applied to the data in Table 6.3.

TABLE 6.3   Selected Values of $F(x)$ for the Example of Book-Club Weekly Payments, Derived from Areas in Figure 6.7

x	0	1	2	3	4	5
$F(x)$	0	0.04	0.16	0.36	0.64	1.00

1. $P(x \leq b) = F(b)$, by definition of the cumulative distribution function. This gives the probability of observing any value equal to or smaller than a given value b. It is represented by the area to the left of the value b under the density function. Using Table 6.3, $P(x \leq 3) = F(3) = 0.36$. This area is hatched in Figure 6.10.

2. $P(x \geq a) = 1 - P(x \leq a) = 1 - F(a)$. The area to the right of a value a in the right tail of a distribution may be found using $F(a)$ and the complement rule. For example, $P(x \geq 2) = 1 - F(2) = 1 - 0.16 = 0.84$. This area is shaded in Figure 6.10.

3. $P(a \leq x \leq b) = F(b) - F(a)$. The probability that x falls between a and b can be found by subtracting the area to the left of a from the area to the left of b, to obtain the amount of area between a and b. Using Table 6.3, $P(1 \leq x \leq 4) = F(4) - F(1) = 0.64 - 0.04 = 0.60$.

The cumulative distribution is an increasing curve starting at zero and rising to the value 1 as more and more probability is accumulated by including larger and larger values of x. The *level* of the cumulative function gives the cumulative probability at any value of x. The *difference* in the cumulative distribution levels between any two values of x gives the probability of the event that x lies in that interval.

This result is identical to that obtained by finding the area under the density function between the same two values of x. In the density function of Figure 6.11(a), the shaded area gives the probability, $P(1 \leq x \leq 4)$. In the cumulative distribution of Figure 6.11(b), the probability of this event is given by the difference in the levels of the function, $F(4) - F(1)$.

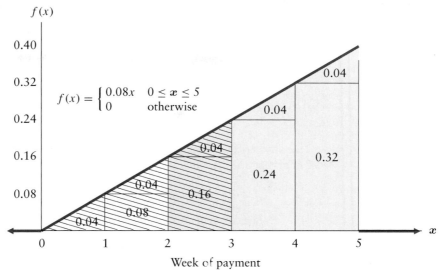

FIGURE 6.10 Reproduction of Figure 6.7

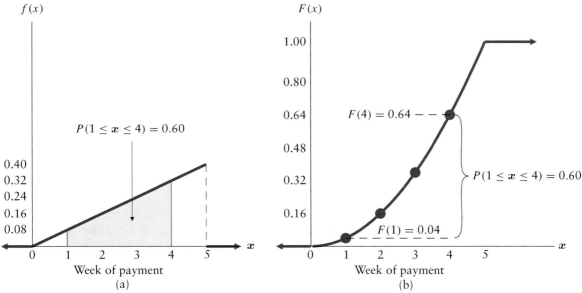

FIGURE 6.11 Probability density and cumulative distribution functions for week of payment

Mean and Variance†

The summary measures of central location and dispersion are as important in describing a density function as they were in describing a mass function. The mean, which we again denote as $\mu = E[x]$, is our measure of central location. It is the centre of gravity, or balance point, of the probability density function. For example, in the book-club example the average payment time can be shown to be $\mu = E[x] = 3\frac{1}{3}$ weeks. That is, the average customer pays the bill $3\frac{1}{3}$ weeks after receiving it. You may picture the book-club p.d.f. (Figure 6.10) as balanced on a fulcrum that is located at $x = 3\frac{1}{3}$.

---

† This section may be omitted without loss of continuity.

The variance and standard deviation of a p.d.f. are denoted by the same symbols used in the discrete case. That is, the variance is $\sigma^2 = V[x]$, and the standard deviation is $\sigma = \sqrt{V[x]}$. For our illustration involving book-club payments, these measures of dispersion can be shown to be:

$$\text{Variance} = V[x] = \sigma^2 = 1.39$$

$$\text{Standard deviation} = \sigma = \sqrt{V[x]} = \sqrt{1.39} = 1.18$$

This standard deviation can be interpreted by using the rule of thumb from Chapter 2. For a p.d.f. this rule is:

$\mu \pm 1\sigma$ will contain approximately 68% of the probability (area)

$\mu \pm 2\sigma$ will contain approximately 95% of the probability (area)

Calculating the probability (area) within ($\mu \pm 1\sigma$) and within ($\mu \pm 2\sigma$) may not be an easy task, even with the use of calculus. A clever reader using geometry, however, should be able to verify the probabilities (areas) given below for the book-club example. [*Hint:* Subdivide the area into a rectangle and a triangle.]

TABLE 6.4   Probability for the Book-Club Example Contained within One and Two Standard Deviations from the Mean

Interval	Probability
$\mu \pm 1\sigma = 3\frac{1}{3} \pm 1.18 = 2.15$ to 4.51	0.6287
$\mu \pm 2\sigma = 3\frac{1}{3} \pm 2(1.18) = 0.97$ to 5.69	0.9623

Note how well these calculated probabilities agree with the rule of thumb despite the fact that the p.d.f. is not symmetric.

For the most part, we will not be concerned in this book with the *process* of calculating $E[x]$ and $V[x]$ for continuous functions, although we emphasize again that it is important for the reader to understand the concepts involved. We therefore present below (but do not elaborate on) the formulas for calculating the mean and the variance for a continuous random variable x. The reader should verify that these formulas are the same as those presented in Chapter 4, except for two features. First, the *summation* in the continuous case is represented by an integral sign ($\int$) in substitution for the summation symbol ($\sum$) used in the discrete case. Second, the probability measures used as *weights* in Formulas 6.3 are areas (height × width) given by $f(x)dx$. These are applicable for the continuous case in substitution for the height of the probability mass function, $P(x)$, which is used for discrete random variables.

Mean of x:	$E[x] = \mu_x = \int_{-\infty}^{\infty} x f(x)dx$	
Expectation of $g(x)$:	$E[g(x)] = \mu_x = \int_{-\infty}^{\infty} g(x)f(x)dx$	(6.3)
Variance of x:	$V[x] = E[(x - \mu_x)^2]$	

PROBLEMS

6.1 The random variable x = time of arrival of the first customer at a certain store (where x = hours) is defined as:

$$f(x) = \begin{cases} 2x & \text{for } 0 \le x \le 1 \\ 0 & \text{otherwise} \end{cases}$$

a) Sketch this p.d.f.

b) Show that the total area under $f(x)$ equals 1.

c) What is the probability that the first customer will arrive before time $x = \frac{1}{2}$?

6.2 Use Problem 6.1 to answer the following.

a) Verify that $x = 0.707$ represents the *median* of the distribution. [*Hint:* Half the area lies to the left of the median.]

b) Would you guess that the mean $E[x]$ of the p.d.f. is larger or smaller than the median? [*Hint:* Remember Chapter 2.]

c) Explain, in words, what significance the mean and median have in this particular example.

6.3 Write down the values of $F(x)$ for the five values of x given in Table 6.5, using the function described in Problem 6.1.

TABLE 6.5

x	0	$\frac{1}{2}$	0.707	1.0	3.7
$F(x)$					

6.4 A study of the length of 20-metre oil pipeline sections found that they varied from 5 cm too short to 5 cm too long. An expert has used the following p.d.f. to describe the error in the case of a randomly selected pipe section:

$$f(x) = \begin{cases} \frac{1}{10} & \text{for } -5 \le x \le 5 \\ 0 & \text{otherwise} \end{cases}$$

a) Sketch this p.d.f. and show that its area is 1.

b) What are the mean and the median length of all pipe sections according to this p.d.f.?

c) What is the probability that a section is more than 3 cm too long? What percent of sections in this population will be more than 2 cm over or under the correct length?

6.5 The cumulative distribution function given below is appropriate for Problem 6.4.

$$F(x) = \begin{cases} 0 & x < -5 \\ \frac{1}{10}x + \frac{1}{2} & -5 \le x \le 5 \\ 1 & x > 5 \end{cases}$$

a) Sketch this function. What are the values of $F(-5)$ and $F(5)$?

b) Find and interpret the value $F(-2)$.

c) Find the value of $F(3)$. Does the complement of this value agree with your answer to the first part of Problem 6.4(c)?

6.6 Consider the p.d.f. shown in Figure 6.12, where x represents the height in inches of lettuce plants one week after planting.

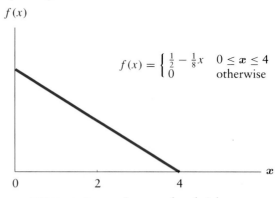

$$f(x) = \begin{cases} \frac{1}{2} - \frac{1}{8}x & 0 \le x \le 4 \\ 0 & \text{otherwise} \end{cases}$$

FIGURE 6.12 Lettuce plant heights

a) Show that the area under this function equals 1.

b) What is the probability that a plant will exceed 2 inches?

c) Find $E[x]$, the average height of the plants. [*Hint:* Do not try a formula unless you know calculus. Instead, note that the mean of our book-club example, which also had a triangular density function, is two-thirds of the distance from the lower end of the triangle.]

d) For this p.d.f., $\sigma = 0.94$. Use this value to find the area between $\mu - 1\sigma$ and $\mu + 1\sigma$. [*Hint:* Find this area by dividing the interval into a rectangle and a triangle.] Is the area you found close to the 68% rule of thumb? If not, can you offer an explanation?

e) Find the area between $\mu - 2\sigma$ and $\mu + 2\sigma$. Is this area close to 95%?

f) Find the values of $F(0)$, $F(2)$, $F(4)$, and $F(5.3)$.

6.7 Because of improved diplomatic relationships with China, numerous business opportunities have opened up. Suppose a manufacturer has decided to export a certain type of printing calculator to China. This manufacturer estimates that annual demand (d) can be represented by the following p.d.f., where d is in thousands of units:

$$f(d) = \begin{cases} (d - 30)/450 & \text{for } 30 \le d \le 60 \\ 0 & \text{otherwise} \end{cases}$$

a) Sketch this function and verify that the area under the function equals 1.

b) Use the hint in Problem 6.6(c) to find $E[d]$ for this p.d.f. If the net profit is $10 per calculator, what is the expected total net profit for the year?

c) Assume that 60,000 calculators are shipped. What is the probability that there will be an inventory of at least 10,000 units at the end of the year?

d) For this problem, $V[d] = 50$. What is the variance of total expected annual profit? [*Hint:* Use Rule 4 from Section 4.4.] Using the rule of thumb from Chapter 2, find two values such that the probability is 0.95 that total expected annual profit lies between these two values.

---

section 6.4

The Normal Distribution

In the eighteenth century, scientists noted a predictable regularity about the frequency with which certain errors occur, especially errors of measurement. Suppose, for example, that a machine is supposed to cut a piece of metal to a width of exactly $\frac{5}{16}$ inches. While this machine produces pieces that are $\frac{5}{16}$ inches wide *on the average*, some pieces are in error — they are slightly too wide or slightly too narrow. Experiments producing errors of this nature were found to form a symmetrical distribution, originally called the *normal curve of errors*. The continuous probability distribution that such an experiment approximates is usually referred to as the *normal distribution*, or sometimes the *Gaussian distribution*, after an early researcher, Karl Gauss (1777–1855).

The normal distribution is undoubtedly the most widely known and used of all distributions. Many natural phenomena — length, height, and thickness of animals or plants; medical counts of sugar, white blood cells, incidence of inner-ear disease; and behavioural, emotional, or psychological measures of human actions, aptitudes, or abilities — tend to result in normal distributions. The distribution of measured errors or deviations from a specified standard in diameters of pistons, cylinders, or gun barrels, weight of packaged products, and even lengths of yardsticks also tends to be normal, as does the distribution of the degree of perfection in production processes of many kinds.

Because the normal distribution approximates many natural phenomena so well, it has evolved into a standard of reference for many probability problems. In addition, under certain conditions the binomial and the Poisson distributions can be approximated by the normal distribution. The normal distribution is so important in the theory of statistics that a considerable portion of the sampling, estimation, and hypothesis-testing theory discussed in the remainder of this book is based on the characteristics of this distribution.

Characteristics of the Normal Distribution

The **normal distribution** is a continuous distribution in which x can assume any value between minus infinity and plus infinity $\{-\infty < x < \infty\}$. Two parameters describe the normal distribution: μ, representing the mean, and σ^2, representing the variance. A normal distribution with mean μ and variance σ^2 often is denoted by the symbol $N(\mu, \sigma^2)$. The normal density function is a symmetrical, bell-shaped probability density function, as it appears in the graph in Figure 6.13.

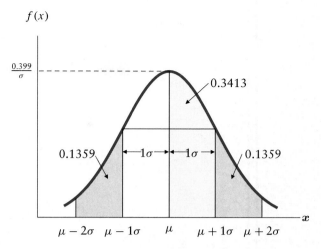

FIGURE 6.13 The normal density function

Note that in Figure 6.13 the area under the curve from μ to $\mu + 1\sigma$ is 0.3413. Thus, $P(\mu \leq x \leq \mu + 1\sigma) = 0.3413$. By symmetry, $P(\mu - 1\sigma \leq x \leq \mu + 1\sigma) = 2(0.3413) = 0.6826$. We can also see that $P(\mu + 1\sigma \leq x \leq \mu + 2\sigma) = 0.1359$, hence:

$$P(\mu - 2\sigma \leq x \leq \mu + 2\sigma) = 0.6826 + 0.1359 + 0.1359 = 0.9544$$

The rule of thumb we have been using throughout this book is now seen to be based on the normal distribution. The extent to which the intervals we have considered previously have differed from our rule of thumb reflects the fact that these distributions have not been normal distributions.

Beginning students of statistics are sometimes confused by the fact that, for the normal distribution, the general symbols μ and σ^2 are used to represent the specific parameters of this distribution rather than some different ones such as n and π in the binomial or λ in the Poisson. This is merely traditional, since the normal is the most commonly used distribution.

The normal p.d.f. contains two constants: $\pi \cong 3.14159$ and $e \cong 2.71828$. The normal p.d.f. is given as follows.

Normal density function, $N(\mu, \sigma^2)$

$$f(x) = \frac{1}{\sigma\sqrt{2\pi}}e^{-\frac{1}{2}\left(\frac{x-\mu}{\sigma}\right)^2} \quad \text{for } -\infty < x < \infty. \qquad (6.4)$$

Since π and e are constants, if μ and σ are known, it is possible to evaluate areas under this function by using calculus (integration). Fortunately, such areas (probabilities) have been tabulated for one special case (the standardized normal), so it is not necessary to use calculus.

It is important to remember that all normal distributions have the same bell-shaped curve pictured in Figure 6.13 regardless of the values of μ and σ. The value of μ indicates where the centre of the *bell* lies, while σ represents how spread out (or wide) the distribution is. Note that in Figure 6.13 the height of the density function at the point $x = \mu$ is $0.399/\sigma$.[5] In this book, however, we will not be concerned with the height of the density function. In fact, in sketching the normal distribution, we often will not indicate any of the values of the vertical axis. Three specific normal distributions, corresponding to $\sigma = 0.5$, $\sigma = 1.0$, and $\sigma = 1.5$, are shown in Figure 6.14.

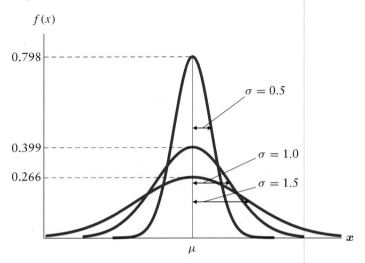

FIGURE 6.14   Three normal distributions with different standard deviations but the same mean

Examples of Normal Distributions

Even with the limited information we have presented thus far about the normal distribution, we can answer a number of probability questions. The following two examples will serve the reader as a review of that information and as illustrations of the use of the normal distribution in statistical problem-solving.

☐ **EXAMPLE 6.3**   The random variable x representing the daily change in the unit value of an income fund is normally distributed with mean $\mu_x = 10$ cents and standard deviation $\sigma_x = 0.8$ cents; that is, $N(10, 0.8^2)$. This information is sufficient to completely determine the probability of any event concerning the values of x.

For instance, what is the probability that, for a randomly selected day, the unit value of the fund will change by more than 10 cents? Since the normal distribution is symmetrical, and 10 is the median as well as the mean, the answer is $\frac{1}{2}$. Now, to move to a slightly more difficult question, what is the probability that the unit value change will be less than 9.2 cents? Using Figure 6.15, we see that 9.2 is the value exactly one standard deviation below the mean $(10.0 - 9.2 = 0.8 = \sigma_x)$. The probability $P(x \leq 9.2)$ is represented by the shaded area under the function $f(x)$.

The probability $P(x \leq 9.2)$ is thus exactly equivalent to the probability as shown in Figure 6.15:

$$P(x \leq \mu - 1\sigma)$$

---

[5] This fact can be derived from Formula 6.4 by substituting μ for x and observing that $e^0 = 1$, and $1/\sqrt{2\pi} = 0.399$. Thus, if $\sigma = 1.0$, then $f(\mu) = 0.399/1.0 = 0.399$. When $\sigma = 0.5$, $f(\mu) = 0.399/0.5 = 0.798$, and if $\sigma = 1.5$, $f(\mu) = 0.399/1.5 = 0.266$.

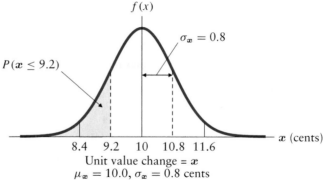

$$\mu_x = 10.0, \sigma_x = 0.8 \text{ cents}$$

FIGURE 6.15   Normal distribution for fund value

There remains the problem of determining how much of the area of the normal distribution lies to the left of $\mu - 1\sigma$. To calculate $P(x \leq \mu - 1\sigma)$, we first recall that, from Figure 6.13, $P(\mu - 1\sigma \leq x \leq \mu + 1\sigma) = 2(0.3413) = 0.6826$. If the probability within this interval is 0.6826, the probability of lying outside this interval is $1 - 0.6826 = 0.3174$. Half of this amount (0.1587) would be in the left tail:

$$P(x \leq \mu - 1\sigma) = \tfrac{1}{2}(\text{complement of area within } \mu \pm 1\sigma)$$

$$P(x \leq 9.2) = \tfrac{1}{2}(1 - 0.6826) = \tfrac{1}{2}(0.3174) = 0.1587$$

Finally, for this same example, suppose that we want to determine the probability that the daily change in unit value is between 11.2 and 12 cents. This probability is given by the area under the curve between 11.2 and 12.0. To find this area using calculus, we would integrate the normal density function in Formula 6.4 with $\mu_x = 10$ and $\sigma_x = 0.8$ using as the lower and upper limits of integration, 11.2 and 12.0. Such an integral could be evaluated using a computer. Another way to determine this area would be to find a table already calculated for a normal distribution with $\mu = 10$ and $\sigma = 0.8$. We will come back to this problem shortly to reject both these methods and seek an easier way. ■

☐ **EXAMPLE 6.4**   Suppose that the random variable y, representing the tread life in miles of a certain new radial tire, is normally distributed with mean $\mu_y = 40,000$ miles, and standard deviation $\sigma_y = 3,000$ miles [$N(40,000, 3,000^2)$]. This information is sufficient to determine completely the probability of any event concerning the values of y. For example, $P(y \geq 40,000) = \tfrac{1}{2}$, since half of the probability in a normal distribution lies on each side of the mean. Or suppose we calculate the probability that a tire of this model selected at random has a tread life greater than 46,000 miles. Using Figure 6.16 we see that 46,000 is exactly two standard deviations above the mean ($46,000 - 40,000 = 6,000 = 2\sigma_y$). The probability $P(y \geq 46,000)$ is represented by the shaded area under the function $f(y)$ in Figure 6.16. The probability $P(y \geq 46,000)$ is also equivalent to the $P(x \geq \mu + 2\sigma)$ in the graph of the normal distribution in Fig. 6.13. Since we already know that $P(\mu - 2\sigma \leq x \leq \mu + 2\sigma) = 0.9544$, the value of $P(x \geq \mu + 2\sigma)$ is clearly equal to one-half of the complement of 0.9544:

$$P(y \geq 46,000) = \tfrac{1}{2}(1.000 - 0.9544) = \tfrac{1}{2}(0.0456) = 0.0228$$

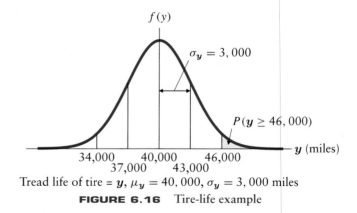

Tread life of tire = y, $\mu_y = 40,000$, $\sigma_y = 3,000$ miles

FIGURE 6.16   Tire-life example

Finally, we might ask about the probability that tread life, for this example, will fall between 44,500 and 47,500 miles. Again, the answer can be determined in two ways. Using calculus, one could integrate the normal p.d.f. from 44,500 to 47,500 with $\mu_y = 40,000$ and $\sigma_y = 3,000$. This integral could be evaluated using a computer. Or one could use a table of areas already calculated for the precise parameters, $\mu_y = 40,000$ and $\sigma_y = 3,000$. Both of these methods are unsatisfactory, however, first because it is too tedious to evaluate a new integral every time one investigates a different set of parameters or new values of the random variable, and secondly because no such tables exist. ■

section 6.5

Standardized Normal

Values of x for the normal distribution usually are described in terms of how many standard deviations they are away from the mean. The value $x = 200$, for example, has little meaning unless we know in what units x was measured (metres, kilometres, litres, et cetera). On the other hand, the statement that x is one standard deviation larger (or smaller) than the mean can be given a very precise interpretation, as it is always meaningful to talk of x being a certain number of standard deviations above (or below) the mean, no matter what value σ assumes or on what scale the variable x is measured. Now, if x is measured in terms of standard deviations about the mean, it is natural to describe probability values in the same terms — that is, by specifying the probability that x will fall within so many standard deviations of the mean. There are three whole-unit intervals, the first two of which we have referred to often as our *rule of thumb*: $\mu \pm 1\sigma$, $\mu \pm 2\sigma$, and $\mu \pm 3\sigma$. Recall that we used the first two of these in the previous section to find probabilities for normally distributed random variables.

Treating the values of x in a normal distribution in terms of standard deviations about the mean has the advantage of permitting all normal distributions to be compared to one common or standard normal distribution. In this standard form, different values of μ and σ no longer generate completely different curves, since x is measured only about μ and all distances away from μ are expressed in terms of multiples of σ. In other words, it is easier to compare normal distributions having different values of μ and σ if these curves are transformed to one common form, which is called the **standardized normal distribution**. The standardized variable represents a *new* random variable, one we discussed in Chapter 4, namely, $z = (x - \mu)/\sigma$. The standardized variable, by definition, has a mean of zero ($\mu_z = 0$) and a standard deviation of one ($\sigma_z = 1$). Note that if the standard deviation is one, the variance must also be one since $\sigma^2 = 1.0$ when $\sigma = 1.0$.

This process of standardization gives a hint about the best method of attack in answering questions concerning a normal probability distribution. Instead of trying to solve directly a probability problem involving a normally distributed random variable x with mean μ and standard deviation σ, an indirect approach is used. We first convert the problem to an equivalent one with a normal variable measured in standard deviation units, called a *standardized normal variable*. A table of standardized normal values (Table III) can then be used to obtain an answer in terms of the converted problem. Finally, by converting back to the original units of measurement for x, we can obtain the answer to the original problem. Figure 6.17 is a schematic outline of this method of solving probability problems.

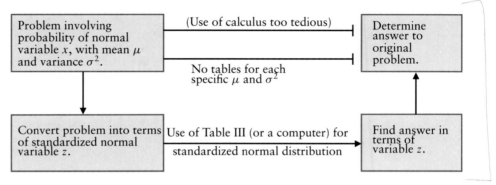

FIGURE 6.17   Problem-solving tactic using the standardized normal

In Section 4.4, we discussed the process of transforming a random variable x (whether normally distributed or not) with mean μ and standard deviation σ into a standardized measure with mean zero and standard deviation one. We now add the additional fact that if the original random variable (x) is normally distributed, then the standardized variable z will also be normally distributed. Thus, $z = (x - \mu)/\sigma$ is $N(0, 1)$ if x is normal.

Standardized normal random variable:

$$z = \frac{x - \mu}{\sigma} \text{ is } N(0, 1)$$ (6.5)

This function is shown graphically in Figure 6.18. The reader should compare Figure 6.18 with Figure 6.13 and verify that the former is merely a special case of the latter where $\mu = 0$ and $\sigma = 1$.

The density function for the standardized normal variable z:

$$f(z) = \frac{1}{\sqrt{2\pi}} e^{-\frac{1}{2}z^2}$$ (6.6)

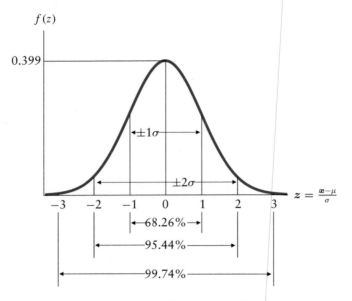

FIGURE 6.18 Standardized normal distribution

The interpretation of z-values is relatively simple. Because $\sigma^2 = V[z] = 1.0$, whatever value z has indicates how many standard deviations x is from the mean. For example, if $z = 1.56$, this indicates that the corresponding x-value is exactly 1.56 standard deviations above the mean of the variable x $((x - \mu) = 1.56\sigma)$. Similarly, if $z = -2.81$, this means that the comparable value of x falls 2.81 standard deviations below the mean.

Using the Standardized Normal

Consider the two examples in the previous section involving normally distributed random variables, where $x =$ daily change in unit value of an income fund with $\mu_x = 10, \sigma_x = 0.8$ and $y =$ tread life of tire in miles with $\mu_y = 40,000, \sigma_y = 3,000$.

Some probability questions were suggested there that we did not completely answer. To repeat, what is $P(11.2 \le x \le 12.0)$ and what is $P(44,500 \le y \le 47,500)$? The answer to each question is shown by the shaded areas under the normal curves in Figures 6.19(a) and (b), respectively. Since we rejected the two proposed direct ways of answering these questions, we proceed now with the indirect approach, using the standard normal distribution.

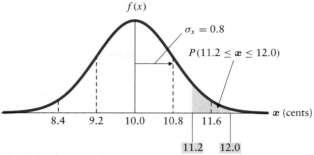

(a) Daily change in the unit value of an income fund x;
$\mu_x = 10.0$, $\sigma_x = 0.8$

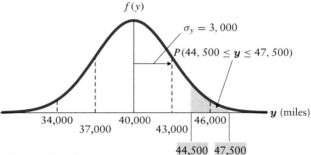

(b) Tread life of tire, y; $\mu_y = 40,000$, $\sigma_y = 3,000$

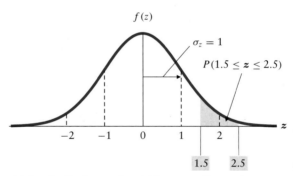

(c) Standardized normal variable z; $\mu_z = 0$, $\sigma_z = 1$

FIGURE 6.19 Comparative normal distributions

In transforming the probability $P(11.2 \leq x \leq 12.0)$ into an equivalent one in standardized normal form, we must apply the transformation $z = (x - \mu)/\sigma$ to each part of the expression in parentheses. The value 11.2 is transformed into its equivalent form by first subtracting $\mu_x = 10.0$, and then dividing the result by $\sigma_x = 0.8$; the value 12.0 is transformed into its equivalent standardized form in exactly the same manner. Finally, we can think of the variable x as being transformed in the same way since the new variable, z, equals $(x - \mu)/\sigma$:

$$P(11.2 \leq x \leq 12.0) = P\left(\frac{11.2 - 10.0}{0.8} \leq \frac{x - \mu}{\sigma} \leq \frac{12.0 - 10.0}{0.8}\right)$$

$$= P(1.5 \leq z \leq 2.5)$$

We follow the same process in transforming the probability

$$P(44{,}500 \le y \le 47{,}500)$$

into standardized normal form, except that in this case $\mu_y = 40{,}000$ and $\sigma_y = 3{,}000$:

$$P(44{,}500 \le y \le 47{,}500) = P\left(\frac{44{,}500 - 40{,}000}{3{,}000} \le \frac{y - \mu_y}{\sigma_y} \le \frac{47{,}500 - 40{,}000}{3{,}000}\right)$$

$$= P(1.5 \le z \le 2.5)$$

It is now obvious that we constructed our two unanswered probability questions to show how two diverse problems such as the unit value of a fund and tire life can both be reduced to the identical question in terms of the standardized normal. The fact that these probabilities are equivalent can be seen by comparing Figs. 6.19(a) and (b) with (c).

Cumulative Distribution of the Standardized Normal

The problem at this point is: How does one evaluate probabilities in standardized form, such as $P(1.5 \le z \le 2.5)$? As we indicated previously, there are tables of standardized normal values (called z-values) for this purpose. Table III in Appendix C is one such table.

Before we describe the use of Table III, let us investigate $F(z)$, the cumulative distribution function for the variable z. This function, shown in Figure 6.20, gives $P(z \le z)$.

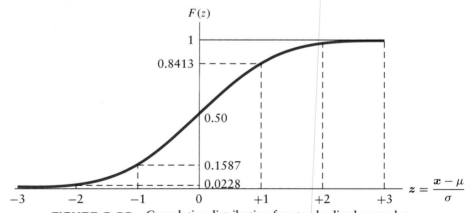

FIGURE 6.20 Cumulative distribution for standardized normal z

Note that we have plotted z-values only from -3 to $+3$, since very little area lies beyond these limits. At $z = 0$ (the mean of z), the value of $F(z)$ must be 0.50, since $z = 0$ represents the median of the z-values. Most of the other values in Figure 6.20 should be familiar to you by now. For example, $F(-1) = 0.1587$. This value agrees with the one calculated in the example on the daily change in the unit value of an income fund, as we saw then that $P(x \le \mu - 1\sigma) = 0.1587$. The value $F(-2) = 0.0228$ should also appear familiar, as this is the same value we calculated in the tire-life problem for $P(y \ge \mu + 2\sigma)$. Because of the symmetry of the normal distribution, $F(-2) = 1 - F(2) = P(y \ge \mu + 2\sigma) = 0.0228$.

Since the normal distribution is completely symmetrical, tables of z-values usually include only positive values of z. Thus, the lowest value in Table III is $z = 0$, and the cumulative probability at this point is $F(0) = P(z \leq 0) = 0.50$. Table III gives other values of z, to two decimal points, up to the point $z = 3.49$. The values of z to one decimal are read from the left margin in Table III, while the second decimal is read across the top. The body of the table gives the values of $F(z)$.

As we illustrate the use of Table III, we will consider four basic rules. The reader should try to understand (visualize) these rules, rather than to memorize them.

Rule 1. $P(z \leq a)$ is given by $F(a)$ when a is positive.

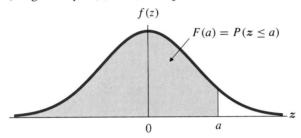

FIGURE 6.21   Illustration of Rule 1, $P(z \leq a)$

We can illustrate this rule by determining the probability $P(y \leq 45,000)$ in the tire-life problem:

$$P(y \leq 45,000) = P\left(\frac{y - \mu_y}{\sigma_y} \leq \frac{45,000 - 40,000}{3,000}\right) = P(z \leq 1.67) = F(1.67)$$

The value $z = 1.67$ in Table III yields a cumulative probability of $F(1.67) = 0.9525 = P(y \leq 45,000)$.

Rule 2. $P(z \geq a)$ is given by the complement rule as $1 - F(a)$.

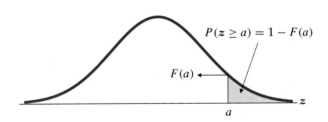

FIGURE 6.22   Illustration of Rule 2, $P(z \geq a)$

Rule 2 is merely the complement of Rule 1. For example, suppose we calculate $P(z \geq 2.00)$ for our tire example. Since $F(2.00) = 0.9772$:

$$P(z \geq 2.00) = 1 - 0.9772 = 0.0228$$

This value agrees with the value calculated earlier:

$$P(y \geq \mu + 2\sigma) = 0.0228$$

Rule 3. $P(z \leq -a)$, where $-a$ is a negative number, is given by $1 - F(a)$.

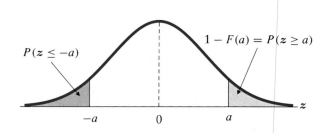

FIGURE 6.23   Illustration of Rule 3, $P(z \leq -a)$

Rule 3 follows directly from Rule 2 because of the symmetry of the normal distribution, for we know that the following is true:

$$P(z \leq -a) = P(z \geq a) = 1 - F(a)$$

For this case, let's return to the problem regarding daily changes in the unit value of an income fund, where

$$P(x \leq 9.2) = P(z \leq -1.00)$$

Since $F(1.00) = 0.8413$, $P(x \leq 9.2) = 1 - 0.8413 = 0.1587$, which agrees with our earlier result.

Rule 4. $P(a \leq z \leq b)$ is given by $F(b) - F(a)$.

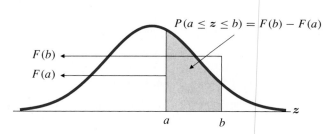

FIGURE 6.24   Illustration of Rule 4, $P(-a \leq z \leq b)$

The area under the curve between two points a and b is found by subtracting the area to the left of a, $F(a)$, from the area to the left of b, $F(b)$. This difference gives the area between the values a and b.

Using this rule, we can solve the problem with which we began this section:

$$P(1.50 \leq z \leq 2.50) = F(2.50) - F(1.50)$$

From Table III, $F(2.50) = 0.9938$ and $F(1.50) = 0.9332$:

$$P(1.50 \leq z \leq 2.50) = 0.9938 - 0.9332 = 0.0606$$

In the above example, both a and b are positive, which makes calculating $F(b) - F(a)$ quite easy. Suppose, however, that we want to calculate a probability where either a or both a and b are negative. The latter case is fairly simple because the following is true, owing to symmetry:

$$P(-a \leq z \leq -b) = P(b \leq z \leq a) = F(a) - F(b)$$
$$P(-2.50 \leq z \leq -1.50) = P(1.50 \leq z \leq 2.50) = 0.0606$$

Now consider the first case, a more complex problem, which is illustrated in Figure 6.25:

$$P(-2.00 \leq z \leq 1.50) = P(z \leq 1.50) - P(z \leq -2.00)$$

From Rule 3, $P(z \leq -2.00) = 1 - F(2.00)$:

$$P(-2.00 \leq z \leq 1.50) = F(1.50) - [1 - F(2.00)]$$
$$= 0.9332 - (1 - 0.9772)$$
$$= 0.9332 - 0.0228$$
$$= 0.9104.$$

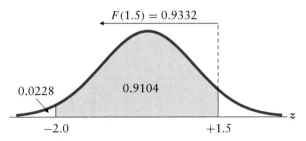

FIGURE 6.25   Finding $P(a \leq z \leq b)$ where a is negative

There are many other types of problems that can be solved using the standardized normal distribution. To illustrate these types of problems, we have included the following two extensions of our tire-life example.

☐ **EXAMPLE 6.5**   An owner of a fleet of rental cars uses tires for which the tread life (miles of safe use) is described by the distribution $y \simeq N(40,000, 3,000^2)$. The owner wishes to establish a policy of replacing tires before they become unsafe or cause downtime for the rental cars. It is decided that all tires should be replaced after a specific number of miles of wear so that, on the average, only two tires out of 100 would wear out prior to replacement. The problem for the owner is to decide on the number of miles (M) at which replacement should occur. We need to find the value M so that $P(y \leq M) = 0.02$.

For this example, we know the probability answer (0.02), but we do not know the value of M. To find M, however, we use the same procedure as before, transforming the problem into standardized terms:

$$P(y \leq M) = P\left[z \leq \frac{M - 40,000}{3,000}\right] = 0.02$$

The probability given in this case is shown by the shaded area in Figure 6.26. Since the value M is smaller than the mean of the distribution, the standardized value corresponding to M will be a negative number. In this type of problem, the probability value closest to that desired is located within the table, and then the corresponding z-value is read from the top and left margins. If $P(y \leq M) = 0.02$, then $P(y \geq M) = 1 - 0.02 = 0.98$. From Table III, the value of z that gives $F(z) = 0.98$ is $z = 2.05$. Remembering that since we want a value below the mean, the *negative* value of z desired in this problem is $z = -2.05$. To convert back to the original problem, we solve the formula $z = (M - \mu_y)/\sigma_y$ for M, as follows:

$$M = \mu_y + z\sigma_y$$

Since $\mu_y = 40,000$, $z = -2.05$, and $\sigma_y = 3,000$, the only unknown value is M. By substitution:

$$M = 40,000 - 2.05(3,000) = 33,850$$

The probability is 0.02 that a tire lasts less than 33,850 miles. The owner can replace tires when they have been used for 33,850 miles and be confident that only 2% of the tires are apt to cause a problem due to wearing out before replacement. ∎

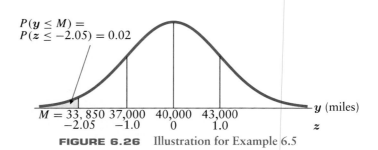

$P(y \le M) =$
$P(z \le -2.05) = 0.02$

$M = 33,850$ $37,000$ $40,000$ $43,000$ y (miles)
-2.05 -1.0 0 1.0 z

FIGURE 6.26   Illustration for Example 6.5

Our final example in this section involves the solution of a probability problem when both endpoints of the desired interval are unknown. The interval desired may be written as $a \le y \le b$, where both a and b are unknown.

Referring to the tread life of the tires as in Example 6.5, we now consider the view of the manufacturer who may wish to set tread-life specifications for the tires produced. A common specification level is to set limits such that 95% of all tires produced will have a tread life within the control limits. To solve this problem, we need to determine two values a and b such that the probability is 0.95 that a randomly selected tire will fall between these values: $P(a \le y \le b) = 0.95$. It should be readily apparent that there is an infinitely large number of such intervals, depending on how the values of a and b are selected. If our interval is to include 95% of the area under the curve and exclude 5%, we could exclude all of the 5% above b, or exclude all of the 5% below a, or exclude part of it below a and part above b. In many cases, the best way to split the percentage to be excluded between the two tails will be specified in the problem. If it is not specified, then *the following is generally agreed:*

> The best way to split the percentage to be excluded is in a manner that makes the interval from a to b as small as possible. The smallest interval in this case is obtained by excluding equal areas in both the upper and lower tail of the distribution.[6]

This result follows from the Neyman-Pearson theorem that is proved in more advanced statistics books. It tells us that the best way to split our 5% to be excluded is to have 2.5% in each tail.

---

[6] As we will discuss later, this nontechnical statement is always true only for unimodal, symmetrical distributions such as the normal. For other types of distributions, further conditions must be specified.

☐ **EXAMPLE 6.6**   Let's now use this result to solve the tire-life problem, $P(a \leq y \leq b) = 0.95$. Since 2.5% is to be excluded above b, we first need to find b so that $P(y \geq b) = 0.025$. Using the standardized transformation:

$$P(y \geq b) = P \left(\frac{y - \mu_y}{\sigma_y} \geq \frac{b - 40,000}{3,000} \right) = 0.025$$

$$= P \left(z \geq \frac{b - 40,000}{3,000} \right) = 0.025$$

From Table III, $F(1.96) = 0.9750$. Thus, $P(z \geq 1.96) = 1 - 0.9750 = 0.025$, so that $z = 1.96$ is the appropriate value. Now, due to symmetry, if $z = 1.96$ cuts off 2.5% from the upper tail, $-z = -1.96$ cuts off 2.5% from the lower tail; hence, the smallest interval containing 95% of the total area under the curve is:

$$P(-1.96 \leq z \leq 1.96) = 0.95$$

We now translate these z-values back into the units in our tire-life problem. Let us use a to designate the value of y which represents the *lower* specification limit of our interval containing 95% of the total area. To find the value of a that corresponds to $z = -1.96$, we first need to substitute the letter a for the symbol y in the standardization formula. That is, when a is substituted for y:

$$z = \frac{y - \mu_y}{\sigma_y} \quad \text{becomes} \quad z = \frac{a - \mu_y}{\sigma_y}$$

The value of a is the only unknown in the latter formula, as $z = -1.96$, $\mu_y = 40,000$, and $\sigma_y = 3,000$. We can solve for a as follows:

$$-1.96 = \frac{a - 40,000}{3,000} \Rightarrow a = 40,000 - 1.96(3,000)$$

$$a = 34,120$$

Similarly, if we let b denote that value of y which represents the *upper* specification limit of our 95% interval:

$$z = \frac{y - \mu_y}{\sigma_y} \quad \text{becomes} \quad z = \frac{b - \mu_y}{\sigma_y}$$

The only unknown is b, since $z = 1.96$, $\mu_y = 40,000$, and $\sigma_y = 3,000$. Hence:

$$1.96 = \frac{b - 40,000}{3,000}$$

$$b = 40,000 + 1.96(3,000)$$

$$b = 45,880$$

The appropriate interval is thus $P(34,120 \leq y \leq 45,880) = 0.95$. The reader should verify that 34,120 to 45,880 is the smallest interval possible by trying several other possible splits of the 5% to be excluded. Figure 6.27 shows the normal distribution for this example.   ■

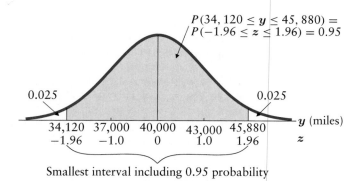

FIGURE 6.27   Illustration for Example 6.6

☐ **STUDY QUESTION 6.1   Guarantee Period for Motors**

The length of life of an electric motor used in a ceiling fan is approximately normally distributed with a mean of 6.4 years and a standard deviation of 1.1 years.

  a) If the fan motor is guaranteed for five years, what is the probability that replacement under the guarantee will be required?
  b) If the manufacturer is willing to replace only 1% of the fan motors, what period of time should be used for the guarantee period?

  • **ANSWER**   Figure 6.28 is helpful in illustrating the relevant events and probabilities.

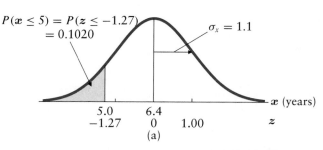

FIGURE 6.28   Illustration for Study Question 6.1

  a) Let x = length of life in years. To find $P(x \leq 5)$, convert to a standardized normal:

  $$P(x \leq 5) = P\left[z \leq \frac{(5 - 6.4)}{1.1}\right] = P(z \leq -1.27)$$

  Using Table III:

  $$P(z \leq -1.27) = 1 - F(1.27)$$
  $$= 1 - 0.8980 = 0.1020$$

  About 10% of the fan motors will need replacement under the guarantee.
  b) If only 1% of the motors are to be replaced, then $P(x \leq a) = 0.01$. In standardized form:

  $$P(x \leq a) = P\left[z \leq \frac{(a - 6.4)}{1.1}\right] = 0.01$$

From Table III, we find $F(z) = 0.99$ for $z = 2.33$. Since a is smaller than the mean of the distribution, then the negative value of z to be substituted into Formula (6.5) is $z = -2.33$. Thus, $a = 6.4 - 2.33(1.1) = 3.837$. The guarantee period desired is 3.837 years. Since 0.837 years is $(0.837)12$ months, or about 10 months, the guarantee period should be 3 years and 10 months if only 1% of the fan motors are to be replaced.   ■

The family of probability problems in which the standardized normal z is useful extends even beyond these instances. Many other distributions applying to other types of problems tend to be normal distributions under certain conditions. One example, discussed in the next section, is that of the binomial distribution. Finally, as we will see in the following chapters, the standardized normal distribution is of primary importance in problems of statistical inference dealing with means of samples from a population whose distribution is unknown.

---

section 6.6

Normal Approximation to the Binomial

Earlier in this chapter, we indicated that the binomial formula is often tedious to use, and that Table I may not contain the desired values of n and π. Statistical packages for the computer are generally the easiest way to solve binomial problems. Still, there are some circumstances where it is convenient to solve binomial problems by approximating the binomial probabilities using the normal distribution. How well the normal approximates the binomial depends on the binomial parameters — in general, the larger the value of n, and the closer π is to $\frac{1}{2}$, the better the approximation.

Using the Normal Approximation to the Binomial

When one distribution is used to approximate another, their characteristics must be fairly similar. In particular, the two distributions should have (1) the same mean, (2) the same variance, and (3) a similar shape.

In approximating the binomial by the normal, we can ensure that their means are equal by setting μ (the mean of the normal) equal to the value of $n\pi$ (the mean of the binomial distribution we are trying to approximate). That is, we

1. Set $\mu = n\pi$.

To ensure that their variances are equal, we set σ^2 (the variance of the normal) equal to $n\pi(1 - \pi)$ (the variance of the binomial): that is, we

2. Set $\sigma^2 = n\pi(1 - \pi)$

It can be shown that as n becomes larger and larger, the shape of the binomial becomes more and more like the normal. In other words:

3. Binomial → normal as $n \to \infty$.

If n is *large*, these conditions ensure that the normal distribution will provide a reasonably good approximation to the binomial. Just how large n needs to be depends on how close π is to $\frac{1}{2}$, and on the precision desired, although fairly good results are usually obtained when $n\pi(1 - \pi) > 3$.

Just as we standardized an x-value in solving problems earlier in this chapter, we again standardize x to approximate the binomial by the normal. In this case, x is standardized by subtracting $\mu = n\pi$ from x, and then dividing this deviation by $\sigma = \sqrt{n\pi(1 - \pi)}$.

Normal approximation to binomial when $n\pi(1-\pi) > 3$:

$$z = \frac{x - n\pi}{\sqrt{n\pi(1-\pi)}}$$

(6.7)

Continuity Correction

One additional factor must be considered in using the normal to approximate the binomial; namely, that a discrete distribution involving only integer values (the binomial) is being approximated by a continuous distribution (the normal) in which x can take on any value between negative and positive infinity. The problem that can arise in this situation is illustrated in Figure 6.29.

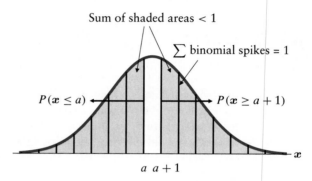

FIGURE 6.29   Illustration of the need for a continuity correction

For the binomial *spikes*, we see that $P(x \leq a)$ and $P(x \geq a + 1)$ will sum to 1 whenever a is an integer. But if we sum the *area* under the normal curve corresponding to $P(x \leq a)$ and $P(x \geq a + 1)$, this area does *not* sum to 1 because the area from a to $(a + 1)$ is missing. The usual way to handle this problem is to *associate one-half of this interval with each adjacent integer*. The continuous approximation to the probability $P(x \leq a)$ would thus be $P(x \leq a + \frac{1}{2})$, while the continuous approximation to $P(x \geq a + 1)$ would be $P(x \geq a + \frac{1}{2})$. This adjustment is called a **continuity correction**.

Without the continuity correction, the normal distribution will generally underestimate binomial probabilities. For small sample sizes, the underestimation may be fairly large. To avoid the tedious mechanics of the continuity correction, we use relatively large values of n to illustrate the normal approximation to the binomial, ignoring the (small) effect of the continuity correction.

☐ **EXAMPLE 6.7**   A survey of households in Toronto found that 53% of all households with annual incomes over $50,000 subscribed to a daily newspaper. If a random sample of 100 such households is taken, what is the probability that at least 45 and no more than 65 of the households interviewed are subscribers to a daily newspaper — what is $P(45 \leq x \leq 65)$ when $n = 100$ and $\pi = 0.53$? Using a computer, or Table I, this probability is found to be:

$$P(45 \leq x \leq 65) = 0.9499$$

Formula 6.7 can be used to approximate this probability by remembering that $n = 100$, $\pi = 0.53$; thus $n\pi = 100(0.53) = 53$, and $\sqrt{n\pi(1 - \pi)} = \sqrt{100(0.53)(0.47)} = 4.99$.

$$P(45 \leq x \leq 65) = P\left(\frac{45 - 53}{4.99} \leq z \leq \frac{65 - 53}{4.99}\right)$$

$$= P(-1.60 \leq z \leq 2.40)$$

$$= F(2.40) = [1 - F(1.60)]$$

$$= 0.9918 - [1 - 0.9452]$$

$$= 0.9370$$

The approximation is fairly good, as we would expect it to be when $n\pi(1 - \pi)$ is much larger than $3[100(0.53)(0.47) = 24.91]$. Using the correction for continuity mentioned above will improve the approximation. ■

☐ **STUDY QUESTION 6.2**   **Repeat Customers at K-Mart**

In a market survey for K-Mart, a researcher has been told that 41.5 percent of K-Mart customers are repeat customers, defined as having visited the store at least once in the previous two weeks. If this assumption is correct, the researcher wants to determine the probability that, in a sample of 1,000 customers, at least 400 but no more than 450 out of 1,000 randomly selected customers at a K-Mart store would be repeat customers.

a) Explain why the normal distribution might be used to find this probability.
b) Find the approximate binomial probability using the normal distribution.

• **ANSWER**   To find $P(400 \leq x \leq 450)$ with $n = 1,000$, and $\pi = 0.415$ where x has a binomial distribution, the normal approximation may be convenient if a computer package is not available for the following reasons:

a) The approximation should be reasonably good because $n\pi(1 - \pi) = 1,000(0.415)(0.585) = 242.775$ which greatly exceeds 3.
   Sample sizes of $n = 1,000$ and $\pi = 0.415$ are not found in binomial tables.
b) In this problem, $n\pi = 1,000(0.415) = 415$ and $\sqrt{n\pi(1 - \pi)} = 15.6$. Formula 6.7, without correcting for continuity, yields the following:

$$P(400 \leq x \leq 450) = P\left(\frac{400 - 415}{15.6} \leq z \leq \frac{450 - 415}{15.6}\right)$$

$$= P(-0.96 \leq z \leq 2.25)$$

$$= F(2.25) - [1 - F(0.96)]$$

$$= 0.9878 - 0.1685$$

$$= 0.8193$$

This approximation is close to the actual probability of 0.8285, which we determined using a computer package. ■

Recall that some binomial-type problems are presented in terms of proportions, rather than the number of successes. In the case of proportions, the appropriate normal approximation is given by Formula 6.8, which is equivalent to Formula 6.7.

Normal Approximation Using Proportions

Recall from Chapter 5 that binomial problems can be phrased in terms of the *proportion* of successes as well as the *number* of successes. For solving problems by the normal approximation method, the following formula using the sample proportion $p = x/n$ is equivalent to Formula 6.7.

Normal approximation to binomial using proportions:

$$z = \frac{p - \pi}{\sqrt{\dfrac{\pi(1 - \pi)}{n}}}.$$

(6.8)

Formula 6.8 should be recognized as the standardization of the variable $p = x/n$. In Chapter 5, it was shown that the variable p has a mean of $E[p] = \pi$ and a variance of $V[p] = \pi(1 - \pi)/n$.

section 6.7   Using the Computer to Determine Normal Probabilities

Statistical packages on the computer are convenient for determining probabilities for continuous distributions, just as they were for discrete distributions in Chapter 5. For the most part, these packages are very easy to use. We illustrate below the Doane package for the normal distribution.

From the main menu in Doane, select the Program Menu (P), and then select the *area* suboption. This option then gives the user the choice of four distributions: 1. F,   2. Student's t,   3. Chi-square, and   4. Normal. After selecting 4 for the normal, the program then asks for the z value. We selected the familiar $z = 1.96$ to illustrate the Doane output (shown in Figure 6.30).

```
Input z? 1.96
```

The area illustrates that $P(z \geq 1.96) = 0.025$, which is the same result given in Table III.

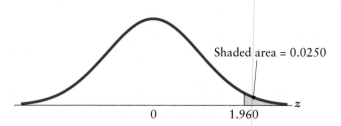

FIGURE 6.30   Output from computer determination of a normal probability

PROBLEMS

6.8 Explain what is meant by the phrase *standardization of a variable*. Why do we standardize variables?

6.9 Sketch the following:

a) the normal density function $N(10, 1)$

b) the curve $N(5, 100)$

6.10 Sketch the following:

a) the cumulative distribution function for the p.d.f. given in Problem 6.9(a)

b) the cumulative distribution function for the p.d.f. given in Problem 6.9(b)

6.11 Assume that x is $N(15, 100)$ where x is the change in a commodity price (¢/bushel). Calculate:

a) $P(5 \leq x \leq 25)$

b) $P(-5 \leq x \leq 35)$

c) $P(-10 \leq x \leq 35)$

d) Use your answer to part (b) to determine each of the following:

$$P(x \geq 35), P(x \leq -5), \text{ and } P(x \leq -5 \text{ or } x \geq 35)$$

6.12 Find the following values:

a) the value of b such that $P(z > b) = 0.01$

b) the value of a such that $P(z < a) = 0.025$

6.13 Suppose that the number of hours per week of lost work due to illness in a certain automobile assembly plant is approximately normally distributed, with a mean of 60 hours and a standard deviation of 15 hours. For a given week, selected at random, what are the following probabilities:

a) The number of lost work hours will exceed 85 hours.

b) The number of lost work hours will be between 45 and 55 hours.

c) The number of lost work hours will be exactly 60.

6.14 The average age of state congressmen in 1935 was 49.65 with a standard deviation of 5 years. Assume that their ages follow a normal distribution; what is the probability that a congressman selected at random would be younger than 38 years old?

6.15 A manufacturer of children's clothing knows that the heights of girls in their third year are normally distributed with mean 40 inches and standard deviation 5 inches. If a sweater is designed that will be suitable for anyone in this population with height between 45 and 55 inches, what is the probability that the sweater would fit a randomly selected girl from this population?

6.16 Over the years, the number of breakfasts served per day in the company cafeteria follows a normal distribution with mean 150 and standard deviation 15. What is the probability that the number of breakfasts served on a randomly selected workday will be between 165 and 180?

6.17 If z is a standardized normal variable, what is the probability of obtaining a value of z between -1.28 and $+1.65$? Use a computer if possible.

6.18 For each of the following, find the specified numerical value and illustrate the interval and area involved on a normal distribution sketch. (The symbol $\sim$ means *distributed as*.)

a) Assuming z is $N(0, 1)$, find $P(1.5 < z < 2.23)$.

b) Assuming z is $N(0, 1)$, find $P(-1.34 < z < +0.62)$.

c) For $z \sim N(0, 1)$, find the value of b that yields $P(-0.05 < z < b) = 0.40$.

d) For $z \sim N(0, 1)$, find the value of b that yields $P(|z| > b) = 0.12$ where $|z|$ denotes the absolute value of z.

e) For $x \sim N(45, 81)$, find $P(33 < x < 51)$.

f) For $x \sim N(15, 3.24^2)$, find $P(x > 20)$.

g) For $x \sim N(100, 400)$, find the value of a that yields $P(x < a) = 0.95$.

6.19 If the income in a community is normally distributed, with a mean of \$19,000 and a standard deviation of \$2,000, what minimum income does a member of this community have to earn in order to be in the top 10%? What is the maximum income one can have and still be in the middle 50%?

6.20 Suppose first that the sales invoices of a certain company have a normal distribution with mean \$32 and standard deviation \$8. Second, suppose that the service life of telephone poles used by public utility companies is normally distributed with average 15 years and variance 25 years.

a) Which of these normal distributions has the larger range? (Careful!)

b) What is the probability that a utility pole selected at random from this latter distribution will have a service life greater than 15 years?

c) Suppose I observe one utility pole that lasts only 3 years, and I also observe an invoice of \$50. Which of these occurrences is the *more* unusual?

6.21 The number of classified ads appearing in a daily newspaper for the sale of used cars is normally distributed with a mean of 100 and standard deviation of 16. Use a computer, if possible, to find the following.

a) The probability that a randomly selected paper will contain more than 140 used car ads.

b) The probability that a paper contains fewer than 80 such ads.

6.22 A traveling circus has found that its average attendance per performance is 6,000 people, with a standard deviation of 1,500. Assume that attendance is normally distributed.

a) Suppose a town asks the circus to come, but the only possible site in town holds only 8,000 people. What is the probability that this site will not be large enough, based on past experience?

b) If the circus loses money on 20% of their performances, what attendance must they have to break even for a given performance? Assume that the profit they make for a given performance depends only on the number of people attending the performance.

6.23 Approximate the binomial probability $P(240 \leq x \leq 260)$, for $n = 400$, $\pi = 0.60$, by using the normal distribution.

6.24 Approximate the binomial probability $P(360 \leq x \leq 390)$, for $n = 750$, $\pi = 0.60$, by using the normal distribution.

6.25 An American senator claims that 75% of his constituents favour his voting policies over the past year. In a random sample of 50 of these people, only 50% favoured his voting policies. Is this enough evidence to make the senator's claims strongly suspect? Use a normal approximation.

6.26 The manager of a service fleet estimates that 50% of all local service calls involve 30 minutes or less of on-site work. A randomly selected set of records on 100 recent service calls are examined. Assuming that the manager's estimate is accurate:

a) Use the binomial probability table or a computer to determine the probability that at least 55 but no more than 60 of these 100 service calls involved 30 minutes or less work time.

b) Use the normal distribution to approximate this same probability.

---

section 6.8	# Exponential Distribution[†]

Another important continuous distribution, the **exponential distribution**, is closely related to a discrete distribution discussed previously, the Poisson. Both the Poisson and the exponential distributions have many applications in operations research, especially in studies of queueing (waiting-line) theory. These two distributions are related in such applications by the fact that if events (such as requests for service, or arrivals) are assumed to occur according to a Poisson probability law, then the exponential distribution can be used to determine the probability distribution of the time that elapses *between* such events. For example, if customers arrive at a bank in accordance with a Poisson distribution, the exponential may be used to determine the probability distribution of the intervals between arrivals. Determination of the time it takes to be serviced (the service time) in these models is another application of the exponential distribution.

The exponential distribution is a continuous function that has the same parameter, λ, as the Poisson. Lambda, as before, represents the mean rate at which events (arrivals or service completions) occur. Thus, a value of $\lambda = 3.0$ may imply that service completions occur, on the average, at the rate of 3.0 per minute (or any other time unit). If a telephone line can handle an average of 20 customers per hour, then λ, defined as the mean number of customers being served by the telephone facilities, is $\lambda = 20$ (per hour) or $\lambda = \frac{1}{3}$ (per minute). Similarly, $\lambda = 3.8$ may imply, as it did in Section 5.7, that an average of 3.8 customers arrives at a checkout counter in a supermarket every minute.

[†] This section may be omitted without loss of continuity.

The basic assumption underlying the exponential distribution is that the longer the time interval becomes, the *less* likely it is that the service completion (or the next arrival) will take that long or longer. Suppose that we let the random variable T represent the amount of time between service completions or arrivals. As the value of T becomes larger and larger, the value of $f(T)$ for the exponential becomes smaller and smaller. In fact, as can be seen in the graph of the exponential distribution in Figure 6.31, $f(T)$ approaches zero as T approaches infinity.

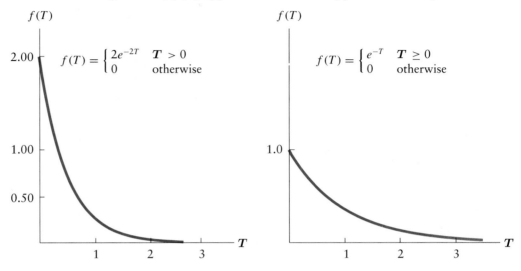

FIGURE 6.31   The exponential distribution: $f(T) = \lambda e^{-\lambda T}$

Note that the exponential distribution, similar to the Poisson, assumes a value other than zero only when T is greater than or equal to zero and when λ is greater than zero. The vertical intercept of the function shown in Figure 6.31 is seen to equal λ, which means that $f(0) = \lambda$. These relationships characterize the exponential distribution, which has the following density function.

Exponential distribution:

$$f(T) = \begin{cases} \lambda e^{-\lambda T} & \text{for } 0 \leq T \leq \infty, \lambda > 0 \\ 0 & \text{otherwise} \end{cases} \tag{6.9}$$

Mean and Variance of the Exponential

Remember that if we interpret λ as the mean arrival (or service) rate, then the exponential gives the probability distribution of the time *between* arrivals (or between service completions). Thus, it should not be very surprising to learn that the mean of the exponential distribution is $1/\lambda$. For example, suppose that the mean service rate of a cashier in a bank equals one-half customer every minute, or $\lambda = \frac{1}{2}$. Since it takes, on the average, one minute to serve half a customer, it takes two minutes to serve one customer; hence, the mean time between service completions is $1/\lambda = 2$. As was true for the Poisson, the mean and the variance of the exponential are both functions of λ. In this case, we could show that the mean and variance of the exponential are as follows:

Mean and variance of the exponential distribution:

$$\text{Exponential mean:} \quad \mu = \frac{1}{\lambda}$$

$$\text{Exponential variance:} \quad \sigma^2 = \frac{1}{\lambda^2}$$

(6.10)

Since the exponential and the Poisson distributions can both be applied to problems of arrivals at a service facility, suppose we reconsider the example in Section 5.7, using the exponential function to describe the time between arrivals at a supermarket checkout counter. The mean number of arrivals is $\lambda = 3.8$ per minute, so the mean time between arrivals will be $1/\lambda = 1/3.8 = 0.263$ minutes (or one customer approximately every 16 seconds).

By substituting $\lambda = 3.8$ into Formula 6.9, the exponential distribution becomes:

$$f(T) = 3.8e^{-3.8T}$$

The variance of this time between arrivals is $1/\lambda^2 = 1/(3.8)^2 = 0.069$ minutes.

Now, suppose we want to calculate the probability that the time between arrivals is greater than one minute, $P(T > 1)$. One procedure utilizing calculus is to integrate the exponential function over the interval in question in order to find the area under the curve. Fortunately, such integrations are not necessary, since tables have been prepared that permit direct evaluation of the exponential function (or a computer may be used). Table IV in this book gives values of the cumulative exponential distribution $F(T)$ associated with selected values of λT.

To find $P(T > 1)$ when $\lambda = 3.8$, we first use the cumulative exponential distribution table (Table IV) to find $F(1)$. The value of $F(1)$ is found in the row labeled $\lambda T = 3.8(1) = 3.8$. Since for $\lambda T = 3.8$, the value of $F(1) = 0.978$, we can write $P(T > 1)$ as follows:

$$P(T > 1) = 1 - P(T \leq 1) = 1 - F(1)$$

$$= 1 - 0.978$$

$$= 0.022$$

Similarly, if one wants to determine the probability that an arrival will occur between one-half and one minute when $\lambda = 3.8$, Table IV can be used to find $P(\frac{1}{2} \leq T \leq 1) = F(1.0) - F(0.5)$. We already know that $F(1.0) = 0.978$. The value for $F(0.5)$ is found in Table IV under $\lambda(0.5) = 3.8(0.5) = 1.9$ and equals $F(0.5) = 0.850$. Thus, $F(1.0) - F(0.5) = 0.978 - 0.850 = 0.128$. This example is illustrated in Figure 6.32.

Calculations of the above nature can be especially useful in the queueing problems mentioned earlier. If, in addition to studying the pattern of arrivals at our supermarket checkout counter, we had also investigated the service time of the cashiers, then we could develop a relationship that would indicate the probability that our cashiers would not be busy for a period of T minutes and the probability that the customers would have to wait more (or less) than T minutes. Ideally, such an investigation could lead to an analysis of the benefits of keeping a customer waiting versus the cost of hiring (or firing) another cashier, the result being a staffing policy designed to balance these costs and benefits. (Too often, it seems, the arrival rate in many supermarkets *exceeds* the service rate for extended periods of time.)

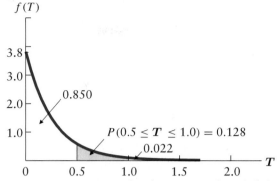

FIGURE 6.32   Example of exponential probability problem with $\lambda = 3.8$

Using the Computer to Determine Exponential Probabilities

To illustrate use of a computer for the exponential distribution, we have selected the package BSTAT. In this package, the user first selects the option *probability distributions* from the main menu, and then selects *exponential normal distribution* from the submenu. To illustrate the BSTAT package, we selected $\lambda = 3.8$, as this is the same mean used in Figure 6.32. Also in that figure, $P(T \leq 1.0)$ can be calculated to equal 0.978; for comparison, we now let $T = 1.00$. The BSTAT questions, user input (in bold), and the program output are shown below.

```
MEAN RATE OF OCCURRENCE: 3.8

OPTIONS:        A. CALCULATE PROBABILITY GIVEN T
                B. CALCULATE T GIVEN PROBABILITY

        ENTER T: 1.0

    EXPONENTIAL DISTRIBUTION

    MEAN RATE OF OCCURRENCE = 3.8
        T = 1
        P = 0.978
```

$P(T < 1.0) = 0.978$ is consistent with the probability presented in Figure 6.32.

Probability Distributions—Summary

The probability distributions presented in Chapters 5 and 6 are summarized in Table 6.6. The first two are discrete distributions, and the latter three are continuous distributions. Although many practical problems in statistical inference and decision-making can be resolved by using these distributions, they are not the only ones upon which statisticians rely. In the forthcoming chapters of this book, we will study three additional continuous distributions, the t, the F, and the χ^2. Table 6.6 serves as the summary for Chapter 6.

TABLE 6.6 Summary of Probability Distributions

Probability Distribution	Parameters	Characteristics	Mass or Density Function Given in Formula	Mean	Variance	Reference Sections	Probability Table
Discrete							
Binomial x	$0 \leq \pi \leq 1$ $n = 0, 1, 2, \ldots$	Skewed unless $\pi = 0.5$, family of distributions	(5.1)	$n\pi$	$n\pi(1-\pi)$	5.2 5.3 5.4	$P(x_{\text{binomial}})$ in Table I
Poisson x	$\lambda > 0$	Skewed positively, family of distributions	(5.6)	λ	λ	5.7	$P(x_{\text{Poisson}})$ in Table II
Continuous							
Normal x	$-\infty < \mu < +\infty$ $\sigma > 0$	Symmetrical, family of distributions	(6.4)	μ	σ^2	6.4	—
Standardized Normal z	—	Symmetrical, single distribution	(6.6)	0	1	6.5	$F(z)$ in Table III
Exponential T	$\lambda > 0$	Skewed positively, family of distributions	(6.9)	$1/\lambda$	$1/\lambda^2$	6.8	$F(T)$ in Table IV

In order to use all these distributions in decision-making about populations, based on sample evidence, we must first be more precise in our study of sampling. In many of our examples, a *sample* or a *random selection* has been mentioned but not formally defined. In Chapter 7, we present the details of sampling and the resulting important probability distributions for sample statistics. These will be used throughout the remainder of this book.

PROBLEMS

6.27 Given the exponential distribution with parameter λ equal to 3.0, complete the following:

   a) Graph the probability density function.

   b) What are the mean and the variance of this distribution?

   c) What percent of the area of this distribution lies within $\pm$ one standard deviation of the mean? Within $\pm$ two standard deviations of the mean?

6.28 Describe how the Poisson and the exponential distributions are related. What assumptions underlie these distributions?

6.29 Suppose that a bank can service, on the average, four customers per six-minute period. Assume that the number of customers serviced is Poisson-distributed.

   a) What is the probability that this bank will be able to service six or more customers in a six-minute period? [*Hint:* Use the Poisson distribution with $\lambda = 4$.]

   b) What is the probability that servicing a customer will take longer than three minutes?

   c) What is the probability that servicing a customer will take between two and four minutes?

6.30 A stockbroker has an average of ten customers call between 9:00 and 10:00 each morning that the stock exchange is open. Customers call according to the Poisson distribution.

a) What is the probability that the stockbroker will have exactly ten customers call between these hours on a given morning?

b) What is the probability that the time between consecutive calls will exceed six minutes?

c) What is the probability that the time between consecutive calls will be between three and six minutes?

6.31 Airplanes land at a small airport at the rate of one every 30 minutes, following a Poisson distribution. Solve using a computer, if possible.

a) What is the probability that the time between arrivals will be less than 15 minutes?

b) What is the probability that the time between arrivals will be greater than three quarters of an hour?

6.32 Suppose that you observe the following service times (in minutes) by a bank teller: 1/2, 1, 1/2, 6, 1, 3.

a) What is the mean service time, given these observations? What is the variance?

b) Graph the probability density function for this application, assuming that times between service completions are exponentially distributed with mean = 2.

c) What is the probability that service will take longer than two minutes? What is $P(1 \le x \le 3)$?

6.33 For the exponential distribution, the interval $\mu \pm 1\sigma$ equals $1/\lambda \pm 1(1/\lambda)$, since $\mu = 1/\lambda$ and $\sigma = 1/\lambda$.

a) If $\lambda = 2$, use Table IV to calculate the probability that T falls between $\mu \pm 1\sigma$. Sketch this area on a graph.

b) Repeat part (a) using $\lambda = 4$.

c) Will the probabilities in parts (a) and (b) hold for any positive λ? Why is this probability greater than the rule of thumb of 68%?

d) Repeat parts (a) and (b) for $\mu \pm 2\sigma$.

6.34 Assume that the interarrival time at a tollbooth is exponentially distributed with a mean interarrival time of $\frac{1}{2}$ minute.

a) What is the value of λ for this problem?

b) What is the variance of the interarrival times?

c) What is the probability that the time between two consecutive arrivals will be between 0 and 1 minute?

d) What is $P(T > 2.0)$? Solve using a computer, if possible.

CHAPTER SUMMARY

KEY TERMS AND EXPRESSIONS

Probability density function: A rule describing the height of $f(x)$ for a continuous random variable x.

Area under the density function from a to b: The probability measure of the event $P(a \le x \le b)$.

Cumulative distribution function $F(x)$: The sum of all the area under the density function to the left of a specified value of the random variable x.

Normal distribution: A symmetrical, bell-shaped, continuous probability density function characterized by its two parameters, the mean and the variance.

Standardized normal distribution: A normal distribution with mean = 0 and variance = 1.

Continuity correction: An extension of the interval defining an event in terms of a discrete random variable so that its probability may be more accurately approximated by a continuous probability distribution.

Exponential distribution: A continuous probability density defined for a random variable T by the function:

$$f(T) = \begin{cases} \lambda e^{-\lambda T} & \text{for } 0 \le T \le \infty, \lambda > 0 \\ 0 & \text{otherwise} \end{cases}$$

This distribution is useful for analysis of the time elapsing between events whose occurrence follows a Poisson distribution.

EXERCISES

[*Note:* Exercises 6.35–6.44 require the use of calculus.]

6.35 The cumulative distribution function for Problem 6.1 is as follows:

$$F(x) = \begin{cases} 0 & \text{for } x \leq 0 \\ x^2 & 0 \leq x \leq 1 \\ 1 & x \geq 1 \end{cases}$$

a) Sketch this function and the p.d.f.,

$$f(x) = \frac{dF(x)}{dx}$$

b) What is the value of $F(\frac{1}{2})$? Does this value agree with $P(x \leq \frac{1}{2})$ calculated in Problem 6.1?

c) Calculate $E[x]$ by evaluating the following:

$$\int_{\text{All } x} xf(x)dx = \int_0^1 2x^2 dx$$

d) Calculate $V[x]$ by evaluating $E[x^2] - \mu^2$, where

$$E[x^2] = \int_{\text{All } x} x^2 f(x)dx = \int_0^1 2x^3 dx$$

6.36 Find the following expectations for continuous random variables.

a) Find $E[x]$ for the p.d.f. shown in part (a) of Figure 6.33 by integrating

$$\int_{\text{All } x} xf(x)dx$$

b) Find $V[x]$ for this same problem by solving $E[x^2] - \mu^2$. [See Exercise 6.35 part (d).]

c) Repeat parts (a) and (b) for the p.d.f. in part (b) of Figure 6.33.

d) Repeat parts (a) and (b) for the p.d.f. in part (c) of Figure 6.33.

$$f(x) = \begin{cases} 2 & 1 \leq x \leq 1.5 \\ 0 & \text{otherwise} \end{cases} \qquad f(x) = \begin{cases} \frac{1}{4} + \frac{1}{8}x & -2 \leq x \leq 2 \\ 0 & \text{otherwise} \end{cases} \qquad f(x) = \begin{cases} e^{-x} & 0 \leq x \leq \infty \\ 0 & \text{otherwise} \end{cases}$$

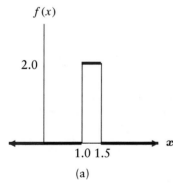

(a)

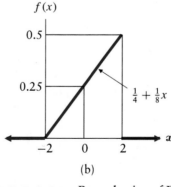

(b)

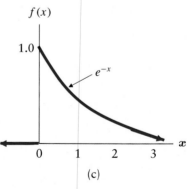

(c)

FIGURE 6.33   Reproduction of Figure 6.8

6.37 Find the cumulative distribution function for each p.d.f. shown in Figure 6.33 by integrating $\int_{-\infty}^x f(x)\,dx$.

a) Verify the following for the first graph:

$$F(x) = \begin{cases} 0 & x \leq 1 \\ 2x - 2 & 1 \leq x \leq 1.5 \\ 1 & x \geq 1.5 \end{cases}$$

b) Verify this function for the second graph:

$$F(x) = \begin{cases} 0 & x \leq -2 \\ \frac{1}{16}x^2 + \frac{1}{4}x + \frac{1}{4} & -2 \leq x \leq 2 \\ 1 & x \geq 2 \end{cases}$$

c) Verify the following for the third graph:

$$F(x) = \begin{cases} 0 & x \leq 0 \\ 1 - e^{-x} & x \geq 0 \end{cases}$$

[*Hint:* $\int e^{-x}\,dx = -e^{-x}$.]

6.38 Find the mean of the distribution defined in Problem 6.6.

6.39 The *uniform* or *rectangular* distribution can be defined in terms of its cumulative distribution function, as follows:

$$F(x) = \begin{cases} \dfrac{x-a}{b-a} & \text{for } a \le x \le b \\ 0 & \text{for } x < a \\ 1 & \text{for } x > b \end{cases}$$

a) Derive the uniform density function for $a \le x \le b$ by differentiating $F(x)$ with respect to x.

b) Sketch both the density function and the cumulative function for the uniform distribution.

c) Show that the uniform distribution satisfies the two properties of all probability functions.

d) Find the mean of this distribution.

6.40 The probability density function for the number of hours behind schedule that the Amtrack Silver Comet arrives in New York from Miami is as follows:

$$f(x) = \begin{cases} \frac{1}{2}x & 0 \le x \le 2 \\ 0 & \text{otherwise} \end{cases}$$

a) Determine the cumulative probability function for this problem, and then sketch both the density and cumulative functions.

b) Show that this function possesses the two properties of a probability density function.

c) What is the probability in a randomly selected trip that the train arrives between 30 and 90 minutes late?

d) Evaluate $F(x)$ at $x = 1$. What probability does $F(1)$ represent?

e) Find the mean of the random variable x.

6.41 A consulting firm studying a large production facility has determined that the peak load on the system always occurs during the 3:00–4:00 p.m. time period. The following p.d.f. accurately describes the moment of the peak load (x = time, in hours).

$$f(x) = \begin{cases} 3x^2 & 0 \le x \le 1 \\ 0 & \text{otherwise} \end{cases}$$

a) Sketch this function. Plot a few points if necessary.

b) Show that the area under the function equals 1 by integrating $\int f(x)dx$.

c) Find a formula for $F(x)$. Use this formula to find $F(\frac{1}{4}) = P(x \le \frac{1}{4})$.

d) Calculate $E[x]$ by evaluating $\int x f(x)dx$.

6.42 Prove the following for the exponential distribution:

$$E[T] = \frac{1}{\lambda} \text{ and } V[T] = \frac{1}{\lambda^2}$$

6.43 Prove the following.

a) The standardized normal density function reaches its maximum height at $z = 0$. [*Hint:* Show that the second derivative is negative.]

b) The points $z = \pm 1$ for the standardized normal density function are inflection points. [*Hint:* Show that the second derivative equals zero.]

6.44 A continuous p.d.f. not presented in this chapter is the *Beta distribution*. This distribution has two parameters, r and n.

$$f(x) = \begin{cases} {}_{n-1}C_{r-1}x^{r-1}(1-x)^{n-r-1} & 0 \le x \le 1 \\ 0 & \text{otherwise} \end{cases}$$

a) Discuss the similarities and differences between this distribution and the binomial distribution.

b) Graph this distribution for $r = 1$, $n = 2$.

c) Determine $E[x]$.

d) If $r \le n/2$, will the distribution be positively or negatively skewed?

6.45 Refer to Exercise 2.40 for the Shark Loan Company.

a) Graph the exponential p.d.f. with $\lambda = 0.02$. Compare this graph with the polygon for Exercise 2.40. Do they seem to correspond well?

b) Elaborate on your answer to part (a) by finding $P(0 \le T \le 20)$, $P(20 \le T \le 60)$, and $P(T > 60)$, and then comparing these answers to the table of values given in Exercise 3.50.

c) What are the mean, median, and standard deviation of an exponential distribution with $\lambda = 0.02$? Are these answers consistent with values for Exercise 2.40(b)?

USING THE COMPUTER

6.46 Sixty percent of all sales at a Gulf Oil Station are charged on credit cards. In a random sample of 200 sales, what is the probability that one-half or more are *cash* sales?

6.47 An auditor reports that 85.2% of the shareholders of a large automobile firm cast votes by proxy at the annual shareholders meeting. What is the probability that in a survey of 900 randomly selected shareholders, at most 5/6 of them vote by proxy?

6.48 Eighty percent of the professional athletes in a sport favour union representation for bargaining with owners. If ABC Sports contacts 50 of the players at random, what is the probability that more than 90% of these will support the union representation?

6.49 The proportion of buyers of long-term government bonds who sell them prior to maturity is 0.655. In a random sample of 120 buyers, what is the probability that more than 70 will sell before maturity? Approximate using the normal distribution.

6.50 Thirty percent of all mutual funds are structured to invest in foreign security markets. In a random sample of 40 such funds, what is the probability that more than 15 may invest in foreign security markets?

6.51 A hospital knows that 25% of its bills are paid prior to the second invoice. In a computerized check of 1,000 accounts, it is found that 770 bills required two or more statements before payment was received. Would you conclude that the 1,000 accounts checked constitutes a random sample from the population of all accounts? Use a probability measure in justifying your answer.

6.52 Table 6.7 shows the percent of vehicles exceeding the speed limit on U.S. highways by state of location of the highway. The figures are based on a study using 1,800 speed detectors that checked hundreds of thousands of vehicle speeds. The chart heading says percent of *drivers* instead of *vehicles*, but this is simply a jump in bureaucratic logic and terminology.

TABLE 6.7 Percent of Drivers Exceeding the Speed Limit

State	(%)	State	(%)
Alabama	39.2	Montana	42.7
Alaska	17.0	Nebraska	39.1
Arizona	49.6	Nevada	51.2
Arkansas	30.0	New Hampshire	39.8
California	45.0	New Jersey	49.5
Colorado	42.7	New Mexico	41.2
Connecticut	44.3	New York	48.3
Delaware	48.9	North Carolina	32.7
Florida	45.7	North Dakota	47.2
Georgia	30.2	Ohio	45.6
Hawaii	43.1	Oklahoma	50.0
Idaho	33.8	Oregon	35.1
Illinois	34.5	Pennsylvania	36.4
Indiana	44.2	Rhode Island	46.3
Iowa	41.4	South Carolina	28.4
Kansas	44.3	South Dakota	37.8
Kentucky	36.8	Tennessee	36.7
Louisiana	43.6	Texas	34.7
Maine	41.6	Utah	47.5
Maryland	44.4	Vermont	50.0
Massachusetts	56.3	Virginia	48.9
Michigan	48.8	Washington	33.1
Minnesota	38.6	West Virginia	18.1
Mississippi	38.0	Wisconsin	33.5
Missouri	47.1	Wyoming	48.4

Source: Federal Highway Administration

a) If the percent specified for Alaska [the state with the lowest percentage of speeders (17.0%)] is correct, what would be the probability of observing 30 or fewer speeders in a random check of 200 vehicles on federal highways in Alaska?

b) Massachusetts wins the booby prize since it has the lowest percentage of drivers obeying the law [highest percentage (56.3%) of speeders]. What would be the probability of observing 100 or fewer speeders in a random check of 200 vehicles on federal highways in Massachusetts?

c) Determine the second best and the second worst states for persons obeying the speed limit on federal highways. For each, find the probability of the same events as in parts (a) and (b), respectively.

d) Find the probability of 60 or fewer speeders among 200 vehicles for the state you are in (or one designated by the instructor).

6.53 Refer to the age distribution for the United States population given in Problem 4.20 on page 135. If a random selection of 80 persons is taken from this population, what are these probabilities?

a) ten or more would be over 65

b) 15 or fewer would be 14 years old or younger

c) fewer than five would be in their forties

CASE PROBLEMS

6.54 A fruit-packing company in Florida uses sorting machines to separate truckloads of oranges into various size categories. One machine is used to separate Class A fruit from all others. Class A oranges must have a diameter between 7 and 9 cm. To check on the sorting machine, oranges are selected at random from the sorted output stream of Class A fruit and checked for sizing. A control chart as shown in Figure 6.34 is used to keep a record of the test results. The size of each orange checked is plotted as a dot on the chart. If the dot falls within the control limits, then it is presumed that the sorting machine is working properly. If the dot falls outside the limits, or if a series of dots occurs all on the same side of the mean, or if a trend of dots occurs approaching one of the limits, then this indicates that the sorting machine may be *out of control*. The process is then halted and the machine adjusted so that it does not select oranges that are either too large or too small. (Note that the rejected fruit proceeds on a different conveyor belt. It is also checked to see whether it contains fruit that *do fall within* the control limits. This result would also indicate a loss of control in the sorting process.)

a) If the machine is properly adjusted, the size of Class A oranges selected will be normally distributed with $\mu = 8$ cm and $\sigma = 0.4$ cm. What is the probability that a single check (using the control chart technique for spotting oranges sized outside the limits) will incorrectly indicate that the process is out of control?

b) Suppose the screening layers within the sorting machine slip so that the machine is now sorting out oranges with $\mu = 7.5$ cm and $\sigma = 0.6$ cm. What is the probability that an orange randomly selected for the check will be within the control limits and indicate incorrectly that the machine is still sorting properly?

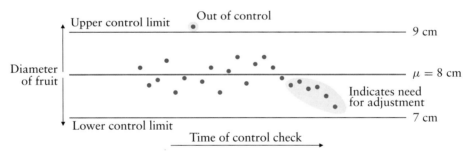

FIGURE 6.34 Control chart for oranges

6.55 At the company in Problem 6.54, the Class A fruit also passes through an eye examination for selection of the best quality fruit in appearance. This *Best Quality* fruit is then used in special Sunshine packages that are mailed throughout the country. Usually, about 20% of the Class A sized fruit are selected for these Sunshine packages.

An electronic device can be used to count all the fruit processed at this stage, both the fruit that is selected for the Sunshine packages and the fruit that is not. At some random time within every half hour, the counting device starts and counts 500 oranges. It automatically prints out in the control supervisor's office the number selected for Sunshine packages and the number not.

Assuming that the trained selectors are consistent in their judgments, variations from the usual 20% of Best Quality fruit indicate that the particular truckload of fruit being processed had a higher (or lower) percentage of high-quality oranges. The supervisor notes these facts along with the name of the producer and the grove of trees from which the fruit originated. On the other hand, if all the fruit being processed throughout the day is known by the supervisor to be from the same groves, then variations from the usual 20% may indicate some loss of efficiency or change of judgment by the selectors due to monotony or whatever.

a) For a population of 20% Best Quality fruit with perfect judgment by the selectors, what is the probability that in a given control lot of 500 oranges, fewer than 18% of the oranges would be selected as Best Quality fruit?

b) Set up a control chart on the number of oranges in a control lot of 500 that might be selected as Best Quality fruit if 20% of the population is that type. Use control limits that include 96% of all the cases that might occur if the selection process is in control.

CHAPTER 7

Sampling and Sampling Distributions

section 7.1

Introduction

This chapter begins the task of relating the probability concepts studied in the past four chapters to the objective of statistics stated in Chapter 1: to draw inferences about population parameters on the basis of sample information.

Recall from Chapter 1 that a major portion of statistics is concerned with the problem of estimating population parameters, or testing hypotheses about such parameters. If we could take a census (examine all items in the population), then the value of the population parameters would be known. Unfortunately, a census of a population is usually not feasible because of monetary and/or time limitations. Hence, we must rely on observing a subset (or *sample*) of the items in the population, and use this information to make estimates or test hypotheses about the unknown parameters. The process of making estimates will be covered in Chapter 9, while the subject of hypothesis testing will be described in Chapters 10 and 11. In these subsequent chapters, we will usually assume that a sample has been taken. It is therefore important that we describe, in this chapter, how a sample is taken and what type of information can be drawn from a sample.

There are four basic questions that must be asked about samples and the process of inference:

1. What are the least expensive methods for collecting samples that best ensure that the samples are representative of the parent population?
2. What is the best way to describe sample information usefully and clearly?
3. How does one go about drawing conclusions from samples and making inferences about the population?
4. How reliable are the inferences and conclusions drawn from sample information?

section 7.2

Sample Designs

By describing various **sample designs**, we will first answer the question of how sample information can be most efficiently collected.

> A sample design is a procedure or plan, specified before any data are collected, for obtaining a sample from a given population.

Nonsampling Errors

The primary requisite for a *good* sample is that it be representative of the population that one is trying to describe. There are, of course, many ways of collecting a *poor* sample. One obvious source of errors of misrepresentation arises when the *wrong population is sampled inadvertently*. The 1936 U.S. presidential election poll conducted by the now defunct *Literary Digest* remains a classic example of this problem. The *Literary Digest* predicted, on the basis of a sample of over two million names selected from telephone directories and automobile registrations, that Landon would win an overwhelming victory in the election that year. Instead, Roosevelt won by a substantial margin. The sample collected by the *Digest* apparently represented the population of predominantly middle- and upper-class people who owned cars and telephones; it misrepresented the general electorate, however, and Roosevelt's support came from the lower-income classes, whose opinions were not reflected in the poll.

Another type of error known as *response bias* frequently affects results in surveys and public opinion polls. Poorly worded questionnaires or improper interview techniques may elicit responses that do not reflect true opinions. Kinsey's research on sex practices, for example, received widespread criticism for reporting responses to questions to which most people are fairly sensitive. Such responses are, therefore, likely to be distorted from the truth. Similarly, it is amazing how the economic well-being of certain college alumni can vary over the interval between the annual homecoming reunion and the annual fund-raising drive.

These types of error are called **nonsampling errors**. Nonsampling errors include all kinds of human errors — mistakes in collecting, analyzing, or reporting data; sampling from the wrong population; and response bias. If the researcher incorrectly adds a column of numbers, this represents a nonsampling error just as much as does the failure of a respondent to provide truthful information on a questionnaire.

Sampling Errors

In addition, even in well-designed and well-executed samples, there are bound to be cases in which the sample does not provide a true representation of the population under study, simply because samples represent only a portion of a population. In such cases, the information contained in the sample may lead to incorrect inferences about the parent population; that is, an *error* might be made in estimating the population characteristics based on the sample information. Errors of this nature, representing the differences that can exist between a sample statistic and the population parameter being estimated, are called **sampling errors**. Sampling errors obviously can occur in all data-collection procedures with the exception of a complete enumeration of the population (a census).

One primary objective in sample design is to minimize both sampling and nonsampling errors. Errors are costly, not only in terms of the time and money spent in collecting a sample, but also in terms of the potential loss implicit in making a wrong decision on the basis of an incorrect inference from the data. An inaccurate public-opinion survey, for instance, could cost a politician votes if a campaign design is based on inferences from these data. Similarly, investment in real estate or stocks might cause an investor to lose a considerable amount of money if the (sample) information that led to a particular investment proved incorrect.

Note that it is the *decisions* resulting from incorrect inferences that may be costly, not the incorrect inferences themselves; hence, it is customary to refer to one objective of sampling as that of *minimizing the cost of making an incorrect decision (error)*. But reducing the costs of making an incorrect decision usually implies increasing the cost of designing and/or collecting the sample. For example, additional effort (or money) devoted to designing a questionnaire, identifying the correct population, or collecting a larger sample usually results in a more representative sample. We can therefore state that the primary objective in sample design is to *balance the costs of making an error and the costs of sampling*.

Designing an optimal sampling procedure may not be easy. One reason is that the elements of a given population may be extremely difficult to locate, gain access to, or even identify. For example, it may be impractical, if not impossible, to identify the population elements of color television owners in a particular city. Another obvious difficulty already mentioned is cost; budget constraints, for example, may force one to collect fewer data or to be less careful about collecting these data than ideal designs would dictate. Also, the costs of making an incorrect decision may be very hard to specify. A discussion of all the problems inherent in sample design, especially those concerned with nonsampling errors and the costs of making an incorrect decision, falls outside the scope of this book. Therefore, we shall concentrate our attention on the problem of determining which sample designs most effectively minimize sampling errors.

Probabilistic Sampling

Probabilistic sampling designs are based primarily on a random selection process. Often, the first criterion for a good sample is that each item in the population under investigation have an *equal and independent chance* to be part of the sample; also, it is often advantageous that each set of *n* items have an equal probability of being included. Samples in which every possible sample of size *n* (every combination of *n* items from the *N* in the population) is equally likely are referred to as *simple random samples*. These are the types of samples that we have used implicitly throughout our discussion of probability theory to illustrate the use of formulas and probability functions.

Simple random sampling requires that one have access to all items in the population. For a small population of elements that are easy to identify and sample, this procedure normally gives the best results. However, simple random sampling of a large population may be difficult, perhaps even impossible, to implement; at best, it will be quite costly. For this case, a more practical procedure must be designed, even though it also will be more restrictive.

In another popular sampling plan, called **systematic sampling**, a random starting point in the population is selected, and then every *k*th element encountered thereafter becomes an item in the sample. For example, every 200th name in a telephone directory might be called in order to survey public opinion. This method is *not* equivalent to simple random sampling because every set of *n* names does not have an equal probability of being selected. Bias *will* result under systematic sampling if there is a *periodicity* to the elements of the population. For instance, sampling sales in a supermarket every seventh day certainly will result in a sample that represents only the sales of a single day, say Monday, rather than the weekly pattern.

Generating Random Numbers

Designing a sample in which each item in the population has an equal probability of being selected usually requires carefully controlled sampling procedures. The stereotype of drawing slips of paper from a goldfish bowl may satisfy the requirements of a simple random sample, but there is no practical way to be certain of this. A more systematic approach to ensuring randomness is to select a sample with the aid of a table of **random numbers**. In such a table, each digit between 0 and 9 is called a *random digit*; here, the word random implies that all of these digits have the same long-run relative frequency (the same probability of occurring), and the occurrence or nonoccurrence of any number is independent of the occurrence or nonoccurence of all other numbers, or of all sets of *n* other numbers. In a table of random numbers, random digits are usually combined to form numbers of more than one digit. For example, random digits taken in pairs represent a population of 100 different numbers (00 to 99), each with a probability of occurring of 1/100, and each independent of all other numbers. Likewise, in a table of random numbers consisting of groups of three random digits, each of the 1,000 numbers between 000 and 999 will have a probability of occurring of 1/1,000 and will be independent of the remaining numbers. Table V in Appendix C is a page of random numbers from a book published by the Rand Corporation, containing one million random digits.[1]

A table of random numbers can be used in the following manner to select a simple random sample of n items from a finite population of size N. First, a unique number between 1 and N must be assigned to each of the N items in the population. The table of random numbers is then consulted. The first n numbers encountered (starting at *any* point in the table and moving systematically across rows or down columns) that are less than N constitute a set of n random numbers. The n elements corresponding to these n numbers form the random sample.

To illustrate this procedure, we will use Table V to select a sample of four items from a population of 75 elements. A random selection of a starting point in the table is customary; let us arbitrarily start with the number that is tenth from the bottom in the first column, 09237. Since our population has less than 100 elements, we need to look at only two digits of each number. Suppose we use the first two digits. Then, the first item in our sample becomes item number 09. Reading down, the next three items in the sample are 11, 60, and 71. We skip 79 because we have only 75 elements in the population. Note that if our sample were to contain five items, the number 09 would have occurred again. This duplication could cause problems, as it may not be possible to sample the same item twice. Its usefulness may be destroyed by the first sample, as would be the case in testing the tread life of a tire or measuring the yield from a new seed variety at an agricultural testing station. For a sample size that is small in relation to the population size, discarding the duplicate item and letting the next element on the list (63) take its place will not seriously distort the usefulness of this method. If an item is discarded, it must be recognized that sampling is now taking place without replacement, rather than with replacement.

Using the Computer to Generate Random Numbers

Many statistical packages for the computer will generate random numbers. In this section we illustrate the use of the Doane package to replicate the process described above, that of generating four random digits from a uniform distribution where all numbers generated have the same probability. The Doane package also generates random numbers from a normal distribution or from a Poisson distribution. In this case we access the program menu (P), and then the RAND submenu. The program questions, our responses (in bold) and the output are as follows:

```
RAND
1. Normal
2. Uniform
3. Poisson

INPUT
    Which option do you want (1, 2, or 3)?  2
    How many random numbers do you want?  4
    For random start, enter any 2-digit number:  34
    What is the lower limit A?  01
    What is the upper limit B?  75
```

---

[1] Each digit in Table V is random; hence, these numbers may be used in pairs of triplets, or combined in many other ways.

```
    12    6    10    51
```

These are the four random numbers generated by the computer. Repeating the process would result in another set of random numbers, quite possibly all different from these four.

Sampling with Prior Knowledge

Two important random sampling plans depend on prior knowledge about the population: stratified sampling and cluster sampling.

Stratified Sampling. The use of **stratified sampling** requires that a population be divided into homogeneous classes or groups, called *strata*. Each stratum is then sampled according to certain specified criteria. The advantage of this procedure is that if homogeneous subsets of the population can be identified, then only a relatively small number of observations is needed to determine the characteristics of each subset. It can be shown that:

> The optimal method of selecting strata is to find groups with a large variability between strata, but with only a small variability within strata.

We illustrate stratified sampling by considering the task of determining the majority political preference in a given Canadian city. Assume that it is known, from previous surveys and elections, that political preferences in this town tend to correspond to various income levels. For instance, upper-income families tend to have similar opinions, as do middle-income and lower-income families. Assume further that in this particular city it is well known that the upper-income families and the lower-income families will have less variability of opinion within their respective groups than will the middle-income group. It may be that upper-income families in general will favour a fiscally conservative candidate, lower-income families will favour a candidate who promises increased city services, and middle-income families will be less predictable.

A *proportional* stratified sampling plan selects items from each stratum in proportion to the size of that stratum. This procedure ensures that each stratum in the sample is *weighted* by the number of elements it contains. If the category *upper-income families* includes 10% of the voting population, then a proportional stratified sampling plan will randomly select 10% of the sample from this group. Many times, however, a more efficient procedure is to select a *disproportionate* stratified sample. A plan of this nature collects more than a proportionate amount of observations in those strata with the most variability, such as the middle-income group in the above example. In other words, by allocating a disproportionate amount of effort (time, money, et cetera) to those groups whose opinions are most in doubt, one often obtains a maximum amount of information for a given cost. Similarly, if it is more costly to sample from a particular stratum, one may elect to take fewer items from that stratum.

Cluster Sampling. **Cluster sampling** represents a second important sampling plan in which the population is subdivided into groups in an attempt to design an efficient sample. The subdivisions or classes of the population in this case are called clusters, where each cluster, ideally, has the same characteristics as the parent population. If each cluster is assumed to be representative of the population, then the characteristics of this population can be estimated by (randomly) picking a cluster and then randomly sampling elements from within this cluster. Since clusters contain sampling units that are geographically or physically close together, the cost of sampling is greatly reduced. Sampling within a cluster may take any of the forms already discussed and may even involve sampling from clusters within a cluster (two-stage cluster sampling). The criterion for the selection of optimal clusters is exactly opposite to that for strata:

> There should be little variability between clusters, but a high variability (representation of the population) within each cluster.

Cluster sampling can be illustrated by extending our previous example. Assume that we now want to sample political preferences in all Canadian cities rather than just one. In this case, a simple random sample would probably be very difficult and expensive, if not impossible, to collect; instead, it may be that a number of cities adequately represent the population of all cities, and it would then be sufficient to sample from just one of these cities. Within the chosen city, one could use simple random sampling, stratified sampling, or systematic sampling, or one could break the city into smaller clusters. In cluster sampling, there is always the danger that a cluster is not truly representative of the population; a geographical bias, for example, may exist when one city is used to represent political preferences in all cities.

Double, Multiple, and Sequential Sampling

One of the most important decisions in any sampling design involves selecting the *size* of the sample. Usually, size is determined in advance of any data collection, but in some circumstances, this may not be the most efficient procedure. Consider the problem of determining whether a shipment of 5,000 items meets certain specified standards. It would be too expensive to check all 5,000 items for their quality, so a sample is drawn, and each item in the sample is tested for quality. Rather than take one large sample, of perhaps 100 items, a preliminary random sample of 25 items could be drawn and inspected. It may often be unnecessary to examine the remaining 75 items; perhaps the entire lot can be judged on the basis of these 25 items. If a high percentage of the 25 components were defective, the conclusion drawn would probably be that the quality of the entire lot may not be acceptable. A low percentage of defectives may lead to accepting the lot. Values other than these extremes may also lead to acceptance or rejection of the entire lot. Nevertheless, there will usually be a range in which there is doubt about the quality of the entire lot. For example, it may be normal to have zero or one defective in a sample of 25. More than four would indicate too many defectives in the lot. Two or three defectives, however, may lead one to suspect the entire lot, but not necessarily to reject it. An additional sample, perhaps the remaining 75 items, could then be taken, and the lot judged on the basis of all 100 items.

Samples in which the items are drawn in two different stages, such as in the sequential fashion described above or from a cluster within a cluster, represent a process referred to as *two-stage sampling*. Virtually all important samples, and certainly all large-scale surveys, represent one form or another of multiple-stage sampling, and the sample design is usually not simple to plan. The major advantage of double, multiple, and **sequential sampling** procedures obviously depends on the savings that result when fewer items than usual must be observed. These procedures are especially appropriate when sampling is expensive, as when inspection destroys the usefulness of a valuable item or when travel expenses of the survey team would be high.

Nonprobabilistic Sampling

In some sense, all **nonprobabilistic sampling** procedures represent **judgment samples**, in that they involve the selection of the items in a sample on the basis of the judgment or opinion of one or more persons. Judgment sampling is usually employed when a random sample cannot be taken or is not practical. It may be that there is not enough time or money to collect a random sample; or perhaps the sample represents an exploratory study where randomness is not too important. On the other hand, when the number of population elements is small, the judgment of an expert may be better than random methods in picking a truly representative sample. For example, you are using judgment sampling when you ask a friend's opinion about a movie or about a particular college course. Similarly, *representative* individuals or animals are often chosen to participate in experiments, and accountants frequently select *typical* weeks for auditing accounts.

In **quota sampling**, each person gathering observations is given a specified number of elements to sample. This technique is used often in public-opinion surveys, in which the interviewer is allocated a certain number of people to interview. The decision as to exactly whom to interview is usually left to the individual doing the interviewing, although certain guidelines are almost always established. With well-trained and trustworthy interviewers, this procedure can be quite effective and can be carried out at a relatively low cost. Great danger exists, however, that procedures left to the interviewers' judgment and convenience may contain many unknown biases not conducive to a representative sample. Quota sampling is often used to obtain market research data or to survey for political preferences. In some of these situations, a quota sample can be thought of as a special form of stratified sampling, in which interviewers are sent out and told to obtain a specified number of interviews from each stratum.

The least representative sampling procedure selects observations on the basis of convenience to the researcher; in other words, a **convenience sample**. Street-corner surveys, in which the interviewer questions people as they go by, seems to be a favourite method of local TV news reporters for collecting public opinions. This method obviously cannot be considered very likely to yield a representative sample; more often, the results are biased and quite unsatisfactory. Convenience sampling is not widely used in circumstances other than preliminary or exploratory studies, or where representativeness is not a crucial factor.

The following table itemizes the sampling procedures described in Section 7.2.

TABLE 7.1   Statistical Sampling Procedures

Probabilistic	Nonprobabilistic
Simple random sampling	Judgment sampling
Stratified sampling	Quota sampling
Cluster sampling	Convenience sampling
Multiple/sequential sampling	

Sample Statistics

As we have indicated previously, the usual purpose of sampling is to learn something about the population being sampled. In selecting a sampling design, the primary considerations are the importance of the information to be gathered and the desired degree of accuracy of what is learned about the population. In view of these purposes, it is important that we structure the problem of taking a sample and analyzing the sample results in terms of the concepts of probability presented in Chapters 3 through 6.

Assume that we are planning on taking a sample of n observations in order to determine the characteristics of some random variable x. The process of taking a sample from this population can be viewed as an experiment, and the observations that may occur in such an experiment make up the sample space. Suppose we let the random variables $x_1, x_2, \ldots, x_n$ represent the observations in this sample. That is, the random variable x_1 represents the observation that occurs first in a sample of n observations, x_2 represents the second observation, and so forth. In simple random sampling, every item in the population has an equal chance of being the observation that occurs first, so in this case the sample space for x_1 would be the entire population of x-values. It is important to remember that $x_1, x_2, \ldots, x_n$ are all *random variables*, and each of these variables has a theoretical probability distribution. Under simple random sampling, the probability distribution of each of the random variables $x_1, x_2, \ldots, x_n$ will be identical to the distribution of the population random variable x since the sample space for each one is the entire population of x-values.

Once we have collected a random sample of n observations, we have one value for x_1, one value for x_2, and so forth, with one value for x_n. We now need to learn more about the characteristics of the random variable x (the population) by making use of the sample values of $x_1, x_2, \ldots, x_n$. In general, the population parameters of interest are usually those described in Chapters 1 and 2, the most important being the summary measures for central location and dispersion. It is intuitively appealing that the best estimate of a population parameter is given by a comparable sample measure (a sample *statistic*). For example, we will see that the best estimate of the central location of a population is a measure of the central location of a sample; and the best estimate of the population dispersion is a measure of the dispersion of the sample. *Thus, a sample statistic is used as an estimate of a population parameter.*

A **sample statistic** can be defined as a function of some (or all) of the n random variables $x_1, x_2, \ldots, x_n$. That is, a sample statistic is a random variable that is based on the sample values of $x_1, x_2, \ldots, x_n$. This means that there is a theoretical probability distribution associated with every sample statistic. For example, suppose we let $R = x_{\max} - x_{\min}$ be the *range* of the values in a sample. In this case, the sample statistic R is a random variable which is a function of only two values in each sample, the largest value ($x_{\max}$) and the smallest value ($x_{\min}$). Since R is a random variable, it has a theoretical probability distribution that we could develop if this statistic were of interest. The method of sampling used will affect the probability distribution of any sample statistic.

Many different sample statistics can be used to estimate the population parameters of interest. Generally, the population parameters of most interest are the mean and variance, since these two measures are so useful in describing a distribution and so necessary in decision-making. Consequently, the most useful sample statistics are the sample mean and the sample variance, which provide the best information about the population mean and variance. As we indicated earlier, there are a number of different sampling procedures that one may use to estimate population parameters. The particular procedure selected will have an effect on one's ability to make inferences about the underlying population. We will assume, at least initially, simple random sampling. In the development to follow, the reader should bear in mind that a similar development could be presented for sample statistics other than the mean and the variance.

Sample Mean

The mean (or average) of a set of observations that represents a sample is calculated in the same manner as demonstrated in Chapter 1 for the mean of a population (Formula 1.1): by summing each value of x in the sample and then dividing this sum by the number of observations in the sample. The letter n is used to denote the number of observations in the sample, and the **sample mean** is denoted by the symbol $\bar{x}$, which is read "ex-bar."

Sample mean:

$$\bar{x} = \frac{1}{n} \sum_{i=1}^{n} x_i \qquad (7.1)$$

The reader may wish to verify the similarity between Formula 7.1 and Formula 1.1. They are both averages of a set of numbers. In the case of Formula 7.1, there are only n numbers (the sample size), while for Formula 1.1, there are N numbers (the population size). The x's of a sample are a subset of the x's of the population.

☐ **EXAMPLE 7.1**   A Saskatoon Chevrolet dealer has ordered a large number of customized Chevy vans. These vans have a list price of $28,500, but each dealer discounts the price down to as low as $24,000 (excluding a trade-in) depending on how hard the customer bargains. The first four vans sold for the following prices (x is the price):

$$x: \quad 25{,}250 \quad 24{,}500 \quad 24{,}750 \quad 24{,}400$$

The dealer considers these four prices to be a random sample of the selling price for all vans at that dealership during the next six months. The average selling price is:

$$\bar{x} = \frac{1}{4}(25{,}250 + 24{,}500 + 24{,}750 + 24{,}400) = \frac{1}{4}(98{,}900) = 24{,}725$$

The sample mean is $\bar{x} = \$24{,}725$.   ∎

The Sample Variance and Standard Deviation

A **sample variance** takes the sum of the squared deviations about $\bar{x}$, or

$$\sum_{i=1}^{n} (x_i - \bar{x})^2$$

For a population, we divided this sum of squared deviations by N, the population size. *For samples, we divide the sum of squared deviations by $n - 1$.*

The reason for dividing by $(n-1)$ is that the resulting measure of variability can be shown to provide the *best* estimate of the (unknown) population variance. This fact will be explained in more detail in Section 7.8 and when we discuss estimation procedures in Chapter 9. For now, we merely show how to calculate a sample variance and a sample standard deviation. A sample variance is denoted by the symbol s^2 and is defined as follows:

Sample variance:

$$s^2 = \frac{1}{n-1} \sum_{i=1}^{n} (x_i - \bar{x})^2 \qquad (7.2)$$

We can use Formula 7.2 to determine the variance of the selling price of the four vans sold by the Chevrolet dealer in Saskatoon. The steps for this calculation are shown in Table 7.2. Remember that the mean of this sample is $\bar{x} = \$24,725$. The second column of Table 7.2 gives the deviation of each x-value about $\bar{x}$. These deviations will always sum to zero. The third column gives the squared deviations about $\bar{x}$. The sum of squared deviations, 432,500, is at the bottom of this column. This sum divided by $n-1=3$ equals the sample variance. That is, $s^2 = 144,166.67$ (dollars squared).

TABLE 7.2   Calculating a Variance

(1) x (Selling Price)	(2) $(x - \bar{x})$	(3) $(x - \bar{x})^2$	
$25,250	$525	$275,625	
24,500	−225	50,625	$s^2 = \frac{1}{3}(432,500)$
24,750	25	625	$= 144,166.67$ (dollars squared)
24,400	−325	105,625	
$\sum(x_i - \bar{x}) = 0$		$432,500 = \sum(x_i - \bar{x})^2$	

As was the case for a population, the standard deviation is the square root of the variance. A sample standard deviation is represented by the symbol s, where s is defined as follows:

Sample standard deviation:

$$s = \sqrt{s^2} \qquad (7.3)$$

For the example of Chevy vans, the standard deviation is:

$$s^2 = \sqrt{144,166.67} = 379.69 \text{ (dollars)}$$

Using the Computer to Determine Sample Statistics

In the past few pages, we have illustrated how to calculate a sample mean and a sample variance. We will continue throughout the remainder of this chapter to illustrate how sample statistics are calculated to demonstrate concepts. For realistic problems, however, one seldom wants to perform the tedious arithmetic necessary for calculating means and variances — it is much easier to let a computer do this work.

We use the Doane package to illustrate a computer output for sample statistics. Consider **Data Set 2**, and suppose our goal is to find the mean and the variance of the first ten price-equity ratios for those data. We put these ten P–E ratios in a file called P-ERATIO, and then used the ANALYZ option of the Doane package to generate the following output. [*Note:* we have omitted irrelevant portions of the output.]

```
Output from Doane Statistical Package
GENERAL FACTS:                    DISPERSION

File = P-ERATIO                   Variance = 6.903 E-2
Observations = 10                 Std. Dev. = 0.263
Minimum = 0.16
Maximum = 1.09
Range = 0.93


CENTRAL TENDENCY
Mean = 0.599
Median = 0.640
```

From the output above, we see that $\bar{x} = 0.599$, the variance is $s^2 = 0.06903$, and $s = 0.263$. Also provided is the fact that the minimum P-E ratio was 0.16, and the maximum was 1.09, resulting in a range of 0.93. The Doane package also will provide a printout of the histogram for the data. We asked the program to provide a histogram with 10 classes, a lower limit of 0.10, and class intervals of size 0.10. The result is shown below.

```
Histogram Output from Doane Package

0.10 < 0.20 │ *    1
0.20 < 0.30 │
0.30 < 0.40 │ **   2
0.40 < 0.50 │
0.50 < 0.60 │ *    1
0.60 < 0.70 │ ***  3
0.70 < 0.80 │ **   2
0.80 < 0.90 │
0.90 < 1.00 │
1.00 < 1.10 │ *    1
```

Sample Statistics Using Frequencies

Recall from Chapter 2 that data are often presented in the form of a frequency distribution. That is, sometimes a value x_i occurs more than once, and the number of times (the frequency) this value occurs is denoted as f_i. Formula 7.1 and Formula 7.2 are really special cases of more general formulas for $\bar{x}$ and s^2 where $f_i = 1$. The general formulas are shown below.

general formulas:

> **Sample mean:**
>
> $$\bar{x} = \frac{1}{n} \sum_{i=1}^{k} x_i f_i$$
>
> **Sample variance:** (7.4)
>
> $$s^2 = \frac{1}{n-1} \sum_{i=1}^{k} (x_i - \bar{x})^2 f_i$$

In Formulas 7.4, we assume that the sample consists of n observations but that there are only k *different* values of x. The frequency of the first value of x, which is denoted as x_1, is f_1. The frequency of the second value (x_2) is f_2 and so forth, with f_k representing the frequency of the last value (x_k). Thus, the sums in Formula 7.4 start with $i = 1$ and end with $i = k$.

□ **EXAMPLE 7.2**   Consider the case of a committee investigating the number of federal grants awarded for local projects in cities with populations ranging from 50,000 to 200,000. In an attempt to measure the characteristics of the population in this case (all cities of that size), ten randomly selected cities were surveyed. Table 7.3 shows the results of this survey (x = number of grants during the past year, f is the frequency of each value of x, and $k = 5$ classes). The sample mean can be calculated by substituting the information from columns (2) and (3) into Formula 7.4.

$$\bar{x} = \frac{1}{n} \sum_{i=1}^{5} x_i f_i = \frac{1}{10}(28) = 2.8$$

The average number of grants in the ten cities sampled is thus 2.8.

TABLE 7.3   Number of Federal Grants to Cities with Populations of 50,000–200,000

(1) x	(2) f	(3) xf	(4) $(x - \bar{x})$	(5) $(x - \bar{x})^2$	(6) $(x - \bar{x})^2 f$
1	2	2	−1.8	3.24	6.48
2	3	6	−0.8	0.64	1.92
3	1	3	0.2	0.04	0.04
4	3	12	1.2	1.44	4.32
5	1	5	2.2	4.84	4.84
	10	28			17.60

To measure the variance of these data, we use Formula 7.4. Using the product of the frequencies times the squared deviations in column (6), we can calculate s^2 as follows:

$$s^2 = \frac{1}{n-1} \sum_{i=1}^{k} (x_1 - \bar{x})^2 f_i = \frac{1}{9}(17.60) = 1.956$$

The sample standard deviation is $s = \sqrt{1.956} = 1.399$. Again, one way to check to see if the result, $s = 1.399$, is reasonable is to use our old rule of thumb. About 68% of the sample values should fall within one standard deviation of the mean, $\bar{x} \pm 1s$. In this case, the result appears reasonable, since seven of the ten observations lie in the interval $\bar{x} \pm 1s = 2.8 \pm 1.399 = 1.401$ to 4.199.   ∎

☐ STUDY QUESTION 7.1   The Usage of a Student Union Building

A study of the usage of the Student Union Building at McMaster University resulted in the following sample data. The variable x represents the number of times per week the Union was used during a one-week period by the 100 students in the survey.

TABLE 7.4   Usage of McMaster's Student Union Building in a Week

x (Times Used)	Frequency	
0	26	
1	31	
2	19	
3	10	
4	6	
5	3	
6	2	
7	2	
8	1	
	$n = 100$	

Find the mean, the variance and the standard deviation of this sample. What percent of the sample data lie within two standard deviations of the mean? If possible, use a computer package such as the GROUP package in Doane to solve this problem.

• **ANSWER**   Using Formula 7.4, we find the mean to be as follows:

$$\bar{x} = \frac{1}{100}[0(26) + 1(31) + 2(19) + \cdots + 8(1)] = \frac{1}{100}[172] = 1.72$$

Using Formula 7.4, the variance is:

$$s^2 = \frac{1}{100 - 1}\left[(0 - 1.72)^2(26) + (1 - 1.72)^2(31) + \cdots + (8 - 1.72)^2(1)\right]$$

$$= \frac{1}{99}(306.16) = 3.09 \text{ (visits squared)}$$

The standard deviation is $s = \sqrt{3.09} = 1.76$ visits. The interval $\bar{x} \pm 2s$ is $1.72 \pm (2)(1.76) = [-1.80 \text{ to } +5.24]$. Since we cannot have a negative number of visits, the interval for practical purposes is [0 to 5.24]. This interval contains the frequencies $26 + 31 + 19 + 10 + 6 + 3 = 95$. Thus, 95% of the sample data lies within two standard deviations. This corresponds precisely to the rule of thumb for the percent of values within plus or minus two standard deviations of the mean.

Statistics for grouped data can also be determined using a computer package. For the Doane package, the appropriate program is called GROUP. Input and output for the data above are shown below. Note that the first class starts at -0.5, and is of size 1.0. The letter m represents the midpoint of each class.

```
                              GROUP

INPUT
          How many classes (up to 15)? 9
          Equal intervals (y/n)? y
          Size of each interval? 1
          Lower limit of first interval? -0.5
OUTPUT
SUMMARY OF CALCULATIONS USING GROUPED DATA
```

Class	f	m	$f*m$	$f*(m-\bar{x})^2$	Cum f
$-0.5 < 0.5$	26	0	26	76.91840	26
$0.5 < 1.5$	31	1	31	16.07040	57
$1.5 < 2.5$	19	2	38	1.48960	76
$2.5 < 3.5$	10	3	30	16.38400	86
$3.5 < 4.5$	6	4	24	31.19040	92
$4.5 < 5.5$	3	5	15	32.27520	95
$5.5 < 6.5$	2	6	12	36.63680	97
$6.5 < 7.5$	2	7	14	55.75679	99
$7.5 < 8.5$	1	5	5	39.43840	100
Total	100		172	306.15997	

```
SUMMARY STATISTICS FOR GROUPED DATA

          MEAN = 1.72
          ST. DEV. = 1.758558
```

Perhaps at this point we should reiterate that one of our objectives in calculating *sample* means and variances is to be able to make statements about the *population* mean and variance. Since different samples from the same population may have different means and variances, the only way to determine the true population parameters is to enumerate every item in the population (a census). But a census is generally too costly and time-consuming. Thus, we must be content to *use sample statistics to estimate the population parameters and then to make statements about how reliable or accurate such a sample statistic is in describing the population parameter of interest.*

To establish the reliability or accuracy with which a sample statistic describes a population parameter, one must know how probable it is that specific values of this statistic will occur (1) for every possible value of the population parameter and (2) for every possible sample size. To begin our discussion of the reliability and accuracy of a sample, let us suppose that we can take a large number of random samples, all of size n, and then calculate $\bar{x}$ for each of these samples. These values of $\bar{x}$ can be put in the form of a frequency distribution. This frequency distribution will have a certain shape, as well as a mean and a variance. Now, if we take *all possible* samples of size n (and the number of samples may be infinite), and determine $\bar{x}$ for each sample, the resulting distribution is the *probability distribution* of all possible values of $\bar{x}$.

The probability distribution of $\bar{x}$ is called a *sampling distribution*. We can also calculate a sampling distribution for s^2 by considering all possible values of s^2 from samples of a given size n. Such sampling distributions are necessary for making probability statements about the reliability and accuracy of sample statistics, and they will be discussed in detail in the remaining sections of this chapter.

PROBLEMS

Use a computer, if possible, to solve these problems.

7.1 Under what conditions is nonprobabilistic sampling more appropriate than probabilistic sampling? Give several examples.

7.2 Distinguish between the following:

a) systematic sampling and simple random sampling

b) stratified and cluster sampling

c) single-stage sampling and multiple-stage sampling

d) judgement, quota, and convenience sampling

e) random variable, random sample, observations selected *at random*

7.3 In designing a sample survey, what factors are most important in establishing the strata in stratified sampling? The clusters in cluster sampling? How will the cost of sampling affect these decisions?

7.4 A company packages lima bean seeds. Obviously not all the seeds in a given lot will germinate. However, the company does not want to package and present for consumer purchase an excessive number of bad seeds. In the long run, about $\frac{3}{4}$ of the seeds germinate, while $\frac{1}{4}$ do not. Before packaging a new lot, the company would like to be sure that at least $\frac{3}{4}$ of the new seeds will germinate. One clever(?) student says that they could test a random sample of only four seeds, and if three of them grew, they could assume that $\frac{3}{4}$ of all the seeds were good.

a) Do you think that the direct relationship between the probability from the sample and the likelihood of good seeds in the entire lot is perfect, as the student suggests? Explain briefly.

b) Suppose exactly $\frac{3}{4}$ of all the seeds were good; what is the probability that exactly three out of four in a random sample would be good? (Although sampling is without replacement, assume that the number of seeds is very large so that the probability of selecting a good seed, $\frac{3}{4}$, remains the same.)

7.5 Refer once again to **Data Set 1**, containing 179 Canadian cities.

a) Use Table V in Appendix C to select a random sample of twenty from the population of 179 cities. Specify how you picked the twenty numbers from Table V.

b) Calculate the mean income for your random sample of cities in part (a). Does your sample mean seem reasonably close to the population mean of 2255.7?

c) Calculate the variance and standard deviation of incomes for your sample of cities. Does the value of s seem reasonably close to σ of 8397.7?

7.6 Use Table V to collect a proportionate stratified sample from **Data Set 1**. Stratify the cities by dividing the sales data into four categories: ≤ 100, $100 \leq 200$, $200 \leq 300$, and > 300. Determine the proportion of cities falling into each of these categories. Collect a sample of size $n = 20$, where the number of cities in each category is the proportion you determined above.

a) Is the sample mean for the income variable close to the population mean of 2255.7? Is the standard deviation close to the population value of 8397.7?

b) Do your sample values in part (a) represent a better approximation to the population values than your answers to Problem 7.5? Did you expect them to? Explain.

7.7 Consider all the undergraduate students at Queen's University as a single population.

a) Specify exactly how you would go about taking a random sample of 50 students. Would a systematic sampling plan be easier in this situation? Would systematic sampling introduce any biases?

b) Specify exactly how you would go about taking a stratified sample, where the strata are the four classes of students (senior, junior, et cetera) and each stratum is sampled in proportion to the number of students in that class.

7.8 Suppose you have been commissioned to design a survey of the age, income, and occupation of the customers who patronize a nationwide chain of stores. Describe how you would proceed with such a study.

7.9 If possible, use a computer to answer each part of the following questions.

a) You decide to take a random sample of $n = 10$ from the 100 companies listed in **Data Set 2**. Identify the ten companies, taking a proportional sample from the first and second set of companies (five each).

b) Find the sample mean and variance of sales for your sample of ten companies.

c) Determine the population mean and variance for all 100 companies. Comment on how well your sample statistics compare to the population parameters.

7.10 In comparing salaries with five friends working as accountants, you learn their monthly salaries are: $4,975, $3,510, $5,870, $3,950, and $4,320. Find the mean and variance of this sample data. Comment on what estimates you can make about the population based on these data.

7.11 An ad in the *Wall Street Journal* reported the following prices for the daily rental of an economy automobile.

1. Boston	$50	5. Miami	$35
2. Detroit	48	6. Phoenix	39
3. Kansas City	44	7. Washinton, D.C	55
4. Los Angeles	42		

a) Find $\bar{x}$ and s^2 for this sample.

b) Would you expect these sample values to represent prices throughout the U.S.? Explain.

7.12 Given the following sample distribution for $x =$ number of soft drink machines needing repair per week at a large business complex:

TABLE 7.5 Weekly Soft Drink Machine Repairs

x	Frequency
1	2
2	7
3	10
4	1

Find $\bar{x}$ and s.

7.13 The distribution of the number of defects per square yard of a cotton textile is given as follows:

TABLE 7.6 Defects per Square Yard of Cotton

No. of defects (x)	Frequency (f)
0	47
1	33
2	14
3	5
4	1
5	0
Total	100

Find the mean and the standard deviation of this sample distribution.

7.14 Given the following sample distribution by class intervals for the number of hours worked last month by a certain group of business executives; find $\bar{x}$ and s.

TABLE 7.7 Hours Worked per Month by Business Executives

Class	Frequency
190–204	3
205–219	5
220–234	9
235–249	6
250–264	7

7.15 If the weekly wages of 100 workers are grouped into classes of $25 each, the distribution in Table 7.8 results.

TABLE 7.8 Weekly Wages for Workers

Wages	f
338–362	4
363–387	15
388–412	20
413–437	30
438–462	15
463–487	10
488–512	6
Total	100

Find $\bar{x}$ for the grouped data, using class marks, $350, 375, 400, \ldots, 500$.

7.16 A manufacturer of razor blades claims that the product will give, on the average, 15 good shaves. Suppose you have five friends who try using one of these razor blades each. The number of shaves reported by your friends are 12, 16, 8, 14, and 10.

a) Find the mean and the standard deviation of this sample.

b) Suggest how you might use this sample evidence to dispute or support the advertiser's claim.

7.17 A fresh-produce distributor has received complaints that bananas have been arriving spoiled at the retail store. The complaint is suspicious, since average delivery time is only 4 days (96 hours) and the bananas are fresh at the time of shipment. The distributor decides to simulate the appropriate conditions by selecting at random a sample of four crates of bananas and measuring the number of hours before spoilage occurs. The results for number of hours, x, are given as 106, 102, 104, and 108.

a) Find the mean hours before spoilage.

b) Find the standard deviation for x.

c) On the basis of these measures, do you think that many of the bananas may indeed be arriving spoiled, or are you also suspicious of the complaints? Explain.

d) Find the range of the sample of x-values.

e) Give one reason why the answer in part (b) is better than that in part (d) as an estimate of dispersion for the entire population of bananas from which the sample was taken.

Sampling Distribution of $\bar{x}$

> The **sampling distribution** of $\bar{x}$ is the probability distribution of *all possible* values of $\bar{x}$ that could occur when a sample (of size n) is taken from some specified parent population.

A sampling distribution is a population. It is a population of *all* possible values of some sample statistic, such as $\bar{x}$. The following example illustrates the sampling distribution of $\bar{x}$ for a very small population.

◻ **EXAMPLE 7.3**   Consider a parent population that has only three values, (1, 2, 3), which occur with equal probability as shown in Figure 7.1. The parent population is thus $x = \{1, 2, 3\}$. This population might represent the number of cable sports channels provided by different cable franchises. The mean of this parent population is easily seen to be $\mu = 2.0$; in other words, the average number of sports channels is 2.0. Now, let us assume that you are not familiar with the parent population, so you decide to take a random sample of size $n = 2$ of the cable franchises. Your sample of size $n = 2$ will look like one of the nine ordered pairs listed in the left-hand column of Table 7.9. The right-hand column lists the sample mean for each of the nine possible samples.

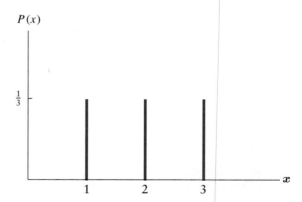

FIGURE 7.1   Distribution of parent population

Each one of the nine samples in column one has the same probability of occurring, $\frac{1}{9}$. This implies that each one of the nine sample means in column two has this same ($\frac{1}{9}$) probability. Now, since only one of the values of $\bar{x}$ in column two equals 1.0, we can write $P(\bar{x} = 1.0) = \frac{1}{9}$. Similarly, there are two instances when $\bar{x}$ equals 1.5; hence $P(\bar{x} = 1.5) = \frac{2}{9}$. A graph (Figure 7.2) and a table (Table 7.4) show the probabilities associated with all these possible values of $\bar{x}$.

TABLE 7.9   All Samples of Size $n = 2$ from $\{1, 2, 3\}$

Sample	Sample Mean $\bar{x}$	
(1, 1)	1.0	
(1, 2)	1.5	
(2, 1)	1.5	
(1, 3)	2.0	This is the population of all possible $\bar{x}$'s
(3, 1)	2.0	when the sample size is $n = 2$.
(2, 2)	2.0	
(2, 3)	2.5	
(3, 2)	2.5	
(3, 3)	3.0	

TABLE 7.10   The Sampling Distribution of $\bar{x}$ for $n = 2$ when $x = \{1, 2, 3\}$

$\bar{x}$	$P(\bar{x})$
1.0	$\frac{1}{9}$
1.5	$\frac{2}{9}$
2.0	$\frac{3}{9}$
2.5	$\frac{2}{9}$
3.0	$\frac{1}{9}$
	1.0

Thus, Figure 7.2 and Table 7.10 present the sampling distribution of $\bar{x}$ for $n = 2$, when $x = \{1, 2, 3\}$. It should be emphasized at this point that *the sampling distribution of $\bar{x}$ is itself a population.* As such, we are interested in the parameters of this population of $\bar{x}$'s, especially its mean and variance. ■

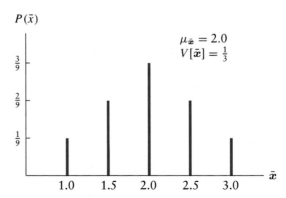

FIGURE 7.2   The sampling distribution of $\bar{x}$ for $n = 2$ when $x = \{1, 2, 3\}$

> The symbol $\mu_{\bar{x}}$, which traditionally denotes the mean of the sampling distribution of $\bar{x}$, is the mean of all possible sample means.[2]

Using the notation of expected values, we can thus write $\mu_{\bar{x}} = E[\bar{x}]$. The variance of this population, which is denoted as $V[\bar{x}] = \sigma_{\bar{x}}^2$, will be discussed shortly.

Mean of $\bar{x}$, or $\mu_{\bar{x}}$

Because you plan to take only *one* sample, of size $n = 2$, you could get a sample mean as low as $\bar{x} = 1.0$ or as high as $\bar{x} = 3.0$ (Table 7.10). A logical question for a researcher to ask in this situation is what would be the **expected value of $\bar{x}$** in such a situation, or what is $E[\bar{x}] = \mu_{\bar{x}}$? That is, what is the average of the p.m.f. in Table 7.10? The mean of these values is calculated in the same manner in which we calculated a mean in Chapter 4, except that now the random variable is $\bar{x}$, and we denote the mean of this variable as $\mu_{\bar{x}}$:

$$\mu_{\bar{x}} = \sum \bar{x} P(\bar{x}) = (1.0)(\tfrac{1}{9}) + (1.5)(\tfrac{2}{9}) + (2.0)(\tfrac{3}{9}) + (2.5)(\tfrac{2}{9}) + (3.0)(\tfrac{1}{9})$$

$$= 2.00$$

Thus we have shown for this population that $\mu_{\bar{x}} = \mu = 2.00$. The fact that these two means are equal is not a coincidence, as it can be shown that $\mu_{\bar{x}}$ equals μ for *any* parent population and *any* given sample size. That is, if μ is the mean of the population of x's and $\mu_{\bar{x}}$ is the mean of the population of $\bar{x}$'s, then:[3]

> Expected value of $\bar{x}$:
> $$E[\bar{x}] = \mu_{\bar{x}} = \mu \qquad (7.5)$$

---

[2] From this point on, we will add a subscript to a population parameter or sample statistic whenever it may be unclear which population or sample is being described. For example, s_y refers to the standard deviation of the sample of y-values, while $\mu_{\bar{x}}$ refers to the mean of the population of $\bar{x}$-values. If *no* subscript is used, such as μ or σ or s, these refer to the distribution of x-values under consideration.

[3] Let $x_1, x_2, \ldots, x_n$ represent independent random variables corresponding to the n observations in a sample from a population with mean μ_x ($E[x_i] = \mu$). Now, since $\bar{x} = (1/n)(x_1 + x_2 + \cdots + x_n)$, we can apply the rules of expectation from Section 4.4 as follows:

$$E[\bar{x}] = E\left[\frac{1}{n}(x_1 + x_2 + \cdots + x_n)\right]$$

$$= \frac{1}{n}E[(x_1 + x_2 + \cdots + x_n)] \qquad \text{(By rule 3)}$$

$$= \frac{1}{n}\{E[x_1] + E[x_2] + \cdots + E[x_n]\} \qquad \text{(By Formula 4.13)}$$

$$= \frac{1}{n}(\mu + \mu + \cdots + \mu) = \frac{1}{n}(n\mu) \qquad \text{(Since } E[x_i] = \mu)$$

$$\mu_{\bar{x}} = \mu$$

The Variance of $\bar{x}$

In addition to knowing the mean of the sampling distribution of $\bar{x}$ for a given sample size n, we also need to know its variance.

> The variance of the values of $\bar{x}$ is denoted by either $V[\bar{x}]$ or $\sigma_{\bar{x}}^2$

The **variance of x** is defined in the same manner in which we previously defined a variance, namely, the average of the squared deviations of the variable ($\bar{x}$ in this case) about its mean ($\mu_{\bar{x}}$ in this case). Thus:

$$\sigma_{\bar{x}}^2 = V[\bar{x}] = \sum (\bar{x} - \mu_{\bar{x}})^2 P(\bar{x})$$

Suppose that we use the data in Table 7.11 to calculate the variance of the $\bar{x}$s, or $V[\bar{x}]$. The variance of the $\bar{x}$'s is shown in column 5 to be $\sigma_{\bar{x}}^2 = \frac{1}{3}$; the standard deviation of the $\bar{x}$'s is $\sigma_{\bar{x}} = \sqrt{1/3} = 0.577$. The reader can verify that this standard deviation appears reasonable by noting that $\mu_{\bar{x}} \pm 1\sigma_{\bar{x}} = 2.00 \pm 0.577$ contains about 78% of the probability distribution of $\bar{x}$, which is not too far from the rule of thumb of 68%.

TABLE 7.11   Calculation of the Variance of a Distribution of Sample Means

(1) $\bar{x}$	(2) $P(\bar{x})$	(3) $(\bar{x} - \mu_{\bar{x}})$	(4) $(\bar{x} - \mu_{\bar{x}})^2$	(5) $(\bar{x} - \mu_{\bar{x}})^2 P(\bar{x})$
1.0	$\frac{1}{9}$	−1.0	1.00	$\frac{1}{9}$
1.5	$\frac{2}{9}$	−0.5	0.25	$\frac{2}{36}$
2.0	$\frac{3}{9}$	0	0	0
2.5	$\frac{2}{9}$	0.5	0.25	$\frac{2}{36}$
3.0	$\frac{1}{9}$	1.0	1.00	$\frac{1}{9}$

Mean 2.0 $V[\bar{x}] = \frac{12}{36} = \frac{1}{3}$

Although we calculated the value of $V[\bar{x}]$ directly in this example, in the many problems in which there is a very large (or infinite) number of values of $\bar{x}$ this approach is impractical, if not impossible. Fortunately, one can calculate $V[\bar{x}]$ without going through this process if one knows the variance of the population from which the samples are drawn ($V[\bar{x}]$). The reason for this is that the variance of the random variable $\bar{x}$ is related to the variance of the parent population and to the sample size (n) by a very simple formula, which we will present shortly.

On the basis of intuition, it should appear reasonable that the variance of $\bar{x}$ will always be less than the variance of the parent population (except when $n = 1$), because there is less chance that a sample mean will take on an extreme value than there is that a single value of the parent population will take on an extreme value. In order for a sample mean to have an extremely large value, most or all of the sample items would have to be extremely large values. But we know from our study of probability that the probability of n extremely large values on n repeated draws is much *smaller* than the probability of a single extremely large value on one draw. It would be very unusual in n trials not to draw some middle values or some extremely low values. Such values would balance out the extremely large values and give a less extreme sample mean. Indeed, this intuitive logic is correct. Not only is the variance of $\bar{x}$ always less than or equal to the variance of the parent population, but it can be shown that σ^2 and $\sigma_{\bar{x}}^2$ are very precisely related. *The variance of the mean of a sample of n independent observations is $1/n$ times the variance of the parent population.* [4]

> Variance of $\bar{x}$:
>
> $$\sigma_{\bar{x}}^2 = \frac{1}{n}\sigma^2$$
>
> (7.6)

When $n = 1$, all samples contain only one observation, and the distributions of x and $\bar{x}$ are identical. That is, $\sigma_{\bar{x}}^2 = \sigma^2/1 = \sigma^2$. As n becomes larger ($n \to \infty$), it is reasonable to expect $\sigma_{\bar{x}}^2$ to become smaller and smaller because the sample means will tend to deviate less and less from the population mean $\mu_{\bar{x}}$. When $n = \infty$ (or for finite populations, when $n = N$), all sample means will equal the population mean and the variance of the $\bar{x}$'s will be zero. To illustrate the relationship described by Formula 7.6, let us return to our example involving the population (1, 2, 3). The variance of this population is:

$$\sigma^2 = \frac{1}{N}\sum(x - \mu_{\bar{x}})^2 = \frac{1}{3}[(1-2)^2 + (2-2)^2 + (3-2)^2] = \frac{2}{3}$$

Since we know that the variance of this population is $\frac{2}{3}$ and the sample size is $n = 2$, we can calculate $V[\bar{x}]$ using Formula 7.6:

$$\sigma_{\bar{x}}^2 = \frac{1}{n}\sigma^2 = \frac{1}{2}\left(\frac{2}{3}\right) = \frac{1}{3}$$

This value of $V[\bar{x}]$ is exactly the same number we calculated using Table 7.11.

Standard Error of the Mean

It is customary to call the standard deviation of the $\bar{x}$'s (which is the square root of $V[\bar{x}]$ and is denoted as $\sigma_{\bar{x}}$) the **standard error of the mean**. The word *error* in this context refers to sampling error, as $\sigma_{\bar{x}}$ is a measure of the *standard* (or expected) error when the sample mean is used to obtain information or draw conclusions about the unknown population mean.

---

[4] Let $x_1, x_2, \ldots, x_n$ be independent random variables, each having the same variance (that is, $V[x_i] = \sigma^2$):

$$V[\bar{x}] = V\left[\frac{1}{n}(x_1 + x_2 + \cdots + x_n)\right] \quad \text{(By definition)}$$

$$= \left(\frac{1}{n}\right)^2 V[x_1 + x_2 + \cdots + x_n] \quad \text{(By rule 4 of Section 4.4)}$$

$$= \left(\frac{1}{n}\right)^2 \{V[x_1] + V[x_2] + \cdots + V[x_n]\} \quad \text{(By Formula 4.13)}$$

$$\sigma_{\bar{x}}^2 = \frac{n}{n^2}(\sigma^2) = \frac{1}{n}\sigma^2 \quad \text{Since } V[x_i] = \sigma^2$$

Standard error of the mean:

$$\sigma_{\bar{x}} = \sqrt{\frac{\sigma^2}{n}} = \frac{\sigma}{\sqrt{n}} \qquad\qquad (7.7)$$

In the above example, the standard error of the mean is:

$$\sigma_{\bar{x}} = \sqrt{\frac{\sigma^2}{n}} = \sqrt{\frac{\frac{2}{3}}{2}} = \sqrt{\frac{1}{3}} = 0.577$$

We must emphasize at this point that $\mu_{\bar{x}}$ and $\sigma_{\bar{x}}$ are parameters of the population of sample averages from all conceivable samples of size n, and these population parameters are *unknown* quantities. In fact, the values of $\mu, \mu_{\bar{x}}, \sigma$, and $\sigma_{\bar{x}}$ are usually *all* unknown quantities, which means that the relationship $\mu_{\bar{x}} = \mu$ and $\sigma_{\bar{x}} = \sigma/\sqrt{n}$ cannot be used to solve for the value of one of these quantities. However, knowledge of the fact that such relationships exist is important in determining how far a sample mean can be expected to deviate from an *assumed* population mean. The advantage of knowing this information is that we can test *hypotheses* about a population by looking at sample results. For example, suppose we had *hypothesized* (but did not know) that our parent population was $x = \{1, 2, 3\}$. If a single sample of size $n = 2$ from the population yielded $\bar{x} = 1.0$, then we might suspect that our assumption about the population $x = \{1, 2, 3\}$ is incorrect. Our knowledge of the sampling distribution for $\bar{x}$ confirms that the $P(\bar{x} = 1.0)$ is only $\frac{1}{9}$ for samples of size 2 from this population — not a frequently occurring event. In Chapter 10, we will formally consider this process of testing hypotheses.

☐ **STUDY QUESTION 7.2**   Rating the Quality of Restaurants

The Mobil Travel Guide rates restaurants with one to five stars, depending on the quality of the food and service. From one source you hear that the Mobil rating staff gives approximately 20% of the restaurants a one-star rating, 20% a two-star rating, and so forth, with 20% receiving 5 stars. You are thinking of taking a sample of ten randomly selected restaurants and looking up the rating of each one.

a) Find the mean and variance of the random variable x, where x is the rating.

b) What is meant by the sampling distribution of $\bar{x}$ for this problem? What mean would you expect for this sampling distribution (sample of size 10) if the source mentioned above is correct? What variance would you expect? What is the standard error of the mean?

c) Based on your answer to part (b), draw a rough sketch of the sampling distribution of $\bar{x}$. We will learn more about sketching this distribution in the next section.

● **ANSWER**

a) Using Formulas 4.2 and 4.4 from Chapter 4, we find the mean and variance of x to be as follows:

$$\mu = \sum x_i P(x_i) = 1(0.20) + 2(0.20) + 3(0.20) + 4(0.20) + 5(0.20)$$

$$= 3.0 \text{ stars}$$

$$\sigma^2 = \sum (x_i - \mu)^2 P(x_i)$$

$$= [(1-3)^2(0.20) + (2-3)^2(0.20) + \cdots + (5-3)^2(0.20)]$$

$$= 2.0 \text{ stars squared}$$

b) The sampling distribution of $\bar{x}$ is the probability mass function for the mean of all possible samples of size 10 drawn from the parent population. The mean of the sampling distribution of $\bar{x}$ is the same as the mean of the parent population. Thus, from part (a):

$$\mu_{\bar{x}} = \mu = 3.0 \text{ stars}$$

The variance of the sampling distribution of $\bar{x}$ is the variance of the parent population divided by $n = 10$. Thus:

$$\sigma_{\bar{x}}^2 = \frac{1}{10}(2.0) = 0.20 \text{ (stars squared)}$$

c) The standard error of the mean is $\sqrt{0.20} = 0.447$ (stars)   ■

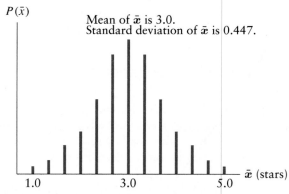

$P(\bar{x})$

Mean of $\bar{x}$ is 3.0.
Standard deviation of $\bar{x}$ is 0.447.

$\bar{x}$ (stars)

1.0   3.0   5.0

FIGURE 7.3   Sampling distribution of $\bar{x}$ for Study Question 7.2

Although we have derived the mean and variance of the $\bar{x}$'s, nothing has been said about the *shape* of the sampling distribution of $\bar{x}$. Recall from Chapter 2 that distributions with the same mean and variance may have distinctly different shapes. It is necessary, therefore, to be more specific about the entire distribution of $\bar{x}$'s. To do so, we will first assume that the parent population is normal and then later drop this assumption.

Sampling Distribution of $\bar{x}$, Normal Parent Population

We already know the mean and variance of the distribution of $\bar{x}$'s, but what is known about its *shape*? It is usually not possible to specify the shape of the $\bar{x}$'s when the parent population is discrete and the sample size is small. However, when the sample is drawn from a parent population (x) that is normally distributed, then the shape of the $\bar{x}$'s can be specified. As you might suspect, in this situation the $\bar{x}$'s are distributed normally.

> The sampling distribution of $\bar{x}$'s drawn from a normal parent population is a normal distribution.

Using the fact that the mean of the $\bar{x}$'s is $\mu_{\bar{x}} = \mu$ (Formula 7.5) and that the variance of the $\bar{x}$'s is $\sigma_{\bar{x}}^2 = \sigma^2/n$ (Formula 7.6), we can now specify that the sampling distribution of $\bar{x}$ is $N(\mu_{\bar{x}}, \sigma_{\bar{x}}^2) = N(\mu, \sigma^2/n)$ whenever the parent population is normal. That is, the mean and variance of $\bar{x}$ are $\mu_{\bar{x}}$ and $\sigma_{\bar{x}}^2$ (or μ and σ^2/n), regardless of the shape of the parent population. The new point is that if the population distribution is normal, so is the distribution of $\bar{x}$.

To illustrate this sampling distribution of $\bar{x}$, we will suppose that all possible samples of size $n = 20$ are drawn from a normal population that has a mean $\mu = 50$ and a variance $\sigma^2 = 80$; that is, $\bar{x}$ is $N(50, 80)$. Because all normal distributions are continuous, an infinite number of different samples of size 20 could be drawn. For any of these samples a mean, x, could be calculated. Since the population mean is $\mu = 50$, the mean of the $\bar{x}$'s is $\mu_{\bar{x}} = 50$. Similarly, since $\sigma^2 = 80$, the variance of the $\bar{x}$'s is $\sigma_{\bar{x}}^2 = \sigma^2/n = \frac{80}{20} = 4$. Finally, because x is normal, $\bar{x}$ will also be normally distributed. All of this information about $\bar{x}$ can be summarized by the following statement: the distribution of $\bar{x}$ is $N(50, 4)$.

This means that 68.3% of the sample means will fall within plus-or-minus one standard error of the mean ($\sigma_{\bar{x}} = \sqrt{4} = 2$):

$$\mu \pm 1\sigma_{\bar{x}} = 50 \pm 1(2) = 48 \text{ to } 52$$

95.4% will fall within plus-or-minus two standard errors of the mean:

$$\mu \pm 2\sigma_{\bar{x}} = 50 \pm 2(2) = 46 \text{ to } 54$$

99.7% of all sample means will fall within plus-or-minus three standard errors of the mean:

$$\mu \pm 3\sigma_{\bar{x}} = 50 \pm 3(2) = 44 \text{ to } 56$$

Figure 7.4 shows the sampling distribution of $\bar{x}$ for all possible samples of size 20 taken from a population with the distribution $N(50, 80)$.

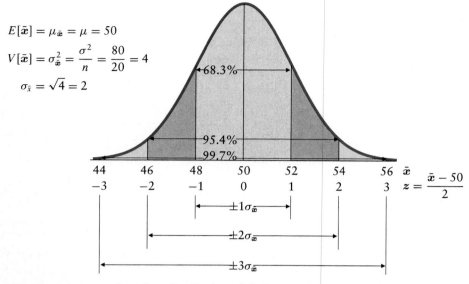

$$E[\bar{x}] = \mu_{\bar{x}} = \mu = 50$$

$$V[\bar{x}] = \sigma_{\bar{x}}^2 = \frac{\sigma^2}{n} = \frac{80}{20} = 4$$

$$\sigma_{\bar{x}} = \sqrt{4} = 2$$

$$z = \frac{\bar{x} - 50}{2}$$

FIGURE 7.4   Sampling distribution of $\bar{x}$ for samples of $n = 20$ taken from a population with distribution $N(50, 80)$

The following statement summarizes what we now know about the distribution of sample means ($\bar{x}$).

> If the parent population ($\bar{x}$) is normally distributed, with mean μ and variance σ^2, then the distribution of $\bar{x}$ for a given sample size n will be:
>
> $$N\left(\mu, \frac{\sigma^2}{n}\right) \tag{7.8}$$

The Standardized Form of the Random Variable $\bar{x}$ (σ Known)[5]

In Chapter 6, we saw that it is usually easier to work with the standard normal form of a variable than to leave it in its original units. The same type of transformation that was made on the random variable x at that point can now be made on the random variable $\bar{x}$. Recall that, in Section 4.4, the variable x was transformed to its standard normal form by subtracting the mean from each value and then dividing by the standard deviation. The resulting variable, $z = (x - \mu)/\sigma$, was shown to have a mean of zero and a variance of one. Although now we are interested in transforming the variable $\bar{x}$ instead of x, and the standard deviation of this variable is $\sigma/\sqrt{n}$ instead of σ, the **standardization of $\bar{x}$** is accomplished in exactly the same fashion. One simply must take care always to subtract the mean and divide by the standard deviation corresponding to the variable being standardized. The mean and variance of the resulting variable will always be zero and 1, respectively.

---

[5] Whenever $\bar{x}$ is normal, the distribution of $\bar{x}$ is $N(\mu, \sigma/\sqrt{n})$, whether or not σ is known. However, in order to make probability statements about $\bar{x}$, we prefer to standardize this variable, and this standardization requires that we know σ.

Standardization of $\bar{x}$:

$$z = \frac{\bar{x} - \mu_{\bar{x}}}{\sigma_{\bar{x}}} = \frac{\bar{x} - \mu}{\sigma/\sqrt{n}} \tag{7.9}$$

The random variable z has a mean of zero and a variance of one. Since we have said that the distribution of the random variable $\bar{x}$ is normal, it follows that the random variable z must also be normally distributed. Thus:

When sampling from a normal parent population, the distribution of $z = (\bar{x} - \mu)/(\sigma/\sqrt{n})$ will be normal with mean zero and variance 1. That is: $z = (\bar{x} - \mu)/(\sigma/\sqrt{n})$ is $N(0, 1)$.

The standardized normal form of the variable $\bar{x}$ is shown on the z-scale in Figure 7.4.

The limitations of the preceding discussion should be apparent, for although the normal distribution approximates the probability distribution of many real-world problems, one cannot *always* assume that the parent population is normal. What, for example, will be the shape of the distribution of $\bar{x}$'s when sampling from a highly skewed distribution? We consider this situation in the next section.

section 7.6 | Sampling Distribution of $\bar{x}$, Population Distribution Unknown, σ Known

When sampling is not from a normal parent population (or when the population is unknown), the size of the sample plays a critical role. When n is small, the shape of the distribution will depend mostly on the shape of the parent population. As n becomes large, however, one of the most important theorems in statistical inference states that the shape of the sampling distribution of $\bar{x}$ will become more and more like a *normal distribution, no matter what the shape of the parent population*. This theorem, called the **central limit theorem**, is stated in formal terms below:

Regardless of the distribution of the parent population (as long as it has a finite mean μ and variance σ^2), the distribution of the means of random samples will approach a normal distribution (with mean μ and variance σ^2/n) as the sample size n goes to infinity.

To summarize this statement and the previous one:

1. When the parent population is normal, the sampling distribution of $\bar{x}$ is exactly normal.

2. When the parent population is not normal (or perhaps unknown), the sampling distribution of $\bar{x}$ is approximately normal as the sample size increases.

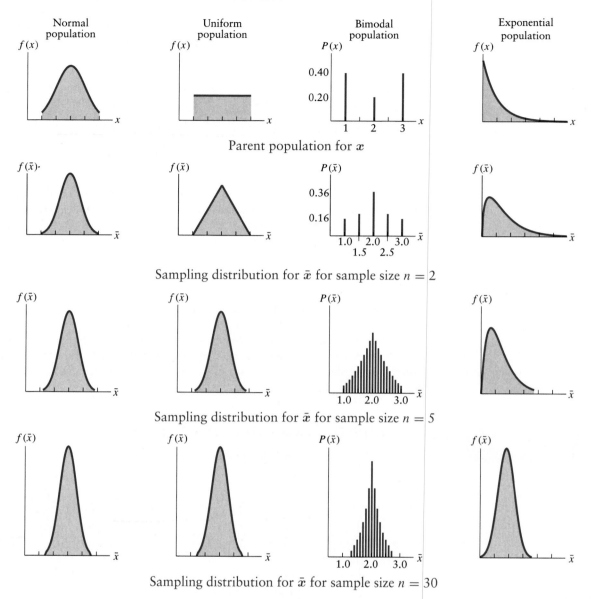

FIGURE 7.5   Sampling distribution of $\bar{x}$ for various population distributions when $n = 2, 5,$ and 30

We will not prove the central limit theorem, but will merely show graphical evidence of its validity in Figure 7.5. The first row of diagrams in Figure 7.5 shows four different parent populations. The next three rows show the sampling distribution of $\bar{x}$ for all possible repeated samples of size $n = 2$, $n = 5$, and $n = 30$, respectively, drawn from the populations shown in the first row. Note in the first column that when the parent population is normal, all the sampling distributions are also normal. Also, note that distributions in the same column have the same mean μ, but their variances decrease as $\sqrt{n}$ increases. This agrees with the central limit theorem.

       The second column of figures in Figure 7.5 represents what is called a *uniform* (or *rectangular*) *distribution*. We see here that the sampling distribution of $\bar{x}$ is already symmetrical when $n = 2$, and it is quite normal in appearance when $n = 5$. As we move to the third column of figures, the parent population is now a bimodal distribution with discrete values of x (the central limit theorem applies whether x is discrete or continuous). Again, by $n = 2$ the distribution is symmetrical, and by $n = 5$ it is quite bell-shaped. The final parent population is the highly skewed exponential distribution. Here we see that for $n = 2$ and $n = 5$ the distribution is still fairly skewed, although it becomes more symmetrical as n increases. When $n = 30$, however, even such a skewed parent population results in a symmetrical, bell-shaped distribution for $\bar{x}$ which, by the central limit theorem, we know to be approximately normally distributed.

In general, just how large n needs to be for the sampling distribution of $\bar{x}$ to be a good approximation to the normal depends, as we saw in Figure 7.5, on the shape of the parent population. Usually the approximation will be quite good if $n \geq 30$, although the third row of Figure 7.5 demonstrates that satisfactory results are often obtained when n is much smaller.

Example of the Use of the Central Limit Theorem

☐ **EXAMPLE 7.4**   A telephone company recently asked for a rate increase for all telephones, including a 25% increase in residential phones. To oppose this increase, a group of concerned citizens decided to investigate the typical phone costs incurred in their town. The information provided by the telephone company was that, for the region they serve as a whole, the average monthly bill for basic service was \$15.30, with a standard deviation of \$4.10. The citizens, however, were curious as to whether or not rates were the same in their town. Since no information was available in this regard, the citizens decided to take a random sample of $n = 36$, in an attempt to obtain further information.

Now, if local phone rates are the same as the population rates reported by the telephone company, we know that the mean of all possible sample means will be $E[\bar{x}] = \mu_{\bar{x}} = \$15.30$, and the standard error of the mean will be $\sigma_{\bar{x}} = \sigma/\sqrt{n} = 4.10/\sqrt{36} = 0.683$. Furthermore, since the sample size is fairly large $(n = 36)$, the central limit theorem tells us that the sampling distribution of $\bar{x}$ will be approximately normal [$\bar{x}$ is $N(\$15.30, 0.683^2)$]. Use of this distribution, shown in Figure 7.6, allows us to answer a number of different probability questions for the telephone example. ■

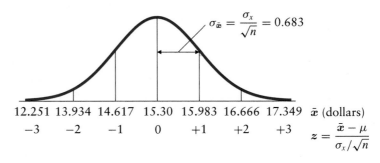

| 12.251 | 13.934 | 14.617 | 15.30 | 15.983 | 16.666 | 17.349 | $\bar{x}$ (dollars) |

$\sigma_{\bar{x}} = \dfrac{\sigma_x}{\sqrt{n}} = 0.683$

$-3 \quad -2 \quad -1 \quad 0 \quad +1 \quad +2 \quad +3$

$z = \dfrac{\bar{x} - \mu}{\sigma_x/\sqrt{n}}$

FIGURE 7.6   Sampling distribution of $\bar{x}$ for telephone bill example

☐ **STUDY QUESTION 7.3** Evaluating the Probability of an Average Telephone Bill

Suppose that in the random sample of 36 residents with phones, we find that the average phone bill is $14.00. A typical question to ask at this point is: What is the probability that a random sample of $n = 36$ will result in an average bill of $14.00 or less, when $\mu_{\bar{x}} = \$15.30$ and $\sigma_{\bar{x}} = 0.683$? Making use of the standard normal transformation, we know that:

$$P(\bar{x} \leq \$14.00) = P\left(\frac{\bar{x} - \mu_{\bar{x}}}{\sigma_{\bar{x}}} \leq \frac{14.00 - 15.30}{0.683}\right) = P(z \leq -1.90)$$

By the central limit theorem, $\bar{x}$ is approximately normally distributed; hence, z is approximately standardized normal and, from Table III in the Appendix:

$$P(z \leq -1.90) = F(-1.90) = 1.0 - F(1.90)$$
$$= 1.0 - 0.9713 = 0.0287$$

The probability that a sample of 36 gives an average no larger than $14.00 is thus 0.0287. The reader should sketch this area on Figure 7.6.

   On the basis of the probability value calculated above, does it appear that local phone bills are part of the same population as residential phone bills in general? We leave such questions concerned with drawing conclusions from sample data for the following chapters, but the reader should keep them in mind to retain a feeling of where we are headed. ■

☐ **STUDY QUESTION 7.4** Evaluating the Probability of an Average Telephone Bill

Rather than finding the probability below a specific value of $\bar{x}$, one often wants to determine values a and b, such that the probability is 0.99 (or some other probability) that the sample mean will fall between these values. Recall that we did a similar calculation in our discussion of the normal distribution in Chapter 6. In the present case, we know that when $n = 36$, $\bar{x}$ will be approximately normally distributed, with mean $\mu_{\bar{x}} = \$15.30$, and $\sigma_{\bar{x}} = 4.10/\sqrt{36} = 0.683$.

   As before, we want the smallest interval including 99%, which means that we must exclude half of the remaining probability [or $\frac{1}{2}(0.01) = 0.005$] in each tail of the distribution of $\bar{x}$. To do this, let us first see what values of the standardized normal distribution exclude 0.005 in each tail. From Table III, $F(z) = 0.995$ if $z = 2.575$[†]; by symmetry, $F(-2.575) = 1.0 - F(2.575) = 0.005$. Thus:

$$P(-2.575 \leq z \leq 2.575) = 0.99$$

Finally, we now have to transform the interval $P(-2.575 \leq z \leq 2.575) = 0.99$ into the original units (dollars) by finding values a and b to satisfy $P(a \leq \bar{x} \leq b) = 0.99$. By standardizing the values of $a, \bar{x}$, and b, we find the following:

$$P(a \leq \bar{x} \leq b) = P\left(\frac{a - 15.30}{0.683} \leq z \leq \frac{b - 15.30}{0.683}\right)$$

[†] The reader could determine the value 2.575 by looking for $1 - 0.005 = 0.995$ in the body of Table III. The closest values to $F(0.995)$ are $F(0.9949) = 2.57$ and $F(0.9951) = 2.58$. Taking into account the nonlinear shape of the normal curve yields the value $F(0.9950) = 2.575$.

Thus, $(a - 15.30)/0.683 = -2.575$ and $(b - 15.30)/0.683 = 2.575$. Solving these two equations, we find $a = \$13.54$ and $b = \$17.06$; this means that the appropriate interval is $P(\$13.54 \le \bar{x} \le \$17.06)$. A diagram of the values in this example is shown in Figure 7.7.

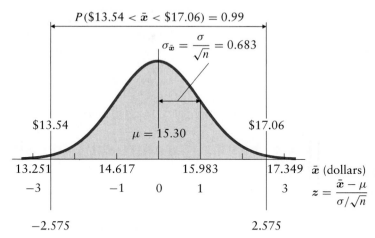

FIGURE 7.7 Standardized normal form of the sampling distribution of $\bar{x}$, sample mean of monthly phone charges; $\mu = \$15.30$, $\sigma = \$4.10$, $n = 36$

☐ STUDY QUESTION 7.5 Restaurant Quality

We continue Study Question 7.2, involving restaurants and their Mobil Travel Guide ratings. Now assume that we are thinking of sampling 100 restaurants. Sketch the sampling distribution of $\bar{x}$, and find values of a and b that give the smallest interval such that the following is true:

$$P(a < \bar{x} < b) = 0.95$$

Recall that in Study Question 7.2, $\mu = 3.0$ (stars) and $\sigma^2 = 2.0$ (stars squared).

• **ANSWER** The mean of $\bar{x}$ is 3.0 (the mean of the original population). The variance of $\bar{x}$ is $\sigma_{\bar{x}}^2 = \frac{1}{100}(2.0) = 0.020$.

The standard error of the mean is $\sigma_{\bar{x}} = \sqrt{0.020} = 0.1414$. The shape of the distribution is approximately normal by the central limit theorem (since n is *large*).

$$P(-1.96 < z < 1.96) = 0.95$$

$$P\left(\frac{a-3}{0.1414} < z < \frac{b-3}{0.1414}\right) = 0.95$$

$$a = 3 - 1.96(0.1414) = 2.723$$

$$b = 3 + 1.96(0.1414) = 3.277$$

Thus, $P(2.723 < \bar{x} < 3.277) = 0.95$.

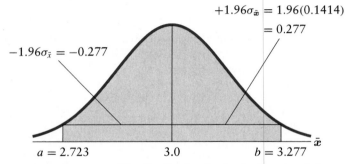

$$+1.96\sigma_{\bar{x}} = 1.96(0.1414)$$
$$= 0.277$$

$$-1.96\sigma_{\bar{x}} = -0.277$$

$a = 2.723$ 3.0 $b = 3.277$ $\bar{x}$

FIGURE 7.8 The distribution for Study Question 7.5

Finite Population Correction Factor

section 7.7

In the standardization for $\bar{x}$ in the previous section, the denominator was $\sigma/\sqrt{n}$. This standard error was calculated under the assumption that sampling occurred either from an infinite population or from a finite population with replacement. But what happens when sampling is *not* of this type — that is, when samples are drawn from a finite population without replacement? In this circumstance, the standard error cannot equal $\sigma/\sqrt{n}$; it must be *smaller*. The fact that the standard error must be smaller than $\sigma/\sqrt{n}$ in the case of a finite population should be evident from the logical fact that the standard deviation of the $\bar{x}$'s must approach zero as the sample size n approaches the population size N. That is, if each repeated sample consists of the whole population ($n = N$), then each sample mean $\bar{x}$ will be identical and equal to the population mean μ. There would be no variation in the values of $\bar{x}$, so $\sigma_{\bar{x}}^2 = 0$. This is not the case for $\sigma/\sqrt{n}$, as it approaches zero as $n \to$ infinity rather than as $n \to N$.

If the sample size is small in relation to the population size, say 10% or less, then Formula 7.6 will be approximately correct even when sampling without replacement. In these cases, we usually do not bother with the correction factor. *However, when the sample size is larger than 10% of N, then the denominator of the formula for z must be multiplied by a correction factor.* This correction factor, called the **finite population correction factor**, is defined as follows:

Finite population correction factor:

$$\sqrt{\frac{(N - n)}{(N - 1)}}$$

Note that this correction factor will always be a number less than 1.0. Multiplying the denominator of (7.9) by this correction factor will decrease the value of the standard error (which is what we wanted). The z-standardization, with the finite correction factor included, is given in Formula 7.10.[6]

---

[6] When the population size itself is very small, say $N \leq 30$, then care must be taken in interpreting this formula.

z-standardization:

$$z = \frac{\bar{x} - \mu}{\frac{\sigma}{\sqrt{n}}\sqrt{\frac{(N-n)}{(N-1)}}} \tag{7.10}$$

We illustrate the finite population correction factor by assuming in our telephone example that the number of local residents with private phones is 300. Since the sampling of 36 residents was without replacement, and a sample of size $n = 36$ equals 12% of this population $(36/300 = 0.12)$, the finite population correction factor should be used. We correct our z calculation from Example 7.4 as follows:

$$P(\bar{x} \le 14.00) = P\left(\frac{\bar{x} - \mu}{\frac{\sigma}{\sqrt{n}}\sqrt{\frac{(N-n)}{(N-1)}}} \le \frac{14.00 - 15.30}{\frac{4.10}{\sqrt{36}}\sqrt{\frac{(300-36)}{(300-1)}}}\right)$$

$$= P\left(z \le \frac{-1.30}{0.642}\right)$$

Comparing this result with that on page 263, we see that the denominator has changed from 0.683 to 0.642. Since $-1.30/0.642 = -2.02$, the new probability is:

$$P(z \le -2.02) = F(-2.02) = 1 - F(2.02) = 1 - 0.9783 = 0.0217.$$

The reader should verify that the finite population correction factor always decreases the value of the uncorrected standard error of the mean.

PROBLEMS

7.18 The balances on Sears charge cards last month is a normally distributed random variable with mean $\mu = 50$ and standard deviation $\sigma = 8$.

a) Find the following:

$$P(x \ge 40), P(x \le 54), \text{ and } P(44 \le x \le 56)$$

b) If a random sample of size $n = 64$ is drawn from this population, find:

$$P(\bar{x} \le 53), P(\bar{x} \ge 49), \text{ and } P(48 \le \bar{x} \le 52)$$

c) Sketch the distribution of x and the distribution of $\bar{x}$.

7.19 What is a sampling distribution? Why is the knowledge of the sampling distribution of a statistic important to statistical inference?

7.20 State the central limit theorem. Why do you think this theorem is so important to statistical inference?

7.21 A telephone company randomly selected 121 long-distance calls and found that the average length of these calls was 5 minutes. The population standard deviation is 45 seconds.

a) What is the probability that a sample mean will be as large as, or larger than, $\bar{x} = 5$ when the true population mean is $\mu = 4\frac{5}{6}$ minutes? What is the probability that a value will be as small as, or smaller than, $\bar{x} = 5$ when $\mu = 5\frac{1}{5}$?

b) Do your answers to part (a) depend on any assumptions about the distribution of the parent population?

7.22 If the mean of all shoe sizes for 13-year-old boys in Canada is 9 and the variance of these sizes is 1, what percent of this population wears a shoe of size 11 or larger? What is $P(\bar{x} > 11)$ if $n = 16$? Assume that the parent population is normally distributed.

7.23 Suppose that a random sample is being drawn from a population of truck drivers known to have a mean age of 30, with a standard deviation of 3 years. The population is normally distributed.

a) What is the probability that a randomly selected truck driver will be over 35 years of age? What is the probability that the executive will be between 25 and 35?

b) What is the probability, in a sample of 36 truck drivers, that the mean age will exceed 31? What is the probability that the mean age will be less than 30.5? What is $P(29 \leq \bar{x} \leq 31)$?

c) Does your answer to part (a) of this question depend on the assumption that the parent population is normally distributed? What about your answer to part (b)? Explain.

7.24 Funds, Inc., sells bonds maturing in 4, 5, 9, and 10 years. The probability distribution for customers purchasing these bonds is given in Table 7.12.

TABLE 7.12 Probability of Bond Sales

x (years)	4	5	9	10
$P(x)$	$\frac{1}{2}$	$\frac{1}{6}$	$\frac{1}{6}$	$\frac{1}{6}$

a) Sketch the probability function and find the mean and the standard deviation.

b) Suppose 115 repeated samples of size $n = 5$ are drawn randomly (with replacement) from this probability distribution. The sample means are calculated and their frequency distribution is given below:

TABLE 7.13 Sample Means for Sample Size $n = 5$

$\bar{x}$	Frequency	$\bar{x}$	Frequency
4.0	2	6.4	15
4.2	6	6.6	6
4.4	2	6.8	2
4.6	1	7.0	3
5.0	2	7.2	5
5.2	15	7.4	7
5.4	12	7.6	8
5.6	5	7.8	1
6.0	3	8.2	2
6.2	17	8.4	1
Total			115

Find the mean and the standard deviation of these values. Compare these values to those defined by the sampling distribution of $\bar{x}$ for all sample means of size 5.

7.25 Use Table V or a computer to collect a random sample of three observations (with replacement) from the population consisting of the digits 0 through 9. Repeat until you have a total of five samples. [*Suggestion:* The Doane package will do the sampling if you first establish a file containing the digits 0 through 9. Then use the subprogram SAMPLER, with $n = 3$.]

a) Calculate $\bar{x}$ for each of your five samples of three observations, and then calculate $\bar{\bar{x}}$, the mean of all five sample means.

b) What is the expected value in the population from which your samples in part (a) were drawn? Is $\bar{\bar{x}}$ reasonably close to $\mu_{\bar{x}}$?

c) Calculate the standard deviation of your five sample means about the grand mean. What is the standard error of the mean in the population from which your samples were drawn? Are the two values reasonably close?

7.26 The five samples you drew in Problem 7.25 represent observations from a population (the digits 0, 1, 2, ..., 9) with mean $\mu = 4.5$ and a variance of $\sigma^2 = 8.25$. This population is not normally distributed.

a) Calculate, for each of your five sample means in Problem 7.25, the value of z:

$$z = \frac{\bar{x} - \mu}{\sigma/\sqrt{n}}.$$

b) Would you expect the distribution of z-values in part (a) to follow a normal distribution? Will these z-values have a mean of zero and a variance of one? If not, explain why not.

7.27 Repeat Problem 7.25 (a), collecting five samples of size $n = 100$ using a computer package.

a) How do your answers change?

b) What is the standard error of the mean for samples of size 100?

c) Will your answer to part (b) in Problem 7.26 change for $n = 100$?

7.28 Collect a simple random sample of size $n = 12$ from the monthly incomes in **Data Set 6** using a computer or the random numbers in Table V. If **Data Set 6** is considered a population, the mean and standard deviation are $851.84 and $1,039.76, respectively.

a) Find the mean of your sample. How many standard errors is your value of $\bar{x}$ away from μ? [*Hint:* Calculate a z-value] What is the probability of a z-value this far, or farther, from μ?

b) Repeat part (a), using a systematic sample. Start with a randomly selected number less than 14, and then take every 17th number. Does this procedure cause any bias in your sample? Repeat the questions in part (a).

c) Take a stratified sample from **Data Set 6**, using the four regions to stratify the data. Find $\bar{x}$ for this sample.

7.29 Answer parts (a) and (b).

a) What is the finite population correction factor, and when is it necessary to apply this factor?

b) If $\sigma_x = 50$, $n = 25$, and $N = 100$, what is the corrected standard error of the mean?

7.30 A company hiring computer programmers has completed a study of 100 randomly selected salary offers, drawn from a population of 500 salary offers. The mean of this sample is $\bar{x} = \$42,985$. What is the probability of a sample mean of \$42,985, or larger, if the population mean is $\mu = \$42,800$ and the population standard deviation is known to be \$1,000? Remember to apply the finite population correction.

7.31 A cereal company checks the weight of each lot of 400 boxes of breakfast cereal by randomly checking 64 of the boxes. This particular brand is packed in 20-ounce boxes.

a) Suppose a particular random sample of 64 boxes results in a mean weight of 19.95 ounces. How often will the sample mean be this low, or lower if $\mu = 20$ and $\sigma = 0.10$? Use the finite population correction factor.

b) What is the percentage difference in the standard error after using the finite population correction factor? If it had not been used, what would have been the percentage error in the probability answer?

---

section 7.8

Sampling Distribution of $\bar{x}$, Normal Population, σ Unknown

In Section 7.5, we discussed the importance in problem-solving of using the following standardization:

$$z = \frac{\bar{x} - \mu}{\sigma/\sqrt{n}}$$

Usually, *our objective in using this type of standardization is to determine the probability of observing some specified value of $\bar{x}$, assuming that the population mean is μ, and then to use this probability in making a decision.* This means we have an assumed value of μ to use in the standardization. But what about the value of σ needed in the denominator? What happens if we do not want to (or cannot) assume a value of σ (if σ is unknown)? In solving a particular problem where σ is unknown, the sample statistic s can be used in place of σ. That is, our standardization now becomes:

$$\frac{\bar{x} - \mu}{s/\sqrt{n}}$$

The substitution of s for σ is reasonable, since it is possible to show that the expected value of s^2 equals σ^2. That is, $E[s^2] = \sigma^2$. We have shown previously that, when $\bar{x}$ is normal, the distribution of

$$\frac{\bar{x} - \mu}{\sigma/\sqrt{n}} \quad \text{is } N(0, 1)$$

Unfortunately, when s is substituted for σ, the resulting distribution is no longer normally distributed, nor is its variance 1.0. Our next task is thus to determine the distribution of the ratio $(x - \mu)/(s/\sqrt{n})$. This distribution can be thought of as being generated by the following process:

1. Collect all possible samples of size n from a normal parent population.
2. Calculate $\bar{x}$ and s for each sample.

3. Subtract μ from each value of $\bar{x}$, and then divide this deviation by the appropriate value of $s/\sqrt{n}$. (Remember, s usually will be different for each sample.)

This process will generate an infinite number of values of the random variable

$$\frac{\bar{x} - \mu}{s/\sqrt{n}}$$

It is not hard to recognize that the mean of this new distribution still equals zero, since the numerator has not changed and it was the numerator that made our original standardization have $E[z] = 0$. The variance of $(x - \mu)/(s/\sqrt{n})$ is no longer equal to $V[z] = 1.0$; it is larger than 1.0. This is reasonable when one recognizes that with the ratio $(\bar{x} - \mu)/(s/\sqrt{n})$ one more element of uncertainty (the estimator s) has been added to the standardization. The more uncertainty there is, the more spread out the distribution.

Several additional aspects of the distribution of $(\bar{x} - \mu)/(s/\sqrt{n})$ are worth noting. First, we would expect this distribution to be symmetrical, since there is no reason to believe that substituting s for σ will make this distribution skewed either positively or negatively. Second, it should be apparent that the variability of this distribution depends on the size of n, for the sample size affects the reliability with which s estimates σ. When n is large, s will be a good approximation to σ; but when n is small, s may not be very close to σ. This implies that the distribution of $(\bar{x} - \mu)/(s/\sqrt{n})$ is a family of distributions in which variability depends on n.

It should be clear from the above discussion that the distribution of $(\bar{x} - \mu)/(s/\sqrt{n})$ is not normal, but is more spread out than the normal. The distribution of this statistic is called the **t-distribution**, and its random variable is denoted as follows:

---

t-distribution:

$$t = \frac{\bar{x} - \mu}{s/\sqrt{n}} \qquad\qquad (7.11)$$

The variable t is a continuous random variable. One of the first researchers to work on determining the exact distribution of this random variable was W. S. Gosset, an Irish statistician. However, the Dublin brewery for which Gosset worked did not allow its employees to publish their research; hence, Gosset wrote under the pen name *Student*. In honor of Gosset's research, published in 1908, the t-distribution is often referred to as the "Student's t-distribution." It is not clear from historical records whether Gosset enjoyed the product of his employer, as do many modern students.

Student's t-distribution

Since the density function for the t-distribution is fairly complex and not of primary importance at this point, we will not present it, but will begin merely by describing the characteristics of this distribution.[7] As we indicated previously, the t-distribution depends on the size of the sample. It is customary to describe the characteristics of the t-distribution in terms of the sample size minus one, or $(n - 1)$, as this quantity has special significance.

---

[7] Mathematically, the random variable t is defined as a standardized normal variable z divided by the square root of an independently distributed chi-square variable, which has been divided by its degrees of freedom; that is, $t = z/\sqrt{\chi^2/\nu}$. The chi-square distribution is discussed in Section 7.9.

The value of $(n-1)$ is called the number of **degrees of freedom** (abbreviated d.f.) and represents a measure of the number of independent observations in the sample that can be used to estimate the standard deviation of the parent population. For example, when $n = 1$, there is no way to estimate the population standard deviation; hence there are *no* degrees of freedom $(n - 1 = 0)$. There is one degree of freedom in a sample of $n = 2$, since one observation is now *free* to vary away from the other, and the amount it varies determines our estimate of the population standard deviation. Each additional observation adds one more degree of freedom, so that in a sample of size n there are $(n - 1)$ observations *free* to vary, and hence $(n - 1)$ degrees of freedom. The Greek letter v (nu) is often used to denote degrees of freedom, where $v = n - 1$ in this case.

> A t-distribution is completely described by its one parameter, $v =$ degrees of freedom. The mean of the t-distribution is zero, $E[t] = 0$. The variance of the t-distribution, when $n \geq 3$, is $V[t] = v/(v - 2)$.

The last sentence above implies that $V[t] \geq 1.0$ for all sample sizes, in contrast to $V[z]$, which is 1.0 no matter what the sample size. For example, when $v = 3$, the variance of the t-distribution is $3/(3 - 2) = 3.0$. The t-distribution with $v = 3$ and the standardized normal are contrasted in Figure 7.9.

For small sample sizes, the t-distribution is seen to be considerably more spread out than the normal. When v is larger, such as $v = 30$, then $V[t] = 30/(30 - 2) = 1.07$, which is not much different from $V[z] = 1.0$. In the limit, as $n \to \infty$, the t- and z-distributions are identical. Tables of t-values are usually completely enumerated only for $v \leq 30$, because for larger samples, the normal gives a very good approximation and is easier to use. For this reason, it is customary to speak of the t-distribution as applying to small sample sizes, *even though this distribution holds for any size n.*

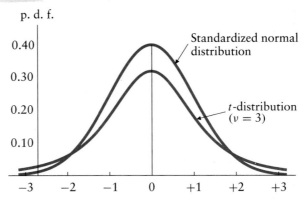

FIGURE 7.9   The standardized normal and t-distributions compared

Probability questions involving a t-distributed random variable can be answered by using a computer or the cumulative distribution function, $F(t)$ in Table VI. This table gives the values of t for selected values of the cumulative probability $[(F(t) = P(t < t)]$ across the top of the table and for degrees of freedom (v) down the left margin. Figure 7.10 shows some values of the t-distribution for $v = 24$ degrees of freedom, taken from Table VI in the Appendix. The four different values from Table VI in the Appendix shown in Figure 7.10 are as follows:

$$P(t \leq 0.685) = 0.75 \qquad P(t \leq 1.318) = 0.90$$
$$P(t \geq 2.064) = 0.025 \qquad P(t \geq 2.492) = 0.01$$

As the latter two values above demonstrate, a probability in the upper tail of the *t*-distribution (beyond one of the cutoff points in Table VI) is obtained by using the complement rule $[1 - F(t)]$. A probability value in the lower tail (a negative *t*-value) is determined by changing the sign to positive and using the same procedure described above (because the *t*-distribution is symmetrical).

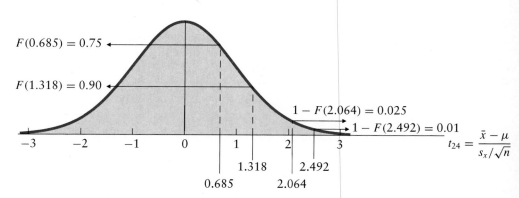

$$F(0.685) = 0.75$$
$$F(1.318) = 0.90$$
$$1 - F(2.064) = 0.025$$
$$1 - F(2.492) = 0.01$$
$$t_{24} = \frac{\bar{x} - \mu}{s_x / \sqrt{n}}$$

FIGURE 7.10 Various probabilities for the *t*-distribution for $\nu = 24$ d.f.

Table VI gives probabilities for seven selected *t*-values for each degree of freedom. More extensive tables are available, and probabilities may be determined mathematically for any *t*-value. The easiest way to determine probabilities for the *t*-distribution is to use a statistical package for a computer.

Examples of the *t*-distribution

As with the normal distribution, the *t*-distribution is often used to test an assumption about a population mean based on the standardization of an observed sample mean.

> The *t*-distribution is the appropriate statistic for inference on a population mean whenever the parent population is normally distributed and σ is unknown.

◻ **EXAMPLE 7.5** A small finance company has reported to an auditing firm that its outstanding loans are approximately normally distributed with a mean of $825. The standard deviation is unknown. In an attempt to verify this reported value of $\mu = \$825$, a random sample of 25 accounts was taken. This random sample yields a mean of $\bar{x} = \$780$, with a standard deviation of $s = 105$. The question facing the auditor is how often might one find a sample mean of $780 or lower when the true mean is $825? That is, what is $P(\bar{x} \leq \$780)$?

To solve this problem, we would like to standardize the values in the parentheses. But such a standardization requires knowledge of σ. Since we do not know σ, we use a new standardization that follows the *t*-distribution:

$$t = \frac{\bar{x} - \mu}{s / \sqrt{n}}$$

Because s is only an estimate of σ, the t-distribution only *approximately* solves specific problems involving $\bar{x}$ such as $P(\bar{x} \leq \$780)$.

In Example 7.5, we would like to find the probability $P(\bar{x} \leq \$780)$. Since $n = 25$, x is normal, and σ is unknown, this probability is approximated by using the t-distribution with $n - 1 = 24$ degrees of freedom. Using the t-standardization:

$$t = \frac{\bar{x} - \mu}{s/\sqrt{n}} = \frac{780 - 825}{105/\sqrt{25}} = -2.143$$

The probability $P(t \leq -2.143)$ is thus our approximation of the probability $P(\bar{x} \leq \$780)$. This probability, which is equivalent to $F(-2.143)$, is evaluated below. ∎

Determining Probabilities for the t-distribution

As usual, determining probabilities such as $F(-2.143)$ is easiest using a computer. Thus, the illustration below demonstrates finding this probability with a statistical package. Because computers are not always readily available, we will also show probabilities determined (as best as possible) from Table VI. For the Doane package, select the Program menu (P), and then select the AREA option from the submenu. From the resulting menu select option 2, "Student's t. The queries by the program, our responses (in bold) for determining $F(-2.143)$ for $\nu = 24$, and the resulting output are shown below.

```
Student's t

Input t? -2.143

Input d.f.? 24
```
STUDENT'S T PROBABILITY DENSITY FUNCTION

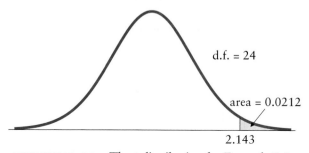

d.f. = 24

area = 0.0212

2.143

FIGURE 7.11   The t-distribution for Example 7.5

Notice that the program has transformed our problem, of finding $F(-2.143)$ to the equivalent problem, that of finding $1 - F(2.143)$. The probability desired is shown in Figure 7.11 to be:

$$P(t \leq -2.143) = 0.0212$$

$P(t \leq -2.143)$ is easy to find using a computer; it is not as easy to find using Table VI because the number $t = 2.143$ does not appear in the row for $\nu = 24$. However, it is possible to use Table VI to find an upper and lower bound for $P(t \leq -2.143) = F(-2.143)$. From Table VI, or Figure 7.10, we know that $F(-2.064) = 1-0.975 = 0.025$. Similarly we know that $F(-2.492) = 1-0.990 = 0.010$. Putting this information together gives

$$0.010 \leq P(t \leq -2.143) \leq 0.025$$

This result says that a sample mean as low as or lower than $780 will occur (approximately) between 1% and 2.5% of the time when $\mu = \$825$. Faced with such low probabilities, the auditor might well be concerned with the accuracy of the assumption that $\mu = \$825$.

Suppose that in the above example, instead of the sample results described there, we found the values $\bar{x} = \$842.60$, and $s = 80.0$. For this result, we want to determine the probability that $\bar{x}$ is greater than or equal to $842.60 when $\mu = \$825$. Using the t-standardization:

$$t = \frac{\bar{x} - \mu}{s/\sqrt{n}} = \frac{\$842.60 - \$825}{80/\sqrt{25}} = 1.100$$

From Table VI, $F(1.100)$ lies between $F(0.685) = 0.75$ and $F(1.318) = 0.90$ when $\nu = 24$. Hence:

$$0.25 > P(t \geq 1.100) > 0.10$$

The exact probability, using a computer, is $P(t \geq 1.100) = 0.1411$. We see from this result that a sample mean of $842.60 is fairly probable when $\mu = \$825$ and $n = 25$. These values are shown in Figure 7.12.

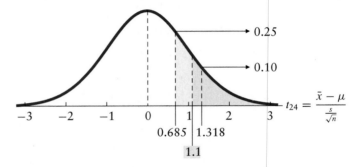

FIGURE 7.12   The t-distribution values for $\nu = 24$

As our second example of the use of the t-distribution, let us determine an interval $[a, b]$ such that $P(a \leq t \leq b) = 0.95$, assuming $n - 1 = \nu = 8$ degrees of freedom. As before, the smallest interval is found by putting half the excluded area, $\frac{1}{2}(0.05) = 0.025$, in each tail of the distribution. For example, we want $P(t \geq b) = 0.025$, which means that, in terms of the cumulative function, we want to find a value t such that $F(t) = 0.975$. From Table VI, for $\nu = 8$, we see that $F(2.306) = 0.975$; hence, $b = 2.306$. Now since the t-distribution is symmetrical, the appropriate value for a is merely the negative of the value of b, or $a = -2.306$. Thus:

$$P(-2.306 \leq t \leq 2.306) = 0.95$$

Recall, from our previous examples using the standardized normal distribution, that $P(-1.96 \leq z \leq 1.96) = 0.95$. The critical values for z that exclude 0.025 probability in the upper and lower tails are ± 1.96, as opposed to ± 2.306 for the t-distribution with $\nu = 8$. The difference reflects the fact that the t-distribution is more spread out than the z-distribution. Note in Table VI that by *increasing* the value of ν from 8 to 10, then 20, then 60, then 120, and moving down the column for $F(t) = 0.975$, the critical values for t *decrease* from 2.306 to 2.228, then 2.086, then 2.000, then 1.98, respectively. For larger values of ν, the spread of the t-distribution closes in to match the spread of the z-distribution. Indeed, when $\nu = \infty$, the critical value for t exactly equals the value 1.96 for z, as shown by the bottom row in Table VI.

Use of the t-distribution When the Population Is Not Normal

It must be emphasized at this point that the t-distribution, as well as the chi-square distribution (discussed in the following section), assumes that samples are drawn from a parent population that is normally distributed. Often there is no way to determine the exact distribution of the parent population. In practical problems involving these distributions, the question therefore arises as to just how critical the assumption is that the parent population be exactly normally distributed. Fortunately, the assumption of normality can be relaxed without significantly changing the sampling distribution of the t-distribution (or the chi-square distribution to be discussed next). Because of this fact these distributions are said to be quite *robust*, implying that their usefulness holds up under conditions that do not conform exactly to the original assumptions. The t-distribution is much more robust than the chi-square distribution.

We should emphasize again that the t-distribution is appropriate whenever x is normal and σ is unknown, despite the fact that many t tables do not list values higher than $\nu = 30$. For practical problems, this does not cause many difficulties; as the reader will note, the t-values in a given column of Table VI change very little above $\nu = 30$. If the appropriate ν is not in Table VI, we suggest looking at the table entries for ν above and below the one desired.[8]

◻ STUDY QUESTION 7.6 Waiting Time for Delivery of New Cars

Volkswagen dealers have been instructed to quote a 100-day wait for delivery of a new Jetta, ordered from the factory. A random sample of 400 such orders resulted in a mean delivery time of $\bar{x} = 120$ days, with a sample standard deviation of $s = 200$. Approximate the probability that the sample mean will be 120 or larger if μ does, in fact, equal 100 and σ is unknown.

• ANSWER

$$P\left(\frac{\bar{x} - \mu}{s/\sqrt{n}} \geq \frac{120 - 100}{200/\sqrt{400}}\right) = P(t \geq 2.00)$$

Although $\nu = 399$ is not listed in Table VI, by looking at $\nu = 120$ versus $\nu = \infty$ we can easily determine that

$$0.025 > P(t \geq 2.00) > 0.01.$$

The exact probability, using a computer, is $P(t \geq 2.00) = 0.0231$. ∎

---

[8] Some texts suggest that the normal distribution be used to approximate the t-distribution when $\nu > 30$, since the t- and z-values will then be quite close. (The normal value will be slightly smaller than the exact t-value). Because of this procedure, the t-distribution sometimes is referred to *incorrectly* as applying only to small samples. We prefer to emphasize that the t-distribution is *always* correct whenever σ is unknown and x is normal.

The Sampling Distribution of s^2, Normal Population

The only sampling distribution considered thus far has been that of $\bar{x}$, the sample mean. But in many practical problems, we need information about the distribution of the sample variance, s^2. That is, we need to investigate the distribution that consists of all possible values of s^2 calculated from samples of size n. The sampling distribution of s^2 is particularly important in problems concerned with the variability in a random sample. For example, the telephone company may be just as interested in the variance in length of calls in a random sample as they are in the mean length. Or a manufacturer of steel beams may want to learn just as much about the variance as the mean of tensile strength of the steel beams. The statistician who first worked with the t-distribution, W. S. Gosset, was also one of the first to describe the sampling distribution of s^2.

Because s^2 must always be positive, the distribution of s^2 cannot be a normal distribution. Rather, the distribution of s^2 is a unimodal distribution that is *skewed* to the right and looks like the smooth curve in Figure 7.13. As with the t-distribution, sampling is from a normal parent population, and the one parameter is the degrees of freedom, ν.

A typical problem in analyzing variances is that of determining the probability that the value of s^2 will be larger (or smaller) than some observed value, given some assumed value of σ^2.

For example, the variance in the amount of cereal in 16-ounce boxes has been $\sigma^2 = 0.0010$ (ounces squared). What is the probability that a random sample of $n = 21$ cereal boxes will result in a sample variance at least as large as $s^2 = 0.0016$? That is, what is

$$P(s^2 \geq 0.0016),$$

assuming $\nu = n - 1 = 20$ and $\sigma^2 = 0.0010$?

Unfortunately, we cannot solve problems like this one directly but must transform them in a way similar to the standardizations for $\bar{x}$. In this case, the transformation is accomplished by multiplying s^2 by $(n-1)$, and then dividing the product by σ^2. This new random variable is denoted by the symbol χ^2, which is the square of the Greek letter chi. The **chi-square distribution** is a family of positively skewed p.d.f.s which depend on one parameter, $\nu = n - 1$, which is its degrees of freedom. Thus,

---

Chi-square random variable:

$$\chi^2_{n-1} = \frac{\nu s^2}{\sigma^2} = \frac{(n-1)s^2}{\sigma^2} \qquad (7.12)$$

In words, this formula says the following:

If s^2 is the variance of random samples of size n taken from a normal population having a variance of σ^2, then the variable $(n-1)s^2/\sigma^2$ has the same distribution as a χ^2-variable with $(n-1)$ degrees of freedom.

The subscript on the χ^2 symbol in Formula 7.12 merely serves to remind us of the appropriate degrees of freedom.

Although Gosset was unable to prove Formula 7.12 mathematically, he did demonstrate this relationship in his empirical work. Gosset took the heights of 3,000 criminals, calculated the value of σ^2 for these heights, and then grouped these heights into 750 random samples of 4. For each of these 750 samples, Gosset, in effect, calculated a value of s^2, multiplied s^2 by $(n-1) = 3$, and then divided this number by σ^2. The results are plotted in the histogram shown in Figure 7.13. Note that Gosset's histogram and the chi-square distribution (for $v = n - 1 = 3$) superimposed on it are not in perfect agreement, a fact that Gosset attributed to the particular grouping of heights that he used.

Solving a problem involving s^2 by using Formula 7.12 follows essentially the same process used to solve problems involving $\bar{x}$.

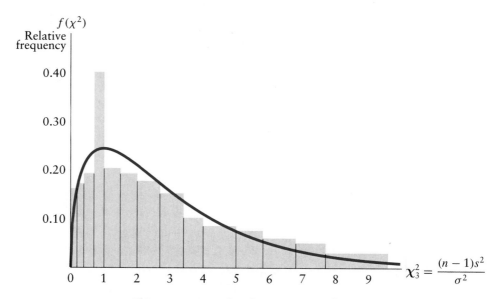

FIGURE 7.13   Chi-square approximation to Gosset's data on the height of criminals

□ **EXAMPLE 7.6**   For example, to solve the cereal problem mentioned earlier, $P(s^2 \geq 0.0016)$, we transform each value in parenthesis as follows:

$$P(s^2 \geq 0.0016) = P\left[\frac{(n-1)s^2}{\sigma^2} \geq \frac{(20)(0.0016)}{0.0010}\right] = P(\chi_{20}^2 \geq 32)$$

The equivalence between $P(s^2 \geq 0.0016)$ and $P(\chi_{20}^2 \geq 32)$ is illustrated in Figure 7.14.

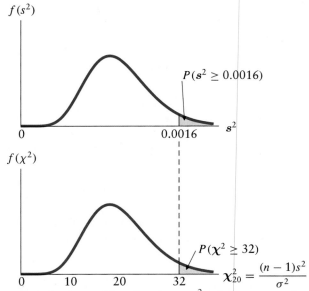

FIGURE 7.14 Transforming an s^2-value into an equivalent χ^2-value with $\nu = n - 1 = 20$

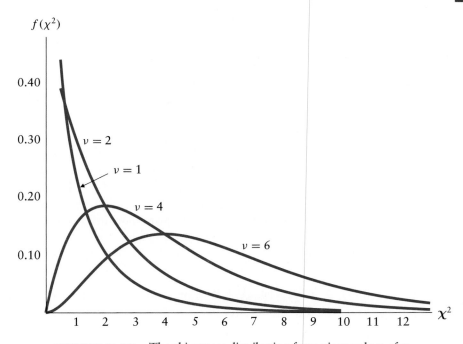

FIGURE 7.15 The chi-square distribution for various values of ν

Properties of the χ^2-distribution

As shown in Figure 7.15, the number of degrees of freedom in a χ^2-distribution determines what shape $f(\chi^2)$ will be. When ν is small, the shape of the density function is highly skewed to the right. As ν gets larger, however, the distribution becomes more and more symmetrical in appearance. Since only squared numbers are involved in calculating χ^2, we know that this variable can never assume a value below zero, but it may take on values up to positive infinity.

The density function for the χ^2-distribution is not of primary importance for our discussion; hence, we will not present its formula, but merely concentrate on its characteristics. The mean and the variance of the chi-square distribution are both related to ν as follows:

$$\text{Mean} = E[\chi_\nu^2] = \nu$$
$$\text{Variance} = V[\chi_\nu^2] = E[(\chi_\nu^2 - \nu)^2] = 2\nu$$

Thus, if we have a chi-square variable involved in a problem using random samples of size $n = 19$, then $\nu = n - 1 = 18$, and:

$$E[\chi^2] = 18, \quad V[\chi^2] = 36, \quad \text{and} \quad \sigma = 6$$

A graph of the chi-square distribution for $n = 19$ ($\nu = 18$) is shown in Figure 7.16. Notice in this figure that $\mu = 18 = \nu$, and the standard deviation is $\sigma = \sqrt{2\nu} = \sqrt{36} = 6$. The distribution in Figure 7.16 is fairly symmetrical in appearance. As ν increases, the χ^2 distribution becomes closer and closer to the normal distribution.

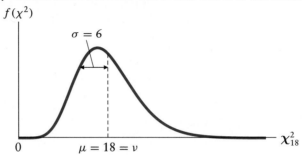

FIGURE 7.16   Chi-square distribution for $\nu = 18$

Chi-square Examples

Table VII in Appendix C gives values of the cumulative χ^2-distribution for selected values of ν and gives (at the bottom) a formula for the normal approximation to χ^2, which can be used when $\nu > 30$. To illustrate the use of the χ^2-distribution, we will assume that we have taken all possible random samples of size $n = 21$ from some normal parent population. For each of these random samples, we then multiply the value of the sample variance (s^2) by $(n-1)$ and divide the result by the (assumed) population variance (σ^2). When we have finished this hypothetical task (there are an infinite number of such ratios), we will have calculated all possible values for this χ^2 distribution:

$$\chi_{20}^2 = \frac{(n-1)s^2}{\sigma^2} = \frac{(20)s^2}{\sigma^2}$$

The distribution of the statistic given above is the chi-square distribution. We can use Table VII in Appendix C to graph a few values of the chi-square distribution for 20 degrees of freedom.

From Figure 7.17, we see that the ratio $(20)s^2/\sigma^2$ will have a value less than 8.26 only 1% of the time, less than 9.59 two and one-half percent of the time, less than 28.4 ninety percent of the time, and so forth.

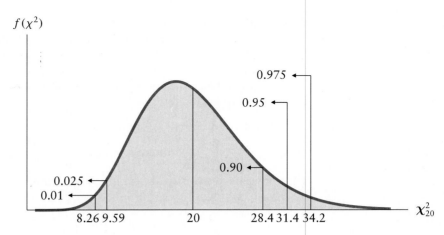

FIGURE 7.17   Chi-square distribution for $v = 20$

⬜ STUDY QUESTION 7.7   Variability of Cereal in 16-Ounce Boxes

Use the chi-square distribution to solve the cereal problem in Example 7.6. That is, find $P(s^2 > 0.0016)$ when $n = 21$ and the population variance is assumed to be $\sigma^2 = 0.0010$.

● ANSWER

$$P(s^2 \geq 0.0016) = P\left(\frac{(n-1)s^2}{\sigma^2} \geq \frac{(20)(0.0016)}{0.0010}\right) = P(\chi_{20}^2 \geq 32.0)$$

From Figure 7.17,

$$0.950 < P(\chi^2 \leq 32) < 0.975$$

This implies that

$$0.05 > P(\chi^2 \geq 32.0) = P(s^2 \geq 0.0016) > 0.025$$

Using a computer package for the chi-square distribution, the exact probability is found to be

$$P(\chi^2 \geq 32) = 0.0433$$

Since a sample variance as high as 0.0016 will occur relatively infrequently when $\sigma^2 = 0.0010$ (less than 5% of the time), we might question this company's statement that $\sigma^2 = 0.0010$.   ◼

PROBLEMS

(Use a computer, if possible, to solve these problems.)

7.32 Determine, for each of the following cases, whether the t-distribution or the standardized normal distribution (or neither) is appropriate for answering probability questions relating to sample means.

a) a small sample from a normal population with known standard deviation

b) a small sample from a nonnormal population with known standard deviation

c) a small sample from a normal population with unknown standard deviation

d) a small sample from a nonnormal population with unknown standard deviation

e) a large sample from a normal population with unknown standard deviation

f) a large sample from a nonnormal population with unknown standard deviation

7.33 Suppose that you collect the following sample of four observations, drawn randomly from a normal population, representing the January heating cost for a 4-bedroom house in Sarnia, Ontario: 199, 215, 191, 179. Compute $\bar{x}$.

a) What is the probability of obtaining this $\bar{x}$ or one smaller if the population has mean $\mu = 210$ and unknown variance? What is the probability that $\bar{x}$ is this large or larger if the population has mean $\mu = 180$ and unknown variance?

b) What is the probability of obtaining this $\bar{x}$ or one smaller if the population has mean $\mu = 210$ and a standard deviation of $\sigma = 14$? What is the probability that $\bar{x}$ is this small or smaller if the population has mean $\mu = 200$ and $\sigma = 10$?

7.34 Answer parts (a) and (b).

a) Describe the difference between the standardized normal distribution and the t-distribution. Under what conditions can each be used?

b) Is $P(z \geq 2.0) = 0.0228$ greater than $P(t \geq 2.0)$ for all sample sizes? How do you explain this fact?

7.35 It is suggested that the average weekly wage of student workers is $110. A random sample of 100 students yields the following distribution:

TABLE 7.14 Average Weekly Wage of Student Workers

Wages	f
38–62	5
63–87	17
88–112	24
113–137	26
138–162	13
163–187	8
188–212	7
Total	100

a) Calculate $\bar{x}$ and s^2 using the class marks 50, 75, 100, ..., 200.

b) How probable is a sample mean this large if $\mu = 110$ and x is normally distributed?

c) Would your result from part (b) lead you to question the supposition that $\mu = 110$?

7.36 Explain why the standardized normal distribution cannot be used for inferences on the population mean whenever the parent population is normally distributed and σ is unknown. What distribution is appropriate in this circumstance?

7.37 Assume that an economist estimates that the number of litres of gasoline used monthly by each automobile in Canada is a normally distributed random variable with mean $\mu = 50$ and variance unknown.

a) Suppose that a sample of nine observations yields a sample variance of $s^2 = 36$. What is the probability that $\bar{x}$ is larger than 54 if $\mu = 50$? What is the probability that $\bar{x}$ is less than 44 if $\mu = 50$? What is the probability that $\bar{x}$ lies between 45 and 55?

b) How would your answers to the above problem change if $n = 36$ and all else remained the same?

7.38 A professional bowler claims that her bowling scores can be thought of as normally distributed with mean $\mu = 215$ and unknown variance. In her latest performance, the bowler scores 188, 214, and 204.

a) Calculate $\bar{x}$ and s^2 for this sample.

b) If these three scores represent a random sample from a normal population with mean $\mu = 215$, what is the probability that $\bar{x}$ will be as low as you calculated it to be in part (a)?

c) Would you conclude from part (b) that the bowler is off her game?

7.39 What is the sampling distribution of s^2? How is this distribution related to the chi-square distribution?

7.40 Suppose that you are drawing samples of size $n = 3$ from a normal population with a variance of 8.25. What is the probability that the value of $(n-1)s^2/\sigma^2$ will exceed 5.99? What is the probability that s^2 will be more than three times as large as σ^2?

7.41 Suppose that a random variable is known to be chi-square-distributed with parameter $\nu = 24$.

a) What are the mean and the variance of the chi-square distribution for this parameter?

b) What is the probability that the value of χ^2 will exceed 43.0? What is $P(\chi^2 \geq 33.2)$? What is $P(\chi^2 \geq 9.89)$?

c) Use your answers to parts (a) and (b) to draw a rough sketch of the chi-square distribution for $\nu = 24$.

d) Superimpose a graph of the normal distribution for $\mu = 24$ and $\sigma^2 = 48$ on your sketch for part (c). How closely do the two distributions agree?

7.42 A hamburger chain is concerned with the amount of variability in its quarter-pounder. The amount of meat in these burgers is supposed to have a variance of no more than 0.2 ounces. A random sample of 20 burgers from one chain yields a variance of $s^2 = 0.4$.

a) What is the probability that a sample variance will equal or exceed 0.4 if it is assumed that $\sigma^2 = 0.2$?

b) Would you suspect that the meat content of the burgers that this chain is selling varies excessively?

7.43 A researcher on agriculture considers the usual variance on yield for corn to be 400 (bushels squared) per acre. This person makes a study of 15 acres selected randomly from one large farm and finds a sample variance of 800. Assuming a normal distribution of yields per acre, is this an unusually high variance?

7.44 A local tax board has determined that the usual variance in property-tax assessment for Type A houses is 1,000,000 (dollars squared). A random sample of 20 houses in the tax area indicated a variance of 600,000. Is this an unusually low variance, assuming a normal distribution of assessments?

TABLE 7.15 Summary of sampling distributions

Random Variable	Situation	Reference Section	Resulting Distribution for Problem-solving	Mean	Variance
$\bar{x}$	Population normal, σ known, sample size n	7.5	$z = \dfrac{\bar{x} - \mu}{\sigma/\sqrt{n}}$	0	1
$\bar{x}$	Population normal, σ unknown, sample size n^*	7.8	$t = \dfrac{\bar{x} - \mu}{s/\sqrt{n}}$	0	$\nu/(\nu - 2)$ (where $\nu = n - 1$)
$\bar{x}$	Population unknown, σ known, n large	7.6	$z = \dfrac{\bar{x} - \mu}{\sigma/\sqrt{n}}$	0	1
s^2	Population normal, sample size n	7.9	$\chi^2 = \dfrac{(n-1)s^2}{\sigma^2}$	ν	2ν (where $\nu = n - 1$)

*If n is "large", $\bar{x}$ will be approximately normally distributed, and s should be close to σ; hence, $(\bar{x} - \mu)/(s/\sqrt{n})$ is approximately $N(0, 1)$.

CHAPTER SUMMARY

KEY TERMS AND EXPRESSIONS

Table 7.15 gives a summary and the reference sections for probability distributions discussed in this chapter.

Figure 7.18 provides a tree diagram that some students have found useful in deciding when to apply each of these distributions.

Sample design: A plan specified for obtaining a sample before any data are collected.

Sampling and nonsampling errors: Sampling errors are those errors that occur because even a perfectly designed sample may not always represent the population exactly. Nonsampling errors are the human, or avoidable, errors.

Random numbers: Numbers selected from a population in such a way that they have the same probability of occurring as does every other number in the population.

Probabilistic sampling: Sample designs that are based primarily on a random selection process.

a) Simple random sampling: Every item and every group of items has the same probability of being in the sample.

b) Systematic sampling: Selection of every kth item, starting from a random point.

c) Stratified sampling: Selects randomly from layers or strata.

d) Cluster sampling: Selects randomly from groups, or clusters, having similar characteristics.

e) Sequential sampling: Sample items not taken simultaneously, but sequentially.

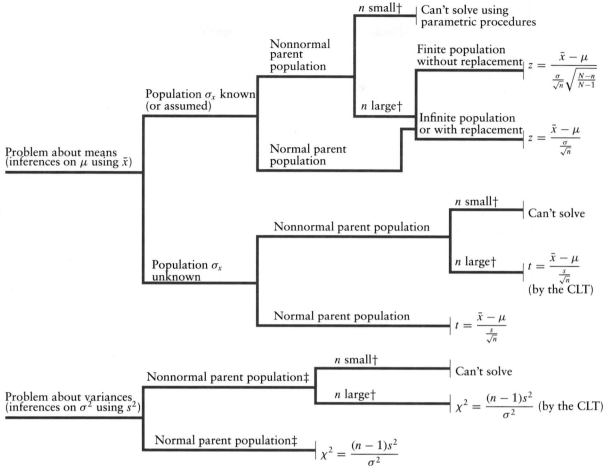

†"Large" and "small" may depend on the accuracy desired and the shape of the parent population. For fairly symmetrical distributions, $n \geq 10$ may be sufficient. In almost all cases, $n \geq 30$ is sufficient for "large."

‡Remember, the t and χ^2 are fairly "robust," meaning that they work well, even if the parent population is not exactly normally distributed but has some normal characteristics (unimodal and not badly skewed).

FIGURE 7.18   Tree diagram for using probability distributions

Nonprobabilistic sampling: Based primarily on a non-random selection process.

a) Judgement sampling: Primary consideration is the judgment of the person in charge.

b) Quota sampling: A specified number of values collected.

c) Convenience sampling: Values taken according to what is convenient.

Sample statistic: A characteristic of a sample.

Sample mean:

$$\bar{x} = \frac{1}{n} \sum x_i f_i.$$

Sample variance:

$$s^2 = \frac{1}{n-1} \sum (x_i - \bar{x})^2 f_i$$

Sampling distribution: The probability distribution of a sample statistic.

Expected value of $\bar{x}$: $E[\bar{x}] = \mu_{\bar{x}} = \mu$

Variance of x: $V[\bar{x}] = \sigma_{\bar{x}}^2 = \sigma^2/n$

Standard error of the mean: $\sigma_{\bar{x}} = \sigma/\sqrt{n}$

Standardization of $\bar{x}$:

$$z = \frac{\bar{x} - \mu}{\sigma/\sqrt{n}}$$

Central Limit Theorem: Regardless of the parent population distribution, as n gets larger, the distribution of $\bar{x}$ will become more and more like a normal distribution.

Finite population correction factor: Corrects the standard error of the mean by multiplying by $\sqrt{(N-n)/(N-1)}$ when sampling more than 10% of a finite population of size N without replacement.

t-distribution: A family of symmetrical p.d.f.s that depend on the parameter v (d.f.) with $E[t] = 0$ and $V[t] = v/(v-2)$ for $v \geq 3$. Used particularly in probability questions involving the sample mean when sampling from a normal parent population with unknown variance, $t = (\bar{x} - \mu)/(s/\sqrt{n})$. The t approaches the normal z as the sample size gets larger.

Degrees of freedom (v): Number of values in a sample that are free to vary when calculating a sample statistic. For example, to calculate s, $v = n - 1$.

Chi-square (χ^2) distribution: A family of positively skewed p.d.f.s which depend on the parameter v (degrees of freedom) with $E[\chi^2] = v$, $V[\chi^2] = 2v$. Used particularly in probability questions about a sample variance when sampling from a normal parent population, $\chi^2_{v=n-1} = (n-1)s^2/\sigma^2$.

EXERCISES

◆ **7.45** A magazine subscription agency, specifically dealing with college students, is interested in the average number of subscriptions held by each student. Denoting x as the number of subscriptions held by a student, a random sample of 900 students was selected and it was found that

$$\sum x = 1,600 \text{ and } \sum (x - \bar{x})^2 = 3,679.18$$

Find a point estimate for the average number of subscriptions held per student. What is the sample standard deviation?

◆ **7.46** A computer manufacturer has determined that the mean time before the first service call on a new PC is $\mu = 184$ days with $\sigma = 22.45$. What is the probability that, in a random sample of 100 new PCs, the sample mean will:

a) exceed 184 days;

b) fall between 180 and 200 days.

◆ **7.47** The following data are a random sample of household incomes (in dollars earned) in the city of Red Deer.

$12,000 $19,800 $56,700 $88,000 $24,500

a) Calculate the mean and standard deviation for this sample.

b) Suppose the true variance of the population from which this sample was drawn is equal to $100 million ($100,000,000). If all possible samples of size 5 were selected from this population, determine the variance and the standard error of the sampling distribution of the sample mean.

c) Assume that household income came from a normal population with $\mu = \$30,000$ and $\sigma^2 = 81,000,000$. What is the probability that a random sample of 5 households would yield a sample mean as high as $40,380?

7.48 Prove the following.

a) $E[s^2] = \sigma^2$ using the fact that the mean of the chi-square distribution is v

b) $V[s^2] = 2\sigma^4/v$

7.49 The auditor's failure to recognize an error in an amount or an error in an internal-control data-processing procedure is described as a

a) statistical error.

b) sampling error.

c) standard error of the mean.

d) nonsampling error.

7.50 In connection with his review of charges to the plant maintenance account, Mr. John Wilson, CA, is undecided as to whether to use probability sampling or judgment sampling. As compared with probability sampling, judgment sampling has the primary disadvantage of

a) providing no known method for making statistical inferences about the population solely from the results of the sample.

b) not allowing the auditor to select those accounts which he believes should be selected.

c) requiring that a complete list of all the population elements be compiled.

d) not permitting the auditor to know which types of items will be included in the sample before the actual selection is made.

7.51 A CA's client wishes to determine inventory shrinkage by taking a sample of inventory items. If a stratified random sample is to be drawn, the strata should be identified in such a way that

a) the overall population is divided into subpopulations of equal size so that each subpopulation can be given equal weight when estimates are made.

b) each stratum differs as much as possible with respect to expected shrinkage, but the shrinkages expected for items within each stratum are as close as possible.

c) the sample mean and standard deviation of each individual stratum will be equal to the means and standard deviations of all other strata.

d) the items in each stratum will follow a normal distribution so that probability theory can be used in making inferences from the sample data.

7.52 In estimating the total value of supplies on repair trucks, Baker Company draws random samples from two equal-sized strata of trucks. The mean value of the inventory stored on the larger trucks (stratum 1) was computed at $1,500, with a standard deviation of $250. On the smaller trucks (stratum 2), the mean value of inventory was computed as $500, with a standard deviation of $45. If Baker had drawn an unstratified sample from the entire population of trucks, the expected mean value of inventory per truck would be $1,000, and the expected standard deviation would be

a) exactly $147.50.

b) greater than $250.

c) less than $45.

d) between $45 and $250, but not $147.50.

7.53 The required size of a statistical sample is influenced by the variability of the items being sampled. The sample standard deviation, a basic measure of variation, is approximately the

a) average of the sum of the differences between the individual values and their mean.

b) square root of the average determined in part (a).

c) average of the sum of the squared differences between the individual values and their mean.

d) Square root of the average determined in (c).

7.54 A student taking statistics suggested that the first ten incomes in **Data Set 2** would constitute a perfectly reasonable random sample. Comment on this suggestion. This same student has a personal computer and used a program called BSTAT to generate the following data on the first ten incomes. Indicate how the BSTAT statistical program calculated each of the following values:

```
        ARITHMETIC MEAN = 38246.2
         SAMPLE STD.DEV = 400469.9
        SAMPLE VARIANCE = 160376179555.7
STD. ERROR OF THE MEAN = 126639.7
                MINIMUM = -57100
                MAXIMUM = 1147000
                    SUM = 3824699
         SUM OF SQUARES = 2906217860061
           DEVIATION SS = 1443385616000.9
```

USING THE COMPUTER

7.55 Some statistical packages have options to demonstrate the central limit theorem. In the Doane package, this option is called MONTE. It is also possible to complete this demonstration using Lotus 1-2-3. Use such a package to collect 100 random samples, each of size $n = 25$, from a uniform distribution (equal frequencies). Have the program calculate $\bar{x}$ and s^2 for each sample.

a) Sketch the distribution of $\bar{x}$, using some convenient class interval for the $\bar{x}$'s. Compare your result with that predicted by the central limit theorem.

b) For each sample in part (a), calculate $t = (\bar{x} - 0.5)/(s/\sqrt{n})$, and then sketch these 100 t-values. Does the distribution correspond to that given in Table VI for $\nu = 24$?

c) For each sample in part (a), calculate $\chi^2 = 24s^2/\sigma^2$, where $\sigma^2 = \frac{1}{12}$. Sketch this distribution. Does this sketch correspond to the distribution of χ^2_{24}?

7.56 Most computer statistical programs will generate random numbers. Use such a program to generate 20 random numbers, where each random number is drawn from the population of integers between zero and 500 (include zero but not 500).

7.57 Many computer statistical programs will provide cumulative probabilities for the distributions discussed in this chapter. Use a computer program to determine the following probabilities.

a) $P(z \leq 1.734)$

b) $P(t \leq 2.661)$ for 45 d.f.

c) $P(\chi^2 \leq 50.00)$ for 35 d.f.

CASE PROBLEM

7.58 The main library in your home town has asked you to help design a survey of the users of the library. The library staff wants to know who is using it (men, women, children), and how often. They also want to know what parts of the library (periodicals, references, stacks, et cetera) these people use. Finally, they want to know something about the people who are *not* using the library – who are they and why they are not using the library. A questionnaire has been designed. Your task is to gather a random sample consisting of approximately 400 responses to the questionnaire. [*Note:* Not everyone who is sent a questionnaire will complete it.] Be very specific as to how you will gather a sample of 400. What might you do to encourage people to respond to the questionnaire? You have a small budget for this study.

CHAPTER 8

Quality Control

Introduction

Much of the origins of quality control (QC) date back to the pioneering work of Walter A. Shewhart and W. Edwards Deming. Dr. Shewhart, a physicist at Bell Labs, initially worked on the problem of designing a standard radio headset for American soldiers in World War I. He measured the head widths of over 9,000 army personnel and found the shape of this distribution to be normal. His research and other studies led Shewhart to develop the concept of a control chart, particularly the $\bar{x}$ chart and the R charts discussed in this chapter.

W. Edwards Deming is a statistician who helped foster the widespread quality control effort in America during World War II. After the war, Deming was asked to help develop the quality movement in Japan, where it became a priority. Evidence that the Japanese listened to Deming is clear from the success they have had exporting a variety of goods noted for their high quality. Deming's research remains among the most referenced work in quality control.

Recently, a great deal of attention has been focused on the problems and rewards of quality. The Malcolm Baldrige award in the United States, for example, is a highly publicized and sought after recognition for total quality management (TQM). Past winners include Cadillac, Federal Express, and Motorola.

The quality of performance is important in all enterprises, whether the product is a good or a service. For example, hospitals and restaurants need to be as concerned with the quality of the product they deliver as are automobile manufacturers, even though the product is classified as a service. Quality control techniques are applied in almost all areas of business. Applications range from monitoring service-oriented functions, such as financial entries in an accounting system, to the traditional application of the quality of manufactured goods. Quality control is now increasingly used in the design of new products as well.

Many major corporations have initiated quality control programs. For example, all three of the major North American automobile manufacturers, General Motors, Ford, and Chrysler, have established elaborate programs to improve quality. Their production workers receive extensive training in the fundamentals of quality control. These programs also extend to their suppliers and dealers. As a result of these initiatives, the quality of cars built by these three companies has improved significantly over the past few years. The computer industry is another industry where quality control programs in manufacturing are well established.

In the service sector, quality control has been applied to banking, insurance, health services, medical care, transportation, retail trade, and public utilities, as well as to a wide variety of local and national government agencies. For example, one application of quality control in monitoring cheques involves the use of magnetic ink character recognition (MICR) equipment. If the device sensing the magnetic characters fails to properly read one or more of the magnetic numbers, a cheque is rejected, resulting in increased processing costs. The rate of rejection is directly affected by the quality of the cheques and typically falls between 0.5% and 1%. Thus, the number of cheques rejected allows the quality of the cheques to be monitored.

In the insurance industry, quality control is used to monitor the accuracy of operations that process information, as well as the time to process claims and audits. Several insurance companies, including United States Fidelity and Guaranty and Blue Cross/Blue Shield, have improved their services because of quality control programs. Quality control programs also exist in many areas of government, ranging from audits for tax returns to customs surveys of imported goods to monitoring the effectiveness of social services.

section 8.2 The Human Side of Quality Control

Although this text presents quantitative methods, it would be remiss not to stress that almost any successful application of quality control depends on numerous human factors. This fact is emphasized in six guiding principles suggested by Deming.

1. Quality is defined by the customer.
2. It is important to understand and reduce the variation in every process.
3. Significant management commitment to quality improvement is vital.
4. Change and improvement must be continuous and omnipresent.
5. Ongoing training is required for continuous improvement.
6. Performance ratings of individual employees are usually destructive.

Much of the literature on quality control involves Deming's six principles and his 14 points (not presented here), and form the basis for the Malcolm Baldridge Quality Award in the United States.

section 8.3 The Concept of a Process

A **process** is any set of conditions that work together to produce a given result. For example, in building an automobile or a refrigerator, each step in the manufacturing line may be considered as a process with its own inputs and outputs. See Figure 8.1.

FIGURE 8.1   A single process

Thus, attaching refrigerator parts, such as doors and handles, to the frame each constitutes a separate process, as does preparing a house for painting, applying the primer, spraying the paint, and drying it. Producing a car or a refrigerator can also be thought of as a series of individual, interrelated processes that make up the manufacturing line, as shown in Figure 8.2.

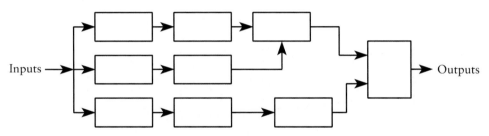

FIGURE 8.2   A typical series of interrelated processes

The quality of the output of these processes can be monitored using statistical methods. There are two basic approaches to monitoring the quality of an output from a process. The first, called the **detection approach**, is shown in Figure 8.3. With this approach, quality control is used to inspect the final product to screen out items that do not meet the specifications. The flaws in the defective items are then used to determine how to correct the process.

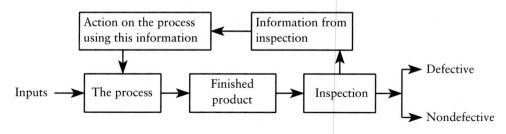

FIGURE 8.3   The detection approach to quality control

Unfortunately, the detection approach focuses on the output of a completed process, and such information may be of limited use in identifying the causes of current problems with the process. For example, it may be difficult to identify, after the fact, such key variables as the quality of batches of materials used, the workers involved, or the equipment used. Thus, it may not be possible to determine exactly which factors were responsible for the defects. Additionally, this approach can be wasteful and uneconomical because it allows for the use of labour and materials before they are tested for defects.

Another approach to statistical process control, called the **prevention approach**, is shown in Figure 8.4. With this approach, the key variables of a process are identified while the process is in operation, the objective being to identify potential problems before defective products are manufactured. The goal is to prevent the production of defective products. If observations on any process deviate too far from those expected under *normal* conditions, the process is investigated until the problem is identified and corrected.

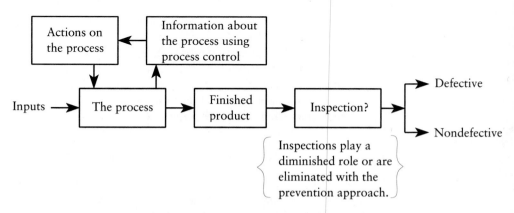

FIGURE 8.4   The prevention approach to quality control

The terms **quality control** and **statistical process control (SPC)** are often used interchangeably, although the latter term is perhaps more representative of the analysis of interest here. A process may involve an assembly line, which has been a typical realm for SPC, or the process may fall into some other field, such as the service industry. In medicine, the **quality assurance (QA)** is frequently used. In all cases, interest focuses on controlling the process so that potential errors or defective components are detected as early as possible and the source of the problem eliminated.

There are two fundamental concerns in the prevention approach to quality control. First, does the process result in a product that meets specifications? In other words, is the output satisfactory? If it is a manufactured part, does it work, or equivalently, does it meet the design standards? For a service, is the process meeting company guidelines and/or satisfying consumer needs? A second concern is whether the process is *in control*, meaning is the process stable over time? When the process is not stable over time, it is said to be *out of control*. Whether a process is in control and whether it is meeting specifications are considered separately in the sections that follow.

section 8.4 — The Use of Control Charts to Determine if the Process is in Control

Whether or not a process is in control is generally determined using a control chart of one form or another. Control charts for SPC are of two types: control charts for attribute data, and control charts for variable data. **Attribute data** occur when there are only two possible outcomes, such as good/defective, male/female, accept/reject, or smoker/nonsmoker, as with the binomial random variable presented in Chapter 5. **Variable data** occur when the measurement of some quantity, such as distance, thickness, or temperature is required. The most common control charts for variable data are $\bar{x}$ charts and R charts, while the most common charts for attribute data are p charts and c charts.

The output of any process is assumed to be subject to variability. If a part is being built, the machine making this part will not always yield an identical output. If clerks are processing data, there will always be some human error. The cause of the variability in a process is of particular concern in SPC. If the variability is caused by the random factors, then we say that the variability is due to **common causes**. On the other hand, if the variability is caused by special factors that can be identified, we say that it is due to **assignable causes**. *A process is said to be in control if the variability is due only to common causes.*

Control charts are used to help determine when a process is out of control. A typical control chart will specify a centreline, upper and lower control limits (UCL, LCL), and a set of points as illustrated in Figure 8.5. Each of the points on a control chart usually represents a *sample* of items from the process, rather than a single output. The letter n is used to denote the number of observations in each sample, and k is used to represent the number of samples.

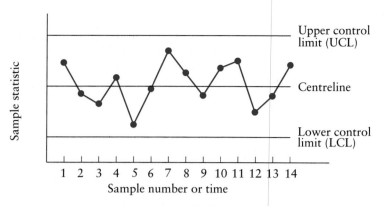

FIGURE 8.5 A typical control chart

To illustrate the meaning of a centreline and upper and lower control limits, consider the problem of controlling the length of the steel mullion (a bar) between the two sides of a side-by-side General Electric (G.E.) refrigerator. The theoretical or ideal dimension of a finished part is called its *nominal dimension*. In the case of the G.E. mullion, the nominal dimension is 58.7650 inches.

To determine if the process producing mullions is in control, G.E. takes a sample of $n = 3$ observations out of every 200 mullions. There are 3,000 mullions made every working day so $3000/200 = 15$ samples are taken each day. For a recent time period (a day), the sample values have averaged 58.7645 inches; this is the *centreline*. Note that the centreline is slightly smaller (by 0.0005) than the desired or nominal dimension.

$$\text{Centreline} = \text{mean of sample averages}$$

G.E. calculates the average value for each consecutive sample of three mullions. By a process to be described shortly, G.E. determines the highest and lowest values expected for each sample of three mullions, assuming only *random variability*, or that there are no assignable causes. The highest and lowest sample values are called the **upper** and **lower control limits** respectively. These are abbreviated as UCL and LCL.

In Example 8.1 the upper and lower control limits for the G.E. mullions will be shown to be 58.7725 and 58.7565, respectively. That is, the average of the three mullions in any sample is expected to fall between these two limits. Note that the difference between UCL and LCL is 0.0160 inches, or about the size of three human hairs.

In SPC applications, the UCL and LCL are determined by taking the centreline plus or minus 3 standard deviations ($\pm 3\sigma$). Hence, the UCL and LCL are known as the **three sigma** limits.

$$\text{UCL} = \text{centreline} + 3\sigma$$

$$\text{LCL} = \text{centreline} - 3\sigma$$

Remember, the variation due to common causes (between the UCL and LCL) is assumed to be the effect of the various random influences that are generally present in all parts of a manufacturing or service process. This variation could arise for a number of reasons, such as precision of the machinery, variability in the raw materials, differences in temperature, et cetera.

For a process to be in control, the common-cause errors are generally assumed to be normally distributed. This means that the interval between UCL and LCL ($\pm3\sigma$) will contain about 99.7% of the common-cause variation because $\pm3\sigma$ contains 99.7% of the normal distribution. Thus, it is very unusual for an observation to fall beyond the UCL and LCL bounds if the process is in control. In SPC, an observation beyond these bounds is assumed to indicate a process that is not in control.

On the other hand, a process may result in sample averages between the UCL and LCL and still not be in control because the values *form a pattern over time*. By definition, patterns cannot exist because the errors must be random if the only source of variability is common causes. The process in Figure 8.5 seems to be in control because the points appear to be random and none falls outside the limits.

There are a variety of rules to use when looking for nonrandom patterns. In Figure 8.6, parts a) to c), three rules are suggested for determining when there is enough of a pattern for the process to be considered out of control.

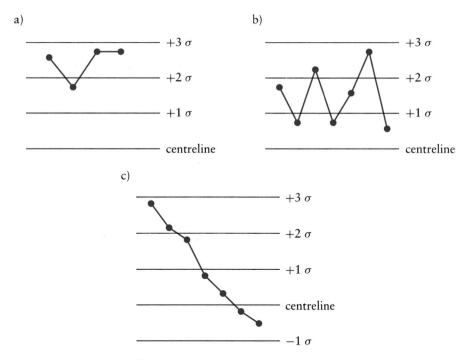

FIGURE 8.6   Patterns indicating nonrandomness (process out of control):
a) 2 out of 3 samples or 2 samples in a row are outside $\pm2\sigma$
b)) 7 consecutive samples appear on one side of the centreline
c) 7 samples in a row run up or down

To summarize, a process is said to be in control when common causes are the only source of variation. That is, the variation is truly random. In terms of a control chart, a process is considered to be out of control when one or more data points fall outside the control limits, or when the points fall within the control limits but a nonrandom pattern has developed.

section 8.5

$\bar{x}$ and R Charts

To monitor variable data, we use x-bar ($\bar{x}$) charts and range (R) charts. The $\bar{x}$ chart measures the changes in the central location of the process, while the R chart measures changes in the variability of the process. Both charts must indicate control before the process can be said to be in control. In some circumstances, the limits for the $\bar{x}$ chart are derived using information from the R chart, in which case, the R chart needs to be constructed first. When automatic measuring and recording equipment are used (usually involving a computer), then this approach is not necessary.

The *range* is the difference between the largest and the smallest values in each sample. The number of observations in each sample is usually kept small, $n = 3$, 4, or 5 being the most common.

A **control chart** has the values of $\bar{x}$ or R plotted on the vertical scale and the sequence of the samples through time on the horizontal axis. The $\bar{x}$ chart is usually presented above the R chart with corresponding sampling points (through time) aligned vertically to make interpretation easier. As we will discuss later, unless the ranges are first in control, the control limits for the $\bar{x}$ chart may be computed incorrectly. The plot of the consecutive sample means on a control chart provides a picture of how the means vary around their long-run average, $\bar{\bar{x}}$, which is called the *grand mean*. Normally, the values of $\bar{x}$ in a control chart will exhibit some natural variation around the grand mean, $\bar{\bar{x}}$. When the process is in control, the sample means should vary around the grand mean in a random manner, with almost all values falling within three standard deviations of $\bar{\bar{x}}$. Assuming a normal sampling distribution, the probability of falling outside these limits is $1 - 0.9974 = 0.0026$. The limits, defined in Section 8.4 as plus or minus three standard deviations, are known as the three-sigma limits.

The probability of a sample falling beyond the three-sigma limits is extremely low. Thus, if one or more of the $\bar{x}$'s deviates beyond these limits, we conclude that the process is not in control due to assignable causes. In estimating probabilities, we need to remember that the sample sizes are generally small; hence the sampling distributions may not be exactly normal.

Range Charts

A range chart (R chart) or a sigma chart (s chart) can be used to track the variability of the process. If the variability is small, the items tend to be similar to one another. A large variability suggests the items are more likely to be different from one another.

The use of the R chart instead of the s chart to monitor variability is somewhat historical. Ranges were used prior to the widespread use of computers because it was easier to hand-calculate ranges than standard deviations. However, with the use of computers, the difference in calculation time generally is not a concern. Still, when n is small, using ranges to track variability is the preferred approach because it is easier for the user to calculate and interpret than the s chart.

An R chart is constructed by plotting the ranges for each consecutive sample taken from the process. The centreline of an R chart is the average of the ranges of the k repeated samples under consideration, and is called R-bar ($\bar{R}$).

R chart centreline:

$$\bar{R} = \text{average of the ranges in the } k \text{ repeated samples} \qquad (8.1)$$

□ **EXAMPLE 8.1**   The ten samples shown in Table 8.1, with $n = 3$ observations, were taken from the G.E. mullion sampling process described previously. What is the centreline for this R chart?

TABLE 8.1   Sample of G.E. mullion lengths, $k = 10$, $n = 3$

Sample Number	Mullion 1	Mullion 2	Mullion 3	Range R
1	58.7610	58.7628	58.7619	0.0018
2	58.7738	58.7582	58.7650	0.0156
3	58.7707	58.7692	58.7682	0.0025
4	58.7580	58.7665	58.7601	0.0085
5	58.7720	58.7638	58.7590	0.0130
6	58.7633	58.7690	58.7610	0.0080
7	58.7645	58.7688	58.7624	0.0064
8	58.7580	58.7666	58.7641	0.0086
9	58.7628	58.7654	58.7629	0.0026
10	58.7669	58.7592	58.7703	0.0111
			Average	0.0078

From the average of the ranges in the last column of Table 8.1, we see that the centreline is

$$\bar{R} = 0.0078.$$ ■

The upper and lower control limits for a range chart are generally constructed by an estimation process. This estimation process is designed to determine

$$\text{UCL}_R = \bar{R} + 3\sigma_R$$
$$\text{LCL}_R = \bar{R} - 3\sigma_R.$$

Actually, $\pm 3\sigma_R$ is not estimated itself, but rather an approximation is used to estimate UCL_R and LCL_R directly. This approximation uses constants (D_3 and D_4) found in Table IX, Appendix C and Formula 8.2 shown below. Although the rationale for this approach is not presented here, the process of calculating the limits is quite straightforward.

R chart, upper and lower limits:

$$\text{UCL}_R = D_4\bar{R}$$
$$\text{LCL}_R = D_3\bar{R}$$ $\qquad (8.2)$

The value of D_3 must be less than 1 since LCL_R is less than $\bar{R}$. This constant depends on the sample size (n) and the assumption of sampling from a normal parent population. Multiplying $\bar{R}$ by D_3 gives an estimate of the LCL, or $\bar{R} - 3\sigma_R$.[†] Similarly, multiplying $\bar{R}$ by the constant D_4 (which must be greater than 1) gives an estimate of $\bar{R} + 3\sigma_R$.

□ **EXAMPLE 8.2** We use the G.E. data to calculate LCL_R and UCL_R. First, we locate $n = 3$ in Table IX of Appendix C, and find that $D_3 = 0$ and $D_4 = 2.575$. Substituting these values into Formula 8.2 yields:

$$UCL_R = 2.575(0.0078) = 0.0182$$

$$LCL_R = 0(0.0078) = 0$$

Thus, G.E. should expect the range for each sample of three mullions to fall between 0 inches and 0.0182 inches. ■

□ **STUDY QUESTION 8.1**

Graph the R chart for the G.E. data given in Table 8.1 and Example 8.2. Show the centreline, both control limits, and the ten data points (ranges). Use a computer program (Lotus, for example) if possible. Does the process appear to be in control?

● **ANSWER** A Lotus plot is shown in Figure 8.7. Because all of the sample ranges fall within the control limits, and because there is no apparent pattern to the sequence of ranges, this chart indicates that the process appears to be in control. ■

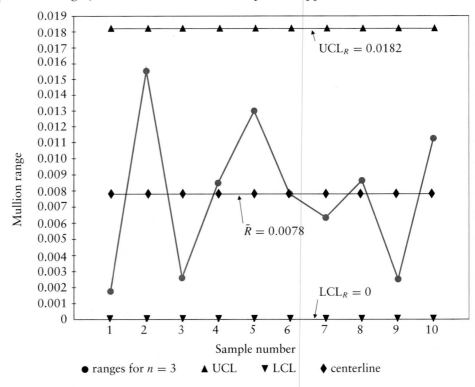

FIGURE 8.7 Range chart for G. E. mullions (using Lotus)

[†] If the number of observations in a sample is 6 or less, this method results in a lower control limit that is negative. Since a negative range is not possible, D_3 is set equal to zero when $n \leq 6$.

$\bar{x}$ Charts

An $\bar{x}$ chart monitors the *central location*, or value of the process. This is in contrast to the R chart, which monitors *variability*. The $\bar{x}$-chart monitors central location by taking a sample of observations at specified time intervals, and monitoring the consecutive sample means. When a reasonably large number of samples have been taken (20 to 25 is usually recommended), the average of all these sample means (denoted as $\bar{\bar{x}}$ and called the grand mean) is used as the centreline.[1]

$\bar{x}$ chart centreline:

$$\bar{\bar{x}} = \left\{ \begin{array}{c} \text{mean of the sample averages from} \\ k \text{ repeated samples of size } n \end{array} \right\} \qquad (8.3)$$

Once the centreline is determined, the upper and lower control limits for an $\bar{x}$-chart ($\text{UCL}_{\bar{x}}$ and $\text{LCL}_{\bar{x}}$) are defined:

Upper and lower limits for $\bar{x}$ chart:
$$\text{UCL}_{\bar{x}} = \bar{\bar{x}} + 3\sigma_{\bar{x}}$$
$$\text{LCL}_{\bar{x}} = \bar{\bar{x}} - 3\sigma_{\bar{x}}$$

The subscript on σ, $\bar{x}$, reminds us that the standard deviation to be applied in this situation represents the variability of the sample averages, rather than the variability of the individual sample observations. In most quality control procedures the value of $3\sigma_{\bar{x}}$ is estimated rather than calculated. Again the constants provided in Table IX of Appendix C are used to estimate both control limits $\text{UCL}_{\bar{x}}$ and $\text{LCL}_{\bar{x}}$. Recall that this was done for UCL_R and LCL_R earlier. In this case, only one constant is needed, A_2, which is multiplied by the average of the ranges, $\bar{R}$ to obtain the desired estimates.

Estimated upper and lower limits for $\bar{x}$ chart:

$$\text{UCL}_{\bar{x}} = \bar{\bar{x}} + A_2\bar{R}$$
$$\text{LCL}_{\bar{x}} = \bar{\bar{x}} - A_2\bar{R}$$

$\qquad (8.4)$

The reader will note that the value of $A_2\bar{R}$ estimates $3\sigma_{\bar{x}}$, rather than $\sigma_{\bar{x}}$ itself. The reason why Formula 8.4 is a good estimate is beyond the scope of this text. From Formula 8.4 it should be clear that the ranges (variability) need to be in control before calculating the limits for $\bar{x}$.

To construct the $\bar{x}$ chart after an R chart has been completed, each value of $\bar{x}$ is calculated. This is typically done using special quality control equipment or a computer. The reader may wish to look ahead to the end of this chapter, to Figure 8.22, to see an R and $\bar{x}$ chart presented together.

☐ **EXAMPLE 8.3** The sample means for the G.E. mullion lengths are shown in the right column of Table 8.2.

---

[1] When the number of samples is less than 20, the nominal dimension is sometimes used as the centreline.

TABLE 8.2 G.E. Data for Calculating the $\bar{x}$ Chart, $k = 10$, $n = 3$

Sample Number	Mullion 1	Mullion 2	Mullion 3	Average $\bar{x}$
1	58.7610	58.7628	58.7619	58.7619
2	58.7738	58.7582	58.7650	58.7657
3	58.7707	58.7692	58.7682	58.7694
4	58.7580	58.7665	58.7601	58.7615
5	58.7720	58.7638	58.7590	58.7649
6	58.7633	58.7690	58.7610	58.7644
7	58.7645	58.7688	58.7624	58.7652
8	58.7580	58.7666	58.7641	58.7629
9	58.7628	58.7654	58.7629	58.7637
10	58.7669	58.7592	58.7703	58.7655
			Grand Mean	58.7645

From the last line in Table 8.2, we see that $\bar{\bar{x}} = 58.7645$. This grand mean is used as the centreline (even though the number of samples, ten, is fairly small). The value $\bar{R} = 0.0078$, calculated in Table 8.1, and the constant $A_2 = 1.023$ from Table IX of Appendix C are used to determine the control limits.

$$\text{UCL}_{\bar{x}} = 58.7645 + 1.023(0.0078) = 58.7725$$

$$\text{LCL}_{\bar{x}} = 58.7645 - 1.023(0.0078) = 58.7565$$

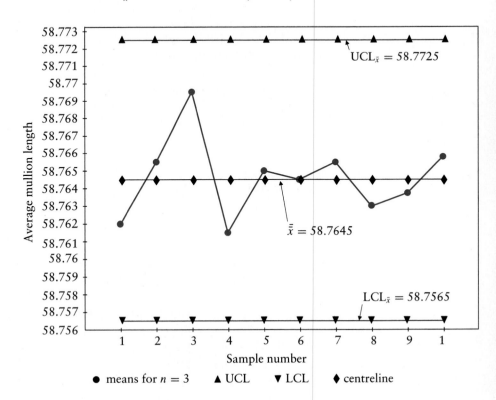

FIGURE 8.8 $\bar{x}$ chart for G. E. mullions

The final step in preparing an $\bar{x}$ chart is to plot the sample points, indicating the centreline and the control limits, as shown in Figure 8.8 (a Lotus graph). Note in this figure that none of the sample means is outside the control limits, and there is no obvious pattern to the sequence of sample means. If either situation had existed, then the process would not be in control. Even though there does seem to be a little bit less variability in the sample means over the last 6 samples, this would be good news for the SPC experts at G.E. Since both the R chart and the $\bar{x}$ chart indicate no special problems with the G.E. data, the process appears to be in control.   ■

If one or more sample means fall outside the control limits, it is usually presumed that a special cause has accounted for the extreme point. Thus, any point outside the control limit should be analyzed immediately to determine its cause. Even if the sample means all fall within the three-sigma limits, the process may not be in control. Unusual patterns or trends, such as shown in Figure 8.6, can indicate a change in the process and a loss of control.

Finally, assuming the sample means are normally distributed (by the CLT), then approximately two-thirds of the sample means should lie in the region one $\sigma_{\bar{x}}$ on either side of the centreline. The other one-third should lie between the one $\sigma_{\bar{x}}$ lines and the control limits. If this is not the case, the statistical control process should be re-evaluated. Generally, in such situations either the control limits and/or the plot points have been incorrectly calculated or the measurements used may have come from more than one process (that is, the process may have been defined incorrectly).

The centreline and control limits are usually not changed with each new sample, but rather need to be updated periodically. Thus, new sample points are typically compared to the control limits established by a set of historical values, where the process has been in control.

◻ STUDY QUESTION 8.2

Is the G.E. mullion process still in control if samples numbers 11 and 12 in the G.E. mullion process yield the following values?

Sample 11   58.7534, 58.7523, 58.7542

Sample 12   58.7729, 58.7538, 58.7699

● **ANSWER**   First, determine the ranges and means for the two new samples.

Sample	Range	Mean
11	0.0019	58.7533
12	0.0191	58.7655

In comparing these values with the control limits determined earlier, we see that the mean for Sample 11 (58.7533) is less than $\text{LCL}_{\bar{x}} = 58.7570$. Thus, Sample 11 indicates that the process is out of control. The range for Sample 12 (0.0191) is larger than the upper control limit for the range ($\text{UCL}_R = 0.0182$); thus, this sample also represents a process out of control. If the process is not in control, it is important to determine why it is out of control, and then correct the problem(s).   ■

The next issue to discuss is whether or not a process is capable of meeting specifications. That is, will it work, or function satisfactorily? This issue is related to, but somewhat independent of the issue of control. It makes little sense to talk about meeting specifications for a process that is not in control, for such a process is changing over time. And if it is changing, then an output meeting specifications today may well not meet specifications tomorrow. Thus, the discussion on capability in Section 8.6 assumes a process that is in control.

PROBLEMS

8.1 Explain the concept of a process. Give an example of a process and identify its inputs and outputs.

8.2 Give two examples of quality control in the service sector other than those described in this chapter.

8.3 Discuss the differences and similarities between the detection and prevention approaches. What role would the detection approach play in a process where extensive use of control charts is made?

8.4 Distinguish between common variation and assignable variation. Which kind of variation is easily detected by the use of control charts? When is a process in control?

8.5 Consider the distributions (Figure 8.9) of a variable of interest from two different manufacturing lines making the same product. What can you say about the variation in these two processes? Which process is in control? Explain.

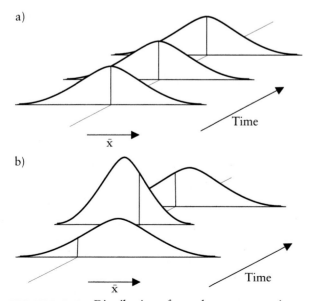

a)

b)

FIGURE 8.9   Distribution of sample means over time

8.6 Consider a manufacturing process that makes precision metal plates used in a clutch assembly for trucks. Engineering design requires the plates to have a thickness of 0.500 ± 0.01 inches. These plates are produced at the rate of approximately 100 per hour. To monitor the quality of the process, three plates are randomly sampled every hour and the thickness of each plate is measured. These measurements are shown in Table 8.3 for 25 different samples. Determine if the process appears to be in control during this time.

TABLE 8.3   25 Hourly Samples of Metal Plate Thickness

Sample	Measurements		
Number	1	2	3
1	0.507	0.502	0.508
2	0.502	0.498	0.497
3	0.497	0.499	0.501
4	0.505	0.502	0.497
5	0.502	0.507	0.503
6	0.506	0.500	0.502
7	0.498	0.495	0.497
8	0.495	0.495	0.501
9	0.504	0.506	0.501
10	0.493	0.496	0.497
11	0.495	0.493	0.500
12	0.506	0.501	0.503
13	0.501	0.495	0.496
14	0.500	0.507	0.506
15	0.504	0.503	0.501
16	0.500	0.498	0.499
17	0.499	0.505	0.503
18	0.492	0.498	0.496
19	0.496	0.499	0.500
20	0.503	0.506	0.506
21	0.505	0.505	0.499
22	0.498	0.496	0.502
23	0.499	0.506	0.505
24	0.500	0.495	0.496
25	0.501	0.506	0.500

8.7 Consider the two sets of distributions of variables of interest from a manufacturing process, Figure 8.10. What can you say about the two processes? Are they in control? Do they meet specifications?

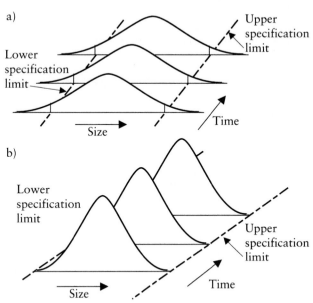

a)

b)

FIGURE 8.10 Distribution of values for Problem 8.7

8.8 A process known to be in control has an output which is normally distributed with mean $\mu = 100$ and standard deviation $\sigma = 10$. Samples of size $n = 4$ are periodically taken for quality control. The quality control process has set the

$$\text{UCL}_{\bar{x}} = \mu + \frac{3\sigma}{\sqrt{n}} = 100 + \frac{3(10)}{\sqrt{4}} = 115$$

The design engineer is concerned with the possibility that the process might shift its mean upwards by one standard deviation, so the new mean is $\mu + 1\sigma = 100 + 10 = 110$. If this happens, the engineer would like to determine how often a sample mean ($\bar{x}$) of $n = 4$ will then exceed the $\text{UCL}_{\bar{x}}$ set above (= 115). Determine this probability assuming the variability of the process does not change, and the distribution is stable with the new mean.

8.9 Consider the charts shown in Figure 8.11. Of these three charts, which one(s) appear to be in control and why? Which do not appear to be in control and why?

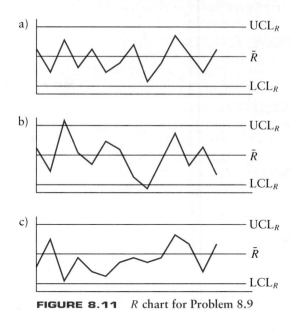

a)

b)

c)

FIGURE 8.11 R chart for Problem 8.9

8.10 Consider the control charts for $\bar{x}$ shown in Figure 8.12. Both of these processes appear to be out of control. Explain why.

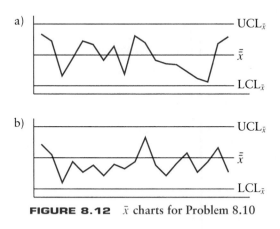

a)

b)

FIGURE 8.12 $\bar{x}$ charts for Problem 8.10

8.11 Consider the control charts for $\bar{x}$ shown in Figure 8.13. What can you say about both these processes? What is a likely explanation and what steps may be taken to correct this situation?

a)

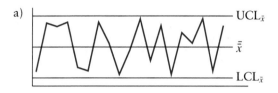

b)

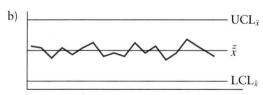

FIGURE 8.13 $\bar{x}$ charts for Problem 8.11

8.12 a) Four of Deming's guiding principles involve human aspects of quality control. Describe these four using your own words, and then indicate why you agree or disagree with Deming on the importance of these factors.

b) Find and report on a list of Deming's 14 points for quality management.

c) What do the letters TQM represent? Describe the concept.

8.13 A production process is monitored for two days by randomly sampling $n = 5$ items every hour. The sample information gives $\bar{\bar{x}} = 22.8$ and $\bar{R} = 10.9$.

a) Use this data to determine the upper and lower control limits for an R chart.

b) Construct the R chart for this process.

c) Explain how this chart will be used.

8.14 Refer to the information in Problem 8.13.

a) Use this information to determine the upper and lower control limits for an $\bar{x}$ chart.

b) Construct the $\bar{x}$ chart for this process.

c) Explain how this chart will be used.

8.15 Suppose for the process described in Problem 8.13 that the next 12 hourly observations result in the following sample means.

$$23.5, \ 21.0, \ 26.5, \ 25.3, \ 19.8, \ 24.5,$$
$$25.6, \ 23.1, \ 25.7, \ 22.4, \ 23.7, \ 24.2$$

Does this process appear to be in control? Explain your answer.

8.16 A manufacturing process is set up to produce fishing line with a 60-lb breaking strength. The specifications require that the actual breaking strength of the line be within 5 lb of that figure. Every shift, five pieces of line, each a few inches long, are taken randomly from the spools produced during that shift. For each of these pieces, the actual breaking strengths are determined. Results from 15 shifts are shown in Table 8.4.

a) Calculate the sample mean and range for each of the 15 samples.

b) Construct the R chart for this process. Does the process variation appear to be in statistical control?

c) Construct the $\bar{x}$ chart for this process. Do the sample means appear to be in control?

TABLE 8.4 Breaking Strength, $k = 15$, $n = 5$

Shift Number	Fishing Line Breaking Strength				
	1	2	3	4	5
1	58.4	62.1	59.3	60.7	59.1
2	59.7	62.7	60.3	61.1	60.6
3	60.2	60.3	63.1	60.0	59.3
4	59.3	58.9	60.6	61.2	60.0
5	60.0	59.3	62.0	61.3	60.1
6	58.1	62.2	59.2	60.7	59.9
7	59.7	60.3	58.2	59.2	61.0
8	60.2	62.0	60.6	57.9	60.0
9	62.7	59.8	60.0	60.1	58.5
10	58.9	60.1	59.7	61.6	60.9
11	59.3	60.2	59.6	62.5	61.3
12	60.7	63.1	59.3	58.4	60.2
13	60.1	61.3	57.8	59.3	58.5
14	59.8	59.4	60.3	61.8	60.4
15	58.5	62.4	61.3	60.8	60.3

8.17 A manufacturing process produces ball bearings. Every hour, three bearings are sampled in order to monitor the variation in the diameters. The engineering specifications require that the bearings have a diameter of 0.75 ± 0.01 inches. Table 8.5 shows the diameter measurements from 20 hourly samples.

a) Calculate the sample mean and range for each of the 20 samples.

b) Construct the R chart for this process.

c) Construct the $\bar{x}$ chart for this process.

d) Does the process appear to be in statistical control? Explain your answer.

e) Do the control limits lie within the specification limits?

process the claim is calculated as the number of days between the receipt of the claim and the mailing of the claim report. Table 8.7 shows the process time data from 20 weeks.

a) Calculate the sample mean and range for each of the 20 samples.

b) Construct the R chart for this process.

c) Construct the $\bar{x}$ chart for this process.

d) Does the process appear to be in statistical control? Explain your answer.

TABLE 8.7 Process time in days, $k = 20$, $n = 5$

Week Number	Claims 1	2	3	4	5
1	17	25	10	14	14
2	23	15	23	23	19
3	22	22	17	15	24
4	13	14	24	19	12
5	20	18	20	18	18
6	22	19	21	17	18
7	12	13	18	14	13
8	12	11	14	18	17
9	13	25	17	24	13
10	17	19	13	16	19
11	19	10	22	15	16
12	21	16	20	25	19
13	22	11	14	17	12
14	10	23	10	22	25
15	11	17	13	19	16
16	13	12	19	22	11
17	18	25	13	13	19
18	17	14	19	20	15
19	22	21	10	19	14
20	15	24	10	10	24

8.20 Monitoring the process in Problem 8.19 for another 10 weeks (weeks 21–30) gives the results shown in Table 8.8.

a) Plot both the sample mean and range for each of these 10 weeks on the R and the $\bar{x}$ charts.

b) What conclusions can you derive from these plots? Does the process variation appear to be in control? Explain your answer.

TABLE 8.5 Ball Bearing Measurements — Diameter, in Inches, $k = 20$, $n = 3$

Sample Number	Bearings 1	2	3
1	0.755	0.748	0.746
2	0.748	0.756	0.752
3	0.743	0.746	0.751
4	0.749	0.753	0.751
5	0.754	0.748	0.750
6	0.752	0.754	0.755
7	0.748	0.753	0.749
8	0.741	0.748	0.747
9	0.750	0.752	0.748
10	0.753	0.749	0.756
11	0.757	0.748	0.750
12	0.743	0.754	0.752
13	0.755	0.753	0.756
14	0.745	0.756	0.752
15	0.750	0.753	0.752
16	0.757	0.753	0.748
17	0.744	0.752	0.751
18	0.756	0.755	0.757
19	0.751	0.748	0.753
20	0.750	0.752	0.752

8.18 The eight samples in Table 8.6 (sample numbers 21–28) were taken the day after the control charts from Problem 8.17 were constructed.

a) Calculate the sample ranges for these eight samples and plot them on the R chart. Does the process variation appear to be in statistical control?

b) Calculate the sample means for these samples and plot them on the $\bar{x}$ chart. Do the sample means still appear to be in control? Explain your answer.

TABLE 8.6 Ball Bearing Measurements — Diameter in Inches, $n = 3$

Sample Number	Bearings 1	2	3
21	0.754	0.753	0.752
22	0.748	0.757	0.753
23	0.752	0.745	0.751
24	0.753	0.754	0.749
25	0.757	0.753	0.755
26	0.748	0.754	0.756
27	0.756	0.753	0.750
28	0.751	0.752	0.749

8.19 An insurance company specializing in health insurance would like to monitor the time it takes to process claims. Every week the company samples five claims finalized that week. For each claim, the time to

TABLE 8.8   Process time in days, $n = 5$

Week Number	Claims				
	1	2	3	4	5
21	24	11	17	12	35
22	10	18	23	14	22
23	20	10	15	20	24
24	14	17	14	17	24
25	10	23	11	24	13
26	23	15	15	25	12
27	20	16	17	21	22
28	15	20	23	18	23
29	11	14	24	25	20
30	23	16	11	13	13

8.21 Terminal connectors are attached to wire leads with a crimping tool by a company producing disk drives. The crimping tool periodically goes bad and needs rebuilding. A sample can be used to determine when this tool begins to go bad, thus avoiding production of useless wire leads. A sample of five observations is always taken. The first three of these samples are shown in Table 8.9. The crimp height specifications are 0.052 ± 0.002 inches. Plot these data on a R and $\bar{x}$ chart, and assume that the sample means have averaged 0.0520 historically and the average range has been $\bar{R} = 0.0015$. Use the constants from Table IX of Appendix C to determine the control limits. What do you conclude?

TABLE 8.9   Crimping tool control, $k = 5$, $n = 3$

Observation Number	Crimp Heights		
	Sample 1	Sample 2	Sample 3
1	0.0530	0.0520	0.0560
2	0.0525	0.0530	0.0530
3	0.0530	0.0525	0.0520
4	0.0526	0.0530	0.0550
5	0.0530	0.0525	0.0530

section 8.6   Process Capability

Meeting specifications means that random variability will not cause the process to exceed the specifications limits. The specification limits often are set by the engineering department for a manufacturing process or by management for a service application. Generally, specification limits are not compared with control limits because the specification limits apply to each *individual* observation ($n = 1$) resulting from the process, while the control limits monitor the process using sample statistics. Recall that the sample statistic $\bar{x}$ was used for each group of three G.E. mullion lengths.

The terminology for specification limits is:

$$USL = \text{upper specification level}$$

$$LSL = \text{lower specification level}$$

In Section 8.5 we assumed that the outcome of a process that was in control would be normally distributed. Figure 8.14 shows a normal distribution of the length of G.E. mullions described earlier plus the USL and LSL set by the G.E. engineers for this process. The specification limits represent the tolerance for this mullion. A **tolerance** is the maximum variability that the specifications permit from the nominal dimension. For the G.E. refrigerators, the tolerance is ± 0.0150, which means that the specification limits are the nominal dimension (58.7650) plus or minus fifteen thousandths of an inch (0.0150).

$$USL = 58.7650 + 0.0150 = 58.7800$$

$$LSL = 58.7650 - 0.0150 = 58.7500$$

Note that these specification limits are symmetrical about the nominal centreline as shown in Figure 8.14.

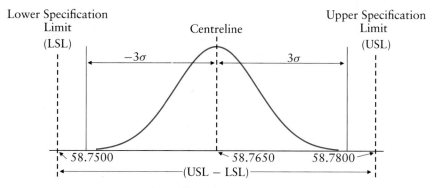

Lower Specification
Limit
(LSL)

Centreline

Upper Specification
Limit
(USL)

-3σ

3σ

58.7500

58.7650

58.7800

(USL − LSL)

FIGURE 8.14   The mullion distribution and specification limits

A process is said to be *capable* if the specifications can be met. This does not mean that specifications must *always* be met, but rather met a certain percentage of the time. A product that falls outside the specifications limits is called **nonconforming**.

There are numerous ways to assess the capability of a process, the most common being *capability indices*. The most often used index is called a *process capability*, or C_p index. Assuming a normally distributed output, the C_p index defines a capable process as one where ±3 standard deviations fall within the specification limits.

A capable process is shown in Figure 8.14. To be capable, the distance between USL and LSL (USL - LSL) must be *greater* than $6\sigma_x$ (the distance between $\pm 3\sigma_x$). Note the subscript x on σ, indicating that in this case we are measuring the variability of the individual x's, whereas previously we measured the variability of the sample averages, $\bar{x}$. To estimate σ_x we use a constant d_2 found in Table IX of Appendix C, and $\bar{R}$, as follows:[2]

$$\text{Estimate of } \sigma_x = \frac{\bar{R}}{d_2}$$

The C_p index, displayed below, measures the capability of the process using the estimate of σ_x, given above.

The C_P index:

$$C_p = \frac{\text{USL} - \text{LSL}}{6\sigma_x} \tag{8.5}$$

If the value of C_p exceeds 1.00, the process is said to be *capable*. When C_p is less than 1.00, the process is *not capable* of meeting specifications. A C_p value of 1.00 indicates a process that is *just capable*. Ideally, we would like the value of C_p to exceed 1.0 because this indicates that the measurements are likely to be within the specifications. When $C_p < 1.0$, the process is not capable of meeting its specifications because one or both control limits will be outside of the specification limits. Figure 8.15 illustrates the values of the C_p index for a distribution of measurements from a process.

---

[2] The values of A_2 and d_2 are related. Problem 8.30 asks the reader to find this relationship.

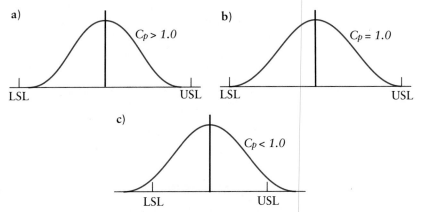

FIGURE 8.15   Interpretation of the capability index:
a) $C_p > 1.0$ (The process is capable)
b) $C_p = 1.0$ (The process is just capable)
c) $C_p < 1.0$ (The process is not capable)

☐ **EXAMPLE 8.4**   Consider the G.E. mullion data in Tables 8.1 and 8.2. The $\bar{x}$ and R charts for this process both showed that the process was in statistical control. Thus, it is now possible to measure the process capability using the C_p index. From our earlier discussion, we know that the USL and LSL are as follows:

$$\text{USL} = 58.7800$$
$$\text{LSL} = 58.7500$$

The value of σ_x for the Table 8.1 data can be estimated, using the value of $\bar{R} = 0.0078$ and the value $d_2 = 1.693$ for $n = 3$ from Table IX of Appendix C.

$$\text{Estimated } \sigma_x = \frac{\bar{R}}{d_2} = \frac{0.0078}{1.693} = 0.0046$$

Thus,

$$C_p = \frac{\text{USL} - \text{LSL}}{6\sigma_x} = \frac{58.7800 - 58.7500}{6(0.0046)} = 1.0870$$

Since $C_p = 1.0870 > 1.0$, this process is capable of staying within its specification limits.   ■

The process capability index, unfortunately, does not take into account the location of the mean of the process; rather, only the spread is used to determine the potential for meeting the specifications. For example, consider a process with $C_p = 1.0$. If the mean of the process is centred midway between the specification limits, there is no problem with the C_p index, as shown in Figure 8.16 (a). However, when the mean of the process is not at the midway point, as in Figure 8.16 (b), the C_p index is misleading.

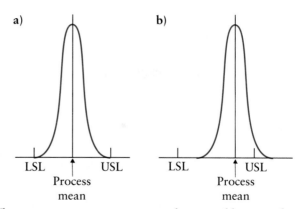

FIGURE 8.16   The process mean may or may not be centred between the specification limits.

An index that does take into account the location of the process mean is the C_{pk} index. The **C_{pk} index** is defined as the minimum of the two distances from the centreline to the specification limits.

$$C_{pk} = \min\left[\frac{\text{USL} - \text{centreline}}{3\sigma_x}, \frac{\text{centreline} - \text{LSL}}{3\sigma_x}\right] \qquad (8.6)$$

If both USL and LSL are equidistant from the centreline, then the C_{pk} index yields the same value as the C_p index. If the distances are not the same, the value of C_{pk} depends on the specification limit closer to the centreline, and the C_{pk} index gives better information about the capability of the process. For example, in Fig. 8.16 (b), the C_{pk} index is calculated on the basis of the distance from the process mean to the USL, a distance shorter than half the distance between the USL and LSL. Thus, C_{pk} is always less than C_p when the process is not centred between its specification limits. Generally, both C_p and C_{pk} are used together to see how well a process is performing when compared with its specification limits.

As with the C_p index, C_{pk} has to be 1.0 or greater for the process to be capable. The larger the value of C_{pk}, the higher the probability will be of staying within the specification limits. A value of 1.33 is considered to be very good and is commonly used as a target in many applications. If the distribution is considered to be approximately normal, a process with the C_{pk} index equal to 1.33 would produce at most 6 of every $100,000$ units that do not conform to the specifications. The reader is asked to verify this fact in Problem 8.44.

Some companies, Motorola in particular, have indicated their desire for an index of 2. This is their *six sigma* program. Motorola's concern is with equipment (such as a cellular phone) that requires many, many parts or steps to produce. If each of these parts/steps could fail to meet specifications, then the probability that the entire output (the cellular phone) is error free decreases dramatically.

Earlier, we calculated $C_p = 1.0870$ for the mullion data. Since C_p is greater than 1.0, we concluded that the process is capable of staying within its limits. However, more information about the capability of this process may be obtained by calculating the C_{pk} index. In general, the C_{pk} index is calculated using the process mean ($\bar{x}$) as the centreline. In this case, we use the centreline and standard deviation from Example 8.3 and Example 8.4. The centreline is $\bar{\bar{x}} = 58.7645$ and the estimated $\sigma_x = 0.0046$.

$$C_{pk} = \min\left[\frac{58.78000 - 58.7645}{3(0.0046)}, \frac{58.7645 - 58.7500}{3(0.0046)}\right]$$

$$= \min\left[\frac{0.0155}{0.0138}, \frac{0.0145}{0.0138}\right] = \min[1.1232, \ 1.0507]$$

$$= 1.0507$$

Since $C_{pk} = 1.0507$ is greater than 1.0, the process appears to be capable of staying within the specification limits. Also, since $C_{pk} < C_p$, the mean of the process is not centred.

Clearly, a process may be in control, and yet not capable. And, as indicated earlier, a process out of control may still be capable of meeting specifications but may not remain capable in the future.

☐ STUDY QUESTION 8.3   Capability for Part AS-132

Engineering requirements for a production process specify that the mean diameter of part AS-132 be 2.50 inches. The tolerance is ±0.004 inches. With the process in control, the last 30 samples of sizes $n = 4$ have resulted in a grand mean of $\bar{\bar{x}} = 2.5015$ inches, and $\bar{R} = 0.0021$.

a) Do these samples indicate the process is capable?
b) What is the estimated value of $\sigma_{\bar{x}}$ from the information given?
c) If the most recent sample of size $n = 4$ resulted in the values 2.4980, 2.5010, 2.5000, and 2.4970, would you conclude that the mean of this process is now out of control?

• ANSWER

a) The process does not appear to be capable because even though C_p exceeds 1.0, C_{pk} does not.

$$\text{Estimated } \sigma_x = \frac{\bar{R}}{d_2} = \frac{0.0021}{2.0590} = 0.0010$$

$$C_p = \frac{\text{USL} - \text{LSL}}{6\sigma_x} = \frac{2.5040 - 2.4960}{6(0.001)} = 1.3333$$

$$C_{pk} = \min\left[\frac{2.5040 - 2.5015}{3(0.001)}, \frac{2.5015 - 2.4960}{3(0.001)}\right]$$

$$= \min\left[\frac{0.0025}{0.003}, \frac{0.0055}{0.003}\right] = \min[0.8333, 1.8333]$$

$$= 0.8333$$

b) Estimated $3\sigma_{\bar{x}} = A_2\bar{R} = 0.729(0.0021) = 0.0015$
Thus, estimated $\sigma_{\bar{x}} = 0.0015/3 = 0.0005$

c) $$\text{UCL}_{\bar{x}} = \bar{\bar{x}} + A_2\bar{R} = 2.5015 + 0.0015 = 2.5030$$
$$\text{LCL}_{\bar{x}} = \bar{\bar{x}} - A_2\bar{R} = 2.5015 - 0.0015 = 2.5000$$

The mean of the last sample is $\bar{x} = 2.4990$. Since this mean is less than the $\text{LCL}_{\bar{x}}(2.5000)$, we conclude that the process is out of control.   ■

The p Chart

A p chart is similar to the $\bar{x}$ and R charts described previously, except that this chart is for attribute data. The variable is typically in binary form, such as conforming/nonconforming, pass/fail, or go/no-go. Often, several characteristics of a process are plotted together on a single chart.

After the $\bar{x}$ and the R charts, the p chart is generally considered to be the most sensitive chart for identifying problems with a process. A p chart is monitored in the same way as an $\bar{x}$ or an R chart. The person monitoring the process looks for points on the p chart that lie outside the limits, or for patterns such as upward or downward trends, or for several successive points on one side of the centreline, and so forth. A p chart is constructed by taking periodic samples from a process and plotting the proportion of nonconforming items for each sample. As with the $\bar{x}$ and R charts, a process is said to be in statistical control if the sample proportions fall within the three-sigma limits of the proportion of defectives, $\bar{p}$. That is, the control limits are $\bar{p} \pm 3s_p$, where s_p is the sample standard deviation and $\bar{p}$ is the sample proportions of defectives across the k repeated samples.

---

p chart centreline

$$\bar{p} = \text{proportion of defectives over } k \text{ samples}$$

$$= \frac{\text{total defectives}}{\text{total observations}} \tag{8.7}$$

The sample standard deviation, s_p, is calculated using Formula 8.8, which is comparable to the standard deviation for the binomial distribution presented in Chapter 5. In this formula, $\bar{n}$ represents the average sample size (since it may not always be possible to take the same size sample). However, this can be done only if the sample sizes do not vary much from each other.

Sample standard deviation:

$$s_p = \sqrt{\bar{p}(1 - \bar{p})/\bar{n}} \tag{8.8}$$

The control limits for a p chart are written as follows:

---

p chart control limits:

$$\text{UCL}_p = \bar{p} + 3\sqrt{\frac{\bar{p}(1 - \bar{p})}{\bar{n}}}$$

$$\text{LCL}_p = \bar{p} - 3\sqrt{\frac{\bar{p}(1 - \bar{p})}{\bar{n}}} \tag{8.9}$$

If Formula 8.9 results in a negative value for LCL_p, which often happens in practice, the lower control limit is set equal to zero.

◻ **EXAMPLE 8.5**   A major bank uses a p chart to monitor, on a daily basis, the proportion of errors made by bank clerks processing cheques. The twenty-five samples shown in Table 8.10 provide the number in each sample, n and the number of errors found in processing the cheques. Determine if the process is in control.

TABLE 8.10   Cheque Processing Errors, $k = 25$, n varies

Day	n	Errors	p	Day	n	Errors	p
1	1000	18	0.0180	16	1020	30	0.0294
2	1000	17	0.0170	17	1024	23	0.0225
3	1020	9	0.0882	18	1040	26	0.0250
4	1120	26	0.0232	19	1010	21	0.0208
5	1024	21	0.0205	20	980	18	0.0184
6	1060	26	0.0245	21	976	19	0.0195
7	920	12	0.0130	22	1010	22	0.0218
8	970	13	0.0134	23	980	32	0.0327
9	980	15	0.0153	24	1020	38	0.0373
10	1020	16	0.0157	25	960	32	0.0333
11	1000	18	0.0180				
12	990	17	0.0172	SUM	25,218	526	
13	1134	26	0.0229	AVG	1009	21	
14	960	9	0.0094				
15	1000	22	0.0222				

For these data, $\bar{n} = 1009$, and $\bar{p} = 526/25{,}218 = 0.0208$

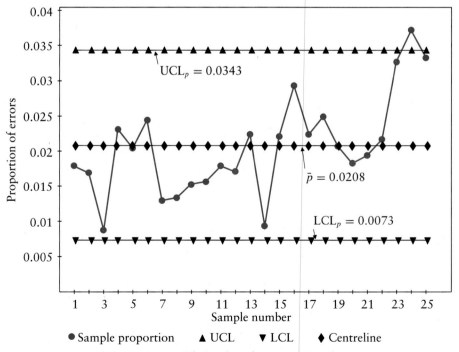

FIGURE 8.17   The p-chart for processing cheques

The control limits are as follows:

$$\text{UCL}_p = 0.0208 + 3\sqrt{0.0208(1 - 0.0208)/1009}$$
$$= 0.0208 + 0.0135$$
$$= 0.0343$$

$$\text{LCL}_p = 0.0208 - 0.0135 = 0.0073$$

The *p* chart shown in Figure 8.12 was constructed using a computer spreadsheet. Because the proportion of errors on day 24 exceeds the upper control limit of 0.0343, the process is out of control. Notice also that the proportions on days 23 and 25 are very close to the upper control limit. ■

section 8.8
The *c* Chart

Besides monitoring the proportion of defectives produced by a manufacturing process, we may be interested in monitoring the number of defects. For example, in the automobile industry, it is common to track the number of defects in the paint job of a new car. Similarly, an important variable in textile manufacturing is the number of defects per square yard. A defect that is simply a flaw or a nonconformity may not lead to an item being declared unusable, for it is possible to have one or more defects in a product that is accepted as being good. A new car, for example, may have a few minor defects in the paintwork.

The number of defects is monitored using a *c* chart. This chart may be used to control a single type of defect or to control all types of defects without distinguishing between types. The *c* chart requires a constant unit of output that will be sampled at regular intervals of time and examined for defects. This constant unit of output is called an **inspection unit**. It may be specified in any units of measurement. For example, an inspection unit may be defined in terms of an area, or volume, or weight. Alternatively, an inspection unit may be specified as a single item or a group of items.

The number of defects per inspection unit is represented by *c*. The sample mean, $\bar{c}$, is the average number of defects per unit across repeated samples and forms the centreline for the *c* chart. As with the other control charts presented, a process is said to be in statistical control if the number of defects falls within the three-sigma limits. For reasons beyond the scope of this chapter, the distribution of *c* is assumed to be Poisson.[3] This distribution possesses a unique property: its standard deviation equals the square root of its mean, a fact we will use to estimate σ_c.

Because of the special property of the Poisson distribution, that its mean and variance are equal, the standard deviation of the process can be estimated by the square root of the sample mean. That is, $\sigma_c = \sqrt{\bar{c}}$. The control limits for a *c* chart are shown below.

---

[3] This distribution was presented in Chapter 5. The material in this section does not assume knowledge of the Poisson distribution. The interested reader will note that the assumptions of the Poisson distribution, presented on page 178, appear reasonable in this context.

> *c* chart control limits:
> $$UCL_c = \bar{c} + 3\sqrt{\bar{c}}$$
> $$LCL_c = \bar{c} - 3\sqrt{\bar{c}}$$
> (8.10)

If LCL_c is negative, it is set equal to zero.

☐ **EXAMPLE 8.6**   Construct a *c* chart using the data in Table 8.11, which represents a carpet manufacturing operation. The 40 samples in the table show the number of defects on each roll of carpet. Additionally, this company has recently undertaken a new training program for its workers. Note that samples 25–40 were manufactured by workers trained under this program. Do you see a trend? What might it imply?

TABLE 8.11   Carpet defect data, $k = 40$

Sample Number	Number of Defects per Roll	Sample Number	Number of Defects per Roll
1	15	21	15
2	11	22	11
3	13	23	13
4	18	24	14
5	16	25	10
6	10	26	9
7	9	27	8
8	15	28	12
9	14	29	11
10	13	30	7
11	11	31	12
12	16	32	13
13	17	33	10
14	12	34	8
15	14	35	12
16	15	36	9
17	11	37	11
18	8	38	10
19	17	39	7
20	16	40	9

The average number of defects per roll is calculated as follows:

$$\bar{c} = \frac{482}{40} = 12.05$$

The control limits are calculated from Formula 8.10.

$$UCL_c = \bar{c} + 3\sqrt{\bar{c}}$$
$$= 12.05 + 3\sqrt{12.05}$$
$$= 22.4639$$

$$\text{LCL}_c = \bar{c} - 3\sqrt{\bar{c}}$$
$$= 12.05 - 3\sqrt{12.05}$$
$$= 1.6361$$

Figure 8.18 shows the c chart for these data. It suggests that a downward trend began around sample number 25. This is a good sign because it shows that the process may be creating fewer defects than normal. This change may be a result of the new training program. Since the process appears to have changed, the control limits should be recalculated using the data in samples 25–40.

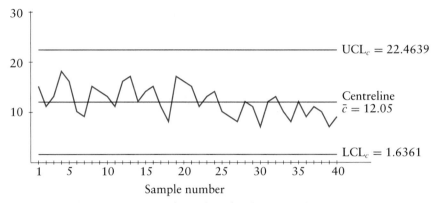

FIGURE 8.18   The c-chart for the carpet data

Acceptance Sampling

section 8.9

The focus in this chapter, thus far, has been on process control, whereby one attempts to detect and correct quality problems as they occur.

Another application of quality control is in acceptance sampling plans. These plans are used to determine whether to accept or reject either an outgoing or an incoming shipment. Generally, raw materials, components to be used in intermediate products, and finished products, are grouped into lots before being shipped to customers. In **acceptance sampling**, each lot is sampled and inspected. This inspection may be performed by a producer before shipping a lot, or by a customer before accepting a lot. In either case, the sampled items are classified as either defective or nondefective. Based on the number of defectives in the sample, the entire lot is either accepted or rejected.

Although acceptance plans have been used extensively in industry, their use in recent years has been declining as more organizations shift to control charts and other statistical methods for quality improvement. Many acceptance sampling plans these days are used simultaneously with statistical process control in the initial stages of a quality control program. As the full impact of process control is achieved, the quality levels may improve to the extent that acceptance sampling techniques may no longer be needed.

An acceptance sampling plan is characterized by two numbers: n the number of items to include in the sample, and a, the acceptable number of defects allowed in the sample before the lot is rejected. Every item in the sample of n is inspected to determine the total number of defectives, x. If x is less than or equal to a, the lot is accepted. If x is greater than a, the lot is rejected. Every sampling plan is completely specified by these two numbers (n and a). Changing one or both of these numbers changes the acceptance sampling plan.

Every lot contains a certain fraction of defectives, p. For the sampling plan to be efficient, the plan must have a high probability of accepting a lot when p is low, and a high probability of rejecting a lot when p is high. For any given acceptance sampling plan, the probability of accepting or rejecting a lot is easily computed if p is known. If n is small compared to the number of items in a lot, the number of defectives follows the binomial distribution.[4] Thus, the probability of accepting a lot may be determined using binomial tables or a computer.

☐ **EXAMPLE 8.7** Consider a plan where the sample size is $n = 20$ and the acceptable number is $a = 1$. If $p = 0.05$, then the probability of accepting the lot is computed using Table I in Appendix C as follows:

$$P(\text{accepting the lot}) = P(x \le 1) = P(x = 0) + P(x = 1)$$
$$= 0.3585 + 0.3774 = 0.7359$$

For this acceptance sampling plan, 73.59% of all lots inspected will pass inspection. Similarly, for $p = 0.10, n = 20$, the probability of accepting the lot (computed from the binomial table for $n = 20$ and $p = 0.10$) is $P(x \le 1) = 0.3918$. As the value of p increases and n remains the same, the probability of accepting a lot decreases. For example, for $p = 0.20$ and $n = 20$, the probability of acceptance decreases to 0.0691. For $p = 0.40$ and $n = 20$, the probability of acceptance is only 0.0006. ■

To see how well an acceptance sampling plan works, we plot the probability of accepting a lot against the fraction of defectives (p). The resulting graph is called the *operating characteristic (OC)* curve for the sampling plan. There is a unique curve for each possible sample size and acceptance number. Figure 8.19 shows the OC curve for the plan where $n = 20$ and $a = 1$. As the values of n and a change, so do the curves. Figure 8.20 shows the curves for various sample sizes. Notice that as n increases, the curve becomes steeper. Consequently, the larger the value of n, the better the curve is able to discriminate lots with a high percentage of defectives. For example, the probability of accepting a lot is lower when $n = 20$ than the probability of accepting the lot when smaller sample sizes are used, such as $n = 5$ or $n = 10$. Figure 8.21 demonstrates the effect of different acceptance numbers. As the acceptance number increases, the entire curve shifts to the right. This increases the probability of accepting a lot.

In practice, a seller and buyer first need to agree on a mutually acceptable fraction of defectives to be tolerated in a lot. This fraction is called the *acceptable quantity level (AQL)*. For example, the seller and buyer may agree that 5% defectives in a lot is tolerable, but no more than 5%. Without a census, the actual proportion of defectives in a lot is unknown. Thus, the sampling plan is of critical importance, especially the choice of the acceptable number of defects allowed in the sample (a). Ideally, a sampling plan should be selected that has a high probability of accepting a lot whose fraction of defectives is less than or equal to the AQL, as well as a high probability of rejecting all other lots.

---

[4] If n is large relative to the lot size, then the hypergeometric distribution should be used.

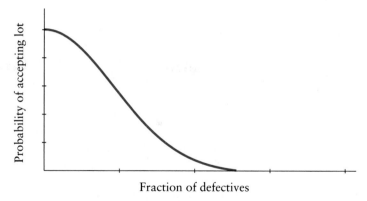

FIGURE 8.19   OC curve for $n = 20$ and $a = 1$.

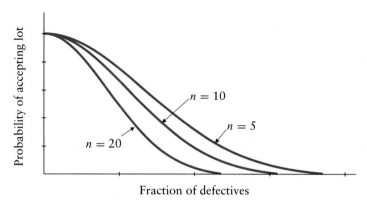

FIGURE 8.20   OC curve for different values of n and $a = 1$.

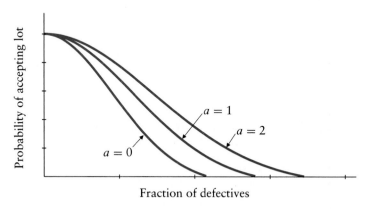

FIGURE 8.21   OC curves for $n = 20$ and different values of a.

❑ **EXAMPLE 8.8**   Suppose the seller and buyer agree on AQL $= 0.05$, and a particular lot has 5% defectives. If the sampling plan uses $n = 50$ and, $a = 0$, the probability of accepting this lot (from the binomial table with $n = 50$ and $p = 0.05$) is $P(x = 0) = 0.0769$. This probability means that on the average, $92.31\%(1 - 0.0769 = 0.9231)$ of all lots with 5% defectives will be rejected. Such a sampling plan is unlikely to be acceptable to the seller.

At the other extreme, suppose there are 10% defectives, $p = 0.10$, and a is set equal to 3. From the binomial table for $n = 50$ and $p = 0.10$, $P(x \leq 3) = 0.2503$. This plan is unlikely to be acceptable to the buyer since approximately 25% of comparable lots will be accepted even though there are 10% defectives.

Generally, adjusting the sample size and the acceptable number will lead to a plan agreeable to both the seller and the buyer. ■

Many different forms of acceptance sampling plans have been developed over the years. One of the most widely used is the Military Standard 105D plan (or MIL-STD-105D in abbreviated form). This plan was developed during the Second World War to control the quality of manufactured war material and has become the standard in many industries, especially those involved in government contract work. The plan consists of a series of tables that tell a user the sample size to employ for a given lot size and the corresponding acceptance number (a) for various AQLs. Thus, it is possible to analyze many different options quickly, thereby making it easy to select a plan that would be acceptable to both the consumer and the producer.

PROBLEMS

8.22 a) Explain the interpretation of the C_p index.

b) Discuss the relationship between the C_p and the C_{pk} indexes. Explain how these indexes may be used to determine how a process is performing.

c) Show that $C_p = C_{pk}$ when the specification limits are equidistant from the process mean.

TABLE 8.12 Sample Observations for Auto Part HR-144

Sample Number	1	2	3	4	5	Mean $\bar{x}$	Range R
1	0.1261	0.1253	0.1245	0.1249	0.1248		
2	0.1259	0.1263	0.1247	0.1240	0.1251		
3	0.1239	0.1265	0.1260	0.1257	0.1243		
4	0.1225	0.1249	0.1265	0.1248	0.1256		
5	0.1259	0.1243	0.1242	0.1257	0.1251		
6	0.1255	0.1273	0.1245	0.1268	0.1263		
7	0.1251	0.1281	0.1239	0.1245	0.1264		
8	0.1288	0.1250	0.1235	0.1240	0.1251		
9	0.1240	0.1252	0.1295	0.1262	0.1275		
10	0.1233	0.1271	0.1280	0.1291	0.1274		
					Grand Mean		

8.23 Table 8.12 provides the data from ten samples taken over time. Each sample consists of 5 observations for a special automobile part (HR-144). The specification limits are 0.1250 ± 0.003. Complete Table 8.12, finding the values of $\bar{x}$ and the ranges. Use these data to construct an R chart and a $\bar{x}$ chart using a computer if possible (a spreadsheet is convenient). Is the process under control? Is it capable?

TABLE 8.13 Windshield control, $k = 25$

Day	Number of Windshields Rejected	Number of Windshields Tested
1	22	425
2	18	435
3	17	392
4	27	421
5	15	405
6	29	427
7	23	397
8	20	402
9	24	401
10	19	430
11	25	417
12	17	411
13	24	404
14	26	427
15	15	423
16	19	398
17	27	421
18	22	409
19	30	438
20	17	418
21	27	409
22	16	422
23	24	409
24	14	395
25	15	422

8.24 To illustrate the technique for constructing a p chart, consider the data in Table 8.13. These data show the number of items determined to be defective from a process manufacturing automobile windshields over a period of 25 days. A windshield is rejected if it contains scratches, cracks, bubbles, dents, or any other visual imperfections. If possible, use a computer to provide answers to the following questions.

a) What are the control limits?

b) Graph the p chart. Does the process appear to be in control?

8.25 To determine whether a machine is capable of meeting the design specifications of a particular operation, it is usual to perform a machine capability analysis. In such an analysis, the objective is to determine if the underlying variability of the machine is small enough to accommodate the design specifications. Consider a part whose outside diameter has to be 2.25 ± 0.001 inches. There are five machines that might be used for this operation. Suppose that the inherent accuracy of these machines is known and is expressed as the standard deviation for work of this kind. These standard deviations are shown in the Table 8.14.

TABLE 8.14

Machine Number	Standard Deviation (inches)
1	0.00010
2	0.00020
3	0.00025
4	0.00035
5	0.00040

Which, if any, of the five machines is capable of meeting specifications? Explain your answer, giving the C_{pk} index in each case.

8.26 A process that is used to fill glass bottles with ketchup is monitored for three days by randomly sampling $n = 5$ bottles every hour. The specifications require that a bottle must contain 16 ± 0.2 ounces of ketchup. The sample information gives $\bar{\bar{x}} = 16.05$ and $\bar{R} = 0.15$. Calculate the C_p and the C_{pk} indices. Is this process capable of meeting its specifications? Explain your answer.

8.27 A production process is monitored for $k = 40$ days by randomly sampling $n = 8$ items per day. From this sample information, we obtain $\bar{\bar{x}} = 25.3$ and $R = 2.5$. If this product is designed to produce measurements with the specifications (25 ± 3), is the process capable of meeting its specifications?

8.28 Refer to Problem 8.16. Recall that the specifications for the breaking strength of the fishing line have to be 60 ± 5 lb. Using the data in Problem 8.16, calculate the C_p and the C_{pk} indexes. Which of the two is a better indicator of the process capability? Explain your answer.

8.29 Refer to Problem 8.17. Calculate the C_p and C_{pk} index and determine if the process is capable of meeting its specifications.

8.30 Determine the mathematical relationship between the constants A_2 and d_2 shown in Table IX of Appendix C. Give an example that demonstrates this relationship.

8.31 Samples of $n = 50$ items were selected every shift for 15 days (3 shifts a day). For each sample, the proportion of defectives is calculated. The proportion of defectives across the 45 samples is 0.045.

a) Calculate the upper and the lower control limits for a p chart.

b) Construct a p chart and explain how this chart will be used.

8.32 The entire daily production of a process that makes circuit boards for a calculator is tested to determine the proportion of defectives. The production levels vary from day to day. In one 30-day period, the average number of boards tested per day was 323. The fraction of defectives for this period was 0.083. Construct a p chart for the period and explain how this chart will be used.

8.33 A bank records the number of complaints it receives from business clients about billing errors on purchases made using the bank's credit card. If this information is maintained on a weekly basis and the average number of errors over a 30-week period is 7.4, find the upper and lower control limits for a c chart. Construct a c chart and explain how it may be used by the management.

8.34 The manager of an information system monitors the number of errors in entries to the data base by sampling 100 entries every day. If the sampling over 20 days produced a total of 72 errors, calculate the average number of errors per entry and construct a c chart for this process.

8.35 An electronics manufacturer produces control assemblies for an AM/FM radio receiver. Each assembly is tested individually. It is expected that a certain proportion of these assemblies will be defective and have to be scrapped. The firm produces 1000 assemblies each day. Each assembly is individually tested after manufacture. Tests for a 20-day period resulted in the data given in Table 8.15.

a) Use this information to construct a p chart and to determine if the process is in control.

b) Suppose that the next eight days' production results in the following number of defects:

$$17 \quad 26 \quad 24 \quad 62 \quad 35 \quad 39 \quad 18 \quad 27$$

What can you say about the process now? Explain your answer.

TABLE 8.15 Control assemblies, $k = 20$, $n = 1000$

Sample Number	Number of Defective AM/FM Receivers	Sample Number	Number of Defective AM/FM Receivers
1	30	11	36
2	40	12	34
3	34	13	28
4	32	14	37
5	20	15	53
6	33	16	19
7	55	17	26
8	21	18	39
9	48	19	30
10	31	20	25

8.36 A subcontractor for a computer manufacturer makes graphics circuit boards for microcomputers. Each circuit board is individually tested and classified as either nondefective or defective. A nondefective board is shipped to the manufacturer; a defective board is discarded. The results of these tests for a 30-day period are shown in Table 8.16. Construct a p chart for the data, using the average sample size method. Determine if the process is in control.

8.37 The management of a weekly news magazine has decided to use quality control techniques to control errors such as misprints, typographical errors, and typesetting errors. Each week after the magazine has been published, 12 pages are randomly selected, and the number of errors are recorded. The results of the procedure for the past 20 weeks are shown in Table 8.17.

a) Construct a c chart for these data.

b) Suppose that in the next eight weeks the magazine records the following number of errors:

$$3 \quad 6 \quad 8 \quad 12 \quad 13 \quad 14 \quad 12 \quad 15$$

What can you say about this process now?

TABLE 8.16 Defective Circuit Boards, $k = 30$, n varies

Day	Number of Defective Circuit Boards	Number of Boards Tested	Day	Number of Defective Circuit Boards	Number of Boards Tested
1	15	327	16	7	330
2	11	356	17	26	344
3	30	344	18	16	349
4	25	338	19	8	339
5	8	345	20	15	330
6	24	353	21	26	357
7	23	332	22	22	353
8	24	324	23	14	332
9	17	360	24	11	327
10	7	347	25	29	359
11	20	352	26	20	339
12	14	334	27	8	331
13	30	356	28	25	350
14	18	343	29	30	355
15	10	328	30	18	352

8.38 Oil filters are sent to an engine assembly plant in large lots. For each shipment, a sample of 50 filters is inspected to determine the number of defectives. A lot is rejected if the number of defectives is greater than or equal to 3. If the actual proportion of defectives is 0.02, what percentage of the lots are rejected with this sampling plan?

TABLE 8.17 Magazine Errors, $k = 20$ for Problem 8.37

Week Number	Number of Errors	Week Number	Number of Errors
1	13	11	10
2	7	12	14
3	8	13	7
4	4	14	4
5	12	15	11
6	9	16	11
7	16	17	6
8	10	18	10
9	7	19	14
10	6	20	8

8.39 Consider a sampling plan with sample size $n = 20$ and acceptance number $a = 1$. Calculate the probability of accepting a lot with the following fraction of defectives, and graph the operating characteristic curve for this plan.

    a) $p = 0$ **b)** $p = 0.05$

    c) $p = 0.10$ **d)** $p = 0.20$

    e) $p = 0.40$ **f)** $p = 0.75$

    g) $p = 1.0$

8.40 Repeat Problem 8.39 for the following sampling plans:

    a) $n = 20$ and $a = 0$

    b) $n = 20$ and $a = 2$

    c) $n = 20$ and $a = 3$

Graph these operating characteristic curves on the same graph as drawn for Problem 8.39. What is the effect of increasing the acceptance number a when n is held constant?

8.41 Repeat Problem 8.39 for the following sampling plans:

    a) $n = 10$ and $a = 1$

    b) $n = 15$ and $a = 1$

    c) $n = 25$ and $a = 1$

Graph these operating characteristic curves for the sampling plan in Problem 8.39 and for parts (a), (b), and (c) of this problem on the same graph. What is the effect of increasing the sample size n when a is held constant?

CHAPTER SUMMARY

KEY TERMS AND EXPRESSIONS

Statistical process control (SPC): Using statistical analysis to investigate and control quality problems.

Process: A set of conditions that work together to produce a given result.

Detection approach: Inspection of final product to screen out items that do not meet specifications.

Prevention approach: Monitoring the key variables of a process in order to identify and correct problems before the process is completed.

Control chart: A plot of data over time, used to determine if a process is in control (stable over time).

UCL and LCL: Upper and lower control limits for a process.

Attribute data: Information on the occurrence of two mutually exclusive and exhaustive states.

Variable data: Information on the measurement or values of quantitative data.

Nonconforming: An output from a process that does not meet specifications.

Capability: The ability of a process to produce results that meet the specifications.

C_p **and** C_{pk} **indices:** Capability indexes to determine if a process is capable of meeting specifications.

Inspection unit: One or more items, or a unit of measurement (area or volume) examined for defects for a c chart.

Acceptance sampling: A process to determine if the quality of a particular lot is acceptable or not based on inspection of some items from that lot.

EXERCISES

8.42 A manufacturing process makes precision shafts for use in lathes. The engineering specifications require that the length of the shaft be 6.625 ± 0.00125 inches. The process is monitored by randomly selecting $n = 4$ shafts every day. Results of these samples for 20 days are shown in Table 8.18.

a) Calculate the sample mean and range for each of the 20 samples.

b) Construct the $\bar{x}$ and the R charts for these data.

c) Does the process appear to be in control? Explain your answer.

d) Calculate the C_p and the C_{pk} indices. Is the process capable of meeting its specifications? Explain your answer.

TABLE 8.18 Data for Problem 8.42, $k = 20$, $n = 4$

Sample Number	Shaft Lengths 1	2	3	4
1	6.6255	6.6251	6.6255	6.6250
2	6.6238	6.6240	6.6250	6.6253
3	6.6248	6.6251	6.6254	6.6255
4	6.6245	6.6247	6.6245	6.6246
5	6.6246	6.6243	6.6244	6.6252
6	6.6246	6.6255	6.6255	6.6248
7	6.6265	6.6256	6.6248	6.6250
8	6.6245	6.6243	6.6253	6.6255
9	6.6250	6.6250	6.6255	6.6251
10	6.6247	6.6257	6.6248	6.6245
11	6.6249	6.6245	6.6243	6.6244
12	6.6250	6.6255	6.6250	6.6240
13	6.6247	6.6248	6.6252	6.6245
14	6.6240	6.6249	6.6245	6.6247
15	6.6260	6.6252	6.6250	6.6255
16	6.6253	6.6253	6.6255	6.6260
17	6.6257	6.6250	6.6257	6.6250
18	6.6250	6.6248	6.6250	6.6250
19	6.6250	6.6252	6.6255	6.6250
20	6.6245	6.6250	6.6249	6.6251

8.43 Refer to the information in Problem 8.42. Suppose that the data for the next eight days gives the results shown in Table 8.19.

a) Calculate the sample mean and range for each sample and plot these on the $\bar{x}$ and the R charts. Does the process appear to be in control over this period? Explain your answer.

TABLE 8.19 Data for Problem 8.43, $n = 4$

Sample Number	Shaft Lengths 1	2	3	4
21	6.6253	6.6247	6.6254	6.6246
22	6.6248	6.6254	6.6253	6.6249
23	6.6253	6.6255	6.6250	6.6254
24	6.6246	6.6253	6.6258	6.6255
25	6.6256	6.6253	6.6255	6.6256
26	6.6237	6.6258	6.6258	6.6259
27	6.6255	6.6256	6.6252	6.6250
28	6.6249	6.6248	6.6254	6.6253

b) Suppose the data from samples 21–28 had given the following sample means.

6.6253 6.6245 6.6248 6.6257 6.6252

6.6242 6.6240 6.6238

What conclusions can you now derive about the process? Explain your answer.

8.44 Verify that a C_{pk} index of 1.33 produces at most 6 out of every 100,000 units that do not conform to specifications, assuming a normal distribution.

8.45 A bank processes cheques using magnetic ink character recognition (MICR) equipment. This equipment has a sensing device that reads magnetic numbers on cheques. If this device fails to read one or more of the magnetic numbers, the cheque is rejected. The rate of rejection is directly affected by the quality of the cheques. In order to monitor the quality of cheques, the bank randomly samples 1,000 cheques each day to determine the number of rejects. The results of the sampling for a 30-day period are shown in Table 8.20.

a) Calculate the proportion of rejects each day.

b) Calculate the centreline and the control limits for a p chart.

c) Construct the p chart and determine if the process is in control.

d) Suppose that over the next 10 days (days 31–40), the number of cheques rejected were as follows.

10 9 14 16 7 9 20 11 6 12

What can you say about the process now? Explain your answer.

e) Suppose the data from days 31–40 had given the following information.

17 5 4 16 3 18 17 5 16

What conclusions can you now derive about the process? Explain your answer.

TABLE 8.20 Cheque Quality Control, $k = 30$

Day	Number of Cheques Rejected	Day	Number of Cheques Rejected	Day	Number of Cheques Rejected
1	6	11	12	21	5
2	12	12	9	22	10
3	11	13	8	23	13
4	10	14	11	24	5
5	14	15	4	25	7
6	6	16	16	26	11
7	10	17	13	27	15
8	5	18	11	28	5
9	10	19	14	29	7
10	8	20	12	30	8

CASE PROBLEMS

8.46 The data in Table 8.21 represents length dimensions of metal speaker screens used in the assembly of television sets by a large international manufacturer of electronics goods. These screens are purchased from a vendor and are measured on an electronic coordinate measuring machine when they arrive at the plant. Engineering has specified 6.690 inches as the lower specification limit and 6.710 inches as the upper specification limit. There have been problems with both the quality of the screens and failure to meet the screen specifications. Consequently, the manufacturer has installed a quality control program to monitor these screens. The data in Table 8.21 were collected by taking $k = 25$ samples, with $n = 5$ observations in each sample.

a) Calculate the sample mean and range for each of the 25 samples.

b) Construct the $\bar{x}$ and the R charts for these data.

c) What conclusions can you derive from these control charts?

d) Calculate the C_p and the C_{pk} indices. What conclusions can you derive from these indices? Is the process capable of meeting its specifications? Explain your answer.

e) If you were analyzing this problem, what recommendations would you make to the management of the organization?

TABLE 8.21

Sample Number	\multicolumn{5}{c}{Speaker Screen Lengths (inches)}				
	1	2	3	4	5
1	6.700	6.703	6.701	6.702	6.702
2	6.703	6.696	6.707	6.705	6.704
3	6.703	6.703	6.700	6.701	6.703
4	6.697	6.712	6.697	6.690	6.701
5	6.709	6.693	6.693	6.703	6.686
6	6.697	6.701	6.692	6.697	6.700
7	6.699	6.702	6.694	6.698	6.694
8	6.698	6.707	6.706	6.700	6.698
9	6.701	6.704	6.693	6.702	6.696
10	6.700	6.699	6.702	6.698	6.690
11	6.703	6.677	6.703	6.697	6.703
12	6.700	6.706	6.690	6.704	6.703
13	6.703	6.703	6.704	6.705	6.702
14	6.704	6.700	6.703	6.705	6.706
15	6.702	6.701	6.705	6.703	6.703
16	6.705	6.708	6.706	6.706	6.707
17	6.708	6.692	6.698	6.698	6.696
18	6.693	6.700	6.697	6.700	6.694
19	6.700	6.692	6.698	6.696	6.699
20	6.694	6.698	6.703	6.700	6.697
21	6.705	6.704	6.693	6.702	6.699
22	6.705	6.695	6.702	6.700	6.702
23	6.702	6.708	6.705	6.707	6.700
24	6.692	6.697	6.696	6.695	6.696
25	6.701	6.699	6.696	6.697	6.701

8.47 Interpret the R and $\bar{x}$ charts shown in Figure 8.22 from the G.E. process producing mullions (described earlier in this chapter). How many mullions were tested? Was the process in control during this period? Write an extensive report to the engineer in charge of manufacturing, summarizing the mullion process. The output shown is an actual output from a system manufactured by Quality Measurement Systems Corporation.

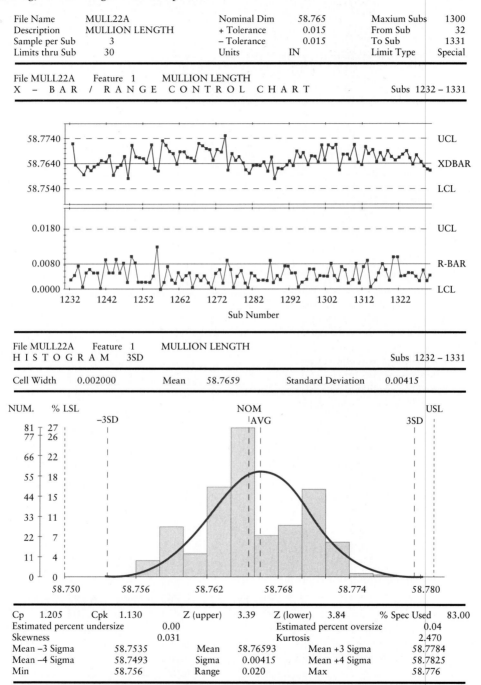

File Name	MULL22A	Nominal Dim	58.765	Maxium Subs	1300
Description	MULLION LENGTH	+ Tolerance	0.015	From Sub	32
Sample per Sub	3	– Tolerance	0.015	To Sub	1331
Limits thru Sub	30	Units	IN	Limit Type	Special

File MULL22A   Feature 1   MULLION LENGTH
X – B A R / R A N G E   C O N T R O L   C H A R T   Subs 1232 – 1331

File MULL22A   Feature 1   MULLION LENGTH
H I S T O G R A M   3SD   Subs 1232 – 1331

| Cell Width | 0.002000 | Mean | 58.7659 | Standard Deviation | 0.00415 |

Cp	1.205	Cpk	1.130	Z (upper)	3.39	Z (lower)	3.84	% Spec Used	83.00
Estimated percent undersize			0.00			Estimated percent oversize		0.04	
Skewness			0.031			Kurtosis		2.470	
Mean –3 Sigma		58.7535		Mean	58.76593	Mean +3 Sigma		58.7784	
Mean –4 Sigma		58.7493		Sigma	0.00415	Mean +4 Sigma		58.7825	
Min		58.756		Range	0.020	Max		58.776	

FIGURE 8.22

CHAPTER 9

ESTIMATION

Introduction

In the preceding chapters, characteristics of a population and of samples have been measured. Also, the concepts of probability distributions for discrete or continuous random variables have been presented. Our next task is to make use of the knowledge of the probability of sampling statistics so that we might reasonably use sample measures to learn about unknown population measures.

In most statistical studies, the population parameters are unknown and must be estimated from a sample because it is impossible or impractical (in terms of time or expense) to look at the entire population. Developing methods for estimating the value of population parameters, as accurately as possible, is thus an important part of statistical analysis.

For example, a firm manufacturing electronic components might wish to investigate the average number of defective units in each batch of 10,000 items without inspecting each and every component before shipment. Likewise, the economist who wants to determine the mean income of all college graduates will undoubtedly have to rely on sample information. In these cases, the value of a sample statistic, such as the sample mean, must be used as an estimate of the population parameter. If the degree of dispersion of defective electronic components from batch to batch or the variability of income is of interest, then this parameter also must be estimated from the sample data. Therefore, our objective in this chapter, which deals with similar estimation problems, is twofold: first, to present criteria for judging how well a given sample statistic estimates the population parameter; and second, to analyze several of the most popular methods for estimating these parameters.

The random variables used to estimate population parameters are called *estimators*, while specific values of these variables are referred to as *estimates* of the population parameters. The random variables $\bar{x}$ and s^2 are thus estimators of the population parameters μ and σ^2. A specific value of $\bar{x}$, such as $\bar{x} = 120$, is an estimate of μ, just as a specific value such as $s^2 = 237.1$ is an estimate of σ^2.

It is not necessary for an estimate of a population parameter to be one single value; instead, the estimate could be a range of values.

> Estimates that specify a single value of the population are called *point estimates*, while estimates that specify a range of values are called *interval estimates*.

A **point estimate** for the average income of college graduates may be $42,000, implying that our best estimate of the population mean is $42,000. An **interval estimate** specifies a range of values, say $30,000 to $54,000, indicating that we think the mean income for the population lies in this interval.

The choice of an appropriate point estimator in a given circumstance usually depends on how well the estimator satisfies certain criteria. The estimators emphasized throughout the remainder of this book are those that have the following four properties of a good estimator.

1. *The property of* **unbiasedness:** On the average, the value of the estimate should equal the population parameter being estimated.
2. *The property of* **efficiency:** The estimator should have a relatively small variance.
3. *The property of* **sufficiency:** The estimator should use all of the information available from the sample.
4. *The property of* **consistency:** The estimator should approach the value of the population parameter with greater probability as the sample size increases.

CUES

An estimator is a random variable, since it is the result of a sampling experiment. As a random variable, it has a probability distribution with a specific shape, expected value, and variance. Analysis of these characteristics of the distribution of an estimator permits us to specify desirable properties of the estimator.

<table>
<tr><td>**section 9.2**</td><td># Four Properties of a Good Estimator</td></tr>
</table>

Unbiasedness

Normally, it is preferable that the expected value of the estimator exactly equal, or fall close to, the true value of the parameter being estimated. If the average value of the estimator does not equal the actual parameter value, the estimator is said to contain a *bias* or to be a *biased estimator*. Under ideal conditions an estimator has a bias of zero, in which case it is said to be *unbiased*. This property can be stated as follows:

> An estimator is said to be *unbiased* if the expected value of the estimator is equal to the true value of the parameter being estimated:
>
> $$E[\text{estimator}] = \text{population parameter}$$

Figure 9.1(a) illustrates one unbiased estimator (1) and one biased estimator (2).

a) Unbiasedness

b) Efficiency

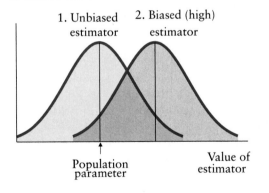

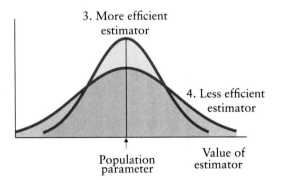

FIGURE 9.1   Illustration of properties of unbiasedness and efficiency a) Unbiasedness b) Efficiency

In the common case of estimating a population mean, it is certainly not difficult to construct examples of a biased estimator. Simply using the largest observation in a sample of size $n > 1$ to estimate μ, and ignoring the rest of the observations, will yield an estimate whose expected value is larger than μ. This is obviously a poor choice for estimating the population mean, especially when there is a much more appealing choice, $\bar{x}$. The sample mean is the most widely used estimator of all, for one of its major advantages is that it provides an unbiased estimate of μ. The fact that $E[\bar{x}] = \mu$ was presented in Section 7.4. The parameter most often estimated other than μ is σ^2, the population variance. An unbiased estimator for σ^2 is s^2, since $E[s^2] = \sigma^2$, as was given in Section 7.9.

As a final example of the property of unbiasedness, consider the problem of estimating π, the population proportion of successes in a binomial distribution. Recall Section 5.6, where we stated that if a sample yields x successes in n trials, then the ratio $x/n = p$ is an unbiased estimator of π:

$$E[p] = E[x/n] = \frac{1}{n}E[x] = \frac{1}{n}(n\pi) = \pi$$

This result implies that if, in a random sample of 100 voters, 60 people indicate that they intend to vote for Candidate A, then $p = 60/100 = 0.60$ is an unbiased estimate of the population proportion of people who would say they intend to vote for Candidate A.

One weakness of the property of unbiasedness lies in the fact that the criterion requires only that the *average* value of the estimator equal the population parameter. It does not require that most, or even *any*, of the values of the estimator be reasonably close to the population parameter, as would seem desirable in a *good* estimator. For this reason, the property of efficiency is important.

Efficiency

For given repeated samples of size n, it is desirable that an estimator have values that are close to each other. It would be comforting in estimating an unknown parameter to realize that the value you computed on the basis of a particular random sample would not be much different from the value you or anyone else would compute on the basis of another random sample of the same size. The *property of efficiency* implies that the variance of the estimator should be small. However, having a small variance does not make an estimator a good one, unless this estimator is also unbiased. For example, an estimator that always specifies 200 as its estimate of the population parameter will have zero variance. But this estimate will be biased unless the true population parameter happens to equal 200. In other words, a small variance is desirable, but so is unbiasedness.

The property of efficiency of an estimator is defined by comparing its variance to the variance of all other *unbiased* estimators.

The *most efficient estimator* among a group of unbiased estimators is the one with the smallest variance.

The most efficient estimator is also called the *best unbiased* estimator, where *best* implies minimum variance. Figure 9.1(b) illustrates the distributions of two different unbiased estimators (labelled 3 and 4) based on samples of the same size. Our definition of efficiency requires that the estimator be *unbiased* and have smaller variance than any other unbiased estimator. Thus, estimator 3 is more efficient than estimator 4.

Relative Efficiency

Since it is generally quite difficult to prove that an estimator is the best among all unbiased ones, the most common approach is to determine the *relative efficiency* of two estimators. Relative efficiency is defined as the ratio of the variances of the two estimators.

$$\text{Relative efficiency} = \frac{\text{Variance of first estimator}}{\text{Variance of second estimator}}$$

As an illustration of the use of relative efficiency, consider the sample mean versus the sample median as estimators of the mean of a normal population. Both estimators are unbiased when we are sampling from a normal population, since the normal is symmetric. From Section 7.4, we know that the variance of $\bar{x}$ equals σ^2/n. It is also possible to find the variance of the sample median as an estimator of the population mean; this variance is $\pi\sigma^2/2n$. The ratio of these quantities gives their relative efficiency:

$$\frac{V[\text{median}]}{V[\bar{x}]} = \frac{\pi\sigma^2/2n}{\sigma^2/n} = \frac{\pi}{2} = 1.57$$

The ratio 1.57 implies that the median is 1.57 times less efficient than the mean in estimating μ. An estimate based on the median of a sample of 157 observations has the same reliability as an estimate based on the mean of a sample of 100 observations, assuming a normal parent population.

In some problems, it is possible to determine precisely the most efficient estimator, that is, the unbiased estimator with the smallest variance. In estimating the mean of a normal population, for example, it can be mathematically proven that the variance of any estimator must be greater than or equal to σ^2/n. Since the variance of $\bar{x}$ in this case exactly equals this lower bound (σ^2/n), the sample mean must be the most efficient estimator of μ.

In the design of a sample, the most efficient estimator may not always be the best choice because of other factors, such as the time available to collect the sample or the accessibility of the observations. Statistical efficiency may have to be sacrificed in order to obtain an estimate in the time allowed; or some other estimator may be less costly to obtain or more meaningful and, therefore, may be preferred over the most efficient one.

A business journal, for example, may publish statements about the managerial competence of various companies in terms of only their ranks relative to each other. For example, Hitachi, Cda. ranks third among all retail firms listed in **Data Set 2** in managerial emphasis on new products. Trying to determine the most efficient estimator in this case (for example, the average managerial characteristics) may be difficult, and such an estimator may not be as meaningful as a measure based on the ranked performance.

Sufficiency

Unbiasedness and efficiency are desirable properties for an estimator, particularly when one is dealing with small samples. Another property of interest is *sufficiency*.

> An estimator is said to be *sufficient* if it uses all the information about the population parameter that the sample can provide.

That is, the sufficient estimator somehow takes into account each of the sample observations, as well as all the information that is provided by these observations. The sample median is not a sufficient estimator because it uses only the *ranking* of the observations to obtain the middle value. The sufficiency property is of importance in that it is a necessary condition for efficiency.

Consistency   Since the distribution of an estimator will change, in general, as the sample size changes, the properties of estimators for large sample sizes (as n approaches the population size or infinity, but prior to the limit of $n \rightarrow \infty$) become important. Properties of estimators based on distributions approached as n becomes large are called *asymptotic properties*, and these may differ from the finite or small-sample properties. The most important of these asymptotic properties is that of *consistency*, which involves the convergence in probability of the estimator to the population parameter as the size of n increases. Since the topic of probability limits is not presented in this text, we shall define a slightly stronger form of consistency called *mean square consistency*.

> The *mean square error* of an estimator is defined as the sum of the variance of the estimator plus the square of its bias:
>
> $$\text{Mean square error} = \text{variance} + \text{bias}^2$$
>
> An estimator is said to be *mean square consistent* if its mean square error approaches zero as the sample size becomes large.

To say that the mean square error of an estimator goes to zero as the sample size becomes very large has the interpretation that the probability distribution of the estimator for large samples becomes more and more compact (small variance) and is centred more and more closely about the true value of the parameter (small bias), as shown in Figure 9.2. At the limit of $n = \infty$, the probability distribution of the estimator degenerates into a single spike at the true value. That is, the estimator always gives the same value, and that value is the true value. In more symbolic terms,

$$\text{when } n \rightarrow \infty, \quad \text{variance} \rightarrow 0 \text{ and bias}^2 \rightarrow 0.$$

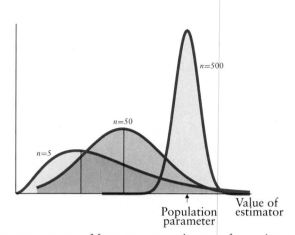

FIGURE 9.2   Mean square consistency of an estimator

Previously, we showed that $\bar{x}$ is an unbiased estimator of the population mean and that p is an unbiased estimator of the population proportion. It is not difficult to show also that both these estimators are consistent as well as unbiased. We shall prove that p is a consistent estimator of π, leaving it to the reader to prove that $\bar{x}$

is also consistent.

$$V[p] = V[x/n] = \frac{1}{n^2}V[x] \qquad \text{(From Section 4.4, Rule 4)}$$

$$= \frac{1}{n^2}n\pi(1-\pi) \qquad \text{(Since } x \text{ is binomially distributed)}$$

$$= \frac{\pi(1-\pi)}{n}$$

Since the value of $\pi(1-\pi)/n$ approaches zero as n approaches infinity, $V[p] \to 0$. Since p is an unbiased estimator of π for any sample size, $(\text{bias})^2 = 0$. Thus, the mean square error also approaches zero and (p) must be a mean-square consistent estimator of π.

While the four properties presented above are certainly all quite desirable, they do not preclude other considerations. We pointed out previously that the inferences (or estimates) made from samples serve as an aid to the process of making decisions and that samples should be drawn with the objective of minimizing the cost of making an incorrect decision (balanced against the cost of sampling). Since one primary purpose in collecting a sample involves estimating parameters, an estimation procedure should be chosen that will minimize the cost (or loss) of making an incorrect estimate from the sample information. This objective is not necessarily incompatible with any of the above properties of good estimators; in fact, in many cases, when these properties are satisfied, the estimator indeed will minimize the cost of making an error.

section 9.3

Estimating Unknown Parameters

In the 1920s, R. A. Fisher developed the method of **maximum likelihood** as a means of finding estimators that satisfy some (but not necessarily all) of the criteria discussed previously. This method is popular because maximum-likelihood estimators are usually intuitively reasonable, have the property of consistency, and are often approximately normally distributed for large samples. The disadvantage of the method is that maximum-likelihood estimates are not necessarily unbiased for small samples and often involve some fairly complex mathematical derivations.

The maximum-likelihood method estimates the value of a population parameter by selecting the most likely sample space from which a given sample could have been drawn. In other words, the sample space is selected that would yield the observed sample more frequently than any other sample space. The value of the population parameter corresponding to the generation of this sample space is called the maximum-likelihood estimate (MLE). The name *maximum-likelihood* is derived from this process of selecting the most likely sample space.

❏ **EXAMPLE 9.1** The University Placement Centre considers its activity to be successful if a graduating senior finds a job as a result of its assistance. In a sample of five graduates, three report finding a job with help from the placement service. Consider the problem of finding the maximum likelihood estimator of the binomial parameter π. The question of interest is, "What sample space (derived from what binomial population) is most likely to give this particular result; or equivalently, what is the most likely value of π given the observed sample?"

The most likely population parameter can be determined by calculating the probability of obtaining exactly three successes in five trials for all possible values of the population parameter and selecting the value that yields the highest probability. Table 9.1 examines nine possible values of π, indicating for each value the probability of three successes in five trials; for example, if $\pi = \frac{1}{10}$, the appropriate probability is:

$$_5C_3 \left(\frac{1}{10}\right)^3 \left(\frac{9}{10}\right)^2 = 0.0081$$

TABLE 9.1 The Probability of Three Successes in a Binomial Situation for Different Values of the Parameter π

Value of π	Probability of Three Successes
0.10	0.0081
0.20	0.0512
0.30	0.1323
0.40	0.2304
0.50	0.3125
0.60 MLE	0.3456
0.70	0.3087
0.80	0.2048
0.90	0.0729

The value of π most likely to yield a sample of three successes in five trials, as given by Table 9.1, is $\pi = 0.60$, where the associated probability is 0.3456. The reader will note that this estimate exactly equals the sample proportion $x/n = 3/5 = 0.60$. ■

It is often true that the most likely value for a population parameter is the intuitively appealing one, the corresponding measure of the sample. For example, it can be shown that the maximum-likelihood estimator of a population mean is the sample mean. That is, the value of $\bar{x}$ is the most likely value of μ that can be found based on a sample of size n.

The particular value chosen as most likely for a population parameter is called a *point estimate*. We know that it would be an exceptional coincidence (because of sampling error) if this estimate were identical to the population parameter. Thus, even though the best possible value is used as the point estimate, we should have very little confidence that this value is *exactly* correct. One of the major weaknesses of a point estimate is that it does not permit the expression of any degree of uncertainty about the estimate. The most common way to express uncertainty about an estimate is to define, with a known *probability of error*, an interval of values in which the population parameter is *likely* to be. This process is known as *interval estimation*.

Confidence Intervals

You will recall that, on a number of occasions thus far, we have determined values a and b so that $P(a \leq \bar{x} \leq b)$ equals some predetermined value. The values a and b were determined from a knowledge about the parent population and its parameters. The interval (a, b) is called a probability interval for $\bar{x}$. For example, if we calculated $P(a \leq \bar{x} \leq b) = 0.90$, based on a random sample of size n drawn from a population with a known mean μ, we know the random variable $\bar{x}$ will fall in the probability interval (a, b) 90% of the time.

In the application of quality control as given in Chapter 8, control limits or specification limits were set based on predetermined population characteristics, such as $\mu \pm 3\sigma$. Although it is important to be able to construct probability intervals or specification limits for $\bar{x}$ based on knowledge of μ, for most practical statistical problems, the process must be reversed; it is μ that is the unknown, and we want to construct a *confidence interval* for μ based on $\bar{x}$. In a confidence interval, the exact sampling distribution of the estimator is used to determine confidence limits that guarantee a preset small probability of error for the interval estimate. The method of confidence interval construction defines an interval based on $\bar{x}$ such that μ is likely to lie in such intervals 90% of the times that the method is used — a 90% confidence interval. This means that, on the average, 90 such intervals out of every 100 calculated on the basis of means of samples of size n will include the population mean μ.

The use of the future tense in explaining a confidence interval is very important because, once such an interval based on a sample is determined, either the true parameter lies in the interval or it does not. The value of μ cannot be said to have a probability of 0.90 of being within the interval because it is not a random variable, but a constant. If it is in a given interval, then the probability that it is in the interval is 1.0; if not, the probability that it is within the interval is 0.0.

Perhaps this concept can be emphasized further by noting that a population parameter, although unknown, is a constant and it does *not* have a probability distribution. Thus, it is improper to make probability statements about values of a population parameter. In finding an interval estimate, the endpoints of the interval are based on sample evidence. They will have different values for each different sample. Thus, these endpoints, or more generally, the intervals themselves, are random variables. Consequently, it is appropriate to make probability statements about the *proportion of intervals* that would include a particular parameter value. But it is *not* appropriate to make probability statements about a parameter.

In order to simplify the language concerning this rather subtle distinction, statisticians use the term *confidence interval* when specifying the upper and lower limits on the likely value of a parameter.

> A 90% confidence interval for a parameter is a shorthand statement for "the probability is 0.90 that the interval to be determined on the basis of the sample evidence would be one that includes the population parameter."

☐ **EXAMPLE 9.2** Consider the following problem in process control. A manufacturer makes large tile pipes. When the production process is working correctly, the interior diameter of the pipe is normally distributed with mean $\mu = 24$ inches and standard deviation $\sigma = \frac{1}{4}$ inch, or $N(24, 0.25^2)$. At random points in time, a sample of four pipe segments is selected from the production process to check the average diameter of all the pipes in the population being produced. The population parameter being investigated here is μ, and we know that in this case $\bar{x}$ has a normal distribution, since x is normal. Because $\sigma/\sqrt{n} = (0.25/\sqrt{4}) = 0.125$ is the standard deviation of the $\bar{x}$'s, the distribution of $\bar{x}$ is $N(24, 0.125^2)$.

Figure 9.3 represents the two types of intervals discussed above. This figure shows the mean of 20 different samples (20 dots), each of size $n = 4$. Part (a) of the figure illustrates a probability interval with its centre at the population mean, $\mu = 24$ inches, and values $a = 23.755$ and $b = 24.245$, chosen so that, theoretically, 95% of the values of $\bar{x}$ will lie between a and b.

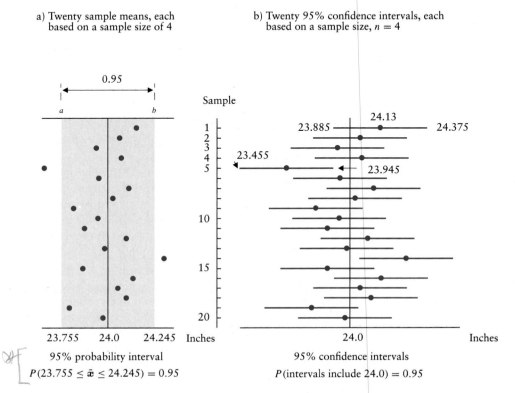

a) Twenty sample means, each based on a sample size of 4

b) Twenty 95% confidence intervals, each based on a sample size, $n = 4$

95% probability interval
$P(23.755 \le \bar{x} \le 24.245) = 0.95$

95% confidence intervals
$P(\text{intervals include } 24.0) = 0.95$

FIGURE 9.3 Illustration of probability intervals and of confidence intervals for an unbiased estimator with a normal distribution: a) 95% probability interval b) 95% confidence intervals

These endpoints are found in the same way as in the probability examples in Chapters 6 and 7. From Table III of Appendix C, the values $z = \pm 1.96$ exclude 0.025 in each tail of the normal distribution. With $\mu = 24$ as the centre of the probability interval, the endpoints are:

$$24 \pm 1.96 \frac{\sigma}{\sqrt{n}} = 24 \pm 1.96(0.125) = 23.755 \quad \text{and} \quad 24.245$$

Owing to the uncertainty of sampling, only 18 of 20 rather than 19 of 20 (95%) of these sample means lie between 23.755 and 24.245. However, over all such conceivable sample means with $n = 4$, we know that

$$P(23.755 \le \bar{x} \le 24.245) = 0.95.$$

In part (b) of Figure 9.3, the confidence intervals for μ based on each of these 20 samples are shown. The centre of each confidence interval is the sample mean $\bar{x}$, shown by the 20 different dots. The endpoints of the intervals are equidistant from these dots as determined by the following equations:

$$\text{upper} = \bar{x} + 1.96(0.125) \quad \text{and} \quad \text{lower} = \bar{x} - 1.96(0.125)$$

Some of the intervals in Figure 9.3(b) do not include the true value of $\mu = 24$, and some do include it. For example, the first interval is centred at the mean of the first sample, 24.13. The upper and lower confidence limits are $24.13 \pm 1.96(0.125)$, which gives 23.885 and 24.375. Thus, this interval does include the value $\mu = 24$. It makes no sense, therefore, to say that the probability that μ lies in this interval is 0.95. It is a *certainty* (probability $= 1.0$) that 24 lies between 23.885 and 24.375. Similarly, consider the fifth sample with a mean of 23.7. The upper and lower confidence limits using this centre value are $23.7 \pm 1.96(0.125)$, which gives 23.455 and 23.945. Again, it is improper to say that the probability that μ lies in this interval is 0.95. Since μ is known to equal 24, we can clearly see that this interval does not include μ. It is *impossible* (probability $= 0.0$) for 24 to be between 23.455 and 23.945. ■

The concept is the same *when the parameter is unknown*. It is still a constant value, whatever it is, and it either will or will not lie in a given interval. The probability of 0.95 *does not refer to the event that μ is in the interval*. The probability of 0.95 refers to the event that *an interval obtained in this manner would include μ*. That is:

$$P(\text{interval would include } \mu) = 0.95$$

This is a probability based on all conceivable repeated samples of four pipe segments from which such intervals could be calculated, not on any one specific interval that has actually been determined.

We express this concept by stating that we are 95% *confident* that the interval covers μ. The term confidence level is used when referring to the uncertainty about the likely value of a population parameter. The term *probability* is reserved for statements of uncertainty about random variables. As the discussion above and Figure 9.3 show, the two concepts are related, but they do not mean the same thing.

❑ STUDY QUESTION 9.1   Interval Interpretation

Write in symbols the appropriate probability statement that corresponds to each of the following:
a) 90% probability interval for the sample variance s^2 of the incomes of college graduates
b) 99% confidence interval for the proportion of persons receiving social security payments
c) 95% confidence interval for the average number of hours worked per week by employees in manufacturing

• ANSWER
a) $P(a \le s^2 \le b) = 0.90$.
b) $P(\text{interval would include } \pi) = 0.99$ [not $P(a \le \pi \le b) = 0.99$].
c) $P(\text{interval would include } \mu) = 0.95$ [not $P(a \le \mu \le b) = 0.95$]. ■

The Probability of an Error, α

It is often more convenient to refer to the probability that a confidence interval will *not* include the parameter than to express the probability that it will. The former probability is denoted by α (the Greek letter "alpha"). The value of alpha is referred to as the probability of making an error, since it indicates the proportion of times that one will be *incorrect* in assuming that the intervals would contain the population parameter. It is customary to refer to confidence intervals as being of size $100(1 - \alpha)\%$. Thus, if α is 0.05, then the associated interval is a 95% **confidence interval**; if a 90% confidence interval is specified, then $\alpha = 1.0 - (90/100) = 0.10$. In Example 9.2 of a process-control problem, α equalled 0.05. This means that the probability is 0.05 of making an error in saying that the interval to be calculated will contain the parameter (the process is in control) when in fact it will not (the process needs adjustment). In other words, if we were to repeat the method of determining confidence intervals many times, we would be incorrect in only 5% of the cases, on the average, in saying that the intervals would include the population parameter.

There is an obvious trade-off between the value of α and the size of the confidence interval: the lower the value of α, the larger the interval must be.[1] If one need not be very confident that the population parameter will be within the interval, then a relatively small interval will suffice; if one is to be quite confident that the population parameter will be in the interval to be calculated, a relatively large interval will be necessary. The value of α is often set at 0.05 or 0.01, representing 95% and 99% confidence intervals, respectively. This procedure, although widely used, does not necessarily lead to the optimal trade-off between the size of the confidence interval and the risk of making an error.

In general, confidence intervals are constructed on the basis of sample information, so that both changes in α and changes in n (the sample size) affect the size of the interval. The more observations collected, the more confident one can be about the estimate of the population parameter, and thus, the smaller need be the interval to ensure a given level of confidence. Although it usually is desirable to have as small a confidence interval as possible, the optimal interval size must be determined by considering the costs of sampling and the amount of risk of making an error that one wants to assume. We shall return several times to this problem of determining the optimal trade-off between the risks of making an error and the sample size. For now, we merely caution the reader to be aware that the task of determining an *optimal* trade-off may not be an easy one and is often done arbitrarily.

Determining a Confidence Interval

One of the first steps in constructing a confidence interval is to specify the size of the sample and how much confidence one wants to have that the resulting interval is likely to include the population parameter. In other words, both n and α are usually fixed in advance. However, it is possible under certain conditions to consider either n or α as an unknown and to solve for the value of the unknown.

In addition to specifying α in advance, one must also specify how much of the total error, α, is attributed to the possibility that the true population parameter might be larger than the upper bound of the confidence interval. The remainder of α is attributed to the possibility that the true parameter might be smaller than the lower bound of the interval. As we indicated previously, this split of α is usually obtained by dividing α *equally* between the upper and the lower tails of the distribution. In the case of a confidence interval, however, the decision on how to divide α should depend on how serious or costly it is to make errors on the high side relative to errors on the low side. Since we normally want to avoid expensive errors, α should be divided in such a way that expensive errors occur less frequently. Unfortunately, determining the costs of making an error may be quite difficult.

---

[1] We assume here that other factors, such as the sample size, are held constant.

> The common procedure for determining confidence intervals is the same as for probability intervals — exclude half of α (that is, $\alpha/2$) on the high side and half of α on the low side.

This procedure is based on the assumption that errors on the high side are just as expensive as errors on the low side.

In the above discussion, we stated that a given confidence interval will depend on α (and the way α is divided) and on the size of the sample. The other factor that influences the boundaries of a particular confidence interval is the *sampling distribution* of the statistic used to estimate the population parameter. The procedure for establishing a confidence interval for a population parameter is first to find a point estimate of this parameter. The uncertainty of this point estimate is then determined by finding that interval of values about the point estimate that yields the desired degree of confidence, on the basis of the sampling distribution of this statistic. Since different sampling distributions are used for estimating different population parameters such as the mean, the binomial parameter π, or the variance, we shall describe the process of constructing intervals for each of these cases in separate sections.

Confidence Intervals for μ (σ known)

In this section, a confidence interval for the population parameter μ is constructed, based on a random sample drawn from a normal parent population with *known* standard deviation. The natural sample statistic for estimating μ is $\bar{x}$, the sample mean, for the reasons discussed in Section 9.2. Recall the sampling distribution of $\bar{x}$ under the conditions listed there: the expected value of $\bar{x}$ equals μ, and $\bar{x}$ has a standard deviation of $\sigma/\sqrt{n}$. Also recall from Section 7.5 that the variable $z = (\bar{x} - \mu)/(\sigma/\sqrt{n})$ has a standardized normal distribution.

We now introduce a useful notational point. The cumulative probability distribution in Table III gives values of $F(z)$, the area under the curve to the *left* of a point z. That is, if 95% of the area under the curve is to the left of z, then $F(z) = 0.95$.

> As an indicator of the proportion of area to the *right* of a point z, we let the symbol z_α represent that point for which the probability of observing values of z greater than z_α is α. By definition, $P(z \geq z_\alpha) = \alpha$, and the *cumulative probability* at this point is $F(z_\alpha) = 1 - \alpha$.

For example, $F(z_{0.01}) = 0.99$, or $F(z_{0.05}) = 0.95$. This notation gives us two ways of representing proportions of the total area under a normal probability density function. We can use the cumulative notation $[F(z)]$ for the area to the *left* of a point z or the subscript notation (z_α) for the point z having an area of α to its *right*. The latter is extremely convenient for denoting the area in the extreme tail of a distribution. If we want to exclude 0.01 in the upper tail, the point is denoted by $z_{0.01}$. If the area in the upper tail beyond a certain point is to be 0.05, we denote that point by $z_{0.05}$. Since the normal distribution is symmetric, the negative value $(-z_\alpha)$ can similarly denote points in the lower tail of the normal distribution below which a proportion α of the area is excluded. Two such points are shown in Figure 9.4.

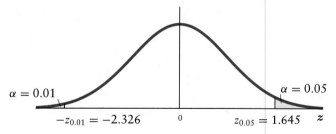

FIGURE 9.4   Values of $+z_{0.05}$ and $-z_{0.01}$

For finding upper and lower bounds of confidence intervals, it is usually convenient to find those points excluding $(\alpha/2)$ proportion of the area (probability) in each tail of the normal distribution so that the total area *excluded* equals α and the area *included* in the interval between the upper and lower limits is $(1 - \alpha)$. To do this, let $z_{\alpha/2}$ represent the value for which the probability $P(z \geq z_{\alpha/2})$, and let $-z_{\alpha/2}$ equal the point at which $P(z \leq -z_{\alpha/2})$. If, for example, $\alpha = 0.05$, the value of $+z_{\alpha/2}$ satisfying $P(z \geq z_{\alpha/2}) = 0.025$ is the same point as $F(z) = 0.975$. From Table III, $z_{\alpha/2} = z_{0.025}$ is seen to be 1.96. The value of $-z_{\alpha/2}$ must be -1.96. The probability that z falls between the two limits, -1.96 and $+1.96$, is

$$P(-1.96 \leq z \leq +1.96) = 1.00 - 0.025 - 0.025 = 0.95,$$

as shown in Figure 9.5.

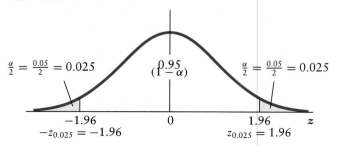

FIGURE 9.5   The values of $\pm z_{\alpha/2}$, cutting off a total area of $\alpha = 0.05$ from the standardized normal distribution, leaving an interval including $100(1-\alpha)$ percent $= 95\%$ of the probability

In more general terms, the probability that z falls between the two limits $-z_{\alpha/2}$ and $+z_{\alpha/2}$ can be written as follows:

$$P(-z_{\alpha/2} \leq z \leq +z_{\alpha/2}) = 1 - \alpha.$$

Note that this interval, $-z_{\alpha/2} \leq z \leq +z_{\alpha/2}$, is a $100(1-\alpha)\%$ *probability interval* for z, *any* standardized normal variable. It is also a $100(1-\alpha)\%$ probability interval for the *particular* standardized normal variable $z = (\bar{x}-\mu)/(\sigma/\sqrt{n})$. Unfortunately, this is not the interval we originally set out to derive because we wanted a $100(1-\alpha)\%$ *confidence interval* for μ, not a probability interval for $(\bar{x} - \mu)/(\sigma/\sqrt{n})$. However, the difference is not hard to resolve. It is simple to find the confidence limits on μ

by rewriting the inequalities in the expression $-z_{\alpha/2} \leq z \leq +z_{\alpha/2}$ as follows:[2]

$100(1 - \alpha)\%$ confidence interval for μ, where σ is known and the parent population is normal:

$$\bar{x} - z_{\alpha/2}\frac{\sigma}{\sqrt{n}} \leq \mu \leq \bar{x} + z_{\alpha/2}\frac{\sigma}{\sqrt{n}} \qquad (9.1)$$

holds for any sample size

❑ **EXAMPLE 9.3**   For decision-making regarding freight rates, track maintenance, diesel fuel consumption, et cetera, a consortium of railroads wishes to estimate, with 80% confidence, the mean number of freight cars hauled per train over a 600-mile segment of track in Alberta and Saskatchewan. We assume that the number of cars is normally distributed and that the population variance is known to be 225.

We first obtain a sample of $n = 25$ trains and determine the sample average of $\bar{x} = 107$ cars. Since we want an 80% confidence interval, $\alpha = 0.20$ and the appropriate z-values are $\pm z_{\alpha/2} = \pm z_{0.10} = \pm 1.28$. Substituting these two values, as well as $n = 25$, $\sigma = 15$, and $\bar{x} = 107$ into Formula 9.1, we find the desired 80% confidence interval:

$$\bar{x} - z_{\alpha/2}\frac{\sigma}{\sqrt{n}} \leq \mu \leq \bar{x} + z_{\alpha/2}\frac{\sigma}{\sqrt{n}}$$

$$107 - (1.28)\frac{15}{\sqrt{25}} \leq \mu \leq 107 + (1.28)\frac{15}{\sqrt{25}}$$

$$107 - 3.84 \leq \mu \leq 107 + 3.84$$

$$103.16 \leq \mu \leq 110.84$$ ■

We can be confident that intervals obtained by using this procedure are likely to contain μ 80% of the time. That is, on the average, for 80 out of 100 such samples of size $n = 25$, the intervals calculated in this manner will include the true population mean μ. We do not know, of course, whether the above interval is one of the correct ones or one of the incorrect ones, since μ is unknown. For the 80% confidence interval, the probability of error is $\alpha = 0.20$ that the interval will not include the true mean μ. If one desires a smaller risk of error α, a larger confidence interval must be used.

---

[2] The solution is:

$-z_{\alpha/2} \leq z \leq z_{\alpha/2}$

$-z_{\alpha/2} \leq \dfrac{\bar{x} - \mu}{\sigma/\sqrt{n}} \leq z_{\alpha/2}$ By substitution

$-z_{\alpha/2}\dfrac{\sigma}{\sqrt{n}} \leq (\bar{x} - \mu) \leq z_{\alpha/2}\dfrac{\sigma}{\sqrt{n}}$ By multiplying each term by $\sigma/\sqrt{n}$

$-\bar{x} - z_{\alpha/2}\dfrac{\sigma}{\sqrt{n}} \leq -\mu \leq -\bar{x} + z_{\alpha/2}\dfrac{\sigma}{\sqrt{n}}$ By adding $(-\bar{x})$ to each term

$\bar{x} + z_{\alpha/2}\dfrac{\sigma}{\sqrt{n}} \geq \mu \geq \bar{x} - z_{\alpha/2}\dfrac{\sigma}{\sqrt{n}}.$ By multiplying each term by (-1), thus changing the direction of both inequalities

For example, in order to have $\alpha = 0.01$ (a 99% confidence interval), the appropriate z-values found in Table III are $z_{\alpha/2} = z_{0.005} = 2.576$ and $-z_{\alpha/2} = -2.576$. The new confidence interval is as follows:

$$107 - (2.576)\frac{15}{\sqrt{25}} \leq \mu \leq 107 + (2.576)\frac{15}{\sqrt{25}}$$

$$107 - 7.728 \leq \mu \leq 107 + 7.728$$

$$99.272 \leq \mu \leq 114.728$$

Since intervals calculated using $\alpha = 0.01$ are wider than intervals calculated using $\alpha = 0.20$, we have greater confidence that the larger interval will include the population parameter μ. We could further increase our confidence and decrease the risk of error α by extending the interval even more. Of course, there is a limit to the usefulness of the interval when it becomes too large. For example, we might have calculated from our sample that the mean number of freight cars almost certainly ($\alpha \rightarrow 0.0$) falls in the interval $27 \leq \mu \leq 187$, but we could have made such a statement from simple experience without knowing anything about statistical inference. We sample to obtain useful information that is more precise. To obtain it, we must be willing to subject our conclusions or inferences to a small controlled level of risk, α.

Relaxation of the Assumption of Normality for the Population

The relationship expressed in Formula 9.1 depends on the assumptions that μ is known and that the parent population is normal. When these assumptions are valid, Formula 9.1 holds for any sample size, whether n is large or small. But suppose that the parent population is *not normal*. In this case, if the sample size n is small, then the distribution of $(\bar{x} - \mu)/(\sigma/\sqrt{n})$ is not normal, and there is no convenient way to determine a confidence interval. On the other hand, when n is large,[3] we know by the central limit theorem that $(\bar{x} - \mu)/(\sigma/\sqrt{n})$ is *approximately* normally distributed; hence the confidence interval specified by Formula 9.1 is still appropriate.

☐ **EXAMPLE 9.4**   Suppose that in Example 9.3 we now drop the assumption of normality, but suppose we increase the sample size to $n = 64$. Since $n > 30$, we can safely rely on the central limit theorem and apply the normal distribution. Let us find a 99% confidence interval if we are again given $\sigma = 15$ and a sample mean of $\bar{x} = 107$. The confidence limits are:

$$107 - (2.576)\frac{15}{\sqrt{64}} \leq \mu \leq 107 + (2.576)\frac{15}{\sqrt{64}}$$

$$107 - 4.83 \leq \mu \leq 107 + 4.83$$

$$102.17 \leq \mu \leq 111.83$$

We have 99% confidence that the interval 102.17 to 111.83 includes the average number of freight cars per train. This interval is smaller than the previous one. Although they have the same level of error, $\alpha = 0.01$, this interval is narrower because it is based on a larger sample size. Figure 9.6 illustrates this 99% confidence interval.

---

[3] We repeat that "large" n depends on the shape of the parent population. For symmetric, unimodel populations, n as small as 5 or 10 may be sufficient for a satisfactory approximation. In almost all cases, $n > 30$ is sufficient.

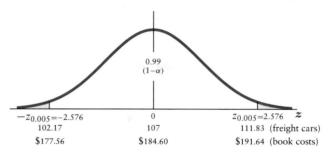

FIGURE 9.6 Illustration of a 99% confidence interval for Example 9.4 and Study Question 9.2

Remember that it is based on only a single sample. If many repeated samples were taken, then 99% of the intervals calculated about the different sample means would include the true value of the unknown μ. Whether this one does or does not is unknown. However, we do have a measure of the uncertainty associated with our statement about the likely value of μ.   ■

As a final remark about sample sizes, recall that one advantage of a large sample is greater reliability. Hence, the finite population correction factor should be used if the population is finite and the sample size becomes so large that it exceeds 10% of the population size. This would modify Formula 9.1 by changing the standard error in the confidence limit from

$$\frac{\sigma}{\sqrt{n}} \quad \text{to} \quad \frac{\sigma}{\sqrt{n}}\sqrt{\frac{N-n}{N-1}}$$

☐ STUDY QUESTION 9.2   Average Book Expenditure per Pupil

A random sample of 18 out of 145 public schools is taken to find the per-pupil expenditures on books this year. The sample average is $184.60. Assuming a normal population with a standard deviation of $12.36 (determined from a census of schools a few years ago), find a 99% confidence interval for the population mean.

• **ANSWER**   From Table III, the appropriate values of z that exclude $(\alpha/2) = 0.005$ of the distribution are ± 2.576. (See Figure 9.6.) Using Formula 9.1 with $\sigma = 12.36$ and $\bar{x} = 184.60$ plus the finite population correction factor gives:

$$184.60 \pm 2.576\left(\frac{12.36}{\sqrt{18}}\right)\left(\sqrt{\frac{145-18}{145-1}}\right)$$

$$= 184.60 \pm 7.50\sqrt{0.882}$$

$$= 184.60 \pm 7.04$$

The upper and lower confidence limits are $177.56 and $191.64.   ■

PROBLEMS

9.1 Differentiate between the following terms.

a) a point estimate and an interval estimate

b) unbiasedness and consistency

9.2 What are the four properties of a *good estimator*? Explain why each one is important.

9.3 Given a normal parent population, which of the following are unbiased estimators of μ?

a) sample mean

b) maximum sample value

c) sample median

d) sample mode

9.4 Consider the population $x = \{5, 15\}$.

a) Calculate μ, σ^2, and σ for this population.

b) Make a list of the eight possible samples of size $n = 3$, with replacement [that is, $(5, 5, 5)$, $(5, 5, 15)$, $(5, 15, 5)$, etc.], and then calculate $\bar{x}$ for each sample.

c) Show from part (b) that $\bar{x}$ is an unbiased estimate of μ (that is, $E[\bar{x}] = \mu$).

d) Calculate s^2 for each sample and then show that $E[s^2] = \sigma^2$.

e) Show that the average of the eight values of s is not equal to σ (that is, $E[s] \neq \sigma$).

f) Calculate the median for each of the 8 samples. Is the average of these medians equal to μ? Is the median an unbiased estimator in this case?

9.5 Calculate the variance of the median values in Problem 9.4(f). Use this variance and the variance of the values of $\bar{x}$ in Problem 9.4(b) to show that $\bar{x}$ is more efficient than the median as an estimator of μ.

9.6 An accountant selected a random sample of 100 of the commercial accounts in a certain bank branch. The mean balance among these accounts was found to be \$749.13. The accountant then stated that the mean balance for all commercial accounts must be \$749.13, since $\bar{x}$ is an unbiased estimate of μ. Discuss the reasonableness of this assertion.

9.7 Explain, in your own words, how the properties of efficiency and consistency both involve the property of unbiasedness. (*Hint:* Consider unbiasedness in small- and large-size samples respectively.)

9.8 Repeat Problem 9.4(b) using $n = 2$. Compare the case in which $n = 2$ with that in which $n = 3$, and show that the results support the fact that the mean is a consistent estimator.

9.9 Forty percent of the clerks in a department store are part-time workers. Let x be the number of part-time workers in a random selection of four clerks.

a) The five possible binomial values of $p = (x/n)$ are $0/4$, $1/4$, $2/4$, $3/4$, and $4/4$. Calculate $E[p]$ by multiplying each of these five values by the appropriate probabilities in Table I ($n = 4$ and $\pi = 0.40$). Is p unbiased (that is, does $E[p] = \pi$)?

b) Calculate the variance of the p-values in part (a). Calculate the variance of p for $\pi = 0.40$ and $n = 5$. Does the variance decrease from $n = 4$ to $n = 5$, supporting the fact that p is a consistent estimator?

9.10 Find the following values.

a) Find the values of z_α when $P(z \geq z_\alpha) = 0.025$ and for $P(z \leq -z_\alpha) = 0.02$.

b) Find the value of $z_{\alpha/2}$ such that $P(-z_{\alpha/2} \leq z \leq z_{\alpha/2}) = 0.98$.

9.11 Explain, in your own words, under what circumstances x does not have to be normally distributed if you wish to calculate a 90% confidence interval for μ.

9.12 When properly adjusted, the period of intense heat applied in a fabricating process is normally distributed with a variance of $\sigma^2 = 0.50(\text{seconds})^2$. Four random cycles of the process are monitored, and the results are heat periods of 51, 52, 50, and 51 seconds.

a) Find an unbiased estimate of μ.

b) Construct a 95% confidence interval for μ.

c) Explain how the width of the confidence interval could be decreased by changing α.

9.13 *Forbes* magazine points out in every issue a number of stocks recommended for purchase. A sample of nine recommendations is followed for six months to determine whether these stocks perform better than the overall Dow-Jones index of stocks. The percentage changes above or below the change for the index are -5, 2, -10, 5, 8, 13, 3, -1, and 3.

a) Find the best point estimate of μ (the mean percentage change, net of the index change, for all such recommended stocks).

b) Construct a 90% confidence interval for μ, assuming a normal population and a variance of $\sigma^2 = 40$.

9.14 Find a 90% confidence interval for the mean number of credit sales per week by a Western Auto store. Assume that the population has a standard deviation of 70 and that a sample of 36 weeks yields a sample mean of 950. Does your answer require the assumption that x is normally distributed?

9.15 A sample of 36 installment loans for used cars bought in 1992 revealed a mean principal amount of $8748. The standard deviation for the parent population is believed to be $970.

a) Find a 95% confidence interval for the mean amount of all used car loans in 1992.

b) The Motor Vehicle Manufacturers Association reported that the average used car installment loan in 1992 was $8975. Does your confidence interval from part (a) include this value? Explain how your result is consistent with the meaning of a 95% confidence interval.

9.16 A recent survey asked respondents to rate, on a scale from 0 to 100, how good a job they thought the manager of the Montreal Expos had done during the past season. Assume that the population variance for this survey is known to be $\sigma^2 = 100$. Construct a 95% confidence interval for μ, assuming that a random sample of 256 adults yielded a mean score of 61.0. Is it necessary in this case to assume that the parent population is normal?

9.17 A production assembly process is scheduled as a 20-minute operation. A time study based on 16 randomly selected observation periods shows a sample average of 24.3 minutes. The population standard deviation is $\sigma = 6$ minutes. Find a 90% confidence interval for the population mean time of this assembly operation, assuming that the population is normally distributed.

9.18 Refer to **Data Set 4** for measures of hours worked per week by a sample of 40 physicians. Assume the population is normal with a standard deviation of 3 hours.

a) Find the best point estimate of the mean hours worked per week.

b) Find a 95% confidence interval for the population mean.

---

section 9.5

Confidence Intervals for μ (σ Unknown)

The major assumption specified at the beginning of Section 9.4 was that the population standard deviation σ is known. This assumption may not realistically be applicable to many practical problems. When the mean of the population is unknown and must be estimated, it is unlikely that the standard deviation about that unknown mean will be known. Instead, the population standard deviation often must be estimated on the basis of the sample standard deviation. Under these circumstances, it is common to use the t-distributed random variable, $(\bar{x} - \mu)/(s/\sqrt{n})$, with $(n - 1)$ degrees of freedom (assuming that the parent population is normal).

The procedure for determining a $100(1 - \alpha)\%$ confidence interval using the t-distribution is the same as that employed when the normal distribution holds, except that different limits must be used. The limits are found by using t-values from Table VI rather than z-values from Table III. Suppose we let $t_{\alpha/2, \nu}$ represent that value of the t-distribution with $\nu = n - 1$ degrees of freedom which excludes $\alpha/2$ of the probability in the upper tail. Note that a t-value is labelled with *two* subscripts, one to denote the value of $\alpha/2$, the other to denote the degrees of freedom (ν) because the t represents a family of distributions that depend on ν. Thus, $t_{0.025, 15}$ denotes that value of the t-distribution with 15 degrees of freedom that cuts off 0.025 of the area in the upper tail of the distribution. Similarly, $-t_{0.025, 15}$ cuts off an area of 0.025 in the lower tail of the t-distribution with 15 degrees of freedom. These values are illustrated in Figure 9.7.

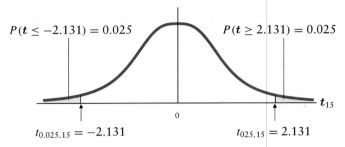

$P(t \le -2.131) = 0.025$ $P(t \ge 2.131) = 0.025$

t_{15}

0

$t_{0.025,15} = -2.131$ $t_{025,15} = 2.131$

FIGURE 9.7   The t-distribution for 15 degrees of freedom

Since each value of $t_{\alpha/2,v}$ cuts off $\alpha/2$ of the t-distribution, the area between $t_{-\alpha/2,v}$ and $t_{\alpha/2,v}$ equals $(1 - \alpha/2) - (\alpha/2) = 1 - \alpha$. That is:

$$P\left(-t_{\alpha/2,v} \le \frac{\bar{x} - \mu}{s/\sqrt{n}} \le t_{\alpha/2,v}\right) = 1 - \alpha$$

Solving the inequalities for μ, we obtain the following formula:

$100(1 - \alpha)\%$ confidence interval for μ, population normal, σ unknown:

$$\bar{x} - t_{\alpha/2,v}\frac{s}{\sqrt{n}} \le \mu \le \bar{x} + t_{\alpha/2,v}\frac{s}{\sqrt{n}}. \qquad (9.2)$$

□ EXAMPLE 9.5   A produce firm in Ontario regularly ships fruit and vegetables to a Great Lakes Distribution Centre. It uses its own trucks, and each round trip follows an identical route — a distance of more than 1500 kilometres. Owing to minor variations in each trip, the actual distance varies. In an audit of ten randomly selected trips, the exact distance is recorded and given in Table 9.2. On the basis of this sample we wish to find a 99% confidence interval for the mean kilometres per trip over all such truck shipments.

The sample mean is $(15,700/10) = 1570$ kilometres. (See column 2 in Table 9.2.) The sample variance is easily calculated by Formula 7.2 rather than relying on a computer:

$$s^2 = \frac{1}{n-1}\sum(x_i - \bar{x})^2$$

The sample standard deviation is $s = \sqrt{65.56} = 8.10$, and $(s/\sqrt{n}) = (8.10/\sqrt{10}) = 2.562$.

From Table VI for the t-distribution, the critical values, $\pm t_{\alpha/2,v}$, for a 99% confidence interval are found. Using the row for $v = (n-1) = 9$ degrees of freedom and the column for $F(t) = 1.0 - \alpha/2 = 1.0 - 0.005 = 0.995$, we obtain $\pm t_{0.005,9} = \pm 3.25$; substituting the appropriate values of x, s, t, and $\sqrt{n}$ into Formula 9.2, the solution is found as follows:

$$\bar{x} - t_{\alpha/2,v}\left(\frac{s}{\sqrt{n}}\right) \le \mu \le \bar{x} + t_{\alpha/2,v}\left(\frac{s}{\sqrt{n}}\right)$$

$$1570 - 3.25(2.562) \le \mu \le 1570 + 3.25(2.562)$$

$$1561.67 \le \mu \le 1578.33$$

TABLE 9.2   Truck Distance in Kilometres

Trip	x (kilometres)	$(x - \bar{x})$	$(x - \bar{x})^2$	Calculations
1	1569	−1	1	
2	1581	11	121	
3	1567	−3	9	
4	1580	10	100	
5	1571	1	1	
6	1570	0	0	$x = \frac{1}{10}(15,700) = 1570$
7	1578	8	64	
8	1568	−2	4	$s = \sqrt{\frac{1}{9}(590)} = \sqrt{65.56} = 8.10$
9	1557	−13	169	
10	1559	−11	121	$s_{\bar{x}} = \dfrac{s}{\sqrt{n}} = \dfrac{8.10}{3.162} = 2.562$
Sum	15,700	0	590	

The interval from 1561.67 to 1578.33 thus represents a 99% confidence interval for the mean kilometres per trip of the produce trucks. ■

This statistical work has given a precise method of estimation. It gives us exact knowledge about how often the true mean is *likely not* to lie in the intervals calculated ($\alpha = 0.01$), if this procedure were repeated over and over.

We can decrease the size of the interval in two ways, either by allowing a greater chance of error (α) or by expending more time and effort (cost) to increase the sample size n. Let us briefly examine the effects of each alternative. First if we are willing to let $\alpha = 0.10$ and obtain only a 90% confidence interval, we find in Table VI that $\pm t_{\alpha/2,v} = \pm t_{0.05,9} = \pm 1.833$. Substituting the same sample values into Formula 9.2, we obtain the following interval:

$$1570 - 1.833(2.562) \leq \mu \leq 1570 + 1.833(2.562)$$

$$1565.30 \leq \mu \leq 1574.70$$

As a second alternative, we could take a sample three times larger than before, $n = 30$, and keep the confidence level at 99%. For comparison purposes, let's assume that the sample of size 30 also yields $\bar{x} = 1570$ and $s = 8.10$, so the only difference from the original problem is the change in the sample size. The reduced standard deviation of the sampling distribution for $\bar{x}$ is $(s/\sqrt{n}) = (8.10/\sqrt{30}) = 1.48$. Since n has increased, the degrees of freedom, $v = n - 1$, has also increased. Thus, the reduced critical values are $\pm t_{\alpha/2,v} = \pm t_{0.005,29} = \pm 2.756$. The smaller interval is:

$$1570 - 2.756(1.48) \leq \mu \leq 1570 + 2.756(1.48)$$

$$1565.92 \leq \mu \leq 1574.08$$

Clearly, either allowing a *greater* risk of error or incurring a *greater* sampling cost results in a *smaller* confidence interval. Note that each interval estimate is centred at the best point estimate, $\bar{x} = 1570$. The reader may now wish to determine an interval estimate allowing *both* the greater risk of $\alpha = 0.10$ and the larger sample size, $n = 30$.

❑ **STUDY QUESTION 9.3** Average Age of Bank Presidents

A sample of the ages of 20 bank presidents is obtained in order to estimate the mean age of the population of nearly a thousand bank presidents. The sample mean and standard deviation are found to be 58 and 8 years, respectively. Find the 95% confidence interval for μ.

● **ANSWER** The t-distribution with 19 degrees of freedom may be used if we assume that the population of ages is normally distributed. From Table VI, the appropriate value of t is $t_{0.025,19} = \pm 2.093$. Using Formula 9.2, the upper and lower limits of the confidence interval are

$$\bar{x} \pm t\left(\frac{s}{\sqrt{n}}\right) = 58 \pm 2.093\left(\frac{8}{\sqrt{20}}\right),$$

which gives 54.26 and 61.74 years as the endpoints of the 95% confidence interval for the average age of bank presidents. ■

In some cases, all the emphasis of interval estimation needs to be placed in one direction. Forming a one-sided confidence statement is simply done by ignoring the other extreme and being sure to use the appropriate cutoff value to place all the error in one end of the distribution. That is, if you wish to have an upper one-sided confidence interval with an error of one percent, you ignore the lower side of the interval and you use the value for $z_\alpha = z_{0.01}$, or $t_\alpha = t_{0.01}$, as appropriate.

❑ **EXAMPLE 9.6** For the produce firm in Example 9.5 and the distance data in Table 9.2, an accountant wishes to know the distance level such that she can be 95% confident that the true mean distance of a trip will not exceed it. Using only the upper side of Formula 9.2, and allowing for all the error of 0.05 in this one end, the solution will be $\bar{x} \pm t_{0.05,9}(s/\sqrt{n})$ where $t_{0.05,9} = 1.833$.

Substituting the correct values, we have $1570 + 1.833(8.10/3.162) = 1570 + 1.833(2.562) = 1574.70$. With 95% confidence, the accountant can assert that the population average distance will be less than 1574.70 kilometres. ■

| section 9.6 | # Confidence Intervals for the Binomial Parameter π |

The random variable x/n was introduced earlier as an estimator of π, the population parameter in a binomial distribution. This statistic is denoted by $p = (x/n)$ and is called the *sample proportion*. It can be used to determine confidence intervals for population proportions in applications involving the binomial distribution, such as the proportion of people in a given population who smoke cigarettes, the proportion of voters favouring a certain candidate, or the proportion of defective items resulting from a given production process.

Using the Binomial Distribution

To estimate the population proportion π, we select the best point estimate, the sample proportion $p = x/n$, where x is the number of successes in n sample trials. We choose the sample proportion p as the likely value for π on which to base the sampling distribution for the number of successes x. According to the binomial distribution formula, the probability of any value of x depends only on the values of π and n. With the probabilities for x calculable, we can easily ascertain the upper and lower limits on x between which $(1 - \alpha)$ of the probability occurs. We simply select as the lower value the largest number of successes for which the cumulative probability remains less than $\alpha/2$. The upper value is the smallest number of successes for which the combined probability of exceeding it is less than $\alpha/2$.

Having determined upper and lower values for the number of successes, we can convert these values to upper and lower limits on the proportion of successes by dividing by n. These upper and lower limits can be used as the endpoints of a $100(1 - \alpha)\%$ confidence interval on π.

☐ **EXAMPLE 9.7**   A set of 36 travel vouchers are randomly selected by an auditor to check their validity compared to company travel policies. Nine are found to be incorrect in terms of including or excluding allowable items or exceeding restrictive limits. Based on this sample, a 98% confidence interval could be determined for the true proportion of vouchers which are incorrect.

The sample proportion, $(9/36) = 0.25$, is the most likely value for the true proportion, so the binomial distribution can be used with $n = 36$ and the likely value of $\pi = 0.25$ as the parameters. If this distribution is not readily available in a table, it could be generated by repeated calculations on a personal computer using this binomial formula:

$$P(\text{success}) = P(x) = {}_{36}C_x(0.25)^x(0.75)^{36-x}$$

The results are given in Table 9.3.

TABLE 9.3   Binomial Probability for $n = 36$ and $\pi = 0.25$

Number of Successes	$P(x)$	Number of Successes	$P(x)$
0	0.0001	11	0.1078
1	0.0004	12	0.0749
2	0.0022	13	0.0461
3	0.0084	14	0.0252
4	0.0231	15	0.0123
5	0.0493	16	0.0054
6	0.0849	17	0.0021
7	0.1213	18	0.0007
8	0.1466	19	0.0002
9	0.1520	20	0.0001
10	0.1368	over 20	0.0001

For a 98% confidence interval, we wish to exclude the upper- and lower-most values that are associated with a probability of no more than 0.01. At the low end, the combined probability for numbers of successes, 0, 1, and 2, is 0.0027. If $P(\text{three successes})$ is added to this, the combined probability exceeds 0.01. Thus, we exclude 0, 1, and 2. At the upper end, values 16 through 36 are excluded as they have a combined probability of 0.0086 which is less than 0.01. But, if 15 successes is added in, the probability exceeds 0.01. Thus, we exclude values of x greater than 15. For this binomial distribution, a total probability of at least 0.98 is assured when $x = 3, 4, \ldots, 15$.

To form a 98% confidence interval on π, we convert from the interval for the number of successes, $3 \leq x \leq 15$, to the corresponding interval on proportions, $3/36 \leq \pi \leq 15/36$. The confidence interval on the proportion of incorrect travel vouchers is $0.0833 \leq \pi \leq 0.4167$. The true proportion incorrect would lie within 98 percent of the intervals which could be calculated this way, based on 36 sample items. ∎

Using the Normal Approximation

Recall from Chapter 6 that when n is large, the number of successes in n independent Bernoulli trials is approximately normally distributed. Thus, we approximate the number of successes, x, by using the standardized normal variable $z = (x - n\pi)/\sqrt{n\pi(1 - \pi)}$, where $n\pi = E[x]$ and $n\pi(1 - \pi) = V[x]$. Now, if the *number* of successes, x, is normal, the *proportion* of successes in n trials, $p = x/n$, must also be normally distributed. Hence, at this point we want to show how the standardized variable z can be used to approximate the *proportion* of successes in n trials in precisely the same manner in which it approximates the *number* of successes.

First, recall that our best estimator of the population proportion π is p, since this estimator has already been shown to be unbiased; that is, $E[p] = \pi$. We also have shown that the variance of p is as follows:

$$V[p] = \frac{\pi(1 - \pi)}{n}$$

Unfortunately, we cannot use this variance to construct a confidence interval because the variance depends on the unknown parameter, π, which we are trying to estimate. The next best thing we can do is to use p, our point estimate of π, in place of π and $(1 - p)$ in place of $(1 - \pi)$. Thus, our estimate of the variance is as follows:

Estimated variance of the proportion of successes:

$$\frac{p(1 - p)}{n} \tag{9.3}$$

An approximately normal standardized variable is now obtained by taking the normal variable (p in this case), subtracting its mean ($E[p] = \pi$) and dividing the result by its estimated standard deviation, which is the square root of the ratio in Formula 9.3. The approximate z-variable (approximated because an estimated standard deviation was used) is:

Approximately normal standardized variable:

$$z = \frac{p - \pi}{\sqrt{\dfrac{p(1 - p)}{n}}} \tag{9.4}$$

Formula 9.4 can now be used to construct a confidence interval in much the same fashion in which the confidence interval for μ was constructed in Section 9.4.[4] When using the confidence interval below, the reader should remember that we are approximating the binomial distribution by using the normal distribution; hence, it is necessary for n to be reasonably *large*. How large n needs to be depends on how close π is to $\frac{1}{2}$. Shortly, we will suggest a procedure for determining whether or not n is large enough that such an approximation will be reasonable.

$100(1 - \alpha)\%$ confidence interval for π:

$$p - z_{\alpha/2}\sqrt{\frac{p(1-p)}{n}} \leq \pi \leq p + z_{\alpha/2}\sqrt{\frac{p(1-p)}{n}} \tag{9.5}$$

☐ **EXAMPLE 9.8**   To plan for fringe benefit costs in a large company with many offices across Canada, an auditor wishes to estimate the proportion of employees with two or more dependents. A random sample of $n = 144$ employees shows that $x = 48$ have two or more dependents. Thus, the best point estimate for the population proportion is the following sample proportion:

$$p = \frac{48}{144} = \frac{1}{3}$$

Our best estimate of the population standard deviation is thus:

$$\sqrt{\frac{p(1-p)}{n}} = \sqrt{\frac{(1/3)(2/3)}{144}} = 0.0393$$

We will now use these values and Formula 9.5 to construct a 95% confidence interval for π. Remember, $z_{\alpha/2} = 1.96$ for $\alpha/2 = 0.025$:

$$\tfrac{1}{3} - 1.96(0.0393) \leq \pi \leq \tfrac{1}{3} + 1.96(0.0393)$$
$$0.333 - 0.077 \leq \pi \leq 0.333 + 0.077$$
$$0.256 \leq \pi \leq 0.410$$

Thus, we have 95% confidence that the interval [0.256 to 0.410] covers the population proportion of employees that have two or more dependents. We can state that 95% of all such intervals that could be calculated using this procedure (on the basis of repeated samples of size 144) would include the true value of π. ■

---

[4] First, form a $100(1 - \alpha)\%$ confidence interval for $p - \pi$:

$$-z_{\alpha/2}\sqrt{\frac{p(1-p)}{n}} \leq p - \pi \leq z_{\alpha/2}\sqrt{\frac{p(1-p)}{n}}$$

Solving this expression for π yields the $100(1 - \alpha)\%$ confidence interval in Formula 9.5.

In some applications, especially in product control, a confidence interval for π can be used to find the confidence interval for the *number* of defectives in a given, very large shipping lot.

☐ **EXAMPLE 9.9**   Consider the problem of a manufacturer who produces ballpoint pen cartridges. Each shipment includes 10,000 cartridges. The producer desires some control over these shipments, in order to ensure that no shipment will contain an excessive number of defective cartridges. A random sample of 400 cartridges is inspected from a shipping lot of 10,000, and nine defectives ($x = 9$) are found. On the basis of this result, we wish to obtain a 90% confidence interval for the number of defectives in the entire shipment. The random variable x, where x = number of defectives, can be approximated by the normal distribution; hence, a 90% confidence interval for the proportion of defectives is obtained by using Formula 9.5. In this case, $n = 400$ and $x = 9$, so $p = 9/400 = 0.0225$. Since $\alpha = 0.10$, $\pm z_{\alpha/2} = \pm z_{0.05} = \pm 1.645$, and the appropriate confidence interval is:

$$0.0225 - 1.645\sqrt{\frac{(0.0225)(0.9775)}{400}} \leq \pi \leq 0.0225 + 1.645\sqrt{\frac{(0.0225)(0.9775)}{400}}$$

$$0.0225 - 1.645(0.0074) \leq \pi \leq 0.0225 + 1.645(0.0074)$$

$$0.0103 \leq \pi \leq 0.0347$$

Thus, the producer may estimate that the population is likely to contain between 1.03% and 3.47% defectives. More precisely, it is expected that in 90% of such repetitions of this process, the true value of π will lie within the interval calculated.

Since the α used in constructing this confidence interval is rather large, we must assume that the producer will be satisfied with an interval that is correct *only* 90% of the time. If this production process involved \$400 stereo speakers rather than 40¢ ballpoint pen cartridges, then a smaller α-level might be used because errors would be more costly.   ■

In Example 9.9, sampling is from a finite population without replacement, which means that the hypergeometric distribution has to be used to give the theoretically correct probability values. However, the population size is so large ($N = 10,000$) in relation to the sample size ($n = 400$) that any inaccuracy resulting from the use of the binomial distribution is negligible. Of course, in the above calculations we used the normal distribution to approximate the binomial. To check whether this approximation is reasonable, let us recall from Section 6.6 the suggestion that when $n\pi(1 - \pi) > 3$, the approximation of the binomial by the normal should be fairly accurate. For this problem we do not know the exact value of π, but we have a likely value for its *lower* bound, namely, $\pi = 0.0103$ (from the confidence interval). Substituting this value of π into $n\pi(1 - \pi)$ we obtain[5]

$$(400)(0.0103)(0.9897) = 4.08.$$

Since this product is greater than 3, we can consider the approximation acceptable; a larger sample is necessary if greater precision is desired.

---

[5] Using the upper bound for π would make $n\pi(1 - \pi)$ even greater. In such cases, always substitute the most extreme value for π, closest to one or to zero, to check the size of $n\pi(1 - \pi)$.

To expand on our solution to this cartridge-inspection problem, let us assume that the decision-maker would like to convert the 90% confidence interval from an interval involving proportions to one involving the *number* of defectives in the shipment of size 10,000. This is done by reversing the process we used in the first part of this section and in Example 9.7.

If π is the proportion of defectives in the lot of size 10,000, then the number of defectives is $n\pi = 10,000\pi$. Using the upper and lower limits for π, we conclude, with 90% confidence, that the number of defectives in the shipment is between $10,000(0.0103) = 103$ and $10,000(0.0347) = 347$. If the producer thinks that these are tolerable values, then the lot can be released for shipment. Much has been saved in inspection costs and some quality control has been maintained over the shipment.

Realistically, the producer will be satisfied if the true number of defectives is less than the *lower* bound of 103 and disappointed only if the true number exceeds 347. In terms of a *one-sided confidence interval*, the producer may have 95% confidence that the interval [0 to 347] will include the true number of defectives. As discussed prior to, and in Example 9.6, such one-sided intervals are often used, in preference to the two-sided confidence intervals, in similar situations for which the error in one of the directions is unimportant.

☐ **STUDY QUESTION 9.4**   **Proportion of Defective Lenses**

A firm that grinds lenses for eyeglasses wishes to estimate the proportion of lenses that are defective. Over a period of six weeks, a random sample of 196 lenses indicates 49 that are defective. Using the approximating normal distribution, find a 98% confidence interval for the true proportion of defective lenses for the population.

● **ANSWER**   The sample proportion is $p = 49/196 = 0.25$. We first need to check for the applicability of the normal distribution. We find $np(1 - p) = 196(0.25)(0.75) = 36.75$. Since this value is larger than 3, we use Formula 9.5 with $z_{0.01} = 2.326$ from Table III. The upper and lower confidence limits are:

$$p \pm z_{0.01}\sqrt{\frac{p(1 - p)}{n}} = 0.25 \pm 2.326\sqrt{\frac{(0.25)(0.75)}{196}}$$

$$= 0.25 \pm 2.326(0.031)$$

which gives 0.178 and 0.322. We have 98% confidence that the interval [17.8% to 32.2%] includes the true percentage of defective lenses.   ■

The applicability of the normal distribution should be *rechecked* by using 0.178, the lower confidence limit for π. The value of $np(1 - p) = 196(0.178)(0.822) = 28.68$. Because 28.68 exceeds 3.0, the normal approximation is acceptable in place of the exact binomial distribution.

| section 9.7 | # Determining the Size of the Sample (n) |

Thus far, we have calculated the width of each confidence interval based on the assumption that the sample size, n, is known. In many practical situations, however, the decision-maker does not know what sample size is optimal. In this situation, it is possible for the decision-maker to calculate the optimal sample size, provided that the following two questions can be answered:

1. What level of confidence is desired? In other words, what is the desired value for $100(1 - \alpha)$?
2. What is the *maximum* difference (labelled D) allowed between the point estimate of the population parameter and the true value of the population parameter?

D is the largest allowable *sampling error* between the estimated and the true values of the population parameter

---

We will investigate the process of determining the optimal sample size for two different situations, estimating a mean μ and estimating a proportion π.

Statistical Inference in Relation to μ

Population Normal, σ Known. First, we consider the problem of determining n when the decision-maker wants a $100(1 - \alpha)\%$ confidence interval for μ, given that the parent population has a normal distribution with a known standard deviation. In this case, we know that the variable

$$z = \frac{\bar{x} - \mu}{\sigma / \sqrt{n}}$$

is $N(0, 1)$. Now, if the required level of confidence is $1 - \alpha$, then the above equation results in the following $100(1 - \alpha)\%$ interval for $\bar{x} - \mu$:

$$-z_{\alpha/2} \frac{\sigma}{\sqrt{n}} \leq (\bar{x} - \mu) \leq z_{\alpha/2} \frac{\sigma}{\sqrt{n}}$$

Since the normal distribution is symmetric, we can concentrate on the right-hand inequality, $(\bar{x} - \mu) \leq z_{\alpha/2}(\sigma/\sqrt{n})$. This inequality means that the largest value $\bar{x} - \mu$ can assume is $z_{\alpha/2}(\sigma/\sqrt{n})$. But we also know that our decision-maker says that the largest sampling error allowed for $\bar{x} - \mu$ is some amount D. This maximum allowable error D can be on either side of the true mean. Thus, we set

$$D = |\bar{x} - \mu| = z_{\alpha/2} \frac{\sigma}{\sqrt{n}}$$

Solving this relationship for n, we obtain the value of n that will ensure with $100(1 - \alpha)\%$ confidence that $|\bar{x} - \mu|$ will be no larger than D.

Minimum required sample size in estimating the mean:

$$n = \frac{z_{\alpha/2}{}^2 \sigma^2}{D^2} \tag{9.6}$$

□ **EXAMPLE 9.10**   We return to the freight car case of Example 9.3. Suppose that we want to find a 95% confidence interval for the mean number of cars such that our sample estimate ($\bar{x}$) and the population mean (μ) differ, either high or low, by no more than five cars; that is,

$$|\bar{x} - \mu| \leq D = 5.$$

If we assume, as before, that the parent population is normal and that $\sigma = 15$, how large must n be to satisfy these conditions?

From Table III, $z_{\alpha/2} = 1.96$ when $\alpha/2 = 0.025$. Substituting this value and $D = 5$, $\sigma = 15$ into Formula 9.6, we find the appropriate value for n:

$$n = \frac{(1.96)^2 (15)^2}{(5)^2} = 34.57$$

We always round *up* in this type of problem to ensure that the sample size is large enough; hence, a random sample of at least 35 trains is needed to ensure that 95% of the time the value of $\bar{x}$ will be within 5 cars of the true population mean, μ. ■

Population Not Normal, σ Known If the population is not assumed to be normal but the standard deviation is known, the above method can be used to determine the minimum sample size necessary to satisfy the conditions of confidence and accuracy. By the central limit theorem, we know that the distribution of sample means approaches the normal distribution as the sample size increases. Thus, once the necessary sample size is obtained, we can check to see if that size n exceeds 30; and if it does, we may be confident that our method of solution was appropriate.

Population Normal, σ Unknown If the population is normal but the standard deviation is unknown, then the appropriate statistic to use is the t variable, $t = (\bar{x} - \mu)/(s/\sqrt{n})$. Again, the maximum sampling error allowed, $|\bar{x} - \mu| = D$, is specified by the decision-maker. In this case, we are stuck for a value of s, since s must be calculated from a sample, and we have not taken a sample yet (the whole purpose is to decide what sample size to take). To make matters even worse, the appropriate t-value to use in calculating a $100(1 - \alpha)\%$ confidence interval is $t_{\alpha/2, \nu}$, where ν depends on the unknown sample size. To make a long story short, the solution for n in this case is not a direct process. The interval can be found by a succession of iterative steps, using sequential sampling, but we will not present this method here.

Statistical Inference in Relation to π

The size of the sample needed to find a desired confidence interval for the binomial parameter π can be determined if the maximum allowable difference between p and π is specified as $D = |p - \pi|$. Two approaches are possible: one using the binomial distribution defined by the sampling process, and one using a normal approximation to this underlying binomial distribution.

To use the binomial distribution directly, one must have extensive tables of the distribution or have a personal computer on which repeated calculations can be performed. A repetitive process, like a *trial and error* method, is used to find the minimum required sample size.

Given a maximum allowable positive error of $D = p - \pi$ in terms of proportions, the process involves increasing the sample size n until $100(1 - \alpha)\%$ of the probability mass function lies within the interval $\pi \pm D$. In our first try, we use a trial value (called a planning value) of $\pi = 0.5$ which gives a symmetric binomial distribution. In the next section, we will discuss why this is the most conservative value to select since, if we succeed in finding a minimum required sample size using this distribution, we will surely have a sufficient size sample for any other binomial distribution defined by a different value of π.

Now, if we are given a desired level of confidence, say 90%, and the desired maximum allowable error, say $D = p - \pi = 0.08$, we may begin calculations. We can select any sample size, say $n = 50$. We first find the maximum allowable error in terms of the number of successes x as $Dn = (0.08)(50) = 4$. Then, we find the combined probability of the events that x successes occur where x is within four units of the expected number of successes, $E[x] = n\pi = 50(0.5) = 25$. That is, we find $\Sigma P(x)$ for $21 \leq x \leq 29$. Using Table 1 in Appendix C or using a personal computer, we find this sum to be as follows:

$$2(0.0598 + 0.0788 + 0.0960 + 0.1080) + 0.1123 = 0.7975$$

This is less than 0.90 for the probability interval that underlies the desired 90% confidence interval. Thus, a larger sample size is needed.

Suppose we try $n = 100$. For $D = 0.08$, the maximum allowable error would be $100(0.08) = 8$. The expected number of successes, again assuming a planning value of $\pi = 0.5$, is $100(0.5) = 50$. We need to calculate the combined probability, $\Sigma P(x)$ for $42 \leq x \leq 58$, which are all those values within eight units of the expected value of x. The sum of the probabilities for these 17 events is 0.9116. This exceeds the desired value of 0.90, so a sample size of 100 is sufficient to obtain a 90% confidence interval on π with a maximum allowable error of 0.08.

Is 100 the minimum sample size that will work? We know that $n = 50$ was too small, and that $n = 100$ is large enough. We would need to try some more sample sizes, say 90 and 95, to refine our possibility set. If 90 were too small and 95 were found to be sufficiently large, we would continue the process with a smaller grid for our search, such as $n = 91, 92, 93,$ and 94. As soon as we found the threshold where the probability exceeds 0.90 of the combined event, number of successes within the desired interval of the expected number of successes, we would have the required minimum sample size.

Changing the planning value Note that if there is any information about the likely value of π, a value different from the planning value of 0.5 could be used. The further away from 0.5 that the likely value is, closer to zero or to one, the smaller the required sample size that would be needed.

For example, if $n = 50$ and $D = 0.08$ as in the first case above, but we think $\pi = 0.10$, we would want to calculate the probabilities of events where $x = 1, 2, \ldots, 9$. These values are those within $(0.08)(50) = 4$ units of the expected value, $E[x] = 50(0.10) = 5$. The sum of these probabilities is 0.9702. For this situation with a planning value of $\pi = 0.10$, a sample size of 50 would be more than sufficient to provide a 90% confidence interval. We should try calculations for $n = 40$ or $n = 30$ and refine the search grid until the solution for n is completed.

Using the normal distribution The second approach takes only one primary step, although it involves an approximating normal distribution rather than the exact binomial distribution. From Formula 9.4, we know that an approximate z-variable involving $p - \pi$ is as follows:

$$z = \frac{p - \pi}{\sqrt{\dfrac{p(1 - p)}{n}}}$$

As in the case with the mean, we can solve this statistic for the unknown value of sample size as follows:

$$z = \frac{(p - \pi)\sqrt{n}}{\sqrt{p(1 - p)}} \quad \text{so} \quad \frac{z\sqrt{p(1 - p)}}{(p - \pi)} = \sqrt{n}$$

By substituting the given value for the maximum allowable difference and choosing the positive cutoff value ($z_{\alpha/2}$) for a $100(1 - \alpha)\%$ confidence interval, we obtain the formula for determining the minimum required sampling size:

Minimum required sample size in estimating a proportion:

$$n = \frac{z_{\alpha/2}^2 \, p(1 - p)}{D^2} \qquad (9.7)$$

Thus, we can find n when we know:

1. $p - \pi$, given by the allowable sampling error D
2. The z-value, determined from Table III for a given $(\alpha/2)$ depending on the level of confidence
3. $p(1 - p)$, based on our best guess (p) of a planning value for the unknown proportion.

     This last point needs careful consideration. Since we are trying to determine what size sample to take, we obviously have not yet taken a sample or calculated a sample proportion, $p = (x/n)$. We may have some prior information, however, on the possible range of values that would be reasonable for p (or π).

Among the set of values for p that might reasonably be considered, the planning value to use is the one value in this set that is closest to $\frac{1}{2}$. When no prior information about p or π is available, the planning value chosen is exactly $p = 1/2$.

The value closest to $\frac{1}{2}$ is chosen because $\frac{1}{2}$ is the proportion between 0 and 1 that maximizes the product, $p(1 - p)$.[†] Hence, this maximum value of $p(1 - p)$ will give a value of n from Formula 9.7 that is at least as large as needed. By using the planning value of $\frac{1}{2}$, we probably obtain a larger sample size n than is necessary to obtain the desired levels of accuracy (D) and confidence ($1 - \alpha$).

◻ **EXAMPLE 9.11**   Returning to Example 9.8, in which an auditor estimated the proportion of employees with two or more dependents, suppose we wish to estimate 100π within plus or minus three percentage points with 95% confidence. What size sample would be needed?

     We know that $z_{\alpha/2} = 1.96$ (since $\alpha = 0.05$) and $D = 0.03$ (since we desire accuracy within three percentage points). Without having any prior planning value for p, we choose $p = \frac{1}{2}$. Using Formula 9.7, we obtain:

$$n = \frac{(1.96)^2 \left(\frac{1}{2}\right)\left(\frac{1}{2}\right)}{(0.03)^2} = \frac{(1.96)^2 \left(\frac{1}{4}\right)}{(0.03)^2} = 1067.1$$

We may conclude that in estimating the desired proportion π, a sample of 1068 employees is needed in order to ensure that a sampling error exceeding 0.03 will not occur more than 5% of the time. See Figure 9.8.

[†] You may try several values of p, $\{\frac{1}{2}, \frac{1}{3}, \frac{1}{5}, \frac{1}{10}\}$, to convince yourself or use calculus as in Exercise 9.55.

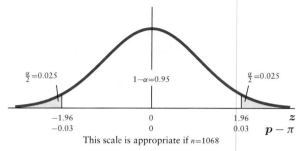

FIGURE 9.8   Approximate probability distribution for Example 9.11

Since a normal approximation was used in this binomial problem, we should now check the necessary condition for its applicability, $np(1 - p) > 3$. If the sample size used is $n = 1068$, this condition will hold even for very small values of p, such as 0.01, since $1068(0.01)(0.99) = 10.6 > 3$. The use of the normal approximation is acceptable. ◼

☐ **EXAMPLE 9.12**   A survey firm reports that 87 percent of the families in Vancouver travel outside the city at least once a year.

We recognize that the value of 87% is simply a *point estimate*. We do not know how accurate this is or what level of confidence we can have in the published statement. Suppose we wish to repeat the survey and be able to have 98% confidence that the proportion estimated will be within plus or minus 0.03 of the true proportion for the population of all families in Vancouver. How large a random sample would we have to take?

For 98% confidence, the value of $(\alpha/2)$ is 0.01. From Table III, the z-value excluding this area in the tail of the normal distribution is $z = 2.326$. The allowable difference (sampling error) is $D = (p - \pi) = \pm0.03$. We can use Formula 9.7 if we substitute a planning value for p. Given the prior information that one point estimate is $p = 0.87$, we can make a reasonable guess that the proportion will be between 0.80 and 0.99. Thus, let us use the feasible value closest to $\frac{1}{2}$ as our planning value. We choose $p = 0.80$; thus, $(1 - p) = 0.20$. This planning value of 0.80 will result in a smaller sample size than if we choose the maximizing value of $p = (1 - p) = \frac{1}{2}$ (as if we had no prior information). The minimum sample size required is:

$$n = \frac{(2.326)^2(0.80)(0.20)}{(0.03)^2}$$

$$= 961.8.$$

We need survey responses from 966 families in this population. Since we used a normal approximation to the binomial distribution, we should check the necessary condition for its applicability, $np(1 - p) > 3$. Using $n = 966, p = 0.80$, and $(1 - p) = 0.20$, we have:

$$966(0.80)(0.20) = 153.9 > 3$$

The use of the normal approximation is quite acceptable. ◼

☐ **STUDY QUESTION 9.5**   Average Commuting Distance

MARTA (Metropolitan Atlanta Rapid Transit Authority) wishes to estimate the *average* number of kilometres that commuters live from their place of work. The population standard deviation is thought to be 3.5 kilometres based on a survey of commuters by Metro in Toronto which is considered comparable. How large a sample of commuters is needed if 95% confidence is desired that the sample mean will be within plus or minus $\frac{1}{2}$ kilometre of the population mean?

● **ANSWER**   Since $\alpha = 0.05$, we use $z_{0.025} = 1.96$ in Formula 9.6 with $\sigma = 3.5$ and $D = |\bar{x} - \mu| = 0.5$:

$$n = \frac{(1.96)^2 (3.5)^2}{(0.5)^2} = 188.24$$

The minimum sample size should be 189 commuters.   ■

☐ **STUDY QUESTION 9.6**   Percentage of Public Transit Commuters

MARTA desires to estimate, with 99% confidence, the *percentage* of commuters who regularly use public transit. They want the estimate to be within plus or minus four percentage points of the true percentage. What size sample should be taken?

● **ANSWER**   We solve this problem in terms of proportions rather than percentages. Since 90% confidence is desired, $(\alpha/2) = 0.05$; the proper z-value is $z_{0.05} = 1.645$. Formula 9.7 is used with $D = |p - \pi| = 0.04$. A planning value might be used instead of $p = \frac{1}{2}$, since a reasonable guess is that the proportion of commuters using MARTA is surely less than $\frac{1}{3}$. If we arbitrarily select $p = 0.34$ and $(1 - p) = 0.66$, the minimum sample size required is:

$$n = \frac{(1.645)^2 (0.34)(0.66)}{(0.04)^2}$$

$$= 379.52$$

MARTA should survey at least 380 commuters.   ■

section 9.8

Confidence Interval for σ^2[†]

Under some circumstances it may be desirable to construct a confidence interval for an estimate of an unknown population variance.[†] The telephone company is often interested in the *variability* of the length of telephone conversations, and a contractor purchasing steel girders may be interested in the *variance* of their tensile strengths. Or a government economist may be just as concerned about the *variability* of the amount of taxes paid by individuals as about the average tax paid, because the income-redistribution effect of taxation is very important. In such cases, it is important to establish limits on just how large or small σ^2 might be. A confidence interval for the population variance is desired.

---

† This section may be omitted without loss in continuity. It assumes the reader has covered Section 7.9.

To construct a $100(1-\alpha)\%$ confidence interval for σ^2 when sampling from a *normal* population, recall from Section 7.9 that the variable $(n-1)s^2/\sigma^2$ has a chi-square distribution with $\nu = (n-1)$ degrees of freedom. Since the values of χ^2 are always positive and the chi-square distribution is not symmetrical, we will *not* be able to use plus and minus values such as $\pm\chi^2_{\alpha/2,\nu}$ as we did with the z or the t-distributions. We will need to look up both upper and lower values for the cumulative chi-square distribution, $F(\chi^2)$ as given in Table VII. The value of χ^2 in the left half of the table such that $F(\chi^2) = \alpha/2$ gives the *lower* (left-hand side) cutoff value. The value of χ^2 from the right half of the table such that $F(\chi^2) = 1 - (\alpha/2)$ gives the *upper* cutoff value for the confidence interval. From Table VII, using $\nu = 9$ and $\alpha = 0.05$, we find the following:

$$\chi^2_{\text{upper}} = 19.0 \text{ for } \alpha/2 = 0.025$$

$$\chi^2_{\text{lower}} = 2.70 \text{ for } F(\chi^2) = 0.025$$

The area of the chi-square distribution lying between these two values must include $(0.975 - 0.025) = 0.95$ of the total area. As shown in Figure 9.9, these values give us a 95% probability interval for a chi-square distributed random variable. Using this interval and substituting the particular chi-square variable $\chi^2 = (n-1)s^2/\sigma^2$, we obtain the following probability interval:

$$P\left[\chi^2_{\text{lower}} \leq \frac{(n-1)s^2}{\sigma^2} \leq \chi^2_{\text{upper}}\right] = 1 - \alpha$$

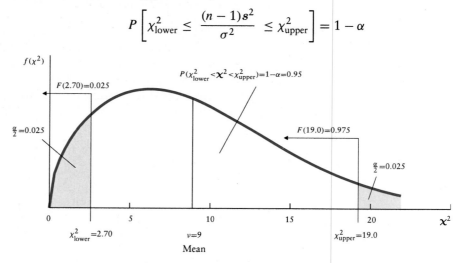

FIGURE 9.9 The values of χ^2 cutting off a total area of $\alpha = 0.05$ from the chi-square distribution with $\nu = 9$, leaving an interval including 95% of the probability in the middle

Again, solving these inequalities for the unknown parameter σ^2, we obtain:[6]

$100(1-\alpha)$ percent confidence interval for σ^2, parent population normal:

$$\frac{(n-1)s^2}{\chi^2_{\text{upper}}} \leq \sigma^2 \leq \frac{(n-1)s^2}{\chi^2_{\text{lower}}} \tag{9.8}$$

[6] In this solution, reciprocals of each term are taken to place σ^2 in the numerator. This changes the sense (direction) of the inequalities.

Note that the upper value of χ^2 now appears in the denominator of the *smaller* endpoint for σ^2, while the lower value of χ^2 is in the denominator of the term giving the *larger* endpoint for σ^2.

☐ **EXAMPLE 9.13** Consider again the sample distances of trips for the produce trucks given in Example 9.5. An auditor is interested in estimating the variance of the population, using the same sample of size $n = 10$ reported in Table 9.2. The best point estimate of σ^2 is s^2, which is computed for this sample to be $s^2 = \left(\frac{1}{9}\right)590 = 65.56$. To achieve an interval estimate for σ^2 with a known level of confidence and a known risk of error, let us compute a 95% confidence interval for σ^2. The values of χ^2 needed here are exactly those used in Figure 9.9, since $v = 9$ and $\alpha = 0.05$. Thus, we substitute the values $\chi^2_{\text{lower}} = 2.70$ and $\chi^2_{\text{upper}} = 19.0$ into Formula 9.8, along with $n = 10$ and $s^2 = 65.56$. This gives the following values:

$$\frac{9(65.56)}{19.0} \leq \sigma^2 \leq \frac{9(65.56)}{2.70}$$
$$31.05 \leq \sigma^2 \leq 218.53$$

The 95% confidence limits on the population variance are 31.05 and 218.53 kilometres squared.

For interpretation, we frequently convert the confidence interval for the variance into one for the standard deviation since we desire a statement in terms of the original units (kilometres in this case). By taking square roots, we calculate 95% confidence limits on the standard deviation (σ) of 5.57 and 14.78 kilometres. Note that this interval is *not symmetric* around the point estimate of $s = 8.10$, since the chi-square distribution is not symmetric. ■

☐ **STUDY QUESTION 9.7** Variance of the Age of Bank Presidents

Determine a 98% confidence interval for the variance of the distribution of ages of bank presidents based on the sample information, $n = 20$ and $s = 8$ years, as given in Study Question 9.3.

● **ANSWER** Since $n = 20$, the degrees of freedom are 19 for the random variable $\chi^2 = (n-1)s^2/\sigma^2$. Since $\alpha = 0.02$, the lower value of χ^2 needed is one such that $F(\chi^2) = 0.01$, and the upper value needed is one such that $F(\chi^2) = 0.99$. From Table VII, these values are $\chi^2_{\text{lower}} = 7.63$ and $\chi^2_{\text{upper}} = 36.2$. Substituting into Formula 9.8 gives the following results in units of years squared:

$$\frac{(19)64}{36.2} \leq \sigma^2 \leq \frac{(19)64}{7.63}$$
$$33.59 \leq \sigma^2 \leq 159.37$$

To measure the limits in terms of years, we take the square root of each term to obtain ($5.8 \leq \sigma \leq 12.6$) years for the 95% confidence interval on the standard deviation of age of bank presidents. ■

section 9.9

Review

Listed in Table 9.4 are the important elements of using probability distributions to find confidence limits or to find the minimum sample size required in an estimation problem.

TABLE 9.4 Summary of Random Variables and Confidence Intervals for Statistical Inference

Unknown Parameter	Population Characteristics and Other Description	Section	Random Variable Involving the Best Sample Estimator	Formula for $100(1-\alpha)\%$ Confidence Interval	Reference Formula
Mean (μ)	Population $N(\mu, \sigma^2)$ or population unknown and $n > 30$; σ known	7.5 9.4	$z = \dfrac{(\bar{x} - \mu)}{\sigma/\sqrt{n}}$	$\bar{x} \pm z_{\alpha/2}(\sigma/\sqrt{n})$	(9.1)
Mean (μ)	Population $N(\mu, \sigma^2)$ σ unknown	7.8 9.5	$t_v = (\bar{x} - \mu)/(s/\sqrt{n})$ where $v = n - 1$	$\bar{x} \pm t_{\alpha/2}(s/\sqrt{n})$	(9.2)
Variance (σ^2)	Population $N(\mu, \sigma^2)$	7.9 9.8	$\chi_v^2 = \dfrac{(n-1)s^2}{\sigma^2}$ where $v = n - 1$	$\dfrac{(n-1)s^2}{\chi^2_{upper}} \leq \sigma^2$ $\leq \dfrac{(n-1)s^2}{\chi^2_{lower}}$	(9.8)
Proportion (π)	$x = $ number of successes in n repeated independent trials, $n\pi(1-\pi) > 3$, if normal approximation is used	6.6 9.6 9.7	$z = \dfrac{p - \pi}{\sqrt{\dfrac{\pi(1-\pi)}{n}}}$	$p \pm z_{\alpha/2}\sqrt{\dfrac{p(1-p)}{n}}$	(9.5)

PROBLEMS

♦ **9.19** A company has a large number of accounts. In order to do a timely audit of its books, a random sample of 9 accounts was chosen. The percentage errors

$$\left[100 \times (\text{book value} - \text{audited value})/\text{book value}\right]$$

of all these accounts were calculated by auditing these accounts completely. The resulting percentage values were: 5, 7, 4, 10, −1, 2, 3, 8, −2.

a) Find the best point estimate of μ, the mean percentage error of all accounts.

b) Construct a 90% confidence interval for μ, assuming a normal population. Interpret this interval.

9.20 Suppose that the following nine values represent random observations from a normal parent population of new car sales (daily) by a Ford dealer: 1, 5, 9, 8, 4, 0, 2, 4, 3. Construct a 99% confidence interval for the mean of the parent population.

9.21 A survey of 16 executives selected at random revealed that the average annual consumption of headache or pain pills per executive was 184, with a sample standard deviation of 20. Establish 90% confidence limits for the average annual per capita consumption of these pills for all executives, assuming that the population is normal.

9.22 Twenty-five small loan applications in a bank were randomly selected in an audit for the purpose of determining the average dollar amount requested for each loan. Construct a 95% confidence interval for μ, assuming that the sample mean was $\bar{x} = \$9000$ and the sample standard deviation was $1500. The population is normally distributed.

9.23 Repeat Problem 9.12(b), but this time assume that the population variance is unknown. How much does the confidence interval change? Explain.

9.24 Repeat Problem 9.13(b), assuming that the population variance is unknown. Explain why the confidence interval changes.

♦ **9.25** A magazine subscription agency, specifically dealing with college students, is interested in estimating the average number of subscriptions held by each student. Denoting x as the number of subscriptions held by a student, a random sample of 900 students was selected and it was found that

$$\Sigma x = 1600 \quad \text{and} \quad \Sigma(x - \bar{x})^2 = 3679.18.$$

a) Find a point estimate for the average number of subscriptions held per student.

b) Suppose the agency wishes to be 99% confident that it obtains an interval that contains μ. Obtain such an interval from the given sample results. What is the margin of error with this interval?

c) How can we decrease the width of the confidence interval without gathering additional information? Explain.

◆ **9.26** In a study undertaken to determine the average amount of time taken to assemble a 16-speed bike, a random sample of 12 assemblies gave $\bar{x} = 54.5$ minutes with $s = 8.3$ minutes.

a) Assuming that the assembly times follow a normal distribution, determine a 99% confidence interval for the mean assembly time.

b) Suppose the population standard deviation was known to be exactly 8.3 minutes. How would the answer to part (a) change?

c) Which of the two intervals is narrower and why?

9.27 A survey of 900 *Wall Street Journal* subscribers indicates that 40% finished college. Set 99% confidence limits on the true proportion of all subscribers with this background.

9.28 In order to estimate the percent of all households using a certain detergent, 196 homes were randomly selected. If 108 of these homes use this product, what would be a 99% confidence interval for the percent of this population of households that uses the detergent?

9.29 An electronics manufacturer would like to know what proportion of television set owners have a VCR. In a sample of 100 randomly selected owners, 60% were found to own a VCR. Construct a 95% confidence interval for the population proportion of television owners who have a VCR. First use the binomial table, then repeat using a normal approximation.

9.30 The total particle removal (TPR) in a certain cigarette filter can be measured on a smoking machine, using a sample of these cigarettes. The standard deviation for TPR for the population of such cigarettes is 2 mg. What size sample is necessary to estimate, with 90% confidence, the average TPR for all such cigarettes, within plus or minus 0.4 mg?

9.31 A population of families has an unknown mean income μ; the standard deviation of these incomes is known to be $1000. How large a random sample would be needed to determine the mean income if it is desired that the probability of a sampling error of more than $50 be less than 0.05?

◆ **9.32** A market research firm is interested in estimating the average annual expenditure, per $1000 of sales, on research and development in the pharmaceutical industry. In a pilot study, a random sample of nine drug firms was chosen. The mean annual expenditure per $1000 of sales was found to be $40 with a standard deviation of $20. Assume that the distribution of annual research and development expenditures across different firms in the industry is normally distributed.

a) On the basis of the pilot study, determine a 95% confidence interval for μ, the actual mean annual expenditure on research and development per $1000 sales.

b) The marketing firm wants its results to be accurate within $5 with 95% confidence. How large a sample size does the firm need to take?

◆ **9.33** You are required to estimate the average annual income of a family in a large industrial township around Nackawic, New Brunswick. The annual incomes follow a normal distribution with $\sigma = \$3000$.

a) Suppose the random sample of 25 observations yielded $\bar{x} = \$29,000$. Construct the 95% confidence interval.

b) Indicate what would happen to the width of the interval (increase, decrease, or remain unchanged), with reference to the one obtained above, under each of these four independent changed scenarios.
i) σ is actually $2500 and not $3000.
ii) The confidence level is changed from 95% to 90%.
iii) The sample size is changed from 25 to 30.
iv) The sample mean was incorrectly calculated.

9.34 Suppose you are a government purchasing agent and you contract with Batpower Company to buy 10,000 batteries according to specifications in the contract. You check 300 batteries and find 42 defective. Use Formula 9.5 to construct a 99% confidence interval on the population proportion of defectives. Is your confidence interval compatible with a 10% defective rate for the entire lot of 10,000?

9.35 A supermarket manager wishes to make a sample estimate of the average time a customer spends at the checkout register. It is known from past experience that the standard deviation is $2\frac{1}{2}$ minutes, and the manager would like to estimate the mean checkout time within plus-or-minus $\frac{1}{2}$ minute. If a 99% confidence level is specified, what is the required sample size to obtain this estimate?

9.36 You wish to estimate the proportion of defectives in a large production lot within plus or minus 0.05 of the true proportion, with 90% confidence. From past experience, it is believed that the proportion of defectives is about $\pi = 0.12$. How large a sample must be used?

9.37 Suppose that the annual earnings of college graduates in their first year job are normally distributed, with $\sigma = \$6,000$.

a) Based on a sample of $n = 16$ with $\bar{x} = \$34,000$, find a 98% confidence interval for μ.

b) How many graduates will you need to sample in order to have 98% confidence that the sample mean to be calculated will be within 600 dollars of the true mean?

9.38 Refer to **Data Set 7** for the designation of risk class for a sample of 48 mutual funds. Suppose two more sample funds are selected (for a total of 50) which have risk class of 3 and 5 respectively. Using Table I for the binomial distribution, find a 90% confidence interval on the proportion of mutual funds that are in risk category 5.

9.39 Use **Data Set 6** to estimate with 99% confidence the proportion of the head of households who live alone (NUMINHSE = 1) in the population of persons over age 54.

9.40 Use **Data Set 6** to estimate with 95% confidence the proportion of the head of households who are female in the population of persons over age 54.

9.41 Use **Data Set 4** to estimate with 90% confidence the proportion of doctors with net income exceeding $120,000.

9.42 Refer to **Data Set 4** for measures of the fee for an office visit recorded for a sample of 40 physicians.

a) Use the first half of the sample to estimate with 90% confidence the proportion of physicians in the population with a fee less than $42.

b) Repeat part (a) using the second half of the sample.

c) Explain how these confidence intervals can be different and if one is to be preferred over the other.

d) Repeat the determination of the confidence interval using all 40 observations as one sample and using the normal approximation to the binomial. Is this result consistent with those in parts (a) and (b)?

9.43 A sample of size 15 has standard deviation 3. The population measure is the distance (kilometres) between home and the work location of commuters (as in Study Question 9.5). Find 90% confidence limits on the true population variance. Assume that the population is normally distributed.

9.44 A manufacturer of steel washers periodically samples the washers produced as a check on the variability of their inside diameter. A sample of size 20 was checked and found to have a standard deviation of 0.002 mm. On the basis of this sample, find a 95% confidence interval for the true variance. Assume that the population is normal.

9.45 Construct a 95% confidence interval for σ^2, based on the data in Problem 9.20.

9.46 Construct a 95% confidence interval for the variance of the bank loans described in Problem 9.22.

9.47 A machine that produces hockey pucks is stopped periodically so that the diameter of the pucks produced can be checked for accuracy. In this particular case, it is not the mean diameter that is of concern, but the variability of the diameters. Suppose that a sample of size $n = 31$ is taken and the variance of the diameters of the pucks sampled is found to be 0.94 mm².

a) Construct a 95% confidence interval for σ^2 assuming that the population is normal.

b) Assume that if this machine is working properly, the variance of the pucks produced will be 0.50 mm². Does this sample indicate that the machine is working improperly? Explain.

CHAPTER SUMMARY

KEY TERMS AND EXPRESSIONS

Point estimate: An estimate of a population parameter that specifies one single value.

Interval estimate: An estimate that specifies a range of values.

Unbiasedness: An unbiased estimator is an estimator that, on the average, equals the parameter being estimated: $E[\text{estimator}] = \text{parameter}$.

Efficiency: An efficient estimator is an unbiased estimator that has the relatively low variance (when compared to other unbiased estimators).

Sufficiency: A sufficient estimator is an estimator that utilizes all the sample information available.

Consistency: A consistent estimator is an estimator with variance and bias (if any) that approach zero as n approaches infinity.

Maximum likelihood: An estimating procedure that selects the value of the population parameter (called the most likely value) for which the observed sample would have the greatest probability of occurring.

100(1 − α)% confidence interval (C.I.): An interval estimate that will include the population parameter $100(1 − α)\%$ of the time.

100(1 − α)% C.I. for μ, σ known, normal parent population, or the central limit theorem applies ($n > 30$):

$$\bar{x} \pm z_{\alpha/2} \left(\frac{\sigma}{\sqrt{n}} \right)$$

100(1 −α)% C.I. for μ, σ unknown, normal parent population:

$$\bar{x} \pm t_{\alpha/2,\nu} \left(\frac{s}{\sqrt{n}} \right)$$

100(1 −α)% C.I. for π, when $np(1 − p) > 3$:

$$p \pm z_{\alpha/2} \sqrt{\frac{p(1 − p)}{n}}$$

Formula for determining the minimum required sample size:

$$n = \frac{z_{\alpha/2}^2 \sigma^2}{D^2}$$ for estimating a population mean where σ is known and D is the maximum allowable sampling error,

or

$$n = \frac{z_{\alpha/2}^2 p(1 − p)}{D^2}$$ for estimating a proportion where a planning value is used for p (or choose $p = \frac{1}{2}$).

100(1 −α)% C.I. for σ^2:

$$\frac{(n − 1)s^2}{\chi_{\text{upper}}^2} \leq \sigma^2 \leq \frac{(n − 1)s^2}{\chi_{\text{lower}}^2} .$$

EXERCISES

9.48 A random sample of 80 highway bridges showed 30 that were unsatisfactory for use by all types of vehicles.

a) Find a 98% confidence interval for the population proportion of unsatisfactory highway bridges.

b) The Highway Administration reported that 44.8% of the nation's bridges were either structurally deficient or functionally obsolete and not satisfactory for use by all types of vehicles. Does your confidence interval in part (a) include this reported population proportion? What does 98% confidence mean in this context?

9.49 A sample of prices of Levis at 24 stores showed a standard deviation of $s = \$2.80$ and a mean of $\bar{x} = \$36.26$. Determine 90% confidence intervals for both the mean and standard deviation (do it for the variance and find the square root) of the population of these prices in all stores. Assume a normal population.

9.50 Suppose that x_1 and x_2 are independent random variables having the Poisson probability distribution with parameter λ. Show that the mean of these variables is an unbiased estimator of λ.

9.51 If $\hat{\theta}$ is an unbiased estimator of the population parameter θ, under what conditions will $\hat{\theta}^2$ be an unbiased estimator of θ^2?

9.52 Which of the properties of a good estimator does $\bar{x}$ have? Prove as many of these as you can.

9.53 Find the amount of bias that results when the statistic $(1/n)\Sigma(x_i − \bar{x})^2$ is used to estimate σ^2.

9.54 The Ryder Corporation manufactures a variety of types and sizes of sheet metal. One of their problems has been that of establishing the exact size of the metal plates after they have been cut and stamped, for in some cases it is extremely important that the size of the plate fall within certain tolerance limits. Ryder recently purchased a special gauge that automatically measures the length of the sheet as it passes the gauge. This gauge, however, is subject to random error that has been found to be normally distributed about the true length of the sheet. To compensate for this error, the manufacturers of the gauge designed it so that, instead of producing just one value for the length of the metal passing by, the device actually gives two readings, and these values are independent of each other. Suppose that we let x_1 represent the first estimator of length and x_2 the second.

a) Is $\frac{1}{2}x_1 + \frac{1}{2}x_2$ an unbiased estimator of length?

b) Is $\frac{1}{3}x_1 + \frac{2}{3}x_2$ an unbiased estimator of length?

c) Which of the estimators in questions (a) and (b) is more efficient?

d) Suppose that one of the sheets passing by the gauge is square, and the people at Ryder wish to estimate the area of this sheet. They are unsure whether they should square the two observations first and then average, or average first and then square — in other words, whether they should use

$$\left(\frac{x_1^2 + x_2^2}{2} \right) \quad \text{or} \quad \left(\frac{x_1 + x_2}{2} \right)^2 .$$

Which method will provide the better estimator?

9.55 Use calculus to show that the maximum value of the function $g(p) = np(1-p)$ for $0 \le p \le 1$, occurs at the value $p = \frac{1}{2}$.

9.56 Use a mathematical statistics text to find proof that, for x normally distributed:

a) $\bar{x}$ is a maximum likelihood estimate of μ.

b) $(1/n)\Sigma(x_i - \bar{x})^2$ is a maximum likelihood estimate of σ^2.

9.57 If the result obtained from a particular sample will be critical, for example, the CPA would not be able to render an unqualified opinion unless every item in the population were examined, which of the following is the most important to the CPA?

a) size of the population

b) estimated occurrence rate

c) specified upper precision limit

d) specified confidence level

9.58 From a very large population, the auditor selects 400 items at random and finds 16 items in error. The auditor can be 95% confident that the error rate in the population does not exceed:

a) $4\% = \frac{16}{400} \times 100$

b) $5.62\% = 1.65\sqrt{\frac{0.04 \times 0.96}{400}} + 0.04$

c) $5.92\% = 1.96\sqrt{\frac{0.04 \times 0.96}{400}} + 0.04$

d) $5.96\% = 1.65\sqrt{\frac{0.06 \times 0.94}{400}} + 0.04$

e) $6.4\% = 1.96\sqrt{\frac{0.064 \times 0.936}{400}} + 0.04$

9.59 Approximately 5% of the 10,000 homogeneous items included in Barletta's finished-goods inventory are believed to be defective. The CPA examining Barletta's financial statements decides to test this estimated 5% defective rate. The CPA learns by sampling without replacement that a sample of 203 items from the inventory will permit specified reliability (confidence level) of 95% and specified precision (sampling error) of ± 0.03. If the specified precision is changed to ± 0.06, and the specified reliability remains 95%, the required sample size is:

a) 51   b) 102
c) 406   d) 812

9.60 An auditor wishes to be 95% confident that the true error rate does not exceed 6%. How large a sample must be taken from a very large population if the auditor estimates an error rate of 4%? Select the closest answer.

a) 150   b) 1250
c) 380   d) 450

9.61 Chalmers asks its Certified Public Accountant to estimate the number of the two thousand charge accounts that are delinquent. A sample of 100 accounts reveals that twenty are delinquent. Thus, at 95% confidence the best estimate is that:

a) at least 320 are delinquent

b) at most 560 are delinquent

c) between 320 and 480 are delinquent

d) between 240 and 560 are delinquent

e) none of the above is close to the number delinquent

9.62 Refer to Example 1.2 and Table 1.3 on page 10 in Chapter 1 for a sample of ten cities drawn from the population of 179 cities in **Data Set 1**. Use the sample mean and variance to find a 95% confidence interval for the mean income of the population of cities given in **Data Set 1**. (Assume a normal population and use the finite population correction.) Does your interval include the true population mean?

9.63 The average years of experience of a group of 50 young union members is 2.55 with a standard deviation of 0.30 years. Find a 99% confidence interval for the population average.

9.64 The quarterly sales of five different franchises of drive-in restaurants are 170, 160, 140, 180, and 140 (in thousands of dollars), respectively. You wish to make an estimate of the average sales for this quarter, for all the outlets in the entire chain.

a) On the basis of this sample information, can you make an estimate that will have a probability of 1.0 of being correct? Why or why not?

b) Make an interval estimate by using the sample mode plus-or-minus $\frac{1}{3}$ its range.

c) Make an interval estimate by using the mean plus-or-minus the standard deviation of the sample.

d) In probability, which of these estimates is better and why, and how could the better one be made even better?

9.65 Suppose that a legislator has engaged a consultant to do a public-opinion survey in an effort to determine the percent of the population who favor her stand on a flat-rate income tax. The survey company will conduct a random survey of public opinion at a cost of 35 cents per interview. How much will the survey cost her if she insists that 95% of the time the sampling error be less than 5%, and if she has no idea what percent of the population favors her stand?

♦ **9.66** A politician is interested in estimating the proportion of constituents, numbering 50,000, who favour the party's stand on the issue of free trade with the United States.

a) How large a sample needs to be taken if we want our estimate of the true proportion to be within plus or minus 2 percentage points with 99% confidence?

b) How would the answer to part (a) change if we had the additional information that approximately 60% of constituents favour the party's stand on free trade?

c) Suppose a random sample of 1600 constituents is taken and it is found that 900 favour the stand. Obtain a 90% confidence interval for the true proportion of the constituent population which favours the party's stand on free trade.

USING THE COMPUTER

9.67 Data Set 8 gives 59 sample observations of monthly returns for stockholders in four companies. Assuming an underlying normal population, use the samples to find a 95% confidence interval on the variance of the population of monthly returns for
a) IBM b) Exxon
c) General Electric d) General Motors.

9.68 Assume a normally distributed population and use the sample evidence in **Data Set 6** to find:

a) a 90% confidence interval for the average education level of persons over age 54.

b) a 95% confidence interval for the average monthly income of persons over age 54.

9.69 Near the end of Section 9.3 we mentioned that the size of the error α is always split into two equal parts to form the narrowest interval around a mean that includes $100(1 - \alpha)\%$ of the distribution of values. That is, for $\alpha = 0.10$ we exclude 0.05 at the lower end of the distribution and 0.05 at the upper end. Refer to Problem 9.14 and find the 90% confidence intervals if the amount excluded at the lower end is 0.045, 0.040, 0.035, 0.030, ..., 0.010, and 0.005. (The amount excluded at the upper end must be adjusted correspondingly so that each interval includes 90% of the distribution.) Use values from Table III and a computer program to repeat the calculations. Find the width of each interval and show that the smallest width interval is the one determined in Problem 9.14.

9.70 Refer to Problem 9.36 in which a sample size was determined to estimate the proportion of defectives within $D = 0.05$ of the true value allowing for 90% confidence in the interval estimate. Use a computer program to solve for the sample size needed if we wish

the estimate to be within plus or minus 0.01, 0.02, 0.03, ..., 0.09, and 0.10 of the true value. Use the same confidence level (90%) throughout. Make a plot of the relation between sample size and the desired difference D.

9.71 Consider the values of income for the population of 179 cities in **Data Set 1**. Use a computer program to randomly select a sample of three items from this population (allowing for replacement after each draw). Repeat the process 200 different times, each time calculating and saving the values of the sample mean $\bar{x}$, the sample statistic

$$\hat{x} = \frac{(x_{max} - x_{min})}{2},$$

and the sample variance s^2.

a) Find the average and the standard deviation of the 200 values of sample means. Compare these to the values expected according to the central limit theorem. (The population mean is $2,255.70 and the population variance is 70,520,969.)

b) Compare the mean and variance of the 200 values of $\hat{x}$ with those for $\bar{x}$. Discuss the results in terms of the properties of unbiasedness, efficiency, and sufficiency for estimators.

c) Repeat the entire process in parts (a) and (b) (called a Monte Carlo experiment) using 200 samples of size 10 each. Compare the values for the mean and variance of $\bar{x}$ between the cases with $n = 3$ and $n = 10$. Discuss the result in terms of the changing variances of the estimators and relate your results to the property of consistency of an estimator.

CASE PROBLEM

9.72 A staff member for a utilities commission gathers information on the average price of electricity prior to a rate hearing for a particular electric utility. Since there are several hundred different utilities serving thousands of different cities, the staff member selects a random sample of 28 Eastern U.S. cities. The average price per kilowatt hour for residential customers over a 12-month period is reported below.

a) Use this sample to determine 95% confidence intervals for the mean and for the standard deviation of the population of rates, assuming that it is normally distributed. A computer printout of some measures for this sample is given below the listing.

b) Use your own computer program to obtain these same summary statistics. (*Hint:* The measure "VARIATION" is the numerator of the variance, that is, the sum of squared deviations about the mean.)

c) Use a computer program to repeat the calculations needed to find confidence intervals for the mean of the population for values of α equal to 0.10, 0.05, 0.02, 0.01, and 0.005.

d) Use a computer program to solve for the limits of both 90% and 99% confidence intervals for the standard deviation of the population. (Use the positive square roots of the confidence limits for the variance.)

TABLE 9.5 Average Price per Kilowatt Hour for Residential Customers

1.	Atlanta, GA, 5.83¢	11.	Hartford, CT, 8.62¢	21.	Richmond, VA, 6.65¢
2.	Baltimore, MD, 6.77¢	12.	Jackson, MS, 6.20¢	22.	Roanoke, VA, 5.25¢
3.	Birmingham, AL, 6.32¢	13.	Miami, FL, 6.91¢	23.	St. Petersburg, FL, 7.23¢
4.	Boston, MA, 9.68¢	14.	Newark, NJ, 10.60¢	24.	Savannah, GA, 6.74¢
5.	Charlotte, NC, 5.41¢	15.	New Haven, CT, 10.12¢	25.	Syracuse, NY, 6.43¢
6.	Cincinnati, OH, 5.83¢	16.	New York, NY, 15.32¢	26.	Tampa, FL, 6.83¢
7.	Cleveland, OH, 8.08¢	17.	Pensacola, FL, 6.23¢	27.	Washington, DC, 6.69¢
8.	Columbia, SC, 6.56¢	18.	Pittsburgh, PA, 8.36¢	28.	Wheeling, WV, 6.12¢
9.	Fairmont, WV, 5.74¢	19.	Philadelphia, PA, 8.83¢		
10.	Gulfport, MS, 6.06¢	20.	Raleigh, NC, 6.19¢		

Computer printout of sample statistics:

```
SUM= 205.60                    SUM OF SQUARES= 1629.362
SAMPLE SIZE= 28                VARIATION= 119.669
MEAN= 7.343                    VARIANCE= 4.432
STANDARD DEVIATION= 2.105
```

CHAPTER 10

Hypothesis Testing: One-Sample Tests

section 10.1

Introduction and Basic Concepts

The procedures presented in Chapter 9 describe the process of making both point and interval estimates of population parameters. One advantage of using an interval estimate is that it permits the expression of uncertainty about the true, but unknown, value of the population parameter. Assumptions about unknown values of population parameters are usually referred to as *statistical hypotheses*. Determining the validity of an assumption of this nature is called the *test of a statistical hypothesis*, or simply *hypothesis testing*.

> The major purpose of hypothesis testing is to choose between two exhaustive and mutually exclusive competing hypotheses about the value of a population parameter.

Types of Hypotheses

In specifying the competing hypotheses about the values that a population parameter might assume, it is convenient to distinguish between *simple hypotheses* and *composite hypotheses*. In a **simple hypothesis**, only one value of the population parameter is specified. If an engineer hypothesizes that the probability of a defective item is $\pi = 0.10$, this represents a simple hypothesis. A financial analyst for McDonald's investigating the hypothesis that the mean income per McDonald's franchise is $\mu = \$130,000$ per month is testing a simple hypothesis. A **composite hypothesis**, on the other hand, specifies not just one value but a *range* of values that the population parameter may assume. The hypotheses, $\pi < 0.10$, or $\mu \neq \$130,000$, represent composite hypotheses because more than one value is specified in each case. As you might suspect, assumptions in the form of simple hypotheses are, in general, easier to test than are composite hypotheses. In the former case, we need to determine only whether or not the population parameter equals the specified value, while in the latter case it is necessary to determine whether or not the population parameter takes on any one of a set (perhaps, very large or even infinite) of values.

The two mutually exclusive hypotheses in a statistical test are referred to as the **null hypothesis** and the **alternative hypothesis**. The term *null hypothesis* developed from early work in the theory of hypothesis testing. This hypothesis corresponded to a theory about a population parameter that the researcher thought did *not* represent the true value of the parameter; hence the word *null*, which means invalid, void, or amounting to nothing. The *alternative hypothesis* generally specified those values of the parameter that the researcher believed did hold true.

Nowadays, it is a generally-accepted common practice for the null hypothesis to be a statement of *no difference*. That is, it is *most* convenient always to have the null hypothesis contain an equality statement using an equal sign. The null and alternative hypotheses are distinguished by the use of two different subscript symbols on a capital H, a zero or nought for H_0, the null hypothesis and an *a* for H_a, the alternative hypothesis.

Suppose, for example, that the automobile industry asserts that new car prices increased by an average of only \$100 in the last year. You believe the average increase was larger than \$100. To test whether μ is equal to or greater than 100 you establish the following null and alternative hypotheses:

$$H_0: \quad \mu = 100 \quad \text{(Null hypothesis)}$$

$$H_a: \quad \mu > 100 \quad \text{(Alternative hypothesis)}$$

Instead of testing for car price increases over a year's period, you may wish to test for differences between the mean price of two groups of cars at one point in time. In this case the null hypothesis established may be that the two groups have equal means, with the alternative hypothesis that their means are not equal:

$$H_0: \quad \mu_1 - \mu_2 = 0 \text{ (Null hypothesis)}$$

$$H_a: \quad \mu_1 - \mu_2 \neq 0 \text{ (Alternative hypothesis)}$$

The null hypothesis and the alternative hypothesis can both be either simple or composite. The simple null hypothesis $H_0: \mu = 100$, for example, may be tested against a simple alternative hypothesis, such as $H_a: \mu = 120$ or $H_a: \mu = 75$; it may be tested against a composite hypothesis, such as $H_a: \mu \neq 100$, $H_a: \mu > 100$, or $H_a: \mu < 100$. Similarly, the composite null hypothesis $H_0: \mu \leq 100$ may be tested against a simple alternative, such as $H_a: \mu = 120$, or against a composite alternative, such as $H_a: \mu > 100$.

Regardless of the form of the two hypotheses, it is extremely important to remember that the true value of the population parameter under consideration *must* be either in the set specified by H_0 or in the set specified by H_a. By testing $H_0: \mu = 100$ against $H_a: \mu = 120$, for example, one is asserting that the true value of μ equals either 100 or 120 and that *no other values are possible*. One means for assuring that either H_0 or H_a contains the true value of the population parameter is to let these two sets be *complementary*. That is, if the null hypothesis is $H_0: \mu = 100$, then the alternative hypothesis will be $H_a: \mu \neq 100$; or if $H_0: \mu \leq 100$, then $H_a: \mu > 100$. From a statistical point of view, it is most convenient to structure the problem so that the null hypothesis can be treated as a simple equality statement even if it is a composite hypothesis.

One- and Two-sided Tests

If the null hypothesis is simple, then the alternative hypothesis may specify one or more values for the population parameter, and these values (or value) may lie entirely above, or entirely below, or on both sides of the value specified by the null hypothesis. A statistical test in which the alternative hypothesis specifies that the population parameter lies either entirely above or entirely below the value specified in the null hypothesis is called a **one-sided test**; an alternative hypothesis that specifies that the parameter can lie on either side of the value indicated by H_0 is called a **two-sided test**. Thus, $H_0: \mu = 100$ tested against $H_a: \mu > 100$ is a one-sided test, since H_a specifies that μ lies on one particular side of 100. The same null hypothesis tested against $H_a: \mu \neq 100$ is a two-sided test, since μ can lie on *either* side of 100.

Whenever possible, we encourage the use of one-sided tests of hypotheses in economics, business, and finance applications. In most real life cases, the decision-maker should know enough about the topic in question to specify the direction of the most expensive or critical error away from the value specified in the null hypothesis. Similarly, a researcher should be able to specify the alternate hypothesis in the direction away from the null value that is most significant to the argument or the issue being considered. If so, then the appropriate alternate hypothesis would lead to a one-sided test in that direction.

A two-sided test bears a strong resemblance statistically to a confidence interval, although we prefer to distinguish between them because they have two different purposes. The confidence interval method uses sample information to make a guess, an interval estimate, about the unknown value of a population parameter. The test of hypotheses procedure uses sample information to help determine between two given, but competing, propositions about the true value of the parameter.

The Form of the Decision Problem

The decision problem that we confront in hypothesis testing is choosing between two mutually exclusive propositions about a population parameter when we are faced with the uncertainty inherent in sampling from a population. The decision-maker has only the sample evidence on which to base the choice of accepting or rejecting the null hypothesis as compared with the alternative hypothesis. The standard method of solving this decision problem is, first, to assume that the null hypothesis is true (just as we presume a person's innocence until he or she is proven guilty in a court of law). Then, using the probability theory from Chapters 5, 6, and 7, we can establish the criteria that will be used to decide whether there is sufficient evidence to declare H_0 false. A sample is then taken, the sample evidence is compared to the criteria, and the decision is made whether to accept or reject H_0.

> When we say "accept a hypothesis" in this context throughout the book, we do not mean accept as true, but accept in a probabilistic decision sense in comparison with the choice of the alternative.

Contrary to practice in a court of law, where innocence is maintained as long as any reasonable doubt about guilt remains, in hypothesis testing we can and do reject H_0 on the basis of a reasonable doubt about its truth. With such a procedure, the probability value, upon which we base our conclusion that there is reason to doubt the truth of H_0, is critical. Moreover, since the decision to accept or reject H_0 is based on probabilities and not on certainty, there are chances of error in the decision. Specifically, there are two types of potential error:

1. One may decide on the basis of the sample result to reject the null hypothesis when this hypothesis is, in fact, true (**Type I error**).
2. One may decide to accept the null hypothesis when this hypothesis is not true (**Type II error**).

There are four possible outcomes of a hypothesis test, as shown in Figure 10.1. This figure presents the basic decision problem in hypothesis testing with reference only to the null hypothesis. A good exercise for the reader would be to construct a similar figure, making reference only to H_a. Remember that accepting H_0 implies rejecting H_a, and vice versa.

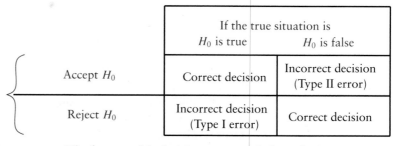

| | If the true situation is | |
	H_0 is true	H_0 is false
Accept H_0	Correct decision	Incorrect decision (Type II error)
Reject H_0	Incorrect decision (Type I error)	Correct decision

FIGURE 10.1 The four possible decision outcomes in hypothesis testing

To illustrate the concept of Type I and II errors, recall our example about the average increase in new car prices, where we established the hypotheses H_0 : $\mu = 100$ and H_a: $\mu > 100$. Now, suppose that the true mean is actually $\mu = 100$. If we decide (on the basis of some sample evidence) to accept H_a: $\mu > 100$, then a Type I error has been made. Let us consider the opposite situation, where the true value of μ exceeds 100. For example, the true mean might be $\mu = 105$. A Type II error is made in this case if we decide to accept the null hypothesis H_0 : $\mu = 100$.

◻ **EXAMPLE 10.1**   Type I and II errors can be specified for the quality-control problem in Section 5.5. In this problem, defective items occur in a production process with one of two probabilities, $\pi = 0.10$ or $\pi = 0.25$. Suppose we establish the null hypothesis H_0 : $\pi = 0.10$ and let the alternative hypothesis be H_a : $\pi = 0.25$. A Type I error is committed if the decision is to accept the alternative hypothesis H_a : $\pi = 0.25$ when the null hypothesis H_0 : $\pi = 0.10$ is true. Similarly, a Type II error is committed if H_0 : $\pi = 0.10$ is accepted when H_a : $\pi = 0.25$ is true. We reiterate at this point that the above hypotheses are based on the assumption that the true population value of π is either 0.10 or 0.25. By specifying two simple hypotheses we are asserting that no other values are possible.   ■

It should be clear that the probabilities of Type I and Type II errors are conditional probabilities which have values between zero and one. The former depends on the condition that H_0 is true and the latter on the condition that H_a is true. The probability of a Type I error is commonly denoted by the lowercase Greek letter alpha (α) and is called the **level of significance**. That is,

$$\alpha = \text{Level of significance} = P(\text{Type I error})$$

$$= P(\text{reject } H_0 \mid H_0 \text{ is true}).$$

The level of significance of a statistical test is comparable to the probability of an error, also called α, discussed in Chapter 9. The value of $(1 - \alpha)$ is called a **confidence level** and represents the complement of $P(\text{Type I error})$.

$$(1 - \alpha) = \text{Confidence level} = 1 - P(\text{Type I error})$$

$$= P(\text{accept } H_0 \mid H_0 \text{ is true}).$$

In constructing a statistical test, we obviously would like to have a small probability of making a Type I error; hence, one objective is to construct the test in such a way that α *is small*. This objective, however, ignores the probability of making a Type II error. The probability of making a Type II error — that is, of accepting a false null hypothesis — is usually denoted by the Greek letter beta (β):

$$\beta = P(\text{Type II error}) = P(\text{accept } H_0 \mid H_0 \text{ is false}).$$

The complement of this probability is known as the power of a statistical test, since it indicates the ability or power of the test to recognize *correctly* that the null hypothesis is false and hence, that H_0 should be rejected.

$$1 - \beta = \text{power} = P(\text{reject } H_0 \mid H_0 \text{ is false}).$$

Thus, one always wishes to construct a test that will yield a large power (close to one), or equivalently, a value near zero for β, when H_0 is false. Figure 10.2 presents the same decision problem shown in Figure 10.1, except that here we identify the *probability* associated with each of the four cells.

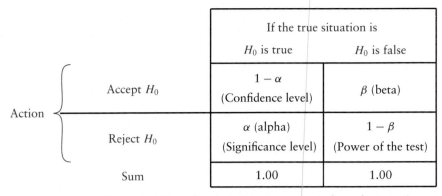

		If the true situation is	
		H_0 is true	H_0 is false
Action	Accept H_0	$1 - \alpha$ (Confidence level)	β (beta)
	Reject H_0	α (alpha) (Significance level)	$1 - \beta$ (Power of the test)
	Sum	1.00	1.00

FIGURE 10.2   The probability of each decision outcome in hypothesis testing

Note that the probability of each decision outcome is a *conditional* probability and that the elements in each column sum to 1.00, since the events with which they are associated are *complements*. By now it should be apparent that α and β need not add to unity, as these two probabilities are not complementary. Thus, a one-unit change in α does not imply a corresponding one-unit change in β, or vice versa. However, α and β are not independent of each other, nor are they independent of the sample size n. When α is lowered, β normally rises, and vice versa (if n remains unchanged). If n is increased, it is possible for both α and β to decrease, because with a larger sample, the sampling error is potentially decreased. Since increasing n usually costs money, the researcher must decide just how much additional money should be spent on increasing the sample size in order to reduce the sizes of α and β. Such analysis, concerned with balancing the costs of increasing the sample size against the costs of making Type I and Type II errors, is a fairly complex subject. We will cover this topic briefly in Section 10.6. Until then, we will assume that the sample size is fixed at some predetermined value n.

section 10.2   The Standard Format of Hypothesis Testing

There are many different population parameters, many different potential forms of hypotheses, and many different sample statistics, random variables, and probability distributions that may be involved in testing hypotheses. It is not, therefore, feasible to catalogue all such tests. However, they all follow a similar procedure, which can be learned and then applied to different situations as they arise. This procedure can be summarized by the following five steps:

1. State the null and alternative hypotheses.
2. Determine the appropriate test statistic.
3. Determine the critical region.
4. Compute the value of the test statistic and its *p*-value.
5. Make the statistical decision and interpretation.

We will illustrate this procedure within the following practical situation.

A financial analyst for McDonald's restaurants has determined that last year the mean monthly income (in thousands of dollars) for a McDonald's franchise was $130. This year, the analyst is concerned that the mean income may be some number other than \$130. For the time being, we will assume that this analyst is unfamiliar with the problem and does not know whether μ exceeds 130 or is less than 130. Also, we will assume that monthly incomes are known to be normally distributed with a standard deviation of $\sigma = 5.4$ (thousands of dollars). A random sample of $n = 25$ franchises is proposed to test whether or not the mean is equal to 130. The five steps for performing this test are described below.

Step 1. State the Null and Alternative Hypotheses. In every hypothesis-testing problem the two conflicting hypotheses must be specified clearly. It is usually convenient to formulate the null hypothesis as a simple hypothesis and the alternative hypothesis as a composite hypothesis, although it is not necessary to do so. In any case, the two conflicting hypotheses must be mutually exclusive, and they must be formulated so that the true value of the population parameter is included in either the null or the alternative hypothesis. *It is not permissible for both hypotheses to be true or both to be false.*

For our McDonald's example, the parameter in the test is the population mean μ. One hypothesis is that $\mu = 130$, and the other is that $\mu \neq 130$. If we let the simple hypothesis containing the equality statement be H_0, then:

$$\text{Null hypothesis: } H_0 : \mu = 130$$

$$\text{Alternative hypothesis: } H_a : \mu \neq 130$$

One of these hypotheses must be true, since the values specified by H_a represent the complement of the value specified by H_0.

Step 2. Determine the Appropriate Test Statistic. The second step in testing hypotheses is to determine which of the random variables that we have studied is appropriate to determine whether we should accept or reject H_0. If the parameter being tested is the population mean, then we know that our best estimate of μ is the sample mean $\bar{x}$. In testing $H_0 : \mu = 130$ versus $H_a : \mu \neq 130$, we would want to determine how close $\bar{x}$ is to 130. A value of $\bar{x}$ far below or far above 130 would lead us to accept H_a. Conversely, a value slightly below, equal to, or slightly above 130 would lead us to accept H_0. In order to decide whether $\bar{x}$ is close enough to 130 to accept H_0 within an allowable risk of error, we need to use probability.

To obtain a sampling distribution which is known to us, we do a transformation to the standardized normal distribution. From the discussion in Section 7.5, we know that if $\bar{x}$ is normal and σ is known, then the standardization of $\bar{x}$ is:

$$z = \frac{\bar{x} - \mu_0}{\sigma / \sqrt{n}}$$

The symbol μ_0 in this standardization is the value of μ specified under the null hypothesis. The random variable z for this example is called the *test statistic*. A **test statistic** is thus a random variable used to determine how close a specific sample result falls to one of the hypotheses being tested. As we will describe in this chapter, most of the random variables studied thus far can be used as test statistics. A valid test statistic must satisfy three conditions:

1. Its p.d.f. must be known under the condition that the null hypothesis is true.
2. It must contain the parameter being tested.
3. All of its remaining terms must be known or calculable from the sample.

In our example, the distribution of z is $N(0, 1)$ when μ is assumed to be $\mu_0 = 130$. Obviously,

$$z = \frac{\bar{x} - \mu}{\sigma/\sqrt{n}}$$

contains the parameter μ. The remaining terms are: σ, which is known to be 5.4, $n = 25$, and $\bar{x}$, which can be calculated from the sample.

Step 3. Determine the Critical Region(s). As we indicated above, certain values of the test statistic lead to acceptance of H_0, while other values lead to the rejection of H_0. In most statistical tests it is important to specify, *before the sample is taken*, exactly which values of the test statistic will lead to rejection of H_0 and which will lead to acceptance of H_0. The former set of values (leading to rejection of H_0) is called the **critical region**, while the latter set (leading to acceptance of H_0) is called the **acceptance region**. The critical value is that point which separates the critical region (rejection region) from the acceptance region. When the alternative hypothesis is two-sided (as in our McDonald's example), these regions are characterized as shown in Figure 10.3.

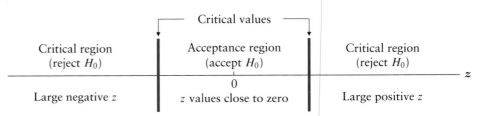

FIGURE 10.3 The acceptance and critical regions for H_0

The problem is to determine the *exact* location of the critical values shown in the figure. These values depend partially on the level of risk of a Type I or Type II error that one is willing to take. For example, the smaller the value of α, the farther outward the critical values in the above figure will move, making the critical regions smaller. This occurs because when α is small, the decision-maker requires a relatively small critical region (α is the probability that the test statistic will be in the critical region when H_0 is true). Figure 10.4 illustrates the effect of increasing the size of α for a given sample size.

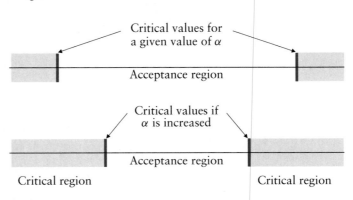

FIGURE 10.4 Increasing the size of α will move the critical values toward the middle. Since the acceptance region becomes smaller, the value of β becomes smaller

As we indicated previously, the ideal is that both α and β be very small in a given situation. It should be clear by now that *decreasing the size of α will increase the size of β*; similarly, if the size of β is decreased, the size of α will increase (assuming that the sample size is fixed).

The traditional method for selecting a critical region is first to establish a value for α and then to choose that critical region that yields the smallest value of β. The rationale behind this procedure is that it is important to establish, beforehand, the risk that one wants to assume of incorrectly rejecting a true null hypothesis. The size of the Type I error in this approach is viewed as so much more important than the size of the Type II error that the size of β is considered only after α has been fixed at some predetermined level.

The practice of selecting a critical region in this manner stems from the early research on hypothesis testing, in which the null hypothesis usually represented current opinion on an issue and the alternative hypothesis represented a viewpoint of the researcher contrary to that commonly accepted. In testing a new drug, such as a cure for cancer, the drug must be assumed to be of no benefit, or even harmful, until it is proven otherwise. The alternative hypothesis is that the drug is indeed beneficial. A most serious Type I error would be made if a harmful drug (H_0 true) were certified as beneficial.

The value of α, or the level of significance, indicates the degree of importance that a researcher attaches to the consequences associated with incorrectly rejecting H_0. Researchers in the social sciences often use a level of significance of $\alpha = 0.05$, indicating that they are willing to accept a 5% chance of being wrong when they reject H_0. For many statistical problems in accounting and finance, α is set, rather arbitrarily, at either 0.05 or 0.01. However, in the medical sciences, α is usually set much lower — perhaps as low as 0.0005 or 0.0001. As we indicated above, medical science has to be *very* concerned about incorrectly rejecting H_0. Although α is rarely set higher than $\alpha = 0.05$, and values such as $\alpha = 0.025$, $\alpha = 0.01$ and $\alpha = 0.001$ are used frequently, other values may be used. If α is set at some predetermined level, then it is extremely important that this value be specified before any data are collected.

In our McDonald's example, a Type I error occurs when it is concluded that $\mu \neq 130$ when μ is truly 130. Suppose we assume that the researcher uses an $\alpha = 0.05$ level of significance. In other words, this researcher wants to have no more than a 5% chance of rejecting $H_0 : \mu = 130$ when this hypothesis is true (a Type I error). This means that the researcher wants the critical region to cut off 5% of the appropriate p.d.f., which from our earlier discussion we know to be the z-distribution. When H_a is two-sided, the optimal critical region will cut off $\alpha/2$ of the area in the upper tail and $\alpha/2$ of the area in the lower tail. This is the same procedure we used to construct a $100(1 - \alpha)\%$ confidence interval. If $\alpha = 0.05$, we know from Table III that the values of z that cut off $\alpha/2 = 0.025$ in each tail of the standardized normal distribution are ± 1.96. Figure 10.5 shows the resulting critical regions.

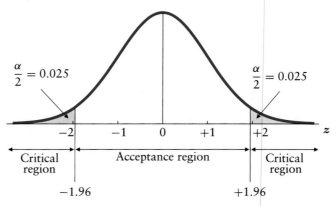

FIGURE 10.5 Critical regions (in terms of z) for testing H_0 : $\mu = 130$ against H_a : $\mu \neq 130$ with $\alpha = 0.05$, $\sigma = 5.4$, $n = 25$

The critical values shown in Figure 10.5 are expressed in terms of the z-distribution. When constructing critical values, we can express these numbers either as a z-value or in terms of $\bar{x}$. The advantage of expressing the critical and acceptance regions in terms of z-values is that it emphasizes the similarity of the solution among many types of problems. Once the normal standardization occurs, each problem looks the same.

The advantage of expressing the critical values in terms of $\bar{x}$ is that it is then possible to compare the sample results directly with these values and to see if the sample result falls in the acceptance region or in the critical regions. Fortunately, it is quite easy to transform a z critical value into its comparable $\bar{x}$ critical value by solving for $\bar{x}$ in the formula that represents the test statistic:

$$z = \frac{\bar{x} - \mu_0}{\sigma/\sqrt{n}}$$

For our McDonald's example, the value of μ_0 is 130 (the null hypothesis), $n = 25$, and the known value of σ is 5.4. Substituting these values and $z = 1.96$ into this formula, we obtain:

$$1.96 = \frac{\bar{x} - 130}{5.4/\sqrt{25}}$$

Solving for $\bar{x}$, we calculate the appropriate upper end critical value:

$$\bar{x} = 1.96 \left(\frac{5.4}{5}\right) + 130 = 132.12$$

Similarly, when the critical value is $z = -1.96$, the appropriate lower end critical value of $\bar{x}$ is derived as follows:

$$-1.96 = \frac{\bar{x} - 130}{5.4/\sqrt{25}} \Rightarrow \bar{x} = -1.96 \left(\frac{5.4}{5}\right) + 130$$

$$\bar{x} = 127.88$$

We could have saved ourselves some work in the above calculation by recognizing that due to symmetry the lower critical value will be the same distance *below* 130 as the upper critical value is *above* 130. They are both 2.12 units away from 130. These critical values are shown in Figure 10.6.

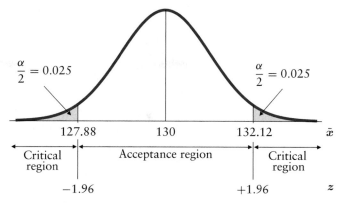

FIGURE 10.6 Critical regions (in terms of $\bar{x}$) for testing $H_0 : \mu = 130$ against $H_a : \mu \neq 130$ with $\alpha = 0.05$, $\sigma = 5.4$, $n = 25$

From Figure 10.6 we know that for random samples of size $n = 25$, 2.5% of the time $\bar{x}$ will be less than 127.88, and 2.5% of the time $\bar{x}$ will be greater than 132.12, assuming that $H_0 : \mu = 130$ is true. We must emphasize that Figures 10.5 and 10.6 are *equivalent* ways of presenting the same critical regions. The only difference is that the former is in terms of the test statistic z, while the latter is in terms of the sample mean itself ($\bar{x}$).

Step 4. Compute the Value of the Test Statistic. Now that we have specified the two conflicting hypotheses, determined the appropriate test statistic, and found the critical region(s), we must see whether the sample result falls in the critical region or in the acceptance region. When the critical values are stated in terms of $\bar{x}$, this process is quite simple. For the most part, however, it will be convenient (and it will help the reader to note the similarities among all problems) to use z-values to denote critical values. To do this, we need to standardize the sample result into its comparable z-value. A value of z calculated on the basis of a sample result is called a computed z-value, and is denoted by the symbol z_c.

Computed z-value:

$$z_c = \frac{\bar{x} - \mu_0}{\sigma/\sqrt{n}}. \qquad (10.1)$$

In general, a **computed value** is a value of the test statistic, calculated by using a specific sample result. To illustrate a computed z-value, we will assume that, in our McDonald's example the random sample of $n = 25$ resulted in $\bar{x} = 128$ (thousand dollars). That is, 25 McDonald's franchises were selected at random, and the average monthly income in this sample was 128. When we substitute this value of $\bar{x}$ into our test statistic, we obtain the following computed z-value:

$$z_c = \frac{128 - 130}{5.4/\sqrt{25}} = -1.85$$

We mention for later use that if the t-variable had been the appropriate test statistic, then we would have denoted the computed value as t_c. Similarly, *computed* values of the chi-square variable will be denoted $\chi_c{}^2$. Some references in statistics use the subscript c to indicate the critical value described in Step 3, which separates the acceptance region from the rejection region. Other symbols are also used, so be sure of the meaning of a symbol when reading different sources.

Step 5. Make the Statistical Decision and Conclusion. If the calculated value of the test statistic lies in the critical region, then H_0 is rejected in favour of H_a. When the calculated value falls in the acceptance region, then H_0 is accepted rather than H_a. In either case, it is important for the researcher to reach a conclusion *in terms of the original problem*, because the results of statistical tests in business and accounting, economics, and the social sciences are often presented to and utilized by people who may not understand statistical terminology.

Let us determine whether or not the sample result $\bar{x} = 128$ or, equivalently, $z_c = -1.85$ leads to rejection or acceptance of $H_0 : \mu = 130$. From Figure 10.6 it is clear that this sample result falls in the acceptance region (above 127.88 for $\bar{x}$, or above -1.96 for z). Thus, we would conclude that the mean may not differ from 130, although we must admit that there is some risk [known as $\beta = P(\text{Type II error})$] that this conclusion is not true.

One-Sided Tests

For the critical regions calculated above, the alternative hypothesis was two-sided, $H_a : \mu \neq 130$. Now let's change this problem because the analyst is not concerned if the mean McDonald's income exceeds 130, but is worried if it is lower than 130. In this case the appropriate alternative hypothesis is $H_a : \mu < 130$.

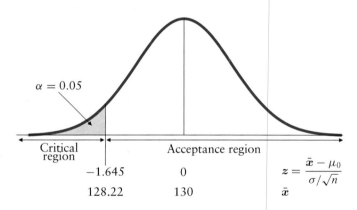

FIGURE 10.7 Critical region for testing $H_0 : \mu = 130$ against $H_a : \mu < 130$ with $\alpha = 0.05, \sigma = 5.4, n = 25$

The only change in our method caused by a one-sided alternative hypothesis is that we now have a single critical region, rather than the two regions shown in Figures 10.5 and 10.6. The single critical value is found in much the same way as in the two-sided test. The only difference is that all of the probability associated with the error α is cut off from a single end of the distribution. Whether this is the upper or the lower end depends entirely on whether the alternative hypothesis is a more than ($>$) or a less than ($<$) relationship. In our McDonald's example with $\alpha = 0.05$, we want to find the single value that cuts off 5% of the distribution. Note in Figure 10.7 that we cut off $\alpha = 0.05$ of the *left-hand* portion of the z-distribution, because the values specified by H_a all lie to the *left* of 130 ($\mu < 130$). If the alternative hypothesis had been one-sided on the upper side ($H_a : \mu > 130$), then the critical region would lie entirely in the upper right-hand tail.

The value $z = -1.645$ in Figure 10.7 was obtained from Table III in Appendix C by interpolating between $z = -1.64 [P(z \leq -1.64) = 0.0505]$ and $z = -1.65 [P(z \leq -1.65) = 0.0495]$. The $\bar{x}$-value comparable to $z = -1.645$ is determined as follows:

$$z = \frac{\bar{x} - \mu_0}{\sigma/\sqrt{n}}$$

$$-1.645 = \frac{\bar{x} - 130}{5.4/\sqrt{25}}$$

$$\bar{x} = -1.645 \left(\frac{5.4}{5} \right) + 130 = 128.22$$

This critical value of $\bar{x} = 128.22$ is also shown in Figure 10.7. Note that now the sample value $\bar{x} = 128$ falls in the critical region, as does the z-value of -1.85, which is less than -1.645.

For the one-sided alternative $H_a : \mu < 130$, we would *reject* the null hypothesis $H_0 : \mu = 130$. Thus, we would conclude that the mean income of McDonald's franchises is probably less than $130,000, although we admit that there is some risk (no more than $\alpha = 0.05$) that this conclusion is not true. This example was designed to emphasize how important is the selection of the significance level or the type of alternative hypothesis in a statistical test. The more specific one can be in specifying H_a, the more powerful will be the resulting test.

Procedure When H_0 Is Composite

The reader may wonder at this point what happens if the null hypothesis is not simple, but composite. For example, suppose that we wish to test

$$H_0: \mu \geq 130 \qquad \text{versus} \qquad H_a: \mu < 130$$

For a composite null hypothesis like this, it is impossible to calculate a critical value as we did in Figure 10.7 because now there is no *one* value for μ specified under the null hypothesis.

> The common approach to this situation is to *construct the critical value (s) by using the most conservative value possible under H_0*. The most conservative value is generally the one closest to the alternative hypothesis.

Thus, if the alternative hypothesis is $H_a : \mu < 130$, the closest value specified by the null hypothesis is the value $\mu = 130$. The critical value(s) can now be constructed by treating the null hypothesis as if it were $H_0 : \mu = 130$. The resulting critical region will look exactly like that shown in Figure 10.7. Rejection of H_0 in favour of H_a for this closest value of μ in the null hypothesis would certainly lead to the same and even stronger conclusions when the other values of μ in the composite null hypothesis H_0 are used.

Reporting a Probability (p) Value

The five steps outlined above occur in almost all tests of hypotheses, even though the step-by-step details of the process may change from one situation to another. We will illustrate the basic process in a number of examples in this chapter and the following chapter. Before doing so, we should point out that a modification of the steps is often used when it is not possible or desirable to specify the value of α (the level of significance) *before* taking the sample. This may happen when the decision-maker (say, the manager) is someone other than the person carrying out the research (the statistical analyst). In some cases the decision-maker is not available to specify an α, or perhaps the analyst is writing a report in which each of the various readers may be thought of as potential decision-makers (all with possibly different α's).

When α is not specified, a common procedure is to determine or report a probability that depends on the computed value of the test statistic, say z_c. To illustrate this procedure, we will apply it to our McDonald's example where the hypotheses are as follows:

$$H_0 : \mu = 130 \qquad \text{versus} \qquad H_a : \mu < 130$$

Recall that the sample result $\bar{x} = 128$ led to a computed z-value of $z_c = -1.85$. The reported **p-value** is the probability that the random variable z would take on a value as extreme as z_c. For this example, the probability calculated from Table III is as follows:

$$p\text{-value} = P(z \le z_c) = P(z \le -1.85) = 1 - 0.9678 = 0.0322$$

The probability value reported to the decision-maker is thus 0.0322. To a decision-maker who knows little about statistical analysis, we might offer the following statement:

"A sample mean of 128 or lower will occur only 3.22% of the time when the true population mean is 130. Since our sample mean was 128, this result casts serious doubt on the validity of the assumption that the mean is, in fact, 130."

A decision-maker with an implicit α *higher* than 0.0322 should reject H_0 because $\bar{x} = 128$ would fall in the critical region. A decision-maker with α *lower* than 0.0322 should accept H_0 because the sample result $\bar{x} = 128$ would fall in the acceptance region. The procedure outlined above is for an alternative hypothesis that is one-sided on the *lower* side of H_0. If H_a is one-sided on the *upper* side of H_0, then the reported p-value is $P(z \ge z_c)$. Otherwise, the procedures described above do not change. Thus, for one-sided tests about μ, a p-value is determined as follows:

When H_a is one-sided on the lower side:

$$p\text{-value} = P(z \le z_c)$$

When H_a is one-sided on the upper side:

$$p\text{-value} = P(z \ge z_c)$$

If the alternative hypothesis is two-sided, the process described must be modified slightly. Suppose, for instance, in the above example that the alternative hypotheses are $H_0 : \mu = 130$ and $H_a : \mu \ne 130$. Since we now have two equi-probable critical regions, the probability to be reported must be *twice as large* as in the one-sided case. The p-value for a two-sided alternative must be twice as large as the p-value for the one-sided case. Thus, the general rule is:

> If H_a is two-sided, the one-sided probability must be doubled to obtain the p-value.

Let us now assume that the same sample result, $\bar{x} = 128$, occurs when testing $H_0 : \mu = 130$ versus $H_a : \mu \neq 130$. To find the p-value, we must double the probability $P(z \leq -1.85)$:[†]

$$2P(z \leq z_c) = 2P(z \leq -1.85) = 2(0.0322) = 0.0644$$

Thus, we would report that, if the null hypothesis is true, a sample result this far away from the hypothesized value of the parameter (either above or below μ) would occur 6.44% of the time. The decision-maker with an α greater than 0.0644 should reject H_0. If α is set at any level of significance below 0.0644, H_0 should be accepted.

For any test, the p-value may be determined (at least approximately or within a range) from interpolation within a probability table such as Table III for z, Table VI for t, or Table VII for x^2. Exact p-values can be found using a computer program for calculating probabilities in common probability distributions. If the p-value approach is used, it can replace steps 3 and 5 in testing a hypothesis. The rejection and acceptance regions need not be determined. The test conclusion is based on the following decision rule.

> If α is greater than the p-value, reject H_0 in favour of H_a.
> If α is less than the p-value, accept H_0 rather than H_a.

These examples have illustrated the general method of hypothesis testing, which may be applied to many tests. The most common tests of hypotheses involve μ, the population mean. Tests about μ are usually designed to indicate, on the basis of a *single* sample, which of two hypotheses about μ should be rejected. In other circumstances, one may be interested in designing a test to indicate, on the basis of a sample from each of *two different* populations, whether or not these *two* samples were drawn from populations having equal means. This breakdown between one- and two-sample tests will be a convenient one for us to follow. Some common one-sample tests are discussed in this chapter; two-sample tests are presented in Chapter 11.

◻ STUDY QUESTION 10.1   Reading Level for a Training Manual

You are in charge of a project to rewrite the training manual for certain GE assembly line workers. A previous study indicated that the mean reading level for these workers is normally distributed with a mean of 9.5 (halfway between the ninth and tenth grade) and a population standard deviation of $\sigma = 1.1$. All recent new employees have been at least high school graduates, which suggests that the mean reading level may have increased. You take a random sample of 50 of these workers and find $\bar{x} = 9.9$. Report a p-value, assuming that the (population) standard deviation is not changed. Would you accept or reject H_0 using $\alpha = 0.05$?

[†] The reader should always make certain that the probability to be doubled is less then 0.50. It would make no sense to double a probability such as $P(z \geq -1.85)$; doing so would yield a p-value greater than 1.0.

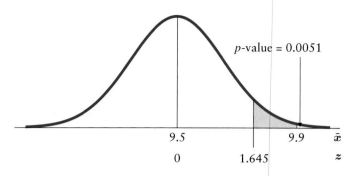

FIGURE 10.8 The p-value for Study Question 10.1

● **ANSWER**

1. Establish the hypotheses: $H_0:\ \mu = 9.5$ versus $H_a:\ \mu > 9.5$ (assuming that μ cannot be less than 9.5).

2. Determine the test statistic:

$$z = \frac{\bar{x} - \mu_0}{\sigma/\sqrt{n}}$$

3. Determine the critical region: Since $\alpha = 0.05$, and the alternative hypothesis is one-sided towards the high side, the critical value is $+z_\alpha = +z_{0.05} = +1.645$.

4. Calculate a test statistic value and report a p-value:

$$z_c = \frac{9.9 - 9.5}{1.1/\sqrt{50}} = \frac{0.4}{0.1556} = 2.57$$

$$p\text{-value} = P(z \geq 2.57) = 0.0051$$

5. Decision and conclusion: Since the calculated value ($z_c = 2.57$) falls in the critical region (beyond 1.645), H_0 should be rejected, and H_a should be accepted. The same conclusion (reject H_0) is reached by noting that α is greater than the p-value. We conclude that the mean reading level is higher than 9.5, although there is some risk (p-value $= 0.0051$) that this conclusion is not true. ■

section 10.3

One-Sample Tests On μ

In this section, we will discuss tests on the mean of a population, μ. In general, there are two types of tests involving μ, one in which σ is assumed to be known and the other in which σ is unknown. In the former case, the z-distribution is the appropriate test statistic. In the latter case, the t-distribution is the appropriate test statistic, although the z is used commonly even in these cases, provided that n is large (where *large* generally means over 30). In all of our examples in Section 10.2, it was assumed that σ was known; hence we used the z test statistic. In this section, we will present another example in which σ is known and then move to the situation in which the t-distribution is appropriate.

Another Example in Which σ is Known

□ **EXAMPLE 10.2**   Reconsider Example 7.4 from Section 7.6 in which a sample of 36 residents was taken to judge whether the average monthly phone charge, claimed to be $15.30, seemed reasonable for the population of local phone subscribers. The standard deviation for this population was $\sigma = \$4.10$. We obtain added information that the town is very small with the total number of local phone customers only $N = 300$. We establish that the null hypothesis is a simple hypothesis and that the alternative hypothesis is two-sided:

$$H_0: \ \mu = 15.30 \qquad \text{versus} \qquad H_a: \ \mu \neq 15.30$$

From the central limit theorem we know that $\bar{x}$ will be approximately normal; hence, we can again use the standardized normal test statistic where $\mu_0 = 15.30$, $\sigma = 4.10$, and $n = 36$. In this case, it is not completely accurate to use a standard error of the mean of $\sigma/\sqrt{n}$, since we are sampling without replacement from a *finite* population. Rather, the finite population correction factor, $\sqrt{(N-n)/(N-1)}$, should be used as explained in Section 7.7. The appropriate test statistic is

$$z = \frac{\bar{x} - \mu_0}{\left(\dfrac{\sigma}{\sqrt{n}}\right)\sqrt{\dfrac{(N-n)}{(N-1)}}}$$

where $N = 300$, and all other terms are known or can be obtained from the sample.

The next step is to specify the level of α and find the critical regions. However, what if we do not know the appropriate level of significance set by the decision-maker. We proceed directly to determining the computed value of the test statistic. A random sample of $n = 36$ yields an average monthly phone bill of $\bar{x} = \$16.90$. The calculated z value is thus:

$$z_c = \frac{\bar{x} - \mu_0}{\left(\dfrac{\sigma}{\sqrt{n}}\right)\sqrt{\dfrac{(N-n)}{(N-1)}}} = \frac{16.90 - 15.30}{\left(\dfrac{4.10}{\sqrt{36}}\right)\sqrt{\dfrac{264}{299}}} = 2.49$$

We can now report the following p-value:

$$2P(z \geq 2.49) = 2(1 - 0.9936) = 0.0128$$

Expressed in words that a nonstatistician might understand more readily, this p-value means that only 1.28% of the time, using this sampling process, would the sample mean be as large as $16.90 when $15.30 is the true mean. This result implies that a decision-maker who has an α larger than 0.0128 should reject $H_0: \ \mu = \$15.30$. If the decision-maker's α is smaller than 0.0128, then he or she should accept the null hypothesis that the true mean is $15.30.

One-sample Test When σ Is Unknown

In many circumstances it is unreasonable to assume that σ is known, for when the mean μ is unknown, the population standard deviation often is unknown also (since σ is a measure based on the size of the squared deviations about μ). And when σ is unknown, the z test statistic is not theoretically correct. Recall from Section 7.8 that, in order to solve problems involving $\bar{x}$ when σ is unknown, we can use the t-distribution if the parent population is normal. In our present context this means that if μ_0 is the value of μ specified by the null hypothesis, then when σ is unknown and the population is normal, the appropriate test statistic for tests on μ is shown as follows:

Test statistic when σ is unknown, population normal:

$$t_{(n-1)} = \frac{\bar{x} - \mu_0}{s/\sqrt{n}}$$

(10.2)

We continue discussion of this test in the context of a practical problem. A marketing adviser suggests to the Ford Motor Company that it extend its service guarantee from 12,000 kilometres to 24,000 kilometres on transmissions, muffler systems, and brakes. This adviser says the change would make good advertising copy and be relatively costless to Ford Motors because such parts seldom require service during this period anyway. The claim is that an average car will run longer than this before the cost of such repairs exceeds \$100.

We will assume that Ford Motors has asked you (as their expert on hypothesis testing) to test this claim. Ford wants you to sample a few car owners, check their service records, and give the company advice on extending its guarantee.

Now, suppose that you decide to check the service record of 15 randomly selected Ford owners from a population of millions. You will let the variable x represent the number of kilometres driven since purchase until the cumulative service repair cost on the parts under study exceeds \$100. Ford Motors wishes to determine whether or not the population mean value (μ) exceeds 24,000 (H_0: $\mu \leq 24,000$, H_a: $\mu > 24,000$). If H_0 can be rejected for the closest value of the null hypothesis, 24,000, it will also be rejected for any value less than 24,000. Thus, although the null hypothesis is H_0: $\mu \leq 24,000$, you will do the test with H_0: $\mu = 24,000$. The alternative hypothesis is H_a: $\mu > 24,000$.

In this situation, a Type I error occurs if you conclude that $\mu > 24,000$ when the null hypothesis ($\mu = 24,000$) is true. The company might then extend the guarantee policy when it should not do so. A Type II error would occur if you accept H_0: $\mu = 24,000$ when $\mu > 24,000$. This error might result in a failure to extend the guarantee when it would be worthwhile to do so.

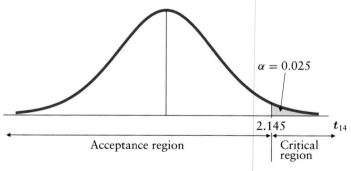

FIGURE 10.9   Critical region (using t) for H_0: $\mu = 24,000$ against H_a: $\mu > 24,000$ when σ is unknown and $n = 15$

On the basis of past experience, Ford Motors expects the distribution of x to be normal, but they do not know its standard deviation. The appropriate test statistic has a t-distribution, $t = (x - \mu_0)/(s/\sqrt{n})$. If the company is willing to accept a risk of $\alpha = 0.025$ of incorrectly rejecting H_0, then the critical region is the 2.5% of the t-distribution that lies in the right-hand tail (since H_a is to the right of H_0).

The boundary point for the acceptance region is found in Table VI for $(n-1) = 14$ degrees of freedom under the heading 0.975 or $\alpha = 0.025$. The critical t-value for a one-sided test is 2.145, as shown in Figure 10.9.

Analysis of the random sample of 15 Ford owners results in the values $\bar{x} = 25,500$ and $s = 4,000$. The **computed value of t** is:

$$t_c = \frac{(\bar{x} - \mu_0)}{\frac{s}{\sqrt{n}}} = \frac{25,500 - 24,000}{\frac{4,000}{\sqrt{15}}} = \frac{1,500}{1,033} = 1.452$$

Since the calculated value $t_c = 1.452$ lies in the acceptance region (it is less than 2.145), you would conclude that Ford Motors should accept the claim that $\mu = 24,000$. Even though our sample result indicated a value more than 24,000, this value is not far enough above 24,000 to lead to rejection of H_0 at the 0.025 level of significance.

The probability value that would be reported is:

$$p\text{-value} = P(t \geq 1.452)$$

Although this probability cannot be determined exactly from Table VI, we can determine from the row for $v = 14$ d.f. that it lies between $0.05 (t = 1.761)$ and $0.10 (t = 1.345)$. Hence, we report the following p-value interval:

$$0.10 > p\text{-value} > 0.05$$

If H_a had been two-sided in this example, the two values 0.10 and 0.05 would have had to be doubled. Using a computer, the exact p-value is found to be

$$p\text{-value} = P(t \geq 1.452) = 0.0843.$$

Let us extend our Ford Motors problem a bit by using a second and considerably larger sample with $n = 81$. For this larger sample, the sample results are:

$$\bar{x} = 24,300 \qquad \text{and} \qquad s = 5,000$$

The calculated value of t in this case is:

$$t_c = \frac{24,300 - 24,000}{5,000/\sqrt{81}} = 0.54$$

We would now like to report a p-value by calculating the value of $P(t \geq 0.54)$ for $n - 1 = 80$ d.f. This calculation poses several problems. First, there is no row in Table VI corresponding to 80 degrees of freedom, so we must move to the closest row, which is 60 d.f. But even for 60 d.f., the value of $t = 0.54$ does not appear among the values listed. From Table VI, row 60, we do know that $P(t \geq 0.679) > 0.25$. Since we also know that $P(t \geq 0) = 0.50$, we can report the following p-value interval:

$$0.50 > p\text{-value} = P(t \geq 0.54) > 0.25$$

Using a computer, the exact p-value is 0.2953.

As we pointed out in Chapter 7, many statistics texts recommend that the z-table be used to approximate the values from the t-table when n is large, which usually means when n is 30 or greater. Using the normal z in the previous example would give $P(z \geq 0.54) = 0.2946$. The best approach is to use a computer package that calculates the exact probabilities.

□ **STUDY QUESTION 10.2**   Marketing Research Study of Mean Age

L.I.M.E., Inc., a marketing research service, has been asked by the city administration to determine whether the mean age of city residents has changed since the 1990 census. At that time the mean age was $\mu = 32.1$ years. The standard deviation that existed in 1990 is unknown. L.I.M.E. takes a random sample of 250 residents and finds $\bar{x} = 33.6$, $s = 14.1$. Establish appropriate hypotheses and report a p-value. Would you accept H_0 or H_a if $\alpha = 0.01$? Write your conclusion in a sentence.

• **ANSWER**   The direction of change is not specified, so a two-sided test is used.
1. Establish H_0 and H_a: H_0: $\mu = 32.1$ versus H_a: $\mu \neq 32.1$.
2. Determine the test statistic:

$$t = \frac{\bar{x} - \mu_0}{\frac{s}{\sqrt{n}}}$$

3. Determine the critical region: The t table has no row for 249 degrees of freedom, but for 120 d.f. and $(\alpha/2) = 0.005$, $t \leq -2.617$ and $t \geq 2.617$.
4. Calculate the test statistic value and report a p-value interval:

$$t_c = \frac{33.6 - 32.1}{14.1/\sqrt{250}} = 1.682$$

$$0.05 \leq p\text{-value} = 2P(t > 1.682) \leq 0.10$$

Using a computer, the p-value for a two-sided test is $2(0.0469) = 0.0938$.
5. Decision and conclusion: Accept H_0 rather than H_a. The sample result is not sufficiently different from the previous census value of 32.1 to conclude with a small risk of error that the mean age has changed. ■

PROBLEMS

10.1 Answer the following.

a) Which is more serious, a Type I or a Type II error?

b) Why is it necessary to be concerned with the *probability* of Type I and Type II errors?

c) What is meant by the phrase "the costs of making an incorrect decision"? How are these costs related to the problem of balancing the risks of making an incorrect decision?

d) How would you go about the process of testing hypotheses in circumstances in which it is impossible to associate, at least directly, any dollar values to the costs of making an incorrect decision? Assume that you are responsible for making an important decision (for example, you are a doctor who must decide whether or not to operate on a patient).

10.2 A Los Angeles bakery was fined $12,000 for selling loaves of bread that were underweight. Assume that the L.A. city attorney has established H_0: $\mu = 24$ oz versus H_a: $\mu < 24$ oz, where 24 oz is the stated weight of each

loaf of bread. A sample of 361 loaves was taken, and σ is known to equal 1.00 oz.

a) Describe, in words, what a Type I and a Type II error would be in this circumstance. What would you guess to be the consequences of each type of error in this situation?

b) Would you accept H_0 or H_a if $\alpha = 0.01$ and the sample mean were $\bar{x} = 23.75$ oz?

c) Do you think $\alpha = 0.01$ is reasonable in this case? Would the decision change if $\alpha = 0.001$?

d) Would you buy bread from this bakery?

10.3 A medical school surveys physicians across the country to determine if the average annual expenses of operating a practice now exceed $110,000. From previous surveys, the standard deviation is thought to be $30,000.

a) Set up the null and alternative hypotheses for a test.

b) Interpret the meaning of a Type I and a Type II error in this context.

c) Data Set 4 reports the survey returns of 40 respondents for which the sample mean is $118,880. Do the test and write your conclusion.

10.4 You are interested in a site for a new restaurant, and a real estate developer claims that, on the average, male resident students at the university eat at least eight meals per week in restaurants located more than one kilometre (beyond walking distance) from their residences. To test this claim, you randomly select six students, and record the number of times they ate beyond the "one-kilometre boundary" in one designated week; the results are 6, 5, 7, 4, 8, and 6. Construct a test, at the 0.01 significance level, assuming that $\sigma = 1.5$ and that the population is normally distributed.

10.5 A Wendy's franchise has been averaging about $5,000 worth of business on a typical Saturday. The manager, concerned that sales are slipping, considers the average sales for four consecutive Saturdays.

    a) What null and alternative hypotheses would you establish to determine whether or not sales are slipping. Let H_a be one-sided. Describe a Type I and a Type II error in this context.

    b) What test statistic should you use if σ is known to equal $500?

    c) Find the critical values for $\bar{x}$ and z, assuming that $\alpha = 0.05$.

    d) What decision should be made in regard to the hypotheses if sales are $4,200, $4,400, $5,200, and $4,800 on the four Saturdays? What probability could be reported in this example?

    e) What p-value should be reported if H_a is two-sided?

    f) Comment on this manager's choice of a random sample.

10.6 A manufacturer of steel rods considers that the manufacturing process is working properly if the mean length of the rods is 8.6 inches. The standard deviation of these rods always runs about 0.3 inches. The manufacturer would like to see if the process is working correctly by taking a random sample of size $n = 36$. There is no indication whether or not the rods may be too short or too long.

    a) Establish the null and alternative hypotheses for this problem. What critical values should be used for z and $\bar{x}$ if $\alpha = 0.05$?

    b) Assume that the random sample yields an average length of 8.7 inches. Would you accept H_0 or H_a? What p-value would you report?

10.7 In a study of family income levels, nine households in a certain rural county are selected at random. The incomes in this county are known to be normally distributed with $\sigma = \$2,400$. An average income of $20,000 is reported from the sample survey. Use a statistical test to decide if average rural incomes are equal to $22,000 or are less than $22,000. Use an 0.05 level of significance.

10.8 A manufacturer of rope produces 22,500 ft of rope a day, in lengths of 50 ft each. Each day, 16 of the 50-ft lengths are tested for tensile strength. The variance of tensile strength is always approximately $\sigma^2 = 256$. The mean tensile strength of one sample of 16 observations was 340 pounds. What probability value would you report if the null hypothesis H_0: $\mu = 350$ is tested against H_a: $\mu \neq 350$? How will your answer change if the alternative is H_a: $\mu < 350$? Assume that the tensile strengths are normally distributed.

10.9 Rework Problem 10.8, but this time assume that only 5,000 ft of rope are produced each day. (*Hint:* Assume that the population size is now $5,000/50 = 100$ lengths of rope, and use the finite population correction factor.)

10.10 In a car paint shop, the desired average painting time is 1.1 hours per car. A recent random sample of 100 paint jobs revealed an average painting time of 1.2 hours per car. The population standard deviation is known to be 0.4 hours. Test whether this sample indicates that the number of hours is different from that desired. Use a two-sided alternative and let $\alpha = 0.01$.

10.11 A statistician is investigating the charge that a minority group of workers is paid less-than-average wages. The population for all comparable workers has a mean wage of $24,500 with a standard deviation of $200.

    a) Establish the appropriate null and alternative hypotheses. Describe possible consequences of a Type I and Type II error.

    b) Find the appropriate critical value if $n = 100$ and $\alpha = 0.05$.

    c) Would you accept H_0 or H_a if $\bar{x} = \$24,300$?

    d) What p-value would you report?

10.12 Under what circumstances is the t-distribution appropriate for testing hypotheses on μ?

10.13 An industrial firm that manufactures small battery-powered toys periodically purchases a large number of batteries for use in the toys. The policy of this company is never to accept a shipment of batteries unless it is possible to reject, at the 0.05 level of significance, the hypothesis that the batteries have a mean life of 50 or fewer hours. The standard deviation of the life of all batteries has typically been 3 hours.

a) What null and alternative hypotheses should be established to implement the company policy?

b) Should the company accept a shipment from which a sample of 64 batteries results in a mean life of 50.5 hours?

c) What is the minimum mean life in a sample of 64 batteries that would lead the company to accept the shipment?

10.14 Rework Problem 10.3, assuming that the population standard deviation is unknown. Table 10.1, obtained from a computer output, gives summary measures for **Data Set 4.**

TABLE 10.1   Financial Information on Physicians

Variable	Label	N	Mean	Std Dev
Cases		40	20.50	11.69
Hours	Reported weekly hours worked	40	50.43	3.13
Income	Reported annual net income of doctor	40	$155,030	$35,483.58
Fee	Average fee charged by doctor	40	$51.80	$13.15
Expenses	Average annual operating expense	40	$118,880	$29,848.88

10.15 Rework Problem 10.5, parts a–e, assuming that σ is unknown and that the population is normal. Calculate s from the four sample values.

10.16 The drive-in window of a First National Bank branch facility in Halifax averaged 24 customers per hour last year. This year the branch manager expects usage to change. Nine observations of usage were taken randomly from the first six months this year: 25, 17, 18, 22, 21, 27, 19, 15, 25.

a) Construct a test assuming that $\alpha = 0.05$, and that the population is normal. What probability value would you report?

b) What p-value would you report if the manager believed that usage has declined (one-tail test)?

10.17 A power shovel was designed to remove 31.5 cubic feet of earth per scoop. On a test run, 25 sample scoops were made; the mean of the samples was 29.3 cubic feet. The standard deviation, computed from sample information, was three cubic feet. Test, at the 99% level of confidence, whether the design

specifications for this equipment should be revised on the basis of the sample information. Describe the two types of error possible in this test. Assume that the population is normal.

♦ **10.18** The Jim Norton chain of coffee shops and doughnut shops has been a successful and stable franchise in Canada for several years. On a typical Saturday, a Jim Norton outlet in Tecumseh, Ontario was averaging sales of $10,000. The manager, Ms. Jimbit, who has just acquired a microcomputer and a statistical software program, is concerned that Saturday sales seem to be declining. If she can be reasonably sure that Saturday sales are really declining, she intends to launch a promotional campaign to boost sales. Accordingly, she records sales for 10 randomly selected Saturdays in the most recent months and runs a program for summary statistics. She asks you to help her analyze the following data and decide whether Saturday sales have slipped below $10,000.

```
File                      = SATURDAY
Observations              = 10
Minimum                   = 9000
Maximum                   = 9900
Range                     = 900
Mean                      = 9584.3
Variance                  = 79960.44
Standard deviation        = 282.7728
Coefficient of Variation  = 2.95
```

a) Set up the null and alternative hypotheses for Ms. Jimbit. Justify your setup.

b) Describe the Type I and the Type II errors in the context of your setup in part (a). What are the consequences for Ms. Jimbit of making these two types of errors?

c) What conclusion would you draw regarding her hypotheses from the computer output using $\alpha = 0.05$? Assume that sales follow a normal distribution.

♦ **10.19** Love Burger, a fast food chain in Paris, France is considering opening a franchise in Montreal. From previous studies, the company has determined that for a site to be acceptable, the number of vehicles traveling that side of the road must be at least 500 per hour. The company wants sufficient statistical evidence to determine if this site is acceptable before it invests in this venture. To collect data, the number of vehicles passing the proposed site was recorded for 100 different randomly chosen hourly periods. From these 100 x-values, it has been found that $\bar{x} = 520$ and $s = 50$.

a) Set up the null and alternative hypotheses. Justify your setup.

b) Describe the Type I error and the Type II error in the context of your setup for part (a). What are the consequences of making each of these two errors?

c) Do the sample data provide sufficient statistical evidence to claim that the proposed site is acceptable? Use $\alpha = 0.01$.

10.20 The daily output of a certain department within an industrial plant is presumed to be normally distributed and has a scheduled average of 85 units. Twenty-five days are selected at random, and the output for each day is observed. The average output calculated from this sample is 81 units, and the standard deviation is 9 units.

a) Test with 99% confidence whether or not the average output is different from that scheduled.

b) What p-value would you report?

c) Explain the meaning of the beta risk for this test.

10.21 A firm that packages tulip bulbs for a mail order nursery designed a process to place 18 bulbs in each box. The process was started and allowed to produce 400 boxes. A sample of 16 boxes was then drawn. On the basis of this sample, the number of bulbs per box averaged 17, while the standard deviation calculated was 2. Would a one-sided test indicate acceptance of the null hypothesis with a mean of 18 if alpha were set at 0.05? Assume that the population is normal.

10.22 Rework Problem 10.4, assuming that σ is unknown and that the population is normal.

♦ **10.23** Nano Computers Ltd. is a major distributor of IBM compatible PCs in the Calgary area. The current warranty provided by the company is 90 days parts and labour. In order to boost its sales, the Marketing Department is proposing to increase the warranty to

180 days. The Finance Department, however, is concerned with the financial implications of such a move. The management would go along with the additional warranty if it can be established, within a reasonable doubt, that the true mean time to first repairs μ is larger than 180 days. To do so, Mr. Williams, the marketing manager, takes a random sample of 100 repair records from the company's 10,000 records. For each record, the time from the date of sale to the date of first repair is recorded in a computer file named REPAIR. Summary statistics are computed as given below:

```
File                          = REPAIR
Observations                  = 100
Minimum                       = 150
Maximum                       = 241
Range                         = 91
Mean                          = 184
Variance                      = 504.0025
St.Dev.                       = 22.45
Coefficient of Variation      = 12.20
```

a) State the null and the alternative hypotheses and justify your answer.

b) Test the hypothesis using $\alpha = 0.05$.

c) Assume that the null hypothesis is in fact true but based on the sample evidence it was rejected in part (b). Explain whether the potential error made is a Type I, a Type II, or both.

d) Based on the sample evidence, what is your best estimate for μ?

e) Obtain a 95% confidence interval for μ.

f) Relate the test in part (b) to the confidence interval in part (e). Also, explain the different purpose of the two methods of statistical inference.

---

section 10.4

Measuring β and the Power of a Test[†]

One of the reasons why we have been avoiding discussion of the calculation of β is that the alternative hypothesis is generally a composite hypothesis. This means that we cannot calculate one value for β because there is no one value specified for μ that makes H_0 false. To illustrate this, we again present our test involving telephone charges, in which $H_0 : \mu = 15.30$ was tested against $H_a : \mu \neq 15.30$. A Type I error (incorrectly rejecting H_0) in this case is well defined, since we know it will occur only when $\mu = \$15.30$. But a Type II error (incorrectly accepting H_0) can occur for any value of μ not equal to 15.30. It should be obvious that the probability of incorrectly accepting $H_0 : \mu = \$15.30$ is much higher when the true value of μ is $\$15.50$ than when the true value of μ is $\$25.00$. The value of β must be different for these two situations.

---

† This section may be omitted without loss in continuity.

The different probability values for β that occur when H_a is composite can be tabled, graphed, or described by a functional relationship. Often it is more useful to present a function describing the values of $(1 - \beta)$, which is called a *power function*, since it indicates the ability or power of the test to correctly reject a false null hypothesis. In general, test statistics and critical regions having the highest power are preferred. Although it is beyond the scope of this book to examine the concepts involved in finding a power function for most statistical tests, we must emphasize that the tests presented thus far have made use of these concepts in that we have always selected the *most powerful critical region*.

To demonstrate the meaning and the calculation of the β error and the power of a test, consider a firm in Quebec that manufactures staples. Control over the number of staples produced in one strip is kept by sampling and testing hypotheses. When the production process is working correctly, the number (x) of staples in each strip has a mean of $\mu = 1,000$, with a standard deviation of 37.5. This variable x is presumed to have an approximately normal distribution; that is, x is $N(1,000, 37.5^2)$.

In this case the company wants to test $H_0: \mu = 1,000$ against $H_a: \mu \neq 1,000$, and the appropriate test statistic is $z = (\bar{x} - \mu_0)/(\sigma/\sqrt{n})$. A Type I error occurs whenever the test results suggest that the process is out of control ($\mu \neq 1,000$), when it actually is in control ($\mu = 1,000$). A Type II error occurs whenever the process is judged to be in control ($\mu = 1,000$) and it actually is out of control ($\mu \neq 1,000$). To make a test of these hypotheses, the company periodically selects a random sample of size $n = 9$, and the company policy is to let $\alpha = 0.05$. The critical values for the test are:

$$\mu_0 \pm z_{\alpha/2}\frac{\sigma}{\sqrt{n}} = 1,000 \pm 1.96\left(\frac{37.5}{\sqrt{9}}\right) = 1,000 \pm 24.5$$

The acceptance region shown in Figure 10.10 is [975.5 to 1,024.5] for the mean of a sample of size 9.

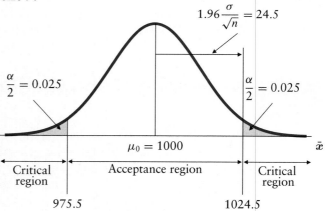

FIGURE 10.10 Critical region for test on $H_0: \mu = 1,000$ against $H_a: \mu \neq 1,000$, $\sigma = 37.5$, $n = 9$, and $\alpha = 0.05$

The question we turn to now is how to calculate β for this problem. Since β is a conditional probability that depends on the value of μ, we will assume that $\mu = 990$. We can now write:

$$\beta = P(\text{Accept } H_0: \mu_0 = 1,000 \mid \mu = 990)$$

From Figure 10.10 we see that H_0 is accepted whenever x lies between 975.5 and 1,024.5. Hence, $\beta = P(975.5 \le \bar{x} \le 1,024.53 \mid \mu = 990)$. This probability can be determined by using the same procedure as in Section 7.6 for working with $z = (\bar{x} - \mu)/(\sigma/\sqrt{n})$. First, we transform the problem to standardized normal terms by letting $\mu = 990$, $\sigma = 37.5$, and $\sqrt{n} = \sqrt{9}$, and then we use Table III to find the appropriate probabilities:

$$P(97.5 \le \bar{x} \le 1,024.5) = P\left(\frac{975.5 - 990}{37.5/\sqrt{9}} \le \frac{\bar{x} - \mu}{\sigma/\sqrt{n}} \le \frac{1,024.5 - 990}{37.5/\sqrt{9}} \right)$$

$$= P(-1.16 \le z \le 2.76)$$

$$= F(2.76) - F(-1.16)$$

$$= 0.9971 - 0.1230 = 0.8741$$

Thus, $P(\text{Type II error}) = 0.8741$, as shown in Figure 10.11. This means that when $\mu = 990$, we will *incorrectly* accept $H_0 : \mu_0 = 1,000$ as being true 87.41% of the time using our test procedure. The *power* of this test is $1 - \beta = 0.1259$, which means that this test will *correctly* recognize this false null hypothesis 12.59% of the time when $\mu = 990$.

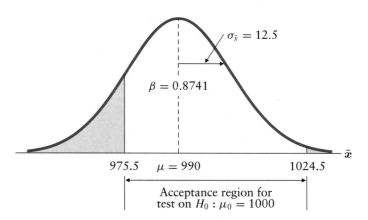

FIGURE 10.11 Probability β of Type II error for the critical region shown in Figure 10.10 if the true mean is $\mu = 990$

Instead of using the value $\mu = 990$ to calculate β, we might have used $\mu = 1,010$. These two values of μ are both an equal distance (10 units) away from $\mu_0 = 1,000$, so it should not be surprising with a *symmetrical* probability distribution to learn that the value of β is the same in both cases ($\beta = 0.8741$). Figure 10.12(a) shows the area corresponding to β for $\mu = 1,010$, while parts (b) and (c) of this figure show the area for β corresponding to $\mu = 970$ and $\mu = 950$, respectively. The calculation of β when $\mu = 970$ is shown below:

$$P(\text{Type II error} \mid \mu = 970) = P(975.5 \le \bar{x} \le 1,024.5 \mid \mu = 970)$$

$$= P\left(\frac{975.5 - 970}{37.5/\sqrt{9}} \le z \le \frac{1,024.5 - 970}{37.5/\sqrt{9}} \right)$$

$$= P(0.44 \le z \le 4.36)$$

$$= F(4.36) - F(0.44) = 1.0000 - 0.6700 = 0.3300$$

Note from Figure 10.12 that the size of β decreases as the value of μ gets farther away from $\mu = 1,000$. That is, the more incorrect H_0 is, the easier it is to correctly reject it, hence, the higher $(1 - \beta)$. This fact is shown in Table 10.2, where we present the value of β and $(1 - \beta)$ for eight different values of μ, four greater than μ_0 and four smaller. The row corresponding to $\mu = 1,000$ is in colour to emphasize that this is the one case in which H_0 is true; hence, β is not defined for $\mu = 1,000$. Figure 10.13 is a graph of the power function $(1 - \beta)$.

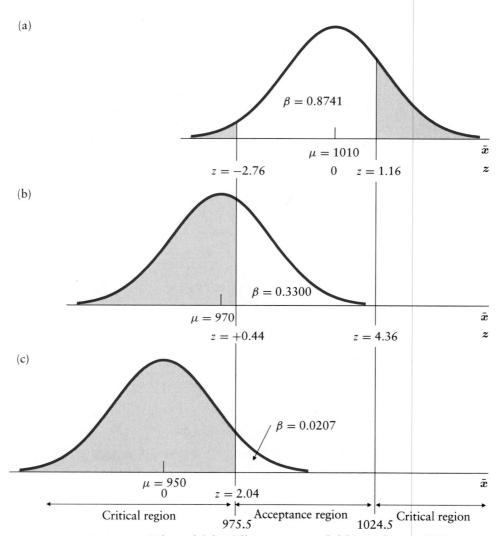

FIGURE 10.12   Values of β for different μ's, $\alpha = 0.05$, $n = 9$, $\sigma = 37.5$

In comparing the power functions of a number of different tests, we look for tests where the power function rises quickly as the value of μ differs by small amounts from μ_0. The most powerful test would be the one with the steepest ascending power function. In other words, we desire a test such that the probability of recognizing a false null hypothesis increases rapidly, even for rather small differences between the hypothesized value of the parameter and the true value.

TABLE 10.2   Value of β and Power for Given True Values of μ

μ	$P(\text{Accept } H_0) = \beta$	$P(\text{Reject } H_0) =$ Power $= 1 - \beta$
950	0.0207	0.9793
970	0.3300	0.6700
980	0.6406	0.3594
990	0.8741	0.1259
1,000	$1 - \alpha = 0.95$	$\alpha = 0.05$
1,010	0.8741	0.1259
1,020	0.6406	0.3594
1,030	0.3300	0.6700
1,050	0.0207	0.9793

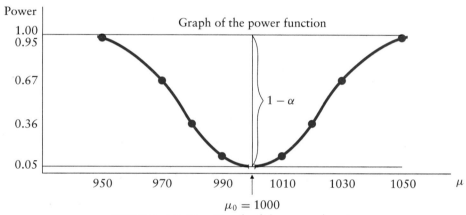

FIGURE 10.13   Graph of the power function

The Trade-offs Between α and β

We have emphasized that when the sample size is fixed, α and β have an inverse relationship. To illustrate this trade-off, we will use the same production-process example described above, but we now will change α from 0.05 to 0.10. Since α has increased, the acceptance region has become smaller, resulting in a reduction of β. Figure 10.14 shows the new acceptance region, calculated by letting $z_{\alpha/2} = z_{0.05} = 1.645$. In this situation, the null hypothesis is accepted if $979.44 \leq \bar{x} \leq 1,020.56$. The result is that the size of β is reduced from 0.3300 (shown in Table 10.2) to the new value, $\beta = 0.2236$. The power of the test has increased correspondingly. These values are shown in Figure 10.14.

If we calculated additional values of the power function, we would find all of them larger when $\alpha = 0.10$ than when $\alpha = 0.05$. As we increase α, we narrow the acceptance region and hence make our test more powerful. Similarly, if we decrease the value of α, then the acceptance region gets larger, β will rise, and the power of the test will drop. Thus, the size of α is related inversely to the size of β and directly to the size of the power, but the trade-off is not one-to-one. In this example, α was increased by 0.05 (0.05 to 0.10), but β decreased by more than 0.10 (0.3300 to 0.2236).

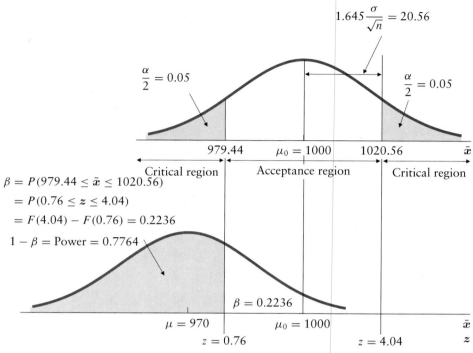

$$1.645 \frac{\sigma}{\sqrt{n}} = 20.56$$

$$\frac{\alpha}{2} = 0.05$$

$$\frac{\alpha}{2} = 0.05$$

979.44 $\mu_0 = 1000$ 1020.56 $\bar{x}$

Critical region | Acceptance region | Critical region

$\beta = P(979.44 \le \bar{x} \le 1020.56)$

$= P(0.76 \le z \le 4.04)$

$= F(4.04) - F(0.76) = 0.2236$

$1 - \beta = \text{Power} = 0.7764$

$\beta = 0.2236$

$\mu = 970$ $\mu_0 = 1000$ $\bar{x}$

$z = 0.76$ $z = 4.04$ z

FIGURE 10.14   Critical region for $H_0: \ \mu_0 = 1,000$ versus $H_a: \ \mu_0 \ne 1,000$ given $\sigma = 37.5, n = 9, \alpha = 0.10$, and the representation of β given that $\mu = 970$

Decreasing α and β by Increasing n

Until now our discussion has been based on the assumption that the size of the sample is fixed in advance. If n is changed, however, the size of both α and β may be changed because the size of n affects the dispersion of the underlying probability distribution and, consequently, the location of the acceptance and critical regions. To illustrate this effect, suppose we return α to its previous level of 0.05 and increase n from 9 to 36. The new critical region for our test, and the determination of β when the true value of μ is 970, are shown in Figure 10.15.

We see that the increased sample size makes our test more sensitive in distinguishing between H_0 and H_a because the standard error of the mean, $\sigma/\sqrt{n}$, is now half its former value (changing from $37.5/\sqrt{9} = 12.5$ to $37.5/\sqrt{36} = 6.25$). The null hypothesis will be accepted in this test if $987.75 < \bar{x} \le 1,012.25$. The probability that H_0 will be accepted given that $\mu = 970$ is now only $\beta = 0.0023$. By comparing Figures 10.14 and 10.15, we see that we have reduced α from 0.10 to 0.05 and reduced β from 0.2236 to 0.0023 merely by increasing n from 9 to 36. Unfortunately, obtaining larger samples is more time-consuming and is often quite costly, so the analyst is faced with the task of balancing the costs of making incorrect decisions against the costs of sampling. We will return to this consideration in Section 10.6 and in Chapter 17.

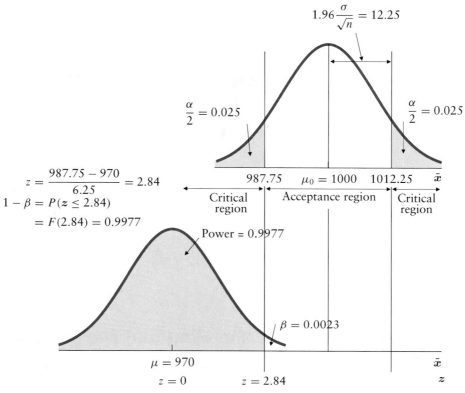

$$z = \frac{987.75 - 970}{6.25} = 2.84$$

$$1 - \beta = P(z \le 2.84)$$

$$= F(2.84) = 0.9977$$

FIGURE 10.15 Critical region for the test on H_0: $\mu_0 = 1,000$ versus H_a: $\mu_0 \ne 1,000$, $\sigma = 37.5$, $n = 36$, $\alpha = 0.05$ and the representation of β when $\mu = 970$

☐ **STUDY QUESTION 10.3**   **Simulation Run-time on a Computer**

The systems department of Stanfield Oil Company typically runs a number of large simulation programs on their mainframe computer. The largest of these simulations takes an average of 31 minutes of running time. A manufacturer of a new simulation software package claims that their program will run this simulation at least 20% faster, on the average. You decide to test H_0: $\mu = 24.80$ versus H_a: $\mu < 24.80$ by using a sample of size $n = 5$ and $\alpha = 0.05$. The hypothesized mean is 20 percent below the current average run time. What is β if the true value of $\mu = 19.50$ and $\sigma = 5.1$?

• **ANSWER**   The low side critical value, denoted L, when $\alpha = 0.05$ is derived in Figure 10.16. Although H_a is one-sided in this problem, the process of finding β is the same as for a two-sided test — namely, we find the area in the acceptance region assuming H_a is true. Hence,

$$\beta = P(\bar{x} \ge 21.05 \mid \mu = 19.50) = P\left(\frac{\bar{x} - \mu}{\sigma/\sqrt{n}} \ge \frac{21.05 - 19.50}{5.1/\sqrt{5}}\right)$$

$$= P(z \ge 0.68) = 0.2483$$

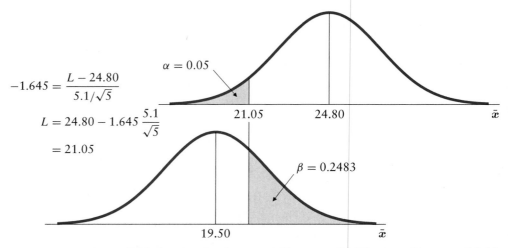

$$-1.645 = \frac{L - 24.80}{5.1/\sqrt{5}}$$

$$L = 24.80 - 1.645\frac{5.1}{\sqrt{5}}$$

$$= 21.05$$

FIGURE 10.16 Critical region for the test on H_0: $\mu = 24.80$ versus H_a: $\mu < 24.80$ where $\sigma = 5.1$, $n = 5$, $\alpha = 0.05$, and the representation of β when $\mu = 19.50$

section 10.5

Test on the Binomial Parameter

The population parameter being examined in a test of hypothesis need not always be the population mean μ. In many situations, the parameter in question is the *proportion* of observations having a certain attribute. When the observations are independent of one another (they are randomly selected with replacement) and the attribute of interest either occurs or does not occur in each observation, then the appropriate test statistic follows the *binomial distribution*. A test involving an unknown binomial proportion π may be one-sided or two-sided, and the values for π may range from zero to one. For example, suppose the null hypothesis is

$$H_0: \pi = \frac{1}{2}.$$

This hypothesis may be tested against the two-sided alternative H_a: $\pi \neq \frac{1}{2}$, or against either of the following one-sided alternative hypotheses: H_a: $\pi < \frac{1}{2}$ or H_a: $\pi > \frac{1}{2}$. As we will demonstrate below, hypotheses involving π can be tested directly by using the binomial distribution or by using the normal approximation to the binomial.

Binomial Tests Using Table I

Recall from Section 9.6 that the best estimator of a binomial proportion π is the sample proportion $p = x/n$. If the value of n used in making this estimate is one of the values of n presented in Table I in Appendix C, or if binomial probabilities can be calculated on a personal computer, we can test hypotheses about π directly. The only substantive difference between this approach and our previous tests involving μ is that now we are dealing with a discrete rather than a continuous test statistic.

The one difficulty in working with a discrete test statistic comes in Step 3, where it is necessary to define a critical region cutting off an area of size α. Unfortunately, when discrete probability spikes are involved, there may be no critical value(s) cutting off an amount exactly equal to α. We have observed this same fact in forming confidence intervals on π in Section 9.6. The usual procedure to ensure that the probability of a Type I error is no larger than α is to find the *extreme value* of x that satisfies the following:

Procedure for finding the critical region in a binomial problem:
For upper-sided test: Find the minimum x such that

$$P(x \text{ or more successes}) \leq \alpha$$

For lower-sided test: Find the maximum x such that   (10.3)

$$P(x \text{ or fewer successes}) \leq \alpha$$

For two-sided test: Use both rules above substituting $(\alpha/2)$ for α

☐ **EXAMPLE 10.3** Consider again the quality control example presented in Section 5.5. In that example, a quality-control engineer is going to sample 20 items from a malfunctioning production process to determine whether to accept H_0: $\pi = 0.10$ (a minor adjustment) or to accept H_a: $\pi = 0.25$ (a major adjustment). Since the alternative hypothesis includes values of π on only one side of the value stated in H_0: $\pi = 0.10$, we need to establish a single critical region that will cut off a probability of α in the *upper* tail of the binomial distribution (the upper tail is used because 0.25 is larger than the null hypothesis value of 0.10). The appropriate binomial distribution in this case has $n = 20$ and $\pi = 0.10$ (representing the null hypothesis).

Let us assume that α has been set at 0.05. This means that we want to find the value of x in Table I, under $n = 20$ and $\pi = 0.10$, such that the probability that the true parameter is larger than this value is no greater than 0.05. Looking in Table I, we see that $P(x \geq 9) = 0.0001$. Similarly, $P(x \geq 8) = 0.0005$. Continuing in this fashion, we can calculate that $P(x \geq 5) = 0.0433$. Thus, if our critical value is $x = 5$, the critical region cut off is of size 0.0433. The next lower value, $x = 4$, cuts off a critical region of size $0.0433 + 0.0898 = 0.1331$, which is too large. Hence, to ensure an α *no larger* than 0.05, $x \geq 5$ is the appropriate critical region. Any sample that results in five or more successes in the 20 trials leads to acceptance of H_a: $\pi = 0.25$. A sample with four or fewer defectives leads to acceptance of H_0: $\pi = 0.10$. The critical and acceptance regions for this problem are shown in Figure 10.17(a). ■

Extending Example 10.3, calculation of the value of β is fairly straightforward, since H_a is a simple alternative hypothesis. Recall that β is the probability that the test statistic falls in the acceptance region when H_a is true. For our problem the acceptance region is $x \leq 4$, and the alternative hypothesis is H_a: $\pi = 0.25$. Hence, β is calculated as follows and shown in Figure 10.17(b):

$$\beta = P(x \leq 4 \mid \pi = 0.25 \text{ and } n = 20)$$

$$= 0.4148$$

The quality-control engineer thus runs a 41.48% chance of accepting H_0 and making a minor adjustment when H_0 is false and a major adjustment is needed. This β-value is quite large in relation to $\alpha = 0.05$. In Section 10.6, we will discuss how one might go about achieving a balance between α and β by considering the costs of making both Type I and Type II errors.

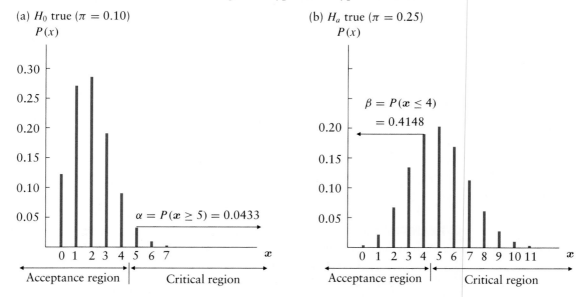

FIGURE 10.17 Critical and acceptance regions for testing $H_0: \pi = 0.10$ versus $H_a: \pi = 0.25$, and representations of α and β risks

In the above discussion, we assumed that α was known in advance. If it is not possible or desirable to specify α in advance, Table I can also be used to report probability values. For example, suppose that α is not given in the quality-control problem described above, but we know that the sample of $n = 20$ resulted in $x = 6$ defectives. The p-value to be reported is the probability of six *or more*[1] defectives in 20 trials when $\pi = 0.10$ (the null hypothesis):

$$p\text{-value} = P(x \geq 6 \mid \pi = 0.10 \text{ and } n = 20) = 0.0114 \qquad \text{(from Table I)}$$

In this case, the decision-maker would have to determine whether $p = 0.0114$ is small enough to reject the null hypothesis $H_0: \pi = 0.10$, or if it is large enough to comfortably accept H_0.

Using the Normal Approximation When n is Large

Recall that it is not always convenient to determine exact binomial probabilities. Fortunately, when the value of n is large and the value of π is not close to either zero or one, then the hypotheses about the binomial parameter π may be tested by using the standardized normal distribution as the appropriate test statistic. An often-used rule of thumb is to assume that the standardized normal approximation can be used when $n\pi(1 - \pi) > 3$, where π is the value specified under H_0, and n is the sample size. The computed value of z for the normal approximation to a binomial proportion is:

---

[1] We must emphasize here that the reported p-value is always the probability of an event that involves a *range* of values and not just a single number. Hence, in this case the probability of six *or more* successes is appropriate. When a p-value is calculated, the range of values used always extends away from the expected value $E[x]$ and toward the critical region. Thus, from Figure 10.17(a) we see that the critical region extends upward in the right-hand tail, and since $E[x] = n\pi = 2$, $x \geq 6$ is used for calculating the p-value.

> Normal approximation to binomial test statistic:
>
> $$z = \frac{p - \pi_0}{\sqrt{\dfrac{\pi_0(1 - \pi_0)}{n}}} \qquad (10.4)$$
>
> where $p = x/n$, the sample proportion.

This standardization is exactly like the one described in Section 6.6, Formula 6.8.

☐ **EXAMPLE 10.4** The marketing division of General Motors wanted an indication of whether or not a majority of the car-buying public desired larger, more luxury-featured automobiles versus smaller and more efficient cars. The hypotheses in this case could be $H_0 : \pi \geq 0.50$ versus $H_a : \pi < 0.50$, where π is the proportion of the public wanting larger cars. However, recall that composite null hypotheses are somewhat more difficult to work with than simple null hypotheses. Making H_0 simple in this example is quite reasonable, as the concern is whether or not the proportion favouring larger cars is less than 0.50. Hence, the appropriate hypotheses are:

$$H_0 : \pi = 0.50 \quad \text{versus} \quad H_a : \pi < 0.50$$

This change in H_0 does not weaken our test. If $\pi_0 = 0.50$ is rejected in favour of $\pi < 0.50$, we are even more confident that larger possible values of π, such as $\pi = 0.55$ or $\pi = 0.60$, would be rejected.

Let α be specified as 0.01 and a random sample of 1,000 adults be taken. Since $n\pi_0(1 - \pi_0) = 1,000(0.50)(0.50) = 250 > 3$, a normal approximation should be quite good. The appropriate normal critical value can be computed by determining from Table III that $z_{0.01} = 2.33$. Since H_a is to the *left* of H_0, we use $-z = -2.33$ in Formula 10.4 in order to solve for the critical value of $p = x/n$:

$$z = \frac{p - \pi_0}{\sqrt{\dfrac{\pi_0(1 - \pi_0)}{n}}}$$

$$-2.33 = \frac{p - 0.50}{\sqrt{\dfrac{(0.50)(0.50)}{1,000}}}$$

$$p = 0.50 - 2.33\sqrt{\frac{(0.50)(0.50)}{1,000}} = 0.4632$$

The critical value for p is 0.4632. If desired, we could have solved for x instead of p, since n is known to be 1,000. In this case, the result would have been $x = np = 463.2$. Both critical values are shown in Figure 10.18.

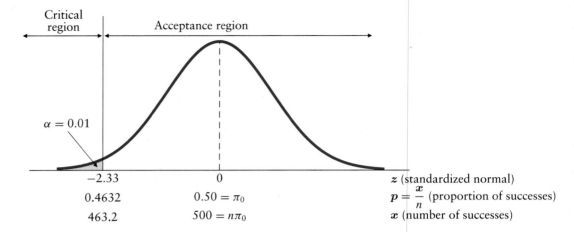

FIGURE 10.18 Standardized normal approximation to the binomial test statistic

The survey results show that 450 out of the 1,000 adults desired larger cars. That is, $x = 450$ and $p = x/n = 450/1,000 = 0.45$. This result is clearly in the critical region shown in Figure 10.18; hence, we reject $H_0: \pi = 0.50$ in favour of $H_a: \pi < 0.50$. A calculated value of z for this result is:

$$z_c = \frac{p - \pi_0}{\sqrt{\dfrac{\pi_0(1 - \pi_0)}{n}}} = \frac{0.45 - 0.50}{\sqrt{\dfrac{(0.50)(0.50)}{1,000}}} = -3.16$$

The reported p-value is thus:

$$P(z \le z_c) = P(z \le -3.16) = 1 - 0.9992 = 0.0008$$

We conclude that less than 50% of the car-buying public desire larger cars. We admit a risk of 0.08% that this conclusion is wrong. ∎

The reader may wonder if a correction for continuity is needed in Formula 10.4 before solving for critical values. The answer is no, because we were not using Formula 10.4 to approximate a *specific* binomial probability. If we were to change our objective somewhat and assume that a sample has been taken and we wish to find the p-value associated with the computed value of z_c, the answer would be yes.

When using the normal distribution to approximate a specific binomial probability, the correction for continuity should be used for exactness. However, if n is large and π is not close to either 0 or 1.0, the change in the results is not great. In all such problems in this chapter, the reader may presume that the gain in exactness is negligible and would not change the conclusion of the decision-maker.

❑ STUDY QUESTION 10.4   A Survey to Determine Soup Preference

The fast-food chain RAX is considering substituting Campbell's soup for its own home-made variety, which is more expensive to make. The substitution will be made if RAX is convinced that more than 40% of their soup customers are indifferent or prefer Campbell's soup. A sample of 150 randomly selected soup customers was asked to taste both types (unlabeled) and to indicate their preference or indifference. Seventy of these people were indifferent or picked Campbell's soup ($x = 70$). Formulate the appropriate hypotheses and report a p-value. Would you accept H_0 or H_a if $\alpha = 0.05$?

• ANSWER

1. Establish H_0 and H_a: H_0: $\pi \leq 0.40$ versus H_a: $\pi > 0.40$.

2. Determine the test statistic: Since $n = 150$, the use of the binomial distribution is inconvenient, and since $n\pi_0(1 - \pi_0) = 150(0.4)(0.6) = 36 > 3$, a normal approximation is used:

$$z = \frac{p - \pi_0}{\sqrt{\dfrac{\pi_0(1 - \pi_0)}{n}}}$$

3. Determine the critical value: $z_{0.05} = 1.645$

4. Calculate a test statistic value and report a p-value: Since $p = 70/150 = 0.467$ and $\pi_0 = 0.40$,

$$z_c = \frac{0.467 - 0.40}{\sqrt{\dfrac{0.40(0.60)}{150}}} = \frac{0.067}{0.04} = 1.675$$

$$p\text{-value} = P(z \geq 1.675) = 0.047$$

5. Decision and conclusion: Reject H_0 and accept H_a, since $\alpha = 0.05$ is greater than the p-value $= 0.0465$. Switch to Campbell's soup, although we admit a risk of 4.7% that less than 40% might be indifferent or prefer the Campbell soup.

---

section 10.6

Balancing the Risks and Costs of Making a Wrong Decision

We now return to the important problem of how to choose the best critical region to weigh the risks and costs associated with making a Type I error against those associated with making a Type II error. As we pointed out in Chapter 7, the objective of sampling can be stated as one of balancing the costs of making an incorrect decision (including sampling costs, which will be considered later). Unfortunately in many circumstances, there may be no easy way even to determine what these costs are, much less to try to balance them. In medical research, for example, it may be difficult if not impossible to assess the costs associated with an incorrect decision involving a new drug or surgical technique. But even if these costs could somehow be assessed, how does one go about balancing costs that may include pain, suffering, and even loss of life? On the other hand, if it is possible to identify the relevant costs and to express them in terms of some comparable basis, such as dollars, then we may be able to balance these costs quite explicitly. The following example describes how to find the critical region by using a process that *minimizes the expected cost of making an incorrect decision.*

Return to the quality-control problem of Section 10.5. It should be noted that, for the first part of this example, we assume that the sample size is fixed at $n = 20$; later we change this assumption and consider a sample of size $n = 50$. Suppose that all the possible costs associated with an incorrect decision, such as losses in profit, and goodwill, are those shown in Figure 10.19. A correct decision is assumed to result in no loss in profit or goodwill.

Decision		Proportion defectives: $\pi = 0.10$, H_0 is true	$\pi = 0.25$, H_0 is false
Decision	Accept H_0 make minor adjustment	Correct decision	\$200
	Reject H_0 make major adjustment	\$500	Correct decision

FIGURE 10.19 Costs of making an incorrect decision

We can calculate for each possible critical region the expected cost (per sample of 20) that will result if the process is producing defectives (**a**) at a rate of 10% or (**b**) at a rate of 25%. These expected costs are calculated by multiplying the probability of making each type of error by the cost of making that error. We have calculated these values for two critical regions: (1) the values $x \geq 5$, which gives a smaller β at the expense of a larger α, and (2) the values $x \geq 4$ used in Figure 10.17.

1. *Critical region* $x \geq 4$ ($\alpha = 0.1331$ and $\beta = 0.2251$)†

a. For $\pi = 0.10$:

$$\begin{aligned}\text{Expected cost} &= P(\text{Type I error}) \times \text{Cost of a Type I error}\\ &= 0.1331(\$500) = \$66.55.\end{aligned}$$

b. For $\pi = 0.25$:

$$\begin{aligned}\text{Expected cost} &= P(\text{Type II error}) \times \text{Cost of a Type II error}\\ &= 0.2251(\$200) = \$45.02.\end{aligned}$$

2. *Critical region* $x \geq 5$ ($\alpha = 0.0433$ and $\beta = 0.4148$)

a. For $\pi = 0.10$:

$$\begin{aligned}\text{Expected cost} &= P(\text{Type I error}) \times \text{Cost of a Type I error}\\ &= 0.0433(\$500) = \$21.65.\end{aligned}$$

b. For $\pi = 0.25$:

$$\begin{aligned}\text{Expected cost} &= P(\text{Type II error}) \times \text{Cost of a Type II error}\\ &= 0.4148(\$200) = \$82.96.\end{aligned}$$

The expected costs given above are conditional values, in that each one was calculated on the assumption that either $\pi = 0.10$ or $\pi = 0.25$. In order to determine which of these critical regions is better, we need to know how often the process is expected to produce defectives at a rate of 10%, relative to the number of times it will be producing defectives at a rate of 25%. Suppose that, if an adjustment is required, the probability that it will be a minor adjustment is 0.70, while the probability that it will be a major adjustment is 0.30. The *total* expected costs associated with each of the two critical regions can now be calculated by taking the product of the expected costs determined above multiplied by the probability that each of these costs will be incurred.

† These probabilities were given in Table 5.4 of Section 5.5. They can also be calculated from Table I using $n = 20$, $\pi = 0.10$.

1. *Critical region $x \geq 4$:*
   Total expected cost

   $= P$(Major adjustment needed) $\times$ Expected cost of Type II error
   $\quad + P$(Minor adjustment needed) $\times$ Expected cost of Type I error
   $= 0.30(\$45.02) + 0.70(\$66.55)$
   $= \$60.09$.

2. *Critical region $x \geq 5$:*
   Total expected cost

   $= P$(Major adjustment needed) $\times$ Expected cost of Type II error
   $\quad + P$(Minor adjustment needed) $\times$ Expected cost of Type I error
   $= 0.30(\$82.96) + 0.70(\$21.65)$
   $= \$40.04$.

Thus, when the process is malfunctioning, the total expected cost for each sample of 20 equals $\$60.09$ if the critical region is $x \geq 4$ and $\$40.04$ if the critical region is $x \geq 5$. In Problem 10.29, we ask the reader to determine that $x \geq 5$ is, in fact, the *optimal* critical region for this problem, with total expected cost smaller than any other critical region.

Changing the Sample Size

Suppose that the size of the above sample could have been increased to $n = 50$ at a cost of $\$10$. Our discussion of trade-offs between α, β, and n in Section 10.4 suggests that this increase in sample size can lead to a decrease in both α and β if an appropriate critical region is used. The question is whether or not the decreased probability of making an error is worth the increased sampling costs of $\$10$. In order to answer this question, let us select a critical region for the new situation (with $n = 50$) and then determine α, β, and the total expected cost for this critical region. This total expected cost can then be compared to the preceding optimal cost of $\$40.04$.

Since n has increased 2.5 times from 20 to 50, let us arbitrarily try a new critical value that is 2.5 times greater than the initial one ($x = 4$); that is, $x = 10$. We leave it as an exercise for the reader to determine if a better critical region than $x \geq 10$ could be found, perhaps $x \geq 12$ or $x \geq 13$ (which are approximately 2.5 times the previous optimal value of $x = 5$). The probability of observing a specific number of defectives when $n = 50$ under the two hypotheses, $H_0: \pi = 0.10$ and $H_a: \pi = 0.25$, is shown in Table 10.3. The probabilities of Type I and Type II errors are seen to be $\alpha = 0.0245$ and $\beta = 0.1636$. Thus, we see that increasing n from 20 to 50 has reduced both α and β.

Critical region $x \geq 10$ ($\alpha = 0.0245$ and $\beta = 0.1636$)
1. For $\pi = 0.10$:
   Expected cost $= P$(Type I error) $\times$ Cost of a Type I error
   $\qquad\qquad = 0.0245(\$500) = \$12.25$
2. For $\pi = 0.25$:
   Expected cost $= P$(Type II error) $\times$ Cost of a Type II error
   $\qquad\qquad = 0.1636(\$200) = \$32.72$
   Total expected cost

   $= P$(Major adjustment needed) $\times$ Expected cost of Type II error
   $\quad + P$(Minor adjustment needed) $\times$ Expected cost of Type I error
   $= 0.30(32.72) + 0.70(12.25) = \$18.39$.

TABLE 10.3   Determining α and β when $n = 50$ and the Critical Region is $x \geq 10$

x	Decision	If $\pi = 0.10$, H_0 Is True $P(x) = {}_{50}C_x(0.10)^x(0.90)^{50-x}$		If $\pi = 0.25$, H_a Is True $P(x) = {}_{50}C_x(0.25)^x(0.75)^{50-x}$
0		0.0052		0.0000
1		0.0286		0.0000
2		0.0779		0.0001
$\vdots$	Accept H_0, make minor adjustment	$\vdots$	Acceptance region	$\beta = 0.1636$ $\vdots$
8		0.0643		0.0463
9		0.0333		0.0721
10		0.0152		0.0985
11		0.0061		0.1194
12		0.0022		0.1294
$\vdots$	Reject H_0, make major adjustment	$\vdots$ $\alpha = 0.0245$	Critical region	$\vdots$
24		0.0000		0.0002
25		0.0000		0.0001
26–50		0.0000		0.0000
Sum		1.000		1.0000

Thus, if we have to choose between a sample of 20 and critical region $x \geq 5$ (with $\alpha = 0.0433$ and $\beta = 0.4148$) in which the costs will average \$40.04 and a sample of 50 and critical region $x \geq 10$ (with $\alpha = 0.0245$ and $\beta = 0.1636$) in which the costs will average \$18.39 for the incorrect decisions plus \$10.00 for the additional observations, it is better to take the larger sample. It may be, of course, that some other critical region will be even better than $x \geq 10$ or that some other sample size gives a lower expected cost. Given calculations of all the possible total expected costs, the optimal sample size and its associated critical region could be determined for this problem. In Chapter 17, we shall return to an extended version of this type of problem and study in more detail the question of sample size.

section 10.7

One Sample Test on $\sigma^{2\dagger}$

Once the procedure for testing hypotheses has been mastered, it can be applied to many other test situations if an appropriate test statistic can be developed. In

---

† This section may be omitted without loss of continuity. It is assumed that the reader has covered Section 7.9.

this section, an example of a test is given which utilizes a test statistic with a chi-square distribution. Table VII, which defines values of the cumulative chi-square distribution, is used to determine the critical region for this test.

Test on a Population Variance, σ^2

In Section 7.9 we formulated a chi-square random variable,

$$\chi^2_{(n-1)} = \frac{(n-1)s^2}{\sigma^2}$$

for a situation in which a random sample of size n is taken from a normal population with standard deviation σ^2. In Section 9.8, a confidence interval for σ^2 was developed using this variable. We now illustrate the use of the χ^2 variable in testing hypotheses about the unknown population variance σ^2 based on a sample estimator s^2.

For a client, you are analyzing a possible purchase of a franchise for Western Bar-B-Q ribs and sandwiches. So far, you have learned that the monthly profits from such franchises is normally distributed with a mean of $9,200. What concerns you now is the variability in monthly profits, as this variability is a measure of the risk being assumed. Your client decides that if the standard deviation of profits is $800 or more, the investment is too risky.

From a statistical point of view, we do not test hypotheses about standard deviations, but rather about variances. Therefore, you clarify that the client will not invest unless the hypothesis that σ^2 is $800^2 = 640,000$ or more can be rejected in favour of the hypothesis that σ^2 is less than 640,000. The most convenient structure for the hypotheses in this problem is to make H_0 a *simple* hypothesis by assigning the most extreme (lowest) value that would cause the client not to invest, that is, $\sigma^2 = 640,000$, and test

$$H_0: \ \sigma^2 = 640,000 \qquad \text{versus} \qquad H_a: \ \sigma^2 < 640,000$$

Thus, if H_0 is accepted, the client should not invest; if H_0 is rejected in favour of H_a, the client should invest. For this type of problem the following chi-square test statistic is appropriate.

Test statistic for hypotheses about a population variance for $v = (n-1)$ d.f.:

$$\chi^2_{(n-1)} = \frac{(n-1)s^2}{\sigma_0{}^2} \qquad\qquad (10.5)$$

In Formula 10.5, $\sigma_0{}^2$ is the hypothesized value of σ^2 when H_0 is true, and s^2 is the sample estimator of the variance based on the random sample of size n.

The next step is to construct the critical region for this test of hypotheses. Since the alternative hypothesis is one-sided to the left of H_0, the appropriate critical region is associated with 100α percent of the values in the left-hand tail of the chi-square distribution. You decide on a sample of size $n = 12$ (chosen randomly among a set of franchises) and you set $\alpha = 0.05$. From Table VII, the critical value for $v = 11$ is $\chi^2_{11} = 4.57$. The critical region for this example is all values of χ^2 less than 4.57, as shown in Figure 10.20.

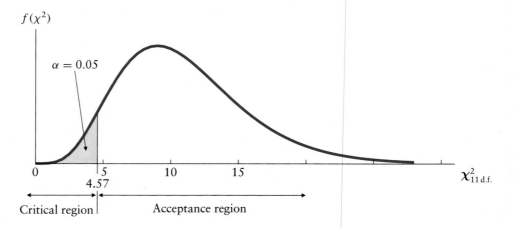

FIGURE 10.20 Critical region for a one-sided chi-square test with $v = n - 1 = 11$ and $\alpha = 0.05$

A sample of $n = 12$ monthly profits yields a sample variance equal to $s^2 = 360,000$. The **computed value of the chi-square test statistic** is:

$$\chi_c^2 = \frac{(n-1)s^2}{\sigma^2} = \frac{11(360,000)}{640,000} = 6.19$$

The sample result falls in the acceptance region and the p-value is 0.1396. This means that even though the sample variance is much less than the hypothesized value for the population variance, it is not sufficiently smaller to warrant rejection of H_0. Hence, you report to your client that an investment in Western Bar-B-Q is risky because it is sufficiently likely that the variance of monthly profits may be as large as 640,000. The standard deviation of monthly profits may exceed $800.

The reader should note that, while the standard deviation may be the more easily interpreted measure of risk or variability, the χ^2 test deals with the square of σ, the variance. Similar tests on σ^2 in other situations may be one-sided upper-tail tests or two-sided tests. All of these tests, however, follow the same general procedure.

☐ STUDY QUESTION 10.5 A Study of the Variance in Gas Mileage

Honda has developed a new fuel-efficient automobile engine and has already determined average gas mileage estimates for highway driving. Assume that Honda is now interested in testing hypotheses about the *variability* in MPG (miles per gallon) for the new engine relative to the old one. The engineers are unsure if variability will increase or decrease. The variance of MPG for the previous engine was $\sigma^2 = 3.9$ (MPG squared). In a test of highway driving with a sample of nine of the new engines, the sample variance was $s^2 = 5.1$. Formulate appropriate hypotheses and report a p-value. Would you accept H_0 or H_a if $\alpha = 0.05$?

• ANSWER
1. Establish the hypotheses: H_0: $\sigma^2 = 3.9$ versus H_a: $\sigma^2 \neq 3.9$.
2. Determine the test statistic:

$$\chi^2 = \frac{(n-1)s^2}{\sigma^2}$$

3. Determine the critical region: For $(\alpha/2) = 0.025$ and $d.f. = 8$, the two-sided critical region is $\chi^2 \leq 2.18$ and $\chi^2 \geq 17.5$.

4. Calculate a test statistic value and report a p-value:

$$\chi_c^2 = \frac{(8)(5.1)}{3.9} = 10.46$$

$2P(\chi^2 \geq 10.46) > 0.20$ (from Table VII, $v = 8$, after doubling) The exact p-value using a computer is $2(0.2342) = 0.4684$.

5. Decision and conclusion: Do not reject H_0 because α is less than the p-value resulting from a computed chi-square value which lies in the acceptance region. The variance from the sample of new engines is not different enough from the previous variance to conclude that the variability in MPG has changed. ∎

PROBLEMS

♦ **10.24** Consider the following null and alternative hypotheses.

$$H_0: \mu = 100$$

$$H_a: \mu \neq 100$$

The population standard deviation is known to be 30. A random sample of 100 is planned for testing the hypothesis. The decision rule for this test is: reject the null hypothesis if the sample mean is more than 106 or less than 94; accept H_0 otherwise.

a) What is the probability of making a Type I error for this decision rule?

b) If μ is actually 109, what is the probability of making a Type II error?

c) What would be the answers to both parts (a) and (b) if the same decision rule were based on a sample of size 400?

10.25 Reconsider Problem 10.2, assuming that the true weight of the loaves of bread in this population is 23.90 oz. What is the value of β if $\alpha = 0.01$? What is the power of the test if $\mu = 23.90$? Using words a nonquantitative decision-maker might understand, interpret the meaning of the values of α and β in this problem.

10.26 Use the critical value calculated in Problem 10.5(c).

a) What is the value of β if the true value of μ is $4,900? What is the power of the test?

b) Repeat part (a), assuming that the true values are $4,800, $4,700, $4,600, and $4,500. Construct a graph of the power function, using these values.

10.27 Sketch the power function for Problem 10.10, assuming that the true values of μ are 0.90, 0.95, 1.00, 1.05, and 1.20.

10.28 Return to Problem 10.13, in which the sample size was $n = 64$ and $\alpha = 0.05$.

a) Find β if $\mu = 51$.

b) Show that for the hypotheses and critical region presented in part (a), the values of both α and β will decrease if n is increased to 100.

10.29 In the discussion in Section 10.6, we calculated the probability of making an incorrect decision concerning adjustments to a production process. The values of α and β were determined for the critical region $x \geq 4$ and for the critical region $x \geq 5$, assuming a sample size of 20.

a) Calculate α and β for this problem for the critical region $x \geq 6$.

b) Calculate the expected cost associated with this critical region when the probability of a defective is 0.10. Do the same thing for the probability of a defective equal to 0.25.

c) Calculate the total expected cost associated with this critical region, assuming that the probability of a minor adjustment is 0.70 and the probability of a major adjustment is 0.30.

d) Is the cost that you determined in part (c) better or worse than the cost calculated in Section 10.6 for the critical region $x \geq 5$? Do you think $x \geq 5$ is the best critical region for this sample size? Explain why, and then try to draw a graph relating the location of the critical region to the total expected costs. Let the horizontal axis be the lower bound of the critical regions.

10.30 In Section 10.6 it was shown that, for the production process under investigation, a sample size of 50 results in a lower expected cost than a sample size of 20 if the additional observations cost only an extra $10. Suppose that we now have the opportunity to buy 50 more observations (for a total n of 100) for $15 more (sampling cost of $25). Estimate, as best you can, the optimal critical region for this size of sample. Is the total expected cost in this case lower or higher than the cost when $n = 50$?

10.31 The manager of food services at Rost Labs claims there is more support for the lunch food this year than last year, when 80% of the employees were dissatisfied. A sample of 50 randomly selected employees finds that 20 think the food is satisfactory this year. The others express some dissatisfaction. Test with an alternative hypothesis that dissatisfaction has decreased, using $\alpha = 0.01$ and Table I. Repeat the test, using a normal approximation. Report a p-value in both cases.

10.32 At the Capital plant in Edmonton, at least two-fifths of the 5,500 employees are reported to be 45 years old or older. A random sample of 100 employees finds that 35 are at least 45 years old. Construct a test of the claim at the 0.05 significance level, using both Table I and the normal approximation.

♦ **10.33** An auditor believes that the proportion of invoices containing at least one error has changed significantly since last year when this proportion was 0.05.

    a) Set up the null and the alternative hypotheses for the auditor, defining each symbol clearly.

    b) Describe the Type I and Type II errors in the context of the setup in part (a).

    c) Find the critical values for z assuming $\alpha = 0.03$. State the decision rule based on these critical z values.

    d) In a random sample of 50 invoices, 46 were error-free and four invoices were found to contain at least one error. Does this sample evidence support the auditor's claim? Use $\alpha = 0.03$.

    e) What p value would you report for this test?

10.34 The national proportion of accountants who passed the entire CGA exam on the first attempt is $\frac{1}{3}$. In British Columbia last year, 36 people took the test for the first time, and 18 passed. Using $\alpha = 0.05$, is this sufficient evidence to indicate a proportion of first-time passes that is greater than the national proportion?

10.35 A supermarket has agreed to advertise through a local newspaper if it can be established that the newspaper's circulation reaches more than 50% of the supermarket's customers.

    a) What null and alternative hypotheses should be established in this problem in trying to decide, on the basis of a random sample of customers, whether or not the supermarket should advertise in the newspaper?

    b) A sample of size $n = 64$ is collected, and $\alpha = 0.01$. Before a decision should be made to advertise, what number (critical value) is needed of supermarket customers who regularly look at this newspaper's advertisements?

10.36 A nationally known insurance company has been advertising on TV that "9 out of 10 claims are in the return mail two days after receipt." Suppose that you decide to test this assertion and you believe the actual proportion is smaller.

    a) What critical region would you establish if $\alpha = 0.05$ and $n = 100$? Use Table I.

    b) Would you accept H_0 or H_a if 85 claims were returned within the two days? What p-value would you report?

    c) Repeat parts (a) and (b) using a normal approximation.

    d) What p-value would you report in part (c) if the sample result found 95 claims settled within two days?

10.37 The telephone company is continually studying the variability in length of phone calls, as well as the average length. Suppose that the national population variance of length of calls is $\sigma^2 = 4$ minutes squared. The telephone company wants to test whether a certain community's calls differ in variability from the national value. The length of calls is assumed to be normally distributed.

    a) What null and alternative hypotheses would you establish for the test described above?

    b) What critical region(s) would you use for this test if $\alpha = 0.05$ and $n = 25$?

    c) Would you accept or reject H_0 if the sample of $n = 25$ resulted in $s^2 = 3.0$?

10.38 Recent studies of life insurance policies have criticized the industry for the large variability in premiums for what is often very similar coverage. The industry has responded that more standardization has been achieved over the past several years. The variability in yearly premiums for $100,000 in whole life insurance for a 30-year-old male was $\sigma^2 = 900$ (dollars squared) five years ago. A random sample of 15 comparable premiums this year resulted in $s^2 = 700$. Establish appropriate null and alternative hypotheses. Report a p-value, and then determine whether you would accept or reject H_0 if $\alpha = 0.05$. Assume that the parent population is normal.

10.39 The Folbert 100-watt light bulb is known to last an average of 3.0 years, with $\sigma = 1$ (year). A sample of five of Folbert's new improved 100-watt bulbs resulted in lives of 1.3, 4.1, 7.8, 3.4, and 2.9 years.

a) Write down H_0 and H_a to test the alternative hypothesis that the new variance is larger than the old.

b) What test statistic is appropriate if the distribution of the life of all 100-watt bulbs is normal?

c) What critical region is appropriate if $\alpha = 0.05$?

d) Would you accept H_0 or H_a on the basis of this sample?

e) What p-value would you report?

10.40 A fast-food chain is considering purchasing a soft-drink machine that automatically fills each cup to the correct level. Previously, employees filled a cup by holding down on a handle. The company has been willing to accept a variance of up to 0.25 (ounces squared) in a 16-ounce cup. Now they are concerned that the variance is significantly larger than 0.25. A random sample of 30 fillings resulted in $s^2 = 0.45$. Assume that the parent population is normally distributed. Establish appropriate hypotheses and report a p-value. Would you accept H_0 or H_a if $\alpha = 0.025$?

CHAPTER SUMMARY

The test statistics and test situations described in this chapter are summarized in Table 10.4.

TABLE 10.4 Summary of One-sample Test Statistics

Unknown Parameter	Population Characteristics and Other Description	Reference Sections	Test Statistic
Mean (μ)	Large sample or population $N(\mu, \sigma^2)$, σ *known*	10.2 9.4 7.5 7.6	$z = \dfrac{(\bar{x} - \mu_0)}{\dfrac{\sigma}{\sqrt{n}}}$
Mean (μ)	Population $N(\mu, \sigma^2)$ σ *unknown*	10.3 9.5 7.8	$t_v = \dfrac{(\bar{x} - \mu_0)}{\dfrac{s}{\sqrt{n}}}$ where $v = n - 1$
Proportion (π)	Repeated independent trials, $n\pi_0(1 - \pi_0) \geq 3$	10.5 9.6 6.6 5.6	$z = \dfrac{(p - \pi_0)}{\sqrt{\dfrac{\pi_0(1 - \pi_0)}{n}}}$
Variance (σ^2)	Population $N(\mu, \sigma^2)$	10.7 9.8 7.9	$\chi_v^2 = \dfrac{(n - 1)s^2}{\sigma_0{}^2}$ where $v = n - 1$

KEY TERMS AND EXPRESSIONS

Simple hypothesis: A statement that specifies a single value for the population parameter.

Composite hypothesis: A statement that specifies more than one value for the population parameter.

Null and alternative hypotheses: The two mutually exclusive and exhaustive hypotheses about the feasible values of the population parameter.

One-sided test: All values specified by H_a lie to one side of those given in H_0.

Two-sided test: The values of H_a lie on both sides of the values specified in H_0.

Type I error: Rejecting H_0 when H_0 is true.

Type II error: Accepting H_0 when H_0 is false.

α level of significance: Probability of a Type I error.

$(1 - \alpha)$: Confidence level.

β: probability of a Type II error.

$(1 - \beta)$: Power of a test.

Test statistic: The random variable used in a test of hypothesis. It must have a known p.d.f., given that H_0 is true, and contain the parameter being tested; all of its other terms must be either known or calculable from the sample.

Critical region: Values of a test statistic that lead to rejection of H_0.

Acceptance region: Values of a test statistic that lead to acceptance of H_0 (fail to cause rejection of the null hypothesis, based on the sample evidence).

Computed value: A value of the test statistic, calculated by using a specific sample result. For example, computed value of z (σ known) for a test on the population

mean:

$$z_c = \frac{\bar{x} - \mu_0}{\frac{\sigma}{\sqrt{n}}}$$

p-value: The probability, given that H_0 is true, of observing a sample result as or more extreme than the one observed or calculated.

Computed value of t (σ unknown) for a test on the population mean:

$$t_c = \frac{\bar{x} - \mu_0}{\frac{s}{\sqrt{n}}}$$

Computed value of z for the normal approximation to a binomial proportion:

$$z_c = \frac{p - \pi_0}{\sqrt{\frac{\pi_0(1 - \pi_0)}{n}}}$$

Chi-square computed value for a test on variance:

$$\chi_c^2 = \frac{(n - 1)s^2}{\sigma_0^2}$$

EXERCISES

10.41 A sample survey firm is contracted by an advertising agency to determine whether or not the average income in a certain large metropolitan area exceeds $27,500. The agency wants the results of this survey to reject the null hypothesis H_0: $\mu = \$27,500$ in favour of H_a: $\mu > \$27,500$ at the $\alpha = 0.05$ level of significance when the true mean is as small as $27,600. If the population standard deviation of incomes in this area is assumed to equal $5,000, how large a sample will the survey firm have to take in order to meet the requirements of the advertising agency?

10.42 Suppose that, in Exercise 10.41, the survey firm charges $5 for each observation it collects for the advertising agency. How much more will it cost the agency to be able to reject H_0: $\mu = \$27,500$ at the $\alpha = 0.01$ level rather than at the $\alpha = 0.05$ level?

10.43 Dataland has the local franchise for the Marvel business microcomputer. A shipment of six Marvels has just arrived. In the past, about half of the arriving Marvels have required more than routine adjustment before they were sold. Let θ = the number of computers in this shipment needing more than routine adjustment. You decide to test H_0: $\theta = 3$ against H_a: $\theta \neq 3$ by

inspecting two computers from the shipment. You will reject H_0 if both computers need more than routine adjustment or if both need only routine adjustment. Otherwise, you will accept H_0.

a) If sampling occurs with replacement, find the probability of a Type I error. Find the probability of a Type II error, assuming that $\theta = 0, 1, 2, \ldots, 5$, or 6.

b) Repeat part (a), assuming that sampling occurs without replacement.

10.44 A *Time* article suggested that the new overseas airfares and gateways may encourage up to a million more visits from Europe to North America per year. A similar article in *Newsweek* suggested the increase may range up to 2 million visits per year. To model this situation, you decide on the following p.d.f.:

$$f(x) = \begin{cases} 1/\theta & \text{for } 0 \leq x \leq \theta \text{ (millions)} \\ 0 & \text{otherwise.} \end{cases}$$

a) You decide to test the null hypothesis H_0: $\theta = 1$ against the alternative hypothesis H_a: $\theta = 2$ by means of a single observation. What are the values of α and β if you select the interval $x \leq 0.5$ as the critical region? Sketch this density function under both the null and alternative hypotheses, and indicate the critical region on this graph.

b) What are the values of α and β if you select $x \leq 0.75$ as the critical region?

c) Which of these two critical regions would be more appropriate if a Type II error is more serious than a Type I error?

10.45 It has been estimated that most families in the United States spend approximately 95% of their yearly income and save no more than 5% of their yearly income. Suppose that a random sample of 100 families with high incomes (exceeding $80,000) shows that 60% of these people save more than 5% of their income.

a) Does this sample support the hypothesis that a majority of families with incomes exceeding $80,000 save more than 5% of their income? What is the null hypothesis in this case? Given these sample results, what is the probability that the null hypothesis is true?

b) Would you conclude from the sample in this problem that families with high incomes will tend to save more than families with more average incomes? Why or why not?

USING THE COMPUTER

10.46 Using **Data Set 1**, create a new variable of household size (called HLDSIZE) for each city by dividing POP by HSHOLDS. Sort the cities into two groups depending on whether the number of residents exceeds 100,000 or not.

a) For each group, do a test of hypotheses on whether the average household size for the population of cities of this size is less than 3.

b) Report and interpret the meaning of the p-value for each test.

10.47 Using **Data Set 2** and $\alpha = 0.05$, test if the mean debt-equity ratio exceeds 1.0 for the population of large firms represented by the first 50 sample firms.

10.48 Repeat 10.47 for the population of medium size firms represented by the last 50 sample firms in **Data Set 2**.

10.49 Use the computer output in Table 10.1 under Problem 10.14 and $\alpha = 0.05$.

a) Test if the average office fee exceeds $50 for the population of physicians underlying **Data Set 4**.

b) Test if the population variance for this variable exceeds $144(\sigma = 12)$.

10.50 Use the variable NUMINHSE in **Data Set 6** to find the necessary sample statistics for this problem.

a) Do a test of hypotheses on whether the mean household size is less than 2 for the population of elderly persons from which the sample was drawn.

b) Explain if any assumption about the normality of the population is necessary.

c) Interpret the meaning of the p-value in relation to a Type I error.

10.51 From **Data Set 7**, select the funds with risk level 5 as a sample of moderately risky mutual funds.

a) Using $\alpha = 0.10$, test if the average 5 year return is less than 8.0 for the population of all funds in this same risk group.

b) Do the same test on the average 10 year return.

c) For each variable, 5 year return and 10 year return, test using $\alpha = 0.01$ if the population standard deviation exceeds 2.0.

CASE PROBLEM

10.52 The Harlem Globetrotters are trying to decide whether or not to book an appearance in a small town of about 40,000 people. The local spokesperson insists that they will have no trouble filling the 4,000-seat gym for the appearance. The Globetrotters, however, have found that in comparable towns the usual attendance is only about 5% of the town's population, which in this case would be 2,000 people. If 4,000 people attend, the Globetrotters figure that they will earn a profit of about $12,000. If only 2,000 attend, they will lose about $20,000. The Globetrotters decide to use statistics in this case, and let H_0: $\pi = 0.05$ (only 2,000 attend) versus

H_a : $\pi = 0.10$ (4,000 people attend), where π is the proportion of the population that will attend.

a) Set up a table comparable to that in Figure 10.19, showing each decision and its consequences.

b) Assume that a sample of size $n = 100$ is to be taken to determine how many people in the town say they would attend. What is the appropriate critical region if α is not to exceed 0.03? What is β for this critical region?

c) Calculate the value of α and β if the critical region used is $x \geq 9$, where x is the number of people who say they will attend.

d) Suppose the Globetrotters estimate that there is only one chance in four that H_a is true. Use this information to decide whether the critical region in part (b) or the critical region in part (c) has the larger expected profit.

CHAPTER 11

Hypothesis Testing: Multi-Sample Tests

<table>
<tr><td>

</td><td>

Introduction

</td></tr>
</table>

This chapter is a continuation of the presentation on hypothesis testing begun in Chapter 10. The major difference between the two chapters is that, whereas the methods presented in Chapter 10 involved collecting a *single* sample, the methods to be discussed in this chapter all involve collecting *two or more samples*. We must emphasize that neither the listing of multi-sample tests in this chapter nor the listing of single-sample tests in Chapter 10 is meant to be exhaustive. Presumably, the reader who can understand and use these particular test statistics will be able to perform similar tests in other situations. Probably more than 100 such test statistics are commonly used in practical applications of statistical methods of hypothesis testing.

<table>
<tr><td>

</td><td>

Test on the Difference between Two Means ($\sigma_1{}^2$ and $\sigma_2{}^2$ Known)

</td></tr>
</table>

In Section 10.3, we presented tests about a single population mean μ. The approach outlined there can also be used to test hypotheses about two populations. One quite common test is the test for the effect of different treatments on two groups, where one group is a *control* group and the other is given special treatment. The special treatment may be on-the-job training, a different diet, or a different type of paint, or painkiller, or razor. (Recall those ads on television?)

If we designate μ_1 as the mean of one population and μ_2 as the mean of a second, a number of different null and alternative hypotheses are possible. If the null hypothesis is restricted to a simple hypothesis, then the most common form is H_0: $\mu_1 - \mu_2 = 0$, which asserts that the two means are equal. The alternative to this hypothesis might be that μ_1 exceeds μ_2 (H_a: $\mu_1 - \mu_2 > 0$), or that μ_2 exceeds μ_1 (H_a: $\mu_1 - \mu_2 < 0$), or perhaps merely that μ_1 and μ_2 are not equal (H_a: $\mu_1 - \mu_2 \neq 0$). It is also possible to hypothesize that the two means differ by some constant amount k, for which the null hypothesis would be H_0: $\mu_1 - \mu_2 = k$.

As was the case in Chapter 10, an important part of the hypothesis-testing procedure is the specification of the appropriate test statistic. Since the heading of this section indicates that $\sigma_1{}^2$ and $\sigma_2{}^2$ are known, the reader may well guess that the standardized z-distribution will again save the day. It does, but we have to specify a new point estimator (to replace x) and a new standard error (to replace $\sigma/\sqrt{n}$). As with all standardizations, the z-variable in this case takes the following form:

$$z = \frac{\text{point estimator} - \text{hypothesized mean}}{\text{standard error of point estimator}} \qquad (11.1)$$

When we are testing hypotheses about $\mu_1 - \mu_2$, it should not surprise you to learn that the best point estimator of $\mu_1 - \mu_2$ is $(\bar{x}_1 - \bar{x}_2)$, representing the difference between the mean of the first sample ($\bar{x}_1$) and the mean of the second sample ($\bar{x}_2$). The standard error of $(\bar{x}_1 - \bar{x}_2)$ is denoted by the symbol $\sigma_{\bar{x}_1 - \bar{x}_2}$, and can be shown to be[1]

$$\sigma_{\bar{x}_1 - \bar{x}_2} = \sqrt{\frac{\sigma_1^2}{n_1} + \frac{\sigma_2^2}{n_2}}$$

where n_1 = sample size from population 1 and n_2 = sample size from population 2, and σ_1^2 and σ_2^2 are (known) variances of the two populations. Finally, it can be shown that if $\bar{x}_1$ and $\bar{x}_2$ are normal, then the distribution of $(\bar{x}_1 - \bar{x}_2)$ will also be normal. Thus, we can write the following test statistic for finding **the two-sample computed z-value**, assuming that the null hypothesis is some specified value of $(\mu_1 - \mu_2)$.

Two sample z-test statistic for testing $\mu_1 - \mu_2$:

$$z = \frac{(\bar{x}_1 - \bar{x}_2) - (\mu_1 - \mu_2)}{\sqrt{\left(\frac{\sigma_1^2}{n_1}\right) + \left(\frac{\sigma_2^2}{n_2}\right)}} \qquad (11.2)$$

□ **EXAMPLE 11.1** Let us use Formula 11.2 to test hypotheses about the mean starting salaries of college graduates in two cities, Toronto (μ_1) and Montreal (μ_2). Assume that we decide to test

$$H_0: \mu_1 - \mu_2 = 0 \quad \text{against} \quad H_a: \mu_1 - \mu_2 \neq 0,$$

using a level of significance of $\alpha = 0.05$. Figure 11.1, which looks remarkably like Figure 10.5, shows the critical regions for this test.

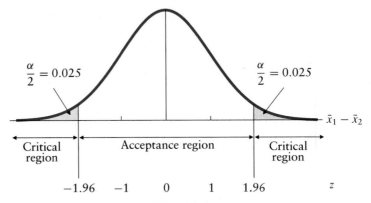

FIGURE 11.1 Two-sided test on $\mu_1 - \mu_2$

---

[1] The variance of the difference, $V\,[\bar{x}_1 - \bar{x}_2]$ (or $\sigma_{\bar{x}_1 - \bar{x}_2}^2$) can be derived as follows, assuming that the samples are drawn independently:

$$V\,[\bar{x}_1 - \bar{x}_2] = V\,[\bar{x}_1] + V\,[-\bar{x}_2]$$

$$= V\,[\bar{x}_1] + (-1)^2 V\,[+\bar{x}_2] \quad \text{(See Formula 4.12)}$$

$$= \frac{\sigma_1^2}{n_1} + \frac{\sigma_2^2}{n_2} \quad \text{(Since } V\,[\bar{x}] = \sigma^2/n\text{)}$$

Now suppose that a random sample of size $n_1 = 100$ from Toronto yields $\bar{x}_1 = \$36,650$, while a random sample of size $n_2 = 60$ from Montreal results in $\bar{x}_2 = \$36,360$. If we assume that the known variances are $\sigma_1{}^2 = 240,000$ and $\sigma_2{}^2 = 332,300$, then the computed z_c value is:

$$z_c = \frac{(36,650 - 36,360) - (0)}{\sqrt{(240,000/100) + (332,300/60)}} = 3.25$$

Since this value of z_c exceeds the critical value of 1.96 shown in Figure 11.1, the null hypothesis must be rejected in favour of the alternative hypothesis. In other words, the difference between these two means appears to be too large to be attributed entirely to chance. If the analyst in this example wants to report a p-value, then the appropriate probability is:

$$p\text{-value} = 2P(z \geq 3.25) = 2(1 - 0.9994) = 0.0012$$

The reported probability is thus 0.0012. For any α larger than 0.0012, the decision-maker should reject H_0. The mean starting salaries of college graduates differ significantly between Toronto and Montreal. ∎

section 11.3

Test on the Difference Between Two Means ($\sigma_1{}^2$ and $\sigma_2{}^2$ Unknown but Assumed Equal)

The two-sample z-test described in Section 11.2 is appropriate only when both $\sigma_1{}^2$ and $\sigma_2{}^2$ are known. When $\sigma_1{}^2$ and $\sigma_2{}^2$ are unknown, the t-distribution can be applied if both parent populations (x_1 and x_2) are normal. If x_1 and x_2 are not normal, but both n_1 and n_2 are reasonably large (say each ≥ 15), then again the t-distribution can be used. In addition, this two-sample t-test assumes that the variances of the two populations are equal ($\sigma_1{}^2 = \sigma_2{}^2$), although there is a t-test, which we shall describe shortly, that does not require this assumption. Fortunately, the t-test is a fairly robust distribution, as was pointed out in Section 7.8, so that minor deviations from the above assumptions may not destroy the usefulness of this approach.

Using the t-distribution

It may seem that a t-test for the difference between two means would have the same format as Formula 11.2, with sample variances $s_1{}^2$ and $s_2{}^2$ substituted for the population variances. However, this is not true, owing to the stipulation that $\sigma_1{}^2 = \sigma_2{}^2$. This equality means that both $s_1{}^2$ and $s_2{}^2$ must represent two estimates of the *same* population variance. In other words, because the two populations are assumed to have the same variance, the two sample variances are merely two separate estimates of this population variance. But if $s_1{}^2$ and $s_2{}^2$ differ, which of these two values should be used to estimate the unknown population variance? The answer is that a *weighted average* of $s_1{}^2$ and $s_2{}^2$ is the best estimate and is more reliable than either one alone. The weights applied are the respective degrees of freedom relative to the total number of degrees of freedom. The weighted average of $s_1{}^2$ and $s_2{}^2$ is as follows:

$$\frac{(n_1 - 1)}{n_1 + n_2 - 2}s_1{}^2 + \frac{(n_2 - 1)}{n_1 + n_2 - 2}s_2{}^2 = \frac{(n_1 - 1)\,s_1{}^2 + (n_2 - 1)\,s_2{}^2}{n_1 + n_2 - 2},$$

where each sample variance has $(n - 1)$ degrees of freedom, and the total number of degrees of freedom is $(n_1 - 1) + (n_2 - 1) = n_1 + n_2 - 2$. The reader should verify that the two weights shown above will always sum to 1.0.

Let us now rewrite Formula 11.2, letting σ^2 denote the two equal variances, that is, $\sigma_1^2 = \sigma_2^2 = \sigma^2$. Factoring σ^2 out of the denominator permits us to rewrite Formula 11.2 as follows:

$$\frac{(\bar{x}_1 - \bar{x}_2) - (\mu_1 - \mu_2)}{\sqrt{\sigma^2 \left(\dfrac{1}{n_1} + \dfrac{1}{n_2} \right)}} = \frac{(\bar{x}_1 - \bar{x}_2) - (\mu_1 - \mu_2)}{\sqrt{\sigma^2 \left(\dfrac{n_1 + n_2}{n_1 n_2} \right)}}$$

Substituting our weighted-average formula for σ^2 yields the appropriate t-test statistic:

Two-sample t-test statistic for testing $\mu_1 - \mu_2$, assuming equal variances in the normal parent populations:

$$t_{n_1 + n_2 - 2} = \frac{(\bar{x}_1 - \bar{x}_2) - (\mu_1 - \mu_2)}{\sqrt{\left(\dfrac{(n_1 - 1) s_1^2 + (n_2 - 1) s_2^2}{n_1 + n_2 - 2} \right) \left(\dfrac{n_1 + n_2}{n_1 n_2} \right)}} \qquad (11.3)$$

This t-variable has $(n_1 + n_2 - 2)$ degrees of freedom.

☐ **EXAMPLE 11.2** Formula 11.3 can be illustrated by applying it to Example 11.1, on starting salaries of college graduates in Toronto and Montreal. Let us now assume that much smaller samples were taken, namely, $n_1 = 11$ and $n_2 = 9$, the population variances are unknown but can be assumed equal, and that the parent populations are normal. Suppose that the decision-maker has set $\alpha = 0.05$, and established the following hypotheses.

$$H_0: \mu_1 - \mu_2 = 0 \quad \text{versus} \quad H_a: \mu_1 - \mu_2 \neq 0$$

The results of the two samples are given in Table 11.1:

TABLE 11.1 Data for College Graduates' Salaries

Sample 1	Sample 2	Statistic
$n_1 = 11$	$n_2 = 9$	sample size
$\bar{x}_1 = 36,600$	$\bar{x}_2 = 36,300$	mean
$s_1^2 = 350,000$	$s_2^2 = 400,000$	variance

Substituting these values into Formula 11.3, we obtain the following computed t-value:

$$t_c = \frac{(36,600 - 36,300) - (0)}{\sqrt{\left(\dfrac{10(350,000) + 8(400,000)}{11 + 9 - 2} \right) \left(\dfrac{11 + 9}{(11)(9)} \right)}}$$

$$= \frac{300}{274.22} = 1.09$$

Since this calculated t-value lies between the two critical values for a two-sided test when $\alpha = 0.05$ and $v = n_1 + n_2 - 2 = 11 + 9 - 2 = 18$ $[t_{0.025,18} = \pm 2.101]$, the decision-maker cannot reject H_0. The difference of $300 between $\bar{x}_1$ and $\bar{x}_2$ in these small samples is not large enough to conclude that mean starting salaries differ. The appropriate p-value to be reported has the following form:

$$p\text{-value} = 2P(t \geq 1.09).$$

From Table VI we know that

$$0.25 > P(t \geq 1.09) > 0.10.$$

Doubling these values, we obtain the expression:

$$0.50 > p\text{-value} > 0.20.$$

Using a computer, $2P(t \geq 1.09) = 0.29$. Thus, for any α less than 0.29, the decision-maker should accept H_0 rather than H_a. ∎

Again, we must point out that many statistics texts recommend using a normal approximation to the t-distribution when $n_1 + n_2 - 2$ is relatively large (such as ≥ 30). We have not emphasized that process (although it is quite straightforward), but rather remind the reader that the t-distribution is *always* the appropriate distribution when σ_1 and σ_2 (in normal populations) are unknown. If a computer program is not available and if the exact value of $n_1 + n_2 - 2$ for a particular problem cannot be found in Table VI, make a rough interpolation between the two closest ones.

☐ STUDY QUESTION 11.1 A Comparison between Two Versions of a Program

An operations research program was written in both FORTRAN and PASCAL for the IBM personal computer. The program written in PASCAL is supposed to run faster, but some experts believe that the running times will be approximately equal. A random sample of similar problems was run using each program, with the following results (in minutes). Assume that the populations are normal.

TABLE 11.2 Time to Run an Operations Research Program

	PASCAL (minutes)		FORTRAN (minutes)
1	0.8	1	3.3
2	4.4	2	7.5
3	1.3	3	1.3
4	3.9	4	6.3
		5	8.1

a) Establish appropriate null and alternative hypotheses for testing whether the population means differ significantly. Report a p-value. Assume that the population variances are equal.

b) Assume that the population standard deviations are known to be $\sigma_1 = 1.1$ (PASCAL) and $\sigma_2 = 2.3$ (FORTRAN). Test to see whether the sample means are significantly different. Accept or reject H_0 using $\alpha = 0.05$.

• **ANSWER**

a) H_0: $\mu_1 - \mu_2 = 0$ where μ_1 is PASCAL versus H_a: $\mu_1 - \mu_2 \neq 0$.
$\bar{x}_1 = 2.6$, $s_1^2 = 3.29$; $\bar{x}_2 = 5.3$, $s_2^2 = 8.42$

$$t_c = \frac{(\bar{x}_1 - \bar{x}_2) - (\mu_1 - \mu_2)}{\sqrt{\left(\dfrac{(n_1 - 1)\,s_1^2 + (n_2 - 1)\,s_2^2}{n_1 + n_2 - 2}\right)\left(\dfrac{n_1 + n_2}{n_1 n_2}\right)}}$$

$$= \frac{(2.6 - 5.3) - 0}{\sqrt{\left(\dfrac{(3)(3.29) + (4)(8.42)}{7}\right)\left(\dfrac{4 + 5}{(4)(5)}\right)}} = -1.614$$

Using Table VI with 7 d.f.:

$$0.10 < 2P(t \leq -1.614) < 0.20$$

The exact p-value is 0.1506. For traditional α-levels ($\alpha \leq 0.10$), we accept H_0 rather than H_a. We conclude that the population means for program running time using PASCAL or FORTRAN are perhaps equal.

b)
$$z = \frac{(\bar{x}_1 - \bar{x}_2) - (\mu_1 - \mu_2)}{\sqrt{\dfrac{\sigma_1^2}{n_1} + \dfrac{\sigma_2^2}{n_2}}} = \frac{2.6 - 5.3}{\sqrt{\dfrac{(1.1)^2}{4} + \dfrac{(2.3)^2}{5}}} = -2.31$$

The critical values from Table III are $z = \pm 1.96$. Since $z_c = -2.31$ falls in the critical region, we reject H_0 and conclude that the mean running times are significantly different. The p-value is $2P(z \leq -2.31) = 0.0208$. ∎

---

section 11.4

Matched Pairs t-Test

There is another way to test for significant differences between two samples involving small values of n that does *not* use the assumption that the variances of the two populations are equal. In this test, it is necessary that the observations in the two samples be collected in the form called *matched pairs*. That is, each observation in the first sample must be paired with an observation in the second sample in such a manner that these observations are somehow matched or related. This is an attempt to eliminate extraneous factors that are not of interest in the test.

In our test for differences in starting salaries, for example, the graduates sampled in the Toronto area may be considerably older than the graduates sampled in the Montreal area, or they may represent a substantially different mix of undergraduate majors. If such differences are not of interest, then they can be systematically eliminated by selecting a sample in which each person in the Toronto area is carefully matched — in terms of age, sex, undergraduate major, or any other criterion — with a person in the Montreal area. One of the most common methods of forming matched pairs is to let a subject *serve as one's own control*. The observation or case is matched with itself at different points in time, as in a *before-and-after* treatment study.

If the observations can be collected in the form of matched pairs, then a *t*-test for differences between the two samples can be constructed on the basis of the *difference score* for each matched pair. This score is calculated by subtracting the score or value associated with the one person or object in each pair from the score of the paired person or object. The *t*-test requires the assumption that these difference scores are normally distributed and independent.

If we denote the average difference in scores between the two populations by the capital Greek letter delta Δ, then the hypothesis being tested is H_0: $\Delta = k$ where k is the hypothesized average difference ($k = 0$ in a test of significance). If the values from the two matched samples are denoted by x_i and y_i, and the difference score between matched pairs by $D_i = x_i - y_i$, then the average of D_i is our best estimate of Δ. The sample values of D_i can be used in a test similar to a one-sample test on a mean with σ unknown and the population assumed to be normal. The sample standard deviation of the difference scores, s_D, and the sample mean of the difference scores, $\bar{D}$, are used to form the following statistic:

Test statistic for matched pairs:

$$t_{n-1} = \frac{\bar{D} - \Delta}{\frac{s_D}{\sqrt{n}}}$$

(11.4)

In Formula 11.4, n is the number of matched pairs in the two samples, and s_D is computed as follows:

Computation of sample standard deviation (s_D) of the difference scores.

$$s_D = \sqrt{\frac{\sum\limits_{i=1}^{n} (D_i - \bar{D})^2}{n - 1}}$$

(11.5)

Suppose, for example, that the observations in Table 11.3 represent the starting salaries for ten matched pairs from Toronto and Montreal. The null and alternative hypotheses to be tested are as follows:

$$H_0: \Delta = 0 \quad \text{versus} \quad H_a: \Delta \neq 0$$

From Table 11.3, we know that $\bar{D} = \$100$. Using the ten values of $D_i = x_i - y_i$ in the last column of Table 11.3 and Formula 11.5 for s_D, we find $s_D = 240.37$. Substituting these values into Formula 11.4, we obtain the following computed *t*-value:

$$t_c = \frac{\bar{D} - \Delta}{\frac{s_D}{\sqrt{n}}} = \frac{100 - 0}{\frac{240.37}{\sqrt{10}}} = 1.32$$

TABLE 11.3 Data for Matched-Pairs Test

Pair	Toronto (x_i)	Montreal (y_i)	Difference $D_i = x_i - y_i$
1	$ 40,400	$ 40,000	$ 400
2	39,800	39,900	−100
3	39,700	40,000	−300
4	40,500	40,400	100
5	40,600	40,600	0
6	40,100	39,900	200
7	40,300	40,400	−100
8	39,900	39,700	200
9	40,400	40,300	100
10	40,700	40,200	500
Sum	402,400	401,400	1,000
Mean	40,240	40,140	100

For $(n - 1) = 9$ degrees of freedom and an α-level of 0.05, the critical values for a two-sided alternative are $t_{0.025,9} = \pm 2.262$. Since t_c falls between these values, the decision should be to accept H_0 rather than H_a. In other words, the difference between these samples is not large enough to reject the assumption that average starting salaries are equal. If we wish to report a p-value, the appropriate probability is:

$$p\text{-value} = 2P(t \geq 1.32)$$

The value of $P(t_9 \geq 1.32)$ is larger than 0.10 and less than 0.25, as shown in Table VI. By doubling these probabilities, we find the following:

$$0.50 > p\text{-value} > 0.20$$

Using a computer, the exact p-value is $2P(t_9 \geq 1.32) = 0.2194$. The statistician now can report that a difference in mean starting salaries as large as $100 will occur relatively frequently (nearly 22% of the time) when the two cities do, in fact, have equal average starting salaries.

Although the matched pairs t-test involves simple calculations, it generally involves considerably more sampling time and effort than does the use of Formula 11.3 for testing means. This time and effort is necessary, however, if there are systematic differences between the two populations that must be eliminated.

section 11.5

Test on the Difference Between Two Proportions

In Section 10.5, we presented a one-sample test involving the binomial parameter π. The comparable test in this chapter is designed to distinguish between two population proportions, π_1 and π_2. One illustration of this situation involves a politician interested in comparing the proportion of people who intend to vote for him or her in one city relative to the proportion of supporting voters in another city. Or perhaps the politician wants to learn how the proportion in a single city changes over time. A similar example is a business firm interested in comparing, between two time periods, the proportion of units of its product that are defective or in comparing its proportion of defectives to that of another company.

The usual null hypothesis in testing population proportions is that π_1 and π_2 are equal:

$$H_0: \pi_1 - \pi_2 = 0$$

The alternative hypothesis can take any of the forms used previously, such as the following:

$$H_a: \pi_1 - \pi_2 \neq 0 \quad \text{or} \quad H_a: \pi_1 - \pi_2 > 0 \quad \text{or} \quad H_a: \pi_1 - \pi_2 < 0$$

The test statistic appropriate in this case has the z-distribution, provided that n_1 and n_2 are both sufficiently large. If we let p_1 and p_2 represent the sample proportions from the first and second populations, respectively, then the appropriate formula for z_c is the computed z-value for the normal approximation of the difference between two proportions:[2]

Calculated z-value for testing $\pi_1 - \pi_2$:

$$z_c = \frac{(p_1 - p_2) - (\pi_1 - \pi_2)}{\sqrt{\dfrac{p_1 (1 - p_1)}{n_1} + \dfrac{p_2 (1 - p_2)}{n_2}}} \tag{11.6}$$

This test statistic should not be totally unfamiliar, since it merely represents an extension of Formula 10.4 to the two-sample situation.

☐ **EXAMPLE 11.3**   An economist is interested in the effects of the recession in 1990–1992 on various industries. In particular, this person is interested in comparing the change in profits from 1991 to 1992 for companies in retailing (nonfood) with banks and bank holding companies. This economist has decided that a listing in a 1992 issue of *Canadian Business* containing these data on 65 companies in the first category and 50 in the second category would be a good random sample. For retailing, 40 of the companies showed a decrease in profits, and 25 had a profit increase. For the banks and bank holding companies, 36 had a profit decrease, and 14 had a profit increase.

Assuming that the *Canadian Business* listing of companies is representative of all companies in any given category, the economist may wish to test for a significant difference in the proportion of companies showing a decrease in profits. Let π_1 = proportion of retailing companies showing a decrease, and let π_2 = proportion of banks and bank holding companies showing a decrease. The relevant hypotheses are:

$$H_0: \pi_1 - \pi_2 = 0 \quad \text{versus} \quad H_a: \pi_1 - \pi_2 \neq 0$$

The sample proportions are:

$$p_1 = \frac{x_1}{n_1} = \frac{40}{65} = 0.615 \quad \text{and} \quad p_2 = \frac{x_2}{n_2} = \frac{36}{50} = 0.720$$

---

[2] Formula (11.6) could be made more precise by adding a correction for continuity. We will assume that n_1 and n_2 are large enough that this correction changes z_c by a negligible amount.

Substituting these values into Formula 11.6 gives z_c:

$$z_c = \frac{(0.615 - 0.720) - (0)}{\sqrt{\dfrac{(0.615)(1 - 0.615)}{65} + \dfrac{(0.720)(1 - 0.720)}{50}}} = \frac{-0.1050}{0.0876} = -1.20$$

$P(z \leq -1.20) = (1 - 0.8849) = 0.1151$ (from Table III). Because this is a two-tailed test, the *p*-value equals $2P(z \leq -1.20) = 2(0.1151) = 0.2302$. Thus, any usual α-value is less than the *p*-value, and H_0 should not be rejected. The proportion of companies showing a decrease in profits may be the same for retailing firms as for banks and holding firms. ∎

section 11.6

Two-sample Tests for Population Variances

Two populations with equal variances are called *homoscedastic*.[3] A test for homoscedasticity is important in a number of contexts. For one example, we know that the *t*-test of Section 11.3 requires the underlying assumption of equal population variances, $\sigma_1^2 = \sigma_2^2$. Or it may be that a quality-control engineer wants to determine whether or not the variance of the quality of the product is changing over time. Similarly, an economist may wish to know whether the variability in incomes or in hours worked differs across two populations. Finally, a financial adviser may wish to investigate the risks inherent in two speculative portfolios by comparing the variance of their market values.

The null hypothesis in testing two population variances is usually given as follows:

$$H_0: \sigma_1^2 = \sigma_2^2$$

The most common alternative hypothesis is

$$H_a: \sigma_1^2 \neq \sigma_2^2.$$

The sampling distribution for testing hypotheses about two variances is called the *F*-distribution, named in honor of R. A. Fisher, who first studied it in 1924. The *F*-distribution tests the hypothesis $\sigma_1^2 = \sigma_2^2$, by taking the *ratio* of the two sample variances, s_1^2 and s_2^2. Knowledge of the degree to which the ratio s_1^2/s_2^2 differs from 1.0 can be used to test $\sigma_1^2 = \sigma_2^2$. When $\sigma_1^2 = \sigma_2^2$, we would expect the ratio s_1^2/s_2^2 to be close to 1.0. Thus, the more the ratio s_1^2/s_2^2 differs from 1.0, the less confidence we have that $\sigma_1^2 = \sigma_2^2$.

How closely the ratio s_1^2/s_2^2 can be expected to approach 1.0 when $\sigma_1^2 = \sigma_2^2$ depends on the size of the two samples or, more precisely, on the number of degrees of freedom in each sample. We will let $v_1 = (n_1 - 1)$ denote the degrees of freedom for the first sample and $v_2 = (n_2 - 1)$ denote the degrees of freedom for the second sample. If the samples are drawn from normal parent populations, the following test statistic is used for testing $\sigma_1^2 = \sigma_2^2$:

---

[3] This word is derived from two words, *homo* (meaning "the same") and *scedastic* (referring to variability).

Test statistic for testing $\sigma_1^2 = \sigma_2^2$:

$$F_{\nu_1, \nu_2} = \frac{s_1^2}{s_2^2} \qquad (11.7)$$

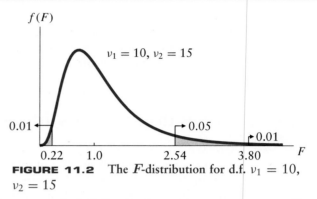

FIGURE 11.2   The F-distribution for d.f. $\nu_1 = 10$, $\nu_2 = 15$

Figure 11.2 shows a typical F-distribution; this one represents all possible values of s_1^2/s_2^2 when $\nu_1 = 10$ and $\nu_2 = 15$. Note that the F-values are always positive or zero and the F-distribution is positively skewed. This is reasonable, since the ratio s_1^2/s_2^2 can never be negative but can assume *any* positive value. The fact that the F-distribution looks something like a chi-square distribution is not coincidental, since these distributions are mathematically related.[4] Three particular probabilities are indicated in Figure 11.2, namely, $P(F \geq 2.54) = 0.05$, $P(F \geq 3.80) = 0.01$, and $P(F \leq 0.22) = 0.01$.

☐ **EXAMPLE 11.4**   The economist in Example 11.3 is also interested in the variability of price–earnings ratios of firms between various industries. To illustrate the use of the F-distribution and Formula 11.7, a random sample of 11 companies was drawn from a listing in *Business Week* of firms in miscellaneous manufacturing, and a random sample of 16 companies was drawn from the list of firms in service industries. The economist desires to test the following hypotheses:

$$H_0: \sigma_1^2 = \sigma_2^2 \quad \text{versus} \quad H_a: \sigma_1^2 \neq \sigma_2^2.$$

The companies sampled and their price–earning ratios are shown in Table 11.4.

The F-distribution is appropriate here, assuming the two samples were drawn from normal parent populations. Using the sample variance formula,

$$s^2 = \frac{\sum_{i=1}^{n}(x - \bar{x})^2}{n - 1}$$

the sample variances are:

$$s_1^2 = 59.2546 \quad \text{and} \quad s_2^2 = 16.7292$$

---

[4] The F-distribution is the ratio of two independent chi-square distributions, each divided by its degrees of freedom.

TABLE 11.4 Sample of Companies and Their Price-Earnings (P–E) Ratio

	Manufacturing Company	P–E Ratio		Service Company	P–E Ratio
1	Corning Glass Works	22	1	National Education	16
2	West	14	2	Amfac	10
3	Norton	32	3	Flour	12
4	Rubbermaid	20	4	KDI	11
5	Alleghany	10	5	Spectro Industries	15
6	Emhart	7	6	Premier Industrial	21
7	Borg-Warner	12	7	Wetterau	11
8	Trane	14	8	Comdisco	20
9	Penn Central	8	9	Dynalectron	9
10	American Standard	25	10	ARA Services	11
11	Snap-on Tools	16	11	IU International	13
			12	Williams	20
			13	Nielsen	18
			14	Manor Care	19
			15	Kay	14
			16	Humana	19

The appropriate F-distribution for this problem has $v_1 = 11 - 1 = 10$ degrees of freedom, and $v_2 = 16 - 1 = 15$ d.f., which is the distribution shown in Figure 11.2.

To test the economist's hypotheses about variances, we compute the following value of the F-statistic for two variances:

$$F_c = \frac{s_1^2}{s_2^2} = \frac{59.2546}{16.7292} = 3.542$$

From Figure 11.2, we see that $P(F \geq F_c) = P(F \geq 3.542)$ is greater than 0.01, but less than 0.05. Hence, we can write the following:

$$0.01 < P(F \geq 3.542) < 0.05$$

Since H_a is two-sided in this example, we double these values, and the reported p-value would be $0.02 < p\text{-value} < 0.10$. Using a computer, the exact p-value is $2P(F_{10,15} \geq 3.542) = 0.0274$. Thus, the decision-maker should reject H_0, that the variances of price–earnings ratios are equal for manufacturing and service industries, if α is higher than 0.0274. ∎

☐ STUDY QUESTION 11.2

In the course of a leather elongation study, with data presented in **Data Set 3**, a worker reports that the weather was much warmer during the days in which the first seven samples were taken for the Tannery Lab compared to that during the days when the last eight samples were taken. This provides a reason for testing if there may be a significant difference between the mean percent elongation in leather between these two subsets of sample periods. As you know, the two-sample test statistic (Formula 11.3) on means for small samples is based on the assumption of equal variances. Using $\alpha = 0.01$, test if the population variance for percent elongation is greater during the moderate weather period.

• **ANSWER**   The test statistic to be used is in Formula 11.7, assuming that the underlying populations are normal. Designating the moderate weather period by the subscript m and the warmer period by w, the hypotheses are:

$$H_0: \text{equal variances, } \sigma_m^2 = \sigma_w^2 \text{ versus}$$

$$H_a: \text{higher variance during moderate weather, } \sigma_m^2 > \sigma_w^2$$

The sample variance for the eight moderate weather observations is 10.268 and that for the first seven observations is 1.238. The degrees of freedom for the F-statistic are 7 in the numerator and 6 in the denominator. The upper critical value from Table VIII(b) is 8.26. We would reject the null hypothesis and conclude that the variances are different only if the computed F-value exceeds 8.26. The computed value of the test statistic is $F_c = s_m^2/s_w^2 = 10.268/1.238 = 8.29$. Since this value exceeds the critical value, we conclude that the variance of percent elongation in leather is greater under the moderate weather conditions. Therefore, it would be inappropriate to use Formula 11.3 for testing the difference in means.   ∎

Using the F-Table

As has been the case for all the probability distributions studied thus far, the F-distribution has been extensively tabled. Table VIII in Appendix C gives values of the cumulative F-distribution. In the case of the F-distribution, the number of values that could be given in a table is so large (because two parameters are involved) that only certain values are listed. First, in most F-tables, it is customary only to give values of F that are greater than 1.0. This means that only upper-tail critical regions can be obtained directly from Table VIII. The other major characteristic of Table VIII is that only two values of the cumulative F-distribution are given. Table VIII(a) shows the critical values of F for the cumulative probability of 0.95 or the α-value of $P(F \geq F) = 0.05$. Table VIII(b) shows the critical values of F for the cumulative probability of 0.99 or the α-value of $P(F \geq F) = 0.01$.

To illustrate the use of these tables, we present the hypothesis $H_0: \sigma_1^2 = \sigma_2^2$, versus the one-sided alternative $H_a: \sigma_1^2 > \sigma_2^2$. Suppose that a random sample of $n_1 = 25$ yields $s_1^2 = 200$, while another sample of $n_2 = 16$ yields $s_2^2 = 75$. Both samples are from normal parent populations. The F-ratio in this case is $F_c = 200/75 = 2.67$, with $25 - 1 = 24$ degrees of freedom in the numerator and $16 - 1 = 15$ degrees of freedom in the denominator. A graph of the F-distribution for 24, 15 d.f. is shown in Figure 11.3.

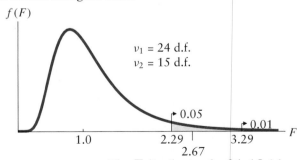

FIGURE 11.3   The F-distribution for 24, 15 d.f.

From Table VIII(a) the intersection of the column corresponding to $v_1 = 24$ and the row corresponding to $v_2 = 15$ shows a value of $F(24, 15) = 2.29$. Hence, $P(F \geq 2.29) = 0.05$. Since our observed ratio of $F = 2.67$ is larger than 2.29, we can conclude that the probability of drawing two such samples from normal populations with the same variance is less than 0.05. Similarly, from Table VIII(b), for 24 and 15 d.f., we find that $P(F \geq 3.29) = 0.01$; this means that the probability is greater than 0.01 that two such samples will be drawn from normal populations whose variances are equal. Putting these results together we can state that

$$0.01 < P(F_{(24, 15)} \geq 2.67) < 0.05$$

or that a ratio as large as 2.67 or larger will occur between 1% and 5% of the time when the population variances are equal. If our observed ratio had been larger than 3.29, then we would report that the p-value is less than 0.01. If the value of F_c had been less than 2.29, then we would report that the p-value exceeds 0.05.

Low Side *F*-Test

In some cases, a non-statistician may present a question which is most conveniently portrayed and interpreted in terms of a one-sided low tail test of difference between two variances. When such a one-sided low tail test is appropriate, we need to determine critical values for the left tail of the F-distribution. To obtain this, we use the following rule:

> A lower-tail critical value of **F** can always be found by reversing the degrees of freedom of the numerator and the denominator, determining the corresponding value in the upper tail of the **F**-distribution, and then taking the reciprocal of this number:
>
> $$F_{(\text{lower critical value, } \nu_1, \nu_2)} = \frac{1}{F_{(\text{upper critical value, } \nu_2, \nu_1)}} \qquad (11.8)$$

As an illustration of the calculation of a lower-tail critical value, we find $P(F_{(15, 24)} \leq a) = 0.01$. From Table VIII(b) and reversing the degrees of freedom, we find $F_{(0.01, 24, 15)} = 3.29$ (Figure 11.3). The reciprocal of this value is what we need. Thus, the lower critical value with $\alpha = 0.01$ for an F-distribution with 15 and 24 degrees of freedom is $(1/3.29) = 0.30$. As in previous situations, the use of tabled values can be replaced by the use of a computer program which calculates the probability exactly.

☐ **EXAMPLE 11.5**   Several legislators are interested in conducting tests involving the variance of incomes between two communities. The null hypothesis in this case is that the two variances are equal (H_0: $\sigma_1^2 = \sigma_2^2$), while the alternative hypothesis is that the first community has a smaller variance (H_a: $\sigma_1^2 < \sigma_2^2$). It is assumed that the two populations are normally distributed and that $\alpha = 0.01$. Random samples of size $n_1 = 11$ for the first community and $n_2 = 16$ for the second result in $s_1^2 = (2,000)^2$ and $s_2^2 = (2,400)^2$. The calculated F-value in this case is:

$$F_c = \frac{s_1^2}{s_2^2} = \frac{(2,000)^2}{(2,400)^2} = 0.69$$

Since we hypothesized that σ_1^2 is less than σ_2^2, we may use a lower-tail critical value. This value can be determined from the F-table using Formula 11.8 as follows:

$$F_{(\text{lower critical value, } 10, 15)} = \frac{1}{F_{(0.01, 15, 10)}} = \frac{1}{4.56} = 0.219$$

Using a computer, the lower critical value is obtained directly and is 0.219. Recall from Figure 11.2 that the lower-tail critical value for $\alpha = 0.01$, when $v_1 = 10$ and $v_2 = 15$, is given as 0.22. As Figure 11.2 illustrates, values of F based on 10 and 15 degrees of freedom will exceed 3.80 one percent of the time and will be less than 0.22 one percent of the time. Since the F-value determined in this example was $F_c = 0.69$, and this value is larger than the critical value of 0.22, the economist cannot reject H_0: $\sigma_1^2 = \sigma_2^2$. The variances of incomes in the two communities may be equal. ∎

□ **STUDY QUESTION 11.3** Quality Control in the Bleaching of Pulp

An article in the *Journal of Quality Technology* reported on the need for quality control in the bleaching of pulp. In some cases the mean effects on pulp brightness of different types of bleach may be equal, but the variabilities differ. In order to guarantee pulp specifications, the company prefers as much uniformity in the pulp brightness as possible. The populations are assumed to be normal. Two chemical bleaches are being considered. The company would like to test the null hypothesis that the use of the two chemicals results in the same variance of brightness, using a two-sided alternative and $\alpha = 0.02$. Two samples of size $n_1 = 11$ and $n_2 = 10$ are taken from pulp treated with these two chemicals. Table 11.5 shows their pulp brightness.

TABLE 11.5 Pulp Brightness

	Chemical 1	Chemical 2
1	78.00	77.20
2	78.36	74.47
3	77.54	82.75
4	77.36	76.21
5	77.55	82.87
6	75.91	76.22
7	78.04	78.06
8	78.95	76.39
9	77.15	76.15
10	77.39	78.05
11	78.36	

• **ANSWER** H_0: $\sigma_1^2 = \sigma_2^2$ versus H_a: $\sigma_1^2 \neq \sigma_2^2$. The sample variances, using the sample variance formula, are as follows:

$$s^2 = \frac{\sum_{i=1}^{n} (x_i - \bar{x})^2}{n - 1}$$

$$s_1^2 = 0.6405 \qquad s_2^2 = 7.9453$$

$$F_c = \frac{s_1^2}{s_2^2}$$

$$= \frac{0.6405}{7.9453}$$

$$= 0.0806$$

Since F_c is less than 1, it surely does not lie in the *upper* critical region. For $\alpha/2 = 0.01$, the lower critical value for $(10, 9)$ degrees of freedom is 0.202. F_c is less than this value. Correspondingly, the risk level, $\alpha = 0.02$, is greater than the p-value $= 2P(F \leq 0.0806) = 0.0003$. We reject H_0 and conclude that the population variances of brightness using two different chemicals are not equal. ■

PROBLEMS

11.1 Review the five steps in hypothesis testing from Chapter 10. Are any modifications necessary to apply these steps to two-sample tests?

11.2 Two types of new cars are tested for gas mileage. One group, consisting of 36 cars, averaged 24 miles per gallon of gas, while the other, consisting of 72 cars, averaged 22.5 miles per gallon.

a) What null and alternative hypotheses would you establish to determine whether or not the mileage differs between the two types of cars?

b) What test statistic is appropriate if $\sigma_1{}^2 = 1.5$ and $\sigma_2{}^2 = 2.0$?

c) Construct the appropriate critical values, assuming $\alpha = 0.01$. Would you accept H_0 or H_a?

d) What p-value would you report if α is not specified?

e) Is it necessary in this problem to assume that x_1 and x_2 are normally distributed? Explain.

11.3 International Farm Equipment, Inc. is considering purchasing bolts from a different manufacturer. The company being considered claims the *yield point* of its bolt (where the bolt begins to bend under pressure) is significantly higher than that of the bolt currently being used.

a) What null and alternative hypotheses would you establish in this situation?

b) What test statistic is appropriate if $\sigma_1{}^2 = 400$, $\sigma_2{}^2 = 800$, and the parent populations are normal?

c) What critical value is appropriate if $\alpha = 0.02$?

d) Assume that the $n_1 = n_2 = 12$ sample values yield the following data on the yield point: $\bar{x}_1 = 370$ and $\bar{x}_2 = 400$. What test conclusion would you reach?

e) What type error might you be making and what is its meaning in this context?

11.4 Select the funds in **Data Set 7** which have risk levels of 4 and of 5 respectively as two samples. Use $\alpha = 0.05$ and determine if the average returns for the population of funds in risk group 4 is more than that of risk group 5 for the following returns:

a) ten year returns

b) five year returns

c) one year return

◆ **11.5** A market researcher hypothesizes that items put on the shelves at eye level sell faster than those kept at other levels. To substantiate her claim, the researcher selects 100 weeks at random. For 50 out of these weeks, the product is kept at eye level and for the remaining 50 weeks the same product is kept at other than eye level. The sales data giving the number of units sold per week for each of these 100 weeks is collected. It is found that:

$$\bar{x}_1 (\text{average weekly eye level sales}) = 50$$
$$\bar{x}_2 (\text{average weekly other than eye level sales}) = 48$$

a) State the null and alternative hypotheses. Justify your setup.

b) Given that $\sigma_1{}^2 = \sigma_2{}^2 = 15$, do the sample data provide sufficient evidence to support the researcher's claim? Use $\alpha = 0.01$.

11.6 Air Australia is interested in determining whether the time is longer for its flights from Sydney to Melbourne than the flight times from Melbourne to Sydney. The airline picks flights that are full and records the data shown in Table 11.6.

TABLE 11.6 Time of Flights

Sample	Sample Size	Mean Time (minutes)	Standard Deviation
Syd–Mel	10	123	$\sqrt{225}$
Mel–Syd	6	108	$\sqrt{185}$

Construct a test using $\alpha = 0.05$. What p-value would you report? Assume normal parent populations.

11.7 Quality Conditioning, Inc. is testing two models of window air conditioners to determine how long the condensers will last under heavy use. The results of the test are as follows:

TABLE 11.7 Life of Window Air Conditioner Condenser

	Model A	Model B
Number of units tested	8	10
Average time to failure (years)	7.0	5.5
Standard deviation (years)	1.0	$\sqrt{1.7}$

Model A is the more expensive model and is hypothesized to last longer. Formulate the appropriate hypotheses and perform a one-sided test, using $\alpha = 0.01$. Assume that the parent populations are normal.

11.8 All the staff employees at a firm making microcomputers took a test to determine their familiarity with microcomputers. A sample of nine scores was randomly selected from the set of employees with business degrees, and a sample of four was randomly drawn from the set of employees with liberal arts degrees. The resulting scores are arranged in ascending order:

TABLE 11.8 Staff Employees' Knowledge of Microcomputers

Business degrees: 65, 68, 72, 75, 82, 85, 87, 91, 95
Liberal arts degrees: 50, 59, 71, 80

a) What assumptions about the parent populations are necessary if we wish to use the t-test to test for significant differences between the means of these two groups?

b) Construct such a test at the 0.05 level of significance.

c) Interpret the meaning of the p-value for this test.

11.9 The speed of an assembly line process is carefully controlled so that each worker has sufficient time (but not too much time) for the assigned task. A time study for one task on an automobile assembly line was conducted by using two workers. At four randomly selected points, each worker was timed for this task. The results, in seconds, are given in Table 11.9. Assume that the populations of times are normally distributed.

TABLE 11.9 Automobile Assembly Line Time Study

	Worker A	Worker B
1	30.7	31.1
2	31.2	31.2
3	31.3	31.4
4	30.9	31.6

On the basis of these times, can you detect, with 99% confidence, any difference between the performance of the two workers?

11.10 An article in the *Journal of the Indiana Dental Association* reported that, in a random sample of 25 entering students each of two consecutive years, the average G.P.A. of the 25 predental majors decreased from 3.68 to 3.60. The standard deviations were 0.33 and 0.36, respectively. Do these G.P.A.s differ significantly using $\alpha = 0.05$ and assuming normal populations?

11.11 All restaurants are rated for cleanliness and quality by government inspectors. A sample of six restaurants gives the ratings (for two inspectors) shown in Table 11.10. Determine, at the $\alpha = 0.05$ level of significance, whether the two inspectors differ in their mean rating or whether the differences can be attributed to sampling error. Assume that the parent populations are normal, and use a matched-pairs t-test.

TABLE 11.10 Cleanliness and Quality Ratings of Six Restaurants

Inspector	1	2	3	4	5	6
A	99	90	66	75	85	92
B	95	49	48	71	80	93

11.12 The manager of a fleet of automobiles is trying to determine statistically which of two different gasolines provides better mileage. This person measures gas mileage (for one car) for eight consecutive tankfuls, using Brands A and B alternately. The mileage difference (B − A) after every two tankfuls is computed. The average difference is 2.5 mpg, and the standard deviation of the differences is $s_D = 2.0$ mpg. Since the dealer selling Brand A is a friend, the manager will switch to Brand B only if he is 90% sure that the Brand B mileage will be *at least one* mile per gallon better. What should the manager do? Assume that the D-values are normally distributed.

11.13 The purchasing manager for Foltz, Inc. is replacing the office copying machine with a model that is supposed to be faster for the staff to use. The manager decides to run six major duplicating projects on each machine. Each project on one machine is carefully matched with a project on the other machine, and the difference in times is recorded. The manager finds that the new machine took, on the average, 9.1 minutes less than the old machine, with a standard deviation (of the difference scores) of $s_D = 4.4$ minutes. Test with 95% confidence whether the manager should switch to the newer machine. Assume that the differences are normally distributed.

11.14 A farm agent experiments with eight acres of land. Half the acreage is treated with fertilizer F210 and half is treated with fertilizer N220. The average difference in yield between paired acres is ten bushels. The standard deviation of differences is 4. Would you conclude that there is a significant difference of yield between the two differently-fertilized tracts? You should have 99% confidence if you do find a difference. Assume that the differences in yields are normally distributed.

11.15 Ten male and ten female production line workers were matched according to age and work experience. The number of absent days for each pair (over the past five years) was then recorded.

TABLE 11.11 Absent Days for 10 Matched Pairs of Line Workers

Pair	Male	Female
1	21	17
2	13	15
3	7	12
4	18	9
5	3	6
6	9	8
7	24	10
8	8	7
9	16	20
10	10	5

a) Use a matched-pairs *t*-test to determine whether there is a significant difference between the number of absent days for males and females. Assume that $\alpha = 0.05$.

b) Use Formula 11.3 to determine whether a significant difference exists.

c) Is the *p*-value for part (a) the same as that for part (b)? Explain why or why not. Which approach is the correct one?

d) Explain the meaning of the type error you might be making in your test conclusion.

11.16 A sample of 10 rolls of carpet has been found to have an average of 10 flaws per roll, with a standard deviation of 3.2. Another sample of 17 rolls has an average of 20 flaws per roll, with a standard deviation of 3.0. Test, at the 0.05 level of significance, whether the second type can be expected to have an average of *at least 5* more flaws per roll than the first type. Assume that the populations are normally distributed.

11.17 Sixty out of 100 randomly selected shoppers who were classified as having rural backgrounds said they prefer to purchase camera equipment in discount stores. In a comparable study involving 250 shoppers with urban backgrounds, 50% said they prefer the discount stores. Use a two-sided test to determine whether these groups differ in the proportion who prefer discount stores. Use $\alpha = 0.01$.

11.18 Contractor Bryan from Regina claims to be better at winning major construction contracts than his friend from Hamilton, contractor Tillman. They have never bid against one another. In a random sample of 200 projects, contractor Tillman was the winner 55% of the time. Contractor Bryan was the winner on 65% of 150 projects. Use a one-sided test and $\alpha = 0.05$ to determine whether contractor Bryan can claim to be better at winning bids.

11.19 A cereal manufacturer will switch to a new TV advertising campaign if the new campaign will increase, by *at least 0.10*, the proportion of viewers who rate the ad as highly attractive. In a random sample of 400 viewers, 23% rated the current campaign as highly attractive. After viewing the new campaign, 35% of a random sample of 100 viewers rated the new campaign as highly attractive. Would you recommend the company switch if $\alpha = 0.01$?

11.20 A bank is comparing the service given by two of its branches. In one branch, 70% of a random sample of 280 customers indicated that they were satisfied with the service. In the other branch, 50% of a random sample of 140 customers indicated that they were satisfied with the service. Would you conclude that the first branch has a significantly higher proportion of satisfied customers? Use $\alpha = 0.01$ and a two-sided test.

♦ **11.21** Mr. Tim O'Russ, the manager of the G-assembly department, believes that under the new system the productivity of his department would improve. In order to demonstrate to the president the improvement in production rate under the new system, six workers are randomly selected to participate in an experiment in which each worker assembles one unit under the old system and one unit under the newly proposed system. The assembly times in minutes are given in Table 11.12.

TABLE 11.12 Time to Assemble One Unit

Worker	Old System (minutes)	New System (minutes)
1	15	14
2	21	18
3	17	18
4	18	16
5	17	17
6	24	23

Assume that the assembly times are normally distributed.

a) Set up the null and alternative hypotheses. Justify your setup clearly.

b) Draw your conclusions assuming $\alpha = 0.05$.

♦ **11.22** A pharmaceutical company wants to test the effectiveness of an experimental sleeping pill. An experiment is conducted over two nights, with ten subjects who have difficulty sleeping at night. On the first night, each of the ten persons is given the sleeping pill one hour before bedtime, and the time needed to fall asleep is recorded. On the second night, the same persons are given a placebo, which is a pill that looks exactly like the sleeping pill but has no medication, and again the time needed to sleep is recorded. All subjects think that they are being given the same sleeping pill. The results in Table 11.13 were obtained:

TABLE 11.13   Time to Fall Asleep

Subject Number	Sleeping Pill (minutes)	Placebo (minutes)
1	4	7
2	7	9
3	8	8
4	15	16
5	6	10
6	13	15
7	6	8
8	12	15
9	1	4
10	9	10

The company wants to have sufficient statistical evidence to claim that the pill is effective before it is marketed.

a) State the null and the alternative hypotheses for the company. Justify your setup.

b) Test for the effectiveness of the pill, using $\alpha = 0.01$.

11.23 What assumptions are necessary for using the F-test to test the null hypothesis $H_0: \sigma_1^2 = \sigma_2^2$?

11.24 The materials manager for International Farm Equipment, Inc. (Problem 11.3) is interested in the *variability* of *yield point* for the new bolts, as compared with the variability of the bolts currently being used. Assume that the manager has no idea of the population variances and no idea of which bolt has more variability, but believes that the parent populations can be considered normally distributed.

a) What null and alternative hypotheses would you establish in this situation?

b) Assume that a sample of 25 of the new type of bolts yields $s_1^2 = 475$ and a sample of 36 of the old type of bolts yields $s_2^2 = 236$. Assuming that these are random samples, what test conclusion would you reach if $\alpha = 0.02$? What p-value would you report?

11.25 Use an F-test to determine whether or not the assumption of equal variances in Problem 11.6 is reasonable. Use $\alpha = 0.02$ and a two-sided alternative hypothesis.

11.26 Answer the following questions involving the F-distribution.

a) Sketch the F-distribution for 15 d.f. ($n_1 = 16$) in the numerator and 12 d.f. ($n_2 = 13$) in the denominator.

b) Two independent samples are drawn from normal populations. The first, of size $n_1 = 16$, results in $s_1^2 = 100$. The second, of size $n_2 = 13$, yields $s_2^2 = 250$. Test to determine whether or not the first has a smaller variance at $\alpha = 0.05$.

c) Explain the meaning of the potential error involved in your test conclusion.

11.27 Find the two lower-tail values for the F-distribution excluding 0.01 and 0.05 respectively, if $v_1 = 24$ and $v_2 = 15$ (Figure 11.3).

11.28 A public-policy researcher is studying the variance in the amount of money requested by certain government agencies. The alternative hypothesis is that the variance this year (σ_1^2) is larger than the variance five years ago (σ_2^2). Random samples of size $n_1 = 21$ and $n_2 = 25$ yield variances of $s_1^2 = (67, 233)^2$ and $s_2^2 = (37, 178)^2$. Assume that the two populations are normally distributed. Make the proper test at $\alpha = 0.01$. What p-value would you report?

11.29 Crafton Leathers of Calgary makes leather covers for books. The leather is tested for average strength as well as variability in strength because tears may occur if part of the leather is weak. Two types of leather are tested. The first type, using a random sample of $n_1 = 60$, indicated a strength (before tearing) of 112 pounds per square inch, with a standard deviation of 6. The second type was tested with a sample of size $n_2 = 40$ and indicated a mean strength of 114, with a standard deviation of 4. Assume that the parent populations are normal.

a) Would you accept or reject the assumption that the two population variances are equal, using a two-sided alternative hypothesis and $\alpha = 0.10$?

b) Would you accept or reject the hypothesis that the two populations have equal means, using $\alpha = 0.01$? Does your answer to part (a) influence your approach to part (b)?

11.30 As part of a study on response and nonresponse biases described in the *Journal of Marketing*, 549 business customers responded to a questionnaire mailed to them concerning the number of telephone lines they have. Personal visits were made to 131 businesses, asking the same question. The mean response to the mail survey was 1.49, with a variance of 0.39. The mean response to the personal visits was 1.54, with $s^2 = 0.56$. Assume normal populations.

a) Do the variances differ significantly? Let $\alpha = 0.02$.

b) Do the means differ significantly, using $\alpha = 0.05$?

c) Is the answer to part (b) dependent on the answer to part (a)? Explain.

CHAPTER SUMMARY

KEY TERMS AND EXPRESSIONS

Two-sample computed z-value:

$$z_c = \frac{(\bar{x}_1 - \bar{x}_2) - (\mu_1 - \mu_2)}{\sqrt{\left(\frac{\sigma_1^2}{n_1}\right) + \left(\frac{\sigma_2^2}{n_2}\right)}}$$

Two-sample computed t-value $(n_1 + n_2 - 2 \text{ d.f.})$:

$$t_c = \frac{(\bar{x}_1 - \bar{x}_2) - (\mu_1 - \mu_2)}{\sqrt{\left(\frac{(n_1 - 1)s_1^2 + (n_2 - 1)s_2^2}{(n_1 + n_2 - 2)}\right)\left(\frac{n_1 + n_2}{n_1 n_2}\right)}}$$

Computed t-value for matched pairs $(n - 1 \text{ d.f.})$:

$$t_c = \frac{\bar{D} - \Delta}{\frac{s_D}{\sqrt{n}}}$$

Computed z-value for normal approximation to the difference between two proportions:

$$z_c = \frac{(p_1 - p_2) - (\pi_1 - \pi_2)}{\sqrt{\frac{p_1(1 - p_1)}{n_1} + \frac{p_2(1 - p_2)}{n_2}}}$$

Computed F-value for two variances $(n_1 - 1$ and $n_2 - 1 \text{ d.f.})$:

$$F_c = \frac{s_1^2}{s_2^2}$$

EXERCISES

11.31 Explain why the smallest value in Table VIII is 1.0 despite the fact that s_1^2/s_2^2 can take on values between zero and infinity.

11.32 Go to **Data Set 2** and collect two random samples of sales values from the first 50 cases. The first sample should be of size $n_1 = 4$ and the second of size $n_2 = 6$. Calculate the sample means and variances. Assume that you do not know that these samples came from the same population.

  a) Use a two-sided F-test to test for equal variances, setting $\alpha = 0.01$. Are the necessary assumptions for use of the F-test met in this case?

  b) Use a two-sided t-test for equal population means, setting $\alpha = 0.01$. Are the assumptions required for this test met?

11.33 Repeat Exercise 11.32 choosing the samples from the second set of 50 firms in **Data Set 2**.

11.34 Information provided by the Business Research and Education Foundation compared the standard of living in various cities around the world. Part of their data compared the cost of a commodity basket in Washington and that in Paris, as measured by the minutes of work time (average of manufacturing workers) required to earn enough to purchase the item (after taxes). Use the following data to test whether there

is a significant average difference in costs between Washington and Paris for the population of costs of all commodities. Use $\alpha = 0.05$ and a two-sided alternative. Do you see any problems with this comparison?

TABLE 11.14 Minutes of Work Time

Commodity	Washington	Paris
Bread, 1 kg	16	18
Hamburger meat, beef, 1 kg	37	80
Sausages, 1 kg	33	75
Sugar, 1 kg	9	9
Butter, 1 kg	55	47
Milk, 1 litre	6	8
Cheese, 1 kg	100	59
Eggs, 10	8	13
Potatoes, 1 kg	7	4
Carrots, 1 kg	11	7
Apples, 1 kg	10	15
Tea, 100 g	10	17
Beer, 1 litre	11	7
Vodka, 0.7 litre	61	107
Cigarettes, 20	9	8

11.35 Consider the incomes information in **Data Set 6** as a sample of $n = 165$ (excluding the outlier case number 80) from a normal population. Compare the incomes of males and females in that sample to determine whether there is a significant difference in the mean incomes. Use $\alpha = 0.01$.

11.36 Use the values in Table VI and VIII to show that $t^2(\alpha/2, \nu) = F(\alpha, 1, \nu)$. Try at least three different degrees of freedom and α-levels of both 0.01 and 0.05.

11.37 Prove that Formula 11.3 and Formula 11.2 yield identical values of t and z when $n_1 = n_2$, $s_1{}^2 = \sigma_1{}^2$, and $s_2{}^2 = \sigma_2{}^2$.

11.38 Consider the sample results for the University Lab and the Industrial Lab in **Data Set 3** as coming from normal populations of measures of percent leather elongation.

a) Test for equal variances of these two populations using $\alpha = 0.10$.

b) Test to determine if the mean for the University lab is less than that for the Industrial lab. Use $\alpha = 0.025$. and Formula 11.3.

c) Repeat the test of hypothesis as in part (b), considering the 15 samples as matched pairs.

USING THE COMPUTER

11.39 Sort **Data Set 1** as was suggested in Problem 10.46 into cities with 100,000 persons or more and cities with less than 100,000. Test if the means and variances of household size differ between the two groups.

11.40 Sort **Data Set 1** as was suggested in Problem 10.46 into cities with 100,000 persons or more and cities with less than 100,000. Test if the means and variances of the percent change in population differs between the two groups.

11.41 Find (or write) a computer program that will generate random samples, and then generate 100 samples, each of size $n = 10$. Compute the mean and variance of each sample. For parts (a) and (b), compare sample 1 with 2, 3 with 4, 5 with 6, and so forth.

a) Determine the variance of the *population* from which you took the 100 samples. Let this variance be both $\sigma_1{}^2$ and $\sigma_2{}^2$ because you are sampling from the same population. Run 50 z-tests to determine whether the means in each pair of samples can be considered significantly different, using $\alpha = 0.05$. How many of the 50 pairs would you expect to have significantly different means? How many did?

b) Repeat part (a), but now assume that you do not know the population variance. Run 50 t-tests, using the sample variances and $\alpha = 0.05$. How many pairs were significantly different?

11.42 Use a statistical computer package on the data in Example 11.4 (Table 11.4) to verify the F-values presented there.

11.43 Use a statistical computer package on the data in Study Question 11.3 (Table 11.5) to verify the F-value presented there.

11.44 Use a statistical computer package on the data in Problem 11.8 to determine whether the sample means differ significantly.

11.45 Use a statistical computer package to verify the answers in the back of the book for the following problems:

a) Problem 11.11

b) Problem 11.15

11.46 For a finance workshop, you wish to compare debt-equity ratios between large firms and medium size firms. As in Problem 10.47, consider the first 50 cases in **Data Set 2** as a sample of large firms in industrial countries, and use the second set of 50 observations in this dataset as a sample of medium size firms in industrial countries. Do two-sample tests on these data to determine whether there is any difference in the variance or in the average of debt-equity ratios between large and medium size firms.

11.47 From **Data Set 7** select those cases with risk level 5. Consider these as a sample of growth funds. Use a matched pairs format to test if there is a significant difference in the average 10 year return compared to the average 5 year return.

CASE PROBLEM

11.48 You are working in a group producing a documentary on changes in Canadian markets. Some sense of key statistical differences between regions is desired by the writers and photographers so they know what to look for and what to emphasize as they do their work. Use **Data Set 1** and a Canadian map, Atlas, or Gazeteer to establish four different regions in Canada and to identify each city within a specific region. Do a series of two samples tests on measures of interest from **Data Set 1** between pairs of the regions and write a short report of your conclusions to provide background for the writers and photographers. Assume that the parent populations are normal, whenever necessary.

CHAPTER 12

Analysis of Variance

section 12.1

Introduction

The tests of hypotheses in Chapter 11 were designed to test for differences between two population means. Often, practical situations may arise in which we want to compare more than two populations. Comparison of the yields of several varieties of corn plants, the gasoline mileage obtained by four automobiles, and the working hours of five groups of college graduates are examples of such situations. In these circumstances, one normally does not want to (and usually should not) consider all possible combinations of two populations at a time and test for differences in each pair. Rather, we want to *simultaneously* investigate the differences among the means of all the populations.

The method for performing this simultaneous test is called ANOVA, which is an abbreviation for **ANalysis Of VAriance**. The essence of ANOVA is that the total amount of variation among categories of data is broken down into two types: the amount of variation which can be attributed to chance and the amount of variation which can be attributed to specified causes. ANOVA tests thus involve a comparison between these amounts.

In general, one can investigate any number of factors that are hypothesized to influence the dependent variable. For example, one may wish to investigate the effect on gasoline mileage (the dependent variable) of such things as the speed of the automobile (factor I), the horsepower of the engine (factor II), and the brand of the car (factor III). In addition, the categories within each of these factors may have a large number of possible values. For example, there are an infinite number of car speeds we might investigate. Therefore, it should not be difficult, even for the beginning student of ANOVA, to see that the relationship among the factors may become quite complex. For example, how do horsepower and the speed of an automobile interact in their effect on gasoline mileage?

In Chapter 7, we introduced the phrase *sample design* to represent the process of designing samples to gain the most precision for a certain level of cost. For ANOVA, the comparable process is called *experimental design*. In experimental design, the statistician is attempting to design an experiment in which the extraneous factors are controlled, so that the factors of interest can be systematically studied. For instance, in the gasoline mileage example just mentioned, the business analyst may use only cars of the same weight so that the weight of the car is not a factor that might contribute to different mileage figures. Similarly, the same type of tires should be used on all cars, unless tires are a factor being studied.

In an ANOVA model, each factor is divided into levels. For example, the factor, automobile speed, may be divided into four speeds (levels): 25 mph, 35 mph, 45 mph, and 55 mph. Similarly, the factor, automobile brand, might be divided into three categories (levels): Ford Taurus, Dodge Spirit, and Buick Regal. A model with only one factor under study is called a *one-factor model*. A *randomized blocks* model is an extension of the one-factor model that permits the analyst to control for an extraneous factor. In our gasoline mileage test, for example, we might want to control for the type of gasoline used. Perhaps three different types could be randomly assigned to each brand of car. The term, randomized blocks, represents the fact that the assignment of gasolines to cars is random. In all cases, ANOVA tests for different effects due to various factors.

The One-Factor Model

Consider the problem of measuring the gasoline mileage, y, of three different brands of compact automobiles. Four cars of each brand are sampled, and each car selected has a standard transmission, four-cylinder engine, and no power equipment. All cars are run on the same trip (city and country driving), using the same drivers, fuel, and tire conditions. In other words, all possible influences except for the brand are controlled as carefully as possible; of course, there may be factors that are not (or cannot be) controlled, such as traffic conditions and weather conditions, but these factors are assumed to be random in their effect. Assume that the sample results for this test are those shown in Table 12.1. (We will return to this problem shortly.)

TABLE 12.1   Gasoline Mileage Test

	Brand of Car (Treatment Number, j)			
Observation (i)	1	2	3	
1	28	24	31	
2	25	23	32	
3	27	18	37	
4	28	27	24	
Means	$\bar{y}_1 = 27$	$\bar{y}_2 = 23$	$\bar{y}_3 = 31$	$\bar{y} = 27$

The One-Factor Model

In a one-factor model, we want to test the null hypothesis that the means of J different populations are all equal. To perform this test, we will take a sample from each of the J populations. Analysis-of-variance methods test for differences among the means of the populations by examining the amount of variation *within* each of these samples, relative to the amount of variation *between* the samples. For example, in testing for differences in gasoline mileage attributable to the brand of automobile used (the one factor), we could take a sample of J different brands.

In ANOVA, the J different samples are often called the J *treatments*. This term originated from early applications of ANOVA to agricultural problems, where, for example, the amount of crop yielded by a certain type of soil was tested by treating the soil with various kinds of fertilizer.

The first step in building an ANOVA model is to specify the underlying population relationships. To do this, we will denote the different treatments by the letter j, where $j = 1, 2, 3, \ldots, J$. If we let N_j be the size of the jth population, then the values within the jth population can be denoted as $i = 1, 2, 3, \ldots, N_j$. Assume that y_{ij} represents the ith value of the jth population under investigation. If we now denote the mean value of y in the jth population as μ_j and the mean of all values of y_{ij} in all J columns as μ (or equivalently, μ is the **grand mean** of the values of μ_j), then Table 12.2 represents this situation.

As we indicated above, in ANOVA we are interested in determining the variation within and between the populations. In terms of the variation *within* a given population, we will assume that the values of y_{ij} differ from the mean of this population (μ_j) only because of random effects. That is, there are influences on y_{ij} that are unexplainable (random) in terms of our one-factor model. The difference

TABLE 12.2 J Populations (Treatments)

		1	2	3	$\cdots$	j	$\cdots$	J	
	1	y_{11}	y_{12}	y_{13}	$\cdots$	y_{1j}	$\cdots$	y_{1J}	
	2	y_{21}	y_{22}	y_{23}	$\cdots$	y_{2j}	$\cdots$	y_{2J}	
	3	y_{31}	y_{32}	y_{33}	$\cdots$	y_{3j}	$\cdots$	y_{3J}	
	.	.	.	.		.		.	
Values within	.	.	.	.		.		.	
each population	.	.	.	.		.		.	
	i	y_{i1}	y_{i2}	y_{i3}	$\cdots$	y_{ij}	$\cdots$	y_{iJ}	
	.	.	.	.		.		.	
	.	.	.	.		.		.	
	.	.	.	.		.		.	
Mean of the									
jth population		μ_1	μ_2	μ_3	$\cdots$	μ_j	$\cdots$	μ_J	μ = Grand mean
Population size		N_1	N_2	N_3	$\cdots$	N_j	$\cdots$	N_J	

between y_{ij} and μ_j is usually denoted by the symbol ϵ_{ij} (ϵ is the Greek letter epsilon) and is calculated as follows:

Random effect in ANOVA:

$$\epsilon_{ij} = y_{ij} - \mu_j$$

or

$$y_{ij} = \epsilon_{ij} + \mu_j \tag{12.1}$$

for $j = 1, 2, \ldots, J$ and $i = 1, 2, \ldots, N_j$

In examining differences *between* populations, we will assume that the difference between the mean of the jth population (μ_j) and the grand mean (μ) is attributable to what is called a treatment effect. That is, μ_j is not exactly equal to μ because of the effect of the jth treatment. We will label this treatment effect τ_j (τ is the Greek letter tau). It is calculated as follows:

The treatment effect in ANOVA:

$$\tau_j = \mu_j - \mu$$

or

$$\mu_j = \tau_j + \mu \tag{12.2}$$

for $j = 1, 2, \ldots, J$

The one-factor ANOVA model can be formulated by substituting Formula 12.2 into Formula 12.1:

One-factor ANOVA model:

$$y_{ij} = \mu + \tau_j + \epsilon_{ij} \qquad \begin{matrix} (j = 1, 2, \ldots, J), \\ (i = 1, 2, \ldots, N_j) \end{matrix} \qquad (12.3)$$

This model means that the value of y_{ij} is composed of three components (or effects): a common effect (μ) plus a treatment effect (τ_j) plus a random-error term (ϵ_{ij}). The null hypothesis in the one-factor model is that the treatment effects are all zero shown as follows:

$$H_0 : \tau_1 = \tau_2 = \cdots = \tau_J = 0$$

An equivalent form of this hypothesis is that all the treatment (column) means are equal to the grand mean and equal to each other.

$$H_0 : \mu_1 = \mu_2 = \cdots = \mu_J = \mu$$

We stress that the two null hypotheses stated above are equivalent, as can be seen from the ANOVA model in Formula 12.3. The alternative hypothesis is that not all of the treatment effects are equal to zero, or

$$H_a : \text{at least one } \tau_j \neq 0.$$

To test these hypotheses, we will assume that a sample of size n_j has been taken from each of the J populations. For each sample, the mean value is $\bar{y}_j$ for $j = 1, 2, \ldots, J$. The grand sample mean is $\bar{y}$. Thus, for the gasoline mileage problem, the null and alternative hypotheses are:

H_0: $\tau_1 = \tau_2 = \tau_3 = 0$ (All three brands have the same gas mileage.)

H_a: at least one $\tau_j \neq 0$ (All three brands do not have the same gas mileage.)

If H_0 is true, the observed differences among $\bar{y}_1$, $\bar{y}_2$, and $\bar{y}_3$ in Table 12.1 can be attributed to random effects and not treatment effects. Note that we can use the column means in Table 12.1 to make estimates of the treatment effects. Our estimates are denoted as $\hat{\tau}_j$:

$$\hat{\tau}_1 = \bar{y}_1 - \bar{y} = 27 - 27 = 0$$

Estimated treatment effects: $\quad \hat{\tau}_2 = \bar{y}_2 - \bar{y} = 23 - 27 = -4$

$$\hat{\tau}_3 = \bar{y}_3 - \bar{y} = 31 - 27 = 4$$

In effect, the ANOVA test is concerned with determining whether the estimated values of τ_j are large enough to convince us that H_0 is not, in fact, true.

Whenever H_0 is true, we would expect the variability between the J means to be the same as the variability within each sample, since in this case the random effects (ϵ_{ij}) are the only source of variation. If the treatment effects are not all zero, then the variability between samples should be larger than the variability within the samples. Our measure of variability in ANOVA is similar to that used in calculating variances; in other words, we first calculate the sum of the squared deviations about the mean, called the **sum of squares**.

The variation *within* the J samples is calculated by first summing the squared deviations of y_{ij} about $\bar{y}_j$ for each sample as follows:

$$\sum_{i=1}^{n_j}(y_{ij} - \bar{y}_i)^2$$

If we now sum this variation over all J samples, the result is called the **sum of squares within** (abbreviated **SSW**):

Sum of squares within: $SSW = \sum_{j=1}^{J}\sum_{i=1}^{n_j}(y_{ij} - \bar{y}_i)^2$

We now must find the amount of variation *between* samples, which is called the **sum of squares between (SSB)**. In this case, we first take the squared deviation of the jth column mean and the grand mean, which is $(\bar{y}_j - \bar{y})^2$. This deviation is multiplied by (weighted by) the number of observations in the jth sample and summed over all values of j as follows:

Sum of squares between: $SSB = \sum_{j=1}^{J} n_j(\bar{y}_i - \bar{y})^2$

There is one other variation in ANOVA — the total variation among all observations in the sample. This variation, denoted as SST (**sum of squares total**), is the sum of squared deviations of all values of y_{ij} about the grand mean $\bar{y}$:

Sum of squares total: $SST = \sum_{j=1}^{J}\sum_{i=1}^{n_j}(y_{ij} - \bar{y})^2$

A fundamental equation of ANOVA states that total variation equals the sum of the between and within variations:

$$SST = SSB + SSW \qquad (12.4)$$

We will illustrate the calculation of these three measures of variation using the data in Table 12.1. Applying the formula for SSW:

$$SSW = \sum_{i=1}^{4}(y_{i1} - \bar{y}_1)^2 + \sum_{i=1}^{4}(y_{i2} - \bar{y}_2)^2 + \sum_{i=1}^{4}(y_{i3} - \bar{y}_3)^2$$
$$= 6 + 42 + 86 = 134$$

When the formula for SSB is used to calculate the variation between the column means, $n_1 = n_2 = n_3 = 4$, SSB is calculated as follows:

$$SSB = n_1(\bar{y}_1 - \bar{y})^2 + n_2(\bar{y}_2 - \bar{y})^2 + n_3(\bar{y}_3 - \bar{y})^2$$
$$= 4(0) + 4(16) + 4(16) = 128$$

Finally, using Formula 12.4 $SST = SSB + SSW = 128 + 134 = 262$. The reader may wish to verify this value, using Table 12.1 and the formula for SST.

Mean Squares and the ANOVA Table

As shown previously, the first step in ANOVA is to calculate SSB and SSW. In order to compare the variability within samples to the variability between samples, we need to divide these sums by their respective degrees of freedom (for the same reason that $\Sigma(x_i - \bar{x})^2$ is divided by its d.f. $(n-1)$ in calculating the sample variance s^2). The d.f. for SSB is always one less than the number of populations, or $J - 1$. Similarly, for SST the number of d.f. is one less than the total sample size, which is $(\sum_{j=1}^{J} n_j) - 1$. For SSW, the expression $(\sum_{j=1}^{J} n_j) - J$ gives the degrees of freedom. Note that these d.f. sum in the same manner as do the sums of squares:

$$\text{Sums of squares:} \quad SST \quad = \quad SSB \quad + \quad SSW$$

$$\text{d.f.} \quad \left(\sum_{j=1}^{J} n_j\right) - 1 = (J - 1) + \left(\sum_{j=1}^{J} n_j\right) - J$$

A sum of squares divided by its degrees of freedom is called a **mean square** (abbreviated MS). Hence,

$$\text{Mean square between:} \quad MSB = \frac{SSB}{J - 1}$$

$$\text{Mean square within:} \quad MSW = \frac{SSW}{\left(\sum_{j=1}^{J} n_j\right) - J}$$

$$(12.5)$$

The various components necessary for ANOVA are usually presented in what is called an *analysis-of-variance table* or **ANOVA table**. The general format of such a table is shown in Table 12.3.

TABLE 12.3 Analysis-of-Variance Table

Source of Variation	SS	d.f.	$MS = SS/\text{d.f.}$
Between samples (treatments)	$\sum_{j=1}^{J} n_j (\bar{y}_j - \bar{y})^2$	$J - 1$	$\dfrac{SSB}{(J-1)}$
Within samples	$\sum_{j=1}^{J}\sum_{i=1}^{n_j} (\bar{y}_{ij} - \bar{y}_j)^2$	$\sum_{j=1}^{J} n_j - J$	$\dfrac{SSW}{\left(\sum_{j=1}^{J} n_j\right) - J}$
Total	$\sum_{j=1}^{J}\sum_{i=1}^{n_j} (y_{ij} - \bar{y})^2$	$\left(\sum_{j=1}^{J} n_j\right) - 1$	

We can illustrate this type of table with our gasoline mileage example. These data are shown in Table 12.4.

TABLE 12.4 ANOVA for Gasoline Mileage Test

Source of Variation	SS	d.f.	MS
Between samples (brands)	128	2	64.0
Within samples	134	9	14.9
Total	262	11	

In ANOVA we test the null hypothesis by comparing the value of MSB to the value of MSW. If the variability between samples (MSB) is small in relation to the variability within samples (MSW), then we should conclude that H_0 cannot be rejected since the differences may simply be due to random causes. On the other hand, if MSB is large in relation to MSW, then we must reject H_0 and conclude that the treatment effects are significant. We can determine whether the size of MSB to MSW is large enough to reject H_0 by using a test statistic with an **F**-distribution.

section 12.3

The F-Test in ANOVA

In ANOVA, the hypotheses are:

$$H_0 : \tau_1 = \tau_2 = \cdots = \tau_j = 0$$

versus

$$H_a : \text{at least one } \tau_j \neq 0$$

The appropriate statistic for testing these hypotheses is the following **F**-ratio:

F-test for ANOVA:

$$F_{(J-1, \Sigma n_j - J)} = \frac{MSB}{MSW}$$

(12.6)

Formula 12.6 gives us a method for testing the size of MSB relative to MSW. Note that for this test the critical region lies in the *upper* tail of the **F**-distribution, since H_0 is rejected only for large values of **F**. That is, when MSB is large in relation to MSW, we reject H_0 because it appears that the treatment effects are not all equal to zero. On the other hand, when the treatment effects are all equal to zero (that is, $\mu_1 = \mu_2 = \cdots = \mu_J = 0$), then we expect the ratio of MSB to MSW to be relatively small and H_0 to not be rejected. If the number of treatments (J) is equal to 2, then the **F**-test in Formula 12.6 is equivalent to the two-sided **t**-test presented in Section 11.3 for differences between means of two populations.

Using the gasoline mileage problem, we can show how to compare MSB and MSW by using the **F**-distribution. First recall, from Table 12.4, that $MSB = 64.0$ and $MSW = 14.9$, and $v_1 = 2$, $v_2 = 9$. The value of F_c is shown as follows:

$$F_c = \frac{MSB}{MSW} = \frac{64.0}{14.9} = 4.30$$

Using a computer, the p-value is $P(F_{2,9} > 4.30) = 0.0489$. Also, referring to Table VIII(a) for 2 and 9 degrees of freedom, we see that the critical value for $\alpha = 0.05$ is $F_{2,9} = 4.26$. Thus, using $\alpha = 0.05$, we conclude that the treatment effects are not all equal to zero; in other words, that a difference does exist in the gas mileage among the three brands of automobiles.

The reader should note that not all samples need to have the same number of observations and that the number of populations (levels) may be two or more. In order to test the null hypothesis that the treatment effects are all equal to zero, it is necessary to make the following two assumptions about the random-error terms:

1. For each sample ($j = 1, 2, \ldots, J$) the random error terms ϵ_{ij} are normally distributed with mean, zero, and variance, σ^2, and the variance is the same for all samples.
2. The random-error terms are independent.

We will presume throughout the examples and problems in this chapter that these ANOVA assumptions are met. Tests of these assumptions are similar to those presented in Chapter 15 for the assumptions in regression.

☐ **EXAMPLE 12.1**   To illustrate ANOVA when the sample sizes are not equal, we present the problem of a statistician who is interested in the yield of fruit from orchards located near each other and similar in all ways except that different treatments of fungicides and pesticides are applied. A random selection of fruit trees is made, and three treatments are used. The appropriate null and alternative hypotheses are:

$$H_0 : \tau_1 = \tau_2 = \tau_3 = 0$$

$$H_a : \text{at least one } \tau_j \neq 0$$

Table 12.5 shows the results of this experiment in bushels per acre.

TABLE 12.5   Experiment Crop Yields (Bushels/acre)

Sample Number	Treatment 1	Treatment 2	Treatment 3
1	130	126	131
2	126	127	128
3	128	129	133
4	132	124	130
5	126	126	130
6		130	132
7		125	
8		126	
9		128	
10		126	

As was the case with regression analysis, statistical programs for the computer are used to solve most ANOVA problems; otherwise, the computational drudgery can be overwhelming. Typically these packages are fairly straightforward to use, and provide the user with all of the values in an **ANOVA table**, such as Table 12.4, plus the *F*-ratio, and often the associated *p*-value. The following printout shows the computer output for the data in Table 12.5.

```
            EXPERIMENTAL CROP YIELDS (Bushels)
            GROUP        MEAN      N
              1        128.400     5
              2        126.700    10
              3        130.667     6
         GRAND MEAN    128.589    21
```

```
                 SUM OF            MEAN
      SOURCE     SQUARES   D.F.    SQUARE   F-RATIO    PROB.
      BETWEEN    59.176     2      29.588   7.333     0.0047
      WITHIN     72.633    18       4.035
      TOTAL     131.810    20
```

The first half of the printout shows the means of each of the treatment groups, and the sample size. The second half gives the ANOVA table. Note that $SSB = 59.176$ and $SSW = 72.633$. The mean squares are the sum of squares each divided by their respective degrees of freedom: $MSW = 59.176/2 = 29.588$ and $MSW = 72.633/18 = 4.035$. The F-ratio is thus:

$$F_c = \frac{29.588}{4.035} = 7.333$$

Finally, using a computer, the p-value is $P(F_{2,18} > 7.33) = 0.0047$. The critical value for (2, 18) degrees of freedom using $\alpha = 0.01$ is, from Table VIII(b) $F_{2,18} = 6.01$. Thus we reject the null hypotheses of no difference in yield due to different treatments. That is, there *is* a significant difference among the means that were subjected to the three treatments. Referring to the computer printout, we find for this particular sample that Treatment 3 was the most effective in increasing yield.

□ STUDY QUESTION 12.1   A Pricing Study of Shampoos

A study investigated the average price (per ounce) of three leading brands of shampoo to determine whether prices are significantly different. A random sample of prices was taken for each brand. Write the null and alternative hypotheses, construct the ANOVA table, and draw a conclusion, letting $\alpha = 0.01$. Use the conceptual formulas or a computer package. Calculate the estimated treatment effects.

TABLE 12.6   The Price per Ounce of Three Leading Shampoos

Brand A (¢)	Brand B (¢)	Brand C (¢)
16	23	19
16	25	15
17	21	17
15	22	
15		

• **ANSWER**   Letting $j = 1, 2, 3$ represent brands A, B, and C, respectively,

$$H_0 : \tau_1 = \tau_2 = \tau_3 = 0$$

$$H_a : \text{at least one } \tau_j \neq 0$$

TABLE 12.7   ANOVA for Shampoo Prices

Source of Variation	SS	d.f.	MS	
Due to treatment	$SSB = 115.367$	2	57.6833	
Due to error	$SSW = 19.55$	9	2.172	$F = 26.56$
Total	$SST = 134.917$	11		

Reject H_0, since $P(F_{2,9} > 26.56) = 0.0002$, and $26.56 > 8.02$ (the critical value for $F_{0.01}$ with 2, 9 d.f.). The conclusion is that there is a significant difference between brands. The estimated treatment effects are:

$$\hat{\tau}_1 = -2.617, \qquad \hat{\tau}_2 = 4.333, \qquad \hat{\tau}_3 = -1.417.$$ ■

PROBLEMS

Assume for all problems that the ANOVA assumptions are met.

12.1 Explain in your own words how variances can be used to test for differences in means.

12.2 Describe the assumptions necessary for one-way ANOVA.

12.3 A survey was conducted in five industries to determine whether there are significant differences in the number of executives using electronic mail. The survey included 250 executives per industry over a three-week period.

TABLE 12.8   Number of Executives Using Electronic Mail

			Industry		
Week	I	II	III	IV	V
1	114	171	147	151	167
2	120	166	134	179	177
3	150	143	121	150	199

Complete an ANOVA test on these data, using a computer or the formulas in Section 12.2. At the $\alpha = 0.05$ level of significance, what do you conclude? Specify H_0 and H_a.

12.4 An experiment was designed to test the length of life of light bulbs from three different manufacturers. A random sample of 5 bulbs was selected from each manufacturer, and the life (in hours) of each bulb was recorded.

Manufacturer I: 120, 90, 105, 100, 125

Manufacturer II: 100, 130, 125, 140, 120

Manufacturer III: 110, 75, 100, 90, 100

Run an ANOVA test on these data. Use either a computer package or the formulas in Section 12.2. Specify H_0 and H_a. What do you conclude?

12.5 During the recession from 1990–1992, some workers were not laid off, but rather had to work reduced hours. To study the effect on four industries, consider the following data representing the hours worked over a 14-week period by randomly selected workers in the four industries.

TABLE 12.9   Hours Worked in Four Different Industries

	Industry		
A	B	C	D
490	525	475	527
450	506	460	507
478	473	525	492
510	526	420	505
504	502	499	530
482	505	472	555

Specify H_0 and H_a and then run an ANOVA test, using a computer. Let $\alpha = 0.01$.

12.6 The students in a computer programming course are complaining that significant differences exist between the average final exam grades given out in four sections (A, B, C, D). All four sections took different final exams. Specify H_0 and H_a and then use ANOVA to determine whether the students have a valid complaint if random samples from each section yielded these results:

Section A: 68, 85, 87, 95, 72, 68, 91, 75, 82

Section B: 59, 50, 80, 71

Section C: 77, 62, 68, 57, 73, 90, 55, 63

Section D: 94, 86, 70, 92

12.7 All restaurants are rated for cleanliness and quality by three different health inspectors. A sample of six restaurants gives the ratings shown below. Determine at the $\alpha = 0.05$ level of significance whether the inspectors differ significantly in their average rating score, or whether the variation in the average scores can be attributed to sampling error. Use a computer program.

TABLE 12.10 Average Rating Scores (%)

Inspector	Restaurant					
	1	2	3	4	5	6
A	99	90	66	75	85	92
B	95	49	48	71	80	93
C	97	62	60	76	90	88

12.8 The information in **Data Set 3** represents the percent elongation of randomly selected pieces of leather. Fifteen pieces of leather were tested by a tannery lab, 15 by a university lab, and 15 by an industrial lab. Run an ANOVA test, using $\alpha = 0.05$, and specifying H_0 and H_a. What do you conclude?

12.9 A study in the *Journal of Quality Technology* reported on the brightness of random samples of pulp after being treated by four different chemicals. Determine whether the average values of brightness differ significantly across chemicals, using $\alpha = 0.01$.

TABLE 12.11 Brightness of Pulp Samples (Rank)

Chemical 1	Chemical 2	Chemical 3	Chemical 4
77.2	80.5	79.4	78.0
74.5	79.3	78.0	78.3
82.7	81.9	81.5	77.5
76.2	80.3	80.8	77.3
82.8	78.3	80.2	77.5
76.2	81.8	79.0	75.9
78.0	82.7	80.5	78.0
76.3	80.9	78.4	79.4
76.1	79.1	81.7	77.1
78.0	80.0	80.9	77.3

12.10 A tax review board wants to determine whether property taxes have been assessed fairly in five cities. The board takes a random sample of nine pieces of property in each city and then reassesses each property. Each of the new assessments is divided by the old assessment. Use the following computer output to determine whether the average ratios (new assessment/old assessment) differ significantly across cities. Use $\alpha = 0.01$. Write down your null and alternative hypotheses. Interpret the computer output.

GROUP	MEAN	N
1	1.118	9
2	1.142	9
3	1.213	9
4	1.258	9
5	1.129	9
GRAND MEAN	1.172	45

SOURCE	SUM OF SQUARES	D.F.	MEAN SQUARE	F-RATIO	PROB.
BETWEEN	0.133	4	0.033	7.257	1.716E-04
WITHIN	0.183	40	4.5739E-03		
TOTAL	0.316	44			

12.11 Interpret the following one-way ANOVA computer printout, where the dependent variable is the number of absent days by workers in different job classifications. Indicate what the null and alternative hypotheses might be and the number of observations in each column. What conclusion would you reach? Estimate the treatment effects.

ANALYSIS OF VARIANCE
ONE-WAY ANOVA

GROUP	MEAN	N
1	3.500	10
2	6.600	10
3	7.300	10
GRAND MEAN	5.800	30

ANALYSIS OF VARIANCE
NUMBER OF CASES: 30   NUMBER OF VARIABLES: 1
ONE-WAY ANOVA

SOURCE	SUM OF SQUARES	D.F.	MEAN SQUARE	F-RATIO
BETWEEN	81.800	2	40.900	13.305
WITHIN	83.000	27	3.074	
TOTAL	164.800	29		

| section 12.4 |

Two-Factor Analysis of Variance

Recall from Section 12.1 that some ANOVA models are one-factor models, while others are designed to study more than a single factor. In this section we begin study of the two-factor model.

In a **two-factor model**, two *treatments* are hypothesized to influence the dependent variable. In an agricultural experiment, for example, the dependent variable may be the yield per acre, while the two factors could be (**1**) the amount of fertilizer and (**2**) the amount of irrigation used. Similarly, the sales of a new product may depend on (**1**) its price and (**2**) the amount of advertising. Finally, the productivity of a worker may depend on (**1**) wages and (**2**) skills.

Just as we used a tabular format for the one-factor model, the same approach is useful now. We will call the two treatments, Factor A and Factor B. Columns will represent the various levels of Factor A ($1, 2, \ldots j, \ldots, J$), and rows will represent the various levels of Factor B ($1, 2, \ldots, k, \ldots, K$). The resulting matrix is shown in Table 12.12.

TABLE 12.12 The Matrix for a Two-factor Model

		Factor A					
		1	2	$\cdots$	j	$\cdots$	J
	1						
	2						
	$\vdots$						
Factor B	k				$\left.\begin{array}{l} y_{1jk} \\ y_{2jk} \\ y_{3jk} \\ y_{4jk} \end{array}\right\}$		
	$\vdots$						
	K						

Notice in Table 12.12 that there are J levels for Factor A. These J levels are represented by the letter j, where $j = 1, 2, \ldots, J$. The K levels for Factor B are represented by the letter k, where $k = 1, 2, \ldots, K$. Finally, within each cell there are n observations. The letter i designates the number of replications, where $i = 1, 2, \ldots, n$. Thus, y_{ijk} represents the value of the dependent variable corresponding to the ith replication using the jth level of Factor A and the kth level of Factor B.

For the experiment illustrated in Table 12.12, the researcher is interested in three questions:

1. Do the column means differ significantly? If they do, we say that there is a *significant main effect A*. The effect of a single factor (such as A) is called a **main effect**.
2. Do the row means differ significantly? If so, we say there is a *significant main effect B*.
3. Is there a *significant interaction effect*? An **interaction effect** is a systematic effect due *not* to Factor A or B alone, but rather to a *combination* of a particular level of A with a particular level of B.

If either main effect is significant, or if the interaction effect is significant, the analyst usually wants to make estimates of these effects.

❏ **EXAMPLE 12.2** Return to the study mentioned in Table 12.1, in which the dependent variable is gas mileage (MPG). Assume now that only six-cylinder engines are used, and we hypothesize that two factors influence MPG: (**1**) the brand of the car (labelled I, II, and III), and (**2**) the speed at which it is driven (25, 35, 45, and 55 miles per hour [MPH]). Factor A (brand) thus has three levels ($J = 3$), and Factor B (speed) has four levels ($K = 4$). For each combination of brand and speed there will be four cars tested ($n = 4$). The experimental results of this two-factor ANOVA are given in Table 12.13.

TABLE 12.13 Results of Two-factor MPG Test

| | | Factor A (Brand) | | | |
		I	II	III	Means
		29.2	29.8	33.7	
		28.6	30.4	34.1	
	25	28.8	28.5	30.2	30.4
		29.8	30.1	31.6	
		23.9	24.7	26.4	
		24.1	26.4	26.2	
	35	25.5	26.1	27.3	25.7
		24.9	25.2	27.7	
Factor B (Speed)		24.4	25.5	24.4	
		20.9	23.7	22.6	
	45	23.1	23.9	26.3	23.7
		21.6	22.5	25.5	
		26.2	28.6	30.1	
		27.7	27.9	29.5	
	55	25.6	28.0	32.2	28.6
		26.9	29.1	31.4	
Means		25.7	26.9	28.7	27.1 = Grand mean

For this experiment, an EPA officer is interested in the following questions:

1. Are there significant differences in the MPG of the three brands of cars? This is main effect A.
2. Are there significant differences in the MPG across the four speeds? This is main effect B.
3. Do speed and brand interact in a systematic way that is independent of the two main effects? This is the interaction effect.

For the two-factor model, the following definitions will be useful.

y_{ijk} = the ith observation in the cell that is the jth level of Factor A and the kth level of Factor B.

μ = the grand mean of all values in the population.

τ_j = the effect of level j of Factor A on y_{ijk}.

λ_k = the effect of level k of Factor B on y_{ijk}.

$(\tau\lambda)_{jk}$ = the interaction effect on y_{ijk} of the jth level of Factor A and the kth level of Factor B.

$\epsilon_{ijk} =$ the (random) error of the ith observation in column j and row k.
The two-factor model can be written as follows:

Two-factor ANOVA model:

$$y_{ijk} = \mu + \tau_j + \lambda_k + (\tau\lambda)_{jk} + \epsilon_{ijk} \qquad (12.7)$$

This formulation says that each observation in the population is the sum of five components: (1) the grand mean, (2) the effect of Factor A, (3) the effect of Factor B, (4) the interaction effect, and (5) an error term.

Sums of Squares in Two-factor ANOVA

The two-factor ANOVA proceeds exactly like one-factor ANOVA; the total sum of squares is separated into distinct parts that correspond to the components of y_{ijk} described above.

$$SSTotal = SSColumns + SSRows + SSInteraction + SSError:$$
$$SST = SSC + SSR + SSI + SSE \qquad (12.8)$$

Table 12.14 lists these four components, the degrees of freedom for each component, and the mean squares. Recall that a mean square is a sum of squares divided by its degrees of freedom. For most practical problems the sums of squares presented above are calculated by using a computer. In Section 12.6, however, the formulas for determining these sums of squares are presented.

TABLE 12.14   Two-factor Components

Sum of Squares	Abbreviation	d.f.	Mean Square
Columns (τ)	SSC	$J - 1$	$MSC = SSC/(J - 1)$
Rows (λ)	SSR	$K - 1$	$MSR = SSR/(K - 1)$
Interaction ($\tau\lambda$)	SSI	$(J - 1)(K - 1)$	$MSI = SSI/(J - 1)(K - 1)$
Error	SSE	$JK(n - 1)$	$MSE = SSE/JK(n - 1)$
Total	SST	$JKn - 1$	

The sums of squares presented in Table 12.15 are from Example 12.2, in which the dependent variable is MPG and the two factors are (1) the brand of the car in the columns and (2) the speed of the car in the rows. There are $J = 3$ brands, $K = 4$ speeds, and $n = 4$ replications per cell. ∎

section 12.5   Testing Hypotheses in the Two-Factor Model

In order to test hypotheses about the two-factor model, the following assumptions are necessary.

TABLE 12.15   ANOVA Table for Example 12.2

Sum of Squares	SS	d.f.	MS
SSC	72.96	2	36.480
SSR	319.92	3	106.640
SSI	7.84	6	1.307
SSE	45.54	36	1.265
SST	446.26	47	

1. For each combination of Factors A and B, the random-error terms ϵ_{ijk} are normally distributed with mean, zero, and variance, σ^2. The variance is the same for all combinations jk.

2. The random-error terms are independent.

We will assume throughout this chapter that the ANOVA assumptions are met for all examples and problems. These assumptions can be tested by advanced methods.

There are three sets of hypotheses for a two-factor model.

1. a) $H_0 : \tau_1 = \tau_2 = \cdots = \tau_J = 0$. This null hypothesis says that no level of Factor A has any influence on the dependent variable (no main effect A).

   b) H_a : at least one $\tau_j \neq 0$. The alternative hypothesis is that one or more of the levels of Factor A *do* influence the dependent variable (significant main effect A).

2. a) $H_0 : \lambda_1 = \lambda_2 = \cdots = \lambda_K = 0$. This null hypothesis says that no level of Factor B has any influence on the dependent variable (no main effect B).

   b) H_a : at least one $\lambda_k \neq 0$. The alternative hypothesis is that one or more of the levels of Factor B *do* influence the dependent variable.

3. a) $H_0 : (\tau\lambda)_{jk} = 0$ for all combinations of j and k. This null hypothesis says that there is no interaction effect for any combination of Factor A and Factor B.

   b) $H_a : (\tau\lambda)_{jk} \neq 0$ for at least one combination of j and k. The alternative hypothesis is that there is interaction.

As was the case for the one-way analysis, two-factor ANOVA hypotheses are tested by calculating an **F**-ratio. The three **F**-ratios used for testing the three sets of hypotheses given above are as follows:

F-test for a Two-factor ANOVA:
1. Main effects A:

$$F = \frac{MSC}{MSE} \quad \text{with } J - 1, \ JK(n - 1) \text{ d.f.}$$

2. Main effects B:

$$F = \frac{MSR}{MSE} \quad \text{with } K - 1, \ JK(n - 1) \text{ d.f.} \qquad (12.9)$$

3. Interaction effects:

$$F = \frac{MSI}{MSE} \quad \text{with } (J - 1)(K - 1), \ JK(n - 1) \text{ d.f.}$$

Notice that the denominator in each of these F-ratios is MSE.

If there are significant main effects A, each main effect A can be estimated by taking the difference between the column mean and the grand mean. Significant main effects B can be estimated by taking the difference between the row means and the grand mean.

☐ **EXAMPLE 12.3** We can test hypotheses concerning the effect of brand and speed on mileage using $\alpha = 0.05$ and the data in Tables 12.13 and 12.15.

1. $H_0 : \tau_1 = \tau_2 = \tau_3 = 0$ (brand has no influence on gas mileage).
   H_a : at least one $\tau_j \neq 0$ (brand influences MPG).
   Using the mean squares from Table 12.15,

$$F_c = \frac{MSC}{MSE} = \frac{36.480}{1.265} = 28.84$$

Using a computer, the p-value is $P(F_{2,36} > 28.84) \simeq 0$ which is less than 0.05. We reject the null hypothesis and conclude that there are significant main effects A. That is, it appears that car brand *does* influence MPG. From Table 12.13, the estimated main effects for brand are:

$$\hat{\tau}_1 = 25.7 - 27.1 = -1.4$$
$$\hat{\tau}_2 = 26.9 - 27.1 = -0.2$$
$$\hat{\tau}_3 = 28.7 - 27.1 = 1.6$$

(Notice that the sum of the estimated main effects equals zero. This is true only when the sample sizes are equal.)

2. $H_0 : \lambda_1 = \lambda_2 = \lambda_3 = \lambda_4 = 0$ (car speed has no influence on MPG).
   H_a : at least one $\lambda_k \neq 0$ (speed influences MPG).

$$F_c = \frac{MSR}{MSE} = \frac{106.64}{1.265} = 84.30$$

From Table VIII(a) this **F**-ratio lies in the critical region; hence, we reject H_0 and conclude that car speeds *do* significantly influence MPG. The *p*-value to be reported here is $p \simeq 0$. The estimated main effects for speed are:

$$\hat{\lambda}_1 = 30.4 - 27.1 = 3.3$$

$$\hat{\lambda}_2 = 25.7 - 27.1 = -1.4$$

$$\hat{\lambda}_3 = 23.7 - 27.1 = -3.4$$

$$\hat{\lambda}_4 = 28.6 - 27.1 = 1.5$$

Again, the sum of these estimated main effects equals zero.

3. $H_0 : (\tau\lambda)_{11} = (\tau\lambda)_{12} = \cdots = (\tau\lambda)_{43} = 0$ (no interaction effect on MPG between brand and speed).

H_a : at least one $(\tau\lambda)_{jk} \neq 0$ (interaction between brand and speed influences MPG).

$$F_c = \frac{MSI}{MSE} = \frac{1.307}{1.265} = 1.033$$

From Table VIII(a) this value of F does not fall in the critical region; hence, we accept the null hypothesis that there is no interaction. The *p*-value to be reported here is $P(F_{6,36} > 1.033) = 0.4202$, using a computer. ∎

---

section 12.6

Calculating the Sums of Squares[†]

When the total sample size in a two-way ANOVA problem is not small, it is not practical to determine the sums of squares by hand calculations. In Section 12.7 we will present a computer output for ANOVA to show how easy it is to interpret. The formulas presented below give the same answers but involve a lot more work. These formulas assumed an equal sample size (*n*) in all cells.

$$SST = \sum_i \sum_j \sum_k (y_{ijk} - \bar{y})^2$$

This is the sum of squared deviations of each observation in a cell (y_{ijk}) about the grand sample mean ($\bar{y}$).

$$SSC = Kn \sum_j (\bar{y}_j - \bar{y})^2$$

This sum of squared deviations measures the variability due to differences between the column means ($\bar{y}_j$) and the grand mean ($\bar{y}$). The Kn in the formula assures us that SSC represents the same total number of terms as SST.

$$SSR = Jn \sum_k (\bar{y}_k - \bar{y})^2$$

This sum of squared deviations measures the variability due to differences between the row means ($\bar{y}_k$) and the grand mean ($\bar{y}$). The Jn in the formula assures us that SSR represents the same total number of terms as SST.

$$SSI = n \sum_j \sum_k (\bar{y}_{jk} - \bar{y}_j - \bar{y}_k + \bar{y})^2$$

[†] This section may be omitted without loss of continuity.

This sum of squared deviations measures the variability due to differences between the mean of each cell ($\bar{y}_{jk}$) and the grand mean ($\bar{y}$) after eliminating (subtracting) the effect of both the column mean ($\bar{y}_j$) and the row mean ($\bar{y}_k$).

$$SSE = \sum_i \sum_j \sum_k (y_{ijk} - \bar{y}_{jk})^2$$

This sum of squared deviations measures the (residual) variability between each observation in a cell (y_{ijk}) and the mean of that cell ($\bar{y}_{jk}$).

☐ **EXAMPLE 12.4** We calculate below the five sums of squares using the data given in Table 12.13. Table 12.16 presents the same data as Table 12.13, except that the mean of each cell is also provided. Using the information in Table 12.16 and the formulas for sums of squares, we illustrate the sums of squares calculated in Table 12.15.

TABLE 12.16   Results of Two-factor MPG Test

| | | Factor A (Brand) | | | |
		I	II	III	Means
		29.2	29.8	33.7	
		28.6	30.4	34.1	
	25	28.8	28.5	30.2	30.4
		29.8	30.1	31.6	
	means	29.1	29.7	32.4	
		23.9	24.7	26.4	
		24.1	26.4	26.2	
	35	25.5	26.1	27.3	25.7
		24.9	25.2	27.7	
	means	24.6	25.6	26.9	
Factor B (Speed)		24.4	25.5	24.4	
		20.9	23.7	22.6	
	45	23.1	23.9	26.3	23.7
		21.6	22.5	25.5	
	means	22.5	23.9	24.7	
		26.2	28.6	30.1	
		27.7	27.9	29.5	
	55	25.6	28.0	32.2	28.6
		26.9	29.1	31.4	
	means	26.6	28.4	30.8	
Means		25.7	26.9	28.7	$27.1 = \bar{y} =$ Grand mean

$$SST = (29.2 - 27.1)^2 + (28.6 - 27.1)^2 + \cdots + (31.4 - 27.1)^2$$
$$= 446.26$$

$$SSC = (4)(4)\left[(25.7 - 27.1)^2 + (26.9 - 27.1)^2 + (28.7 - 27.1)^2\right]$$
$$= 72.96$$
$$SSR = (3)(4)\left[(30.4 - 27.1)^2 + (25.7 - 27.1)^2 + (23.7 - 27.1)^2\right.$$
$$\left. + (28.6 - 27.1)^2\right]$$
$$= 319.92$$
$$SSI = (4)\left[(29.1 - 25.7 - 30.4 + 27.1)^2 + (29.7 - 26.9 - 30.4 + 27.1)^2\right.$$
$$\left. + \cdots + (30.8 - 28.7 - 28.6 + 27.1)^2\right]$$
$$= 7.84$$
$$SSE = (29.2 - 29.1)^2 + (28.6 - 29.1)^2 + \cdots + (31.4 - 30.8)^2$$
$$= 45.54$$

There are computational formulas (which we do not present) that make calculating these sums of squares somewhat easier. As indicated earlier, the easiest method is to use a computer program such as SAS, SPSS, Minitab or BMDP.

section 12.7

Interpreting a Computer Output

There are a variety of computer programs for ANOVA, most of which differ only slightly in the format of their output. The computer output in Study Question 12.2 illustrates a typical output, this particular one resulting from the program SPSS (Statistical Package for the Social Sciences).

▢ STUDY QUESTION 12.2   A Pricing Study of Weed Cutters

A study investigated the price of a certain brand of weed cutter. Three cities were considered (City A, City B, and City C). Three types of stores were considered in each city: department store, hardware store, and garden store. Four observations were taken in each cell, with the following results (cell values are the observed prices).

TABLE 12.17   Data for Study Question 12.2

	City A	City B	City C
Department store	64, 70, 78, 72	77, 81, 68, 75	56, 62, 63, 60
Hardware store	71, 75, 69, 82	72, 76, 78, 74	62, 65, 61, 59
Garden store	70, 84, 72, 74	69, 77, 73, 79	78, 70, 75, 73

Prepare an analysis of this two-way ANOVA problem using a computer program. State the hypotheses and interpret your output.

• **ANSWER**   The hypotheses are as follows:
1. $H_0: \tau_1 = \tau_2 = \tau_3 = 0$ (no city effect) versus H_a : at least one $\tau_j \neq 0$.
2. $H_0: \lambda_1 = \lambda_2 = \lambda_3 = 0$ (no store effect) versus H_a : at least one $\lambda_k \neq 0$.
3. $H_0: (\tau\lambda)_{jk} = 0$ for all combinations of (j, k) (no interaction effect) versus $H_a: (\tau\lambda)_{jk} \neq 0$ for at least one (j, k) (interaction effect).

The following output is part of that generated by the SPSS program. The column significance of F is comparable to a p-value, except significances lower than 0.001 are listed as 0.001.

```
CITY     CITY A, B OR C
STORE    TYPE OF STORE
```

SOURCE OF VARIATION	SUM OF SQUARES	DF	MEAN SQUARE	F	SIGNIFICANCE OF F
MAIN EFFECTS					
CITY	638	2	319.000	15.27	.001
STORE	207	2	103.500	4.95	.010
2-WAY INTERACTIONS					
CITY STORE	285	4	71.25	3.41	.036
RESIDUAL	564	27	20.89		.001
TOTAL	1694	35			

The conclusions based on the F-ratios in this ANOVA analysis are as follows:
1. There is a significant main effect due to city ($F_c = 15.27$, $p \leq 0.001$). That is, prices *do* appear to differ across cities.
2. There is a significant main effect due to store ($F_c = 4.95$, $p \leq 0.010$). That is, prices *do* appear to differ across stores.
3. There is a significant interaction effect ($F_c = 3.41$, $p = 0.036$). That is, the best type of store to shop for this weed cutter in one city is not necessarily the best type in another city.   ■

PROBLEMS

For these problems, assume that the ANOVA assumptions are met.

12.12 Explain why three null hypotheses are needed for two-way ANOVA. Write each of the three null hypotheses.

12.13 Describe a real-world situation in which two-way ANOVA would be useful. Do not use an example presented in the text.

12.14 Describe the assumptions necessary for testing hypotheses for two-way ANOVA.

12.15 What would you conclude if, in a two-way ANOVA test, the F-test for one of the main effects equals zero? What would you conclude if the F-value for interaction equals 0?

12.16 Return to **Data Set 3**, representing 45 observations on the elongation of leather. Assume that these data came from three different types of leather (I, II, and III). In each column the first five observations came from I, the second five came from II, and the last five came from III. Complete a two-way ANOVA test on these data, using $\alpha = 0.01$. Specify your hypotheses.

12.17 For the experimental data reported in Problem 12.9, the suggestion has been made that pulp brightness may depend on the batch from which each

sample was drawn. Use the first nine observations in each column, assuming the first three were from Batch A, the second three from Batch B, and the next three from Batch C. Determine if there are significant main effects (batch or chemical) or significant interaction effects. Let $\alpha = 0.01$.

12.18 Describe, in your own words, why considering main effects alone is not sufficient for two-way ANOVA.

TABLE 12.18   Compression Results for Three Types of Chewable Pills

	Amount of Compression (psi)		
	Brand A	Brand B	Brand C
Type I	0.72, 0.58, 0.74, 0.56	0.81, 0.70, 0.64, 0.67	0.68, 0.60, 0.66, 0.61
Type II	0.52, 0.78, 0.56, 0.62	0.64, 0.69, 0.58, 0.67	0.73, 0.55, 0.61, 0.70
Type III	0.68, 0.76, 0.77, 0.71	0.82, 0.80, 0.79, 0.85	0.91, 0.84, 0.82, 0.66

12.19 Floristan, Inc. has run compression tests on three types of chewable pills (to determine the pressure it takes for a pill to crumble). There are three different brands being tested. The results are in Table 12.18. Use a computer program to determine whether there is a significant difference across brands and across types, using $\alpha = 0.05$. Estimate the brand effects and the type effects if they are significant. Is the interaction effect significant?

12.20 Return to the data in Problem 12.10. These data represent the ratio of new assessments to prior assessments for five cities. The one-way analysis grouped all nine observations in a single column together. Now we learn that observations 1–3 represented farm property, observations 4–6 represented commercial property, and observations 7–9 represented residential property. What do you conclude from the computer output given below?

```
                 SUM OF           MEAN
SOURCE          SQUARES   D.F.   SQUARE   F-RATIO   PROB.
COLS            0.133        4   0.033    20.744    2.765E-08
ROWS            8.3733E-03   2   4.1867E-03  2.617  0.0896
INTERACTION     0.127        8   0.016     9.889    1.296E-06
ERROR           0.048       30   1.6000E-03
TOTAL           0.316       44
```

12.21 Three different brands of radial tires were tested to determine how long the tread would last under various

temperatures. The tires were tested in dry weather using temperatures of 60°, 70°, and 80°. Use the following data to run a two-factor ANOVA test with $\alpha = 0.01$. Be sure to specify your hypotheses and interpret your results. Entries in the table represent mileage, in thousands of miles. Use a computer package, if possible.

TABLE 12.19 Tread Durability

Temperature	Tire Mileage (thousands of miles)		
	A	B	C
80°	46, 49, 49, 48	50, 52, 59, 52	42, 45, 46, 44
70°	48, 50, 50, 51	57, 55, 58, 52	47, 43, 43, 44
60°	44, 42, 45, 44	44, 41, 40, 44	43, 45, 45, 46

12.22 For Problem 12.21, estimate the main effect for each type of tire and for each temperature. Which tire would you buy?

KEY TERMS AND EXPRESSIONS

Analysis of variance (ANOVA): A method for testing hypotheses about the means of two or more populations.

Grand mean: The mean of all values under investigation.

Treatment effect: An effect associated with a particular population.

Random-error term: A term representing the variability within a column (one-way analysis) or within a cell (two-way analysis).

Sum of squares: A sum of squared deviations about a mean.

SSW: The sum of squares within a column (one-way analysis).

SSB: The sum of squares between columns (one-way analysis).

SST: The sum of squares total: $SST = SSW + SSB$ (one-way analysis).

Mean square: A sum of squares divided by its degrees of freedom.

MSB: Mean square between: $MSB = SSB/(J-1)$.

MSW: Mean square within:

$$MSW = SSW \left/ \left(\sum_{j=1}^{J} n_j \right) - J \right.$$

F-ratio: $F = MSB/MSW$, used to test hypotheses of equal means.

ANOVA table: A table showing the sources of variation with sums of squares, degrees of freedom, and mean squares.

Two-factor model: A model of an experiment in which the dependent variable is hypothesized to depend on two variables.

Main effect: An effect associated with a single variable.

Interaction effect: An effect associated with a combination of factors after eliminating the main effects of each separate factor.

SST **(two-way analysis):** The sum of squares to-tal composed of *SS*Columns plus *SS*Rows plus *SS*Interaction plus *SS*Error.

MSC, MSR, MSI, MSE: Mean square columns, rows, interaction, and error.

EXERCISES

12.23 Prove that $SST = SSW + SSB$ for one-way ANOVA.

12.24 Describe the main effects and the interaction effects that might occur in a three-factor ANOVA.

12.25 Make up a problem unlike any in this text for which a three-way ANOVA would be appropriate.

12.26 Consider the two graphs in Figure 12.1 representing a two-way ANOVA. Each number represents the mean of a cell.

a) Would you *guess* that in Figure 12.1(a) there are significant main effects A or B? Would you estimate significant interaction effects? The sample size is 20 for each cell.

b) Repeat the analysis using Figure 12.1(b).

12.27 Consider the diagram of a two-factor model in Figure 12.2. Each number represents a cell mean, and each cell contains 50 observations. From this diagram, would you guess there are significant (a) main effects A, (b) main effects B, or (c) interaction effects?

(a)   (b)

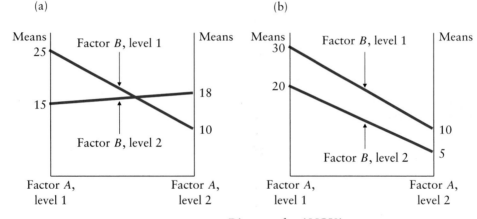

FIGURE 12.1   Diagrams for ANOVA

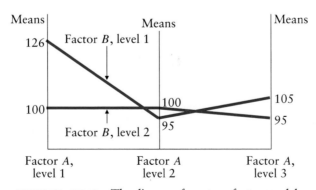

FIGURE 12.2   The diagram for a two-factor model

12.28 An administrator of a medical insurance plan is concerned with the length of time various patients stay in the hospital. To study this situation, the administrator has picked three comparable hospitals and categorized patients in these hospitals as male or female and either under 40 or 40 or older. All patients studied had comparable illnesses. Conduct a threeway analysis of variance on the data in Table 12.20.

TABLE 12.20   Length of Stay in Hospital (Days)

		Hospital A	Hospital B	Hospital C
Males	< 40	29, 36, 28,	14, 5, 10,	22, 25, 23,
	≥ 40	35, 33, 38	8, 7, 16	20, 30, 32
Females	< 40	25, 35, 31,	3, 5, 8,	18, 7, 15,
	≥ 40	32, 26, 34	9, 4, 6	11, 8, 10

12.29 The National Federation of Independent Business Research and Education Foundations has provided data on the minutes of work time (average of manufacturing workers) required to earn enough income to purchase items in a weekly food basket. Use ANOVA to determine whether the average times in the cities listed below differ at the $\alpha = 0.05$ level of significance.

TABLE 12.21   Number of Minutes Required to Purchase a Weekly Food Basket

Commodity	Washington	Toronto	Paris	Munich
Bread, 1 kg	16	16	18	27
Hamburger meat beef, 1 kg	37	63	80	70
Sausages, 1 kg	33	51	75	75
Sugar, 1 kg	9	11	9	10
Butter, 1 kg	55	50	47	52
Milk, 1 litre	6	9	8	7
Cheese, 1 kg	100	65	59	65
Eggs, 10	8	16	13	12
Potatoes, 1 kg	7	3	4	4
Carrots, 1 kg	11	13	7	10
Apples, 1 kg	10	23	15	15
Tea, 100 g	10	5	17	10
Beer, 1 litre	11	18	7	8
Vodka, 0.7 litre	61	131	107	74
Cigarettes, 20	9	25	8	16

USING THE COMPUTER

12.30 A management training program is interested in the effect of sex and age on the ability of trainees to perform certain computational tasks. The higher a person's score, the better they performed on the task. A study of 32 men and women resulted in the following computer output, using the statistical package by David P. Doane, *Exploring Statistics with the IBM PC*. In this output, the columns represent different age groups, from youngest to oldest; row 1 is female, row 2 is male.

a) What do you conclude from this output? Indicate carefully the hypotheses being tested, and the hypotheses supported by the data.

b) How many age groups were there? Estimate the treatment effect for the various age groups.

c) Show how the three *F*-ratios were calculated. What is the *p*-value for each of these ratios?

TABLE OF SUMS FOR EACH CELL

ROW	COL1	COL2	COL3	COL4	TOTAL:
1	48	45	26	33	152
2	41	40	34	29	144
TOT:	89	85	60	62	296

ANOVA TABLE

SOURCE OF VARIATION	SUM OF SQUARES	D.F.	MEAN SQUARE	F-RATIO
BETWEEN ROWS:	2	1	2	0.40
BETWEEN COLS:	85.75	3	28.58333	5.76
INTERACTION:	17.25	3	5.75	1.16
ERROR:	119	24	4.958334	
TOTAL:	224	31	7.225806	

12.31 For the following computer output, the experiment involves the rating by consumers (of various ages) of different brands of coffee.

```
    AGE                CONSUMER AGE CATEGORY
    BRND               BRAND OF COFFEE

SOURCE OF      SUM OF      MEAN              SIGNIFICANCE
VARIATION      SQUARES DF  SQUARE    F        OF F
MAIN EFFECTS
  AGE          10.667   2   5.333   1.426     .266
  BRND        354.889   2 177.444  47.436     .001
2-WAY
INTERACTIONS
  AGE BRND      1.778   4    .444    .119      .974
RESIDUAL       67.333  18   3.741
TOTAL         434.667  26  16.718
```

a) How many age categories are there? How many brands? How many replications? What is the total sample size?

b) Are the main effects significant? Is there a significant interaction effect? Is the total amount explained significant?

12.32 The output below was generated by a computer program called B-STAT. The dependent variable is the weight loss by men participating in one of four diets. The men are divided into two age groups — under 40 and 40 or older.

```
ANALYSIS OF VARIANCE
    TWO-WAY ANOVA
COL    MEAN     N
 1    11.12     8
 2     8.75     8
 3    10.62     8
 4     7.75     8

ROW
 1   10.125    16
 2    9.00     16

CELL   MEANS
ROW    COL    MEAN     N
 1      1    12.00     4
 2      1    10.25     4
 1      2     9.00     4
 2      2     8.25     4
 1      3    11.25     4
 2      3    10.00     4
 1      4     8.50     4
 2      4     7.25     4
     GRAND MEAN  9.56  32
```

SOURCE	SUM OF SQUARES	D.F.	MEAN SQUARE	F-RATIO
COLS	60	3	20.00	7.49
ROWS	10	1	10.00	3.75
INTERACTION	2	3	0.67	0.25
ERROR	64	24	2.67	
TOTAL	136	31		

Determine whether there is a significant main effect for rows or columns. Estimate the main effects. Interpret these results in terms of diets and the age of the men.

CASE PROBLEM

12.33 Data Set 1 contains information for Canadian cities on population, number of households, personal income, retail sales, and taxable returns. Suppose you are interested in using ANOVA to determine if per capita income is related to the size of the city, and to the percent change (1981 to 1991) in the population of the city. Do this by selecting (randomly) ten cities with population 100,000 and over, ten cities with populations 30,000–100,000, and ten cities with populations 10,000–30,000. Determine for these 30 cities the per capita income, and the median percent change in population from 1981 to 1991. Conduct a two-way ANOVA test, with three columns (population levels), and two rows: (1) $\geq$ median % population change and (2) < median % population change. The observations in the table are the per capita income values. State your hypotheses. What do you conclude, using $\alpha = 0.05$?

CHAPTER 13

Simple Regression and Correlation Analysis

Introduction

In the past several chapters, we have discussed the process of using sample information to make inferences, test hypotheses, or modify beliefs about the characteristics of a population. In this chapter and the next, we turn to a related problem, describing or estimating the value of one variable, called the *dependent* variable, on the basis of one or more other variables, called *independent* or *explanatory* variables.[1] A description of the *nature* of the relationship between two or more variables is called *regression analysis*, while investigation into the *strength* of such relationships is called *correlation analysis*.

Sir Francis Galton, an English expert on heredity in the late 1800s, was one of the first researchers to work with the problem of describing one variable on the basis of one or more other variables. Galton's work centred on the heights of fathers compared to the heights of their sons. He found that there was a tendency toward the mean — both exceptionally short fathers and unusually tall fathers tended to have sons of more average height. Galton said that the heights of the sons *regressed* toward the mean, thus originating the term *regression*. Nowadays the term *regression* more generally means the description of the nature of the relationship between two or more variables.

Suppose, for example, that a business manager is trying to predict sales for next month (the dependent variable) on the basis of indices of disposable income, price levels, or any of numerous other independent variables, or using one or more of a battery of tests to evaluate the ability of prospective employees for new jobs. In these cases, regression analysis is used in an attempt to model and *predict* the value of the dependent variable on the basis of one or more other measured characteristics, which are the given independent variables. In other cases, regression may be used to *describe* the functional relationship between two or more variables. An economist may use it for this purpose as an aid to understanding the relationship of consumption to current and past levels of income and wealth or the relationship of lifetime earnings to explanatory factors such as education level, job experience, occupation group, race, and sex.

No matter whether regression analysis is used for descriptive or predictive purposes, one cannot expect to be able to forecast or describe the *exact* value of sales, profits, consumption, or any other dependent variable. There always are extra-model variations in government policy and laws, the economy, society, the weather, or just plain differences in human ability and motivation. Because of these possible variations, we shall be interested in determining the *average* relationship between the dependent variable and the independent variables. In this chapter, we will confine our analysis to the case of *simple* linear regression — *one* independent variable. *Multiple* linear regression, which involves two or more independent variables, will be presented in Chapter 14.

The Regression Models

For most regression analysis, the average population relationship between the dependent variable (usually denoted by the letter y) and the independent variable (denoted by the letter x) is assumed to be linear. A straight line is used because it

---

[1]   This label of dependent and independent variables in a regression model is different from our previous *statistical* definitions of independent and dependent events or of independent random variables.

is mathematically simple and yet still provides an approximation to the real-world relationship that is sufficient for most practical purposes.[2]

The Population Regression Model

Since we are interested in determining the mean value of y for a given value x, we are interested in the expectation $\mu_{y \cdot x}$, which is read as *the mean of the y-values for a given x-value*. In the equation representing the population straight-line relationship between x and the mean of the y-values, called the **population regression line**, the Greek letter α (alpha) represents the *y-intercept* and β (beta) is used to denote the slope which is the derivative of y with respect to x. The regression line is expressed in slope-intercept form as in Appendix B, but the symbols used to represent the slope and intercept differ from those in Appendix B. The mean value of y for a given value x is denoted by the symbol $\mu_{y \cdot x}$.

$$\text{Population regression line:} \qquad \mu_{y \cdot x} = \alpha + \beta x \qquad (13.1)$$

To illustrate a population line, suppose that y represents the total cost of a production run and x represents the number of units. The value of $\mu_{y \cdot x}$ is the average total cost for producing some given number of units. The intercept α measures the fixed cost of the production process and the slope β measures the marginal cost per unit.

The difference between an actual value y_i and the expectation of y for a given x_i, $\mu_{y \cdot x_i}$, is the unpredictable element in regression analysis. This difference is usually called the *random error* and is denoted by the Greek letter epsilon, ϵ_i.

$$\text{Error in the population model:} \quad \epsilon_i = y_i - \mu_{y \cdot x_i} \quad \text{or} \quad y_i = \mu_{y \cdot x_i} + \epsilon_i \qquad (13.2)$$

The **population regression model** consists of all the terms combined from Formulas 13.1 and 13.2 which sum to y_i.

Population regression model:

$$y_i = \alpha + \beta x_i + \epsilon_i \qquad (13.3)$$

An illustration of this model is shown in Figure 13.1, in which each dot represents one observation in the population. When values of x and y are plotted in this fashion, the diagram is called a *scatter diagram*. In such a scatter diagram, the dependent variable y is plotted on the vertical axis. The model in Figure 13.1 is a straight line because we are assuming that *linear* regression is appropriate. The point at which this line intersects the vertical axis is the intercept denoted by α. The rate of change in the vertical direction for each one-unit change on the x-axis is the slope of the line (denoted by β). For any value of the independent variable (x_i), the corresponding expected value for the dependent variable is $\mu_{y \cdot x_i}$. The error ϵ_i is the vertical distance measured between the actual point observed (x_i, y_i) and the line for the same x_i-value.

---

[2] The variables y and x may, of course, be transformations of economics or business data, such as $y = $ (change in sales)^2 or $x = 1/$(interest rate). Thus, theoretical nonlinear relationships may be expressed in a linear regression model. See Section 15.6 for further discussion of this point. Also, we shall usually treat the independent variable as a given set of values, not as a random variable.

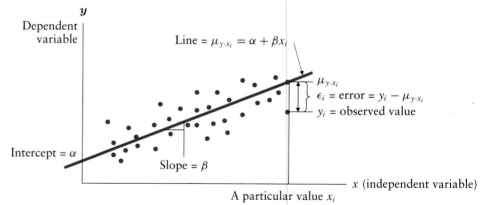

FIGURE 13.1   The population regression model

To aid our introduction in the use of regression models, let us construct a simple model relating a worker's characteristics as measured by a test score (Test) to the worker's output on a specific job assignment (Output). Many electric utility companies are offering customers a discount on the regular rate schedule if they convert to a load control or time-of-day pricing program. To make the conversion, special monitoring and control devices must be installed at the residence. Sometimes this is quite simple; other times it is a rather complex and lengthy installation. The difference depends on the wiring, the location of the main line, and separate devices for electric heating or air-conditioner units and for electric water heaters. Prior to assignment on this type of installation, utility employees or subcontractors must complete a training course and pass an examination. A score of 300 is required to pass; the maximum is 800. The electricians usually require two or three hours to install and check out the new devices at a residence. Thus, it is typical for them to complete at least two, more often three, and sometimes four or more installations in a day.

We wish to examine the relation, if any, between the typical number of installations completed per day (y = Output) and the training program test results (x = Test). Observations are taken for a number of electricians over randomly selected days. We expect to find that electricians who score higher on the test generally complete a greater number of installations per day. They have demonstrated more knowledge and a higher level of the requisite skills.

The population regression model is   Output $= \alpha + \beta(\text{Test}) + \epsilon_i$

or $$y_i = \alpha + \beta x_i + \epsilon_i$$

The slope β measures the marginal product of the extra training which is implicit in an increase in the test score. The intercept is the average number of conversions per day by an electrician before, or without, the training course. We must be careful in interpreting intercepts too literally since they are often not realistic. Electricians are not allowed to work on such a conversion unless they have taken the training course and scored at least 300. It is risky to conjecture about the number of conversions based on a test score of zero since that value is outside the range of possible experience.

The values of α and β are, of course, unknown, as are the random disturbances ϵ_i. Usually, α and β can only be estimated on the basis of sample data, and the properties of the estimators obtained depend on the assumptions about the disturbances ϵ_i. The following discussion introduces the sample regression model as the basis for estimating α and β.

The Sample Regression Model

Following the process we started in Chapter 7, we use sample data to estimate population parameters. In the case of regression analysis, the two population parameters to be estimated are α and β. Since α and β are used to determine $\mu_{y \cdot x}$ for a specified value of x, once we have an estimate of α and β we can also derive an estimate of $\mu_{y \cdot x}$ for any specified x-value. The **sample regression line** has the following form:

Sample regression line:
$$\hat{y} = a + bx \qquad\qquad (13.4)$$

Let us explore how this sample line relates to the population regression line in Formula 13.1. The sample value of a is our best estimator of the intercept α, while the sample value of b is our best estimator of the slope β. Values of a and b, together with a given value of x, yield a predicted value of y, which is denoted $\hat{y}$. This $\hat{y}$-value is our best estimator of the population value $\mu_{y \cdot x}$. We can add the subscript i to these variables to indicate specific values, just as we did for the population regression line. Thus, if x_i is a specific value of x, the equation for finding $\hat{y}_i$ is $\hat{y}_i = a + bx_i$.

We can also specify a *sample regression model*, just as we specified a population regression model. Again, we need to define an error term, denoted by e_i, which is the difference between the predicted value $\hat{y}_i$ and the actual value y_i. The e_i values in regression analysis are often referred to as *residuals*, since they represent what is left over, or unexplained, after we use the predicted value $\hat{y}_i$ to estimate the actual value y_i:

Residuals: $\quad e_i = y_i - \hat{y}_i \quad$ or $\quad y_i = \hat{y}_i + e_i$.

If we use the estimator $\hat{y}_i = y_i - e_i$ in Formula 13.4, we obtain the **sample regression model**:

Sample regression model:
$$y_i = a + bx_i + e_i \qquad\qquad (13.5)$$

To illustrate the concept of a sample regression model, multiple observations are taken for a number of electricians to find an average number of installations completed per day by each. Figure 13.2 shows these sample observations, including one for electrician Joe Egan, in a scatter diagram. The line drawn free-hand through these points has an intercept of $a = 0.7$ and a slope of $b = 0.005$ and represents one possible sample regression line. We call this the *eyeball* fit. In the next section, an objective way to compute a *best fit* line for a scatter diagram will be discussed.

This sample regression line is:

$$\hat{y} = 0.7 + 0.005x$$

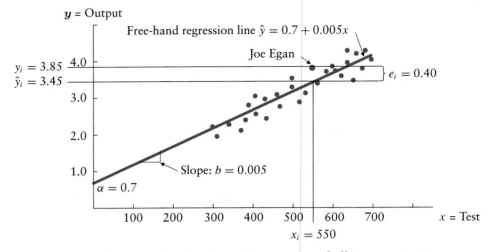

FIGURE 13.2 Sample scatter diagram and *eyeball* fit regression line

On the basis of this sample regression line, we can calculate a predicted value for output for any electrician with a given test score, such as $x_i = 550$, by substituting the value 550 for x_i in the equation:

$$\hat{y}_i = 0.7 + 0.005(550) = 3.45$$

Company records show that for the particular electrician, Joe Egan, with a test score of 550, the actual output of installations completed per day is 3.85. Thus, we can determine the amount of error in predicting Joe Egan's output by comparing his actual installation record of $y_i = 3.85$ per day to the predicted value of y_i (given $x_i = 550$) of 3.45.

$$e_i = y_i - \hat{y}_i = 3.85 - 3.45 = 0.40$$

The electrician, Joe Egan, overachieves compared to the average relationship which underestimates his number of completed installations per day. Table 13.1 summarizes the terms and the symbols used in the regression model.

TABLE 13.1 Regression Model: Terms and Symbols

Term	Population Symbols	Sample Symbols
Model	$y_i = \alpha + \beta x_i + \epsilon_i$	$y_i = a + bx_i + e_i$
Error	ϵ_i (disturbance)	e_i (residual)
Slope	β	b
Intercept	α	a
Equation of line	$\mu_{y \cdot x_i}$	$\hat{y}_i$

☐ **EXAMPLE 13.1** In a production process, the total cost y (fixed plus variable) depends on x, the number of units produced in a given run. Samples of different production runs are taken where the lot sizes vary from 20 to 80 units. The sample regression line is found to be:

$$\hat{y} = 25.75 + 1.225x$$

We interpret the intercept of 25.75 to be the fixed cost for a production run which is independent of the number of units produced. The slope of 1.225 represents the variable cost per unit.

If two production runs are needed, one for 75 units and the other for 200 units, estimated values of the total costs can be determined by substituting these values for x in the regression line:

For $x = 75$, $\hat{y} = 25.75 + 1.225(75) = 117.625$
For $x = 200$, $\hat{y} = 25.75 + 1.225(200) = 270.75$

The latter prediction for $x = 200$ is made with reservations since this value of 200 lies well beyond the upper value of the sample data observed.

If a run of 75 units is made and the actual total cost is determined to be 120, then the residual $e = (y - \hat{y})$ is $120 - 117.625 = 2.375$. The model underestimated total costs for this case. ◼

☐ STUDY QUESTION 13.1 Housing Price Model

A report on housing in metropolitan areas provides information on many variables related to housing. One part of this report (based on a census of cities) suggests a population regression model relating the mean price y of a housing unit to the median income x of households in that city (each measured in thousands of dollars):

$$\mu_{y \cdot x_i} = \alpha + \beta x_i + \epsilon_i$$

A sample of 25 cities was taken and the regression line based on this sample is:

$$\hat{y} = -4.047 + 4.693x$$

a) Interpret the meaning of the slope and the intercept.
b) For the city of Eagle Bay, the average housing price is $93,800, and the median income is $21,100. Find the sample model residual for this city.

● ANSWER

a) The slope of 4.693 is the marginal change in the average housing price for a unit change in median income. That is, if median income in a city increased by $1,000, the average housing price would be predicted to increase by $4,693. The intercept of $-\$4,047$ is the value of the average housing price in a city with median income of zero. Of course, this is not realistic; zero median income is below any observed city in the sample, and there is no experience of a home-buyer being given $4,047 to take a new house.

b) Substitute the median income of $21,100 into the sample regression line to find the value predicted by the model for the average price of a housing unit:

$$\hat{y}_i = -4.047 + 4.693(21.1) = 94.975 \quad \text{or} \quad \$94,975$$

The sample residual is:

$$e_i = y_i - \hat{y}_i = 93.800 - 94.975 = -1.175 \quad \text{or} \quad -\$1,175$$

The model overestimates the actual average housing price in Eagle Bay. ◼

Estimating the Values of α and β by Least Squares

A first step in finding a sample regression line of best fit is to plot the data in a scatter diagram. Such a plot allows us to visually determine whether a straight-line approximation to the data appears reasonable and to make eyeball estimates of α and β. Although this approach often yields fairly satisfactory results, there are at least two reasons for having a more systematic approach to finding the *best* straight-line fit to the data. First, different people are likely to find different values for a and b by the freehand drawing method. Second, the freehand estimation procedure provides no way of measuring the sampling errors, which are always important in forming confidence intervals or doing tests of hypotheses on population parameters.

What we need is a mathematical procedure for determining the sample regression line that best fits the sample data. The first step is to determine the criterion for defining *best fit*. Perhaps the most reasonable criterion is to find values a and b so that the resulting values for $\hat{y}$ (in the equation $\hat{y} = a + bx$), are as close as possible to the observed values y_i. The approach used in Chapter 2 to measure closeness of values to the mean (variance) is the same one we will use now to measure closeness of estimated values to observed values — the sum of the *squared deviations* (this sum is called a *variation*). That is, we will find the line of best fit in regression analysis by determining the values of a and b that minimize the sum of the *squared residuals*. This procedure is known as the *method of least squares*.

There are other criteria that might be used for determining a sample regression model and they would result in different estimated values. In this text, we emphasize the method of least squares because it is the one most commonly used and has desirable characteristics. Since the residuals are represented by $e_i = \hat{y}_i - y_i$, the **least-squares estimation method** is defined as follows:

Method of least-squares estimation:

$$\text{Minimize} \quad \sum_{i=1}^{n} e_i^2 = \sum_{i=1}^{n} (y_i - \hat{y}_i)^2$$

The sample regression line determined by minimizing Σe_i^2 is called *the least-squares regression line*. Since $\hat{y}_i = a + bx_i$, minimizing

$$\Sigma e_i^2 = \Sigma(y_i - \hat{y}_i)^2$$

is equivalent to minimizing $\sum_{i=1}^{n} [y_i - (a + bx_i)]^2$.

Finding the value of the two unknowns, a and b, that minimizes the sum of squared residuals is a problem solvable by calculus.[3] By minimizing Σe_i^2, the estimates a

---

[3] For convenience, let us denote the function to be minimized as:

$$G = \sum_{i=1}^{n} [y_i - a - bx_i]^2$$

Since this function is to be minimized with respect to a and b, it is necessary to take the partial derivatives of G with respect to these two variables, set each of these partials equal to zero, and then and b that provide the line of best fit, according to the least-squares criterion, are found to be as shown in the following formulas.

$$\text{Slope of least-squares line:} \quad b = \frac{\sum_{i=1}^{n}(x_i - \bar{x})(y_i - \bar{y})}{\sum_{i=1}^{n}(x_i - \bar{x})^2} \quad (13.6)$$

$$\text{Intercept of least-squares line:} \quad a = \bar{y} - b\bar{x} \quad (13.7)$$

The solution for the intercept, a, depends on the means of the variables x and y and the slope b. Thus, the slope b should be calculated first.

Let us examine the formula for the slope. Its denominator is the *sample variation* of the explanatory variable x. Variation, you recall, is the sum of squares of deviations from the mean. The numerator of the expression for b in Formula 13.6 is the sample **covariation** of x and y which is the sum of cross–products of deviations from the mean. If a variation or covariation is divided by degrees of freedom, a sample variance or covariance is obtained.

Table 13.2 lists terms used in regression analysis along with their respective symbols.

TABLE 13.2 Identification of Sample Terms Used in Regression Analysis

Item	Name	Symbol
Value of x or y	Observation	x_i or y_i
Difference between a value and the mean of the values	Deviation	$x_i - \bar{x}$
The sum of the squared deviations for one variable x	Variation	$SSx = \Sigma(x_i - \bar{x})^2$
The sum of the cross-products of deviations for two variables	Covariation	$SCxy = \Sigma(x_i - \bar{x})(y_i - \bar{y})$
A variation divided by d.f.	Variance	s_x^2
A covariation divided by d.f.	Covariance	s_{xy}

We will abbreviate a sample **variation** as SSx or SSy, where SS reminds us these are *sums of squares* of deviations and the lower case symbol x or y indicates the variable involved. We denote the sample **covariation** of variables x and y as $SCxy$, since it is a *sum of cross-products* of deviations. Using these definitions, the formulas for finding the least-squares estimates (a and b) are as follows:

---

solve the resulting two equations simultaneously. The partial derivatives are:

$$\frac{\partial G}{\partial a} = \sum_{i=1}^{n} 2(y_i - a - bx_i)(-1) \qquad \frac{\partial G}{\partial b} = \sum_{i=1}^{n} 2(y_i - a - bx_i)(-x_i)$$

Setting these equal to zero yields the following two equations (called *the normal equations*), which can be solved to obtain Formula 13.6:

$$\Sigma y_i = na + b\Sigma x_i \qquad \Sigma x_i y_i = a\Sigma x_i + b\Sigma x_i^2$$

Note also that setting the first partial equal to zero is identical to requiring that the sum of the residuals be zero, since the term in parentheses is the residual $e_i = (y_i - a - bx_i)$.

Slope and intercept of least-squares regression line:

$$b = \frac{(\text{covariation of } x \text{ and } y)}{(\text{variation of } x)} = \frac{SCxy}{SSx} \qquad (13.8)$$

$$a = \bar{y} - b\bar{x}$$

Two features of the sample regression line should be noted. First, if we substitute the intercept $a = \bar{y} - b\bar{x}$ into the line $\hat{y}_i = a + bx_i$, we obtain

$$\hat{y}_i = \bar{y} + b(x_i - \bar{x})$$

This means that if a prediction is calculated at the given value of the mean, $x_i = \bar{x}$, then $\hat{y} = \bar{y} + b(0)$; the predicted value for y is its mean. The population regression line always goes through the point $(\bar{x}, \bar{y})$.

Second, in order to minimize Σe_i^2, it is necessary to set $\sum_{i=1}^{n} e_i = 0$. (See the preceding footnote.) Thus, the sample regression line splits the scatter diagram of observed points so that the positive residuals (underestimates of the true point) always exactly cancel the negative residuals (overestimates of the true points). Such a sample regression line therefore estimates, without bias, the population regression line.

We will illustrate the technique of finding a least-squares regression line by applying it to our Output–Test problem for a random sample of eight observations (eight electricians).[4] Columns (1) and (2) in Table 13.3 give the data, ordered from the lowest test score to the highest. For a small sample, it is an aid to learning to calculate the sample regression line at least once by hand. For hand calculation, an alternative and equivalent formula for finding the slope is

$$b = \frac{SCxy}{SSx} = \frac{\Sigma x_i y_i - \dfrac{1}{n}(\Sigma x_i)(\Sigma y_i)}{\Sigma x_i^2 - \dfrac{1}{n}(\Sigma x_i)^2} \qquad (13.9)$$

This is commonly used when the raw data are not available but means and sums of squares or variations are reported. Ordinarily, you should learn how to determine the least squares regression results by a statistics software package on a computer available to you. Printouts from regression software will be illustrated throughout Chapters 13–16.

---

[4] For most practical purposes, a sample size of eight would not be sufficient. We use small samples here and later only for expositional convenience in illustrating the computations and formulas.

TABLE 13.3   Sample Points for Test and Output, and Calculations of Their Means, Variations, and Covariation

Obs	(1)	(2)	(3)	(4)	(5)	(6)
	Test (x_i)	Output (y_i)	($x_i - \bar{x}$)	($y_i - \bar{y}$)	($x_i - \bar{x}$)($y_i - \bar{y}$)	($x_i - \bar{x}$)^2
1	480	2.70	−60	−0.40	24	3,600
2	490	2.90	−50	−0.20	10	2,500
3	510	3.30	−30	+0.20	−6	900
4	510	2.90	−30	−0.20	6	900
5	530	3.10	−10	0.00	0	100
6	550	3.00	+10	−0.10	−1	100
7	610	3.20	+70	+0.10	7	4,900
8	640	3.70	+100	+0.60	60	10,000
Sum	4,320	24.80	0	0.00	SCxy = 100	SSx = 23,000
Mean	$\bar{x} = 540$	$\bar{y} = 3.10$				

FIGURE 13.3   Scatter diagram and least-squares regression line for data in Table 13.3

Our first step in analyzing the data in the first two columns of Table 13.3 is to construct a scatter diagram, to see whether the assumption of linearity is a reasonable one in this case. Figure 13.3 indicates that it is. The upward sloping line drawn in the diagram can be determined by the method of least squares.

The sums in columns (5) and (6) of Table 13.3 give the information necessary to calculate the slope. Using Formula 13.8, we can determine b as follows:

$$b = \frac{SCxy}{SSx} = \frac{\sum_{i=1}^{n}(x_i - \bar{x})(y_i - \bar{y})}{\sum_{i=1}^{n}(x_i - \bar{x})^2}$$

$$= \frac{100}{23{,}000} = 0.004348$$

Using this value of b and the means of x and y shown in columns (1) and (2) of Table 13.3, we obtain the following value of a:

$$a = \bar{y} - b\bar{x} = 3.10 - 0.004348(540) = 0.7521$$

Rounding to three significant digits, the least-squares regression line for this example is

$$\hat{y} = 0.752 + 0.00435x$$

Since the line in Figure 13.3 was determined by the method of least squares, there is no other line that could be drawn so that the sum of the squared residuals between the points and the line (measured in a vertical direction) would be smaller than for this line. The residuals and the estimated values of y_i for all eight sample points are given in Table 13.4. Note that the sum of the residuals for the least squares regression line is zero.

TABLE 13.4   Observed, Estimated, and Residual Values for the Least-squares Regression Shown in Figure 13.3

Obs	x_i	Observed Value (y_i)	Predicted Value	Residual $e_i = (y_i - \hat{y}_i)$
1	480	2.70	2.8391	−0.1391
2	490	2.90	2.8826	0.0174
3	510	3.30	2.9696	0.3304
4	510	2.90	2.9696	−0.0696
5	530	3.10	3.0565	0.0435
6	550	3.00	3.1435	−0.1435
7	610	3.20	3.4043	−0.2043
8	640	3.70	3.5348	0.1652
Sum	4,320	24.80	24.8000	−0.0000

Knowing the regression line described above enables us to predict the value of the dependent variable given a value of the independent variable.

☐ **EXAMPLE 13.2**   The regression model relating Output and Test scores can be used to predict the number of installations per day depending on the Test scores after the training program (other worker characteristics being ignored). If $x_i = 500$, the best estimate for Output given by $\hat{y} = 0.752 + 0.00435x$ is:

$$\hat{y}_i = 0.752 + 0.00435(500) = 2.927 \text{ per day}$$

The slope of the relation, $b = 0.00435$, gives the estimated average change in output for a unit change in the test scores. An increase in the test score of 100 points indicates an increase in installations completed of $0.00435(100) = 0.435$ per day. ■

Figure 13.4 presents a computer printout for the sample regression determined from the data in Table 13.3. The items discussed so far are in colour.

```
                        LINEAR REGRESSION
    DEP VAR: OUTPUT    N: 8    MULTIPLE R: .812    SQUARED MULTIPLE R: .659
    ADJUSTED SQUARED MULTIPLE R: .602    STANDARD ERROR OF ESTIMATE: .194


        VARIABLE    COEFFICIENT    STD ERROR    T        P(2 TAIL)
        CONSTANT    0.752          0.6932       1.085    0.320
        TESTSCOR    0.00435        0.001278     3.404    0.014


                        ANALYSIS OF VARIANCE


    SOURCE        SUM-OF-SQUARES    DF    MEAN-SQUARE    F-RATIO    P
    REGRESSION    0.435             1     0.435          11.583     0.014
    RESIDUAL      0.225             6     0.0375


                    PEARSON CORRELATION MATRIX


                          TESTSCOR    OUTPUT
                TESTSCOR  1.0000
                OUTPUT    0.8116      1.0000
```

FIGURE 13.4   Computer printout based on the data in Table 13.3

At this time, the reader may wish to check his or her understanding of the least-squares procedure by verifying that the point of means $(\bar{x}, \bar{y}) = (540, 3.1)$ does lie on the least-squares regression line given in $\hat{y} = 0.752 + 0.00435x$. Also, note from Figure 13.3 that a positive residual such as $e_3 = 0.3304(y_3 - \hat{y}_3)$ means that the line lies below the point (x_3, y_3) and, therefore, $\hat{y}_3$ underestimates y_3. On the other hand, a negative residual such as $e_7 = -0.2043(y_7 - \hat{y}_7)$ corresponds to an overestimation of y_7 by $\hat{y}_7$, in that the regression line is above the point (x_7, y_7).

☐ STUDY QUESTION 13.2   Sample Regression Line for Housing Price

The sample observations given in the top portion of Table 13.5 are used to obtain the summary measures in the bottom portion. Find the sample regression line relating housing price y to median income x. The result should match the sample regression equation given in Study Question 13.1.

● **ANSWER**   The values for the slope and intercept are:

$$b = (\text{covariation of } y \text{ and } x)/(\text{variation of } x)$$
$$= SC_{xy}/SS_x = 743.6969/158.4544 = 4.69344$$
$$a = \bar{y} - b\bar{x} = 95.604 - 21.232(4.69344) = -4.047$$

In dollars, $a = -4.047(\$1,000) = -\$4047$. The sample regression line is $\hat{y}_i = -4047 + 4.693x_i$ ■

TABLE 13.5 Housing Price and Median Income in Thousands of Dollars

Obs	Income	Price	Obs	Income	Price
1	22.1	90.1	14	24.7	133.7
2	23.3	101.4	15	20.2	87.9
3	24.3	93.2	16	16.8	77.4
4	18.6	88.8	17	23.0	96.8
5	22.2	99.1	18	22.2	96.6
6	24.5	112.2	19	23.3	115.9
7	21.6	81.5	20	20.4	106.6
8	17.6	77.6	21	18.9	83.5
9	23.5	96.5	22	17.9	77.4
10	18.1	86.4	23	26.6	128.8
11	21.1	88.4	24	18.4	75.5
12	20.4	100.2	25	20.1	95.3
13	21.0	99.3			

Variable	Symbol	n	Sum	Mean	Variation
Income	x	25	530.8	21.232	$\Sigma(x_i - \bar{x})^2 = 158.4544$
Price	y	25	2,390.1	95.604	$\Sigma(y_i - \bar{y})^2 = 5{,}460.3096$
				Covariation $= \Sigma(x_i - \bar{x})(y_i - \bar{y}) = 743.6969$	

Figure 13.5 presents a computer printout for this regression problem. As mentioned in Chapter 2, there is a great time saving in using an existing computer program if it provides what is needed. If some specific form of printout or specific statistical measures are desired, a specific computer program may need to be written. The relevant parts of Figure 13.5 for the current discussion are in colour. Some other parts will be referred to later in this chapter.

```
DEPENDENT VARIABLE..        PRICE    HOUSING PRICE
VARIABLE(S) ENTERED IN MODEL   INCOME   HOUSEHOLD MEDIAN INCOME


                      ANALYSIS OF VARIANCE



MULTIPLE R          0.79953              DF   SUM OF SQUARES   MEAN SQUARE
R SQUARE            0.63925   REGRESSION   1    3490.4990      3490.4990
ADJUSTED R SQUARE   0.62357   RESIDUAL    23    1969.8106        85.6439
STANDARD ERROR      9.25444       F = 40.756         SIGNIF F = 0.0001



                   VARIABLES IN THE EQUATION



   VARIABLE         B         SE B        T       SIG T
   INCOME        4.69344    0.73518    6.3840    0.0001
   (CONSTANT)   -4.04720   15.71878   -0.2575    0.7991
```

FIGURE 13.5 Computer printout for the housing price regression

Interpretation and Use of a Sample Regression Model

Several aspects of the method of least squares must be emphasized at this point. First, in using a regression line to make predictions about the dependent variable, the amount of uncertainty increases when values of the independent variable fall outside the range of past experience (historical data or sample observations), since it may be that these values cannot be represented by the same equation. The regression equation described previously, for example, predicts that the number of completed installations per day of electricians scoring only 100 points on the test would be $\hat{y}_i = 0.752 + 0.00435(100) = 1.187$. This is below the practical minimal value for the number of installations completed daily. Moreover, there are no observations of electricians with this low test score, since the minimum passing score is 300. There is really no appropriate way of applying this regression equation to predict the output when $x_i = 100$. Similarly, the equation would predict an output of 5.10 per day by electricians who score 1,000 on the test:

$$\hat{y}_i = 0.752 + 0.00435(1,000) = 5.10$$

Again, no persons were observed near this test score, since the maximum possible is 800.

The point is that special care must be taken in using a regression equation to make predictions. It must be remembered that the equation describes only an average relationship between the variables included in the model. *Other variables not included in the model* may cause deviations and errors from the values predicted by this simple relation. Also, since it is an *average* representation, it may not be accurate for any particular observation. It can be expected to represent only the average relation for values of x and y within the range of the sample data used in the estimation. In the above example, the equation should not be used for predictions when the input variable x has values outside the interval of about 400 to 700. The relation may be quite different for especially high or low values of x.

Second, the method of least squares can be adapted to apply to nonlinear populations. Although the computations necessary for applying the method of least squares to a nonlinear relationship naturally will differ from those used for linear relationships, the objective in fitting the curve is the same in the two cases — to find the line minimizing the sum of the squared residuals. Nonlinear regression models, which are often quite complex, can be found in more advanced texts on regression analysis.

As we have indicated, the method of least squares is just one curve-fitting technique in which the values of a and b are derived by finding the sample regression line that fits the sample data. The advantage of this approach is that if certain *assumptions* are made about the population, then the resulting estimators a and b can be shown to be unbiased, efficient, and consistent. Furthermore, these assumptions permit us to construct more easily the confidence intervals and to test the hypotheses that are so crucial to regression analysis. Economists, for example, use regression analysis in an attempt to form interval estimates and to test various hypotheses about population parameters in economic models, such as the marginal propensity to consume, the price elasticity of demand, and the factor shares of labor and capital in production. Policy-makers might use regression models to study the effect of changes in one variable, for example, of a tax change on one or more other variables such as employment, consumption, prices, interest rates, or the federal deficit. Business forecasters use regression for finding trend lines (as seen later in Chapter 16) and for predicting sales or for planning employment and advertising levels. Auditors would use least squares sample regressions to predict average values of production costs, or travel expenditures, or inventory balances to judge the validity of claims or the feasibility of new ideas. In any such uses, however, the analyst must be satisfied that the underlying assumptions are reasonable.

In Chapter 14, the role of the common assumptions underlying least squares regression analysis will be explained. Also, some tests to examine the validity of the assumptions and some calculational methods to adjust for possible violations of the assumptions will be presented. In the next section, we shall give only a brief statement of the assumptions and the derivable properties of the estimators. Following that, we proceed with the mechanics of regression analysis as if the assumptions are valid.

Assumptions and Estimator Properties

The assumptions underlying regression analysis are primarily concerned with the random variable ϵ. Making assumptions about the probability density function of ϵ enables us to make deductions about the sampling distribution of the random variable e from the sample regression model. In turn, this knowledge allows us to determine the sampling distributions of the estimators a for the intercept, b for the slope, and $\hat{y}_i$ for the predicted value of the dependent variable. With such probability distributions known, we can formulate confidence intervals or perform tests of hypotheses to learn about the overall population regression model. Such methods parallel those already presented in Chapters 9–12.

Many possible sets of assumptions could be formulated about the distribution of the variables in the population regression model. Five assumptions are commonly used because they yield estimators possessing the desirable properties of unbiasedness and efficiency (refer to properties of estimators in Section 9.2), and they result in test statistics that follow common distributions (z, t, F). These **five assumptions** are sometimes called the *ideal assumptions* for linear regression because they lead to the simple and best situation for the resulting estimators of the coefficients in the model. More formally, they are sometimes referred to as the *Gauss–Markov* assumptions which are the basis for an important theorem that was formulated by the German mathematician and astronomer, Karl F. Gauss (1777–1855), in his early works published in 1807 and 1821. Since these involved applications in physics and planetary motion, they generally remained unknown to social scientists and business analysts until they were restated by A. A. Markov in 1912 in a study of linear processes. Markov extended his work in the 1930s and the Gauss–Markov Theorem assumed its identity.

> Gauss-Markov Theorem: Given the five basic assumptions itemized below, the least squares estimators in the linear regression model are Best Linear Unbiased Estimators (BLUE).

In this context, *linear* means that the estimators are simply calculated, straight-line functions of the values of the dependent variable *y*. *Unbiased* has the standard meaning that the estimator has an expected value equal to the true population value. *Best* is a term meaning the estimator is efficient, having as small a variance as any other unbiased estimator that might be derived.

We here present the five assumptions with a brief explanation of their importance in leading to the desirable properties for the least squares estimators. In Chapter 16, more discussion is given about their validity and the effect on the estimators when they are not valid. Fuller treatments can be found in specialized books on linear models or econometrics.

The Five Assumptions

Assumption 1. (independence) *The random variable ϵ is assumed to be statistically independent of x.* In other words, the covariance is zero between the independent variable and the corresponding error term at each observation i. This assumption always holds when x is considered to be a set of given values and not a random variable.

Assumption 2. (normality) *The random variable ϵ is assumed to be normally distributed.* Figure 13.6 illustrates the meaning of this assumption (and assumptions 3 and 4 as well) by showing the normal distribution of errors ϵ_i about the population regression line.

Assumption 3. (balance) *The random variable ϵ is assumed to have a mean of zero; that is, $E[\epsilon] = 0$.* For a given x_i, the differences between y_i and $\mu_{y \cdot x_i}$ are sometimes positive, sometimes negative, but on the average are zero. Thus, the distribution of ϵ_i about the population regression line $\mu_{y \cdot x_i}$ (as shown in Figure 13.6) is always centred on the line for any given value of x.

$f(y \mid x)$

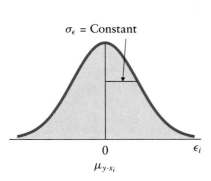

σ_ϵ = Constant

0

$\mu_{y \cdot x_i}$

ϵ_i

Side view of one of the
normal distributions of ϵ_i

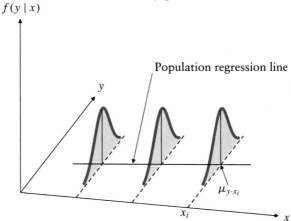

Population regression line

y

$\mu_{y \cdot x_i}$

x_i

x

FIGURE 13.6 Normally distributed error ϵ_i about $\mu_{y \cdot x_i}$, for any value x_i, given that assumptions 3 and 4 also hold.

Assumption 4. (homoscedasticity) *The random variables ϵ_i are assumed to have a finite variance σ_ϵ^2 that is constant for all given values of x_i.* In other words, the dispersion of points in the population about the population regression line must be constant. In Figure 13.6, this constant variance of ϵ_i is represented by depicting all the normal distributions about $\mu_{y \cdot x_i}$ as having the same standard deviation. No one distribution is more spread out or more peaked than another for a different value of x.

Assumption 5. (non-autocorrelation) *Any two errors, ϵ_i and ϵ_t, are assumed to be statistically independent of each other.* Since they are normally distributed, this implies that their covariance is zero, $C[\epsilon_i, \epsilon_t] = 0$. In other words, the error of one point in the population cannot be related systematically to the error of any other point in the population. Knowledge about the size or sign of one or more errors does not help in predicting the size or sign of any other error.

Properties of the Regression Coefficients

The good properties of least-squares estimators and the common forms of test statistics that result given these five assumptions account for the widespread use of the least-squares procedure. Given assumption 2, it can be shown that the estimators of α, β, and $\mu_{y \cdot x_i}$ obtained by using the least-squares criterion are normally distributed and are *identical* to the estimators that would result using the principle of maximum likelihood estimation. (Refer to Section 9.3.) Such estimators have the very important property of consistency.

Assumptions 1 and 3 are critical for the least-squares estimators to have the desirable property of unbiasedness. Assumptions 4 and 5 allow a proof that the least-squares estimators have the property of efficiency. In summary, by using these assumptions it is determinable that each estimator (a, b, or $\hat{y}$) is a random variable with a *normal* probability distribution with means and variances that can be easily derived by using the rules for expectations (Section 4.4). Examination of these gives us the comforting information that each of these estimators (a, b, or $\hat{y}$) has three desirable properties:

1. correct on the average (unbiasedness)
2. relatively reliable on a single try (efficiency)
3. more and more accurate, on the average, if larger-sized samples are used (consistency)

In Sections 13.7–13.10, we will make use of this probability knowledge about the estimators in order to make inferences about the population regression model relating variables y and x.

PROBLEMS

13.1 Explain why a disturbance term ϵ is included in the population regression model.

13.2 Explain what is meant by desirable properties of the estimator b.

13.3 Suppose that $y =$ average test score on college entrance boards and $x =$ hundreds of dollars of expenditures per pupil in the student's respective high school. Given that a regression of y on x gives $\hat{y} = 320 + 50x$, what is the interpretation of the value 50 and what value would you predict for y if $x = 5$?

13.4 Given the data in Table 13.6 on five observations for the variables y, sales of cordless phones, and x, years with $1991 = 0$.

a) Find the slope and intercept for the least-squares estimating line using Formula 13.8, and write the complete estimating equation.

b) Interpret the meaning of the values of a and b.

TABLE 13.6   Sales of Cordless Phones (y) Over a Number of Years (x)

y	3	19	18	22	23
x	−2	−1	0	1	2

13.5 A manufacturing firm bases its sales forecast for each year on government estimates for total demand in the industry. The data in Table 13.7 give the government estimate for total demand and this firm's sales for the past ten years.

TABLE 13.7   Sales Versus Demand

Demand Estimate	Sales
200,000	5,000
220,000	6,000
400,000	12,000
330,000	7,000
210,000	5,000
390,000	10,000
280,000	8,000
140,000	3,000
280,000	7,000
290,000	10,000

a) Draw a scatter diagram and verify that a linear approximation would be appropriate in this problem.

b) Find the least-squares regression line.

c) What sales figure represents the least-squares estimate if the government estimates total demand to be 300,000?

13.6 A study was conducted to determine the relationship (if any) between the number of persons in a household (x) and the number of radios in that household (y). The sample shown in Table 13.8 was collected.

TABLE 13.8 Data for Number of Persons in a Household versus Number of Radios

persons x	3	1	5	2	4
radios y	3	2	6	4	5

a) Plot these data on a scatter diagram to verify that a linear relation might be suitable.

b) Verify that the least-squares regression line is $\hat{y} = 1.3 + 0.9x$, using Formula 13.8. Show that this line goes through the point $(\bar{x}, \bar{y})$.

c) Calculate a $\hat{y}$-value for each x_i. Show that $\Sigma(y_i - \hat{y}_i) = 0$ for these values.

d) If $x_i = 7$, what value would you predict for $\hat{y}_i$?

13.7 Table 13.9 gives values for x = number of injuries and y = number of games missed for major league baseball players.

TABLE 13.9 Injuries and Games Missed

x	5	1	7	6	4
y	22	2	83	38	15

a) Plot the scatter diagram for these data. Does a linear relation seem appropriate?

b) Determine the least-squares regression line for these data.

c) Calculate $(y_i - \hat{y}_i)$ for each value of x_i. Is there any pattern to these deviations?

d) What value does the regression line predict if $x_i = 8$?

13.8 For Problem 13.7, find the regression line $\hat{x} = a + by$, assuming that y is the independent variable. Is this the same line as $\hat{y} = a + bx$? Sketch the two least-squares lines on the same scatter diagram.

13.9 The data in Table 13.10 pertain to selling prices and number of pages of new accounting manuals.

TABLE 13.10 Accounting Manuals' Selling Price versus Number of Pages

Price ($)	Number of Pages
45	400
47	600
47	500
45	300
43	400
43	200

Find the regression equation of y (price in dollars) on x (number of pages in hundreds), using the method of least squares.

13.10 The data in Table 13.11 on production of spark plugs and average cost were collected.

TABLE 13.11 Average Cost of Spark Plugs Based on Number Produced

Average Cost (¢)	Production per Month (000s)
13	25
19	20
40	10
25	20
33	15

a) Does the scatter diagram for these observations indicate a possible linear relation?

b) Find the regression equation of cost (y) on production (x), using the method of least squares.

c) What is the value of s_{xy} for these data?

d) Find $\hat{y}$ for each x-value, and then calculate $(y_i - \hat{y}_i)$ for each x-value.

♦ **13.11** By observing the total costs associated with publishing 30 different paperback books, a paperback publishing company has employed simple linear regression and obtained the following estimates for 1000 copies:

   Fixed cost per book title = $7,500
   Marginal cost per page = $3

a) State the regression equation. Be sure to indicate clearly the independent and the dependent variable.

b) Estimate the total cost of publishing 1,000 copies of a 500-page book.

♦ **13.12** Pierre Croissant, the owner/chef of Chez Pierre, an exclusive French restaurant in Winnipeg, is keenly interested in the relationship between the size of a party eating in his restaurant and their beverage consumption. He wonders, in particular, if larger parties tend to drink more, on a per-person basis. He has gathered a small random sample of data from his sales records as given in Table 13.12:

TABLE 13.12   Number in Group versus Beverage Charge

Number in Party	Beverage Charge per Person ($)
2	7.50
1	3.25
7	9.75
4	8.00
8	12.00
3	6.50
4	4.50
10	9.50
6	10.00
2	6.00

a) Estimate the linear regression line to predict values of beverage charge per person (y) as a function of number in party (x). Clearly show the values of the parameter estimates, and the prediction equation.

b) If a party of 5 persons comes in on a typical evening, what is your best estimate of their *total* beverage bill?

c) Below is a computer printout for this regression analysis. Identify the parts that relate directly to your solution in part (a).

```
                LINEAR REGRESSION
DEP VAR: BEVERAGE    N: 10    MULTIPLE R: .797
SQUARED MULTIPLE R: .635
ADJUSTED SQUARED MULTIPLE R: .589
STANDARD ERROR OF ESTIMATE: 1.731
```

```
VARIABLE   COEFFICIENT   STD ERROR   T       P(2 TAIL)
CONSTANT   4.264         1.071       3.980   0.0041
PARTYSZ    0.731         0.196       3.732   0.0058
```

```
              ANALYSIS OF VARIANCE

              SUM-OF-        MEAN-
SOURCE        SQUARES   DF   SQUARE   F-RATIO   P
REGRESSION    41.747    1    41.747   13.928    0.0058
RESIDUAL      23.979    8    2.997
```

◆ **13.13** The Wonder Sam Company in British Columbia operates a chain of retail outlets. It is attempting to evaluate the efficiency of various stores by measuring how total store expenses (excluding cost of goods sold) varies with the number of employees. Last month, data were randomly selected from ten of its many outlets. The following calculations were obtained using x as the number of employees and y as the overhead expenses.

$$\Sigma x = 609, \ \Sigma x^2 = 39{,}717, \ \Sigma y = 612,$$
$$\Sigma y^2 = 39{,}846, \ \Sigma xy = 39{,}637$$

a) Using simple linear regression and Formula 13.9 estimate the fixed cost per store and the variable cost per employee.

b) Estimate the fixed cost of a store with 55 employees.

13.14 Use the data on housing prices and median income in Table 13.5 and the sample regression line from Study Question 13.2. Find the residuals for observations 4 and 24 and interpret their meaning.

---

section 13.5

Measures of Goodness of Fit

In this section, we will present two primary measures of goodness of fit. The first is a measure of the *absolute* fit of the sample points to the sample regression line, called the *standard error of the estimate*. The second measure is an index of the *relative* goodness of fit of a sample regression line, called the *coefficient of determination*. Our presentation of these measures will be easier if some of the components of variability in regression analysis are understood first.

Deviations

In regression analysis, the difference between y_i and the mean of the y-values ($\bar{y}$) is often called the *total deviation of y*; that is, it represents the total amount that the ith observation deviates from the mean of all y-values. By a mathematical identity, this total deviation can be written as the *sum* of two other deviations; one is $(y_i - \hat{y}_i)$, and the other is $(\hat{y}_i - \bar{y})$.

You will recognize the first of these two deviations, $(y_i - \hat{y}_i)$, as the residual value e_i discussed in Section 13.4. Since the e_i are the unpredictable (or random) deviations, the term $(y_i - \hat{y}_i)$ is referred to as the *unexplained deviation*. While we cannot explain $(y_i - \hat{y}_i)$, it *is* possible to explain that $\hat{y}_i$ differs from $\bar{y}$ because x_i differs from $\bar{x}$. This deviation $(\hat{y}_i - y)$ is explained (or accounted for) by the regression line; hence, it is called the *explained deviation*. Putting all this together, we obtain the following relationship:

Total deviation in regression analysis:

$$\text{Total deviation} = \text{Unexplained deviation} + \text{Explained deviation}$$
$$(y_i - \bar{y}) \quad = \quad (y_i - \hat{y}_i) \quad + \quad (\hat{y}_i - \bar{y}) \qquad (13.10)$$

This relationship is illustrated in Figure 13.7 in the context of our Output–Test example.

The deviations emphasized in Figure 13.7 are for the first and the eighth electricians in our sample. (See Table 13.4.) For the first electrician, the deviations are:

$$\text{Total deviation} = \text{Unexplained deviation} + \text{Explained deviation}$$
$$-0.400 \quad = \quad -0.139 \quad + \quad -0.261$$

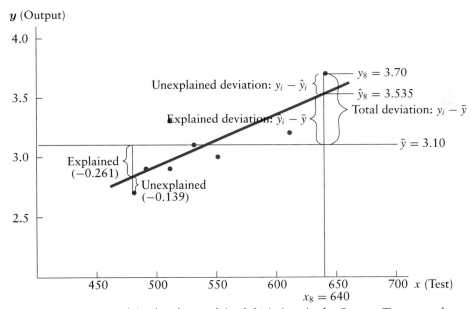

FIGURE 13.7   Explained and unexplained deviations in the Output–Test example

The reader can determine the deviations for the eighth case.

Because the two parts of the total deviation shown in Formula 13.10 are independent, it can be shown that this same relationship holds when we *square* each deviation and sum over all n observations as follows:

$$\sum_{i=1}^{n}(y_i - \bar{y})^2 = \sum_{i=1}^{n}(y_i - \hat{y}_i)^2 + \sum_{i=1}^{n}(\hat{y}_i - \bar{y})^2 \qquad (13.11)$$

The left-hand side of Formula 13.11 is referred to as the *total variation*, or as the *sum of squares total* (which is abbreviated as **SST**). The first term on the right is the *unexplained variation*, or equivalently, the *sum of squares error* (**SSE**). You should recognize SSE as Σe_i^2, the term that was minimized in finding the least-squares regression line. The last term in 13.11, which is the sum of squares of the values of $\hat{y}_i$ about $\bar{y}$, is called the *explained variation due to the regression model*, or the *sum of squares regression* (**SSR**). Thus, we can identify terms in 13.11 as follows:

Variation in regression analysis:

Total variation = Unexplained variation + Explained variation

$$\sum_{i=1}^{n}(y_i - \bar{y})^2 \quad = \quad \sum_{i=1}^{n}(y_i - \hat{y}_i)^2 \quad + \quad \sum_{i=1}^{n}(\hat{y}_i - \bar{y})^2 \quad (13.12)$$

$$\text{SST} \quad = \quad \text{SSE} \quad + \quad \text{SSR}$$

The advantage of breaking total variation into these two components is that now we can talk about goodness of fit in terms of the size of SSE. For example, if the line is a perfect fit to the data, then SSE = 0. Usually, however, the line is not a perfect fit; hence, SSE $\neq$ 0.

Calculation of SST, SSR, and SSE

We can calculate SST, SSE, and SSR for our Output–Test relation from the data in Tables 13.3 and 13.4. First, SST can be derived by squaring the values in column 4 of Table 13.3. These values are shown in column 1 of Table 13.13. The value of SSE is derived by squaring the errors $e_i = (y_i - \hat{y}_i)$ shown in the final column of Table 13.4. These squares (rounded to three decimals) are shown in column 2 of Table 13.13. Finally, we can calculate

$$\text{SSR} = \sum_{i=1}^{n}(\hat{y}_i - \bar{y})^2$$

by subtracting $\bar{y} = 3.10$ from each value of $\hat{y}_i$ in column 3 of Table 13.4 and then squaring these differences. These values are shown in column 4 of Table 13.13.

TABLE 13.13 Calculation of SST, SSE, and SSR for the Output–Test Example

(1) $(y_i - \bar{y})^2$	(2) $e_i^2 = (y_i - \hat{y}_i)^2$	(3) $(\hat{y}_i - \bar{y})$	(4) $(\hat{y}_i - \bar{y})^2$
0.16	0.019	2.8391 − 3.10	0.068
0.04	0.000	2.8826 − 3.10	0.047
0.04	0.109	2.9696 − 3.10	0.017
0.04	0.005	2.9696 − 3.10	0.017
0.00	0.002	3.0565 − 3.10	0.002
0.01	0.021	3.1435 − 3.10	0.002
0.01	0.042	3.4043 − 3.10	0.093
0.36	0.027	3.5348 − 3.10	0.189
SST = 0.66	SSE = 0.225		SSR = 0.435

We find that

$$\text{SST} = \text{SSE} + \text{SSR}$$
$$0.660 = 0.225 + 0.435$$

> In any regression analysis, the components (SSR and SSE) of total variation (SST) need to be determined. They are useful in finding summary measures for the goodness of fit and for aiding in the interpretation of the regression.

Thus, it is convenient to have a simpler way to determine these variation measures that avoids all the calculations used to determine the entries in columns 2, 3, and 4 in Table 13.13, or to have these measures included in computer calculations and printouts.

Since SST is simply the measure of the variation to be explained in the dependent variable y, it can be found as in column 1 of Table 13.13 or by using an equivalent formula for the variation of the variable y.

Total variation in the dependent variable y:

$$\text{SS}y = \text{SST} = \sum_{i=1}^{n} y_i^2 - \frac{1}{n}\left(\sum_{i=1}^{n} y_i\right)^2 \qquad (13.13)$$

The amount of variation explained by the regression equation can be determined without first calculating SSE. A roundabout procedure can be used that avoids the calculation of each estimated value ($\hat{y}_i$). A formula for finding SSR using values already calculated from Formula 13.8 is as follows:

> Explained variation: $\text{SSR} = b(\text{SC}xy)$ (13.14)

Once both SST and SSR are found, the unexplained variation SSE is found by subtraction using the relation in Formula 13.12, namely, $\text{SSE} = \text{SST} - \text{SSR}$.

☐ **EXAMPLE 13.3**   For the Output–Test example, the terms needed for finding SST using Formula 13.13 are found directly from the original data in Table 13.3. For $n = 8$ we have $\Sigma y_i = 24.80$, and the sum of squares is $\Sigma y_i^2 = 77.54$:

$$\text{SST} = 77.54 - \frac{1}{8}(24.80)^2 = 0.660$$

This is identical to SST at the bottom of column 1 in Table 13.13. The variation explained is easily found by using Formula 13.14. We know that the slope is $b = 0.00435$ and the covariation of x and y was found earlier to be 100.0. Thus,

$$\text{SSR} = 0.00435(100.0) = 0.435$$

It follows that the sum of squares of the errors is

$$\sum_{i=1}^{8} e^2 = \text{SSE} = \text{SST} - \text{SSR} = 0.660 - 0.435 = 0.225,$$

which is the number determined previously by the direct (but more cumbersome) method shown in Table 13.13.

Figure 13.8 repeats the computer printout of Figure 13.4 for the regression analysis of output on test scores. Various entries relevant to goodness of fit are in colour. As is usually the case, the components of total variation are found in the ANALYSIS OF VARIANCE section. Under the column for SUM-OF-SQUARES and in the row for REGRESSION is the value of 0.435 for the explained variation, SSR, due to the regression model. In the row labeled RESIDUAL is SSE, the unexplained variation of 0.225. ∎

```
                              LINEAR REGRESSION
DEP VAR: OUTPUT    N: 8    MULTIPLE R: .812    SQUARED MULTIPLE R: .659
ADJUSTED SQUARED MULTIPLE R: .602    STANDARD ERROR OF ESTIMATE: .194


              VARIABLE   COEFFICIENT   STD ERROR     T      P(2 TAIL)
              CONSTANT      0.752        0.6932    1.085      0.320
              TESTSCOR      0.00435      0.001278  3.404      0.014

                        ANALYSIS OF VARIANCE


         SOURCE       SUM-OF-SQUARES   DF   MEAN-SQUARE   F-RATIO     P
         REGRESSION        0.435       1      0.435       11.583   0.014
         RESIDUAL          0.225       6      0.0375


                    PEARSON CORRELATION MATRIX


                              TESTSCOR    OUTPUT
                   TESTSCOR   1.0000
                   OUTPUT     0.8116    1.0000
```

FIGURE 13.8 Computer printout based on the data in Table 13.3

Standard Error of the Estimate

One of the most useful measures of goodness of fit in regression analysis is called the **standard error of the estimate,** which is nearly the same as a standard deviation for the variable e, the residuals in the sample regression model. It is denoted by the symbol s_e and defined as follows:

Standard error of estimate:

$$s_e = \sqrt{\frac{1}{n-2}\sum_{i=1}^{n}(y_i - \hat{y}_i)^2} = \sqrt{\frac{\text{SSE}}{n-2}} \qquad (13.15)$$

Its square s_e^2, known as the *mean square error (MSE),* represents an unbiased estimate of the variance of the errors (ϵ_i) about the *population* regression line. You may recall from Sections 7.9 and 9.8 that an unbiased sample variance was calculated by dividing the sum of squared deviations by $(n-1)$, the degrees of freedom. The number of degrees of freedom in this case is $n-2$ because *two* sample statistics (a and b) must be calculated before the value of $\hat{y}_i$ can be computed (since $\hat{y}_i = a + bx_i$). Each of those calculations imposes a linear restriction on the sample values y_i, so that only $n-2$ of these values are free to vary once a and b are determined. Throughout *simple* regression analysis, we use $n-2$ for the degrees of freedom in any statistics that require use of the residuals (e_i).

☐ **EXAMPLE 13.4**   We calculate s_e for the Output–Test relation beginning with column 2 of Table 13.13 from which the sum of squares of the errors is:

$$\sum_{i=1}^{8} e_i^2 = \text{SSE} = 0.225$$

Since $n = 8$, the value of s_e is:

$$s_e = \sqrt{\frac{\text{SSE}}{n-2}} = \sqrt{\frac{0.225}{6}} = 0.1936$$

The value of s_e can be interpreted in a manner similar to that for a sample standard deviation. The typical error in using the regression model to predict output for the given sample values of test scores is 0.1936 completed installations per day.   ■

Given the *ideal* assumptions 2, 3, and 4 for a normal distribution of errors with mean zero and constant variance, approximately 68 percent of the sample observations for the Output-Test example will lie within $\pm 1 s_e$, or 0.1936 units, of the regression line. A band of $\pm 1 s_e$ measured vertically about $\hat{y}$ is illustrated in Figure 13.9. We see that 6 of the 8 residuals (75%) are less than ± 0.1936 and lie within the band. Carrying the *rule of thumb* further, a band of $\pm 2 s_e$ should include about 95% of the points.

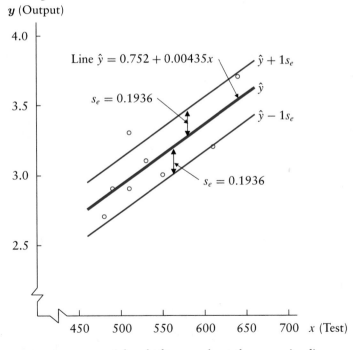

FIGURE 13.9   A band of one s_e about the regression line

This information gives a good indication of the fit of the regression model and the typical size of residuals that result from its use. The units of s_e are always the same as those for the variable y since e is a leftover (residual) component of y. To help judge if s_e is large or small, it is common to compare it to the average size of y. Using a *coefficient of variation* type measure, we can define the typical percentage error in predicting y using the sample data and regression line as follows:

Coefficient of variation for regression residuals:

$$\text{C.V. residuals} = \left(\frac{s_e}{\bar{y}}\right) 100 \qquad (13.16)$$

For the Output–Test regression, C.V. residuals $= (0.1936/3.1)100 = 6.25$. In predicting installations completed per day in this sample with the estimated model, the value will be incorrect by 6.25 percent, on the average.

The Coefficient of Determination

Our second measure of goodness of fit, which is useful in interpreting the *relative* amount of the variation that has been explained by the sample regression line, is called the **coefficient of determination** and is denoted by the symbol r^2.

Remember from Formula 13.12 that SST $=$ SSE $+$ SSR. Suppose that we divide each term in this equation by SST and note that SST divided by itself equals 1.0. We obtain:

$$\frac{\text{SST}}{\text{SST}} = 1.0 = \frac{\text{SSE}}{\text{SST}} + \frac{\text{SSR}}{\text{SST}}$$

Since the two ratios on the right-hand side of this equation sum to one, they must be a pair of mutually exclusive proportions. As one increases, the other decreases. Since SSE is the unexplained variation in y, the ratio SSE/SST is the *proportion* of total variation that is unexplained by the regression relation. The other ratio SSR/SST, is the *relative* measure of goodness of fit and is called the *coefficient of determination*. It measures the *proportion* of total variation that is *explained* by the regression line.

Relative measure of goodness of fit, coefficient of determination:

$$r^2 = \frac{\text{SSR}}{\text{SST}} = \frac{\text{Variation explained}}{\text{Total variation}} \qquad (13.17)$$

If the regression line *perfectly fit* all the sample points, all residuals would be zero. SSE $= \Sigma(\text{residuals})^2$ would be zero, SSR would equal SST, and the coefficient of determination would achieve its maximum value of 1.0. In other words, a perfect fit would result in a value of $r^2 = 1$.

As the degree of fit becomes less accurate, less and less of the variation in y is explained by the relation with x (SSR decreases), which means that r^2 must decrease. The lowest value of r^2 is 0, which will occur whenever SSR $= 0$ and SSE $=$ SST. By definition this means that $\Sigma(y_i - \hat{y}_i)^2 = \Sigma(y_i - \bar{y})^2$, implying that $\hat{y}_i = \bar{y}$ for all observations. Thus, the case of no explanation by the regression model occurs when the least-squares line $\hat{y}$ is the horizontal line at $\bar{y}$, the mean of y. For a horizontal line the slope is $b = 0$, meaning that the regression model reduces to $\hat{y} = \bar{y} + 0x$. The zero coefficient makes it obvious in this case why x has no effect in explaining changes in y. Whether an x-value is high or low, the corresponding value of y would be unaffected.

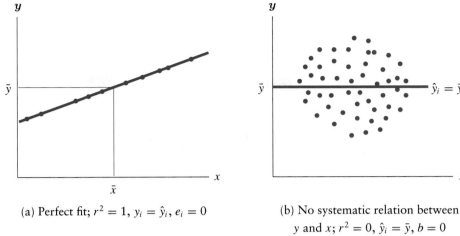

(a) Perfect fit; $r^2 = 1$, $y_i = \hat{y}_i$, $e_i = 0$

(b) No systematic relation between y and x; $r^2 = 0$, $\hat{y}_i = \bar{y}$, $b = 0$

FIGURE 13.10   Simple regression examples of $r^2 = 1$ and $r^2 = 0$

Figure 13.10(a) illustrates a line of perfect fit where SSE = 0 and SSR = SST so that $r^2 = 1.0$. Figure 13.10(b) suggests a case where SSR = 0 and SSE = SST so that $r^2 = 0$. In business applications of regression analysis, these extreme cases are usually not found; typically, $0 < r^2 < 1$.

Once the value of r^2 is calculated in a regression analysis, we have a *relative measure of goodness of fit*. For example, if $r^2 = 0.70$, this means that 70% of the total variation in the y-values (SST or SSy) is explained by the regression. Similarly, we know that 30% of the variation in y has *not* been explained. The proportion of variation unexplained is $(1 - r^2) = \text{SSE}/\text{SST}$.

◻ **EXAMPLE 13.5**   Let us calculate r^2 in our Output–Test relation. In this case, we already know that SSR = 0.435 and SST = 0.660. Hence,

$$r^2 = \frac{\text{SSR}}{\text{SST}} = \frac{0.435}{0.660} = 0.659$$

The interpretation of this result is that 65.9% of the total sample variation in output is explained by the linear relation of output with test scores.[5] The remaining 34.1% of the variation in output is still unexplained. Some other worker or job characteristics that are omitted from our regression model could help explain some additional portion of the variation. If these other factors could be measured and included as additional independent variables, we would have a *multiple regression model*, which is the topic considered in Chapter 14.   ■

◻ **STUDY QUESTION 13.3**   Goodness of Fit in the Housing Price Model

Find the goodness-of-fit measures for the regression model relating housing price to income. Interpret their meaning. The data are given in Table 13.5 and Study Question 13.2.

● **ANSWER**

$$\text{SST} = \text{SSy} = 5{,}460.3$$

$$\text{SSR} = b(\text{SCxy}) = 4.6934(743.7) = 3{,}490.5$$

$$\text{SSE} = \text{SST} - \text{SSR} = 5{,}460.3 - 3{,}490.5 = 1{,}969.8$$

---

[5] The similarity in size between SST and r^2 is purely coincidental.

The absolute measure of goodness of fit is the standard error of regression:

$$s_e = \sqrt{\frac{SSE}{n-2}} = \sqrt{\frac{1969.8}{23}} = \sqrt{85.643} = 9.254$$

Using the regression line on this sample data gives a typical prediction error of 9.254, an error of $9,254 in housing price. Since the mean housing price for the 25 cities is $95,604, the coefficient of variation for the residuals is:

$$\text{C.V. residuals} = \frac{9,254}{95,604} \times 100$$
$$= 9.68$$

This represents an error of about 9.7 percent, on the average, which is rather large for most prediction purposes.

The relative measure of fit is the coefficient of variation, $r^2 = SSR/SST = 3,490.5/5,460.3 = 0.639$. Almost 64 percent of the variation in housing price is explained by the relationship to median income. The percent of variation still unexplained is 36. ∎

Correlation Analysis

Although we have presented the relative measure of goodness of fit (r^2) in terms of the regression relationship between y and x, the strength or closeness of the linear relationship between two variables can be measured *without* estimating the population regression line. The measurement of how well two (or more) variables vary together is called *correlation analysis*.

One measure of the population relationship between two random variables is the **population covariance**:

$$C[x, y] = E\big[(x - \mu_x)(y - \mu_y)\big]$$

Although the covariance has many important statistical uses, this measure in general is *not* a good indicator of the relative strength of the relationship between two variables because its magnitude depends so highly on the *units* used to measure the variables. For example, the covariance between two measures of lengths x and y will be $\frac{1}{12}$ as large if x is scaled in feet than if x is scaled in inches. For this reason, it is necessary to *standardize* the covariance of two variables in order to have a good measure of fit. This standardization is accomplished by dividing $C[x, y]$ by σ_x and σ_y. The resulting measure is called the **population correlation coefficient** and is denoted by the Greek letter ρ (rho):

Population correlation coefficient:

$$\rho = \frac{\text{Covariance of } x \text{ and } y}{(\text{Std. dev. of } x)(\text{Std. dev. of } y)} = \frac{C[x, y]}{\sigma_x \sigma_y} \qquad (13.18)$$

Three values of ρ serve as benchmarks for interpretation of a correlation coefficient. First, let us consider the population in which the values of x and y all fall on a single straight line with a positive slope. In this case, which is referred to as a *perfect positive linear relationship* between x and y, ρ will equal $+1$.

When the relationship between x and y is a perfect *negative* linear relationship, all values of x and y lie on a straight line with a negative slope. In this case, ρ will equal -1. If x and y are not linearly related (if they are independent random variables), then the value of the correlation coefficient will be zero, since in this case $C[x, y] = 0$.

Thus, ρ measures the strength of the linear association between x and y. Values of ρ close to zero indicate a weak relation; values close to $+1.0$ indicate a strong *positive* correlation; and values close to -1.0 indicate a strong *negative* correlation. Figure 13.11 illustrates some representations of values of ρ for selected scatter diagrams.

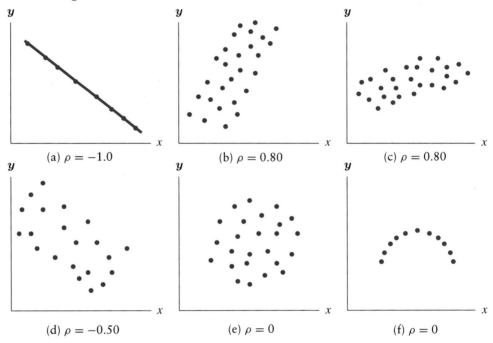

FIGURE 13.11 The population correlation coefficient

Note, from Figures 13.11(b) and 13.11(c), that two populations which appear quite different can have the same correlation coefficient. Figures 13.11(c) and 13.11(d) show the difference between positive and negative correlation. The last two diagrams show different examples of a population with zero correlation. In Figure 13.11(f), x and y are related in a nonlinear fashion, yet still $\rho = 0$, which emphasizes the fact that ρ measures the strength of the *linear* relationship.

The Sample Correlation Coefficient

As in all estimation problems, we use sample data to estimate the population parameter ρ. In this case, the sample statistic is called the **sample correlation coefficient** and denoted by the letter r. The value of r is defined in the same way as ρ, except that we substitute for each population parameter its best estimate based on the sample data. For instance, the best estimate of $C[x, y]$ in Formula 13.18 is the sample covariance, denoted by the symbol s_{xy}:

$$s_{xy} = \frac{1}{n-1} \sum_{i=1}^{n} (x_i - \bar{x})(y_i - \bar{y})$$

Similarly, the best estimates of σ_x and σ_y are the respective sample standard deviations, s_x and s_y. Substituting these estimates in Formula 13.18, we obtain the following defining formula for r:

Sample correlation coefficient:

$$r = \frac{s_{xy}}{s_x s_y} = \frac{\text{Covariance of sample values of } x \text{ and } y}{\left(\begin{array}{c}\text{Sample standard} \\ \text{deviation of } x\end{array}\right)\left(\begin{array}{c}\text{Sample standard} \\ \text{deviation of } y\end{array}\right)}$$

$$= \frac{\dfrac{1}{n-1} \displaystyle\sum_{i=1}^{n} (x_i - \bar{x})(y_i - \bar{y})}{\sqrt{\dfrac{1}{n-1} \displaystyle\sum_{i=1}^{n} (x_i - \bar{x})^2} \sqrt{\dfrac{1}{n-1} \displaystyle\sum_{i=1}^{n} (y_i - \bar{y})^2}} \tag{13.19}$$

A sample correlation coefficient is interpreted in the same manner as ρ, except that it measures the strength of the *sample* data rather than the population values. For example, where $r = \pm 1$, there is a perfect straight-line fit between the sample values of x and y; hence, they are said to have a perfect correlation. This is the same extreme case as discussed for the coefficient of determination when $r^2 = 1$. At the other extreme, if the sample values of x and y have no relationship, both r and r^2 will be zero.

Correlation coefficients are commonly calculated in computer programs for statistical analysis of measures of association between variables. If the measure r needs to be calculated by hand, note that the common term, $1/(n-1)$, can be factored from the fraction in Formula 13.19. The numerator becomes simply the sample covariation and the denominator terms within the redicals are the samples variations of x and y.

Simplified formula for r:

$$r = \frac{SCxy}{\sqrt{(SSx)}\sqrt{(SSy)}} \tag{13.20}$$

☐ **EXAMPLE 13.6** We can calculate the correlation coefficient between output and test scores using Formula 13.20. The essential measures have already been calculated. In Table 13.3, we find the following:

$$SCxy = 100.0$$

$$SSx = 23{,}000$$

From the previous section, we know that $SST = SSy = 0.66$. The sample correlation coefficient is:

$$r = \frac{100}{\sqrt{(23,000)(0.660)}} = 0.8116$$

The correlation between output and test in this example is 0.8116, indicating a moderately strong positive linear relationship. ■

Correlation and Regression

There are several connections and comparisons to be made between correlation and regression. First, there are some similarities and duplication of information. The correlation coefficient provides information on the strength and the direction of the association between x and y. In regression analysis, the coefficient of determination is also a measure of the strength of the association; indeed, for a model with only one explanatory variable, the measure r^2 is the square of the correlation measure r as they measure the same relationship.[6] When the association is very weak, both measures are near zero. A strong relationship is indicated between the two variables y and x when when r approaches -1 or $+1$, and in either case, the square of r is positive and r^2 approaches $+1.0$.

The additional information about the direction of association given by the sign of the correlation coefficient is obtained in regression by the sign of the slope coefficient b. A positive correlation must always correspond to a regression line with a positive slope indicating a direct relation; a negative r indicating an inverse relation is matched by a regression line with a negative slope. Thus, all the information contained in r about the strength and direction of the association is present in the analysis of a regression.

Refer to the computer printouts in this chapter for examples of these connections. In Figure 13.4 for relating installations completed to test scores, note that $r = +0.812$. The slope also has a positive sign, and the coefficient of determination is 0.659 which is the square of r. In Figure 13.5 for relating average housing price

---

[6] Recall from Formula 13.17 that $r^2 = SSR/SST$ and follow these steps to show the equivalence with $(r)^2$.

$$r^2 = \frac{SSR}{SST} = \frac{b(SCxy)}{SS_y}$$

since the explained variation is $SSR = b(SCxy)$ by Formula 13.14, and the total variation SST is the variation in the dependent variable y (SSy). Next, substituting the formula for the slope b from Formula 13.8, we obtain

$$r^2 = \left(\frac{SCxy}{SSx}\right)\left(\frac{SCxy}{SSy}\right) \qquad r^2 = \frac{(SCxy)^2}{(SSx)(SSy)}$$

which is exactly the square of r in Formula 13.20. By multiplying the right-hand side of Formula 13.20 for r by $1 = \sqrt{SSx}/\sqrt{SSx}$ and simplifying, we obtain the following:

$$r = \frac{(SCxy)}{\sqrt{(SSx)}\sqrt{(SSy)}}\left[\frac{\sqrt{SSx}}{\sqrt{SSx}}\right]$$

Since $\qquad b = \frac{SCxy}{SSx}, \qquad r = b\frac{\sqrt{SSx}}{\sqrt{SSy}}$

Since the sums of squares are never negative and their meaningful square roots are positive, the *signs* of r and b will always be the same.

to median income, the correlation coefficient is $+0.79953$. The slope is also positive indicating a direct upward sloping relation and $r^2 = 0.63925$, the square of r.

There are some differences in the two approaches. In correlation between x and y, both variables are considered to have probability distributions while in regression, the independent variable x can be considered as a set of fixed or given values.[7]

Further, in measuring correlation, there is no implied dependent-independent variable designation. In regression, the analyst has imposed a situation where the variable y is dependent on the explanatory variable x. If the roles of y and x are reversed, the regression line and the slope will be different although its sign will still be the same. The values of r and r^2 maintain their correspondence. The difference is not in the statistical association, which is symmetric, but in the implied causality introduced by the specification of the regression model. A high correlation or a good fit to a regression line does not imply that x is *causing* y. The belief in causation does not come from the statistics, but from the mind of the model-builder. The regression results do not imply or prove causation, but they are useful in predicting the value of y for some other observation on x or for anticipating the likely effect on y from some proposed policy that would change the level of x.

☐ STUDY QUESTION 13.4   Correlation Between Cost and Lot Size

Find the correlation coefficient between total costs and lot size using the data in Table 13.14. Interpret it with respect to its relation to b and r^2 for the regression line.

TABLE 13.14   Sample Data on Total Costs and Lot Size

Obs	Lot size (x)	Total Costs (y)	x^2	y^2	xy
1	60	100	3,600	10,000	6,000
2	40	80	1,600	6,400	3,200
3	80	120	6,400	14,400	9,600
4	20	45	400	2,025	900
5	50	90	2,500	8,100	4,500
Sum	250	435	14,500	40,925	24,200
Mean	50	87			

● **ANSWER**   Using the data we determine $SCxy = 2,450$, $SSx = 2,000$ and $SSy = 3,080$. The sample regression slope is

$$b = \frac{SCxy}{SSx} = \frac{2,450}{2,000} = 1.225$$

and the intercept is

$$a = \bar{y} - b\bar{x} = 87 - (1.225)50 = 25.75$$

---

[7] If the independent variable x is not a random variable, but is a *fixed* variable, ρ is not even defined (since the terms $C[x, y]$ and $V[x]$ are zero). Nevertheless, even when x is fixed, r is still a good descriptive statistic for the association between sample values of y and x.

The sample regression line is

$$\hat{y} = 25.75 + 1.225x$$

Next, we use Formula 13.20 to calculate the correlation coefficient:

$$r = \frac{SCxy}{\sqrt{(SSx)}\sqrt{(SSy)}} = \frac{2,450}{\sqrt{(2,000)}\sqrt{(3,080)}} = \frac{2,450}{2,481.9} = +0.987$$

This indicates a strong positive association. The sign is the same as for the slope b in the regression line indicating an upward sloping line.

The square of the correlation coefficient, $(0.987)^2 = 0.974$, should equal the coefficient of determination for the regression model. We know that the total variation in y to be explained in this data is SST $= 3,080$. We find the explained variation due to the regression using Formula 13.14 as

$$SSR = b(SCxy) = 1.225(2,450) = 3001.25$$

The ratio SSR/SST gives

$$r^2 = 3,001.25/3,080 = 0.974$$

The model explains 97.4% of the variation in total costs by relating this variable to the lot size. ∎

PROBLEMS

13.15 In a simple regression and correlation analysis based on 72 observations, we find $r = 0.8$ and $s_e = 10$.

a) Find the amount of unexplained variation.

b) Find the proportion of unexplained variation to the total variation.

c) Find the total variation of the dependent variable.

13.16 In a simple regression, explain the importance of r^2 and s_e, and differentiate between them.

13.17 Use the data from Table 13.15 to compute the regression equation of sales (y) on advertising expenditures (x). Then compute a measure that describes the proportion of the variation of sales that is explained by the regression.

TABLE 13.15 Sales versus Advertising Expenses in Various Regions

Region	Sales, y	Advertising Expense, x ($10,000)
A	31	5
B	40	11
C	25	3
D	30	4
E	20	2
F	34	5

13.18 The least-squares estimating line of the number of motel rooms that are rented (y), based on the number of advance reservations made (x), for a certain Holiday Inn is $\hat{y} = 26 + (3/4)x$ with an average $\bar{y} = 60$.

a) For a particular night, 60 advance reservations are received. Suppose that the manager needs one maid for each nine rooms occupied. Advise this manager on the minimum number of maids that should be employed in this particular case, based on your estimate of the number of rooms that will be occupied and will need cleaning.

b) Suppose that, for one day, the number of advance reservations received is 36 and the number of rooms occupied turns out to be 55. Find the total, explained, and unexplained deviations for this case.

13.19 An economist wishes to study the demand relation for a hand calculator. Over several years the product has improved somewhat while its price has fallen considerably. The price per unit (x) and the number of units (in thousands) purchased annually (y) are given in Table 13.16.

TABLE 13.16   Demand for Hand Calculators

Price ($)	120	100	70	50	30	20
Quantity (000s)	10	15	20	35	45	55

a) Estimate the linear demand function relating the quantity demanded to the price using the method of least squares.

b) Although price is the independent variable, it is common to graph a demand relation with price on the vertical axis and quantity on the horizontal axis. Following this convention, sketch the observations and the regression line. Interpret the meaning of the values obtained for the estimates of α and β.

c) If the price in another year was $25, what is your estimate of the quantity demanded in that year?

d) Find the proportion of the variation in quantity that is explained by your demand relation.

e) Find the coefficient of variation (C.V.) for the residuals.

13.20 We wish to explore the relationship between family monthly food consumption y and family monthly income x, both measured in hundreds of dollars. We are given information for 100 families in Table 13.17.

TABLE 13.17   Family Food Consumption versus Monthly Income

$n = 100$	$\bar{y} = \$6$	$\bar{x} = \$8$
$\Sigma xy = 6{,}000$	$\Sigma y^2 = 4{,}500$	$\Sigma x^2 = 10{,}000$

a) Find the regression equation $\hat{y} = a + bx$, using the method of least squares.

b) Using the regression equation, make an estimate of consumption for a family with a monthly income of $1,500.

c) Compute an absolute measure of goodness of fit of the regression equation and interpret its meaning.

d) Find C.V. residual and interpret.

◆ **13.21** Refer to the information on the Wonder Sam Company in Problem 13.13.

a) What percentage of the variability in costs is explained by the regression on the number of employees?

b) Find the correlation coefficient between y and x and relate it to the answer in part (a).

◆ **13.22** Any manufacturing operation essentially incurs three kinds of expenses — raw material expenses, direct labour expenses, and overhead expenses. A manufacturer of certain auto-parts is interested in knowing if a linear relationship exists between its monthly overhead (in thousands of dollars) and total number of parts produced per month (in thousands). The data have been collected for 12 consecutive months. Number of parts is called NPARTS, and the corresponding overhead costs are called OVRHD. Following is the partial output from a regression program:

```
          TABLE OF MEANS AND STANDARD DEVIATIONS
Variable      Mean       St. Dev.
OVRHD        41.1167      7.50937
NPARTS       18.8917      4.95167

        MATRIX OF CORRELATION COEFFICIENTS
                        OVRHD     NPARTS
            OVRHD       1.0000    0.9859
           NPARTS      0.9859    1.0000

                   ANOVA TABLE
Source of      Sum of                  Mean
Variation      Squares      D.F.      Square
Regression    602.9756       1       602.9756
Error          17.3210      10         1.7321
Total         620.2966      11
           TABLE OF ESTIMATED COEFFICIENTS

              Estimated    Estimated   Computed
Variable      Coefficient  St. Dev.    t-Value
NPARTS          1.4952      0.08014     18.658
Intercept      12.8697
```

$$SSx = 269.709$$

Standard error of estimate = 1.3161.

a) State *and* interpret the regression equation.

b) Predict the overhead costs for manufacturing 18,000 parts. Is it reasonable to make such a prediction? Explain.

c) What is the proportion of variability explained by the regression?

13.23 In a simple regression based on 20 observations, it is found that $r^2 = 0.6$ and $s_e^2 = 0.81$. Find the total, explained, and unexplained variations.

13.24 Given the data in Table 13.18 for quiz scores (y) and class absences (x) for a certain statistics class:

TABLE 13.18   Class Absence Versus Quiz Scores

$\Sigma y = 1,800$	$\Sigma xy = 4,750$	$\Sigma y^2 = 113,000$
$\Sigma x = 90$	$n = 30$	$\Sigma x^2 = 400$

a) Find the estimating equation $\hat{y} = a + bx$, and interpret the meaning of b.

b) Find the coefficient of determination.

c) Determine a student's expected quiz score if this person had six absences. Comment on the validity of using the estimating equation for subsequent classes or quizzes.

13.25 In a regression analysis using 16 observations, the explained variation is 40 out of a total variation of 60. Find the standard error of estimate for the regression equation.

13.26 Given the information in Table 13.19 for retail stores, compute the measures required:

TABLE 13.19   Daily Costs for Retail Stores Versus Number of Clerks

No. of clerks	x	2	4	6	8	10	12
Daily costs ($000s)	y	3	4	4	6	6	7

a) regression equation of y on x, estimate of fixed cost, and of variable cost per clerk

b) coefficient of determination

c) standard error of estimate and C.V. residual

d) the total deviation, the explained deviation, and the unexplained deviation for the fifth observation.

13.27 Define or describe briefly each of the following:

a) covariance

b) coefficient of determination

c) method of least squares

d) normal equations

13.28 In any simple correlation analysis, state what the logical limits are for values of r, and explain why.

13.29 We have data on the number of sheep x (in thousands) and production of wool sweaters y (in thousands) for a certain region of the United Kingdom, as given in Table 13.20:

TABLE 13.20   Production of Wool Sweaters versus Number of Sheep

Year	Wool Sweaters y (000s)	Sheep x (000s)
1940	2	1
1950	3	2
1960	5	4
1970	7	5
1980	8	4
1990	6	3

a) Find the estimating equation for $\hat{y} = a + bx$, by the method of least squares.

b) Find the sample coefficient of correlation between y and x, and relate it to the regression line.

13.30 What is the coefficient of correlation between two variables if:

a) one of the variables is constant?

b) the value of one variable always exceeds the value of the other variable by 100?

c) the unexplained variation is twice the explained variation?

♦ **13.31** In an attempt to understand the factors that influence the crime rate, information about the following two variables is extracted from a database for 25 of the 50 U.S. states:

PCRIME: U.S. state burglary rate per 100,000 population
URBAN: Percent of population in urban areas.

A simple linear regression model was developed in order to identify any relationship between these two variables. Following is a partial computer printout of the results.

TABLE OF MEANS AND STANDARD DEVIATIONS

Variable	Mean	St. Dev.
PCRIME	1597.04	376.0792
URBAN	63.524	21.6304

MATRIX OF CORRELATION COEFFICIENTS

	PCRIME	URBAN
PCRIME	1.0000	0.6938
URBAN	0.6938	1.0000

TABLE OF ESTIMATED COEFFICIENTS

Variable	Estimated Coefficient	Estimated St. Dev.
URBAN	12.0625	2.6109
Intercept	830.7821	

Standard error of estimate = 276.6722
n = 25

a) Show, from the computer output that the sum of squares for the independent variable URBAN is $SS_x = 11,228.98$.

b) What is the proportion of variability explained by the regression line?

c) State and interpret the regression model.

13.32 What is the difference between regression analysis and correlation analysis? When should each be used?

13.33 A Peace Corps representative in Chad works with five farmers in a cooperative shop rebuilding small gasoline motors for use in water pumps. She recognizes a difference in the workers' individual ability to learn the new job and to do it properly without supervision. After several weeks, she records the following information, where y = average weekly output of correctly rebuilt motors, and x = years of education of each of the five Chadian workers.

TABLE 13.21 Output of Motors Versus Years of Education

x	7	5	6	10	4
y	15	7	10	20	8

a) Find the regression equation $\hat{y} = a + bx$, and interpret the meaning of b.

b) Find the value of r.

c) Find SSE and SSR.

d) What percent of the variability in y is explained by the regression?

e) Show for these data that $r = b\sqrt{SSx}/\sqrt{SSy}$.

♦ **13.34** The data in Table 13.22 represent the dollar value of sales and advertising for a company for five different periods.

TABLE 13.22 Sales Versus Advertising Expenditure

Period	Advertising (in thousands)	Sales (in thousands)
1	20	300
2	30	450
3	40	550
4	50	600
5	60	900

a) Find the least squares regression line, using advertising expenditure as the independent variable and sales as the dependent variable.

b) What sales value would you predict if the advertising expenditure were zero? Is it appropriate to make such a prediction from the estimated regression equation?

c) Determine the sample correlation coefficient.

♦ **13.35** The Pac Ford Company in St. John's, Newfoundland wants to predict how overhead costs vary with production levels. The company is uncertain about the measure to use for representing production activity. The two measures about which it has data are the direct labour hours (DLH) and the number of units produced (NOU). Monthly data for the preceding six months is given in Table 13.23.

TABLE 13.23 Number of Labour Hours, Units Produced, and Overhead Costs

Month	DLH	NOU	Overhead Costs (000s)
September	120	115	$27.7
August	140	160	$39.9
July	135	144	$32.4
June	143	147	$36.4
May	140	125	$31.2
April	118	125	$28.9

a) Using correlation analysis, determine which measure, DLH or NOU, is most strongly, linearly associated with the firm's overhead costs.

b) Based on your analysis in part (a), determine the best estimated regression equation. Using this equation, estimate the overhead costs when the independent variable has a value of 120.

---

section 13.7

Test on the Significance of the Sample Regression Line

We have presented a way of estimating the best regression line fitting the linear relation between y and x, and we have discussed measures of the strength of the linear relationship. However, we have not given any rules or guidelines to help determine whether knowledge of the independent variable x is useful in predicting the values of y.

Any use of inference to learn about a population based on a sample requires knowledge about the probability distribution of the relevant random variables. In regression, the random variables of interest are the estimators from the sample model, such as the slope b, or a forecast $\hat{y}_i$, or a measure of fit. The needed probability distributions depend directly on the random variable ϵ_i, representing the errors in the population model.

In Section 13.4, the common assumptions about the errors ϵ_i were presented. If these hold for a regression model, the probability distribution of the sample estimator for the slope b, intercept a, or forecast $\hat{y}_i$ is found to be normally distributed with mean equal to the respective population parameter β, α, or $\mu_{y \cdot x_i}$. Also, each has a variance that depends on the unknown variance σ_ϵ^2 of the errors. Thus, the variance of each of these estimators is also *unknown*. If we denote these unknown variances as σ_b^2 for the slope, σ_a^2 for the intercept, and $\sigma_{\hat{y}}^2$ for the forecast, we can specify the probability distributions of these random variables as shown in Table 13.24.

TABLE 13.24   Probability Distributions for Regression Analysis

Random Variable	Mean	Variance	p.d.f.	Standardized Form
Disturbance, ϵ_i	0	σ_ϵ^2	$N(0, \sigma_\epsilon^2)$	
Slope, b	β	σ_b^2	$N(\beta, \sigma_b^2)$	$z = (b - \beta)/\sigma_b$
Intercept, a	α	σ_a^2	$N(\alpha, \sigma_a^2)$	$z = (a - \alpha)/\sigma_a$
Forecast, $\hat{y}_i$	$\mu_{y \cdot x_i}$	$\sigma_{\hat{y}_i}^2$	$N(\mu_{y \cdot x_i}, \sigma_{\hat{y}_i}^2)$	$z = (\hat{y}_i - \mu_{y \cdot x_i})/\sigma_{\hat{y}_i}$

We must repeat that each of these estimators has a variance that is unknown and that depends on the variance of the population disturbance. In order to make inferences, we will follow the familiar procedure of using a sample estimate of this unknown variance. We use the square of the standard error of estimate (s_e^2) to estimate the unknown variance of the population error. Using s_e as a substitute for σ_ϵ, we will compute sample measures of variance for each estimator and denote the corresponding standard deviations by the symbols s_b or s_a. We will substitute these sample standard deviations for the unknown population standard deviations into the standardized forms of the random variables given in Table 13.24. In doing so, we recognize that the probability distribution is no longer normal (denoted by z), but is a *t*-distribution that allows for the extra uncertainty in estimating a true variance σ^2 by a sample variance s^2.

Test on the Slope

We will follow this procedure of inference in several applications. First, we wish to examine the significance of the relation between the dependent variable y and the explanatory variable x. Suppose that the population relationship is such that $\beta = 0$. This means that the term $\beta x = 0$ and can be dropped from the model. The population regression line is simply a horizontal line at the level of μ_y (similar to Figure 13.10(b) for the sample regression line). In other words, when there is no systematic relation between y and x, our best predictor of the expected value of y is the mean of y. This agrees with our analysis throughout Chapters 9–11 when we emphasized the use of the mean to estimate the level expected for a single variable.

On the other hand, *if β is not equal to zero*, some systematic direct ($\beta > 0$) or inverse ($\beta < 0$) relation does exist between y and x. In this case, the term βx in the model does *not* drop out; hence, the changes in x are meaningful in predicting changes in the level of y. Thus, to determine whether or not the estimation of the y-values is improved by using the regression line, we can test the null hypothesis $H_0 : \beta = 0$. Rejecting H_0 in this case means concluding, on the basis of the sample information given, that β does not equal zero and, hence, that the regression line *is* useful in estimating the dependent variable. The alternative hypothesis for this test is usually one-sided. For example, we could use the one-sided alternative that the slope is greater than zero ($H_a : \beta > 0$) or the one-sided alternative that the slope is less than zero ($H_a : \beta < 0$). A two-sided alternative would be to hypothesize merely that the slope does not equal zero ($H_a : \beta \neq 0$). The two-sided test is appropriate only if no *a priori* knowledge or theory is available about the expected direction of the relation between y and x.

Although the above forms of hypotheses are always used to test the significance of a regression coefficient, the hypothesized value need not be zero. To illustrate a problem in which β is not assumed to be zero, consider that an economist wishes to test the null hypothesis that the slope of the regression line relating personal income and consumption (slope = marginal propensity to consume) has not increased from some historical value, such as $\beta = 0.90$. The appropriate test is $H_0 : \beta = 0.90$ against $H_a : \beta > 0.90$. The assumed value of β in such a test is usually denoted by β_0.

A *t*-test (with $n - 2$ degrees of freedom) uses the sample estimate b and the standardized form of a test statistic given by the following formula:

Test statistic for inference on the regression slope β:

$$t_{(n-2)} = \frac{b - \beta_0}{s_b}$$

(13.21)

The estimated standard error s_b is defined as follows:

Estimated standard error of regression coefficient b:

$$s_b = \frac{s_e}{\sqrt{SSx}}$$

(13.22)

The value s_b is a measure of the amount of sampling error in the regression coefficient b, just as $s_{\bar{x}}$ was a measure of the sampling error of $\bar{x}$ in *t*-tests on a mean (Section 10.3).

☐ **EXAMPLE 13.7**   We can apply Formula 13.21 to our Output–Test example. Suppose that the null hypothesis $H_0 : \beta = 0$ is tested against $H_a : \beta > 0$. We use the one-sided test because we expect electricians with higher test scores, on the average, to complete more installations per day. First we must calculate s_b by substituting the previously determined values into Formula 13.22:

$$s_e = 0.1936 \quad \text{and} \quad SSx = 23,000$$

Therefore, $$s_b = 0.1936\sqrt{\frac{1}{23{,}000}} = 0.001278$$

Thus, the calculated value t_c is as follows:

$$t_c = \frac{b - \beta_0}{s_b} = \frac{0.00435 - 0}{0.001278} = 3.404$$

For $n - 2 = 6$ degrees of freedom, the probability that t is larger than 3.406 falls between 0.005 and 0.01 (Table VI in the Appendix). Using a computer, the p-value is $p(t_6 \geq 3.404) = 0.007$. Thus, it is highly unlikely that a slope of $b = 0.00435$ will occur by chance when $\beta = 0$. We reject H_0 and conclude that the regression line does seem to improve our ability to estimate the dependent variable. ∎

Figure 13.12 repeats the computer printout for this regression; the results relating to inference are in colour. In the row for the variable TESTSCOR and the column STD ERROR, we find $s_b = 0.001278$. In the next column is the t-value, $t = 3.404$. In the last column is printed the p-value for a two-sided test of significance. We usually can hypothesize the direction of the relation in advance, so we use one-half of the p-value for a one-sided test. We can reject H_0 with a risk of type I error no larger than 0.007.

```
                        LINEAR REGRESSION
DEP VAR: OUTPUT    N: 8   MULTIPLE R: .812    SQUARED MULTIPLE R: .659
ADJUSTED SQUARED MULTIPLE R: .602    STANDARD ERROR OF ESTIMATE: .194

          VARIABLE   COEFFICIENT   STD ERROR      T     P(2 TAIL)
          CONSTANT     0.752         0.6932     1.085     0.320
          TESTSCOR     0.00435       0.001278   3.404     0.014

                      ANALYSIS OF VARIANCE

     SOURCE      SUM-OF-SQUARES   DF   MEAN-SQUARE   F-RATIO      P
     REGRESSION      0.435        1      0.435       11.583    0.014
     RESIDUAL        0.225        6      0.0375

                PEARSON CORRELATION MATRIX

                          TESTSCOR    OUTPUT
              TESTSCOR     1.0000
              OUTPUT       0.8116     1.0000
```

FIGURE 13.12   Computer printout based on the data in Table 13.3

In addition to being able to test hypotheses about β, it is possible to construct a $100(1 - \alpha)\%$ confidence interval for β. Since the regression coefficient b follows a t-distribution with $(n - 2)$ degrees of freedom and standard deviation s_b, the desired interval is shown in the following formula:

Confidence interval for the regression slope β:

$$b - t_{(\alpha/2, n-2)}s_b \ \leq \ \beta \ \leq \ b + t_{(\alpha/2, n-2)}s_b \tag{13.23}$$

☐ **EXAMPLE 13.8** A 95% confidence interval for the population slope in the Output–Test relation, given that $n = 8$, $t_{(\alpha/2, n-2)} = t_{(0.025, 6)} = 2.447$, and $s_b = 0.001278$, is found by using Formula 13.23:

$$0.00435 - (2.447)(0.001278) \leq \beta \leq 0.00435 + (2.447)(0.001278)$$

$$0.00122 \leq \beta \leq 0.00748$$

Thus, based on our sample of eight electricians, an increase in completed installations per day of between 0.122 and 0.748 could be expected for each 100-point increase in test scores. This is a rather wide interval for any precise forecasting of output. This degree of uncertainty suggests the need to consider other factors and to take a larger sample of electricians. ■

Test on the Correlation Coefficient

In addition to the t-test presented above for testing $H_0 : \beta = 0$, there is an equivalent t-test based on the null hypothesis $H_0 : \rho = 0$. The following t-distributed random variable using the sample correlation coefficient r (which is our best estimate of ρ) with $(n - 2)$ degrees of freedom, can be used:[8]

t-statistic for test on a correlation coefficient ρ:

$$t_{(n-2)} = \frac{r\sqrt{n - 2}}{\sqrt{1 - r^2}} \qquad (13.24)$$

☐ **EXAMPLE 13.9** The t-statistic in Formula 13.24 can be used to test the null hypothesis of no correlation, $H_0 : \rho = 0$. We again use our Output–Test example, in which $r = 0.8116$. For the same reason that we used $H_a : \beta > 0$, we now use the alternative hypothesis $H_a : \rho > 0$. To determine the probability that a value such as 0.8116 would occur by chance, given that $\rho = 0$ and $n = 8$, we use Formula 13.24 to calculate t:

$$t_c = \frac{0.8116\sqrt{8 - 2}}{\sqrt{1 - (0.8116)^2}} = 3.404$$

The value of t obtained in this analysis, $t_c = 3.404$, is *exactly* the same result as that obtained when testing $H_0 : \beta = 0$ in Example 13.8. This equivalence is no mere coincidence, since the outcome of a simple regression analysis and a correlation analysis on the same data must yield identical results when the same hypothesis of *no* relationship between x and y is being tested.[9] Finally, we should mention that the p-value $P(t_6 \geq 3.404)$ for this test is identical to the one in Example 13.8. ■

---

[8] The use of this statistic requires that the combined random variables x and y have a bivariate normal distribution. Although this is not necessarily the case in business and economic applications, the statistic in Formula 13.24 is still useful as an index of association.

[9] These tests are *not* equivalent if the null hypothesis specifies that the slope is equal to some value other than zero, although the previous test on β (Formula (13.21)) is still appropriate. In that case, the test on β (using Formula (13.21)) is not a test of the significance of the linear relationship, but rather a test on some proposed population parameter β_0. Therefore, such a test would not be equivalent to the t-test in this section for the *significance of ρ*.

☐ **STUDY QUESTION 13.5**   **Testing the Housing Price Model**

Use the regression model relating housing price to income as in Study Question 13.2 and the results computed in Study Question 13.3.

a) Test the significance of the correlation coefficient to see whether income is useful in explaining changes in price.
b) Find a 99% confidence interval on the true slope relating price and income in the population regression model.
c) Relate the calculated values in parts (a) and (b) to the computer printout for this regression given in Figure 13.13 (repeated from Figure 13.5).

● **ANSWER**

a) Formula 13.24 is used to test the significance of the relation between price and income. Let $H_0 : \rho = 0$ and $H_a : \rho > 0$, since a positive relation is expected. Since $r^2 = 0.639$ from Study Question 13.3, its square root is $r = +0.799$. It has a positive sign because the correlation coefficient always has the same sign as the slope b which was positive. The calculated test statistic is as follows:

$$t_c = \frac{r\sqrt{n-2}}{\sqrt{1-r^2}} = \frac{0.799\sqrt{23}}{\sqrt{1-0.639}} = 6.38$$

From Table VI with 23 degrees of freedom, the p-value for the test is:

$$P(t_{23} \geq 6.38) < 0.0005$$

This low p-value leads to the conclusion to reject H_0 and accept the alternative hypothesis that median income is strongly positively correlated with housing price.

b) A confidence interval on β is found by using Formula 13.23. For 90% confidence and 23 degrees of freedom, the appropriate t-value from Table VI is $t_{0.05,23} = 1.714$. The estimated standard error for the estimate b is $s_b = s_e/\sqrt{SSx}$ from Formula 13.22. Using $SSx = 158.4544$ as in Study Question 13.2 and $s_e = 9.254$ from Study Question 13.3:

$$s_b = \frac{9.254}{\sqrt{158.4544}} = 0.7352$$

The desired limits of the confidence interval are

$$b \pm ts_b = 4.693 \pm 1.714(0.7352) = 4.693 \pm 1.260,$$

which gives 3.433 and 5.953.

```
DEPENDENT VARIABLE..      PRICE       HOUSING PRICE
VARIABLE(S) ENTERED IN MODEL E       INCOME E      HOUSEHOLD MEDIAN INCOME

                      ANALYSIS OF VARIANCE

    MULTIPLE R           0.79953                 DF   SUM OF SQUARES   MEAN SQUARE
    R SQUARE             0.63925   REGRESSION     1      3490.4990      3490.4990
    ADJUSTED R SQUARE    0.62357   RESIDUAL      23      1969.8106        85.6439
    STANDARD ERROR       9.25444   F = 40.756          SIGNIF F = 0.0001


                    VARIABLES IN THE EQUATION
```

```
VARIABLE          B         SE B        T       SIG T
INCOME         4.69344    0.73518     6.3840    0.0001
(CONSTANT)    -4.04720   15.71878    -0.2575    0.7991
```

FIGURE 13.13   Computer printout for the housing price regression

c) The values of r and r^2 are given in the left column of the printout labeled MULTIPLE R and R SQUARE. The positive slope is in the second last line in the column headed B. The calculated t-value (6.38) on the significance of ρ is the same as the t-value on the significance of β given in the same row as the slope and in the column headed T. Its p-value is 0.00005, one-half the value in the same row and in the column headed SIG T. This is more exact than the table limit of 0.0005 as determined in part (a). The estimated standard error of b (0.73518) used in the confidence interval in part (b) is given in the same row under the heading, SE B.   ∎

Test on the Intercept

A test similar to that for the slope can be applied to test hypotheses about the true value of the intercept α in the population model. The appropriate statistic based on the assumptions of Section 13.4 and the distribution as given in Table 13.24 is t-distributed with $n - 2$ degrees of freedom:

t-statistic for inference on the intercept α:

$$t_{n-2} = \frac{a - \alpha}{s_a} \tag{13.25}$$

The sample standard deviation of the estimator a is found by using Formula 13.26:

Estimated standard error of the regression intercept a:

$$s_a = s_e \frac{\sqrt{\sum_{i=1}^{n} x_i^{2}}}{\sqrt{n(\mathrm{SS}x)}} \tag{13.26}$$

Confidence limits on the true intercept α can also be found by using this same statistic. The endpoints would be $a \pm t_{(\alpha/2, n-2)} s_a$, where the appropriate value of t depends on the level of confidence desired and the degrees of freedom $(n - 2)$. Typically, inference on the intercept is not as common as inference on the slope. The purpose of regression is more to relate the two variables y and x and to determine how changes in x affect changes in y than to determine the base level of y when $x = 0$. The latter involves extrapolation back to the value $x = 0$, which is often outside the meaningful or observed domain of the x-values.

section 13.8

Constructing a Forecast Interval

One of the important uses of the sample regression line is to obtain forecasts of the dependent variable, given some extra-sample value of the independent variable.

The estimated value $\hat{y}_i = a + bx_i$ is the best estimate we can make of both $\mu_{y \cdot x_i}$ (the mean value of y, given a value x_i) and of y_i (the actual value of y that corresponds to the given value x_i). Forecasts of both types are frequently desired. Economists may wish to forecast the average or expected level of unemployment, given assumed values of independent variables under policy control. From such forecasts they might argue which variables should be affected by policy, by how much, and in what direction, so that a policy goal of 5% unemployed might be expected. The forecast of the actual value of the dependent variable may be desired in other cases, such as predictions of the level of unemployment for the second quarter of the next year, or of the level of the price of General Motors common stock at the end of this year, or of the total sales this year for Simpsons.

Point Estimates of Forecasts

To obtain the best point estimate for forecasts of both the mean value and the actual value of y, the given value of the independent variable (call it x_g) is substituted into the estimating equation to obtain the **forecast value**:

$$\hat{y}_g = a + bx_g$$

Suppose that in our Output–Test example we wish to predict y for the test score of another electrician given as $x_g = 500$. Using the estimated regression coefficients $a = 0.752$ and $b = 0.00435$, we obtain

$$\hat{y}_g = a + bx_g = 0.752 + 0.00435(500) = 2.927$$

Thus, our best estimate of completed installations per day for this electrician who has a score of 500 is $\hat{y}_g = 2.927$.

Similarly, our estimate for the mean output of *all* electricians having scores of 500 is also $\hat{y}_g = 2.927$. Although these estimates both equal the same value, we must emphasize that they are interpreted differently. The confidence interval for estimating a single value will necessarily be larger than the confidence interval for estimating the mean value because the former will always have a larger standard error.

Interval Estimates of Forecasts

Recall from Section 9.3 that an interval estimate is centred, in probability terms, at the values of the point estimate. Then the endpoints of the interval are found by using information about the probability distribution of the point estimator and its standard error. From the above discussion, we know that the point estimate for forecasts of both the mean value and the actual value of y is always the same value of $\hat{y}_g$. However, the endpoints of interval estimates of these two types of forecasts based on a new extra-sample value x_g will be different because their *standard errors* will be different. Each of these is a multiple of the standard error of estimate, s_e, which was used in Section 13.5 for estimating the interval or band around sample values of y based on the *original sample values* of x. (Figure 13.9)

Let us consider first the interval estimate of the forecast of the actual value of y_g. The appropriate standard error to use for this interval is usually called the **standard error of the forecast**, which we denote by s_f:

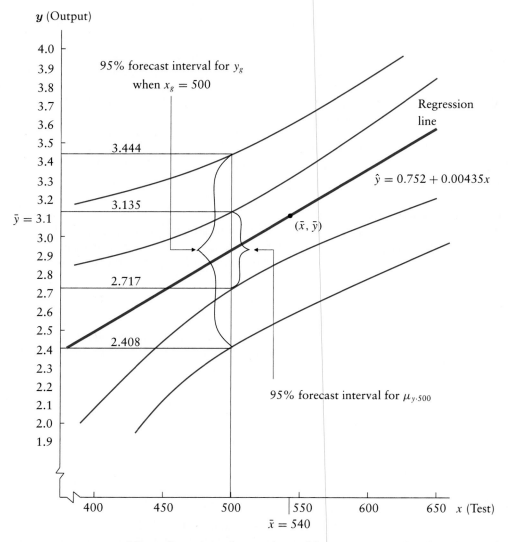

FIGURE 13.14   Ninety-five percent forecast interval for $\mu_{y \cdot x_i}$ (narrow band) and y_g (wide band) in the Output–Test example

Estimated standard error of the forecast:

$$s_f = s_e \sqrt{1 + \frac{1}{n} + \frac{(x_g - \bar{x})^2}{SSx}} \qquad (13.27)$$

Note that s_f will always be larger than s_e, since the term under the square root will always be greater than one. Also, note that s_f depends on the particular value of x_g that is given. This is an important concept: the farther the new value x_g is from the mean of the values used in estimating the sample regression line, the less accurate will be the forecasts based on that line. For this reason, one must be cautious in making forecasts beyond the range of the observed data. Due to the squared term $(x_g - \bar{x})^2$, which is always positive, the forecast error becomes larger at an increasing rate as x_g differs more and more (in either direction) from the original mean of the independent variable $\bar{x}$. This is shown in Figure 13.14 by drawing the confidence bands as curved rather than straight lines. The forecast will be most accurate near the point of means $(\bar{x}, \bar{y})$.

We can now use our point estimate $\hat{y}_g$, and the standard error s_f, to construct a $100(1 - \alpha)\%$ **forecast interval** for y_g. The appropriate test statistic in this case has the t-distribution with $(n - 2)$ degrees of freedom:

Endpoints of a $100(1 - \alpha)\%$ forecast interval for y_g:

$$\hat{y}_g \pm t_{(\alpha/2, n-2)} s_f \tag{13.28}$$

If we wish to construct a forecast interval for $\mu_{y \cdot x_g}$, the *mean* of the y-values, the appropriate standard error denoted by the symbol $s_{\bar{y} \cdot x}$ is as follows:

Estimated standard error for the mean forecast:

$$s_{\bar{y} \cdot x} = s_e \sqrt{\frac{1}{n} + \frac{(x_g - \bar{x})^2}{\text{SS}x}} \tag{13.29}$$

As was the case for s_f, $s_{\bar{y} \cdot x}$ depends on n, x_g, and s_e. The value of $s_{\bar{y} \cdot x}$, however, will always be smaller than s_f in Formula 13.27, because we are averaging the potential error over all possible predictions for a given value x_g rather than hedging our forecast for one particular case. The confidence bands about $\hat{y}$ are narrower when we are forecasting the mean prediction as shown in Figure 13.14. Again the appropriate test statistic is the t-distribution, with $(n - 2)$ degrees of freedom.

Endpoints for a $100(1 - \alpha)\%$ forecast interval on $\mu_{y \cdot x_g}$:

$$\hat{y}_g \pm t_{(\alpha/2, n-2)} s_{\bar{y} \cdot x} \tag{13.30}$$

□ EXAMPLE 13.10   Suppose that we want to construct, on the basis of our sample of $n = 8$, a 95% forecast interval for the output of an electrician with a test score of 500. From Table VI, the value of $t_{(0.025, 6)} = 2.447$, and we know the following from our previous analysis:

$$\hat{y}_{500} = 2.927, \quad s_e = 0.1936, \quad \bar{x} = 540, \quad \text{and} \quad \text{SS}x = 23,000$$

Substituting these values into Formula 13.27 for s_f and using Formula 13.28, we obtain the following endpoints for the forecast interval:

$$2.927 \pm 2.447(0.1936)\sqrt{1 + \frac{1}{8} + \left[\frac{(500 - 540)^2}{23,000}\right]}$$

$$= 2.927 \pm 2.447(0.1936)(1.09296)$$

$$= 2.927 \pm 0.518$$

$$= 2.409 \quad \text{and} \quad 3.445$$

We can expect that 95% of the intervals determined by this method will include the true value. In this case of estimating the number of installations completed per day for a single electrician who scored 500 on the training test, this interval is quite wide. This results partly from using a very small sample, $n = 8$, which gave us a relatively large standard error (s_e). ■

◻ STUDY QUESTION 13.6 Forecast for Housing Price

Using the data and results in Study Questions 13.2 and 13.3, find the 90% forecast interval for the actual housing price in a city given that its median income is $20,000. Repeat for another city with median income of $25,000. Contrast the spread of the two intervals.

● ANSWER A forecast is obtained by substituting the given income value (in $000s) into the sample regression equation. For $x = 20$:

$$\hat{y}_{20} = -4.047 + 4.6934(20) = 89.821$$

The standard error of the forecast is found by using Formula 13.27:

$$s_f = 9.254\sqrt{1 + \frac{1}{25} + \frac{(20 - 21.232)^2}{158.4544}}$$

$$= 9.254\sqrt{1.0496} = 9.254(1.0245) = 9.481$$

By using Formula 13.28 and $t_{0.05, 23} = 1.714$ from Table VI the limits are:

$$89.821 \pm 1.714(9.481)$$

$$89.821 \pm 16.250$$

Multiplying by 1,000 to return to units of dollars, we have the 90% confidence limits on $\hat{y}_{20}$ of $73,571 and $106,071 with a spread of $32,500.

For $x = 25$:

$$\hat{y}_{25} = -4.047 + 4.6934(25) = 113.288$$

$$s_f = 9.254\sqrt{1 + \frac{1}{25} + \frac{(25 - 21.232)^2}{158.4544}}$$

$$= 9.254\sqrt{1.1296} = 9.254(1.0628) = 9.835$$

The limits on $\hat{y}_{25}$ are:

$$113.288 \pm 1.714(9.835),$$

$$113.288 \pm 16.857$$

When multiplied by 1,000, this gives the endpoints of the forecast interval of $96,431 and $130,145 with a spread of $33,714.

The spread of the two intervals differs by $1,214 because the given value of $25,000 differs more from the original mean of $21,232 than does the given value of $20,000. ∎

section 13.9

The F-Test[†]

In Section 13.7, we presented some t-statistics for testing the significance of the relation between y and x as expressed by the regression model. There is still another way of testing the null hypothesis $H_0 : \beta = 0$, using the measures of unexplained and explained variation. Before the reader bemoans the presentation of one more test to learn, we must point out that the test in this section is particularly important because it can be generalized to problems involving more than just one independent variable (to the multiple-regression case). This use will be discussed in Chapter 14.

[†] It is assumed that the reader has studied the use of an F-distributed random variable presented in Section 11.6 or in Chapter 12.

Recall that SST = SSE + SSR. You may also recall that the degrees of freedom associated with SST are $n - 1$ (since only $\bar{y}$ must be calculated before SST can be computed), while the d.f. for SSE are $n - 2$ (both a and b must be calculated before computing SSE). Since the d.f. for SST must equal the sum of those for SSE and SSR, we see by subtraction that the d.f. for SSR = 1. A sum of squares divided by its degrees of freedom is called a **mean square**. The two mean squares we will need are **mean square error** (MSE) and **mean square regression** (MSR):

$$\text{Mean square error:} \qquad \text{MSE} = \frac{\text{SSE}}{n - 2} = s_e^2$$

$$\text{Mean square regression:} \qquad \text{MSR} = \frac{\text{SSR}}{1}$$

It is customary to present information about MSE and MSR in an *analysis-of-variance* (ANOVA) table, as shown in Table 13.25.

TABLE 13.25   Analysis-of-Variance (ANOVA) Table for Simple Regression

Source of the Variation	Sum of Squares	Degrees of Freedom	Mean Square
Regression	SSR	1	MSR = SSR/1
Error (or residual)	SSE	$n - 2$	MSE = SSE/$(n - 2)$
Total	SST	$n - 1$	

One word of caution is necessary here: although the sums of squares and the degrees of freedom are additive, the mean square terms are *not* additive. Note that, in the analysis-of-variance table, no MS term is given in the row labeled *Total*. The SST and the degrees of freedom total are given in the table, so it can be verified that elements in the body of the table do sum to these values.

We can use the mean squares for a new test on the hypothesis $H_0 : \beta = 0$. The test statistic is the *F*-ratio shown in Formula 13.31:

F-statistic for testing the fit of the linear model:

$$F_{(1, n-2)} = \frac{\text{MSR}}{\text{MSE}} \qquad\qquad (13.31)$$

Remember that either a positive or a negative value of β can lead to a significant linear relation between y and x. However, this *F*-test cannot distinguish between $\beta < 0$ and $\beta > 0$ because the calculated values of F_c are always positive. Thus, the alternative hypothesis used in this test is two-sided, $H_a : \beta \neq 0$. That is, the hypotheses are:

H_0 : no significant relation and $\beta = 0$

H_a : there is a significant relation between y and x and $\beta \neq 0$

Figure 13.15 illustrates the critical region for the *F*-test. It has only one section (in the upper tail), even though this is a two-sided test on β.

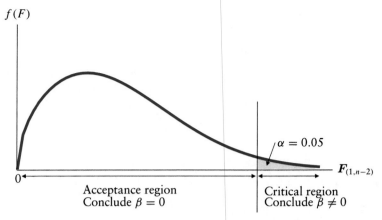

FIGURE 13.15   The critical region for the analysis-of-variance test on a regression

We recognize that if $\beta = 0$, then the variable x is not useful in the equation and there is no association between x and y. When this occurs, the goodness of fit of the model is poor; that is, the explained variation SSR and the MSR are relatively small and the unexplained variation SSE and the MSE are relatively large. The calculated F-value will be small and H_0 will not be rejected. Obversely, if $\beta \neq 0$, then there is a significant amount of variation explained, the sum of squares of errors is smaller, the calculated F-value will be large, and H_0 is rejected in favour of the alternative hypothesis that the slope is not zero and the model has a useful fit.

◻ **EXAMPLE 13.11**   An ANOVA table for regression analysis is constructed for the Output–Test example and given in Table 13.26. Similar information is contained in the computer printout in Figure 13.12. Recall from Section 13.5 that:

$$SST = 0.660 \qquad SSE = 0.225 \qquad \text{and} \qquad SSR = 0.435$$

Hence:

$$MSR = \frac{SSR}{1} = \frac{0.435}{1} = 0.435 \qquad \text{and} \qquad MSE = \frac{SSE}{n-2} = \frac{0.225}{6} = 0.0375$$

TABLE 13.26   Analysis-of-Variance (ANOVA) Table for the Regression of Output on Test

Source	SS	d.f.	Mean Square	F-value
Regression	0.435	1	0.435	11.6
Error	0.225	6	0.0375	
Total	0.660	7		

If we choose a significance level of $\alpha = 0.05$, the critical value [from Table VIII(a)] is $F_{(1,6)} = 5.99$. The **F**-statistic calculated in this example is:

$$F_c = \frac{MSR}{MSE} = \frac{0.435}{0.0375} = 11.6$$

The calculated F-value is larger than the critical value. From Figure 13.12, the p-value is 0.014. We reject the null hypothesis and conclude that the linear model relationship *does have* a useful fit. Knowing the test score does help to determine the number of installations completed (as we already concluded in previous tests on this relation). ■

The F-test in this section is related to the previous t-tests for regression analysis. The F-test indicates that a significant linear relation exists between the variables y and x when a significant amount of variation in y is explained by x. This can occur only if there is a significant correlation between y and x, $\rho \neq 0$, as shown by one t-test [Formula 13.24] and only if there is a significant slope of the line relating y and x, $\beta \neq 0$, as shown by the other t-test [Formula (13.21)]. The calculated F-value in Formula 13.31 equals the *square* of the calculated t-values in Formulas 13.21 and 13.24. Theoretically, an F-distributed random variable with 1 and $n-2$ degrees of freedom (in the numerator and denominator, respectively) is exactly the square of a t-distributed random variable with $n-2$ degrees of freedom. In our Output–Test example, the t-values were 3.404 and the F-value is 11.6, which is the rounded value of $(3.404)^2$.

This same relation between the t- and F-statistics for a test on the null hypothesis, $H_0 : \beta = 0$, can be observed for the Price–Income regression discussed in the Study Questions in this chapter. Looking back to the computer printout in Figure 13.13, we note that the value of F associated with the significance test for β is $F = 40.756$. It also gives a value of the t-statistic [Formula 13.21] associated with the significance test for β of 6.3840. The square of this t-value is the F-value.

> In summary, for the simple regression model with only one explanatory factor x, F-test on the fit, the t-test of significance on the coefficient of x, and the t-test on the significance of the correlation coefficient ρ are all equivalent tests. They all test whether or not y and x are significantly linearly related.

In Chapter 14, we will consider a multiple regression model in which several explanatory variables are used to explain changes in y. In that situation, the t-tests will help us learn about the significance of the *individual relation between y and one* of the explanatory variables. The F-test will give us information about the significance of the *overall relation among y and all* the explanatory variables. The advantage of the F-test is that it can be generalized to a test of significance when there is more than one independent variable, while the t-test cannot. The advantage of the t-test is that it can be used to test for values of β other than zero.

section 13.10 — An Example Problem

Having specified all the concepts and formulas essential for a simple regression and correlation analysis, the best way to review them is by interpreting and analyzing a fresh problem. Suppose a government economist is interested in estimating a model determining the investment for all firms in the economy.

Any textbook of macro-economics includes some theoretical relationships between private investment and other variables. Generally, it is recognized that the level of investment depends on the availability of funds for investment and on the need for expanding productive capacity. Thus, any variables that reflect these supply or demand factors may be appropriate to explain or predict changes in levels of investment. Such variables as the existing amount of plant and equipment that is depreciating, current and past levels of profits, the interest rate at which funds could be borrowed, indicators of the current general economic conditions, expected sales, and stock values, etcetera, may be selected as independent variables to help explain variation in investment.

For simplicity, suppose we specify that the population regression model is $y_i = \alpha + \beta x_i + \epsilon_i$, where x_i represents a composite price index for 500 common stocks during a given time period and y_i represents the amount of aggregate investment *during the following time period*. We might postulate such a relationship because we believe that stock market prices are indicative of the general level of business expectations for the future. For this example, we will estimate the population regression line on the basis of 20 quarterly observations. The data, shown in Table 13.27, represent investment measured at an annual rate in billions of dollars. The sample statistics needed for computing the least-squares regression line follow the table. Computer printouts for this regression are given in Figure 13.16. Comparing parts (a) and (b) reveals differences in calculations, rounding, or formatting of regression results between software programs.

TABLE 13.27   Data for Estimating the Investment Equation

Observation Number	Investment (y)	Stock Index (x)	Observation Number	Investment (y)	Stock Index (x)
1	62.3	398.4	11	84.3	581.8
2	71.3	452.6	12	85.1	707.1
3	70.3	509.8	13	90.8	776.6
4	68.5	485.4	14	97.9	875.3
5	57.3	445.7	15	108.7	873.4
6	68.8	539.8	16	122.4	943.7
7	72.2	662.8	17	114.0	830.6
8	76.0	620.0	18	123.0	907.5
9	64.3	632.2	19	126.2	905.3
10	77.9	703.0	20	137.0	927.4

$$\text{Mean of } y = \tfrac{1}{20}\sum_{i=1}^{20} y_i = 88.915 \qquad \text{Mean of } x = \tfrac{1}{20}\sum_{i=1}^{20} x_i = 688.92$$

Variation of $y = SSy$

$$= \sum_{i=1}^{20}(y_i - \bar{y})^2$$
$$= 11{,}485.7$$

Variation of $x = SSx$

$$= \sum_{i=1}^{20}(x_i - \bar{x})^2$$
$$= 628{,}713.46$$

Covariation of x and $y = SCxy$

$$= \sum_{i=1}^{20}(x_i - \bar{x})(y_i - \bar{y})$$
$$= 77{,}626.0$$

We know that the line that provides the least-squares fit to these data has the following slope and intercept using Formula 13.8:

Sample slope: $\quad b = \dfrac{SCxy}{SSx} = \dfrac{77{,}626.0}{628{,}713.46} = 0.12347$

Sample intercept: $\quad a = \bar{y} - b\bar{x} = 88.915 - 0.12347(688.920) = 3.855$

The least-squares estimating line is $\hat{y}_i = 3.855 + 0.12347x_i$. The positive value for b confirms our assumption that investment increases when stock prices increase. We see that, for these data, a 10-unit increase in the stock index x in one quarter is associated with an increase in the annual rate of investment during the next quarter of about 1.23 billion dollars.

FIGURE 13.16 Computer printouts for a regression using the data in Table 13.27

a) Printout from a BASIC program of formulas in this chapter:

```
Sample size = 20          SUM of x = 13778.4          SUM of y = 1778.3
MEAN of x = 688.92                MEAN of y = 88.915
VARIANCE of x = 33,090.182        VARIANCE of y = 604.510
STD DEV of x = 181.907            STD DEV of y = 24.587
SCxy = 77,626.0           SSx = 628,713.46            SSy = 11,485.69
SLOPE = 0.12347                   y-INTERCEPT = 3.8550
SST = 11,485.7           SSR = 9584.4                 SSE = 1901.3
SE = 10.277                                           R-SQUARED = 0.8345
SB = 0.01296             T-RATIO = 9.526              F-TEST = 90.74
```

b) Statistical software program printout:

```
DEPENDENT VARIABLE.      INV       PRIVATE INVESTMENT, $BIL
VARIABLE(S) ENTERED IN MODEL       STKPR      STOCK PRICE, PREVIOUS QUARTER
                                   ANALYSIS OF VARIANCE
```

		DF	SUM OF SQUARES	MEAN SQUARE	
MULTIPLE R	0.9135				
R SQUARE	0.8345	REGRESSION	1	9584.4258	9584.43
ADJUSTED R SQUARE	0.8253	RESIDUAL	18	1901.2597	105.63
STANDARD ERROR	10.2774		F = 90.74	SIGNIF	F = 0.0001

```
                         VARIABLES IN THE EQUATION
```

VARIABLE	B	SE B	T	SIG T
STKPR	0.12347	0.01296	9.5257	0.0001
(CONSTANT)	3.85498	9.22048	0.4181	0.6808

To obtain the goodness-of-fit measures, the components of total variation must be found. The total variation in y to be explained is $SST = SSy = 11{,}485.7$. Its components are found by using Formula 13.12:

$$\text{Explained variation} = SSR = b(SCxy)$$

$$= 0.12347(77{,}626.0) = 9{,}584.4$$

$$\text{Unexplained variation} = SSE = SST - SSR$$

$$= 11{,}485.7 - 9{,}584.4 = 1{,}901.3$$

The value $SSE = \Sigma e_i^2 = 1{,}901.3$ can be used to find the standard error of the estimate by using Formula 13.15:

$$s_e = \sqrt{\frac{SSE}{n-2}} = \sqrt{\frac{1{,}901.3}{18}} = 10.277$$

The reader may wish to check (Problems 13.76 and 13.77) whether approximately 68% of the data points lie within 10.277 vertical units (billions of dollars) above or below the estimating line.

Our second measure of goodness of fit is the sample coefficient of determination r^2, given by Formula 13.17:

$$r^2 = \frac{\text{Explained variation}}{\text{Total variation}} = \frac{\text{SSR}}{\text{SST}} = \frac{9,584.4}{11,485.7} = 0.8345$$

This means that 83.45% of the variation in investment has been explained by the relationship between it and the stock price index.

The correlation coefficient r is the positive (since $b > 0$) square root of this, $r = 0.9135$, which indicates a relatively strong positive association. This measure could also be calculated directly using Formula 13.20:

$$r = \frac{\text{SC}xy}{\sqrt{(\text{SS}x)}\sqrt{(\text{SS}y)}} = \frac{77,626}{\sqrt{(628,713)}\sqrt{(11,486)}} = 0.9135$$

Any of the tests or confidence intervals on the population parameters, as described in the preceding sections, can be calculated easily by using the information from Figure 13.16. For example, the test of the significance of the slope parameter involves:

$$H_0 : \beta = 0 \qquad \text{versus} \qquad H_a : \beta > 0$$

The test statistic with a t-distribution and $n - 2 = 18$ degrees of freedom using Formula 13.21 is:

$$t_{18} = \frac{b - \beta_0}{s_b},$$

where $\beta_0 = 0$ and $s_b = s_e/\sqrt{\text{SS}x}$. Using a significance level of $\alpha = 0.005$, we find in Table VI that the critical region is all values of t such that:

$$t > t_{(0.005,18)} = 2.878$$

The calculated value of s_e is 10.277 and

$$s_b = \frac{10.277}{\sqrt{628,713.46}} = 0.01296$$

Thus, the calculated value t_c is:

$$t_c = \frac{b - 0}{s_b} = \frac{0.12347}{0.01296} = 9.526$$

The value of t_c exceeds the critical value ($9.526 > 2.878$). Also the p-value is no larger than 0.00005, half of the reported two-sided probability in the column labelled SIG T in Figure 13.16(b). We reject the null hypothesis and conclude that there is a positive linear relationship between current investment and the stock-market index of the previous quarter. If the stock prices do reflect business expectations, then these data support the theory that business firms are more willing to expand their plant and equipment when they foresee good times (higher incomes, greater demands, and more potential sales and profits) ahead.

The significance of the positive linear relationship can be found by using the **F**-test of Section 13.9 and the hypotheses $H_0 : \beta = 0$ and $H_a : \beta \neq 0$. The test statistic is given by the **F**-ratio in Formula (13.31) with 1 and 18 degrees of freedom. From Table VIII and a significance level of 0.01, the critical value is $F_{(0.01;1,18)} = 8.29$. Note that this is the square of the critical value of the previous one-sided **t**-test, $(2.878)^2$, using $\alpha = 0.005$. From Figure 13.16, SSR = 9,584.4, SSE = 1,901.3, and $(n-2) = 18$:

$$\text{MSR} = \frac{\text{SSR}}{1} = 9,584.4 \quad \text{and} \quad \text{MSE} = \frac{\text{SSE}}{18} = 105.63$$

The calculated value of the **F**-statistic is as follows:

$$F_c = \frac{\text{MSR}}{\text{MSE}} = \frac{9,584.4}{105.63} = 90.74$$

This is the square of the calculated **t**-statistic, $(9.526)^2$, in the previous test. Again, we reject the null hypothesis and conclude that there is a significant linear relation between investment and stock index.

Finally, the regression model can be used to predict investment by using the procedures of Section 13.8. If a quarterly observation for the stock index is given as $x_g = 800$, the best point estimate for the value of investment is obtained by substitution into the sample regression equation,

$$\hat{y}_g = a + bx_g = 3.855 + 0.12347(800) = 102.63 \ (\$\text{billions})$$

To obtain an interval estimate with 90% confidence, Formulas 13.27 and 13.28 are used. The **t**-value obtained from Table VI is $t_{0.05,18} = 1.734$. The value of the standard deviation for an individual forecast is:

$$s_f = s_e\sqrt{1 + \frac{1}{n} + \frac{(x_g - \bar{x})^2}{\text{SS}x}}$$

$$= 10.277\sqrt{1 + \frac{1}{20} + \frac{(800 - 688.92)^2}{628,713.46}}$$

$$= 10.277\sqrt{1 + 0.05 + 0.0196}$$

$$= 10.277(1.034) = 10.626$$

The 90% forecast interval has limits $\hat{y}_g \pm t_{(0.05,18)}s_f = 102.63 \pm 1.734(10.626)$, which gives $102.63 + 18.43 = 121.06$ and $102.63 - 18.43 = 84.20$. The width of this interval ($84.20 to $121.06 billion) illustrates the uncertainty involved with predicting investment based on this sample regression model.

PROBLEMS

13.36 In a regression of the amount of sales y on the number of customers x based on 11 observations, the value of the coefficient of determination is 0.36.

a) Does this indicate a significant correlation between

y and x at the 0.05 significance level if proper normality assumptions are made? Let H_a be two-sided.

b) What is the proportion of variation left unexplained in this regression?

13.37 The ten observations in Table 13.28 were obtained in a survey in Queensland to determine the relationship between an individual's educational level past 4th form and this person's salary.

TABLE 13.28   Salary versus Education

Years of Extra Education	Income
3	$40,000
4	38,000
7	43,000
9	50,000
1	36,000
0	35,000
2	38,000
1	37,000
8	44,000
5	39,000

a) Assuming normal distributions, what is the correlation between extra years of education and income for this sample?

b) Use $\alpha = 0.05$ and your answer to part (a) to test the null hypothesis $H_0 : \rho = 0$ against the alternative hypothesis $H_a : \rho > 0$.

13.38 Given a regression equation, $\hat{y} = 14 + 6x$, based on 12 observations, test the hypotheses $H_0 : \beta = 0$ versus $H_a : \beta > 0$ using a significance level of 0.05. The standard error of b is $s_b = 1.5$.

13.39 In a correlation between corporate net investment and long-term interest rates, using quarterly observations from the third quarter of 1983 through the fourth quarter of 1992, a correlation coefficient of +0.60 is obtained. Determine whether this is a significant positive correlation, using $\alpha = 0.01$, a one-sided alternative hypothesis, and assuming normality.

13.40 In analyzing the relationship between 26 observations of two variables, dividends (y) and profits (x), you find SST equal to 120.0 and SSR equal to 13.2. The slope of the sample regression line is positive. Assume that the populations are normal.

a) What is the coefficient of determination for this problem? What percent of the sample variation in dividends has been explained?

b) Use the t-test described in Section 13.7 to test the null hypothesis $H_0 : \rho = 0$ against $H_a : \rho \neq 0$. Can the null hypothesis of no linear correlation be rejected at the 0.05 level of significance?

c) Compute the F-value necessary for testing the null and alternative hypotheses equivalent to those in part (b). Is this value of F consistent with the t-value calculated in part (b)?

♦ **13.41** Continuing with the analysis of results in Problem 13.31, answer the following items.

a) Test the hypothesis that U.S. states with lower percentage of urban population have lower crime rates. Set up H_0 and H_a, and use 5% as the level of significance.

b) The state of Wyoming is not part of the sample. Only 15.1% of its population lives in urban areas. Estimate Wyoming's crime rate.

c) Obtain a 90% forecast interval for Wyoming's true crime rate.

d) The percentage of urban population in the state of Wyoming is lower than that of every one of the 25 states in the sample. Is it reasonable to make a prediction about its crime rate based on the sample data?

♦ **13.42** Continuing with the analysis of results in Problem 13.22, answer the following items.

a) The manufacturer wants to test whether the overhead cost increases as the number of parts manufactured goes up. Set up null and alternative hypotheses and justify your setup. Use $\alpha = 0.01$ for the test.

b) Construct a 99.9% confidence interval for the slope of the population regression line.

c) Construct a 99.9% confidence interval for the mean overhead for manufacturing 25,000 parts.

13.43 Let x represent income (billions of dollars) in Western Australia and let y represent retail sales (millions of dollars) in jewelry stores in Western Australia. The regression equation is $\hat{y} = 8.505x - 7.41$. The standard error of the estimate is 3.5, and the correlation coefficient is 0.95.

a) For a year in which income payments are $10.0 billion, what is the best estimate of sales in jewelry stores?

b) What proportion of the variation in the retail jewelry sales is explained by the variation in income payments?

c) This correlation indicates that in Western Australia higher retail jewelry sales cause higher incomes. Comment.

13.44 The data in Table 13.29 represent the dollar value of sales and advertising for a retail store.

TABLE 13.29 Sales versus Advertising

Advertising, x (in Thousands)	Sales, y (in Thousands)
$600	$5,000
400	4,000
800	7,000
200	3,000
500	6,000

a) Draw the scatter diagram for these data. Fit a line by the freehand method. Does the linear approximation seem appropriate?

b) Find the least-squares regression line.

c) What value for sales would you predict if advertising were $700? What value would you predict if advertising were zero?

d) Given the standard assumptions, construct a 95% confidence interval for the *mean* value of sales when advertising is $500 ($\mu_{y \cdot 500}$).

e) Construct a 95% confidence interval for the actual value of sales when advertising is $500.

f) Test the null hypothesis that the slope of the regression line is zero against $H_a : \beta > 0$ using $\alpha = 0.05$.

g) Find the sample correlation coefficient.

h) Assuming normality, test the null hypothesis $H_0 : \rho = 0$ against the alternative $H_a : \rho \neq 0$. At what level of significance can H_0 be rejected? Relate this answer to part (f).

13.45 Given the following least-squares regression line, ANOVA table, and the standard assumptions, where $y =$ rental cost ($) of a charter bus and $x =$ number of hours rented during the day.

TABLE 13.30 An ANOVA Table

$\hat{y} = 112 + 9.6x$

Source	SS	d.f.
Regression	144	1
Error	342	38

a) What was the sample size in this problem? What is SST?

b) Use an *F*-test to accept or reject $H_0 : \beta = 0$ versus $H_a : \beta \neq 0$ using $\alpha = 0.05$.

c) Calculate the value of s_b based on the fact that SS$x = 1.5625$.

13.46 Use the value of s_b from Problem 13.45.

a) Construct a *t*-test to accept or reject $H_0 : \beta = 0$ versus $H_a : \beta \neq 0$ using $\alpha = 0.05$. Is your answer consistent with your answer for part (b) of Problem 13.45?

b) Construct a 95% confidence interval for β.

c) Assume, for this problem, that when $x_g = 5$, $s_f = 3.20$ from Formula 13.27. Use this information to construct a 95% confidence interval for y_g.

d) If $s_{\bar{y} \cdot x} = 1.965$ when $x_g = 5$ from Formula 13.29, construct a 95% confidence interval for $\mu_{y \cdot x_g}$.

13.47 For the data in Problem 13.44, find s_x, s_y, and s_{xy}. Show that the value of r you calculated for Problem 13.44 equals $s_{xy}/s_x s_y$.

13.48 For $y =$ (delivery time in minutes of pizza orders) and $x =$ (distance in quarter-miles from the pizza shop to the customer) the least-squares regression line fitted to 62 observations yields the equation $y = 16.9 + 1.225x$. SST for this sample was determined to be 594, while SSE was found to be 540.

a) Construct an ANOVA table for these values.

b) Find the standard error of b by assuming that SS$x = 36$. Use this information to test the null hypothesis $H_0 : \beta = 0$ versus $H_a : \beta \neq 0$ by means of a *t*-test. Use $\alpha = 0.05$.

c) Test the same relation as in part (b), but this time use an *F*-test. Are your answers to parts (b) and (c) consistent?

d) Assuming normality, test the null hypothesis $H_0 : \rho = 0$ versus $H_a : \rho \neq 0$ at $\alpha = 0.05$. Compare this result to those in parts (b) and (c).

13.49 Use the information provided in Problem 13.48 to answer the following questions.

a) Assume that the given value of x is $x_g = 7$ and $\bar{x} = 10$. Find the standard error of the forecast, s_f. Use this information to construct a 95% forecast interval for y_g.

b) Repeat part (a) for $x_g = 8, 9, 10, 11,$ and 12. Draw a graph similar to Figure 13.14, illustrating a 95% forecast interval for y_g from $x = 7$ to $x = 12$.

c) Find the values of $s_{y \cdot x}$ for $x = 7$ through 12. Draw the 95% forecast interval for $\mu_{y \cdot x_g}$ on your graph from part (b).

◆ **13.50** Refer to the regression for beverage charge per person determined in Problem 13.12, and answer the following.

a) Calculate the sample correlation coefficient between the two variables.

b) Test the hypothesis that there is no linear relationship between the two variables. State your hypotheses and your conclusion precisely. Use $\alpha = 0.05$.

c) Construct a 90% confidence interval for the true slope of the linear relationship between the two variables.

♦ **13.51** Continuing with the analysis of results given in Problem 13.11, use statistical inference for the following parts:

a) The standard error of marginal cost is estimated to be 1.250. Test the null hypothesis that the slope of the regression line is zero against $H_a : \beta > 0$, using $\alpha = 0.10$.

b) The standard error of the forecast is estimated to be $140. Obtain a 90% forecast interval for the actual cost of publishing 1,000 copies of a 500-page book.

CHAPTER SUMMARY

KEY TERMS AND EXPRESSIONS

Population regression line $[\mu_{y \cdot x} = \alpha + \beta x]$: For the population, the intercept (α) plus the slope (β) times x equals the mean of the y-values for a given x-value.

Population regression model $[y_i = \alpha + \beta x_i + \epsilon_i]$: An error term ($\epsilon_i$) is added to the regression line to describe the actual value of the ith observation (y_i).

Sample regression line $[\hat{y} = a + bx]$: Estimate of population regression line.

Sample regression model $[y_i = a + bx_i + e_i]$: Estimate of population regression model.

Least-squares estimation method: Process of finding regression coefficients a and b by minimizing

$$\text{SSE} = \sum_{i=1}^{n} e_i^2 = \text{unexplained variation, the sum of}$$

squared deviations between the actual and the estimated values of y_i.

b (least-squares estimate of population slope β):

$$b = \frac{\text{SC}xy}{\text{SS}x}$$

a (least-squares estimate of population intercept α):

$$a = \bar{y} - b\bar{x}$$

Variation, Covariation: These are the sample measures of variance and covariance multiplied by $(n - 1)$.

Variation of $x = \text{SS}x = $ sums of squares of

deviations for $x = \sum_{i=1}^{n} (x_i - \bar{x})^2$

Variation of $y = \text{SS}y = $ sums of squares of

deviations for $y = \sum_{i=1}^{n} (y_i - \bar{y})^2$

Covariation of x and $y = \text{SC}xy = $ sums of cross products of deviations of x and $y =$

$$\sum_{i=1}^{n} (x_i - \bar{x})(y_i - \bar{y})$$

Five *ideal* assumptions: The population error terms ϵ_i are assumed (**1**) to be independent of x, (**2**) to be normally distributed, (**3**) to have a mean of zero, (**4**) to have a finite variance (σ_ϵ^2) that is constant, and (**5**) to be independent of one another.

SST, SSE, SSR: total, unexplained, and explained variation of y in a regression where SST = SSR + SSE.

$$\text{SST} = \text{sum of squares total} = \text{SS}y = \sum_{i=1}^{n} (y_i - \bar{y})^2;$$

$$\text{SSE} = \text{sum of squares error} = \sum_{i=1}^{n} e_i^2 = \sum_{i=1}^{n} (y_i - \hat{y}_i)^2;$$

$\text{SSR} = $ sum of squares explained by the regression

$$= \sum_{i=1}^{n} (\hat{y}_i - \bar{y})^2$$

Standard error of the estimate (s_e): Typical deviation of sample points about the sample regression line; $s_e = \sqrt{\text{SSE}/(n-2)}$ represents an unbiased estimate of σ_ϵ.

Coefficient of determination: $r^2 = \text{SSR}/\text{SST} = $ explained amount of variation in y relative to the total to be explained; $0 \leq r^2 \leq 1$.

Population covariance: $C[x, y] = E[(x - \mu_x)(y - \mu_y)]$ describes how x and y covary in the population.

Population correlation coefficient: $\rho = C[x, y]/\sigma_x \sigma_y$, which is a measure of the population linear association between x and y; $-1 \leq \rho \leq +1$.

Sample Covariance (s_{xy}): Unbiased estimate of $C[x, y]$:

$$s_{xy} = \frac{1}{n-1} \sum_{i=1}^{n}(x_i - \bar{x})(y_i - \bar{y})$$

Sample correlation coefficient: It is the best estimate of ρ.

$$r = \frac{s_{xy}}{s_x s_y} \quad \text{or} \quad r = \frac{SCxy}{\sqrt{(SSx)}\sqrt{(SSy)}}$$

Hypothesis of no linear regression: $H_0 : \beta = 0$.

t-statistics for inference on the regression coefficients: $t = (b - \beta_0)/s_b$ for the slope, and $t = (a - \alpha)/s_a$ for the intercept, both with $n - 2$ degrees of freedom.

Standard error of b (s_b): Indicates the uncertainty of the least-squares estimate of β:

$$s_b = s_e\sqrt{\frac{1}{SSx}}$$

t-test for $H_0 : \rho = 0$: $t = r\sqrt{n-2}/\sqrt{1-r^2}$ with $n - 2$ degrees of freedom.

Confidence limits for the regression coefficients: $b \pm t_{(\alpha/2, n-2)}s_b$ for the slope, and $a \pm t_{(\alpha/2, n-2)}s_a$ for the intercept.

Forecast value ($\hat{y}_g$): Obtained by substituting a given value x_g into the estimating equation, $\hat{y}_g = a + bx_g$.

Standard error of the forecast (s_f): A measure of the uncertainty of the least squares forecast y_g:

$$s_f = s_e\sqrt{1 + \frac{1}{n} + \frac{(x_g - \bar{x})^2}{SSx}}$$

Forecast interval for y_g:

$$\hat{y}_g - t_{(\alpha/2, n-2)}s_f \leq y_g \leq \hat{y}_g + t_{(\alpha/2, n-2)}s_f$$

Mean square: A sum of squares divided by its degrees of freedom. For a simple regression, mean square error $MSE = SSE/(n-2) = s_e^2$, and mean square regression $MSR = SSR/1$.

F-statistic for the fit of the linear model: $F = MSR/MSE$ with 1 and $n - 2$ degrees of freedom.

EXERCISES

13.52 How would you choose among alternative unbiased estimators of the slope in the population regression model?

13.53 Explain the relation between the t-test on the significance of a slope β and the F-test on the significance of the linear relation between y and x.

13.54 What assumptions about the parent population are necessary to fit a least-squares regression line to a set of observations? What assumptions about the parent population are necessary to make interval estimates on the basis of a least-squares regression line?

13.55 Find the formula for the least-squares estimator for β in the function $y = \beta x^3$, based on n sample observations of y and x.

13.56 Use the following data to answer parts (a)–(d).

TABLE 13.31 Salary versus Age

Age (Years)	Salary ($000)
65	150
70	170
75	160

a) Estimate the salary of a corporate executive who is 71 years old, using a least squares estimator.

b) Estimate the age of an executive whose salary is $153,000, using a least squares estimator.

c) Plot the regression lines you calculated for parts (a) and (b). Why do these lines differ?

d) Find the sample correlation coefficient. Does the value of the correlation coefficient depend on which variable is dependent and which is independent in the regression equation?

13.57 If you used some method other than least-squares to get linear unbiased estimates of the coefficients in a regression model, discuss how your values for s_e and r^2 would compare to those determined by means of a least-squares regression based on the same sample data.

13.58 Derive the normal equations for the least-squares estimation of the function $y = \alpha + \beta x^2$.

13.59 Discuss the following statement: "Cause-and-effect inferences can never be made from regression analysis."

13.60 If it is true that (under the five assumptions) the distribution of the least-square estimator of a coefficient is *normal*, then why does statistical inference on a regression coefficient use the *t*-distribution instead of the *z*-distribution?

13.61 In a regression, the estimated value of β is $b = 2.5$ with $s_b = 0.8$. Find a 90% confidence interval on the true parameter β if $n = 22$.

13.62 Given that, for a sample of 17 pairs of observations on y and x, the total variation is 28,416, the SSR is 7,104, and the covariation of x and y is $-42,624$.

    a) Find s_e and r and explain their meaning.

    b) Assuming normality, test the hypothesis that there is no correlation between y and x. Use a two-sided alternative hypothesis and let $\alpha = 0.10$.

13.63 Define or describe briefly each of the following:

    a) standard error of the estimate, s_e

    b) standard error of the forecast, s_f

    c) standard error of the regression coefficient, s_b

13.64 In a simple regression based on 32 observations, it is found that $r = 0.6$ and $s_e^2 = 100$.

    a) Find SST, SSR, and SSE.

    b) Do an analysis-of-variance test to determine whether the linear relationship is significant at the 0.01 level.

13.65 The number of rooms to be occupied (y) in a large hotel is estimated to be $\hat{y} = 10 + 3x$, where x is the number of advance guaranteed room reservations. Also, $\bar{y} = 160$ and $\bar{x} = 50$. Explain whether there is any difference in the precision of forecasts (y) based on this model in the cases where the given values of x_g are 40 and 100.

13.66 Consider a model $y_i = \alpha + \beta x_i + \epsilon_i$, where y is the long-term AAA corporate bond yield and x is the income velocity of money defined as

$$\log(\text{GNP/money supply}).$$

Using quarterly data for over six years, we obtain

$$n = 26 \qquad \Sigma y = 118.27 \qquad \Sigma y^2 = 541.77$$

$$\Sigma xy = 477.05 \qquad \Sigma x = 104.42 \qquad \Sigma x^2 = 420.72$$

    a) Find the least-squares estimates for α and β based on these data. Interpret the meaning of your estimated model by considering the effect on the interest rate of a 0.2-unit decrease in income velocity due to an increased desire by consumers to hold cash.

    b) If income velocity is 4.0, find the estimated value for y. If the true interest rate at this level of income velocity is 4.29%, determine the residual e.

    c) Compute and interpret the meaning of r^2 and s_e.

13.67 Examine the relation between imports and national income for a country over an eleven year period using the data in Table 13.32.

TABLE 13.32   Imports versus National Income

Imports y (million dollars)	National Income x_2 (million dollars)
11.6	331
12.9	351
13.4	366
13.4	368
15.7	400
15.1	414
14.8	427
16.5	458
17.2	482
18.8	517
21.4	559

Source: *International Financial Statistics, Supplement.*

    a) By the least-squares method, estimate the model $y_i = \alpha + \beta x_i + \epsilon_i$.

    b) Find and interpret the meaning of r^2 and s_e.

    c) Test the significance of ρ at the 0.01 level, assuming normal populations.

    d) Test at the 0.01 level whether the marginal propensity to import (β) satisfies $(0.02 < \beta < 0.05)$ by making a one-sided test on each endpoint of the interval.

    e) Fifteen years ago, national income was 280. Test whether a level of imports of 10.5 for that year is consistent with the recent experience. Use the 0.05 level of significance. [Hint: Form and use the t-distributed test statistic implied in Formula 13.28.]

13.68 A significant change occurred in U.S. federal government expenditures on defense in the period 1940–1948. Use the data in Table 13.33 for $y = $ GNP and $x = $ expenditures on national defense, both in billions of dollars.

TABLE 13.33 GNP versus Expenditures

Year	y	x
1940	99.7	1.5
1941	124.5	6.1
1942	157.9	24.0
1943	191.6	63.2
1944	210.1	76.8
1945	211.9	81.3
1946	208.5	43.2
1947	231.3	14.4
1948	257.6	11.8

a) Estimate the relation $y_i = \alpha + \beta x_i + \epsilon_i$ by the least-squares method.

b) Interpret the meaning of the estimate of β.

c) Determine the residuals for these nine observations.

d) Find and interpret the meaning of r^2 and s_e.

e) By examining these results, discuss the adequacy of this linear representation when enormous structural changes take place. Suggest a better specification of the relation between GNP and defense expenditures for the period 1940–1948.

f) Find the U.S. expenditure on GNP and defense for the current year. Using the relation estimated above, find the residual (unexplained deviation). Explain what this calculation shows about using a regression line for forecasts given extra-sample values of x.

13.69 The data in Table 13.34 measure $y =$ current corporate investment and $x =$ retained earnings in the previous year.

a) Formulate a linear regression model relating these two variables. Estimate and interpret the meaning of your specification and your results.

TABLE 13.34 Corporate Investment versus Retained Earnings

y	x	y	x
37.0	16.0	37.3	13.5
30.5	14.2	39.2	16.0
32.5	10.8	44.9	16.6
35.7	16.0	52.0	20.6
34.4	13.2	60.6	25.4

b) Test the hypothesis $H_0 : \beta = 1.5$ at the 0.05 significance level against the alternative $H_a : \beta \neq 1.5$.

c) What proportion of the variation in investment is explained by the regression line on retained earnings? Compare this to the similar measure for the example problem in Figure 13.16. On this basis, can you argue whether retained earnings or stock price is a better variable for a model explaining investment?

13.70 Prove that b in Formula 13.9 is equivalent to the b-value in Formula 13.8.

13.71 Prove that the normal equations in the footnote 3 of this chapter do, in fact, lead to the values of a and b in Formula 13.8.

13.72 Using the appropriate definitions, explain why the following equations are correct: $\text{SSR} = r^2(\text{SST})$ and $\text{SSE} = (1 - r^2)(\text{SST})$. Use these formulas to prove that the F-value in Formula 13.31 is the square of the t-value in Formula 13.24.

13.73 Prove that $r = b(s_x/s_y)$ and $r^2 = \text{SSR}/\text{SST}$.

◆ **13.74** Refer to the regression results of Problem 13.34 to answer the following items.

a) Test the null hypothesis that the slope of the population regression line is zero against the alternative hypothesis that it is positive. Use 0.10 as the level of significance.

b) Test the null hypothesis $H_0 : \rho = 0$ against the alternative hypothesis $H_a : \rho \neq 0$. Use $\alpha = 0.01$. Relate this result to part (a).

c) Given the standard assumptions of the regression model, construct a 99% confidence interval for the mean sales with an advertising expenditure of $40,000.

d) Construct a 99% forecast interval for the actual value of sales with an advertising expenditure of $40,000.

◆ **13.75** An observational study of 19 managers from a medium-sized manufacturing plant attempted to determine if a manager's success can be explained in part by the degree of the manager's interactions with people outside the manager's work unit. For each of the 19 managers, the 'manager success index' was named MSI and the 'number of interactions with outsiders' was called NIO. Table 13.35 gives results relevant to this potential relationship. Analyze it by answering the following questions.

TABLE 13.35 Manager Success Index

Table of Means and Standard Deviations

Variable	Mean	Standard Deviation
MSI	67.42105	25.81196
NIO	44.15789	24.52269

Matrix of Correlation Coefficients

	MSI	NIO
MSI	1.0000	0.7413
NIO	0.7413	1.0000

ANOVA Table

Source of Variation	Sum of Squares	D.F.	Mean Square
Regression	6589.707	1	6589.707
Error	5402.924	17	317.819
Total	11992.63	18	

Table of Estimated Coefficents

Variable	Estimated Coefficent	Estimated Standard Deviation	Computed t-Value
NIO	0.78024	0.17135	4.554
Intercept	32.96727		

NOTE: $SS_x = 10,824.52185$
Standard error of estimate $= 17.82748$

a) State and interpret the regression equation.

b) Test for the hypothesis $H_0 : \beta = 0$ versus $H_a : \beta > 0$, using a significance level of 0.05.

c) What is the proportion of variability explained by regression?

d) Test the null hypothesis $H_0 : \rho = 0$ against $\rho \neq 0$ with $\alpha = 0.05$. Relate this result to part (b).

e) Obtain a 95% confidence interval for the slope of the regression line.

f) Construct a 95% confidence interval for the mean value of *manager success index* for 40 interactions with outsiders.

g) Construct a 95% forecast interval for the actual value of *manager success index* for a manager who has 40 interactions with outsiders.

USING THE COMPUTER

13.76 Use the data in Section 13.10. Have a computer program do a plot of investment against stock index. Draw in the sample regression line and two bounding lines parallel to the regression line but a vertical distance of $s_e = 10.28$ units above and below it. Determine what proportion of the 20 observations lie within one standard error of the regression line.

13.77 Use a computer program to recalculate the sample regression line using the same data as in Section 13.10 on investment and stock index. Also, have the list of 20 residuals printed out.

a) Determine what proportion of these values of e_i are smaller in absolute value than s_e.

b) Compare this result to the proportion determined graphically in Problem 13.76.

13.78 Use the observations on sales and employees in **Data Set 2** for the largest 50 firms and make the standard assumptions.

a) Find the least squares regression line between sales (y) and employees (x). Use sales values in terms of

billions of dollars and employees in thousands with two decimal places. For example, General Motors sales and employees are 18.458 and 42.555 respectively.

b) Test the significance of the slope using a t-test at the 0.01 level.

c) Find a 90% forecast interval for the actual value of sales for a firm with 15,000 employees.

13.79 Use the observations in **Data Set 1** on income and sales for the cities that begin with the letter "C".

a) Find the least-squares regression equation between sales (y) and income (x) and make the standard assumptions.

b) Do an *F*-test on the significance of the relation using the 0.05 level.

c) Find a 98% confidence interval for the true slope of the relation.

13.80 Refer to **Data Set 4**, which gives 40 observations from a survey of doctors (general practitioners) in private practice. Make the standard assumptions.

a) Do a least-squares regression between the reported annual net income (y) and the average weekly hours worked (x).

b) Find s_e and r^2 and interpret their meaning.

c) Explain why you do or do not think this is a useful model for explaining the different levels of net income of these doctors.

13.81 Repeat Problem 13.79 for the cities that begin with the letter "S".

13.82 Compare the results of Problems 13.79 and 13.81.

a) Can you say which group of cities provides the better estimate of the true β relating income and sales?

b) Repeat Problem 13.79 for all cities in **Data Set 1**. Does the value of b obtained in this case lie within the confidence intervals for β that were calculated in part (c) of Problems 13.79 and 13.81?

13.83 Refer to **Data Set 5** giving 41 annual observations for 1950–1990 of some economic measures for Canada. We would expect a positive relation between the level of exports and the gross domestic product (GDP).

a) Find the least-squares regression equation between GDP (y) and exports (x).

b) Using a significance level of 0.025 and the standard assumptions, determine whether the change in GDP for a unit change in exports is less than 4.

13.84 Refer to **Data Set 6** taken from a survey of persons over age 54 and make standard assumptions.

a) Find the least-squares regression line using the number of persons in the households as the independent variable (x) to explain the variation in monthly income (y).

b) Test the fit of the relation using an **F**-test with $\alpha = 0.05$.

c) Make an upper-sided **t**-test of significance on the slope β using $\alpha = 0.025$.

d) Compare and interpret the results of the tests in parts (b) and (c).

13.85 Repeat Problem 13.84 using the education level of the person as the independent variable (x) and compare the results of the goodness of fit measures. Which explanatory variable is preferred if only one is included in the model?

CASE PROBLEMS

13.86 (Highway Safety) The data below give the number of motor vehicle deaths for a recent year and the number of licensed drivers per 10,000 population in the District of Columbia and all states except Hawaii.

OBS	STATE	NUMDEATH	NUMDRVRS
1	AL	968	158
2	AR	640	92
3	CA	4743	952
4	CO	566	109
5	CT	325	167
6	DE	118	30
7	DC	115	35
8	FL	1545	298
9	GA	1302	203
10	IL	2207	544
11	IN	1410	254
12	IA	833	150
13	KS	669	136
14	KY	911	147
15	LA	1037	146
16	ME	196	46
17	MD	616	157
18	MA	766	255
19	MI	2120	403
20	MN	841	189
21	MS	648	85
22	MO	1289	234
23	NB	450	89
24	NH	158	37
25	NJ	1071	329
26	NY	2745	744
27	NC	1580	226
28	OH	2096	530
29	OK	785	137
30	OR	575	108
31	PA	1889	570
32	RI	100	46
33	SC	870	122
34	TN	1059	177
35	TX	3006	515
36	UT	295	57
37	VT	131	20
38	VA	1050	208
39	WV	467	88
40	WI	1059	207
41	AK	43	11
42	AZ	588	91
43	ID	262	41
44	MT	259	38
45	NE	215	23
46	NM	387	54
47	ND	185	38
48	SD	270	40
49	WA	730	160
50	WY	148	22

a) Find the least-squares regression between the number of deaths (y) and the number of drivers (x).

b) Find the two measures of goodness of fit, s_e and r^2.

c) Assuming normality, do a test of significance on the population correlation coefficient at a level of 0.01.

13.87 Stock analysts look at the total risk premium of a given security to compare those stocks which are safer to hold versus those that are more risky. The risk premium is often determined relative to an average market risk level and depends on the returns or total yield for the given stock. A measure of the risk level for a given stock is called the beta coefficient. If beta exceeds unity, the stock is classified as risky; holding it is associated with taking an aggressive posture in the market. An investor who wishes to take a more defensive position would buy and hold stocks with a beta coefficient smaller than unity, which corresponds to a stock which is safer than the market on the average. One way to estimate the beta coefficient is with a regression analysis of the monthly return of company j stock as the dependent variable r_j and the monthly return of the market r_m as the explanatory variable. The model is:

$$r_j = \alpha + \beta r_m + \epsilon$$

The beta coefficient is estimated by the slope of the model, b. **Data Set 8** gives a set of monthly returns for four stocks and for a *market* group of stocks.

a) Use these data to estimate the beta coefficient for each given stock (IBM, Exxon, GE, GM) and interpret its meaning.

b) Construct a portfolio of the GE and GM stocks by averaging their returns. Estimate beta for this portfolio and compare it to the B's of GE and GM separately.

CHAPTER 14

Multiple Regression and Correlation Analysis

Introduction to Multiple Regression

In Chapter 13, the method of least-squares estimation was found to yield estimates that have the desirable properties of unbiasedness, efficiency, and consistency, given a set of five standard assumptions. Measures of the goodness of fit and methods of statistical inference were discussed for the *simple* linear regression model involving one dependent variable y and *one* independent variable x. In this chapter, we extend the analysis to *multiple* linear regression models involving *two or more* independent or explanatory variables. In the next chapter, we will give a more thorough discussion of the underlying assumptions for regression analysis, including some tests for the validity of the assumptions.

The Extended Population Model

In most applications, many factors may be related to the dependent variable, any of which could help explain its variation. Suppose we assume that there are m independent variables and that the population model relating these variables to the dependent variable y is given by the following linear model. Remember that the variables in the model may be functions of original measures so that a non-linear relation may be represented in the context of the linear model. Refer to Section 15.6.

Population regression model:

$$y_i = \alpha + \beta_1 x_{i1} + \beta_2 x_{i2} + \beta_3 x_{i3} + \cdots + \beta_m x_{im} + \epsilon_i$$

As was the case for simple linear regression, the subscript i on each variable represents one of the values in the population. Also, α equals the y-intercept, β_1 equals the slope of the relationship between y and x_{i1}, β_2 equals the slope between y and x_{i2}, and so forth. The conditional mean of the dependent variable is given by the following **population multiple regression equation.**

Population multiple regression equation:

$$\mu_{y \cdot x_1, x_2, \ldots, x_m} = \alpha + \beta_1 x_1 + \beta_2 x_2 + \cdots + \beta_m x_m \qquad (14.1)$$

The coefficients $\beta_1, \beta_2, \ldots, \beta_m$ are called **partial regression coefficients,** since they indicate the (partial) influence of each independent variable on y, when the influence of all the remaining independent variables is *held constant.*

☐ **EXAMPLE 14.1**   Let us consider a simplified example of multiple regression. Applicants for college admission, for graduate school, or law school admission, for jobs, for loans, and so on, always have to fill out some form or present some documented evidence about their qualifications. The appropriate official (school administrator, personnel manager, or loan officer) must somehow weigh the different qualifications and make a judgment about the suitability of the applicant. This involves an estimate of the probability of success, perhaps measured by some subsequent accomplishment.

Suppose that the admissions board for a graduate school tries to predict y = grade point average (GPA) expected in graduate school for new enrollees given their individual characteristics. It is common to use several explanatory variables to help make such a prediction. Among these are the Under Graduate Grades (UGG), the quality of the undergraduate school, letters of recommendation, and the scores on standardized Graduate Record Examinations (GRE). Given sufficient historical information on enrollees' characteristics and their eventual graduate-school grade record, a mathematical relation can be determined among these variables. The relation, allowing for uncertainty, is a regression equation that can be used to make predictions for other enrollees.

Assuming there are only two explanatory variables in the equation, the population regression equation is:

$$\mu_{y \cdot x_1, x_2} = \alpha + \beta_1 x_1 + \beta_2 x_2$$

with

y = graduate grade point average (GPA)

x_1 = graduate record examination scores (GRE)

x_2 = undergraduate grade average (UGG) ■

The Extended Sample Model

The process of using sample information to estimate the parameters of a multiple linear regression equation involves the same techniques used in the simple linear regression case. Suppose that we have a sample consisting of n observations for each of the variables. The problem is to find the sample regression equation that provides the *best fit* to these data and to use the coefficients of that equation as estimates of the parameters of the population regression equation. For multiple regression the sample equation is as follows:

Sample multiple regression equation:

$$\hat{y} = a + b_1 x_1 + b_2 x_2 + \cdots + b_m x_m \qquad (14.2)$$

The value of $\hat{y}$ is the estimate of $\mu_{y \cdot x_1, x_2, \ldots, x_m}$; a is the estimate of the intercept α; and $b_1, b_2, \ldots, b_m$ are the estimates of the partial regression coefficients $\beta_1, \beta_2, \ldots, \beta_m$. The multiple regression equation reduces to the simple regression line when $m = 1$.

For the grade point average example, suppose we estimate the *sample* equation to be the following:

$$\hat{y} = -1.75 + 0.005 x_1 + 0.70 x_2$$

The value $b_1 = 0.005$ in this case indicates that, after eliminating or taking into account the influence on GPA of x_2 (UGG), a one-unit increase in x_1 (GRE) will increase the mean value of y (GPA) by 0.005 units. Similarly, since $b_2 = 0.70$, a one-unit increase in x_2 (UGG) will increase the mean GPA by 0.70 units, assuming that the influence of GRE is being held constant. Figure 14.1 is a graph of the plane represented by this multiple regression equation.

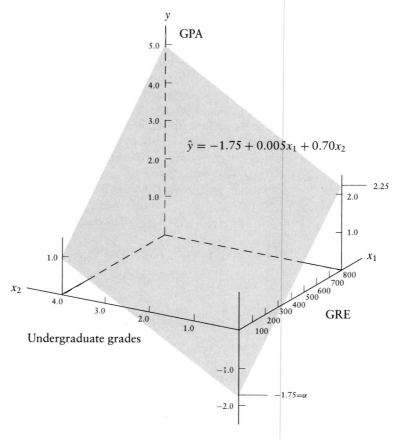

$$\hat{y} = -1.75 + 0.005x_1 + 0.70x_2$$

FIGURE 14.1   The regression plane $\hat{y} = -1.75 + 0.005x_1 + 0.70x_2$

Predicting Levels or Changes in Y

The sample equation can be used to find predicted levels for y, given values for the independent variables in the equation. Substitution of the x-values, multiplied by the appropriate slopes and added to the intercept, will give the value of $\hat{y}$.

Note in Figure 14.1 that when $x_1 = 0$ and $x_2 = 0$, the regression plane intersects the y-axis at $\alpha = -1.75$. When $x_1 = 800$ and $x_2 = 0$, the value of $\hat{y}$ is 2.25. Similarly, when $x_1 = 800$ and $x_2 = 4.0$, the regression plane yields $\hat{y} = -1.75 + 0.005(800) + 0.70(4.0) = 5.05$.

These extreme points are at the boundaries of the positive coordinates for the multiple regression plane in three-dimensional space. As we saw before for the simple regression model, care must be taken in extending the regression results toward the upper or lower limits of the explanatory variables. The regression model is the expected or *average* relation and may not be meaningful at the extremes. Clearly, no one enrolled in graduate school could obtain a GPA of -1.75 (which occurs when $x_1 = x_2 = 0$. Making predictions for these low levels of x_1 and x_2 is inappropriate, since the population of graduate school enrollees does not include anyone who has a GRE score of zero and an undergraduate grade point average of zero. The model cannot be linearly extrapolated to the extremes.

Using more likely values, we can find the estimated grade point average for an applicant with an exam score of 620 and undergraduate grade average of 3.2.

$$\hat{y} = -1.75 + 0.005(620) + 0.70(3.2) = 3.59$$

Expected changes in grade point average can be predicted based on suggested changes in the independent variables. Using Δ as a change symbol so that Δy means the change in y and Δx is a change in x, we see from the general form of a sample regression equation that the following is true.

$$\Delta\hat{y} = \Delta a + \Delta(b_1 x_1) + \Delta(b_2 x_2) + \Delta(b_3 x_3) + \cdots + \Delta(b_m x_m)$$

Since there can be no change in the constants, $a, b_1, b_2, \ldots, b_m$, this becomes:

$$\Delta\hat{y} = b\Delta x_1 + b_2\Delta x_2 + b_3\Delta x_3 + \cdots b_m\Delta x_m$$

If only one independent variable (say x_2) changes and the others are held fixed, the resulting impact on y is simply $\Delta\hat{y} = b_2\Delta x_2$. For example, let us find the change predicted for grade point average if an applicant retakes the test and scores 40 points higher so $\Delta x_1 = +40$.

$$\Delta\hat{y} = 0.005(40) = 0.2$$

The predicted change in graduate grade average would be an increase of 0.2. Note that in calculating predicted changes, you do not need to involve the intercept value. Finding predicted values or forecasts in this way only determines *point* estimates. The computation of *interval* forecasts with a stated level of confidence (or of error) is quite cumbersome for the multiple regression model. Since this computation is best presented by using matrix operations, it is not described in this text.

On the intuitive level, we must remember that the sample model gives results for only one set of data. Even if it has a high level of fit, it is not necessarily true that its predictions will be accurate for other situations. If there is some change in the underlying behaviour or in some legal, social, political, regulatory, economic, or military factor (and so forth), the mathematical mechanism described by the equation may not hold. The equation is most accurate near the point of means for the given variables and for no changes in the environmental or business conditions surrounding the time or place setting in which the data were gathered.

Acknowledging these points of caution, the objective information of point forecasts is not to be dismissed. Forecasts may provide the decision-maker with insights just as worthwhile as those obtained from subjective experience or from discussion with experts. Forecasts are calculated under the assumption that conditions do not change substantially.

◻ STUDY QUESTION 14.1 Predicting Bicycle Sales from a Regression Equation

In a relatively flat, moderate climate, medium-sized college town, a bicycle dealer tries to stock bicycles and parts based on expectations of sales. Over the years this dealer has gathered data and estimated the following relation:

$$\text{Bicycle Sales} = -15 + 35 \text{ STU} + 0.5 \text{ GASPR} - 0.2 \text{ PRICE}$$

where STU is the number of students (in thousands) enrolled in the nearby college, GASPR is the price of a gallon of gas (in cents), and PRICE is the average price of new bicycles (in dollars).

a) Determine the predicted bicycle sales for next year if there are 5,000 students, the price of gas is $1.20 per gallon, and the average price of bicycles is $450.

b) Find the expected change in bicycle sales if their average price is raised $35, other factors remaining constant.

c) Find the expected change from one year to the next in bicycle sales if yearly changes are anticipated of 100 more students, ten cents lower price of gasoline, and an increase in the average bicycle price of $27.

● ANSWER

a) Values are substituted into the sample regression equation to obtain the following:

$$\hat{y} = -15 + 35(5) + 0.5(120) - 0.2(450) = 130$$

The expected number of bicycles to be sold is 130.

b) $\Delta\hat{y} = -0.2(35) = -7$. An average increase in price of $35 for bicycles has an impact of decreasing sales by 7 bicycles, holding the other two variables constant.

c) $\Delta\hat{y} = 35(0.1) + 0.5(-10) - 0.2(27) = -6.9$. The total impact of these changes is predicted to be a decrease in bicycle sales of 6.9 units. ∎

---

section 14.2

Multiple Least-Squares Estimation

The least-squares estimates for multiple regression are again based on the principle of minimizing the sum of the squares of the residuals. As before, each residual (e_i) is the difference $e_i = y_i - \hat{y}_i$, where y_i is the observed value and $\hat{y}_i = a + b_1 x_{i1} + b_2 x_{i2} + \cdots + b_m x_{im}$ is the predicted value. For least-squares estimates, we want to find the values of $a, b_1, b_2, \ldots, b_m$ (given observations on y and on the x_j's) that minimize the following function:

$$G = \sum_{i=1}^{n} e_i^2 = \sum_{i=1}^{n} (y_i - a - b_i x_{i1} - b_2 x_{i2} - \cdots - b_m x_{im})^2$$

The procedure for minimizing this function is the same as in the simple linear regression (shown in a footnote in Section 13.3). In this case, the result is a set of $m + 1$ *normal equations* that, when solved simultaneously, yield the $(m + 1)$ estimates $a, b_1, \ldots, b_m$. See Problem 14.28 for an example when $m = 2$. Although solving for these estimates is not a particularly difficult task, the process usually requires tiresome arithmetic that is prone to computational errors. For this reason, computer programs based on the techniques of matrix algebra are generally employed to calculate the sums, sums of squares, and sums of cross-products of the sample observations and to solve such systems of normal equations. Students who wish to study more advanced methods and applications of multiple regression or correlation analysis in business and economics are well advised to include a course in matrix algebra in their program of study and to become familiar with typical computer program outputs for regression analysis. In this chapter, we will emphasize the understanding and interpretation of multiple regression rather than its computational aspects.

We extend the investment model introduced in Section 13.10 by including a second independent variable in our analysis of the dependent variable (investment). Recall that our first independent variable, which we now label x_1, was the *price index* of 500 common stocks. Our second variable, which is denoted by x_2, is the *retained earnings of firms*. Retained earnings are the portion of profits after taxes that is not distributed to owners (stockholders), but is kept within the firm as working capital. Since these retained earnings are often the source of funds used to purchase new land, buildings, and equipment, we presume that a positive relationship exists between x_2 and y. We will attempt to relate the value of retained earnings (in billions of dollars measured at an annual rate) in one quarter with investment in the following quarter. The 20 observations of x_2 are shown in Table 14.1, along with the corresponding values for y and x_1 that were given in Table 13.27. The simple and multiple regression equations using least squares estimation on these data are given in Figure 14.2 (a) and (b) respectively. Part (a) is the same as Figure 13.16.

TABLE 14.1 Data for Multiple Regression Model for Investment

Observation	y (Investment)	x_1 (Stock Price Index)	x_2 (Retained Earnings)
1	62.3	398.4	16.2
2	71.3	452.6	17.4
3	70.3	509.8	14.8
4	68.5	485.4	14.6
5	57.3	445.7	8.2
6	68.8	539.8	14.9
7	72.2	662.8	15.1
8	76.0	620.0	14.3
9	64.3	632.2	10.9
10	77.9	703.0	16.0
11	84.3	581.8	16.2
12	85.1	707.1	16.4
13	90.8	776.6	20.4
14	97.9	875.3	20.5
15	108.7	873.4	26.1
16	122.4	943.7	29.0
17	114.0	830.6	24.6
18	123.0	907.5	27.8
19	126.2	905.3	23.3
20	137.0	927.4	21.6

from Table 13.27

Since there are two variables in our model, the population equation to be estimated is as follows:

$$\mu_{y \cdot x_1, x_2} = \alpha + \beta_1 x_1 + \beta_2 x_2$$

The least-squares regression equation is:

$$\hat{y} = 1.677 + 0.07856 x_1 + 1.7984 x_2$$

The unexplained variation is now as shown:

$$\text{SSE} = \sum_{i=1}^{20} e_i^2 = \sum_{i=1}^{20}(y_i - \hat{y}_i)^2 = 1,263.77$$

Note how these results compare with those of the analysis involving only x_1 and y, where the regression line was

$$\hat{y} = 3.855 + 0.12347 x_1$$

and the unexplained variation was

$$\sum_{i=1}^{20} e_i^2 = \text{SSE} = 1,901.3$$

a) Simple regression:

```
DEPENDENT VARIABLE..        INV            PRIVATE INVESTMENT, $BIL

VARIABLE(S) ENTERED IN MODEL      STKPR      STOCK PRICE, PREVIOUS QUARTER
                          ANALYSIS OF VARIANCE
MULTIPLE R            0.9135              DF    SUM OF SQUARES   MEAN SQUARE
R SQUARE             0.8345   REGRESSION    1      9584.4258      9584.43
ADJUSTED R SQUARE    0.8253    RESIDUAL    18      1901.2597       105.63
STANDARD ERROR      10.2774    F = 90.74           SIGNIF F = 0.0001

--------------VARIABLES IN THE EQUATION --------------------

VARIABLE         B       SE B       T                 SIG T

STKPR         0.12347   0.01296   9.5257             0.0001
(CONSTANT)    3.85498   9.22048   0.4181             0.6808
```

b) Multiple regression

```
DEPENDENT VARIABLE..        INV            PRIVATE INVESTMENT, $BIL

VARIABLE(S) ENTERED IN MODEL      STKPR      STOCK PRICE, PREVIOUS QUARTER
                                  RETEARN    RETAINED EARNINGS, PREVIOUS QUARTER
                          ANALYSIS OF VARIANCE
MULTIPLE R            0.9434              DF    SUM OF SQUARES   MEAN SQUARE
R SQUARE             0.8900   REGRESSION    2     10221.9157      5110.96
ADJUSTED R SQUARE    0.8770    RESIDUAL    17      1263.7698        74.34
STANDARD ERROR       8.6220    F = 68.75           SIGNIF F = 0.0001

--------------VARIABLES IN THE EQUATION --------------------

VARIABLE         B       SE B       T                 SIG T

STKPR         0.07856   0.01880   4.1786             0.0006
RETEARN       1.79840   0.61413   2.9284             0.0094
(CONSTANT)    1.67713   7.77099   0.2158             0.8317
```

FIGURE 14.2   Computer printout for the investment model

As suggested by this example, the introduction of a new variable into the sample regression model usually has several effects:
1. The coefficients of previously included variables change.
2. More of the variation of y is explained (SSE gets smaller).
3. The values of t- (or F-) distributed statistics change.

Change (1) will occur unless the correlation coefficient $r_{x_i x_j} = 0$, where x_i is the included variable and x_j is the new variable. Change (2) occurs unless $r_{x_i x_j} = 1.0$ or -1.0. Change (3) occurs with any change in the model specification or the set of observations. Throughout this chapter we explore, in depth, the causes and the meaning of these changes.

We note that the estimate for the coefficient of x_1 (stock index) changes from 0.12347 to 0.07856 when the variable x_2 (retained earnings) is included in the estimating equation for y (investment). That is, a ten-point rise in the stock index last quarter is now associated with an increase in investment (annually) of only about \$0.79 billion rather than \$1.23 billion. Obviously, the new estimate b_1 must have a different meaning from the estimate b in the simple model. The estimate $b_1 = 0.07856$ is obtained by considering the influence of x_2 on y and its relationship with x_1, as well as the simple relationship of x_1 on y and of x_1 with x_2.

The technique of multiple regression is similar to a laboratory-controlled experiment in which one independent variable at a time is varied to examine its influence on the dependent variable, while holding all other controlled factors constant. In this case, the variables included in the model are the only ones being controlled; other factors are subsumed into the error term.

> The partial regression coefficient measures the influence of one variable on y while holding the influence of the other variables constant.[1]

Thus, b_1 measures the partial effect of changes in last quarter's stock prices on investment as if we had controlled the real world in such a way that the amount of *retained earnings* in the previous quarter was constant. The value of b_1 depends on the selection of the other factors included in the model. This is a critical concept. If another factor, such as interest rate, were included in addition to (or instead of) retained earnings, then the value of b_1 would change because the controlled environment in which the influence of x_1 is being measured would be different. Only if all the additional explanatory variables includable in the model are independent of x_1 would the estimate of b_1 remain unchanged when these variables are included.

Similarly, the value of $b_2 = 1.7984$ represents the partial influence of retained earnings on current investment, where the influence of the index of *stock prices* is held constant. Using a familiar term in economics — *ceteris paribus* (holding other factors constant) — the effect of a one-billion-dollar increase in retained earnings is an increase of about \$1.8 billion in investment.

☐ **EXAMPLE 14.2** In Chapter 13, several study questions dealt with a simple regression model relating median income (here denoted as x_1) to the average home price (y) in a city. Other factors affecting the price of housing might be included in an extended model. Table 14.2 gives data for an extended model where Rent (x_2) is the average monthly rental rate of new units and Vacant (x_3) is the percentage of housing units that are vacant. Figure 14.3(a) gives the computer results for the *simple* regression model ($m = 1$), and Figure 14.3(c) gives the output for the *multiple* regression model ($m = 3$). Figure 14.3(b) will be used in a later explanation.

---

[1] Students with a knowledge of calculus can interpret a simple regression coefficient of x as the derivative dy/dx, whereas the partial regression coefficient of x_1 is the partial derivative, $\partial y/\partial x_1$, obtained by treating every other $x_j (j \neq 1)$ as if it were a constant.

TABLE 14.2 Data for the Housing Price Regression

Obs	Income	Price	Rent	Vacant
1	22.1	90.1	392	10
2	23.3	101.4	402	9
3	24.3	93.2	394	12
4	18.6	88.8	345	15
5	22.2	99.1	406	11
6	24.5	112.2	455	8
7	21.6	81.5	315	23
8	17.6	77.6	330	20
9	23.5	96.5	370	12
10	18.1	86.4	368	16
11	21.1	88.4	335	14
12	20.4	100.2	412	8
13	21.0	99.3	380	10
14	24.7	133.7	442	6
15	20.2	87.9	306	20
16	16.8	77.4	322	23
17	23.0	96.8	357	13
18	22.2	96.6	366	10
19	23.3	115.9	441	8
20	20.4	106.6	422	7
21	18.9	83.5	345	16
22	17.9	77.4	339	15
23	26.6	128.8	444	7
24	18.4	75.5	305	18
25	20.1	95.3	375	11

Several comparisons between the results of the simple and multiple regression models highlight the three effects listed previously. First, the coefficient on the explanatory variable Income changes when other variables are included in the model. In the simple model, a change in median income of one dollar leads to a change in housing price of $4.693 ($b = 4.693$). In other words, a city with a median income $1,000 higher is expected to have housing prices $4,693 higher. Income is the only explanatory variable in the model and is serving as a proxy for many hidden relationships.

When the factors of rent and vacancy rates are included in the multiple regression, the estimated changes are very different. Higher rents indicate a strong housing market and allow correspondingly higher prices for housing units ($b_2 = 0.1812$). Higher vacancy rates indicate a less competitive housing market in which units are more easily found. This puts pressure on housing prices to decline ($b_3 = -0.3143$). The coefficient on Income has decreased to $b_1 = 2.0180$. We see that when more direct factors are included to explain the competitiveness in the housing market, the more indirect factor of income becomes less important. If another factor, such as the average size of the housing unit (square-foot measure) were included, it would probably have an even more direct effect on the housing price. All the coefficients of previously included variables would again change. Thus, it is important for the decision-maker to correctly specify all the relevant factors in a regression model under analysis.

A second change between the results of the simple and multiple regressions is in the amounts of variation unexplained. Referring to Figure 14.3(a), the *unexplained variation* (SSE) for the simple model is 1,969.81. In the multiple model with two additional variables helping to explain the variation in housing price, the unexplained variation is reduced to SSE = 874.04.

Looking at the relative measure of goodness of fit, $R^2 = $ SSR/SST, we note its increase from 0.64 in the simple model to 0.84 in the multiple model. Income alone explained 64% of the variation in housing price, whereas income, rent, and vacancy rate together explained 84% of the variation in housing price.

FIGURE 14.3   Computer output for the housing price models

a) One explanatory factor

```
DEPENDENT VARIABLE..      PRICE        HOUSING PRICE

VARIABLE(S) ENTERED IN MODEL      INCOME      HOUSEHOLD MEDIAN INCOME

                       ANALYSIS OF VARIANCE
MULTIPLE R          0.7995             DF   SUM OF SQUARES   MEAN SQUARE
R SQUARE            0.6392  REGRESSION   1       3490.4990     3490.4990
ADJUSTED R SQUARE   0.62367   RESIDUAL  23       1969.8106       85.6439
STANDARD ERROR      9.25447   F = 40.756          SIGNIF F = 0.0001

- - - - - - - - - - - - - VARIABLES IN THE EQUATION - - - - - - - - - - - - - - - - - -

VARIABLE             B         SE B         T         SIG T
INCOME          4.69344     0.73518      6.384        0.0001
(CONSTANT)     −4.04720    15.71878     −0.258        0.7991
```

b) Two explanatory factors

```
DEPENDENT VARIABLE..      PRICE        HOUSING PRICE

VARIABLE(S) ENTERED IN MODEL      INCOME      HOUSEHOLD MEDIAN INCOME
                                  RENT        AVERAGE MONTHLY RENTAL RATE

                       ANALYSIS OF VARIANCE
MULTIPLE R          0.9153             DF   SUM OF SQUARES   MEAN SQUARE
R SQUARE            0.8378  REGRESSION   2       4574.8327     2287.4164
ADJUSTED R SQUARE   0.8231    RESIDUAL  22        885.4769       40.2490
STANDARD ERROR      6.3442    F = 56.832          SIGNIF F = 0.0001

- - - - - - - - - - - - - VARIABLES IN THE EQUATION - - - - - - - - - - - - - - - - - -

VARIABLE             B         SE B         T         SIG T
INCOME          2.06752     0.71411      2.895        0.0084
RENT            0.21031     0.04052      5.190        0.0001
(CONSTANT)    −27.10220    11.65533     −2.3255       0.0297
```

c) Three explanatory factors

```
DEPENDENT VARIABLE..        PRICE        HOUSING PRICE

VARIABLE(S) ENTERED IN MODEL        INCOME      HOUSEHOLD MEDIAN INCOME
                                    RENT        AVERAGE MONTHLY RENTAL RATE
                                    VACANT      PERCENTAGE UNITS VACANT

                            ANALYSIS OF VARIANCE
MULTIPLE R          0.9165              DF    SUM OF SQUARES    MEAN SQUARE
R SQUARE            0.8399    REGRESSION   3       4586.2701      1528.7567
ADJUSTED R SQUARE   0.8171    RESIDUAL    21        874.0395        41.6209
STANDARD ERROR      6.4514    F = 36.730           SIGNIF F = 0.0001


-------------- VARIABLES IN THE EQUATION ------------------
VARIABLE               B          SE B        T            SIG T
INCOME            2.01796      0.73231     2.756          0.0118
RENT              0.18124      0.06909     2.623          0.0159
VACANT           -0.31426      0.05995    -0.524          0.6056
(CONSTANT)      -11.10911     32.73019    -0.339          0.7377
```

Finally, the values of *F*-statistics for the overall fit of the model and of *t*-statistics for the significance of individual coefficients of each explanatory variable are also shown in Figure 14.3. A comparison quickly reveals that the *F*-values have changed and the *t*-value for the variable Income has changed. In the following sections of this chapter, more explanation is given of the meaning and the use of these test statistics and goodness-of-fit measures. ∎

Goodness-of-Fit Measures

As in the case of simple regression, some goodness-of-fit measures are needed to judge how well the multiple regression equation fits the observed data. Again, an absolute measure and a relative measure are common; they have an interpretation completely analogous to those discussed in Section 13.5. Before presenting these measures, we emphasize two *conditions* that are necessary for least squares estimation to work meaningfully so that these measures may be calculated and interpreted.

Condition 1.   *None of the independent variables is an exact linear combination of the other independent variables.* This means that no one variable x_j is an exact multiple of any other independent variable. Further, if $m \geq 2$, this assumption means that no one variable x_j can be written as follows where the *a*'s are constants.

$$x_j = a_1x_1 + a_2x_2 + \cdots + a_{j-1}x_{j-1} + a_{j+1}x_{j+1} + \cdots + a_mx_m$$

This assumption is a weak condition, since it requires only that the variables not be *perfectly* related to each other in a linear function. In practice, the independent variables often are partially linearly related to each other, or related to each other in some nonlinear way. Although least-squares estimates can be calculated in these situations, problems do arise in their interpretation.

Condition 2.   *The number of observations (n) must exceed the number (m + 1) of coefficients being estimated; that is, n > m + 1.* Since there are $m + 1$ coefficients to be estimated in the multiple regression equation, the number of degrees of freedom is $n - (m + 1)$. This condition merely specifies that there be at least one degree of freedom. In practice, the sample size must be quite a bit larger than $m + 1$ in order to obtain meaningful information about the underlying relation.

Standard Error of Estimate

The standard error of the estimate for the multiple regression equation is defined just as it is for simple regression by the following formula:

$$s_e = \sqrt{\frac{\text{unexplained variation}}{\text{degrees of freedom}}}$$

However, since $(m + 1)$ parameters must be estimated before a residual from the multiple regression equation can be calculated, the degrees of freedom in this statistic are $n - (m + 1)$.

Standard error of estimate in multiple regression:

$$s_e = \sqrt{\frac{\text{SSE}}{n - m - 1}} = \sqrt{\frac{1}{n - m - 1} \sum_{i=1}^{n} e_i^2} \qquad (14.3)$$

As before, we know that about 68% of all sample points should lie within one standard error of the estimated values of y_i; about 95% should lie within two standard errors. Since the amount of variation explained in a regression model (SSR) can never be reduced by the addition of another variable, the variation unexplained (SSE) can never be increased, so s_e will usually decrease. If a weakly related independent variable is added, however, the reduction in unexplained variation could be so small that it would not compensate for the loss of one degree of freedom due to its inclusion. In this case, s_e would increase when the extra variable is included. This is a signal that the new variable should be reconsidered and possibly omitted from the equation.

Just as in the simple regression, we can compare the size of the standard error of estimate to the mean of the dependent variable to get a typical percentage error. In Formula 13.16, this measure was called the coefficient of variation of the residuals, and computed as C.V. residuals = $(s_e/\bar{y})(100)$.

❑ **EXAMPLE 14.3** In our multiple regression example for investment, the value of $\epsilon_i^2 = 1,263.77$, $m = 2$ (two independent variables), and $n = 20$. See Figure 14.2b. Thus, the standard error of the estimate is:

$$s_e = \sqrt{\frac{1,263.77}{20 - 2 - 1}} = \sqrt{\frac{1,263.77}{17}} = \$8.622 \text{ billion}$$

Using $\bar{y} = 88.915$ from Figure 13.16(a), the typical percentage error is C.V. residuals = $(8.622/88.915)(100) = 9.70$ percent.

Comparing these values of s_e with that obtained by using the simple regression model (Figure 14.2a), where the standard error was \$10.277 billion with C.V. residuals $(10.277/88.915)100 = 11.56$ percent, we observe that the values have decreased. The inclusion of retained earnings in the model contributes to its explanatory value and decreases the typical error in predicting investment with this model. ■

Multiple Coefficient of Determination

For the multiple regression model, the relative measure of goodness of fit is designated by the symbol R^2, to differentiate it from the simple coefficient of determination r^2. This multiple coefficient of determination R^2 is the ratio of the variation explained by the multiple regression equation (SSR) to the total variation of y (SST). The only difference between R^2 and r^2 is that, in the multiple case, the explained variation results from m independent variables rather than from only a single independent variable. It is customary to write the multiple coefficient of determination as $R^2_{y \cdot x_1, x_2, \ldots, x_m}$, where the dependent variable is specified *before* the dot and the independent variables are listed *after* the dot.

Multiple coefficient of determination:

$$R^2_{y \cdot x_1, x_2, \ldots, x_m} = \frac{\text{Variation explained by all } x\text{'s (SSR)}}{\text{Total variation of } y \text{ (SST)}} \qquad (14.4)$$

❑ **EXAMPLE 14.4**   We can calculate R^2 for the multiple regression model on investment (Figure 14.2b). With x_1 and x_2 in the analysis, we found that SSE = 1,263.770 and that SSR = 10,221.916. The total variation in y is the sum of these unexplained and explained components of variation,

$$\text{SST} = \text{SSR} + \text{SSE}$$

$$\text{SST} = 10,221.916 + 1,263.770 = 11,485.686$$

Therefore,

$$R^2_{y \cdot x_1, x_2} = \frac{\text{SSR}}{\text{SST}} = \frac{10,221.916}{11,485.686} = 0.8900$$

This means that 89% of the variation in investment is explained by the linear relationship between investment, stock prices, and retained earnings. In comparing the value of $R^2 = 0.8900$ to the value $r^2 = 0.8345$ obtained from the simple model (using stock prices alone), we see that the addition of variable x_2 to the analysis adds 5.55% to the variation in investment that is explained by the regression. ■

Remember that a single variable in a model may serve as a proxy for the influence of other related variables not explicitly included. When one of these other related variables is included, the two variables share the explanatory role. In Example 14.4, the fact that x_1 explains 83.45% of the variability in y and x_2 explains only an additional 5.55% *does not imply that stock prices (x_1) are better predictors of investment than are retained earnings (x_2).* If retained earnings had been the variable considered first and then controlled during the addition of stock prices to the analysis, then retained earnings would appear to explain the greater share of total variation. By reversing the order, it can be shown that x_2 alone would explain 77.7% of the variation in y and the addition of x_1 would explain an extra 11.3%, giving the same joint total explained as before, 89%. Each explanatory variable has its separate role, and each shares some explanatory power of other nonincluded variables to which it is linearly related. When a third or fourth variable is included, similar results occur. Separate effects of each explanatory variable are partially distinguished and, collectively, all included variables may still share some role as a proxy for other relevant variables that are not yet included. Also, recall that the model-builder is responsible for the specification of the cause-and-effect nature of the relationships among the variables. The statistical regression results show only *association*, not *causal linkages*.

We can gain further insights into the meaning of R^2 from the correlations between all pairs of variables associated with the sample regression model, *including the variables $\hat{y}$ and e, the predicted values, and the residuals from the regression.* The correlation between the original values of y and the predicted values given by $\hat{y}$ tells us the strength of the predictive capability of the model. The method of least squares, remember, calculates the regression coefficients so that the predicted values calculated as $\hat{y}$ will have the maximum possible association of fit to the values of the dependent variable. The closer this correlation is to 1.0, the better the predictive value of our model. The square of this correlation is the *coefficient of determination*.

Similarly, the correlation of the residuals with the values of the dependent variable can be squared to obtain $1 - R^2$, the proportion of the variation which is not predictable by the model. The sum of the squares of these two correlations must be 1.0, since the variation is either explained (predictable) or not. The correlation of the residuals with $\hat{y}$ calculated on the basis of the model or with any of the independent variables in the model should be zero. The residuals are the leftover components of the dependent variable after all the explanatory power (in terms of the linear relationship) of the independent variables has been extracted.

□ **EXAMPLE 14.5** Table 14.3 gives the correlations for the variables in the multiple regression model for the investment relation in Example 14.4. We note that the correlation between the original values of y, Investment, and the calculated values, Yhat, is 0.94338. The model demonstrates a rather strong predictive capability. The square of this correlation is 0.89, the value of R^2.

TABLE 14.3 Correlations Underlying the Investment Regression

	Investment	Stock Price	Retearn	Yhat	Residual
Investment	1.00000				
Stock price	0.91349	1.00000			
Retearn	0.88145	0.81576	1.00000		
Yhat	0.94338	0.96832	0.93435	1.00000	
Residual	0.33171	0.00000	0.00000	0.00000	1.00000

The correlation of the values of Investment with the Residuals is 0.33171. Its square is 0.11, which is the proportion of the variation in investment that is not explained by the model. Of course, 0.89, the proportion explained and, 0.11, the proportion unexplained, add to 1.0.

We can also note the correlations are zero between the Residuals and the independent variables or $\hat{y}$ calculated as a function of those variables. Other interesting items are the blanks in Table 14.3. There is no causation implied in correlation; the association between any two variables is the same regardless of which is considered first or second. Thus, the table would be symmetric if the blank spaces were filled in. The diagonal values are always 1.0 since any variable is perfectly correlated with its own values. Finally, the correlation between Investment and Stock Price of 0.91349 is the correlation coefficient for the simple model (Figure

14.2a). Its square is the R-square in the simple model which gives the proportion of variation in Investment explained by Stock Price only. ∎

Since the explained variation (SSR) can never be decreased by the addition of another independent variable, the coefficient of determination R^2 will always either increase or remain the same as more variables are included in the model. Even if the new variable is totally unrelated to y, the new R^2 would be no lower than the old R^2. The estimation process would compute a coefficient of zero for the new variable so the fit could be no worse than before.

If the new variable has just a small effect, SSR would be a little larger, and the new R^2 would be higher than before. Theoretically, it is possible to continue adding nearly irrelevant variables to the model and boosting R^2 higher and higher with each addition. If you continue until you have $n - 1$ explanatory variables in the model, least squares estimation will find a perfect, but meaningless fit, with $R^2 = 1.0$. Just as we can draw a line (one-dimensional) through two points, or a plane (two-dimensional) through three points, we can theoretically determine an $(n - 1)$ dimensional hyperplane that perfectly goes through all n sample points for y.

This effect on R^2 differs from that on the absolute measure of goodness of fit, s_e. Recall that when a new variable is largely irrelevant, the reduction in unexplained variation does not always make s_e smaller. The difference is due to the fact that s_e takes into account the degrees of freedom in the model, but R^2 does not. Thus, if we wish to judge whether or not an extra variable in a model improves the fit, we examine the standard error of estimate, s_e, to see if it has decreased, not whether R^2 has increased.

Adjusted Coefficient of Determination

There is a method of adjusting the R^2 measure for degrees of freedom so that it does not overstate the fit as extra variables are added to a model. The new statistic is called the **adjusted coefficient of determination** which we will denote by R^2_{adj}. Some analysts find it convenient to use this measure of fit rather than s_e and R^2. It does allow a fair comparison between models of the same dependent variable that have a different number of explanatory variables or a different number of observations. However, R^2_{adj} is not a strict proportional measure for the interpretation of variation explained as is R^2, and it provides no new information on the goodness of fit that is not already known from s_e which adjusts for the degrees of freedom in the usual way of all measures of standard errors.

If you wish to derive the adjusted R^2 measure, rewrite the numerator for R^2 as

$$R^2 = SSR/SST = 1 - SSE/SST$$

and adjust for the degrees of freedom by dividing SSE by $n - m - 1$ and dividing SST by $n - 1$. A convenient form for the answer is

Adjusted coefficient of determination:

$$R^2_{adj} = 1 - (1 - R^2)\left[\frac{n - 1}{n - m - 1}\right] \tag{14.5}$$

Note that R^2_{adj} will always be smaller than the unadjusted R^2.

☐ **EXAMPLE 14.6** For a numerical comparison, suppose two regression equations (A and B), are determined for the same dependent variable y, each based on 20 observations. Let equation A have two explanatory variables and a value of $R^2 = 0.80$; let equation B have six explanatory variables and a value of $R^2 = 0.82$. The adjusted values of R^2_{adj} would be as follows:

Equation A:
$$1 - (1 - 0.80)\frac{19}{17} = 0.776$$

Equation B:
$$1 - (1 - 0.82)\frac{19}{13} = 0.737$$

Considering the number of variables included, equation A has the relatively better fit. ∎

☐ **STUDY QUESTION 14.2** **Multiple Regression Fit for Housing Price**

Using the computer output in Figure 14.3, find the adjusted coefficient of determination for the simple and multiple regression equations. Discuss the results in comparison with the changes in s_e.

● **ANSWER** The simple model has $n = 25$, $m = 1$, and $R^2 = 0.6392$. The adjusted measure is:

$$R^2_{adj} = 1 - (1 - 0.6392)\frac{24}{23} = 0.624$$

For the extended model including the variable Rent, $n = 25$, $m = 2$, and $R^2 = 0.8378$. The adjusted measure is:

$$R^2_{adj} = 1 - (1 - 0.8378)\frac{24}{22} = 0.823$$

For the multiple regression model including Vacant as well as Income and Rent, $n = 25$, $m = 3$, and $R^2 = 0.8399$. The adjusted measure is:

$$R^2_{adj} = 1 - (1 - 0.8399)\frac{24}{21} = 0.817$$

Table 14.4 summarizes the results. As expected, R^2 increases with the addition of each variable. When Rent is included, R^2 increases from 0.6392 to 0.8378, meaning that the percent of explained variation is increased from 63.9 to 83.8. Since the most that could ever be explained is 100 percent, this is a gain of $(19.9/36.1)(100) = 55$ percent towards perfection. The extra proportion of variation explained by the inclusion of Vacant is very small, from 0.8378 to 0.8399. ∎

TABLE 14.4 Comparison of Goodness of Fit Measures for Housing Price Models

Variables Included in Model	s_e	R^2	R^2_{adj}
Income	9.25	0.6392	0.623
Income, Rent	6.34	0.8378	0.823
Income, Rent, Vacant	6.45	0.8399	0.817

When an extra variable is added, the standard error, s_e, changes proportionately the same as R^2_{adj}, but in the opposite direction. Each corrects for the loss of one more degree of freedom while measuring the extra goodness of fit. With the inclusion of Rent, for example, the standard error of estimate *decreases* from 9.25 to 6.34 (about a 32 percent drop) and R^2_{adj} increases from 0.623 to 0.823 (about a 32 percent rise).

In the multiple regression model including the variable Vacant, the extra amount of variation explained is more than offset by the loss of one more degree of freedom. The standard error rises instead of getting smaller and R^2_{adj} turns back down instead of increasing. In terms of improving fit, Vacant is not a satisfactory variable for inclusion in the model.

One may still wish to include Vacant for theoretical specification purposes. The fit is not much affected by its inclusion and its coefficient does have the correct theoretical negative sign. Thus, if the purpose of the model is to obtain a numerical value for the impact of income on housing price, and controlling for rent and vacancy levels is important, then the variable Vacant may be kept in the model. Goodness of fit and forecasting are not always the primary purpose of constructing and estimating models.

The Coefficient of Multiple Correlation

Multiple linear correlation bears the same relationship to simple linear correlation as multiple linear regression does to simple linear regression: It represents an extension of the techniques for handling the relationship among *more than two* variables. In multiple linear correlation, the objective is to estimate the *strength* of the relationship between a variable y and a group of m other variables $x_1, x_2, \ldots, x_m$. The measure usually used for this purpose is called the **multiple correlation coefficient** and is denoted by the symbol $R_{y \cdot x_1, x_2 \ldots, x_m}$. A multiple linear correlation coefficient represents the simple linear correlation coefficient between the sample values of y and $\hat{y}$, the estimates of these values provided by the multiple regression equation. (Refer to Example 14.5.) However, the value of R is never negative, but rather $0 \leq R \leq 1$. This is so because the sign of R does *not* indicate the slope of the regression equation, since it is not possible to indicate *all* the signs of the regression coefficients that relate y to the variables $x_1, x_2, \ldots, x_m$ by a *single* plus or minus sign. Also, the square of the multiple correlation coefficient (R^2) indicates the proportion of the total variation in y accounted for by the regression equation and is identically the multiple coefficient of determination.

As shown in Figure 14.2(b) for our investment example, the value of R is the square root of R^2:

$$R_{y \cdot x_1, x_2} = \sqrt{R^2_{y \cdot x_1, x_2}} = \sqrt{0.89} = 0.943$$

Partial Correlation Coefficient

The value of R measures the degree of association between the variable y and *all* of the variables $x_1, x_2, \ldots,$ and x_m. One may, however, be more interested in the degree of association between y and *one* of the variables $x_1, x_2, \ldots,$ or x_m *with the linear effect of all the other explanatory variables removed*. A measure of the strength of the relationship between the dependent variable and one explanatory variable, with the linear effect of the rest of the variables eliminated, is called a *partial correlation coefficient*. A partial correlation coefficient is analogous to a partial regression coefficient, in that all other factors are held constant. Simple correlation, on the other hand, ignores the effect of all other variables, even though these variables might be quite strongly related to the dependent variable y, or to the explanatory variable x, or to one another.

Partial correlation measures the strength of the relationship between y and a single independent variable by considering the *relative* amount that the unexplained variation is reduced by including this variable in the regression equation. We might want to calculate the partial correlation between y and x_2, when the linear effect of x_1 is held constant (eliminated). This partial correlation is denoted by the symbol $r_{y,x_2 \cdot x_1}$, where the variables *before the dot* indicate those for the correlation being measured (y and x_2), and the variable(s) *after the dot* indicate those with influence held constant (x_1). For instance, in the investment example, $r_{y,x_2 \cdot x_1}$ would be a measure of the strength of the relationship between investment (y) and retained earnings (x_2), with the influence of stock prices (x_1) held constant.

As before, the square of a correlation coefficient is usually easier to interpret than the coefficient itself. In the case of a partial correlation coefficient, this square is called a **partial coefficient of determination**. The partial coefficient of determination measures the *additional* proportion of the unexplained variation in y that is explained by the variable that is *not* being held constant.

Partial coefficient of determination:

$$r^2_{y,x_2 \cdot x_1} = \frac{\left(\begin{array}{c} \text{Extra variation in } y \text{ explained} \\ \text{by the additional influence of } x_2 \end{array} \right)}{\text{Variation in } y \text{ unexplained by } x_1 \text{ alone}} \qquad (14.6)$$

Total variation in y = 11,485.7

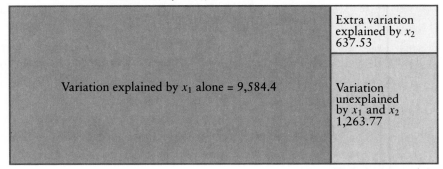

FIGURE 14.4   The elements of variation used in a partial coefficient of determination, $r^2_{y,x_2 \cdot x_1}$, for the investment example

☐ **EXAMPLE 14.7**   Figure 14.4 illustrates the determination of the value of $r^2_{y,x_2 \cdot x_1}$ for our investment equation. The total variation in y (investment) to be explained is:

$$\sum_{i=1}^{20} (y_i - \bar{y})^2 = 11,485.7$$

The total amount of variation is represented by the area of the entire rectangle. Based on the simple relationship between y and x_1 (stock prices), the amount of unexplained variation when x_1 is the only independent variable is SSE $= 1901.3$. The denominator of Formula (14.6) is thus 1901.3.

Recall from Figure 14.2(b) that the amount of unexplained variation with both x_1 and x_2 in the analysis is 1,263.77. Thus, the *extra* amount of variation explained by adding x_2 to the analysis is $(1,901.3 - 1,263.77) = 637.53$, which is the value needed for the numerator of Formula (14.6). The proportion of previously unexplained variation in investment that is explained by the addition of retained earnings x_2 is:

$$r^2_{y,x_2 \cdot x_1} = \frac{637.53}{1,901.3} = 0.335$$

The square root of this value gives the partial correlation coefficient between investment and retained earnings when stock prices are held constant:

$$r_{y,x_2 \cdot x_1} = \sqrt{0.335} = 0.579 \qquad\blacksquare$$

Such partial coefficients of correlation or partial coefficients of determination can be extended to more than two explanatory variables. If a third variable is included, or a group of new variables, the partial coefficient of determination measures the *additional* proportion of the *previously unexplained* variation in y that is explained by the newly included variables. For each such case, all that is needed to find the value of the partial coefficient of determination is the amount of variation left unexplained at each step. If the variables already included in the model are designated as group A and the newly added variables are designated as group B, then the multiple partial coefficient of determination is given as follows:

Multiple partial coefficient of determination:

$$r^2_{y,A \cdot B} = \frac{\left[\begin{array}{c}(\text{Variation unexplained by group A}) \\ -(\text{Variation unexplained by groups A and B})\end{array}\right]}{\text{Variation unexplained by the variables in group A}} \qquad (14.7)$$

The numerator in Formula 14.7 is the extra variation explained by the variable or variables in group B.

☐ STUDY QUESTION 14.3   Partial Fit Measures in the Housing Price Model

Using Figure 14.3 (a) and (b), find $r^2_{y,x_2 \cdot x_1}$ and $r_{y,x_2 \cdot x_1}$ and interpret their meaning. Symbolically, $x_1 =$ Income and $x_2 =$ Rent.

● **ANSWER**

$$r^2_{y,x_2 \cdot x_1} = \frac{(\text{SSE with only } x_1) - (\text{SSE with } x_1 \text{ and } x_2)}{\text{SSE with only } x_1}$$

$$= \frac{1,969.811 - 885.477}{1,969.811} = 0.55$$

Rent explains 55% of the residual variation in housing price that was not explained by income. Refer to the answer to Study Question 14.2 and note that this result is identical to the improvement in fit measured by R^2 relative to the perfect (maximum possible) improvement. Finding the square root gives r as follows:

$$r_{y,x_2 \cdot x_1} = \sqrt{0.55} = 0.74$$

The linear association measure is 0.74 between Rent and Housing Price with the linear effect of Income held constant. ∎

PROBLEMS

14.1 Discuss the usefulness and value of the extension of regression analysis to include more than one explanatory factor.

14.2 Explain the difference in meaning between the simple regression coefficient in a simple regression analysis and a partial regression coefficient in a multiple regression analysis.

14.3 Figure 14.5 is a computer printout using the variable measures in **Data Set 4** for doctor's income, fees,

hours, and expenses. Use these results to compare the multiple regression to the simple regression of Problem 13.80.

a) Consider the causes and meaning of the changes in coefficients and in the measures of goodness of fit.

b) Use Formula 14.5 and compare the values of R^2_{adj}.

c) Find and interpret the partial coefficient of determination, $r^2_{y,x_2 \cdot x_3 \cdot x_1}$, where $x_1 = $ hrs, $x_2 = $ fee, and $x_3 = $ expenses.

```
HEADER DATA FOR:    Prob. 14.3        LABEL:   income of doctors
NUMBER OF CASES:    40       NUMBER OF VARIABLES:    4

INDEX       NAME            MEAN        STD.DEV.
Y           INCOME          155.030     35.484
X1          FEE              51.797      13.152
X2          HRS              50.430       3.131
X3          EXPS            118.880      29.849

DEPENDENT VARIABLE: INCOME

VARIABLE    COEFFICIENT     STD. ERROR    T(DF = 36)    PROB.

FEE            1.4257         0.2145        6.648        .0001
HRS            5.2191         0.9822        5.314        .0001
EXPS           0.2676         0.1097        2.439        .0198
CONSTANT    -213.8266

STD. ERROR OF EST. = 16.3461
        R SQUARED = 0.8041
      MULTIPLE R = 0.8967

                    ANALYSIS OF VARIANCE TABLE

SOURCE        SUM OF SQUARES   D.F.       MEAN SQUARE    F RATIO    PROB.
REGRESSION    39485.2230        3         13161.7410     49.259     .0001
RESIDUAL       9619.0610       36           267.1961
TOTAL         49104.2840       39
```

FIGURE 14.5   Printout for multiple regression on doctor's income

14.4 Using the estimated investment equation reported in Figure 14.2(b), determine the forecasted level of investment for the next quarter if the values in the current quarter are 950 for the stock price index and 25

for retained earnings. Discuss potential reasons why your forecast may be wrong.

14.5 In Problem 13.12, results of a simple regression

model were presented in which the beverage charge per person at a restaurant was predicted on the basis of the number of persons in a dining party. Suppose we add another explanatory variable which is the time in minutes between the first beverage service and the service of the dinner. The new regression equation is:

$$\text{Bevcharge} = 4 + 0.6(\text{Party}) + 0.3(\text{Minutes})$$

a) What would be the predicted beverage charge per person for a party of six that waits 35 minutes between the first drink service and the dinner service?

b) Find the expected change in the beverage charge per person if one extra person joins the party and the service is delayed an extra 20 minutes.

14.6 A health economist believes that two factors considered by doctors when they set their fees for office visits are the costs of operating the practice and the number of hours worked per week.

a) Using Figure 14.6, based on Data Set 4, compare the multiple and simple regression results interpreting the changes in coefficients and in the measures of goodness of fit.

b) Use Formula 14.5 to verify the printed value of R^2_{adj} in the multiple regression.

a)
Dependent Variable: FEE   AVERAGE FEE CHARGED BY DOCTOR

Analysis of Variance

Source	DF	Sum of Squares	Mean Square	F Value	Prob>F
Model	1	126.40070	126.40070	0.726	0.3996
Error	38	6619.66870	174.20181		
C Total	39	6746.06940			

Root MSE	13.19855	R-square	0.0187	
Dep Mean	51.79725	Adj R-Sq	−0.0071	
C.V.	25.48119			

Parameter Estimates

Variable	DF	Parameter Estimate	Standard Error	T for H0 Parameter=0	Prob> |T|
INTERCEP	1	22.802110	34.10291	0.669	0.5078
HRS	1	0.574958	0.67498	0.852	0.3996

b) Model: Model2
Dependent Variable: FEE   AVERAGE FEE CHARGED BY DOCTOR

Analysis of Variance

Source	DF	Sum of Squares	Mean Square	F Value	Prob>F
Model	2	936.06402	468.03201	2.981	0.0631
Error	37	5810.00538	157.02717		
C Total	39	6746.06940			

Root MSE	12.53105	R-square	0.1388	
Dep Mean	51.79725	Adj R-Sq	0.0922	
C.V.	24.19250			

Parameter Estimates

Variable	DF	Parameter Estimate	Standard Error	T for H0 Parameter=0	Prob> |T|
INTERCEP	1	46.403885	34.00560	1.365	0.1806
HRS	1	−0.314835	0.75115	−0.419	0.6775
EXPS	1	0.178924	0.07880	2.271	0.0291

FIGURE 14.6 Printout for models on doctor's fees

♦ **14.7** Tables 14.5 and 14.6 provide partial results from a simple and multiple regression analysis where the dependent variable is Pcrime, the burglary rate per 100,000 population in the U.S., and the independent variables are Urban, the percent of the state population living in urban areas, and Divorce, the divorce rate per 1,000 persons. The simple regression model of Pcrime on Urban was previously studied in Problem 13.31.

TABLE 14.5 Simple Regression on Percent of Population that is Urban

Variable	Estimated Coefficient	Estimated Standard Deviation
Urban	12.062	2.6109
Intercept	830.7821	

TABLE 14.6 Multiple Regression Including Divorce Rate per 100,000 Population

Variable	Estimated Coefficient	Estimated Standard Deviation
Urban	14.1189	3.1046
Divorce	83.8271	15.7621
Intercept	157.3256	

Compare the simple and multiple regression results by interpreting the coefficient values.

14.8 In a multiple regression analysis of changes in annual average mortgage rates (y) on three explanatory variables (x_1, x_2, and x_3), the following results are found. The variation explained jointly by x_1 and x_2 is 350.

$$\sum_{i=1}^{n}(y_i - \bar{y})^2 = 600 \qquad \sum_{i=1}^{n}e_i^2 = 150$$

a) Find the multiple coefficient of determination, and explain its meaning.

b) Find $r^2_{y.x_3 \cdot x_1 x_2}$, and interpret its meaning.

14.9 Suppose the variation in y is 500 units and the sample equation, $\hat{y} = a + b_1 x_1 + b_2 x_2$, leaves 240 units unexplained (based on 15 observations). Extending the model to include variable x_3 explains 80 more units of variation in y. Find $R^2_{y.x_1 x_2 x_3}$ and $r^2_{y.x_3 \cdot x_1 x_2}$.

14.10 Suppose that in a multiple regression of y (profits) on three types of expenses, x_1, x_2, and x_3, we obtain SST = 1,000 and SSE = 200; the variation explained by only x_2 and x_3 is 400. Find $R^2_{y.x_1 x_2 x_3}$ and $r^2_{y.x_3 \cdot x_1 x_2}$.

14.11 Refer to Figure 14.3. Let x_1 = Income, x_2 = Rent and x_3 = Vacant. Find and interpret the meaning of $r^2_{y.x_3 \cdot x_1 x_2}$.

14.12 Table 14.7 gives a correlation matrix for variables associated with the multiple regression on housing price discussed in the text and reported in Figure 14.3(c).

a) Relate the correlations between Yhat and Price and between Residual and Price to the R-square in the regression.

b) Explain if it is unusual that the correlations of Residual with the other variables are zero.

TABLE 14.7 Correlations Underlying the Housing Price Regression

	Price	Income	Rent	Vacant	Yhat	Residual
Price	1.0000					
Income	0.7995	1.0000				
Rent	0.8809	0.7085	1.0000			
Vacant	−0.8239	−0.6754	−0.8963	1.0000		
Yhat	0.9165	0.8724	0.9612	0.8990	1.0000	
Residual	0.4001	0.0000	0.0000	0.0000	0.0000	0.0000

14.13 Discuss whether each of the following statements is true or false.

a) If $s_e = s_y$, then $b = 0$.

b) If $R_{y.x_1 x_2 x_3} = 1$, then $r_{y.x_1 \cdot x_2 x_3} = 0$.

c) If $R_{y.x_1 x_2 x_3} = R_{y.x_1 x_2}$, then $r_{y.x_3 \cdot x_1 x_2} = 0$.

d) $R^2_{y.x_1 x_2 x_3} \geq R^2_{y.x_1 x_2}$.

e) $r^2_{y.x_1} + r^2_{y.x_2} = R^2_{y.x_1 x_2}$.

14.14 In a multiple regression of y (sales) on three characteristics of retail outlets, x, z, and w, the total variation is 200, the residual variation is 20, and the variation explained by only variables z and w is 120 units.

a) Find $R^2_{y.x,z,w}$.

b) Find $r^2_{y.x \cdot zw}$.

14.15 Given a multiple regression equation, $\hat{y} = a + b_1 x_1 + b_2 x_2 + b_3 x_3$ based on 24 observations on each variable, suppose that the total variation, SST, equals 300, the unexplained variation is 60, and the amount of variation explained by variables x_1 and x_2 together is 160.

a) Calculate the value of the multiple coefficient of determination and interpret its meaning.

b) Find R^2_{adj} and explain its difference from R^2 in part (a).

c) Prepare a diagram similar to Figure 14.4 to explain the meaning and value of $r^2_{y.x_3 \cdot x_1 x_2}$.

| section 14.4 | # Analysis-of-Variance Tests[†] |

We must emphasize that the least-squares procedure does not require *any* assumptions about the population, since this procedure is merely a curve-fitting technique. However, just as in simple regression, in order to be able to make inferences based on the sample regression equation, it is necessary to make certain assumptions about the error term ε in the population regression model. Throughout this and the following sections, we assume that the *ideal* assumptions itemized in Section 13.4 apply, extended in the appropriate way for the model with multiple explanatory factors. Further formal discussion of these assumptions is delayed until the next chapter.

A variety of test procedures involving the multiple correlation coefficient and the parameters of the multiple regression model have been developed. Not all will be discussed here, since the complexity of many of them is better handled in a more advanced text. The primary questions of interest in a multiple linear relationship usually concern the goodness of fit and the significance of the partial regression parameters.

Analysis-of-Variance Test

The test of the significance of the entire multiple linear regression is similar to the test of the significance of the simple linear relationship. Hence, the same type of **ANOVA (analysis-of-variance) table** and an F-distributed statistic can be utilized. See Table 13.25 and Formula 13.31. In simple linear regression, we tested the null hypothesis $H_0: \beta = 0$ (the hypothesis of no linear association between y and x). In multiple linear regression, we test the null hypothesis of no linear association between y and *all* the explanatory variables x_j, $j = 1, 2, \ldots, m$. We use the following hypotheses:

H_0: the x_j are *not* linearly related to y;

H_a: the x_j as a group *are* linearly related to y.

If the linear regression equation of Formula 14.2 fits the data well, the amount of variation in y that is explained (SSR) should be large in relation to the amount of variation that is left unexplained (SSE). If each of these amounts of variation is divided by its degrees of freedom, then a mean square is obtained. The ratio of the mean square explained (MSR) to the mean square unexplained (MSE) has an F-distribution. In multiple regression, $(m + 1)$ parameters are estimated on the basis of n observations, so the unexplained variation will have $n - (m + 1)$ degrees of freedom. The degrees of freedom for the explained variation equal the number of independent variables (m) included in the model to do the explaining. Total variation always has $(n - 1)$ degrees of freedom. Table 14.8 is the analysis-of-variance table for multiple linear regression, analogous to Table 13.25 for simple regression analysis.

The appropriate statistic to test the significance of the entire multiple regression equation follows an F-distribution with m and $(n - m - 1)$ degrees of freedom:

[†] It is assumed that the reader of this section has studied Section 13.9 concerning the F-distributed statistic for ANOVA in regression analysis.

TABLE 14.8   Analysis-of-Variance (ANOVA) Table for Multiple Regression

Source of the Variation	Sum of Squares	Degrees of Freedom	Mean Square
Multiple regression	SSR	m	$SSR/m = MSR$
Residual	SSE	$n - m - 1$	$SSE/(n - m - 1) = MSE$
Total	SST	$n - 1$	

F-statistic for fit of the multiple regression model:

$$F_{(m, n-m-1)} = \frac{SSR/m}{SSE/(n - m - 1)} = \frac{MSR}{MSE} \tag{14.8}$$

□ **EXAMPLE 14.8**   We apply this F-test to our investment equation for which the computer output is repeated in Figure 14.7 with relevant items in colour. Since there are $m = 2$ independent variables, we are testing H_0: x_1 and x_2 are *not* linearly related to y versus H_a: they are. From Figure 14.7, we find the sums of squares SSR = 10,221.92 and SSE = 1,263.77. By addition, SST = 11,485.69.

```
DEPENDENT VARIABLE..      INV          PRIVATE INVESTMENT, $BIL

VARIABLE(S) ENTERED IN MODEL      STKPR       STOCK PRICE, PREVIOUS QUARTER
                                  RETEARN     RETAINED EARNINGS, PREVIOUS QUARTER

                             ANALYSIS OF VARIANCE
MULTIPLE R          0.9434              DF    SUM OF SQUARES   MEAN SQUARE
R SQUARE            0.8900  REGRESSION   2       10221.9157       5110.96
ADJUSTED R SQUARE   0.8770    RESIDUAL  17        1263.7698         74.34
STANDARD ERROR      8.6220        F = 68.75      SIGNIF F = 0.0001

- - - - - - - - - - - - - - VARIABLES IN THE EQUATION - - - - - - - - - - - - - - - - - - -

VARIABLE        B         SE B        T              SIG T

STKPR       0.07856    0.01880     4.1786           0.0006
RETEARN     1.79840    0.61413     2.9283           0.0094
(CONSTANT)  1.67713    7.77099     0.2158           0.8317
```
FIGURE 14.7 Computer printout for the investment multiple regression model

In this example, $n = 20$ and $m = 2$. From the analysis-of-variance table in Figure 14.7, we find the calculated value of F to be:

$$F_c = \frac{MSR}{MSE} = \frac{5,110.96}{74.34} = 68.75$$

This value far exceeds the critical value (Table VIII(b)) for $\alpha = 0.01$ with 2 and 17 d.f.:

$$F_{(2, 17)} = 6.11$$

The printout provides a p-value for this test of 0.0001, labelled SIGNIF F. Given this type of software printout, all the analyst has to do is observe the calculated F-value and the associated p-value for the test, and write a conclusion. We conclude that the null hypothesis of no linear relationship can be rejected. Thus, *stock prices* and *retained earnings* jointly appear to have a significant linear association with investment.   ∎

□ **STUDY QUESTION 14.4**   *F*-test for the Housing Price Model

Use the housing price model and the computer printout in Figure 14.8, which repeats Figure 14.3(c), to do an *F*-test on the linear relation between housing price and the three variables, income, rent, and vacancy rate.

• **ANSWER**   From the analysis of variance table in Figure 14.8, we learn the values of SSR and SSE with 3 and 21 degrees of freedom respectively.

```
DEPENDENT VARIABLE..        PRICE              HOUSING  PRICE

VARIABLE(S) ENTERED IN MODEL        INCOME      HOUSEHOLD MEDIAN INCOME
                                    RENT        AVERAGE MONTHLY RENTAL RATE
                                    VACANT      PERCENTAGE UNITS VACANT
                     ANALYSIS OF VARIANCE
MULTIPLE R          0.9165              DF    SUM OF SQUARES    MEAN SQUARE
R SQUARE            0.8399   REGRESSION   3       4586.2701      1528.7567
ADJUSTED R SQUARE   0.8171   RESIDUAL    21        874.0395        41.6209
STANDARD ERROR      6.4514   F = 36.730           SIGNIF F = 0.0001

------------- VARIABLES IN THE EQUATION -----------------

VARIABLE              B         SE B        T          SIG T

INCOME           2.01796     0.73231     2.756        0.0118
RENT             0.18124     0.06909     2.623        0.0159
VACANT          -0.31426     0.05995    -0.524        0.6056
(CONSTANT)     -11.10911    32.73019    -0.339        0.7377
```

FIGURE 14.8 Computer output for the housing price multiple regression model

The mean square explained due to the regression is:

$$MSR = \frac{SSR}{m} = \frac{4,586.27}{3} = 1528.76$$

Similarly, the mean square unexplained is MSE = SSE/21 = 41.62.
Using Formula 14.8, the value of the *F*-statistic for this sample equation is:

$$F_c = \frac{MSR}{MSE} = \frac{1,528.76}{41.62} = 36.73$$

This is larger than the critical value, $F_{0.01} = 4.87$, in Table VIII(b) for 3 and 21 degrees of freedom. The printout in Figure 14.8 gives this same value for the F-ratio. It also gives a *p*-value = 0.0001. That is,

$$P(F_{3,21} \geq 36.73) \leq 0.0001$$

which is surely below any usual level of risk α. The conclusion is to reject the null hypothesis of no linear relation and to argue that the sample model indicates that the three variables together do have a significant linear association with y. ■

Test on a Subgroup of Variables

Sometimes a hypothesis needs to be tested regarding the linear relation between y and a *subset* of all the explanatory variables. This subset of variables may be those that are subject to policy manipulation, or they may be all the same type of economic or business measures, such as a set of expenditure class measures, a set of interest rate measures, or a set of demographic measures. We denote the number of these variables of special interest by the letter J. We wish to develop a test to determine whether these J variables together are significantly related to *y* *given the other variables included in the model.* That is, for the equation $y = \alpha + \beta_1 x_1 + \cdots + \beta_m x_m$, suppose there are $(m - J)$ variables that we definitely wish to include in the equation and J variables that are to be tested for their joint contribution. An analysis-of-variance type test can be used to determine if the amount of *extra* variation in *y* that the J variables explain is significant.[2] The hypotheses to be tested are:

H_0: the extra contribution jointly of the J explanatory variables is *not* significant.

H_a: the group of J variables do contribute significantly to the explanation of the remaining variation in *y* after accounting for that explained by other variables in the model.

An appropriate test statistic is based on the comparison between the amount of unexplained variation (SSE) when *all* the variables are included in the model and the amount of unexplained variation when the group of J variables is *not included*.

We label the latter sum of squares as SSE_S for the unexplained variation in the *shorter* or *smaller* form of the model (including only $m - J$ variables). The F-ratio is calculated as follows:

For a test on the significance of a subgroup of J variables in a multiple regression:

$$F_{(J, n-m-1)} = \frac{(\text{SSE}_S - \text{SSE})/J}{\text{SSE}/(n - m - 1)} \tag{14.9}$$

◻ **EXAMPLE 14.9** For the housing price model with results in Figure 14.8, use Formula 14.9 to test the joint contribution of the two variables, Rent and Vacant, after accounting for the variation explained by the single variable Income. There are $m = 3$ variables in the complete model, $J = 2$ variables to be jointly considered as a subgroup, and $m - J = 1$ variable in the *shorter* model. We have already determined, from Figure 14.3(a), that the unexplained variation in the shorter model with Income as the only explanatory variable is 1,969.81 million, now denoted as SSE_S. The unexplained variation in the complete model with all three explanatory variables (including the $J = 2$ added variables) is SSE = 874.04. The difference between these two is a measure of the extra variation explained by the addition of the variables Rent and Vacant into the model. The hypotheses are:

H_0: the extra contribution of the variables Rent and Vacant is *not* jointly significant in the model including the independent variable Income.

H_a: Rent and Vacant do contribute significantly to the *extra* explanation of the variation in *y* after accounting for the variation explained by Income.

For our sample, the number of observations is $n = 25$ and $m = 3$, so we shall use the F-distributed random variable with $J = 2$ and $n - m - 1 = 21$ degrees of freedom. The calculated value using Formula 14.9 is:

$$F_c = \frac{(1,969.81 - 874.04)/2}{874.04/21} = \frac{547.89}{41.62} = 13.2$$

---

[2] This concept is identical to a test of significance on a partial coefficient of correlation when the variables in group B are the J variables of special interest and group A includes the other $(m - J)$ variables. A similar test would involve the null hypothesis $H_0 : \rho_{y, B \cdot A} = 0$.

This is larger than the critical value, $F_{0.01} = 5.78$, in Table VIII(b) for 2 and 21 degrees of freedom. Using a computer, the exact p-value is $P(F_{2.21} \geq 13.2) = 0.0002$. We conclude that the joint contribution of rent and vacancy rate is significant in this multiple regression model. ∎

From prior discussion, the reader may recall that this joint contribution is due almost entirely to the variable Rent since the variable Vacant contributes very little. However, F-tests do not reveal which of the jointly contributing variables is most or least useful in this regard. Information on the individual usefulness of a particular explanatory variable is most quickly obtained by a t-test on its coefficient, the subject of the next section.

Tests on Parameters

In the previous section, we dealt with tests related to the overall fit and the joint contribution of variables in a multiple regression model. In addition to knowing whether or not a significant amount of extra variation in y has been explained by any specific variable, other important questions of statistical inference on the parameters in the model must be asked. Is the impact on y of a particular variable direct (positive slope) or inverse (negative slope), or could it be zero? What is the confidence interval on the unknown variance of the disturbances in the model? What are the confidence limits on the coefficient associated with the most critical explanatory variable (most critical meaning the one of special interest for policy purposes, for decision-making, for forecasting, or for theoretical cause-and-effect relationships)?

Examining the Size of the Variance of the Disturbances[†]

Since the true distributions of the estimators of the coefficients in the model depend on the variance of the disturbances, σ_ϵ^2 (Table 13.24), we first present a method for obtaining a confidence interval on the size of this parameter. The resulting confidence limits also serve as a guide to the accuracy of the model, since they enable us to put bounds on the typical size of the error σ_ϵ.

The best estimate of the variance of the disturbance term (σ_ϵ^2) is given by the estimated variance of the residuals, s_e^2. This is, of course, the square of the standard error of estimate and is the same as the mean square error (MSE) in the analysis of variance table for a multiple regression. Conversely, the square root of the mean square error is s_e, which is denoted in some books and computer printouts by the name, *root mean square error* (RMSE). By whatever name, the best estimate of variance of the population model disturbances is the observed variance of the sample model residuals.

If the model fits well, the variance of the errors about the regression equation should be relatively small in comparison to the variance in the dependent variable y. That is, the clear channel representation of the relation among y and the x's is not drowned out by the static and random noise due to the disturbance term (the errors due to mismeasurement or misspecification or behavioral changes).

[†] This discussion assumes that Section 7.9 on the chi-square random variable has been studied.

A test statistic involving these terms has a known distribution given the *ideal* assumptions underlying our regression model. The formula is similar to that presented in Chapters 7 and 9 for the variance of a population, except that the degrees of freedom are $n - m - 1$, not $n - 1$, where m is the number of explanatory variables in the model.

Chi-square statistic for inference on the variance of the disturbance:

$$\chi^2_{(n-m-1)} = \frac{(n - m - 1)s_e^2}{\sigma_\epsilon^2} \tag{14.10}$$

This statistic is most frequently used to set confidence limits on the size of this variance of errors for the particular regression model. As such, the limits give a guide to the goodness of fit of the model and to the likely range of values for the unknown error ϵ_i. To find the confidence limits, two values must be obtained from the chi-square table (Table VII in the Appendix) for $n - m - 1$ degrees of freedom and the $100(1 - \alpha)\%$ level of confidence. The χ^2_{upper} value should *exclude* $100(\alpha/2)\%$ of the *upper tail* of the relevant distribution; the χ^2_{lower} value should *exclude* the same percent of the *lower tail*, leaving $100(1 - \alpha)\%$ in the middle. The confidence limits are shown in the following formula:

Confidence limits for σ_e^2:

$$\frac{(n - m - 1)s_e^2}{\chi^2_{upper}} < \sigma_\epsilon^2 < \frac{(n - m - 1)s_e^2}{\chi^2_{lower}} \tag{14.11}$$

Once the end points of this confidence interval on σ_ϵ^2 are determined, square roots can be taken to obtain an interval for the typical size of the population disturbance, σ_ϵ. These lower and upper limits can be used for σ_ϵ in a coefficient of variation similar to Formula 13.16 to gauge the potential percentage error in predictions using this model.

$$\text{C.V. Residuals} = \left(\frac{\sigma_\epsilon}{\bar{y}}\right) 100 \tag{14.12}$$

As suggested earlier, actual forecast intervals are more complex and not presented in this text. This quick alternative is justifiable only at the mean point of the data for providing a measure for comparison across different models of the same dependent variable.

□ EXAMPLE 14.10   We can use Formula 14.11 to find the 95% confidence interval on the variance of the disturbances in the regression model for investment. Figure 14.7 provides the results of the estimation of investment in terms of stock price index and retained earnings. The values of n and m are $n = 20$ and $m = 2$, so $n - m - 1 = 17$. We find $s_e^2 = \text{MSE} = (1,263.77/17) = 74.34$, reported on the printout as MEAN SQUARE for RESIDUAL. For $(\alpha/2) = 0.025$, we look in Table VII for the chi-square values in the row for 17 degrees of freedom and the columns for 0.025 and 0.975 to obtain $\chi^2_{lower} = 7.56$ and $\chi^2_{upper} = 30.2$, respectively. The

95% confidence limits on σ_ϵ^2 are:

$$\frac{17(74.34)}{30.2} = 41.85 \quad \text{and} \quad \frac{17(74.34)}{7.56} = 167.17$$

By using square roots, the typical size of the error has the following limits:

$$6.47 < \sigma_\epsilon < 12.93$$

Note that these endpoints are not equally distant from the standard error of estimate, $s_e = 8.62$, because the chi-square distribution is not symmetrical.

Using these endpoints in Formula 14.12 along with the mean of the variable, investment, $\bar{y} = 88.915$, for the data in Table 14.1, we can find the relative measure of percent error:

upper C.V. Residual $= (12.93/88.915)100 = 14.5$ percent

lower C.V. Residual $= (6.47/88.915)100 = 7.3$ percent

For this model and data, we can anticipate potential errors in predicting investment of about 7–15 percent. ∎

Tests on a Particular Coefficient

To determine the significance of an individual coefficient (β_j) in the regression model, a test similar to that for the slope in the simple regression equation is used. The null hypothesis H_0: $\beta_j = 0$ means that the term, $\beta_j x_j$ is zero in the model, so the variable x_j has no significant linear relationship with y, *when the effect of the other independent variables is held constant.*

The best linear unbiased estimator of β_j is the sample partial regression coefficient b_j. Again, if the *ideal* assumptions hold (particularly the normality of ϵ_i), the test for this null hypothesis follows the *t*-distribution with $(n - m - 1)$ degrees of freedom, as given in the following formula:

---

t-statistic for inference on a partial regression coefficient β_j:

$$t_{(n-m-1)} = \frac{b_j - \beta_j}{s_{b_j}} \tag{14.13}$$

Here s_{bj} is the estimated standard error of the estimator b_j. Calculation of s_{bj} is quite tedious, but its value is readily available in the computer output of any standard regression analysis program.

For a test of significance, $\beta_j = 0$ is substituted in Formula 14.13. Thus, the determination of t in a practical application is accomplished simply by forming the ratio of the coefficient to its estimated standard error. When the calculated value of t exceeds the critical value, $t_{(\alpha, n-m-1)}$ determined from Table VI, the null hypothesis of no significance can be rejected. It is then concluded that the variable x_j does have an important influence on the dependent variable y, after accounting for the influence of all other independent variables included in the model. Analysts usually report such *t*-ratios for tests of significance in any discussion of multiple regression results.

☐ **EXAMPLE 14.11** In the investment model of Figure 14.7, the estimated standard errors of the coefficients b_1 and b_2 of the variables x_1 (stock prices) and x_2 (retained earnings) are

$$s_{b_1} = 0.0188 \quad and \quad s_{b_2} = 0.6141,$$

respectively. Since $n = 20$ and $m = 2$ in this case, the critical value for a one-sided test on either coefficient (using a significance level of $\alpha = 0.01$) is:

$$t_{(\alpha, n-m-1)} = t_{(0.01, 17)} = 2.567$$

Thus, the critical region for a one-sided test when $H_0: \beta_1 = 0$ or $H_0: \beta_2 = 0$ includes *all values of t that exceed* 2.567. We choose a one-sided upper-tail test because our *a priori* theoretical propositions were that both x_1 and x_2 were positively related to y.

The value of b_1 is 0.07856, hence for the test on β_1, the calculated value of the test statistic follows:

$$t_c = \frac{b_1}{s_{b_1}} = \frac{0.0786}{0.0188} = 4.18$$

The value of b_2 is 1.798, so for the test on the significance of β_2,

$$t_c = \frac{b_2}{s_{b_2}} = \frac{1.798}{0.614} = 2.93$$

These *t*-values as calculated by a computer are shown in Figure 14.7 in the column headed T. To make the test conclusion, we compare the calculated *t*-value to the critical value from Table VI and find that the result for both b_1 and b_2 is to reject H_0. We conclude that these coefficients are positive and their associated variables of stock price index and retained earnings are each useful in the model. ■

In Figure 14.7, the *p*-value for a two-sided test of significance is given in the column headed SIG T. For use in a one-tailed test, we compare one-half of the reported value to our acceptable Type I error. If it is less than the risk we are willing to assume, we are comfortable in deciding to reject H_0 and claiming a useful relation. From the printout, we find the one-sided *p*-value = (1/2)0.0006 = 0.0003 for the test on β_1 and *p*-value = (1/2)0.0094 = 0.0047 for the test on β_2. These are both less than $\alpha = 0.01$, so we could make the same conclusion as before. Thus, a quick way to judge the usefulness of any variable in a regression model with a one-sided test is to see if the *p*-value (one-half the reported value) is less than the acceptable risk of error.

A similar test using a *t*-ratio and a corresponding *p*-value can be used for inference on the intercept in the model. The printout reports this information in the row labeled (CONSTANT). For the regression result in Figure 14.7, the *t*-ratio for significance of the intercept is only 0.2158, and the *p*-value is large. We conclude that the intercept in the population model for investment could be zero even though the point estimate is $a = 1.677$.

We repeat that it is standard operating procedure in any multiple regression analysis to report the coefficients, the *t*-ratios, and the *p*-values for tests of significance. This allows a quick check to determine whether any variable is *not* contributing significantly to the explanation of the variation in y. The *t*-values also quickly reveal which variable has the most significant coefficient in terms of having the greatest *t*-value in absolute size. For the investment regression, we conclude that the variable x_1 (stock prices) is the more influential of the two explanatory variables since it has the higher *t*-value.

These t values for tests of significance may not be the only ones of interest to a decision-maker. Previous regression results may have already shown which variables tend to have significant coefficients. For example, we know that the level of income is important in explaining the amount of household expenditures. However, we may not know exactly the value of the coefficient (β_j, which is the marginal propensity to consume) relating income and expenditures for a particular group of households. We may wish to determine whether the coefficient for households in rural areas, or those of a certain ethnic group, or those which have only a single adult, is similar to the coefficient that has been determined for some other group or for the whole population. In such a case, we would do a test of hypothesis using Formula 14.13 with the value of β_j set to the previously accepted value. For example, if a population of households is thought to have a marginal propensity to consume of $\beta_j = 0.8$, the null hypothesis would be $H_0: \beta_j = 0.8$ and the value 0.8, not zero, would be substituted into the numerator of the t-statistic.

In many cases of applied regression analysis it is also desirable to find an interval estimate for the partial slope β_j rather than simply the point estimate b_j. Formula 14.14 can be used in the usual way to find $100(1 - \alpha)\%$ confidence limits on β_j. These limits would be as follows:

$100(1 - \alpha)\%$ confidence limits on β_j:

$$b_j \pm t_{(\alpha/2, n-m-1)} s_{b_j} \qquad (14.14)$$

☐ STUDY QUESTION 14.5 t-test for the Housing Price Model

Use the housing price model and the regression results shown in Figure 14.8.

a) Interpret the meaning of the individual t-ratios for the coefficients of each included variable.

b) Report and interpret the p-values for one-sided tests of direct relations of housing price to income and rent, but an inverse relation to vacancy rates.

c) Find and interpret the meaning of a 90% confidence interval for the coefficient of the variable that is most influential in explaining changes in the variation of y.

d) Do the results show any cause and effect among the variables?

• ANSWER

a) The estimated equation and the corresponding t-values (given below each coefficient) are:

$$\text{PRICE} = -11.109 + 2.018 \text{ (Income)} + 0.181 \text{ (Rent)} - 0.314 \text{ (Vacant)}$$
$$\phantom{\text{PRICE} = } (-0.339) \qquad (2.756) \qquad\qquad (2.623) \qquad\qquad (-0.524)$$

The coefficients for Income and Rent are significant at $\alpha = 0.01$ since the critical value from Table VI is $t_{0.01,21} = 2.518$. The coefficient for Vacant is not significant since its t-value is only -0.524. Thus, the variables Income and Rent are useful in the model to explain the variation in housing price, but vacancy rate is not.

b) The *p*-values for one-sided tests indicate that the risks of falsely concluding that Income and Rent have a significant direct relation to Price are 0.0059 and 0.00795 respectively. On the other hand, the probability is 0.30 of observing this negative a sample estimate of $b_3 = -0.314$ when the true population value is $\beta_3 = 0$. This is too large a risk of error so we accept the null hypothesis that there may not be a systematic linear relation between housing price and vacancy rate when controlling for income and rent.

c) The most influential variable is Income, which has a significantly positive coefficient and has the largest absolute value of the *t*-ratios. The 90% confidence interval on β_1 associated with the variable Income is found by using Formula 14.14, the *t*-value of 1.721 for $(\alpha/2) = 0.05$, and the standard error for the estimator from Figure 14.8 of $s_{b_1} = 0.7323$. The limits are $2.018 \pm 1.721(0.7323)$, which gives 0.758 and 3.278.

  Based on the sample regression results, a \$1,000 rise in median income (assuming no change in rent or vacancy rates) indicates an increase in the average housing price of \$758 to \$3,278. A different set of sample observations or a different set of control variables in the model may lead to a different estimate and a different confidence interval. Theoretically, 90% of such confidence intervals would include the true value of the slope (β_1).

d) Whether or not there is any cause and effect between rent or income and housing price is not determinable from these statistical results. The analysis gives information only on the linear association among these variables. The *analyst* specifies the cause and effect linkage by designating rent and income as explanatory (causal) variables that affect the dependent variable, housing price. In an alternative model, another analyst might have these causal roles reversed and be predicting rent based on housing price. ■

PROBLEMS

14.16 In multiple regression analysis:

a) What measures are used to determine whether the equation fits the data well and may be useful for forecasting?

b) How can you determine which of the explanatory factors included in the model has the most significance in explaining the variation of the dependent variable *y*?

14.17 The following results are given for a multiple regression analysis, for *y* = tax revenue using 53 observations (standard errors are in parenthesis).

$$\hat{y} = \underset{(1.5)}{6} + \underset{(2)}{3x_1} + \underset{(4)}{10x_2} - \underset{(0.8)}{4x_3}.$$

a) What value of *y* would you predict if $x_1 = -1, x_2 = 3$, and $x_3 = 2$?

b) Calculate the values of the *t*-statistic for one-sided tests of the significance of each individual estimate of the regression coefficients, and find the critical value for such tests using a significance level of 0.05.

c) Determine which independent variable is most important and which is least important for explaining the variation in the dependent variable.

d) Suppose that x_1, x_2, and x_3 are policy variables that can be manipulated. If x_1 and x_2 are increased by 20 units each while x_3 is increased by 50 units, what is your best estimate of the change in tax revenue?

14.18 Refer to Problem 14.3 and Figure 14.5 to answer the following:

a) Find a 90% confidence interval on the typical size of the disturbance in the population model. Find measures of the C.V. Residuals as in Formula 14.12 and comment on the likely percent error in predicting income.

b) Report on tests of significance for a positive relation between each explanatory variable and income.

14.19 Continue the analysis of the regression output in Figure 14.5.

a) Use an F-test to determine the significance of the overall contribution of both explanatory variables in the model.

b) Find a 95% confidence interval on the impact on annual income of a unit decrease in the number of hours worked per week.

14.20 Given the following information on a linear multiple-regression model:

y = average yield in bushels of corn per acre on a farm

x_1 = amount of summer rainfall

x_2 = average daily use in machine hours of tractors on the farm

x_3 = amount of fertilizer used per acre

The sample includes observations for ten crop years.
Results:
$\hat{y} = 16 + 75x_1 + 6x_2 + 48x_3$ Regression equation
      (10)   (25)   (4)   (8)   Standard errors
$n = 10$, $s_e = 20$ bushels, $s_y = 40$ bushels,
$r^2_{y \cdot x_1 \cdot x_2 x_3} = 0.60$
Answer parts (a) through (f):

a) What are the degrees of freedom for t-distributed test statistics for regression?

b) Explain which variable appears to be the most important in explaining the variation of yield.

c) From the regression results, is it proper to argue that more machine hours of tractor use causes more yield or that more yield requires more machine hours of tractor use? Explain.

d) Find the coefficient of multiple correlation, $R^2_{y \cdot x_1 x_2 x_3}$.

e) Account for the different values of

$$R^2_{y \cdot x_1 x_2 x_3} \quad \text{and} \quad r^2_{y \cdot x_1 \cdot x_2 x_3}$$

by explaining the different meanings of the two coefficients.

f) Determine a 90% confidence interval on σ_ϵ.

14.21 Using 12 weekly observations, a model to estimate tourism revenue, $y = \alpha + \beta_1 x_1 + \beta_2 x_2 + \beta_3 x_3 + \beta_4 x_4 + \epsilon$, is estimated by the method of least squares. Here SST = 400, SSE = 170, and the amount of variation explained jointly by x_1, x_2, and x_3 is 200.

a) Find $r^2_{y \cdot x_4 \cdot x_1 x_2 x_3}$ and explain what it means.

b) Do an ANOVA test with $\alpha = 0.05$ to determine whether this linear relationship is significant.

14.22 In a multiple regression to explain monthly new car sales by a dealer, based on 40 observations, the following results are obtained with standard errors in parentheses:

$$\hat{y} = 10 + 4x_1 + 6x_2 - 2x_3$$
$$\qquad\quad (1.2) \quad (5.0) \quad (0.4)$$

a) Explain the meaning of the coefficient for the variable x_2, which measures the number of full-time salespeople.

b) Using some test statistic, explain which of the independent variables is the most significant.

c) Explain one probable effect of dropping variable x_2 from the regression model and reestimating.

d) What value of y would you predict if $x_1 = 4$, $x_2 = 1$, and $x_3 = 2$?

♦ **14.23** The following results were obtained from a multiple regression analysis for predicting personal income tax. The model used three independent variables x_1, x_2, and x_3. The regression equation obtained using a sample of 32 observations was as follows with standard errors of coefficients in parentheses.

$$\hat{y} = 1500 + 6x_1 - 10x_2 + 4x_3$$
$$\qquad\qquad (2) \quad (4) \quad (0.8)$$

a) What would be the predicted value of the personal income tax if $x_1 = 100$, $x_2 = 10$, and $x_3 = 1000$?

b) Test for the significance of the coefficient of each independent variable of the regression model. Use $\alpha = 0.05$. State the null and the alternative hypotheses in each case.

♦ **14.24** A firm has developed a regression model to forecast its yearly sales for different sales regions. The model under consideration is:

$$y = \alpha + \beta_1 x_1 + \beta_2 x_2 + \beta_3 x_3 + \epsilon$$

where y = annual regional sales
      x_1 = population of the sales region
      x_2 = annual regional advertising expenditure
      x_3 = prosperity index for the region

A random sample of observations is used to obtain the results in Table 14.9.

TABLE 14.9   Annual Sales Forecast

ANOVA Table

Source of Variation	Sum of Squares	Degrees of Freedom	Mean Square
Regression	28612.16	3	*
Error	*	7	
Total	38762.55	*	

Table of Estimated Coefficients

Variable	Estimated Coefficient	Estimated Standard Error
Population	−0.025	0.039
Advertising expenditure	1.823	1.117
Prosperity index	11.068	3.245

a) Fill in the blanks indciated by * in the ANOVA table.

b) What is the total number of sample observations for sales that were used in the regression analysis?

c) Find R^2.

d) Test for the usefulness of the model at $\alpha = 0.05$.

e) For a given region, population increases by 10 units, advertising expenditure increases by 1 unit and prosperity index increases by 0.5 unit. What impact would this have on the sales for the region?

14.25 Consider a linear-regression model

$y = \alpha + \beta_1 x_1 + \beta_2 x_2 + \epsilon$ where,

$y =$ learning by grade 12, as measured by an academic test score composite, with mean 300 and standard deviation 150, for the entire population of twelfth-graders

$x_1 =$ school expenditures per pupil during three years of high school (in hundreds of dollars)

$x_2 =$ an index of socioeconomic status of the individual, with mean 10 and standard deviation 2, for the entire population of twelfth-graders

Based on a sample of 25 twelfth-grade individuals who were arrested on drug possession charges, the following results are obtained. Analyze, interpret, and explain the results in Table 14.10 in the way you think most appropriate and meaningful.

TABLE 14.10   Drug Possession Arrests

Variable	Mean	Standard Deviation
y	306.67	175.98
x_1	12.58	9.31
x_2	11.17	8.95

Correlations:

$r_{yx_1} = 0.83$ $r_{yx_2} = 0.35$ $r_{x_1 x_2} = 0.10$

Coefficient	Estimate	Standard Error	t-value
a	10.16	11.90	0.85
b_1	17.60	0.62	28.30
b_2	4.30	2.90	1.48

Multiple $R = 0.92$ $s_e = 3.015$

Analysis of Variance	SS	d.f.	Mean Square
Regression	1090	2	545.00
Residual	200	22	9.09

14.26 Using the results for the investment model given in Figure 14.2 and using the F-test for a subgroup of coefficients (Formula 14.9), test the significance of the contribution of the single variable $x_2 =$ retained earnings. Treat it as a subgroup of size $J = 1$. Compare the result to the t-test for the significance of β_2. [The calculated F-value should be the square of the calculated t-ratio.]

14.27 Explain how the use of the t-distribution differs from the use of the F-distribution in testing hypotheses in multiple linear regression.

14.28 In a multiple regression problem the data in Table 14.11 are used:

TABLE 14.11   Multiple Regression Data

	y	x_1	x_2	x_1^2	x_2^2	$x_1 y$	$x_2 y$	$x_1 x_2$	y^2
	9	3	2	9	4	27	18	6	81
	10	4	3	16	9	40	30	12	100
	2	1	2	1	4	2	4	2	4
	9	2	3	4	9	18	27	6	81
	20	5	5	25	25	100	100	25	400
Σ	50	15	15	55	51	187	179	51	666
μ	10	3	3						

a) The normal equations for two independent variables are:

$$\Sigma y = na + b_1 \Sigma x_1 + b_2 \Sigma x_2$$

$$\Sigma x_1 y = a \Sigma x_1 + b_1 \Sigma x_1^2 + b_2 \Sigma x_1 x_2$$

$$\Sigma x_2 y = a \Sigma x_2 + b_1 \Sigma x_1 x_2 + b_2 \Sigma x_2^2$$

Find a, b_1, and b_2.

b) Find SSE, SSR, and SST. Use this information to calculate s_e and R_2.

c) Determine a 90% confidence interval on σ_ϵ^2.

d) If $r^2_{y,x_1} = 136.9/166$, and $r^2_{y,x_2} = 140.167/166$, find $r^2_{y,x_1 \cdot x_2}$ and $r^2_{y,x_2 \cdot x_1}$.

e) Test the null hypothesis of no linear association using the *F*-test. Use $\alpha = 0.05$ and include the ANOVA table for this problem.

14.29 A word processing pool supervisor wishes to use the intermediate results provided below to determine a regression equation that can predict the total keyboarding hours, y, for report drafts. She uses as independent variables the number of words in the draft, x_1 (in tens of thousands) and an index x_2 for level of difficulty on a scale of 1 (least difficult) to 5 (most difficult).

$$n = 25, \quad \Sigma y = 200, \quad \Sigma x_1 = 100, \quad \Sigma x_2 = 75,$$
$$\Sigma x_1 y = 1,000, \quad \Sigma x_2 y = 800, \quad \Sigma x_1^2 = 600,$$
$$\Sigma x_2^2 = 325, \quad \Sigma y_2 = 3,800, \quad \Sigma x_1 x_2 = 200$$

a) Calculate the coefficients a, b_1, and b_2 for the estimated regression equation. [Solve the normal equations as in Problem 14.28(a).]

b) Explain the meaning of the values obtained for b_1 and b_2.

c) Calculate and interpret R^2.

d) Test for the significance of the individual coefficients, using an appropriate one-tailed test and $\alpha = 0.05$.

e) Determine a 90% confidence interval on σ_ϵ^2 and use it to obtain upper and lower values of the potential percentage error in prediction with this model.

14.30 In a multiple regression problem, the ANOVA results are shown in Table 14.12.

TABLE 14.12   An ANOVA Table for Regression

Source	SS	d.f.
Regression	36	2
Error	64	32

a) How many independent variables are there? What is the sample size?

b) What is the value of the multiple correlation coefficient R? What percent of the variability in y is explained by the independent variables?

c) Test the null hypothesis that there is no linear regression. Use a two-sided alternative hypothesis and let $\alpha = 0.05$.

d) Find the value of $r^2_{y,x_2 \cdot x_1}$ given that the unexplained variation in a simple regression with x_1 alone is 80.

e) Calculate the standard error of the estimate and interpret its meaning.

14.31 During the summer, ten university students were hired by Disney World as entertainers. Before being hired, each student was given two different aptitude tests. They were then given three days of training, after which they were rated by a committee. The results are shown in Table 14.13.

TABLE 14.13   The Results of Two Aptitude Tests followed by Training and the Resultant Rating

Test Score I (x_1)	Test Score II (x_2)	Rating (y)
74	40	91
59	41	72
83	45	95
76	43	90
69	40	82
88	47	98
71	37	80
69	36	75
61	34	74
70	37	79

a) Calculate a, b_1, and b_2 in the equation $\hat{y} = a + b_1 x_1 + b_2 x_2$. [*Hint:* See Problem 14.28, part (a) or use a computer.]

b) How would you interpret b_1? How would your answer differ if you had estimated the simple regression equation $\hat{y} = a + b_1 x_1$?

c) Calculate SSR and SST for part (a).

d) Use your results from part (c) to test the hypothesis of no linear regression.

e) Determine a 90% confidence interval on σ_ϵ^2 and comment on a typical percentage error in using this model to predict Rating.

section 14.6	# Dummy Variables in Regression Analysis

Thus far, the variables we have used in regression problems have been *quantitative variables*, which means that they represent variables that are either measured or counted. In some types of problems it is desirable to use another type of variable called a *qualitative variable*, which merely indicates whether or not an object belongs to a particular category or possesses a particular quality. For example, in a regression analysis in which the dependent variable is the consumption expenditures of families in Canada, one may be interested in relating y not only to family income (x_1) but also to whether or not the family lives in an urban or rural community. To use a variable indicating location in a regression analysis, we define $L = 0$ if the family lives in a rural community and let $L = 1$ if they live in an urban community. A variable such as L is often called a **dummy variable**.

A Dummy Variable to Change Level

The introduction of a dummy variable does not change the multiple regression process described thus far. All computations are made in the same way as for a regression analysis involving only quantitative variables. One characteristic of the addition of a dummy variable L is that we know that its value for any observation is either zero or one. Hence, we can write two regression equations, one using $L = 0$ and the other using $L = 1$. To illustrate this, we present the following least-squares regression model:

$$y = \alpha + \beta x + \lambda L + \epsilon$$

If $L = 1$, then substituting $L = 1$ into this equation and finding the expected value yields:

$$E[y \mid L = 1] = \alpha + \beta x + \lambda(1) + 0 = (\alpha + \lambda) + \beta x$$

Since $L = 1$ indicates an urban family, this equation represents the regression line for urban families. If we substitute $L = 0$ in the original regression model, we find the expected regression line for rural families:

$$E[y \mid L = 0] = \alpha + \beta x + \lambda(0) = \alpha + \beta x$$

Thus, we have derived two regression lines from the original regression model, as shown in Figure 14.9.

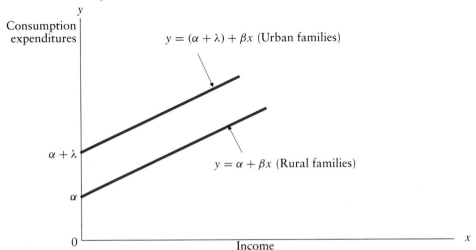

FIGURE 14.9   Two regression lines resulting from the use of a dummy variable

In this example, the distinction between rural and urban families shifts the regression intercept from α to $(\alpha + \lambda)$. Our graph shows a positive value for λ. Note that the slope of both straight lines is the same (β).

A Dummy Variable to Change Slope

If we wish to allow for a different slope in the relation between consumption and income for rural versus urban families, the specification of the model is changed to include an interaction variable between income and the dummy indicator of rural or urban. The new variable is Lx and the new regression equation is $y = \alpha + \beta x + \gamma(Lx)$.

If $L = 1$ for an urban family, the line is:

$$E[y \mid L = 1] = \alpha + (\beta + \gamma)x \text{ with a slope of } (\beta + \gamma)$$

When $L = 0$ for a rural family, the line is:

$$E[y \mid L = 0] = \alpha + \beta x \text{ with a slope of } \beta$$

A positive value of γ would indicate that urban families have a higher propensity to consume out of extra income received than do rural families. A negative value of γ would give evidence of the converse. In both cases, the intercept is the same value α. Figure 14.10 illustrates the situation of a dummy slope variable.

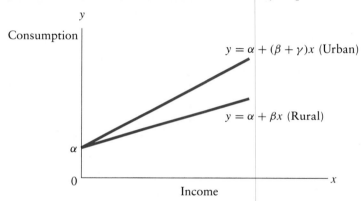

FIGURE 14.10 Two regression lines resulting from the use of a dummy slope variable

The reader should recognize that dummy variables may be used to allow for both different intercepts and different slopes. A model allowing for both different intercepts and slopes due to the urban/rural distinction would be:

$$y = \alpha + \beta x + \lambda L + \gamma(Lx) + \epsilon$$

For $L = 1$, the urban equation is $y = (\alpha + \lambda) + (\beta + \gamma)x$. For $L = 0$ the rural equation is $y = \alpha + \beta x$. The difference in level between the two models is given by λ and the difference between the two slopes for rural and urban families is given by γ.

Also, more than one dummy variable can be used in the same model. We might have included a dummy variable for sex of the head of the family with $S = 1$ for male and $S = 0$ for female, as well as a dummy variable indicating education level of the head of the family as $E = 1$ if the level is at least 12 years and $E = 0$ if not. Each dummy variable (or dummy interaction variable for changing slopes) would have its own coefficient. For example, if we included dummy variables for location (rural or urban), sex, and education level in the model, we could specify it as follows:

$$y = \alpha + \beta x + \lambda_1 L + \lambda_2 S + \lambda_3 E + \epsilon$$

The value estimated for λ_3 would tell how much higher (or lower if λ_3 is negative) the consumption expenditures would be for a family headed by a person with at least 12 years of education compared to one headed by a person with an education level less than 12 years, on average, while keeping constant the family income, its location, and the sex of the head of the family. Dummy variable specifications can be very informative and add much capability to the application of the linear regression analysis.

Some analysts may wish to include the category of suburban for the location of the family, or to include education levels of college graduate or professional certification as separate categories. How this can be achieved is our next topic.

Multiple Category Dummy Variables

If a qualitative variable with multiple categories is to be used as an explanatory variable in a model, a set of dummy variables is used. If there are h categories, each can be represented by a dummy variable which takes on the value 1 or 0 depending on the occurrence of that category for the given observation. Usually, however, not all h dummy variables are used.

> If the model includes an intercept term, only $h - 1$ dummy variables need to be specified to represent h different categories since one category, called the *base category*, is represented by the intercept.

If h dummy variables were included, their sum for each observation would be 1.0 since one of them would always be one and the others would be zero. But 1.0 is also the value in each observation for the intercept so the h dummy variables would be linearly dependent with the intercept. This situation would violate Condition 2 specified in Section 14.3 and the equation could not be estimated.

The coefficients on the dummy variables will give the differential level of the dependent variable between each of these other categories and the base category. For example, if families in the consumption study are classified as living in rural, urban, or suburban locations, we define $L_1 = 1$ if urban and zero otherwise, and $L_2 = 1$ if suburban and zero otherwise. The model is:

$$y = \alpha + \beta x + \lambda_1 L_1 + \lambda_2 L_2 + \epsilon$$

When an observation is for a rural family, both L_1 and L_2 are zero and α represents the intercept for consumption expenditures for rural families. A coefficient such as λ_2 gives the average difference in consumption expenditures between suburban and rural families at any level of income (since the slope β is a constant). Three parallel lines would be defined by this sample regression equation.

A similar representation is used if different impacts on y of an explanatory variable are expected depending on the category of a qualitative variable. Suppose the data provide four levels of education for the head of the household, such as ten or fewer years, 11–13 years, 14–16 years, and graduate or professional education after university study. To represent the four categories, *three* dummy variables are needed. We define them as follows:

$E_1 = 1$ for 11–13 years of education, otherwise zero

$E_2 = 1$ for 14-16 years of education, otherwise zero

$E_3 = 1$ for education beyond the university, otherwise zero

To represent different slopes for the consumption function, the model specification is:

$$y = \alpha + \beta x + \gamma_1(E_1 x) + \gamma_2(E_2 x) + \gamma_3(E_3 x) + \epsilon$$

The base category is 10 or fewer years of education with slope or marginal propensity to consume for this group of families equal to β. The slope for families whose head has 14–16 years of education is given by $\beta + \gamma_2$, and similarly for the other categories. The sample regression equation would define four lines all emanating from the same intercept but having different slopes. Of course, if a coefficient, say γ_1, is estimated and found to be insignificant, it means that no difference is found in the impact of income on consumption expenditures between families whose head has 10 or fewer years of education versus those with 11–13 years.

☐ **EXAMPLE 14.12**   A Canadian economic model is based on quarterly observations and an equation is specified for the dependent variable, y = gasoline price, with independent variables, x_1 = national income per capita, x_2 = unemployment rate, and x_3 = domestic stock of gasoline. It is hypothesized that gas prices should be higher when the national economy is prosperous with higher x_1 and lower x_2, and when the current inventory x_3 is lower. Improvement in the model is sought by including dummy variables for the change in the level of gas price depending on the seasons (winter, spring, summer, or fall) as demands for oil products vary. Also, the impact of the inventory level on gas price is hypothesized to change depending on whether any of the major oil producing countries or any of the highly industrial countries are at war during the quarter because war makes the world's supply of oil more valuable. Dummy variables can be defined to fit and test these hypotheses.

To represent four seasons, three dummy variables are used with one season chosen as the base. We choose to let the base season be the fall, and define dummy variables for the quarterly observations of $Q_1 = 1$ for winter, $Q_2 = 1$ for spring, and $Q_3 = 1$ for summer, and zeros otherwise. These dummy variables for seasons will enter the model directly to provide for potential change in the average level of gas price by season. Also, we define a dummy variable $W = 1$ if any designated countries are involved in a war and $W = 0$ if not. This dummy variable must be entered in the specification as an interaction term with the variable x_3 to allow for a change between war times and other periods in the impact on gas price of the current stock of oil. The model is:

$$y = \alpha + \beta_1 x_1 + \beta_2 x_2 + \beta_3 x_3 + \lambda_1 Q_1 + \lambda_2 Q_2 + \lambda_3 Q_3 + \gamma(W x_3) + \epsilon$$

The coefficient of the last term, γ, gives the differential impact of inventory stock on gas price during war periods. If it is positive, then a unit rise in the domestic stockpile results in a larger change in gas price during war periods than otherwise. Each coefficient on the quarterly dummy variables is interpreted the same. λ_1 gives the change in the level of the gas price, on average, between winter and fall, λ_2 between spring and fall, and λ_3 between summer and fall.   ■

☐ **STUDY QUESTION 14.6**   Dummy Variables in a Health Study

The World Health Organization collected data to study child mortality (measured as the number of children who died relative to the total number of children ever born of the particular mother) among families in a squatter settlement in Onitsha, Nigeria. Some variables included as potential explanatory factors of child mortality are the income of the household and the years of education of the mother. Categorical variables included are the quality of housing as a factor affecting the level of child mortality and the employment sector of the head of the household as a factor affecting the impact of the mother's education on child mortality.

The housing quality categories are low (natural residual materials for wall and roof), middle (cement walls but other roofing, mostly corrugated tin), and good (cement walls and roof). The employment sector categories are formal labour and other (informal home service, weaving, gardening, care-giver, et cetera).

a) Define the dummy variables to use and fully specify the model.

b) Interpret the meaning of the coefficient of each term in the model involving a dummy variable.

c) Give the value estimated for the different intercepts and slopes using the printout of Figure 14.11.

```
Model:      SOCIAL DETERMINANTS OF CHILD MORTALITY
Dependent Variable:    CHIL_MOR            CHILD MORTALITY

                    Analysis of Variance
Source   DF   Sum of Squares   Mean Square   F Value   Prob>F
Model     5       2.51349        0.50270      7.783    0.0001
Error    68       4.39224        0.06459
C Total  73       6.90573

Root MSE    0.25415    R-square   0.3640
Dep Mean    0.37211    Adj R-sq   0.3172
C.V.       68.30016

                        Parameter Estimates

                Parameter    Standard      T for H0:
Variable   DF    Estimate      Error     Parameter = 0   Prob > |T|

INTERCEP    1     0.52098      0.07495        6.951       0.0001
MOTH_EDU    1    -0.07059      0.03035       -2.326       0.0230
INCM        1    -0.00035      0.01199       -0.029       0.9769
H1          1    -0.20189      0.07505       -2.690       0.0090
H2          1     0.09064      0.08114        1.117       0.2679
LX1         1     0.01102      0.02692        0.409       0.6836

Variable   DF   Variable Label
INTERCEP    1   Intercept
MOTH_EDU    1   YEARS OF EDUCATION OF THE MOTHER
INCM        1   MONTHLY INCOME OF HOUSEHOLD, $HNDRDS
H1          1   1 IF CEMENT WALLS & ROOF, 0 IF NOT
H2          1   1 IF RESIDUAL WALLS & ROOF, 0 IF NOT
LX1         1   INTERACTION, LABOUR DUMMY WITH MOTH.EDU
```

FIGURE 14.11 Printout for Regression for Child Mortality Study

• **ANSWER**

a) Let the middle quality of housing be the base. Define $H1 = 1$ for good quality housing and zero otherwise and $H2 = 1$ for poor quality housing and zero otherwise. Also, define $L = 1$ if the head of household is a formal labourer and zero otherwise. An interaction term is designated $LX1$ which is the product of the dummy variable L and the value of mother's education. The model is:

$$y = \alpha + \beta_1(\text{MOTH\_EDU}) + \beta_2(\text{INCM}) + \lambda_1(H1) + \lambda_2(H2) + \gamma(LX1) + \epsilon$$

b) Different levels of child mortality for good and for low housing relative to the middle level of housing, holding other factors constant, are given by the coefficients λ_1 and λ_2 respectively. The slope relating years of education of the mother and child mortality, holding other factors constant, is given by β for families whose head is an informal sector worker and by $(\beta + \gamma)$ for those whose head is a formal labourer.

c) In this answer, we simply report the point estimates shown although only those which are statistically significant by their t-ratios can be considered meaningful. Child mortality is lower, other factors constant, by 0.202 for families that live in good housing compared to those living in middle quality housing. Other factors the same, families living in poor housing compared to those in middle quality housing experience a higher child mortality of 0.091, or nine percent higher. The impact, on average and holding other factors constant, on child mortality of a rise in the education level of the mother by one year in families whose head is an informal sector worker is a decrease of about seven percent (coefficient of -0.0706). Interestingly, in families whose head is a formal labourer, an extra year of education of the mother is indicated to decrease child mortality by only about six percent ($-0.0706 + 0.0110 = -0.0596$). The coefficient on the interaction term, $LX1$, has quite low significance, however, so the true difference could well be zero. ∎

PROBLEMS

14.32 Let y = individual income for persons selected from among full-time workers in manufacturing, and let x = age. A simple regression model is written $y = \alpha + \beta x + \epsilon$.

a) Suppose that I wish to include in the model the factor of sex. Specify and interpret the dummy variable to be included in order to differentiate levels of income depending on sex as well as on age.

b) Suppose that now I wish to allow for different impacts of age on income, depending on whether or not the person completed college. Specify a dummy slope variable to be added to the model, and explain the separate regression lines that can be derived.

c) Make a sketch with income and age on the axes, and illustrate the different potential regression lines you have implied in parts (a) and (b).

d) Finally, add a set of dummy variables to the model to allow for different income levels for three different areas of the country: east, central, and west. In your model, specify the difference in the intercepts for females in the east compared to males in the west.

14.33 Lifetime earnings are explained in a human capital model by various characteristics of the individual, such as the level of schooling attained. Suppose that five such levels are distinguished in the available data: minimum required level, second level certificate or diploma, college graduate, master's degree or equivalent, and doctoral or other professional degree requiring at least three years of postgraduate work. To use the level of schooling as an explanatory variable in a regression model, specify the number of dummy variables you would use. Define them, and make a list of their values for each level of education described.

14.34 Refer to **Data Set 6** for survey data on persons over age 54. Included is a variable identifying the region of the country of the respondent. Suppose that regional differences are thought to be one of the factors determining the monthly income of the respondent along with education level and the number of persons in the household.

a) Explain how to define dummy variables to represent these different regions.

b) Specify a model in which the regional effect changes the *level* of monthly income.

c) Specify a model in which the regional effect changes the *impact* of education on monthly income.

14.35 Sales of a large retailer are cyclical depending on the level of GNP in the economy. They are also seasonal depending on the quarter of the year. Let y = sales, x = GNP, and Q_1, Q_2, and Q_3 represent the first, second, and third quarter of the year.

a) Define the values of the variables Q_1, Q_2, and Q_3.

b) Specify the model for sales.

c) Explain why the fourth quarter does not seem to be represented, but how it really is.

d) Interpret the meaning of the coefficient for Q_1.

14.36 For the situation of Problem 14.35, and based on data for 14 recent quarters, the simple regression of sales (million $) on GNP (billions $) and the multiple regression including quarterly dummy variables are estimated. Figure 14.12 gives the partial printout.

a) Sketch and label the four estimated regression lines with sales on the vertical axis and GNP on the horizontal.

b) What is the difference in the level of sales, on the average, between the first and the second quarters? Between the second and the fourth quarters?

c) Show that all three quarterly dummy variables have significant negative coefficients in a one-tail test.

d) In terms of seasonal sales, explain what it means for the coefficients on all three quarterly dummy variables to be negative. Do you think this retailer could sell primarily toys?

```
DEPENDENT VARIABLE..      SALES              RETAIL SALES

VARIABLE(S) ENTERED ON STEP NUMBER 1 ..      GNP

MULTIPLE R            0.84359     VARIABLE              B     STD ERROR B
R SQUARE             0.71165         GNP         1.064442        0.19560
ADJUSTED R SQUARE    0.68765     (CONSTANT)     -129.6420
STANDARD ERROR      79.55907

ANALYSIS OF VARIANCE        DF   SUM OF SQUARES    MEAN SQUARE          F
REGRESSION                  1.    187455.68491   187455.68491   29.61551
RESIDUAL                   12.     75955.74366     6329.64530

VARIABLE(S) ENTERED ON STEP NUMBER 2 ..                   Q3   THIRD QUARTER
                                                          Q1   FIRST QUARTER
                                                          Q2   SECOND QUARTER

                                       VARIABLE          B     STD ERROR B
MULTIPLE R            0.99297
R SQUARE             0.98599             GNP       0.9716888       0.05031
ADJUSTED R SQUARE    0.97976             Q3       -82.76965       16.59757
STANDARD ERROR      20.25250             Q1      -191.1151        15.61405
                                         Q2       -43.29506       15.48683
                                     (CONSTANT)    76.02249

ANALYSIS OF VARIANCE        DF   SUM OF SQUARES    MEAN SQUARE          F
REGRESSION                  4.    259719.95483   64929.98871   158.30260
RESIDUAL                    9.      3691.47374     410.16375
```

FIGURE 14.12 Computer printout for the retail sales models

CHAPTER SUMMARY

KEY TERMS AND EXPRESSIONS

Population multiple linear regression equation:
$$\mu_{y \cdot x_1 x_2 \ldots x_m} = \alpha + \beta_1 x_1 + \beta_2 x_2 + \cdots + \beta_m x_m$$

Partial regression coefficient: The coefficient of x_j in a multiple regression model that gives the change in y for a unit change in x_j, holding constant the linear effect on y of all other explanatory variables in the model.

Sample multiple regression equation:
$$\hat{y} = a + b_1 x_1 + b_2 x_2 + \cdots + b_m x_m.$$

Standard error of estimate in multiple regression (s_e): Absolute measure of the typical size of the residual in the sample model:

$$s_e = \sqrt{\frac{SSE}{n - m - 1}}$$

Typical percentage error: A coefficient of variation measure for residuals:

$$\text{C.V. Residual} = (\sigma_\epsilon / \bar{y})100$$

Multiple coefficient of determination (R^2): Relative measure of fit for the entire model:

$$R^2 = \frac{SSR}{SST}$$

Adjusted coefficient of determination: Relative measure of fit adjusted for degrees of freedom:

$$R^2_{\text{adj}} = 1 - (1 - R^2)\left(\frac{n - 1}{n - m - 1}\right)$$

Multiple correlation coefficient: Index of linear association among y and two or more explanatory variables:

$$R_{y \cdot x_1, x_2, x_3, \ldots, x_m}$$

Partial coefficient of determination: Relative measures of the extra variation in y explained by a group of variables, A, out of the variation previously unexplained by another group of variables, B:

$$r^2_{yA \cdot B} = \frac{\substack{\text{Extra variation in } y \\ \text{explained by adding group A}}}{\substack{\text{Variation in } y \\ \text{unexplained by group B alone}}}$$

ANOVA tests in multiple regression: Tests using an F-distributed random variable to determine the overall contribution of all or of a subgroup of explanatory variables.

Chi-square statistic: For inference on the variance of a disturbance term in a multiple regression model:

$$\chi^2 = \frac{(n - m - 1)s_e^2}{\sigma_\epsilon^2}$$

with $n - m - 1$ degrees of freedom.

t-test on partial regression coefficients, B_j:

$$t = \frac{(b_j - \beta_j)}{s_{b_j}}$$

with $n - m - 1$ degrees of freedom.

Dummy variable: A qualitative variable with values defined to be either zero or one, depending on the occurrence or non-occurrence of a particular category.

EXERCISES

♦ **14.37** Using 15 weekly observations, a linear equation $\mu_{y \cdot x_1, x_2} = \alpha + \beta_1 x_1 + \beta_2 x_2$ for predicting tourism revenues is estimated by the method of least squares. Partial calculations yield SST = 400 and SSE = 100.

a) Calculate R^2 for this model and interpret this value. Also, find R^2_{adj} and explain the difference between these two measures.

b) Complete an ANOVA table for this regression.

♦ **14.38** Using Tables 14.5 and 14.6 in Problem 14.7, and the information below, answer the following questions concerning the multiple regression.
Given: Sum of squares due to regression = 6,695,543
Standard error of estimate = 277.0397

a) Show that the total sum of squares SST = 10,302,840.43.

b) Complete an ANOVA table for the multiple regression.

c) Test for the usefulness of the model with $\alpha = 0.05$.

d) Was Divorce a useful variable to add? Test with $\alpha = 0.05$.

e) What is the proportion of variability explained by this regression model?

f) Maryland and Connecticut have the same Urban value. The divorce rate for Maryland, however, is higher than that of Connecticut by 0.6 points. According to the regression equation, which state has a higher crime rate, and by how much?

♦ **14.39** A multiple regression equation

$$\mu_{y \cdot x_1, x_2, x_3} = \alpha + \beta_1 x_1 + \beta_2 x_2 + \beta_3 x_3$$

was fitted to data for several weeks with the following definition of variables:

y =Weekly hours of labour

x_1 =Thousands of pounds shipped during the

week (Pounds)

x_2 =Percentage of units shipped by truck during

the week (Truck)

x_3 =Average number of pounds per shipment during

the week (Avship)

Data were collected from the firm's accounting and production records in order to provide the cost information about the shipping department. Part of the computer output is given in Table 14.14 for $n = 20$.

TABLE 14.14 ANOVA Table

Source of Variation	Sum of Squares	Degrees of Freedom	Mean of Squares
Regression	*	*	*
Error	1539.886	*	*
Total	6698.1988	*	

Table of Estimated Coefficients

Variable	Estimated Coefficient	Estimated St. Dev.	Computed t-Value
Pounds	2.7261	2.275	*
Truck	0.0472	0.093	*
Avship	−2.5874	0.643	*
Intercept	131.9243		

a) State the least squares prediction equation.

b) Test for the usefulness of the model with $\alpha = 0.01$, and state your conclusions in the context of the problem.

c) Test $H_0: \beta_2 = 0$ versus $H_a: \beta_2 > 0$, using $\alpha = 0.05$. What conclusion can you draw from this analysis in the context of the problem?

d) Find R^2 and interpret its value.

e) Suppose the shipping department employees are paid $7.50 per hour. How much more or less, on average, will it cost the company if the average number of pounds per shipment increases from 20 to 21? Assume that the other variables remain unchanged.

14.40 Refer to the printout in Figure 14.11 and the model of Study Question 14.6 to answer the following.

a) Determine and interpret the difference between R^2 and R^2_{adj}.

b) Determine a quick estimate of the potential percent error in predicting y.

c) Determine if the contribution of either housing dummy variable is significant.

14.41 A government auditor in the revenue department wishes to predict total income tax collected from residents by cities. A model is estimated with independent economic and demographic variables of retail sales and population in the city. A printout of the results is given in Figure 14.13. Analyze and interpret the results as you think is most appropriate and meaningful, or follow specific directions of your instructor.

```
NUMBER OF CASES: 47      NUMBER OF VARIABLES: 3

INDEX   NAME     MEAN        STD.DEV.
Y       TOTTAX   459.5131    644.1203
X1      POP      118.3045    399.8020
X2      SALES    1004.6006   3753.1717

DEPENDENT VARIABLE: TOTTAX

VARIABLE        COEFFICIENT   STD. ERROR    T(DF = 44)    PROB.
POP             0.4075        1.1565        0.352         .7262
SALES           0.0383        0.1219        0.314         .7547
CONSTANT        175.9801

        STD. ERROR  OF EST.   = 331.9377
                R SQUARED     = 0.7460
                MULTIPLE R    = 0.8637

            ANALYSIS OF VARIANCE TABLE

SOURCE        SUM OF SQUARES      D.F.   MEAN SQUARE   F RATIO   PROB.
REGRESSION    14236946.138        2      7118473.069   64.606    .0001
RESIDUAL      4848035.210         44     110182.618
TOTAL         19084981.348        46
```

FIGURE 14.13 Printout of multiple regression for total income tax

14.42 A legislative staff member also forms a model to estimate income tax receipts from all residents by cities as in Problem 14.41. Explanatory variables in her model are the total personal income and the number of households in the city. A printout of the results is given in Figure 14.14. Analyze and interpret the results as you think is most appropriate and meaningful, or follow specific directions of your instructor.

```
Model: Personal Income Tax
Dependent Variable: TOTTAX      TOTAL TAX PAYABLE ($MIL)

                      Analysis of Variance

                         Sum of          Mean
   Source      DF        Squares        Square       F Value    Prob>F

   Model        2    15073558.455    7536779.2275     82.668    0.0001
   Error       44     4011422.8934     91168.702122
   C Total     46    19084981.348

        Root MSE        301.94155      R-square      0.7898
        Dep Mean        459.51309      Adj R-sq      0.7803
        C.V.             65.70902

                      Parameter Estimates

                     Parameter      Standard     T for H0:
   Variable    DF     Estimate        Error    Parameter = 0   Prob> |T|

   INTERCEP     1    204.03903       50.77980       4.018       0.0002
   HSHOLDS      1     -1.80679        1.01866      -1.774       0.0830
   INCOME       1      0.06806        0.01779       3.826       0.0004
```

FIGURE 14.14   Total personal income tax in cities in Canada

USING THE COMPUTER

14.43 A firm producing detergent has done a market analysis trying to improve its ability to predict annual sales of detergent in particular market areas. Four explanatory variables were measured, including population, unemployment rate, advertising expenditures in the area, and the number of competitors in the market. Observations on 30 market areas are given in Table 14.15. Population and sales are measured in thousands.

a) Use a computer program to find the sample regression equation for sales in terms of the four explanatory variables. [For better computational accuracy, code population and sales in millions and code advertising in thousands of dollars.]

b) Use tests to determine the significance of each coefficient and of the overall fit of the model.

c) Find a 90% confidence interval on the variance of the disturbance σ_ϵ^2.

d) Find a forecast of sales for the Atlanta market area if the values of the explanatory variables are specified to be $x_1 = 9.66$ million people, $x_2 = 6.4\%$ unemployed, $x_3 = \$35,000$, and $x_4 = 2$ competitors.

14.44 Refer to **Data Set 4** for sample observations on the variables: a doctor's net income, hours worked, office fee, and office expenses.

a) Estimate the sample regression equation for a doctor's income based on the other three variables. Compare your results to those given in Problem 14.3.

b) Test the significance of the overall fit of the equation.

c) Find a 95% confidence interval for the partial regression coefficient of the variable office Fee.

d) Do a test to determine the significance of the contribution of the two variables, office Fee and office Expenses. [The simple regression in Problem 13.80 is a starting point.]

e) Compute the predicted value $\hat{y}$ and the residuals $e = y - \hat{y}$. Find the correlation coefficients between y and $\hat{y}$. Find the correlation coefficients between e and each other variable in the model, as well as with $\hat{y}$. Discuss the results.

TABLE 14.15 Data for Detergent Market Analysis

Obs	Population	Unemp. Rate	Advert. Expense	Compet- ition	Sales
1	7,500	5.1	59,000	0	5,170
2	8,710	6.3	62,500	1	5,780
3	10,000	4.7	61,000	1	4,840
4	7,450	5.4	61,000	1	6,000
5	8,670	5.4	6,100	1	6,000
6	11,000	7.2	12,500	1	6,120
7	13,180	5.8	35,800	1	6,400
8	13,810	5.8	59,900	1	7,100
9	14,430	6.2	57,200	2	8,500
10	10,000	5.5	35,800	1	7,500
11	13,210	6.8	27,900	1	9,300
12	17,100	6.2	24,100	2	8,800
13	15,120	6.3	27,700	2	9,960
14	18,700	5.0	24,000	3	9,830
15	20,200	5.5	57,200	3	10,120
16	15,000	5.8	44,300	3	10,700
17	17,600	7.1	49,200	4	10,450
18	19,800	7.5	23,000	4	11,320
19	14,400	8.2	62,700	2	11,870
20	20,350	7.8	55,800	2	11,910
21	18,900	6.2	50,000	3	12,600
22	21,600	7.1	47,600	4	12,600
23	25,250	4.0	43,500	4	14,240
24	27,500	4.2	55,900	5	14,410
25	21,000	7.0	51,200	4	13,730
26	19,700	6.4	76,600	3	13,730
27	24,150	5.0	63,000	3	13,800
28	17,650	8.5	68,100	4	14,920
29	22,300	7.1	74,400	5	15,280
30	24,000	8.0	70,100	5	14,410

14.45 Refer to **Data Set 5** to estimate a model explaining Canadian imports in terms of the gross domestic product, the population, and the consumer price index.

a) Formulate the desired model and hypothesize the sign of the respective coefficients of the explanatory variables.

b) Use a computer to estimate this model and to estimate a model using only gross domestic product as a single explanatory variable. Discuss the changes in the goodness of fit measures and in the coefficients between the two equations.

c) Do a test to determine the significance of the contribution in the extended model of the two extra

variables, population and consumer price index.

14.46 Use the survey data in **Data Set 6**.

a) Estimate a regression model for the dependent variable, y = monthly income, on the explanatory variables: years of education (x_1), number of persons in the household (x_2), and a dummy variable for the sex of the respondent (x_3).

b) Test the significance of the coefficient for the dummy variable at the 0.05 level.

c) Explain the meaning of the coefficient b_3 for the dummy variable.

14.47 The four explanatory variables from Problems 14.41 and 14.42 are included in the same model to determine the total personal income tax of residents by cities. To answer the following parts, use the printout in Figure 14.15 (next page) for this multiple regression based on the same data and cities as the analyses given in Figs. 14.13 and 14.14.

a) Test the joint contribution of total personal income and number of households in the model having four explanatory factors.

b) Compare the contribution determined in part (a) to the contribution of the same two variables when they are the only variables in the model for predicting total tax. Be precise in explaining why these are different.

c) Test the joint contribution of sales and population in the model having four explanatory factors.

d) Compare the contribution determined in part (c) to the contribution of the same two variables when they are the only variables in the model for predicting total tax. Be precise in explaining why these are different.

14.48 Estimate and analyze the results of the model as required in Problem 14.34, parts (b) and (c) combined. Assign region 1 as the base region. Delete the outlier, observation 80, prior to the estimation.

14.49 In **Data Set 7**, there are 48 observations on various yields for a group of mutual funds.

a) Define a dummy variable for risk level to distinguish between lower risk funds (risk of 4 or less) and the higher risk funds (risk of 5 or 6). Specify the model for determining five year yield as a function of assets (put into units of millions of dollars) so that both the intercept and the slope may change depending on the risk category.

b) Estimate the model and interpret the results.

14.50 From the observations in **Data Set 1**, formulate a regression model explaining sales in terms of income, the number of households, and the percent population change. Estimate the model.

a) Compare the change in coefficients and in the goodness of fit measures to the results for the simple regression model of Problem 13.82(b).

b) Do F- and t-tests as appropriate to analyze and interpret the multiple regression results, or follow the specific directions given by your instructor.

14.51 Repeat the same requirements as in Problem

14.50, but use a sample restricted to cities beginning with the letter C. Compare the results to the simple regression in Problem 13.79.

14.52 Repeat the same requirements as in Problem 14.50, but use a sample restricted to cities beginning with the letter S. Compare the results to the simple regression in Problem 13.81.

```
        Dependent Variable: TOTTAX      TOTAL TAX PAYABLE ($MIL)

                               Analysis of Variance

                              Sum of          Mean
        Source      DF        Squares        Square      F Value    Prob>F

        Model        4     16542413.857   4135603.4642    68.315    0.0001
        Error       42      2542567.491     60537.3212
        C Total     46     19084981.348

             Root MSE       246.04333     R-square      0.8668
             Dep Mean       459.51309     Adj R-sq      0.8541
             C.V.            53.54436

                               Parameter Estimates

                          Parameter      Standard     T for H0:
        Variable    DF     Estimate        Error     Parameter = 0   Prob> |T|

        INTERCEP     1     84.15139       55.39020       1.519        0.1362
        POP          1      1.21641        3.54266       0.343        0.7330
        SALES        1     -0.86140        0.17705      -4.865        0.0001
        HSHOLDS      1      3.66298        6.42415       0.570        0.5716
        INCOME       1      0.30054        0.08526       3.525        0.0010
```

FIGURE 14.15 Printout of the multiple regression ($m = 4$) for total income tax

---

CASE PROBLEMS

14.53 As part of an economic study on development, it is desired to estimate a regression explaining literacy rates for population groups in different regions of countries throughout the world. Some explanatory variables may be quantitative, such as newspaper circulation, availability of radios or televisions, school enrollment, or the like. Other variables may not be measurable or may be qualitative. Hoping to represent different levels of some of these other variables, the economist categorizes the state of economic development of each region into one of these four classes:

1 = rapidly developing with sustained growth

2 = some current growth

3 = stagnant but with the prospect of soon experiencing growth

4 = not developing and with little prospect of growth soon.

TABLE 14.16 Summary Table
$(R^2 = 0.283, \bar{y} = 59.297,$
$SST = 73,875.877, n = 79)$

Variable	Coefficient	Standard Error
x_1	1.017	0.125
x_2	0.022	0.023
G_1	21.220	8.235
G_2	16.321	5.353
G_3	9.417	3.985
Intercept = -4.55		

Data source: *Literacy Cookbook*, Louis Harris Political Data Center, University of North Carolina, Chapel Hill.

a) Write a model using three dummy variables, G_1, G_2, and G_3, to represent the four states of growth (letting development group 4 be the base group represented by all zeros), and use x_1 to denote school enrollment as a percent of people aged 5–19 and x_2 to denote the number of radios and televisions per thousand people.

b) Interpret the results of the regression using the summary table of output, Table 14.18. Use tests on the significance of the coefficients and on the fit of the model.

c) Write the equations for regions with development status 1 and for regions with development status 3 and interpret the meaning of the difference between

the equations.

14.54 Problem 13.86 (Highway Safety) gave data for a simple regression on the number of highway deaths in the United States in terms of the number of drivers in 49 states and the District of Columbia. Table 14.19 gives data on another potential explanatory variable, the density of the area as defined by the number of persons per square mile. Include it in the model and reestimate the sample regression equation. Compare the results of the simple and multiple regression equations.

TABLE 14.17 Observations on Population Density by State

OBS	STATE	DENSITY	OBS	STATE	DENSITY	OBS	STATE	DENSITY
1	AL	64.0	18	MA	655.0	35	TX	37.0
2	AR	34.0	19	MI	137.0	36	UT	10.0
3	CA	100.0	20	MN	43.0	37	VT	42.0
4	CO	17.0	21	MS	46.0	38	VA	100.0
5	CT	518.0	22	MO	63.0	39	WV	77.0
6	DE	226.0	23	NB	18.4	40	WI	72.0
7	DC	12524.0	24	NH	67.0	41	AK	0.0
8	FL	91.0	25	NJ	807.0	42	AZ	12.0
9	GA	68.0	26	NY	350.0	43	ID	8.0
10	IL	180.0	27	NC	93.0	44	MT	4.0
11	IN	129.0	28	OH	237.0	45	NE	2.0
12	IA	49.0	29	OK	34.0	46	NM	7.0
13	KS	27.0	30	OR	18.0	47	ND	9.0
14	KY	76.0	31	PA	252.0	48	SD	9.0
15	LA	72.0	32	RI	812.0	49	WA	43.0
16	ME	31.0	33	SC	79.0	50	WY	3.0
17	MD	314.0	34	TN	85.0			

CHAPTER 15

Econometric Analysis

Introduction

In regression analysis, a sample regression equation is estimated on the basis of data on a dependent variable y and a set of explanatory variables, $x_1, x_2, \ldots, x_m$. The significance of the association between y and the explanatory variables has been examined by using various test statistics. The interpretations and conclusions that can be drawn from the regression model depend on the values of the estimates and on the outcome of such tests.

While the use of the method of least squares to find the estimates is merely a technical process, the use of test statistics and methods of inference require knowledge of the probability distribution associated with the estimators and test statistics (which are random variables). Our previous discussion in conjunction with Table 13.24 indicated that these probability distributions depend on the probability distribution of the disturbance term (ϵ_i) in the regression model. When information is provided, *or assumed*, about the characteristics of the random variable ϵ_i across all observations $i = 1, 2, \ldots, n$, properties of the least-squares estimators and various test statistics can be derived.

Such derivations are not our purpose in this text, but we stated in Sections 13.4 and 14.3 the common assumptions and conditions underlying the least-squares regression analysis. We also specified the importance of these assumptions in terms of the properties of the least-squares estimators. We collect all these materials together again, and expand some of them, in the next section. In subsequent sections of this chapter, particular assumptions or conditions will be studied more carefully. We will discuss some situations in which our simple analysis (as done in Chapters 13 and 14) is not the most appropriate because of potential violations of an assumption or a condition. The *effect* of the violation on our previous methods and results will be explained. We will consider some methods of *detection* of such potential violations and briefly examine a possible *remedy* for the situation. In the final section, 15.7, we give a checklist for the preparation of an empirical research report or term paper using a regression model.

This material is commonly included in textbooks on **econometrics,** which present statistical estimation and testing procedures for economics and finance (or other areas of business and social sciences) using the framework of the linear regression model. In scientific and engineering fields, similar methods are studied under the heading of *residual analysis* in texts on linear and nonlinear models. In the sections of this chapter, we will simplify this material and relate it to the regression analysis of Chapters 13 and 14.

The objectives of this chapter are several, but they are also limited. The reader should be able to understand the meaning of the assumptions and the potential problems for least squares regression if they do not hold. Moreover, one should know some basic methods for detecting if the key assumptions are valid or if they seem to be violated. In the latter case, it would be unwise to put too much trust in the exact estimates since an improved estimation method may be more appropriate to help overcome the violation of the assumption. The particulars of such improved estimation methods involving two-stage, nonlinear, or iterative methods are not presented here. The reader who needs to undertake more complex estimation methods should consult an expert or continue with a course or a text in econometric methods. Familiarity with and use of a computer would be essential in such courses.

section 15.2

The Ideal Assumptions and Conditions

Five assumptions for simple linear regression were presented in Section 13.4 and two extra conditions were included in Section 14.3. We repeat this listing below, generalizing to the multiple regression case, and add one other obvious condition. After the listing, more explanation about these items is given. Later sections of this chapter deal extensively with some particular items from this list.

Assumption 1.   The error term ϵ is independent of each of the m independent variables, $x_1, x_2, \ldots, x_m$.

Assumption 2.   The errors ϵ_i for all possible sets of given values $x_1, x_2, \ldots, x_m$ are normally distributed.

Assumption 3.   The expected value of the errors is zero for all possible sets of given values $x_1, x_2, \ldots, x_m$. That is, $E[\epsilon_i] = 0$ for $i = 1, 2, \ldots, n$.

Assumption 4.   The variance of the errors is finite and is the same for all possible sets of given values $x_1, x_2, \ldots, x_m$. That is, $V[\epsilon_i] = \sigma_\epsilon^2$ is a constant for $i = 1, 2, \ldots, n$.

Assumption 5.   Any two errors ϵ_i and ϵ_t are independent; their covariance is zero, $C[\epsilon_i, \epsilon_t] = 0$ for $i \neq t$.

Condition 1.   None of the independent variables is an exact linear combination of, nor highly correlated with, the other independent variables.

Condition 2.   The number of observations (n) must exceed the number ($m + 1$) of coefficients being estimated; that is, $n > m + 1$.

Condition 3.   The true relation between the variables denoted by y and $x_1, x_2, \ldots, x_m$ in the model is a *straight-line* (linear) relation.

Correlation Between x_j and the Disturbance ϵ

The first assumption was used in the previous presentation on least-squares estimation. It concerns the independence between the explanatory variables and the disturbance term in the same observation period. This assumption will be true necessarily when x is a *fixed* variable with values known in advance, rather than a *random* variable with values drawn from an underlying sampling distribution. When x is a fixed variable, it must be independent of the random variable ϵ, since the covariance of a random variable and a constant is always zero. When x is a random variable, this assumption may be violated, and many of our previous results are *not* true.

A violation of assumption 1 most often results from either measurement error or simultaneity between y and x_j. Let us first consider the problem arising from **simultaneity** when the underlying theory suggests not only a causal relation from the variable x_j affecting y, but also from y to x_j. Such a two-way causal ordering cannot be adequately reflected in a single-equation model. Instead, a set of simultaneous equations is needed in which both y and x_j are *jointly* dependent variables based on other explanatory variables and one or more disturbance terms.

❑ **EXAMPLE 15.1**   A typical simultaneous relation between two variables involves the relation between x = national income and y = consumption expenditures. A simple model to determine the level of consumption expenditures is theoretically specified to include national income as an explanatory factor:

$$\text{Consumption} = \alpha + \beta(\text{National income}) + \epsilon$$

Obviously, in this model, consumption depends on the error term. By assumption 1, the independent factor, national income, should be independent of the error term. However, methods of determining national accounts prescribe that one component of national income is consumption expenditures (as well as investment expenditures, government expenditures, and foreign expenditures on our exports).

National income = Consumption + Investment + Government + Net exports

Since the error term affects consumption and since consumption is a component of national income, the error term must be related to national income. This violates assumption 1. ■

Another common problem resulting in a violation of assumption 1 is **error in measurement** of the explanatory variable. If the variable x_j is incorrectly measured, say by a constant percentage, as in a 1% error in measurement, then for larger values of x_j, the size of the error, $\epsilon = 0.01x_j$, would also be larger. The correlation between x_j and ϵ will not be zero, especially if the error-in-measurement component dominates the other components of the overall disturbance. See Figure 15.1 for a sketch of this situation.

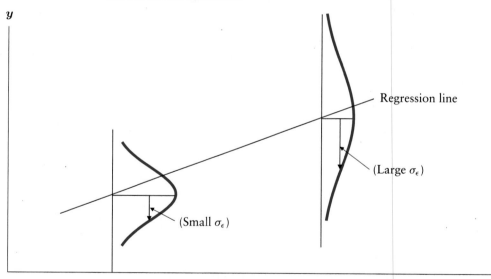

FIGURE 15.1   Violation of assumption 1 and assumption 4

□ **EXAMPLE 15.2**   A food manager for 37 schools in her district has a model to estimate the required re-stocking of paper products at the end of each week. Since school cafeterias have limited storage space, the paper supplies are delivered each weekend for the upcoming week. One factor in the model is x = the number of lunches served in the school during the week. Since the compiling of the information, obtaining supplies from distributors, and loading the delivery truck all take time, the manager requires each school to report the number of lunches it had served during the week by Friday at 9 a.m. Obviously, the Friday lunch data are not available.

The values for x will be inaccurate, and the error term ϵ will be greater in the larger schools, which serve more lunches on a typical Friday than the smaller schools. This inaccuracy of reports, or in other situations, improper accruals, causes the disturbance term to be correlated with the explanatory factor x. The model will still make reasonable projections for the food manager, but the coefficient of x (number of lunches) will be biased high in order to offset the consistently low measurement of this variable. ■

Other violations of assumption 1 may occur when an important variable is omitted from the regression analysis as suggested in Example 15.3 or when the underlying behaviour changes from consistent to erratic as in Example 15.4.

▢ **EXAMPLE 15.3** Let us consider the problem of estimating demand for compact cars, where the quantity demanded is y and the price of compacts is x. For simplicity, suppose that we assume the only variable of importance omitted from this model is the price of the substitute good, larger vehicles. If the price of compacts increases, we would expect a lower demand for compacts, assuming that all other factors are equal. But all other factors are not equal, since demand also depends on the price of larger vehicles. If, as the price of compacts increases, it becomes more and more difficult to predict demand then assumption 1 is violated. In other words, the errors increase because we do not know what will happen to the price of larger vehicles and uncertainty increases in this market. ■

▢ **EXAMPLE 15.4** Suppose that y is investment expenditures by firms and x is annual growth in sales. If sales growth is 5–10%, firms might make corresponding investment expenditures to replace worn-out equipment and buy some new goods to allow for some expansion of production. This behavioural response would be quite consistent across firms. However, suppose that sales growth for a group of firms was 75–100%. More variation in response could be expected. Some firms might feel very optimistic and make large investment expenditures to double their output. Others might be very cautious and feel that the sales growth was a one-time increase. They might save the extra revenues temporarily and not expand at all. They might not even replace what wears out, and instead, use the current sales figures as motivation to sell out at a good price. The errors ϵ and the sales growth x are not independent because the relation fits much better (small ϵ) in the range of x where investment behaviour is consistent and fits much worse (large ϵ) in the range of x where firms make widely different decisions on investment expenditures. ■

All these cases of potential violations of assumption 1 have quite serious implications for our analysis. When assumption 1 is violated, the primary effect is that our estimators, a for the intercept α, b_j for the slope coefficients β_j, and s_e^2 for the variance of the disturbance σ_ϵ^2, are all *biased*. This also affects the correctness of the t- and F-distributed test statistics that we presented in Chapters 13 and 14.

In practice, nearly every model relating economic or business variables will involve some extent of mismeasurement, simultaneity, or changing behaviour that may cause a violation of assumption 1. Unfortunately, there is no good and simple way to detect this violation statistically. The only estimates we have of the disturbance terms ϵ_i are the residuals e_i of the regression equation. One would be tempted to test for possible correlation between an explanatory factor x and the disturbance by examining the correlation of e with x. However, under the method of least squares, this correlation is always zero. Refer to Example 14.5. The best detection method for assumption 1 is careful thinking about the specification to understand any potential simultaneity and a careful examination of the data gathering and reporting process to learn about potential mismeasurement.

When the specified relation among y and $x_1, x_2, \ldots, x_m$ is relatively strong and these potential violations are minor, the extent of the bias in our estimators may not be worth worrying about. In cases in which the problem is potentially severe, a partial remedy is often obtained by using a two-stage method of estimation. We do not pursue this topic further in this text, but interested readers can consult textbooks in econometrics under the topics of *instrumental variable estimation* and *simultaneity.*

Normal Distribution of ϵ with Mean Zero

Assumption 2 is generally not violated in a well-specified model for which a full range of values is available for the measures of the variables. Errors in processes, errors in nature, deviation in measures of behaviour, and other disturbances tend to be normally distributed. Specific errors caused by wars, floods, elections, diseases, or other *shocks* are not. All such error components, as well as other errors due to systematic business, economic, and noneconomic factors not explicitly included in the model, are blotted together in the disturbance term ϵ. Since ϵ is a composite of so many factors and since many of these factors are unrelated to each other, it is reasonable to assume that many of them act to offset each other. Therefore, large values of ϵ are much less likely to occur than small values, giving a bell-shaped distribution of errors. Indeed, when *many independent* factors act together to determine a random variable, a form of the *central limit theorem* guarantees that their joint effect produces a normally distributed random variable. Consequently, when the important explanatory factors are included in the model and *many other linearly independent* factors are components of the error term, it is reasonable to expect *normally distributed errors*. The importance of this assumption of normality and some methods of detecting if it holds or not are presented in Section 15.3.

Similarly, assumption 3 is generally reasonable for the regression model. Both assumptions 2 and 3 are represented in Figure 15.2 by showing the distribution of any ϵ_i to be normal and centred on the regression line. If many independent factors are components of the disturbance term, they will be offsetting to a large degree and quite unpredictable. Thus, for a given set of values for the explanatory variables, the differences between the true and the estimated values of y ought to be sometimes positive, sometimes negative, but on the average zero.

Assumption 3 is important because it establishes the estimability of the intercept α. Along with assumption 1, it is required in order to establish that the least-squares estimators of the coefficients are *unbiased*.

If the data for the dependent variable y are measured incorrectly so that its values are consistently too high or too low, this inaccuracy will be absorbed by the error term. The expected value of ϵ will be different from zero. In the estimation, the least squares computation will adjust for this by providing an estimate of the intercept which is correspondingly biased to offset the measurement discrepancy in y. In using accounting data for the variable y, improper accruals or the failure to adjust for inflation are just two situations which could lead to a violation of assumption 3.

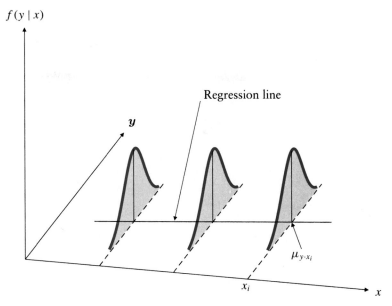

FIGURE 15.2   Normally distributed errors ϵ_i about $\mu_{y \cdot x_i}$ with expected value of zero for any value of x_i

There is no simple and powerful method to test statistically if $E[\epsilon_i] = 0$ or not, and none is presented in this text. The only estimate of ϵ_i for case i is the one residual e_i, and a sample of size one is very weak for testing an average.

You might think that the collection of all n residuals could be used, but least squares computation always requires that $\Sigma e_i = 0$, so the average of e is zero in every estimation regardless of what is the true value of $E[\epsilon_i]$. The analyst must review the desired meaning of the variable y in the model and consider carefully if its measurement given in the available data is accurate, or at least randomly inaccurate, but not consistently wrong in the same direction. Of course, if one knew that it is consistently over- or under-stated, a multiple of the given values could be used to obtain a more correct dataset. For example, if the data on *number of lunches* in Example 15.2 were to be used in some model to represent the dependent variable, and we knew that it only includes lunches on 4 days (Monday to Thursday, omitting Fridays), we could approximate the correct five day value by multiplying each observed value by 1.25.

Constant Variance and Independence of the Disturbances

We specify a constant variance for the disturbances in assumption 4. The variability of points in the population about the true regression equation must not change. In Figure 15.2, this constant variance of ϵ_i is represented by depicting all the normal distributions about $\mu_{y \cdot x}$ with the same standard deviation as opposed to Figure 15.1 where the spread of the distributions of errors change. The distribution of any ϵ_i should not be more spread out or more compact than another.

Assumption 4 is often violated in data measured at the same point of time (*cross-sectional data*). For example, in a study relating certain variables across cities, assumption 4 might be violated because of differing legal codes, climate, or political interests. Similarly, a study relating educational attainment and household income might have different variances of errors for different households due to differing influences of cultures or social biases on the value of formal education. The problem is called *heteroscedasticity* (from Greek for changing dispersion).

Assumption 5 requires serial independence of the disturbances. If each observation on values of y and $x_1, x_2, \ldots, x_m$, is to be used for maximum information about the population regression model, the *noise* (errors) in each observation should not be related. Otherwise, the relationship among our observed values is unduly affected in a nonrandom way by some continuing effects of a one-time *shock* or the temporary effect of an excluded variable. This problem of carry-over effects from one error to the next tends to occur in time-series data, especially when the time intervals are short.

If some underlying factors not specified in the model exert an influence on the fit of the model over several time periods, the disturbances tend to be correlated to each other. Consider a change in corporate tax laws that might affect both the amount of investment (due to investment tax credit or depreciation write-offs) and the amount of retained earnings (due to taxes on profits). This legal factor may not be represented in the model, but its effect may be seen in the errors of the regression equation. The average relationship estimated may give values too high before the tax-law change and too low afterwards. The residuals would then tend to be all negative for observations taken before the tax change and all positive for observations made after the change. Thus, the residuals would not be occurring at random but would systematically be related to each other. This problem is called *autocorrelation* (Greek for related back to itself).

Knowledge about a violation of assumption 5 is critical to the analyst because of its effects on the least squares regression results. Just as with violations of assumption 4, the estimator b_j of a coefficient loses the desirable property of efficiency. The estimators have larger theoretical standard errors than they should.

When assumption 5 is violated, an estimator b_j is still unbiased so that on average it would be correct. However, because the estimator is inefficient, our chances are decreased that the single estimate computed using one set of sample data will be close to the true value. Also, when assumption 5 does not hold, the estimator of the variance of the disturbances is biased. Since the estimate s_e is a crucial element in our methods of inference and testing, the effect is that our test statistics are not as appropriate as the statistical theory defines them to be under *ideal* conditions.

The problems associated with violations of assumptions 4 and 5 and a discussion of methods to detect such violations are deferred to Sections 15.4 and 15.5 for a fuller explanation.

Conditions 1, 2, and 3

These final conditions about the regression analysis are required in order for our least-squares statistics to have the meaningful interpretations and desirable properties that we gave them in Chapters 13 and 14. Condition 1, requiring linear independence among the explanatory variables, is necessary in order for our calculations of estimates to be defined. More on this problem can be found in Section 15.3.

Condition 2, that $n > m + 1$, is essential in order to have positive degrees of freedom in our test statistics. No meaningful conclusions can be drawn from our model unless the results are based on a sufficient number of sample observations.

The number of cases n should be sufficiently greater than the number of coefficients to be estimated in the model so that the results are believable and useful. No one will be convinced by a study based on a sample of 2 or on a regression when $n - (m + 1) = 2$. Degrees of freedom of at least 30 are an aid for robustness of the assumption of normality of ϵ_i and for the t- and F-statistics used in inference. Larger degrees of freedom of 100 or more are desirable, and values in the thousands are common for studies based on cross-sectional survey data. The trade-off is cost; each extra sample case requires associated time and cost.

Condition 3 requires that our model specifies a linear relation between y and x_j. If the variables that are represented by these measures of y and x_j do not have a linear relation, we face an obvious problem of misspecification. This may produce rather unreliable results. The statistical methods of regression analysis are only as good as the data and the specification of the model allow them to be. If the true relation among y and x_j is nonlinear, a transformation of variables might be employed before using the linear model. We examine some nonlinear specifications in Section 15.6.

section 15.3

Normality and Multicollinearity

In this section, we consider two topics. First, we examine more fully the basic assumption of normality for the distribution of ϵ_i, the disturbance term in the regression model. Second, we consider problems that arise when condition 1 specified in Section 15.2 is violated.

The value of assumption 2 of normality for the disturbance term is that the distributions of the estimators for the coefficients in the model depend on the probability distribution of ϵ. Thus, if assumption 2 holds, these estimators will be normally distributed. Also, the implications of the normal distribution for ϵ make it proper to develop and use the t- and F-distributed test statistics as we have described. The question that arises is, how do we know if we have a problem in assuming normality and proceeding in the usual manner of analysis?

In some cases, it may be obvious that there is a potential problem. If the data for the dependent variable y is truncated against an upper or lower bound, the errors might be restricted in one direction. Their distribution might look more like half of a normal distribution, or at least be skewed away from normality. For example, suppose y is measured as the expenditure on new cars by households during the past six months. The sample may include a large proportion of households for which this value is zero. Since the other actual prices of new cars may be \$10,000 and above, the model will predict some positive value for y even for those cases where the actual y is zero. This will give a large number of negative disturbances not symmetrically balanced by positive ones. The distribution of disturbances would not be normal.

If the data are not truncated or censored or limited by some maximum or minimum bound so that the full range of potential values for y can be observed, then assumption 2 does not usually pose any difficulty. However, subtle problems can be missed even by the most clear-thinking analyst so some statistical methods for detecting non-normality are helpful.

Histogram of Residuals

Our only estimates of the true disturbance terms are the residuals from the regression equation. Using the collection of all n residuals, we can approximate the likely shape of the underlying distribution of the disturbances. A first approach is to plot a histogram of the residuals.

We know that the mean of the residuals is zero and we can calculate the standard deviation of the residuals. For large samples, we can use the standard error of estimate s_e as an indication of the spread of the distribution of residuals without introducing any significant error. The residuals can be grouped into categories depending on how many standard errors they lie from zero. The frequencies of each group can be counted and the resulting frequencies plotted.

For a simple example, suppose the standard error of estimate in a regression is $40. Obviously, one-half the standard error is $20. We could use class intervals of width 20 to form categories of zero to $20, over $20 to $40, over $40 to $60, et cetera, until we get to four standard errors above the mean. This upper category would be over $140 to $160. Any residual larger than $160 would indicate an outlier. A similar list of groups would be defined in the negative direction.

For ease of comparison and communication, the class groups are often defined in standardized units rather than the units of the particular problem. We use z-scores by calculating the standardized residuals (e/s_e) and assigning them into groups of zero to 0.5, over 0.5 to 1.0, over 1.0 to 2, over 2 to 3, and over 3 to 4, and symmetrically in the negative direction. The use of half unit intervals close to the mean and larger intervals in the tails of the distribution gives us greater accuracy in detecting if the resulting distribution looks like a normal distribution. Also, it helps to avoid problems of low frequencies in some groups. Figure 15.3 illustrates the resulting histogram from a set of 100 residuals where the standard error was 40. The top scale on the horizontal axis is in terms of standardized units and is the one most commonly used.

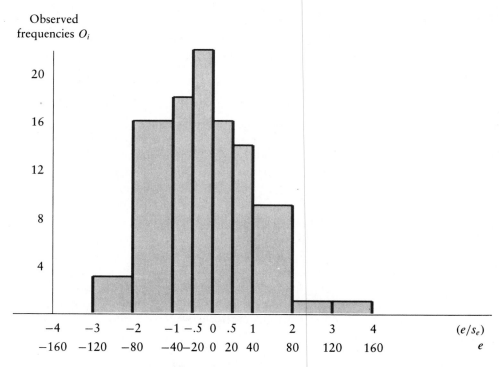

FIGURE 15.3   Histogram of residuals

Examination of the histogram reveals if normality seems acceptable. Remember the guidelines for the bell-shaped normal curve with about two-thirds of all values within $\pm$ one standard error, and lesser amounts symmetrically in the upper and lower tails. In Figure 15.3, some skewness is evident, but the values do tend to concentrate in the middle of the distribution. The observed frequencies within $\pm 1 s_e$ appear to be $18 + 22 + 16 + 14 = 70$, which is 70% of all 100 residuals.

Test for Normality

A statistical test of comparison of the frequencies in the histogram with the theoretical distribution can be made. The test of goodness of fit of an observed distribution to an expected distribution using the chi-square test statistic is presented in Section 18.3. The test of hypotheses applied in this situation are:

$$H_0 : \text{the distribution of disturbances is normal}$$

$$H_a : \text{the distribution of disturbances is not normal}$$

The test statistic compares the observed frequencies of residuals within each class interval with the expected number that would occur in a drawing from a normal distribution. The observed frequencies of the residuals are denoted by O_i and the expected number based on the normal probability table is E_i. The degrees of freedom for the test equal the number of class intervals less one, denoted $k - 1$. The calculated test statistic is found as follows:

Chi-square test statistic:
$$\chi^2 = \Sigma (O_i - E_i)^2 / E_i \tag{15.1}$$
where $i = 1, 2, ..., k$, and the degrees of freedom $= k - 1$

If the calculated value of the chi-square statistic exceeds the critical value for the desired significance level, we conclude that the observed frequencies differ so much from the expected frequencies that the underlying distribution is not normal.

One problem with using this test is that it requires a large enough sample so that none of the expected frequencies is less than 1 and no more than 10 percent of the classes have frequencies less than 5. Categories may have to be combined to fulfill these guidelines. Otherwise, the power of the test is diminished substantially. The grouping of categories by half or full standard error units as in Figure 15.3 suffers from the problem of having too few values occurring in the outer intervals. An alternate grouping that is commonly used defines each of 20 class intervals to include five percent of the theoretical distribution. (See Section 18.3.)

□ **EXAMPLE 15.5**   We use the data in Figure 15.3 to test for normality using the chi-square statistic. The end two categories in each tail are combined into a single class interval as shown in Table 15.1. The resulting number of intervals is $k = 8$ so the degrees of freedom for the test are $k - 1 = 7$. With a significance level of 0.10, the critical value from Table VII is 12.0.

Let us review the method of finding expected frequencies using the standardized normal Table III. Consider one of the intervals, say $1 \leq z < 2$. The cumulative probability for $z = 1.0$ is 0.8413, and the cumulative value for $z = 2$ is 0.9772. The difference is the probability of occurrence in the interval, which is 0.1359. Rounding off we have 13.6 percent of the total number of residuals as the expected frequency in this interval. Since $n = 100$ the expected frequency is $0.136(100) = 13.6$. Each interval is treated similarly; the lower side intervals are symmetric with those on the upper side.

Table 15.1 presents the calculations. Column one gives the class intervals; columns 2 and 3 give the observed and the expected frequencies. Column 4 gives the value of the component of the chi-square test statistic for that interval. The sum of column 4 is the desired value for the test.

TABLE 15.1   Calculation of the Statistic for Testing Normality

Class Interval	O_i	E_i	$(O_i - E_i)^2/E_i$
$-4 \leq z < -2$	3	2.3	0.21
$-2 \leq z < -1$	16	13.6	0.42
$-1 \leq z < -0.5$	18	15.0	0.60
$-0.5 \leq z < 0$	22	19.1	0.44
$0 \leq z < 0.5$	16	19.1	0.50
$0.5 \leq z < 1$	14	15.0	0.07
$1 \leq z < 2$	9	13.6	1.56
$2 \leq z < 4$	2	2.3	0.04
Sum	100	100.0	3.84

Note that the expected frequencies for the similar categories above and below the mean of zero are symmetric. Also, remember it does not matter which end of a class interval includes the endpoint since the normal distribution is continuous. Overlapping values are not allowed so that each residual is unambiguously placed.

The computations in Table 15.1 lead to a calculated chi-square value of 3.84. This is well below the critical value of 12.0, so we fail to reject the null hypothesis. We conclude that the assumption of normality of the disturbances should be accepted. ∎

Dependency Among the Explanatory Variables

We now consider the violation or near violation of condition 1, which specifies that none of the independent variables can be an exact linear combination of the other independent variables. If the independent variables, $x_1, x_2, \ldots, x_m$ are perfectly linearly related to each other, they are linearly *dependent*. In this case, no estimates of the partial regression coefficients can be obtained, since the normal equations will not be solvable; that is, the method of least squares breaks down and no estimates can be calculated. We would be trying to perform calculations that are essentially the same as dividing a number by zero. Computer programs typically check for this dependency and will report an error message indicating that calculations cease or are not to be believed.

Perfect dependence seldom occurs in practice because most investigators are careful not to include two or more explanatory variables that represent the same influence on the dependent variable y in the regression model. Indeed, even if an investigator did accidentally include two or more such variables, it is unlikely that the *sample* observations representing measures of these variables would be perfectly related because some slight errors of measurement and sampling are almost inevitable. A situation to avoid is using dummy variables which have the same values across all observations, such as if all cities in a sample that had a town council form of government, indicated by dummy variable $Gov = 1$, were also all in the same region indicated by a dummy variable $Reg = 1$.

However, special problems even occur when two or more of the independent variables are strongly (but not perfectly) correlated to one another. A near violation of condition 1 causes difficulty in distinguishing the separate effects on y of the included explanatory variables. This problem is called **multicollinearity**.

☐ **EXAMPLE 15.6** In our investment example (Section 14.2), the variable x_2 (retained earnings) was correlated with the stock price index (x_1). By using x_1 alone, 83.45% of the variation in y is explained; by using x_2 alone, 77.7% of the variation in y is explained. However, by using both x_1 and x_2, the combined explained variation is 89% of the total variation. Thus, there is considerable *overlap* in the explanatory roles of the variables x_1 and x_2, probably since both react to other economic, political, and social factors within society. Precisely distinguishing the separate influences of the two variables is the problem caused by multicollinearity. In this example, we realize that there is some collinearity because of the large correlation between x_1 and x_2. The simple correlation between the two independent variables can be shown to be $r_{x_1 x_2} = 0.8158$, indicating a possible multicollinearity problem. ■

Effects of Multicollinearity

When multicollinearity occurs, the least-squares estimates are still unbiased and efficient. The problem is that the estimated standard error of the coefficient (say, s_{b_j} for the coefficient b_j) tends to be inflated. This standard error tends to be larger than it would be in the absence of multicollinearity because the estimates are very sensitive to any changes in the sample observations or in the model specification. In other words, including or excluding a particular variable or certain observations may greatly change the estimated partial coefficient. When s_{b_j} is larger than it should be, the t-value for testing the significance of β_j is smaller than it should be (Formula 14.13). Thus, one is likely to conclude that a variable x_j is not important in the relationship when it really is.

> When the presence of multicollinearity is quite severe, we have less confidence in the estimates of the coefficients. They are prone to have excessively large variances and are not precise in distinguishing the separate effects on y of the individual explanatory variables.

If the purpose of the model is *forecasting* values for the dependent variable y based on new observations of the explanatory variables, the multicollinearity problem may not need any drastic correction. If the multicollinearity can be expected to continue, forecasts are not seriously disturbed, since the individual estimates of the coefficients, and of the forecasts, are unbiased.

To repeat this point in a slightly different way, the effect of severe multicollinearity may be to increase s_{b_j} so much that no coefficient b_j is significantly different from zero. Yet the joint effect of all the explanatory variables in the model is highly significant. The model may have a high value of R^2 based on the sample observations. This high degree of fit indicates that the estimated values will be very close to the observed values within the sample. If this multicollinearity continues for new observations and the specification is not changed, the model will also give a close fit for these new sample values. Forecasts based on them will be close to the actual values.

Detection of a Multicollinearity Problem

The quickest indicator of multicollinearity follows from the above paragraph. In analyzing the results of a regression, you may find a fairly large and significant value of R^2 but low and insignificant values of the t-ratios. The former indicates that the model is useful overall, while the latter indicates that none of the included variables is particularly useful. It is likely in such a case that the explanatory variables are correlated with each other so that the combined effect of them on y is considerable, but that no individual effect is discernable.

Another approach for detecting multicollinearity follows from the discussion in Example 15.6. We see that a high correlation between any pair of explanatory variables x_j and x_k may be used to help identify multicollinearity. It is possible, however, for all independent variables to have relatively small *mutual* correlations and yet to have some multicollinearity among three or more of them. Sometimes it is possible to detect these higher-order associations by using a multiple coefficient of determination that deals only with the explanatory variables. Suppose that we use the symbol R_j^2 to denote the multiple coefficient of determination for variable x_j with all the other $(m-1)$ independent variables, $x_1, x_2, \ldots, x_{j-1}, x_{j+1}, \ldots, x_m$. Such a measure could be determined for each of the independent variables. Generally, if one or more of these values, $R_1^2, R_2^2, \ldots, R_j^2, \ldots, R_m^2$, is approximately the same size, or greater than the multiple coefficient of determination for the model, $R^2 y \cdot x_1 \ldots x_m$, then multicollinearity is a problem. In other words, if the strength of the association among the independent variables is approximately as great as the strength of their combined linear association with the dependent variable, then the amount of overlapping influence may be substantial enough to make the interpretation of the separate influences difficult and imprecise.

If the number of observations is quite small, these comparisons may be made by using adjusted R^2 measures which are corrected for the different number of variables involved. We do not present any statistical method for testing whether these values indicate high multicollinearity or not. *Since multicollinearity is a property of the sample observations, inference about the population is not appropriate.*

☐ **EXAMPLE 15.7**   Consider a model with four independent variables:

$$y = \alpha + \beta_1 x_1 + \beta_2 x_2 + \beta_3 x_3 + \beta_4 x_4 + \epsilon$$

The multiple coefficient of determination for this model is:

$$R^2_{y \cdot x_1 x_2 x_3 x_4} = 0.80$$

To check for multicollinearity, one would first calculate the six simple correlations between pairs of independent variables:

$$r_{x_1 x_2} \qquad r_{x_1 x_3} \qquad r_{x_1 x_4} \qquad r_{x_2 x_3} \qquad r_{x_2 x_4} \qquad r_{x_3 x_4}$$

If one of these is close to unity, so that its square exceeds $R^2 = 0.80$, then imprecise estimation is likely. The next step would be to calculate the multiple coefficients of determination for each explanatory variable with the other three:

$$R^2_{x_1 \cdot x_2 x_3 x_4} \qquad R^2_{x_2 \cdot x_1 x_3 x_4} \qquad R^2_{x_3 \cdot x_1 x_2 x_4} \qquad \text{and} \qquad R^2_{x_4 \cdot x_1 x_2 x_3}$$

If any of these are as large as $R^2_{y \cdot x_1 x_2 x_3 x_4} = 0.80$, then the problem of multicollinearity may be substantial.   ■

☐ **STUDY QUESTION 15.1**   **Multicollinearity in the Housing Price Model**

Examine the extent of multicollinearity in the data for the multiple regression model for housing price (Table 14.7 and Figure 14.3c), where the following is true:

$$\text{Price} = \alpha + \beta_1(\text{Income}) + \beta_2(\text{Rent}) + \beta_3(\text{Vacant}) + \epsilon$$

• **ANSWER**   The value of the multiple coefficient of determination for the model is $R^2 = 0.84$.

The mutual correlation coefficients among all the variables are given in Table 14.7. The largest (in absolute value) correlation coefficient between any two explanatory variables is $r_{\text{Rent, Vacant}} = -0.896$; its square is 0.803. This is large enough to be worrisome.

The next step is to relate each x_j with the other two explanatory variables using a computer program for multiple regression or correlation. It is found that the multiple coefficients of determination for each explanatory variable with the other two are:

$$R^2{}_{\text{Income}\cdot x_2 x_3} = 0.51$$
$$R^2{}_{\text{Rent}\cdot x_1 x_3} = 0.82$$
$$R^2{}_{\text{Vacant}\cdot x_1 x_2} = 0.81$$

None of these is as large as $R^2{}_{y\cdot x_1 x_2 x_3} = 0.84$, but two are very close. Multicollinearity is evident as a potential problem in making coefficients seem less significant than they might be. However, this is probably not a serious problem for this estimation since two of the three coefficients have significant t-ratios anyway.   ■

Correction for Multicollinearity

The primary problem of multicollinearity is that the values of b_j are quite imprecise. Unfortunately, there is no one best remedy for this problem in all cases, nor even a consistent ranking of possible remedies that should be attempted. With some skill and a lot of luck, one of the following alternatives might provide more precise estimates of the desired coefficients.

Changing the Specification. One common procedure is to select the independent variable *most seriously involved* in the multicollinearity and remove it from the model. The difficulty with this approach is that the model now may not correctly represent the population relationship, and all estimated coefficients would contain a *specification bias*. It would be better to try to replace the multicollinear variable with another that is less collinear but may still measure the same theoretical influence.

☐ **EXAMPLE 15.8**   In the specification of an investment model, if the theoretical variable *business expectations* is measured by a stock price index that is highly collinear with retained earnings, then it may be possible to replace the stock index with some other measure, perhaps an index of business expectations obtained by surveying executives in the 500 largest corporations. In this way, the multicollinearity may be reduced while the theoretical base for the model is still retained. Of course, the change in variables is useful only if the new variable is less collinear with the other explanatory variables than was the original variable.   ■

Transformation or Aggregation of Variables. Sometimes the problem of multi-collinearity is resolved by making suitable changes in the definitions of the variables in the model. Two popular suggestions are *aggregations* and *transformations* of variables. An aggregation follows some rule for combining several variables into one *composite variable*. A transformation follows a rule for creating a new variable (call it x^*) as a function of current or past values of one of the given variables.

Transformations that are commonly used are ordinary first differences or logarithmic first differences. For a variable x these are represented by the transformation rules, $x_t^* = x_t - x_{t-1}$ or $x_t^* = \ln(x_t/x_{t-1}) = \ln(x_t) - \ln(x_{t-1})$, for observations $t = 2, 3, \ldots, n$. The error terms in the model must also be transformed accordingly. The assumptions for least-squares estimation from Section 15.2 must apply to the transformed variables and error terms. These do not automatically hold true even if they were true for the model before the transformation.

The logarithmic first difference is often used to eliminate the effect of trends and cycles in a time series of positive values. To the extent that the explanatory variables have trends and cyclical components in common, this transformation helps to reduce multicollinearity.

Such transformations are also useful when forecasts are to be made based on new observations of the explanatory variables. If a growth trend occurs, new values would tend to be larger than any previously observed values. Forecast intervals would be excessively large owing to the large deviation of the new given value from the sample mean of the previous observations (Section 13.8). However, the size of the first difference or of the logarithmic first difference is probably within the range of previous experience of such differences. Thus, the standard error for the forecast of the difference would not be exaggerated, and the confidence interval would not be unduly wide.

The type of aggregation of variables that is most common is a grouping of collinear variables into a composite index that allows a similar interpretation. Index numbers are discussed in Section 16.5. For example, four separate interest rate variables that are highly correlated with each other may be replaced by some single weighted composite of these variables. The total effect of the interest rate variables on the dependent variable may still be reflected by the coefficient of this single variable, and the multicollinearity in the model may be eliminated.

Forming a composite in this way is fruitful only if the variables included in the composite have some useful *combined* interpretation. The meaning of the composite will be unclear if diverse factors are involved. Statistically, the formation of a composite is most useful if the included variables are highly correlated with each other and each has a low correlation with the remaining explanatory variables not included within the composite.

Improvements in the Data or the Calculations. Very frequently, multicollinearity may occur as a result of data that are limited in coverage and do not adequately represent the domain of the variables being sampled. If additional data could be acquired, it is possible that more independent variation would be observed and the multicollinearity would be reduced. The new data may be obtained simply by increasing the sample size. If this is not possible within the restraints of the variable definitions, model specification, and purpose of the analysis, an independent study may be done on a suitable submodel for which other data can be used. On the basis of this submodel, one or more of the coefficients of some collinear variables in the original model may be approximated by these so-called **extraneous estimates.** By using these extraneous estimates, the *other* coefficients in the original model may be estimated from the original data under conditions of reduced multicollinearity.

☐ **EXAMPLE 15.9** Suppose the model $y = \alpha + \beta_1 x_1 + \beta_2 x_2 + \beta_3 x_3 + \epsilon$ is to be estimated, but x_2 and x_3 are highly correlated. If independent data are available that provide evidence on the relation between x_3 and the dependent variable y, an extraneous estimate of β_3 may be obtained, say $\widehat{\beta_3}$. The model can be rewritten with a revised dependent variable and error term:

$$y^* = (y - \widehat{\beta_3} x_3) = \alpha + \beta_1 x_1 + \beta_2 x_2 + \epsilon^*$$

The remaining coefficients, β_1 and β_2, can be estimated on the basis of the original data. ■

The use of extraneous estimates creates some other questions of interpretation and validity. More of the econometric literature on extraneous estimates should be studied before the reader uses this approach.

When multicollinearity is a problem, intermediate calculations used in multiple regression computer programs (to find determinants and inverses of matrices) are subject to roundoff error. These errors affect the calculations of the estimates (b_j) and their standard errors (s_{b_j}), the standard error of estimate (s_e), and the statistics for testing significance. Consequently, when a particular estimation of a model seems to involve multicollinearity, we should try to make the calculation of these inverses as precise as possible. Scaling the data so means of all variables in the model are within a factor of 100 of each other is usually all that is needed for good computational accuracy.

PROBLEMS

15.1 Explain why a disturbance term ϵ is included in the population regression model.

15.2 Explain what is meant by simultaneity in the specification of a regression model.

15.3 Consider which assumption(s) may be violated in each of the following cases for a simple model of the form $y = \alpha + \beta x + \epsilon$.

a) y and x are both growing over time, and the error in measurement of x is a constant 3% of the size of x.

b) x measures unemployment and y measures the change in average wages for quarterly observations from 1980–1995 for a South American country. During 1992–1995 there are externally controlled wage and price guidelines so that the model consistently overpredicts wages during this period.

c) The specified model is erroneous, and the true form of the relation between y and x is similar to the right half of a convex (with respect to x) parabola. [*Hint:* Draw a scatter diagram of such a parabolic relation and draw a straight line through it

representing the best linear fit. Examine the signs of successive residuals.]

15.4 Consider a model specifying annual aggregate consumption dependent on disposable personal income and a disturbance term, as in

$$\text{Consumption} = \alpha + \beta \ (\text{income}) + \epsilon.$$

a) For assumptions 1–5, discuss the implication of each on the underlying economic environment in which this model is presumed to hold.

b) Criticize one of the assumptions and suggest a reason why it may impose an invalid background condition.

15.5 Consider a model specifying quarterly corporate dividends dependent on total corporate profits in the preceding four quarters and a disturbance term. Answer parts (a) and (b) of Problem 15.4 in this context.

15.6 Give an argument that explains why any one of the standard assumptions for regression analysis would be violated, in each of the following situations, for a simple model of the form $y = \alpha + \beta x + \epsilon$. Also, suggest how the violation of this assumption would affect the properties of the ordinary least-squares (OLS) estimators.

a) y measures wealth of an individual and x measures this person's age; $V[y]$ increases with age.

b) Observations on y and x are daily stock averages and volume of trading, respectively.

15.7 Explain the meaning of each of the following assumptions in which ϵ is a random term in a linear-regression model. Give an example of some specified model that might violate each assumption, and explain why.

a) $C[\epsilon_i, \epsilon_t] = 0$ for $i \neq t$

b) $V[\epsilon_i] \neq \sigma_\epsilon^2$ for all i

15.8 For the model specified in Problem 14.25 on academic test scores, select one of the assumptions 1–5 of Section 15.2 and express its meaning in terms of the model. Suggest some real situation for which the assumption would probably be violated.

15.9 Repeat Problem 15.8 for the model on corn yield specified in Problem 14.20.

15.10 Explain the meaning of multicollinearity, and specify one of its effects that you think is important.

15.11 Suppose that the values of y are related to both variables x and w. Data are given in Table 15.2.

TABLE 15.2   Observations for y, x, and w

y	x	w
1.0	1.00	5.0
2.0	1.44	3.5
3.0	1.96	3.0
4.0	3.24	4.0
5.0	4.00	1.0
6.0	7.84	2.0

a) Plot the relationship between y and x, and between y and w. Is the relationship approximately linear in both cases? If not, what would be the problem in fitting an equation of the form $\widehat{y} = a + bx + cw$?

b) Find the simple correlation coefficient of variables x and w. Do you think multicollinearity might be a problem in using x and w as copredictors of y?

15.12 The residuals from a sample regression equation based on 120 cases are placed into 9 classes. The observed frequencies are compared with the expected frequencies for a normal distribution.

a) What is the expected frequency for the interval, $0 \leq z < 0.5$?

b) How many residuals are expected to fall in the interval corresponding to $-2 \leq z < -1$?

c) Interpret the test result if the calculated chi-square value is 10.

15.13 The residuals from a sample regression equation based on 360 cases are placed into 10 classes. The observed frequencies are compared with the expected frequencies for a normal distribution.

a) What is the expected frequency for the interval, $2 \leq z$?

b) How many residuals are expected to fall in the interval corresponding to $-1 \leq z < -0.5$?

c) Interpret the test result if the calculated chi-square value is 18.

15.14 Given the Table 15.3 of observed frequencies of standardized residuals in standard deviation unit intervals,

TABLE 15.3   Frequencies of Standardized Residuals

Interval	Observed Frequency
$z \leq -2$	5
$-2 < z \leq -1$	40
$-1 < z \leq -0.5$	60
$-0.5 < z \leq 0$	120
$0 < z \leq 0.5$	95
$0.5 < z \leq 1$	85
$1 < z \leq 2$	75
$2 < z$	20

a) Explain which assumption underlying regression can be scrutinized based on this information.

b) Sketch a histogram representing this information and interpret it in reference to this assumption.

15.15 Using the information in Problem 15.14,

a) determine the expected frequencies for each class interval if the distribution were normal.

b) calculate a goodness of fit test and interpret the result.

♦ **15.16** With reference to assumption 2, interpret the following computer printout based on residuals from a regression analysis. In Table 15.4, $f(0)$ is the observed frequency, $f(E)$ is the expected frequency, and each $*$ represents one observation.

TABLE 15.4 Residuals from a Regression Analysis

$f(O)$	$f(E)$	z	Scale and Histogram
0	0.1		$\vert$
		-3	$\vdash$
0	1.0		$\vert$
		-2	$\vdash$
8	6.5		$\vert$ ********
		-1	$\vdash$
16	16.4		$\vert$ ***************
		0	$\vdash$
18	16.4		$\vert$ *****************
		1	$\vdash$
5	6.5		$\vert$ *****
		2	$\vdash$
1	1.0		$\vert$ *
		3	$\vdash$
0	0.1		$\vert$

15.17 In Problem 14.41, a model for total personal income tax in cities was estimated with a coefficient of determination of 0.7460. If the correlation coefficient between the two explanatory variables in that model is 0.9981, comment on a potential problem of multicollinearity.

15.18 In a multiple regression with four explanatory variables, $R^2 = 0.82$

a) Explain the meaning of multicollinearity if it occurred in this model.

b) If the correlation coefficient between variables x_1 and x_3 is 0.7, and between x_1 and x_4 is 0.8, what can be implied relative to multicollinearity?

c) What other measures would you want to know?

15.19 In a multiple regression with three explanatory variables, $R^2 = 0.56$.

a) Explain the effects of multicollinearity if it occurred in this model.

b) If the coefficient of determination for x_1 related to x_2 and x_3 is 0.75, what is the interpretation relative to multicollinearity?

15.20 In a multiple regression with five explanatory variables based on 66 observations, the calculated F value from the ANOVA table is 16.5. Also, the calculated t-ratios for coefficients of each variable are 0.77, 1.12, −0.31, 0.68, and 0.04 respectively. Interpret the meaning of this information relevant to condition 1.

15.21 The simple correlation matrix among explanatory variables in a regression model is given in Table 15.5.

a) Explain what values should be in the blank cells and fill them in correctly.

b) Interpret their relevance to a problem of multicollinearity if the R^2 for the model is 0.35 versus the case if the R^2 is 0.95.

TABLE 15.5 Correlation Matrix

	$X1$	$X2$	$X3$	$X4$
$X1$	1.0	0.7		
$X2$		1.0		0.8
$X3$	0.5	0.6		0.3
$X4$	0.4			

Heteroscedasticity

section 15.4

Referring to the disturbance terms in the regression model, **heteroscedasticity** defines the condition where the variance of ϵ is not constant across all observations, $i = 1, 2, \ldots, n$. In this section, we consider the violation of assumption 4 of Section 15.2, which states the desired condition of constant variance, $V[\epsilon_i] = \sigma_\epsilon^2$.

Usually, the assumption of constant variance is not seriously violated when using economic or business data *measured over time* unless some significant structural change occurred to affect the observations, such as a new law, a war, a revolution, or some natural disaster. More often, the problem of heteroscedasticity arises when cross-sectional data, *at a given point in time*, is used, such as employment or production data across firms, or tax and revenue data across cities. In these cases, the disturbances may not have constant variances because of differing factors related to the size or the legal code of the different cross-sectional entities. For example, large corporations have different structures and operate under different tax laws than do small business firms. Thus, one would expect a specified model to represent one of these types better than the other. The variance of disturbances for the one type that it fits best will be smaller than the variance of disturbances for observations of the other type.

Also, as was discussed in association with Figure 15.1, the violation of assumption 4 is not always independent of the violation of assumption 1. Errors in measurement may exist, for example, as a large component of the disturbance term. If there are errors in measurement that are proportional to some x_j or if there are changes in measurement procedures so that some observations have significantly more accuracy than others, the variance of the disturbance term will be smaller for the subset of observations with the smaller errors of measurement.

Effect of Hetero-scedasticity

When only assumption 4 is violated, the distribution and expectations of the least-squares estimators b_j of the coefficients β_j do not change. They are still linear and unbiased estimators with the properties of normality and consistency. The problem is that if the variance changes for different observations, the estimators b_j are not efficient. That is, $V[b_j]$, where the estimators b_j are obtained by the least-squares estimators, are greater than variances of b_j^* determined by some other estimating procedure that uses the additional information about the changing variance of the disturbance term.

The importance of assumption 4 is that it allows us to estimate only one variance of the disturbance rather than many different levels of variance across observations. Since the disturbance variance (σ_ϵ^2) is a term in the specification of the probability distribution of each least-squares estimator or of a forecast based on these estimators (Table 13.24), it is convenient to have one representation for this value rather than many. If assumption 4 does not hold and we fail to utilize the information about the changing variance of ϵ, the least-squares estimators of the coefficients in the regression model lose the desirable property of *efficiency*, having minimum variance compared with any other linear unbiased estimator. Further, computed standard errors for the estimated coefficients will be incorrect.

Plots to Detect Hetero-scedasticity

Sometimes, it is suspected that a population regression model may fit better for some subset of observations and fit worse for another subset or have a gradation of fit across multiple subsets of the observations. Detection of such differences in $V[\epsilon_i]$ cannot be made by using ϵ_i directly, since these are unknown. Instead, it is common to make plots of the residuals e_i to detect any signs of possible heteroscedasticity.

If the observations are time-series data (periodic over time), a useful sketch for detecting heteroscedasticity is a plot of the values of the residuals against time. On the plot, we examine free-hand drawn bounding lines of the scatter of points. A changing variance would be indicated if the bounding lines have any systematic pattern *other than parallel lines*, such as approximately ∧, an inverted V, or if they widened and narrowed in the shape of an egg timer or a football. For the residuals plotted in Figure 15.4, there seems to be an indication of an increasing variance over time, indicated by the ∨-shape of the bounding lines. The spread of the points from zero is increasing as time advances.

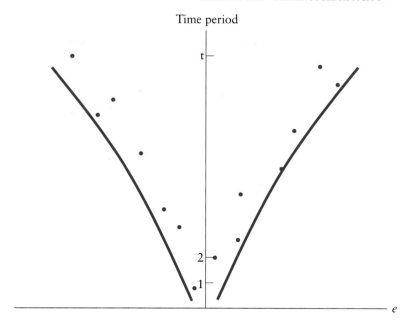

FIGURE 15.4   Residual plot against time, indicating heteroscedasticity

If the observation groups are not consecutive, such as in cross-sectional data, similar information about potential heteroscedasticity is obtained by plotting the residuals against the estimated values of the dependent variable, $\hat{y}$. The interpretation is similar.

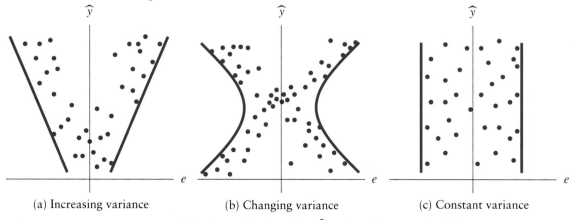

(a) Increasing variance   (b) Changing variance   (c) Constant variance

FIGURE 15.5   Plotting residuals against $\hat{y}$ to detect heteroscedasticity

For example, the V-shaped slope of the boundary lines for the scatter of points in Figure 15.5(a) suggests an increasing variance of the residuals as the value $\hat{y}$ increases. Such a plot may indicate that the fit of the model is not uniform and that the disturbances may not have a constant variance. A changing variance could also be indicated if the boundary lines approximated an inverted V or if they were close together at some points and wider apart at others, as in Figure 15.5(b). Assumption 4 of constant variance does *not* seem to be violated if the boundary lines are approximately parallel, as in Figure 15.5(c).

Finally, the size of the variance of the disturbance might be related to the size of one of the explanatory variables (such as with proportional measurement error) or be a function of one of these variables (such as the square or the logarithm of the variable). In such cases, it is common to order the observations according to the size of that explanatory variable (smallest to largest) and make a plot of the residuals against the values of that variable x_j just as in Figure 15.4, in which the variable was time. The same guidelines for interpretation apply.

☐ **EXAMPLE 15.10**   As an illustration of the usual use of a plot to detect possible heteroscedasticity, we refer to the model on housing price with results in Figure 14.3(c). The residuals and the predicted values of $\widehat{y}$ have been determined and plotted in Figure 15.6(a). Using the free-hand method, approximate bounding lines for the scatter plot are drawn. It appears in this plot that the variance of the residuals is relatively small for observations associated with values of $\widehat{y}$ below 100. For larger values above 100, there is more erratic scatter and larger variance evident among these residuals. A change in the variance of the disturbances seems likely.

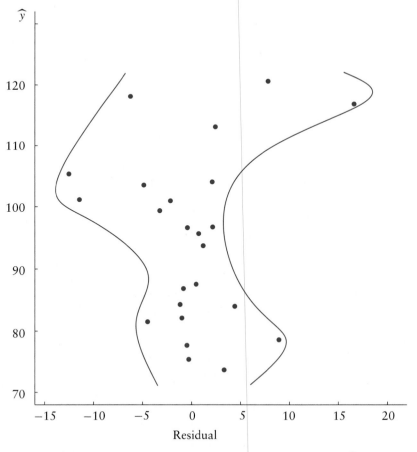

FIGURE 15.6(a)   Plot of residuals in housing model against $\widehat{y}$

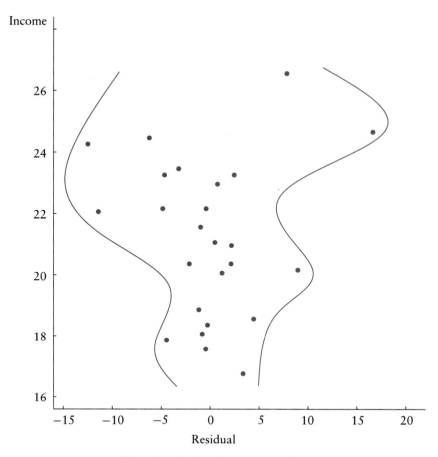

FIGURE 15.6(b)   Plot of residuals in housing model against x_1 = income

In the second plot of Figure 15.6(b), the residuals are plotted against Income, one of the explanatory variables in the model. Again, we examine the bounding lines to see if they are roughly parallel, or if there is some divergence. It appears that a similar change occurs in the variance of the residuals when related to the size of Income as to the predicted values $\hat{y}$. For income values above 22, the spread of the disturbances seems to be greater than for the collection of points when income is less than 22. The possibility of heteroscedasticity is indicated. ■

Detection of heteroscedasticity by plots is not an exact science, and there is no known confidence level in the conclusions derived. Econometricians have developed several tests, simple and complex, some with better properties than others for studying this problem.

Tests for Hetero-scedasticity   Some rather simplistic tests developed for heteroscedasticity involve a few groupings of the residuals between which changes in the variance of the residuals are examined. Some methods discard information on all subgroups except the two with the highest and the lowest sample variance. Such tests have relatively low power since the sub-groupings are arbitrary. Finally, when the residuals of different subgroups all come from the same regression, their calculation depends on the same estimated coefficients which depend in turn on *all* the observations. Hence, statistics based on the different subgroups are not independent as needed for true chi-square and F-distributions.

More powerful tests for heteroscedasticity, using all the available information, are sometimes quite complex. We will describe two tests which are applications of topics already studied and which are quite easy to interpret; the first as in a two sample F-test and the second as in a one sample chi-square test.

Goldfeld-Quandt Test

To satisfy the independence condition between subgroups, we must find the variance of the subgroups of residuals from *separate* regressions based on the corresponding subgroups of observations. If there are n_A observations in one subgroup and an additional n_B observations in the other, the sums of squares of residuals obtained from separate regressions on the group A data and on the group B data would be independent. We test the hypotheses:

$$H_0 : \text{constant variance of } \epsilon_i$$

$$H_a : \text{heteroscedasticity of the disturbances}$$

The ratio appropriate for an F-distributed test statistic is as follows:

F-test for heteroscedasticity:

$$F_{(n_A - m - 1, n_B - m - 1)} = \frac{(\text{SSE})_A / (n_A - m - 1)}{(\text{SSE})_B / (n_B - m - 1)} \qquad (15.2)$$

The terms in the ratio are the mean square errors (MSE) from the separate regressions (Section 14.4) which are readily available from a regression printout. If the calculated F-value is in the upper or lower critical region, we reject the null hypothesis of homoscedasticity. We conclude in a two-sided test that the variance of the disturbance term is different between subgroup A and subgroup B. A one-sided alternative hypothesis together with the upper-tail critical region may be used when the subgroup expected to have the larger $V[\epsilon_i]$ is designated as subgroup A in the numerator of Formula 15.2. This test is named the **Goldfeld–Quandt** (G–Q) **test** after two economists at Princeton University, who first introduced it in 1965. The critical regions are determined by using the standard F-table.

☐ **EXAMPLE 15.11**   Consider a model explaining a firm's level of employment based on four explanatory variables measuring particular firm characteristics. The model is estimated on the basis of data for 68 firms from a Census of Manufacturers. The cross-sectional sample includes 44 firms in the food industry and 24 firms in the primary metals industry. It is suspected that the variance of the errors may be different in the two separate industries. The food industry is denoted as subgroup A with $n_A = 44$, and the primary metals industry is subgroup B with $n_B = 24$. The null hypothesis is $H_0 : V[\epsilon]_A = V[\epsilon]_B$ against a one-sided alternative, $H_a : V[\epsilon]_A > V[\epsilon]_B$. The degrees of freedom are $44 - 4 - 1 = 39$ and $24 - 4 - 1 = 19$. The null hypothesis H_0 will be rejected if the calculated F-value exceeds the critical value from Table VIII of $F_{(0.05; 39, 19)} = 2.02$.

Two regressions are determined, one for each subgroup of data. The sum of squares of errors for each regression is $(SSE)_A = 0.90888$ and $(SSE)_B = 0.25047$. The calculated value of the test statistic using Formula 15.2 is:

$$F_c = \frac{(0.90888/39)}{(0.25047/19)} = \frac{0.0233}{0.01318} = 1.77$$

This calculated F-value does not exceed 2.02, so assumption 4 of constant variance is *not* rejected. ∎

Sometimes, separate subgroups of the data are not so obvious, and the test is to be applied in general to determine whether $V[\epsilon_i]$ is increasing, decreasing, or constant over the complete set of observations (ordered by time or by size of $\widehat{y}$ or by size of some x_j). In this situation, it is recommended that the data be separated into three groups with numbers of observations n_A, n_M, and n_B. The G–Q test statistic (Formula 15.2) can be used on the subgroups A and B, excluding the middle n_M observations. This disuse of some of the data tends to make the test less powerful because some sample information is not used. However, comparing more widely separated observations has the opposite effect of making the test more powerful because it tends to make the difference between $(SSE)_A$ and $(SSE)_B$ larger. Research studies indicate that a good trade-off between these competing uses of the data occur when the middle group of n_M observations includes about 20% of the observations. If exactly 20% cannot be achieved due to discreteness or ties in the data, you should err in the direction toward 16-18% rather than toward 22–24%. This method of ordering the observations and excluding about 20% of the middle observations to form subgroups A and B is quite commonly and successfully used.

☐ **STUDY QUESTION 15.2**   Heteroscedasticity Test in the Housing Price Model

Use the housing price model of Figure 14.3(c) and test for heteroscedasticity using a Goldfeld–Quandt test. Order the observations by the size (smallest to largest) of $\widehat{y}$.

• **ANSWER**   The 25 observations are ordered by the size of the predicted level of housing price. It is hypothesized, based on the plot in Figure 15.6(a), that higher values of price are associated with a larger variance of the disturbances. Thus, we select as subgroup A the ten observations with the largest values of $\widehat{y}$. (Ten cases represents 40% of the total of 25 cases.) The 10 cases with the smallest value of $\widehat{y}$ are placed in subgroup B. The middle 20% or 5 observations are omitted.

Regressions of the same original model (housing price depending on income, rent, and vacancy levels) are run on each of the two subgroups A and B. Partial results of these regressions are given in Figure 15.7(a) and (b).

a) High Subgroup:

Analysis of Variance

Source	DF	Sum of Squares	Mean Square	F Value	Prob>F
Model	3	1725.86170	575.28723	20.046	0.0016
Error	6	172.19430	28.69905		
Total	9	1898.05600			

b) Low Subgroup:

Analysis of Variance

Source	DF	Sum of Squares	Mean Square	F Value	Prob>F
Model	3	138.39668	46.13223	2.576	0.1495
Error	6	107.46732	17.91122		
Total	9	245.86400			

FIGURE 15.7 Housing regression on (a) high and (b) low subgroups of data ordered by $\widehat{y}$

The regression on subgroup A gives a mean square of residuals of $(MSE)_A = 28.699$ and the regression on subgroup B gives a mean square of residuals of $(MSE)_B = 17.911$. Each mean square is based on 6 degrees of freedom since the number of cases is 10 and the number of variables is 3 $(10 - 3 - 1 = 6)$. The calculated value of the G–Q statistic is $F_c = 28.699/17.911 = 1.6$. This value is less than the critical value of 4.28 from Table VIII(a) for 6 and 6 degrees of freedom. We accept the hypothesis that there is not a violation of assumption 4. Although the plots indicated potential heteroscedasticity, this test using subgroups did not find it significant. ■

White Test

A second test for detecting heteroscedasticity is named for the econometrician, H. White, who introduced it in 1980. Since we are concerned with the variance of disturbances and since a variance is a squared deviation measure, it is suggested that the size of e^2 be analyzed. Since the mean of the residuals is zero, the size of $e^2 = (e - 0)^2$ gives an indication of the spread of the distribution. To determine if this spread changes systematically over the sample, a regression is suggested relating e^2 to all second degree terms (squares and cross-products) of explanatory variables in the model used to estimate y. The amount of systematic relation can be measured by the R-square for the goodness of fit of the model. The test statistic is $\chi^2 = nR^2$ with degrees of freedom equal to the number of explanatory factors in this auxiliary regression. If the calculated χ^2 is significantly large, then there is an indication of a problem of heteroscedasticity.

☐ **EXAMPLE 15.12** We again use the housing price model of Figure 14.3(c) to test for possible heteroscedasticity using the **White test**. New variables to be determined on the basis of the original data and the residuals from the original regression are the squares of the residuals (labelled ESQ for e-squared) and the squares of each explanatory variable (labelled X1SQ, X2SQ, and X3SQ for the squares of income, rent, and vacant respectively) and the cross-products of these three variables (labelled X1X2, X1X3, and X2X3). Figure 15.8 gives the output for this regression.

All results indicate that this is a weak fitting model with little significance. The R^2 for this regression is 0.334 which gives a calculated White chi-square statistic of $\chi^2 = nR^2 = 25(0.334) = 8.35$. For six degrees of freedom, the p-value exceeds 0.10. The conclusion is to accept the null hypothesis of no heteroscedasticity since the p-value exceeds any acceptable α-level of risk. ■

```
                 Dependent variable: ESQ Residual squared
                            Analysis of Variance

                            Sum of            Mean
        Source      DF      Squares          Square     F Value    Prob>F

        Model        6    34038.17591      5673.02932    1.506     0.2324
        Error       18    67826.23546      3768.12419
        C Total     24   101864.41137


             Root MSE      61.38505     R-square     0.3342
             Dep Mean      34.96158     Adj R-Sq     0.1122
             C.V.         175.57858


                            Parameter Estimates

                          Parameter        Standard      T for H0:
        Variable    DF     Estimate          Error     Parameter=0    Prob> |T|

        INTERCEP     1     -0.46083       200.57686      -0.002       0.9982
        X1SQ         1     -4.39598         4.62107      -0.951       0.3541
        X2SQ         1     -0.01459         0.01310      -1.114       0.2799
        X3SQ         1      0.50667         0.41593       1.218       0.2389
        X1X2         1      0.52749         0.49163       1.073       0.2975
        X1X3         1     -0.01318         1.43458      -0.009       0.9928
        X2X3         1     -0.04515         0.07363      -0.613       0.5474
```

FIGURE 15.8 Auxiliary model for White test for heteroscedasticity

Correction for Heteroscedasticity

Suppose the variance of the disturbances for a model are determined to have a changing variance in violation of assumption 4. To obtain better estimates than the simple least-squares estimates, the observations for which the disturbance variance is small should be given larger weights in the estimation, and the observations for which the disturbance variance is large should be given smaller weights. Ordinary least squares (OLS), without explicit weights, presumes that each observation is equally precise in estimating the *true* relation. However, the true relation is more easily determined when the level of disturbance noise (variation) is small. Consequently, to obtain the most accurate estimation of this relation, more importance should be given to observations for which $V[\epsilon_i]$ is small. Observations for which $V[\epsilon_i]$ is large should be de-emphasized.

Estimation techniques which use the extra information detected about the changing variance of the disturbances involve transformation of variables and two stage procedures which are not presented here. The student of statistics needs to know the importance of assumption 4 of constant variance and should be able to understand the common plots and tests for detecting a potential problem. Further study in econometrics or consultation with an expert in the estimation of regression models is recommended before the reader tries to make corrections to obtain better estimates. Think of this situation as similar to the electric power temporarily going off in your home. You know some effects of this problem and you can detect the existence of the problem, but correcting it may be beyond your current expertise. The same will be true for correction of a violation of assumption 5 discussed in the next section.

Autocorrelation

Assumption 5 in the list of common assumptions states that each disturbance is independent of each other; that is, $C[\epsilon_i, \epsilon_t] = 0$, for $i \neq t$. If the disturbances tend to be correlated with each other, this assumption is violated. This situation is known as **autocorrelation** and is a frequently occurring problem, especially in time series data.

We will be concerned in this section with first order autocorrelation in which successive error terms are correlated. Clearly, the term, *successive errors*, only has meaning when some ordering of the observations is implied as in observations over time. If the ordering of the cases is arbitrary, such as an alphabetical ordering or survey response sequence as in cross-sectional data, autocorrelation is not relevant. The mix of cases could be re-entered in a different order and the successive residuals would change correspondingly. Within a time series data set, autocorrelation occurs because some extraneous factor changes and causes the behaviour of agents to change in such a way that our model has systematic rather than random, errors for a succession of cases. This is more likely to occur when the successive time periods are shorter in duration.

☐ **EXAMPLE 15.13**   Suppose we are studying the demand for automobiles and we have collected data on sales and economic factors of demand over time. If we have weekly observations, we would have to include in our model variables representing rebates, special financing arrangements, or other marketing features that are introduced and withdrawn, causing changes in weekly sales. If we use annual data, we might assume that these minor variations balance out over the year and are represented well enough by a measure of annual marketing and advertising expenses. The errors ϵ_i from annual data are not as likely to be related to each other, owing to the continuing influence of a one-time shock, as are the errors from weekly data.

Suppose a safety defect for an automobile is announced, and cautious buyers delay purchases of that automobile or buy another brand. The effect could decrease sales of the automobile over *several* weeks. Our model would tend to overpredict during these successive weeks because of the negative values for the disturbance terms. Suppose, after several weeks, another announcement proclaims that further tests indicate that the safety defect is not widespread and no recalls are needed. At the same time, a consumer magazine rates this automobile as one of the best buys of all new cars. Sales may pick up and exceed the predicted value from our model for several weeks. The successive positive disturbances are affected by these factors that are *not* included in the model. Assumption 5 is violated since the errors are correlated with previous values rather than being independent.   ■

Autocorrelation can also be related to some of the same causes as error in measurement or heteroscedasticity. First, suppose that one explanatory variable is measured with error and is available only annually, whereas the other explanatory variables are measured monthly. If we interpolate within the year to approximate a series of monthly values for the annually observed variable, it is likely that we will also apportion a related share of its error of measurement into the successive monthly values. This would introduce autocorrelation into the disturbances.

Second, cross-sectional data that lead to heteroscedasticity may also lead to a violation of assumption 5 called *spatial autocorrelation*. Many of the same excluded factors may be influencing the error term over different observations.

This is particularly true, for example, if the cross-sections are regions such as states and the variables are aggregates of individual measures of economic activity. The state boundaries determine to which aggregate a certain individual measure belongs (such as persons included in a census), but these state boundaries are politically or geographically determined. Economic activity on both sides of the boundary may be affected to a significant extent by the same underlying factors, such as the weather, the quality of the land, the education and culture and productivity of the workers, and so on. Since such common factors are absorbed by the error term, spatial autocorrelation is likely to result among errors for states in the same geographic region.

Effect of Autocorrelation

As stated in Section 15.2, assumption 5 is crucial (along with assumption 4) for obtaining least-squares estimates of the coefficients that are *efficient*. If either or both of these assumptions (4 and 5) are violated, the estimators calculated by the method of least squares would not have the smallest possible variance. Some *other* unbiased estimator that uses *more information* would be the efficient one. Also, s_e^2 would no longer be an unbiased estimate of the variance of the disturbance (σ_ϵ^2). Thus, s_{b_j}, the estimated standard errors of the coefficients, would not be correct, and tests of hypotheses or confidence intervals based on these will not be correct.

Detection of Autocorrelation

The most frequently encountered form of autocorrelation is detected by examining the linear association of successive residuals. If we denote a residual at time period t by e_t and the previous residual by e_{t-1}, first-order autocorrelation corresponds to the simple linear correlation of e_t with e_{t-1} over the entire set of observations, $t = 2, 3, 4, \ldots, n$. A measure of this correlation is given by the correlation coefficient between these two variables, $r_{e_t e_{t-1}}$. A geometric representation can be obtained by making a scatter diagram of the points corresponding to each pair (e_t, e_{t-1}). Figure 15.9 illustrates three cases: (a) positive autocorrelation, (b) negative autocorrelation, and (c) no autocorrelation. When the points are predominantly in the positive quadrants (same signs of $+, +$ or $-, -$) as they are in Figure 15.9(a), this means that successive residuals tend to have the same sign. If most points lie in the negative quadrants (opposite signs of $+, -$ or $-, +$) as in Figure 15.9(b), then successive residuals tend to have opposite signs. If the scatter of points is spread over all quadrants, successive residuals tend to be independent, as in Figure 15.9(c).

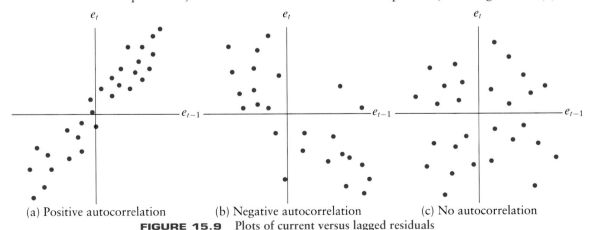

(a) Positive autocorrelation   (b) Negative autocorrelation   (c) No autocorrelation

FIGURE 15.9   Plots of current versus lagged residuals

A second type plot reveals similar information. We can plot the residual e against the time period t and look to see if there is a random or a systematic pattern over time. Figure 15.10(a) and Figure 15.10(b) present sketches indicating problems of a systematic pattern. The graph in part (a) is a typical result when positive autocorrelation is present and the graph in (b) indicates the less common, but equally problematic, case of negative autocorrelation. We would prefer to see a random scatter of points with neither too few nor too many different runs of successive positive or negative signs. A sign test for runs could be applied to these residuals as discussed in Section 18.2.

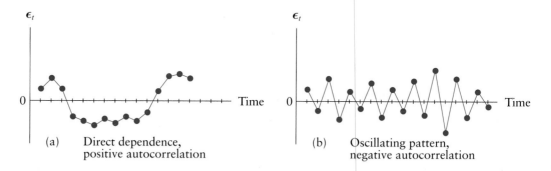

FIGURE 15.10   Time-sequence of autocorrelated errors ϵ_t

□ **EXAMPLE 15.14**   The residuals from our investment example in Figure 14.2(b) are given in Figure 15.11(a). The plot of e_t against e_{t-1} as shown in Figure 15.11(b) tends to look like Figure 15.9(a), indicating positive autocorrelation. The time-sequence plot of residuals given in Figure 15.11(c) also indicates positive autocorrelation. It is similar in appearance to Figure 15.10(a). The signs of the residuals tend to be grouped over time. The first group of five are positive residuals; the second group are mostly negative until the final four residuals, which are all positive. Thus, the least-squares estimates for this model probably are not efficient owing to the problem of autocorrelation.   ■

OBS	Y	YHAT	RESIDUAL	ELAG1
1	62.3	62.109	0.1912	.
2	71.3	68.525	2.7752	0.1912
3	70.3	68.343	1.9576	2.7752
4	68.5	66.066	2.4341	1.9576
5	57.3	51.437	5.8626	2.4341
6	68.8	70.879	−2.0790	5.8626
7	72.2	80.901	−8.7014	−2.0790
8	76.0	76.100	−0.1003	−8.7014
9	64.3	70.944	−6.6442	−0.1003
10	77.9	85.678	−7.7780	−6.6442
11	84.3	76.516	7.7836	−7.7780
12	85.1	86.719	−1.6194	7.7836
13	90.8	99.373	−8.5728	−1.6194
14	97.9	107.306	−9.4063	−8.5728
15	108.7	117.228	−8.5281	−9.4063
16	122.4	127.966	−5.5661	−8.5281
17	114.0	111.168	2.8318	−5.5661
18	123.0	122.964	0.0357	2.8318
19	126.2	114.699	11.5014	0.0357
20	137.0	113.377	23.6225	11.5014

FIGURE 15.11(a)   Residual analysis for the investment model

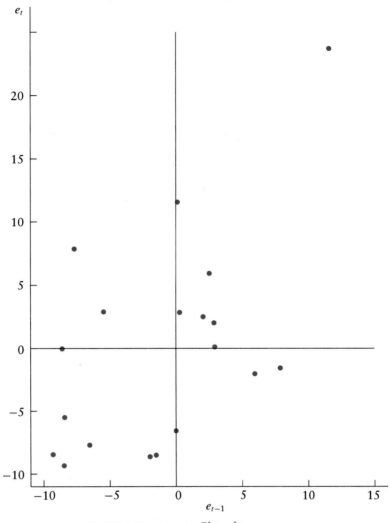

FIGURE 15.11(b)   Plot of e_t versus e_{t-1}

Although autocorrelation appears to exist in both Figure 15.11(b) and Figure 15.11(c), it is generally not reliable to determine whether autocorrelation is present merely by using a scatter diagram. Hence, we need a test statistic to determine whether or not to accept the null hypothesis of independence (no autocorrelation) among successive error terms. The test used most often for this purpose is called the Durbin–Watson test.

The Durbin–Watson Test

The **Durbin–Watson (D–W) test** is designed to test the null hypothesis that there is no first-order autocorrelation among the error terms. The alternative hypothesis is that first-order autocorrelation does exist. To be more precise, let the relationship between the population errors ϵ_t and ϵ_{t-1} be expressed as follows:

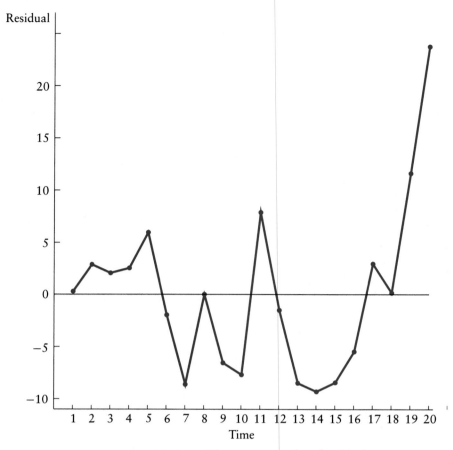

FIGURE 15.11(c)   Time-sequence plot of residuals

First-order autoregressive model of the errors:

$$\epsilon_t = \rho \epsilon_{t-1} + \nu_t \qquad\qquad (15.3)$$

where ρ is the population autocorrelation coefficient between ϵ_t and ϵ_{t-1}

The ν_t in Formula 15.3 are the error terms, and they satisfy assumptions 1–5 as applied to this model. When $\rho = 0$, no autocorrelation exists; the farther ρ is away from zero toward $+1.0$ or -1.0, the greater the autocorrelation.

It might be tempting to test for autocorrelation by finding an estimate of this autocorrelation coefficient ρ based on the residuals from the regression equation. Indeed, computer printouts often include such a coefficient as an indicator of autocorrelation. If it is close to 0, the indication is that the residuals are independent; if it is closer to $+1$ or to -1, a positive or negative autocorrelation is indicated. However, the distribution of this coefficient is not exactly like that of a true correlation coefficient between two variables having a bivariate normal distribution. It is more complicated because the auto-regressiveness, if any, of the explanatory variables in the model affects the distribution. The common test statistic for correlation coefficients is not valid in this context.

A test statistic for autocorrelation which can be used is the value of d determined by the following formula:

Durbin–Watson statistic:

$$d = \frac{\sum\limits_{t=2}^{n}(e_t - e_{t-1})^2}{\sum\limits_{t=1}^{n} e_t^2} \qquad (15.4)$$

Its critical values are given in Table X and are interpreted according to the sketch in Figure 15.12. Values of d close to 2 indicate no problem. Values close to 0 or close to 4 indicate a problem of positive or negative autocorrelation respectively. Between the upper and lower critical values on either side of 2, there is an intermediate region. Recent research confirms that values of d in these intervals indicate a tendency toward a problem, especially if the explanatory variables in the model tend to be auto-regressive themselves. Therefore, we use the d_U and d_L-critical values as indices of the severity of the problem.

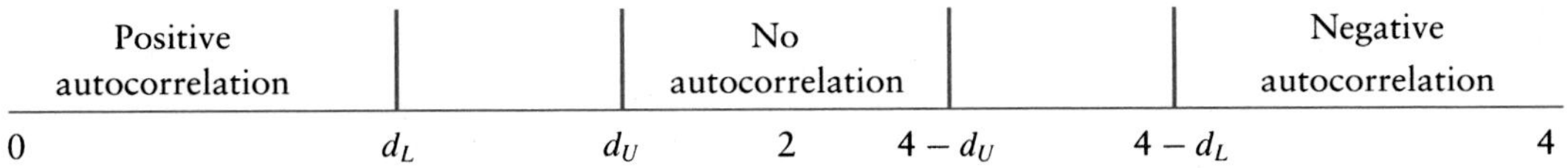

Positive autocorrelation		No autocorrelation		Negative autocorrelation

0   d_L d_U 2 $4 - d_U$ $4 - d_L$ 4

FIGURE 15.12   Alternative conclusions based on the Durbin–Watson d-statistic

$d < d_L$: serious problem of positive autocorrelation that requires correction

$d_L < d < d_U$: weaker problem of positive autocorrelation for which a correction is probably worthwhile

$d_U < d < 4 - d_U$: no problem of autocorrelation worth correcting

$4 - d_U < d < 4 - d_L$: weaker problem of negative autocorrelation for which correction is probably worthwhile

$4 - d_L < d$: serious problem of negative autocorrelation that requires correction

☐ **EXAMPLE 15.15**   We suspect the presence of positive autocorrelation in a particular regression problem involving $m = 3$ independent variables, $n = 45$ observations, and a calculated d-value, from Formula 15.4, of $d_c = 1.31$. The hypotheses are:

H_0 : no autocorrelation $(d = 2)$

H_a : positive autocorrelation $(d < 2)$

Using the left side of Table X for $\alpha = 0.05$, we find $d_L = 1.38$ and $d_U = 1.67$. Since our computed value d_c is below d_L, we conclude that positive autocorrelation is a problem. We have a significant violation of assumption 5 in our model.

In another regression problem we suspect the presence of negative autocorrelation where $m = 4$ independent variables, $n = 70$, $d_c = 2.94$, and $\alpha = 0.01$. The hypotheses are:

H_0 : no autocorrelation $(d = 2)$

H_a : negative autocorrelation $(d > 2)$

Using the right side of Table X for $\alpha = 0.01$, we find $d_L = 1.34$ and $d_U = 1.58$. Since we are testing for negative autocorrelation and Table X gives values only for the test on positive autocorrelation, we must find the transformed critical values, $4 - d_L = 2.66$ and $4 - d_U = 2.42$. Since our computed value $d_c = 2.94$ lies above $4 - d_L$, we conclude that a significant problem of negative autocorrelation exists. ∎

◻ STUDY QUESTION 15.3 Autocorrelation Test in the Investment Model

Compute and interpret the Durbin–Watson d-statistic for the investment model using a significance level of 0.05. The residuals are given in Figure 15.11(a).

● ANSWER By using Formula 15.4, the value of d_c is 0.784. By using Table X for $m = 2$ explanatory variables and $n = 20$ observations, the lower critical value is $d_L = 1.10$. Thus, the null hypothesis of no autocorrelation is rejected. The conclusion is that positive autocorrelation is a problem in this investment model, as suggested by the plots in Figures 15.11(b) and (c). ∎

Correction for Autocorrelation

Sometimes the problem of autocorrelation can be corrected by improving the specification of the model. This is especially true if the cause of the autocorrelation is the significant role of an *excluded* variable that has a strong cyclical pattern. Inclusion of such a variable may often be effective. In other cases, the seeming occurrence of autocorrelation may be a result of estimating a nonlinear relation by a linear specification. A substitution of variable, such as x^2 or $1/x$ or e^x in place of the explanatory factor x, can remedy an incorrect specification. The reader is referred to Section 15.6.

Apart from a potential specification problem, the detection of autocorrelation means that the problem to be corrected is the inefficiency of the ordinary least squares (OLS) estimators of the coefficients in the model and incorrect standard errors of these estimators. An estimating procedure that corrects for violations of assumption 5 is called **generalized least squares (GLS),** which in its calculation explicitly uses information about the variances and covariances of the error terms ϵ_i. The purpose in using this information is to generate a new model situation in which the new error terms are free of the violation of assumption 5. While a complete discussion of a generalized least-squares estimator requires presentation of topics not included in this text, a rather simplified and modified version usually provides a worthwhile improvement in the efficiency of the estimators. It has the advantage of requiring only ordinary least-squares computations.

For example, if the problem is a first-order positive autocorrelation of the errors, the four steps for this practical remedy are as follows:

1. Determine the residuals from the first estimation of the model and use the Durbin–Watson test to detect first-order autocorrelation.

2. Estimate the autocorrelation coefficient ρ using these residuals. Call this estimate $\widehat{\rho}$.

3. Transform all the original variables (including the implicit one associated with the intercept) according to the same autocorrelation pattern uncovered among the residuals in step 2. Call the transformed observations y^* for the dependent variable and x_j^* for each explanatory variable $(j = 1, 2, \ldots, m)$.

4. Using least squares, re-estimate the model using the transformed data with $n - 1$ observations, since the first observation is lost in the transformation process. The new disturbance term, ϵ^*, satisfies assumption 5.

$$y^* = \alpha(1 - \widehat{\rho}) + \beta_1 x_1{}^* + \beta_2 x_2{}^* + \cdots + \beta_m x_m{}^* + \epsilon^*$$

We have already discussed step 1. To complete step 2, there are several methods for finding the estimate of ρ defined in Formula 15.3. One estimate might be the least-squares regression coefficient in the simple model relating current residuals e_t to their previous values e_{t-1}. Another could be the serial correlation coefficient, $r_{e_t e_{t-1}}$. Both of these measures are related to the size of the squared differences between e_t and e_{t-1}, which is the numerator term in Formula 15.4. A third approximation uses the Durbin–Watson statistic d.

Approximation of the autocorrelation coefficient in terms of the Durbin–Watson statistic:

$$\widehat{\rho} \simeq \tfrac{1}{2}(2 - d) \qquad (15.5)$$

Since step 1 requires computation of d, the simplest and quickest way to find $\widehat{\rho}$ for step 2 is to use Formula 15.5.

We find the transformed data in step 3 for observations $t = 2, 3, \ldots, n$, for all variables in the model according to the following rule:

Transformation of variables:

$$(\text{Transformed value})_t = (\text{Original value})_t - \widehat{\rho}\,(\text{original value})_{t-1} \qquad (15.6)$$

In the usual least-squares regression, the correct values of the intercept, an implicit variable x_0, are 1.0 for every observation. In the revised equation with transformed variables, the correct values for x_0 would be $1 - \widehat{\rho}$ for every observation. If it is easiest to use a standard least-squares regression program that automatically includes a standard intercept, the program can still be used. However, to determine the correct value of a and to make inference about α, the reported value of a and of its standard error (s_a) must be multiplied by the factor $1/(1 - \widehat{\rho})$.

Step 4 simply involves a second least squares estimation.

❑ **EXAMPLE 15.16** Since the d-value of the Durbin–Watson statistic in the investment model (Study Question 15.3) is $d = 0.784$, which indicates positive autocorrelation, the four-step remedy for autocorrelation should be applied. Step 1 gives the value of d. In step 2, the approximate value of $\widehat{\rho}$ is found by using Formula 15.5:

$$\widehat{\rho} \simeq \tfrac{1}{2}(2 - 0.784) = 0.608$$

Step 3 requires transformation of the observations for y = investment, x_1 = stock price, x_2 = retained earnings, and the intercept according to Formula 15.6 and substituting $\widehat{\rho} = 0.608$. For example, the new observation for the dependent variable in period nine is:

$$y_9{}^* = y_9 - 0.608 y_8 = 64.3 - 0.608(76.0) = 18.09$$

Using a computer, all variables for all observations are transformed similarly and are shown in Table 15.6. The intercept values are changed from $x_0 = 1$ to $x_0 = 1 - 0.608 = 0.392$ for all 19 observations. Observation 1 is now missing data since the transformation would require values of the previous period, which are not given.

TABLE 15.6 Original and Transformed Observations for the Investment Model

Observation	y	x_1	x_2	y^*	x_1^*	x_2^*
1	62.3	398.4	16.2	—	—	—
2	71.3	452.6	17.4	33.4216	210.373	7.5504
3	70.3	509.8	14.8	26.9496	234.619	4.2208
4	68.5	485.4	14.6	25.7576	175.442	5.6016
5	57.3	445.7	8.2	15.6520	150.577	−0.6768
6	68.8	539.8	14.9	33.9616	268.814	9.9144
7	72.2	662.8	15.1	30.3696	334.602	6.0408
8	76.0	620.0	14.3	32.1024	217.018	5.1192
9	64.3	632.2	10.9	18.0920	255.240	2.2056
10	77.9	703.0	16.0	38.8056	318.622	9.3728
11	84.3	581.8	16.2	36.9368	154.376	6.4720
12	85.1	707.1	16.4	33.8456	353.366	6.5504
13	90.8	776.6	20.4	39.0592	346.683	10.4288
14	97.9	875.3	20.5	42.6936	403.127	8.0968
15	108.7	873.4	26.1	49.1768	341.218	13.6360
16	122.4	943.7	29.0	56.3104	412.673	13.1312
17	114.0	830.6	24.6	39.5808	256.830	6.9680
18	123.0	907.5	27.8	53.6880	402.495	12.8432
19	126.2	905.3	23.3	51.4160	353.540	6.3976
20	137.0	927.4	21.6	60.2704	376.978	7.4336

The computer printout of the least-squares estimation for the revised model is given in Figure 15.13. The output for the original model was given in Figure 14.2(b).

Dependent Variable: y^* Weighted first difference of Investment

```
                       Analysis of Variance

                         Sum of           Mean
Source      DF          Squares         Square      F Value     Prob>F

Model        3      29012.10060     9670.70020      181.676     0.0001
Error       16        851.68724       53.23045
C Total     19      29863.78784


        Root MSE        7.29592     R-square      0.9715
        Dep Mean       37.79419     Adj R-Sq      0.9661
        C.V.           19.30434
```

Parameter Estimates

Variable	DF	Parameter Estimate	Standard Error	T for H0: Parameter=0	Prob> |T|
CONSTANT	1	19.61847	15.58810	1.259	0.2262
X1*	1	0.06120	0.02658	2.303	0.0351
X2*	1	1.63690	0.63023	2.597	0.0194

NOTE: R-square is redefined.

FIGURE 15.13 Investment regression using transformed variables

The new estimates, $a^* = 19.618$, $b_1^* = 0.0612$ and $b_2^* = 1.637$ are preferred to the simple least-squares estimators ($a = 1.677$, $b_1 = 0.0786$ and $b_2 = 1.798$). Tests of significance on the coefficients can use the new t-ratios. Note, however, that goodness of fit information from this proxy regression is not comparable to that for the original regression. The new values for means and sums of squares are in the new scale of weighted first differences of y and are not directly meaningful in terms of the original definition of investment in the model. ■

This method, which makes use of the extra information about the autocorrelation pattern, is expected to give better estimates of b_j than the ordinary least squares method without the transformation. More sophisticated detection and correction procedures for problems of autocorrelation are beyond the level of this text. The interested reader should refer to textbooks and research publications in econometrics.

section 15.6 Use of Linear Regression for Nonlinear Relations

Condition 3 in Section 15.2 made clear again that we have been dealing throughout Chapters 13, 14, and 15 with a *linear* regression model. Any student who has studied relations among economic or business variables knows that these are not always linear. (Recall the graphs used in lectures or textbooks that used curved lines, not straight ones.) Examination of a plot of values of the dependent variable y against those for an independent variable x_j is always useful in helping to determine if the underlying relation is linear or nonlinear. If many interesting relations are nonlinear, is it fair to ask how applicable are the methods of linear regression?

First, although a relation may be nonlinear over its full range, when we consider a segment of the overall curve, it is often approximately correct to assume a straight line. A downward-sloping demand schedule for, say, gasoline (petrol) may be nonlinear. However, over a range of values commonly occurring in the world market, such as a price of 75¢ to $3.50 per gallon, a linear approximation is quite accurate. We need not worry about the fact that the quantity demanded would surely decrease at a nonlinear rate if the price per gallon increased to $10.

A second reason that we study the linear model extensively is that we often only need to obtain a first approximation to the true relation. Depending on our purpose in obtaining numerical estimates of the relation, the linear approach may be satisfactory in providing insights, directions of impacts, and filling gaps in the theory of the relevant relation. It must be emphasized that the linear least squares estimation is *inexpensive and easy* compared to the more complex iterative and nonlinear estimating methods.

Third, the linear model is really quite adaptable for representing various *nonlinear* relations simply by a substitution of variables. That is, the model can be made linear among the measures y and x_j which are *nonlinear functions* of the underlying theoretical variables being studied. The observations y_i may be the reciprocal or the logarithm of an economic variable. Second- and higher-order relations, square roots, or exponential transformations may also be included. A few examples of such transformations and their uses can be listed.

Higher-order Transformations

The linear model can represent a higher-order relation. A complete second-order model with two independent variables Z and W might be represented as

$$y = \alpha + \sum_{j=1}^{5} \beta_j x_j + \epsilon$$

where $x_1 = Z$, $x_2 = W$, $x_3 = Z^2$, $x_4 = W^2$, and $x_5 = ZW$. Such a model allows for nonlinear, second-degree curves (parabolic or hyperbolic) including an interaction term (ZW). However, the analysis involves only a linear model in terms of the observations of y and x_j. Third-, fourth-, or higher-order models can be developed similarly.

One particular use of such models is in forecasting and in fitting series of values over time. The use of powers of $t = $ time as values of x_j, such as $x_1 = t$, $x_2 = t^2$, $x_3 = t^3$, et cetera, allows for nonlinear trends (Section 16.2) to be built into the forecasting model. We also used this type of representation for the auxiliary equation to test for heteroscedasticity (Figure 15.8).

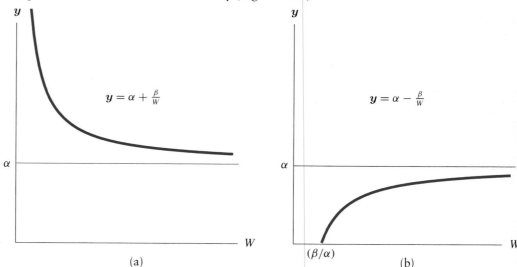

FIGURE 15.14   Nonlinear functions with asymptotes

Reciprocal Transformations

Often the theoretical relation between two variables may be nonlinear and contain the implication of an asymptotic level on one variable for extreme values of the other. An example in economics is the Keynesian liquidity trap described by the relation $y = \alpha + (\beta/W)$, where y is investment (expenditure for plant and equipment) and W is the interest rate. Figure 15.14(a) depicts such a relation of a negative slope (for all values of W) that decreases in absolute value as W increases. Thus, investment approaches the asymptotic level given by the value α. If β is negative, y approaches the asymptote α from below with positive but decreasing slope as in Figure 15.14(b). For such cases, the simple transformation of variable using the reciprocal, $x = 1/W$, provides the linear model $y = \alpha + \beta x$ with constant slope β and intercept α.

□ **EXAMPLE 15.17** Suppose the true relation for a particular industry is $y = 5 + (40/I)$, where y is investment and I is the interest rate. Selected values for y and I are given in Table 15.7. Then, the reciprocal of I $(1/I)$ is used to obtain x. Use of the reciprocal transformation allows estimation of the linear model to learn about a nonlinear relation. Plots of the original nonlinear function and the linear function using the reciprocal variable are shown in Figure 15.15. ■

TABLE 15.7 Example Values of Investment (y), Interest Rate (I), and $x = (1/I)$

y	∞	45	25	15	13	10	9	7	6	5
I	0	1	2	4	5	8	10	20	40	∞
x	∞	1	0.5	0.25	0.20	0.125	0.10	0.05	0.025	0

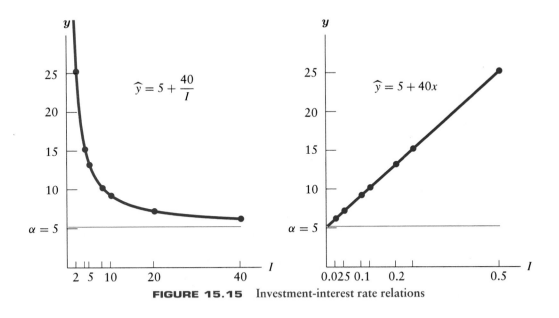

FIGURE 15.15 Investment-interest rate relations

Logarithmic Transformations on y and x

Many theoretical relations between economic or business variables may be expressed in multiplicative models rather than additive ones. They have the form $y = \alpha X_1^{\beta_1} Z_2^{\beta_2} W_3^{\beta_3}$. This is a common representation for production functions where y is output and the different x_j are input factors (labour, machines, management). Also, economists frequently are interested in the values of the elasticity of a relation rather than the slope of the function. The slope is the relative *unit* change in y for a *unit* change in x and is easily measured by β_j in the linear model. The **elasticity** (denoted by the Greek letter eta, η) is the relative *percentage* change in y for a one *percent* change in x. It is easily measured by β_j in a multiplicative model. Using variable transformations, the linear regression can treat the multiplicative model and measures of elasticity.

In the equation $y = \alpha + \beta^* x$, the slope is β^*, a constant. The elasticity is $\eta = \beta^*(x/y)$, and it changes all along the line as values of x and y change. If the theoretical relation suggests a *constant* rather than a changing elasticity, a logarithmic transformation on both variables, y and x, may be applied. The model obtained is linear in the logs, $\ln y = \alpha + \beta \ln x$ where $\ln$ symbolizes "the logarithm of." This double-log transformation corresponds to a model with a constant elasticity of y with respect to x (given by β). Depending on the size of this elasticity, various nonlinear curves as illustrated in Figure 15.16 may be represented by a linear model.

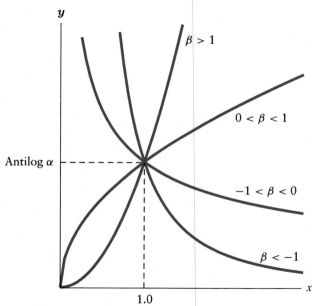

FIGURE 15.16   Double-log transformation, $\ln y = \alpha + \beta \ln x$

□ **EXAMPLE 15.18**   The well-known Cobb–Douglas production function has the form $Q = \lambda L^{\beta_1} K^{\beta_2}$, where Q is output, L is labour, and K is capital (building and equipment). If the double-log transformation is used, the model becomes linear, $y = \alpha + \beta_1 x_1 + \beta_2 x_2$, where $y = \ln Q, x_1 = \ln L, x_2 = \ln K$, and $\alpha = \ln \lambda$. ∎

Logarithmic Transformation on x Only

Some nonlinear relations between economic or business variables may be represented in a linear model if a semi-log transformation is used. The model, $y = \alpha + \beta \ln x$, has a changing slope given by (β/x), which decreases as x increases. It also has a changing elasticity given by $\eta = (\beta/y)$, which decreases as y increases.

☐ **EXAMPLE 15.19** Consider a model where y = output of wheat and x = expected price of wheat. The semi-log model, $y = \alpha + \beta \ln x$, may be appropriate for this situation, represented in Figure 15.17. No wheat would be produced for sale unless the price were above some minimal level ($e^{-\alpha/\beta}$). Also, the percentage increase in wheat produced is limited at high output levels by production constraints, such as the available amount of cultivated land. Thus, the elasticity is decreasing as output increases, and the slope is decreasing as price increases. ∎

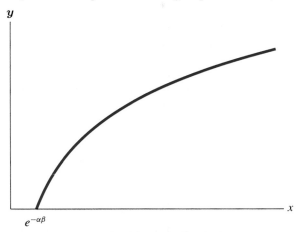

FIGURE 15.17 Semi-log transformation, $y = \alpha + \beta \ln x$

Exponential Model

The exponential model shown in Figure 15.18 has the form $y = \alpha\beta^x$. It is often used to represent a variable that has a constant rate of growth (β) over time and for estimating nonlinear trends (Section 16.2) or compound interest at a fixed rate over x years. Taking logs of both sides, we have $\log y = \ln \alpha + (\ln \beta)x$. This is seen to be a semi-log representation where we use the logarithm of y but not of x, opposite to the above case. Using least squares, we can estimate values for $\ln \alpha$ and $\ln \beta$. We find the antilogs to obtain estimates a and b of the original α and β.

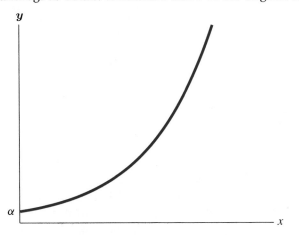

FIGURE 15.18 Exponential model, $y = \alpha\beta^x$

□ **EXAMPLE 15.20** Population growth in some regions over some periods may be represented by a constant rate of growth function. We let y = population and x = time in years. For the nonlinear function, $y = \alpha\beta^x$, β is the constant rate of growth to be estimated. It is obtained by a semi-log transformation to obtain the linear form of the model, $\ln y = \ln \alpha + (\ln \beta)x$. ■

More Complex Transformations

It is fairly obvious that combinations of these or other simple transformations allow for a wide variety of nonlinear representations within the context of the simple linear regression model. Often, only the limits of cleverness of the model-builder restrict the formulation of meaningful nonlinear relations in terms of the linear model. Other times, the limitation may be mathematical. There are some relations that are intrinsically nonlinear and cannot be put into a linear form by any combination or series of transformations of variables. The following specifications are nonlinear in the parameters:

$$y = \alpha + \beta_1 e^{(\beta_2 x)}$$
$$y = \alpha + \beta_1 x_1 + \beta_2 (\beta_3)^{x_2}$$

These models cannot be changed into the standard linear model. Special methods for estimating nonlinear functions must be used. These involve iterative procedures that require more complex statistical and mathematical procedures than the linear case. These nonlinear techniques are not considered in this text, although some computer programs for estimation will include at least one nonlinear method.

section 15.7

Doing a Multiple Regression Research Report

One way to learn why the linear regression model is the most commonly used statistical technique is to apply the process yourself to a question of interest. In this section, a *checklist* is given for the steps to follow in using multiple regression for a research report. This checklist serves as a summary of the topics in Chapters 13, 14, and 15. It emphasizes that statistical procedures do not make a model good or bad, useful or not. The model-builder or analyst must use good sense and good theory before using good statistical or econometric methods.

The following steps provide one way of proceeding through a complete analysis of a linear regression model. Not all the items are always necessary, and some may be done in a different order.

Phase I: Specification

1. Specify the dependent variable of interest. State clearly the relevance of this dependent variable to some purpose of forecasting, decision-making, or problem-solving.
2. On the basis of reading, experience, theory, derivations, optimization solutions (such as minimizing costs or maximizing utility), or results of other studies, specify the explanatory variables in the model. Keep in mind the purpose in step 1. Variables useful for good forecasting may differ from variables that can be manipulated for policy changes or from variables that are theoretically supposed to be causal factors.

3. State clearly the expected shape of the function relating each explanatory variable to the dependent variable. That is, try to specify the most reasonable functional form (linear or nonlinear) and to understand the expected direction of the effect (positive or negative).

4. Find the best measures of the variables desired in the model. Be sure to note the definitions, the units, the time periods, the number of cases, and the source of the data.

Phase II: Prior Analysis and Respecification

5. In view of the likely functional relations from step 3 and the data available from step 4, define the symbols $y, x_1, x_2, \ldots, x_m$, for the *linear* regression model. These may be transformations, substitutes, composites, or dummy variables developed from the theoretically specified variables.

6. Specify the expected sign (and approximate size, if possible) of the regression coefficients β_j relating y to x_j. These propositions must take account of the functional relations in step 3 and any variable changes in creating y or x_j in step 5. These propositions will provide the testable hypotheses for later analysis so they should relate directly to the point of the project as stated in step 1. They may involve separate regressions for different subsets of the data or several regressions with and without particular explanatory variables.

7. Consider the possible outcomes of your analysis. Suppose the testable statements in step 6 are *confirmed* by tests on the sample model. What will you have shown? Suppose such tests and results *falsify* one or more of the prior suppositions. Will you have anything meaningful to argue or any worthwhile information to provide relative to the purpose of your project?

   The answers to these hypothetical questions help to assure that you understand the model and its limitations relative to the intended purpose of the project. This step also helps you to review whether or not you will be able to make the required tests. Some of your theoretical or practical propositions may require testing and inference methods that are more complex and unknown to you (and to others). In this case, think about how you can examine the same issue in a simpler way.

8. Think about the underlying set of five assumptions and three conditions in Section 15.2. Question the validity of each of these for your model and think of situations or reasons why they might be violated. Keep note of arguments that seem to support the applicability of these assumptions for your model. During this conceptual process, do not make use of the data found in step 4. Rather, you should review the background conditions during the time period or across the various firms, households, or cities in your data set. Consider the real-world setting for your theoretical relations.

   Your efforts in steps 6, 7, and 8 may lead to modifications in the model and to the inclusion or exclusion of some variables. If so, be sure to repeat the process from step 3 for the revised specification.

Phase III: Estimation and Testing

9. Use a computer program and your data to obtain the results for the multiple regression estimation, using the method of least squares. Remember that you may have to estimate several models, such as models excluding one, two, or a subgroup of variables, in addition to the full model. Also, include a listing of the data with labels and be sure to instruct the computer to provide the estimated values $(\widehat{y}_i)$ and the residuals (e_i) for each regression. Looking ahead to steps 11

and 12, you may also wish to program the computer to reorder the observations and do some plots.

10. Do the standard analyses for the goodness of fit of your model, and do one-sided tests of significance of the coefficients corresponding to your propositions in step 6. Interpret these results to see whether a more detailed analysis of this model is worthwhile.

11. Complete any other useful analysis of the regression results, including tests of any remaining hypotheses suggested in step 6. These may involve computing forecasts or making comparisons of results from different regressions for subgroups of the data or for different specifications of the set of explanatory variables.

12. Examine the correlation coefficients among the explanatory variables for detection of multicollinearity. Examine plots and tests of residuals for detection of non-normality, heteroscedasticity, or autocorrelation.

Phase IV: Revision

13. If one or more of the problems in step 12 are detected, a re-estimation of the model may be needed. Make clear what problem has been detected and its effects. With more study or consultation, you may consider using additional data or a revised specification, probably involving a transformation of the original variables to obtain a better estimation of your model.

14. If part of the analysis suggests the need for another statistical result that you did not compute the first time, or the need for a different regression, do the extra procedure to obtain what is needed.

Phase V: Interpretation and Conclusion

15. Compile a detailed list of each result with its separate meaning. From this, formulate the interpretation of the complete set of results. Relate the individual and collective results to the purpose of your project. Understand which results contribute to your conclusions and which make it dubious or ambiguous.

16. Write a report including the following:

    a) An abstract or executive summary of the project

    b) Statement of the purpose of the project

    c) Statement of the model(s) and its relevance to the issue

    d) Definition of variables and source of their statistical measures detailing the units and cases being used in each regression

    e) Hypotheses to be tested, forecasts to be calculated, and their relevance to the issue

    f) Summary of results, including any residual analysis and revised estimations

    g) Conclusions based on the results and their overall bearing on the issue raised in item (b)

Use your computer output as an appendix to your paper, and clearly mark the crucial results referred to in your written report. It is often convenient to include the formulas and calculated values of the test statistics on the computer output as well.

Item (a) is a one-paragraph synopsis of the purpose, interesting methods or results of analysis, and the principal conclusions. Try to write parts (b) and (c) of the report on about one page. Items (d) and (e) may require more pages, depending on the number of variables and regressions involved. A reasonable limit is three pages. Item (f) will probably correspond in length to items (d) and (e) together. Two pages should suffice for item (g). Thus, a typical research report may be concisely written in about ten pages or less, plus computer output. In the context of a term paper the instructor may request some longer detail on a particular part of the report. In the context of a job, if the report is especially relevant, containing important and unambiguous results, the supervisor who requested it may ask for an expanded version and a presentation to a policy or review group.

PROBLEMS

15.22 Given the residuals in Table 15.8 for a regression of y = consumption and x = income over ten years, plot e_t against time and plot e_t against e_{t-1}. Interpret the plots as indicators of possible autocorrelation.

TABLE 15.8 Regression Residuals for y = consumption and x = income over ten years

Year	e_t	Year	e_t
1984	−0.4	1989	+0.3
1985	−0.1	1990	+1.2
1986	−0.1	1991	+0.6
1987	−0.8	1992	−0.1
1988	+0.4	1993	−1.0

15.23 For the residuals in Table 15.8, perform a Durbin–Watson test for autocorrelation.

15.24 Use the residuals from the regression model for imports in Problem 13.67. Make a plot of e against $\hat{y}$. Calculate the Durbin–Watson d-statistic. Interpret the results in terms of possible violations of assumptions 4 and 5.

15.25 Repeat Problem 15.24 using the residuals given below for the simple regression model for investment reported in Figure 13.16.

OBS	Y	X1	YHAT	RESID
1	62.3	398.4	53.045	9.2551
2	71.3	452.6	59.737	11.5631
3	70.3	509.8	66.799	3.5007
4	68.5	485.4	63.787	4.7133
5	57.3	445.7	58.885	−1.5850
6	68.8	539.8	70.503	−1.7034
7	72.2	662.8	85.690	−13.4900
8	76.0	620.0	80.406	−4.4055
9	64.3	632.2	81.912	−17.6119
10	77.9	703.0	90.653	−12.7534
11	84.3	581.8	75.689	8.6110
12	85.1	707.1	91.160	−6.0597
13	90.8	776.6	99.741	−8.9407
14	97.9	875.3	111.927	−14.0271
15	108.7	873.4	111.692	−2.9925
16	122.4	943.7	120.372	2.0277
17	114.0	830.6	106.408	7.5920
18	123.0	907.5	115.903	7.0972
19	126.2	905.3	115.631	10.5689
20	137.0	927.4	118.360	18.6402

15.26 The application of OLS treats all observations as equally important. State one situation in which this may be an inappropriate procedure, and explain the general principle or method of a better procedure.

15.27 Consider a simple model, $y_t = \alpha + \beta x_t + \epsilon_t$ for which it is known that $\epsilon_t = 0.3\epsilon_{t-1} + v_t$ where the v_t are normally and independently distributed with constant variance and mean zero.

a) Explain the problem of using ordinary least squares in this situation.

b) Construct the appropriate expression that will minimize the sum of squares, if the variables are transformed to correct for the problem. (*Hint:* Let the new variables be $y_t^* = y_t - 0.3y_{t-1}$ and $x_t^* = x_t - 0.3x_{t-1}$.)

15.28 Repeat Problem 15.24 using the results in Table 15.19 from the simple regression model of sales on GDP in Problem 14.36.

TABLE 15.9 Residuals of Sales on GDP

Obs	Observed Sales	Predicted Sales	Residual
1	978.000	1054.550	−76.550
2	1123.000	1087.015	35.985
3	1125.000	1115.010	9.990
4	1260.000	1152.691	107.309
5	1121.000	1199.740	−78.740
6	1275.000	1230.608	44.392
7	1257.000	1263.606	−6.606
8	1381.000	1300.968	80.032
9	1172.000	1316.722	−144.722
10	1368.000	1343.333	24.667
11	1382.000	1377.927	4.073
12	1454.000	1393.468	60.532
13	1260.000	1378.247	−118.247
14	1462.000	1404.113	57.887

15.29 Answer parts (a) and (b).

a) Suppose an individual's personal income tax liability t is related to personal adjusted gross income I by the model, $t = \alpha I^{\beta+1}(10)^{\epsilon}$. Determine a representation of this theory that allows estimation of α and β as parameters in the simple linear model.

b) Let E denote hours of work per capita per week, and let I denote per capita national income in the model, $E = \alpha I^{\beta}\epsilon$. Sketch the relation between E and I. Determine a representation of this theory that allows estimation of α and β as parameters in the simple linear model.

15.30 Given the values of x and y in Table 15.10:

TABLE 15.10 Data for a concave function

x	1.00	1.44	1.96	3.24	4.00	7.84
y	1.0	2.0	3.0	4.0	5.0	6.0

a) Plot these six values of x and y on a graph, and then make a freehand estimate of the curve relating the two variables. Would a linear function be appropriate in this circumstance? What type of relationship to the values of x does y appear to have?

b) Transform the variable x into a new variable by taking the square root of x, and then plot this new variable against y. Is this relationship approximately linear?

c) Use the transformation in part (b) to establish a least-squares regression line for the relationship between y and $\sqrt{x}$. Calculate a list of the residuals.

d) Find the sample coefficient of determination for the original data and then find it for the transformed data. Explain if the different values give a hint to the best-fitting form of model relating y to x.

15.31 The data in Table 15.11 represent the growth pattern of the price of a mutual fund unit where x is in months and y is in dollars.

TABLE 15.11 Growth of a Mutual Fund

x (months)	1	2	3	4	5	6	7
y ($)	0.80	1.10	1.70	2.60	3.80	5.70	8.50

a) Find the least-squares equation relating x and y, of the form $\widehat{y} = ab^x$. Take the logarithm of both sides of this equation, letting $\log \widehat{y} = \log a + (\log b)x$.

b) Plot the original data and your least-squares estimate, and use this sketch to find the error of prediction for these seven observations.

15.32 Given the five observations on y and x in Table 15.12,

a) Determine the least-squares estimate assuming that $\widehat{y} = ax^b$. Let $\ln \widehat{y} = \ln a + (\ln x)b$.

b) Plot the original data and the least-squares estimate on graph paper, and compute the residuals $e_i = y_i - \widehat{y}_i$.

c) Find s_e using Formula 13.15.

TABLE 15.12 Data for Problem 15.32

x	1	2	3	4	5
y	1.0	2.1	4.3	8.1	13.0

d) Determine the least-squares estimate using the line $\widehat{y} = a + bx$ and find s_e. By comparing s_e for both forms of the estimation, determine which model specification provides the best fit.

15.33 The observations in Table 15.13 represent the price movement of a certain common stock over a ten-year period.

TABLE 15.13 Price Movement of Common Stock

x (Year)	y (Price)	x (Year)	y (Price)
1	100	6	35
2	120	7	60
3	75	8	75
4	50	9	80
5	40	10	70

a) Sketch the relationship between x and y. What type of function does this relationship seem to follow for the given ten years?

b) Use the method of least squares to fit the equation $\widehat{y} = a + bx$.

c) Determine the residuals for these ten observations, and test to see whether autocorrelation may be a problem in this estimation. Relate this result to your answer to part (a).

CHAPTER SUMMARY

KEY TERMS AND EXPRESSIONS

Econometrics: A study of methods of statistical analysis of economic models.

Simultaneity: Two-way causal relation among variables in a model.

Error in measurement: Inaccuracies in the values of the explanatory variable.

Multicollinearity: A condition in which two or more of the independent variables are strongly (but not perfectly) related to one another in a linear relationship.

Extraneous estimates: Values of coefficients in a model that are obtained from a result external to the estimation of the model.

Heteroscedasticity: The variance of the error terms is not constant.

Goldfeld–Quandt test: An F-test using regressions on subgroups of data to detect heteroscedasticity.

White test: A chi-square test using an auxiliary regression to detect heteroscedasticity.

Autocorrelation: There is a correlation among the error terms.

Durbin–Watson test: A test on residuals to detect autocorrelation.

Generalized least squares (GLS): Estimation method based on the least-squares principle that incorporates information about the variance and covariance of the disturbance terms into the estimation.

Transformation of variables: Algebraic changes in the definitions of y and x so that the linear model can better represent an underlying nonlinear relation or so that the underlying assumptions for multiple regression are better satisfied.

Elasticity: The percentage change in y for a one percent change in x.

EXERCISES

15.34 A study was made of 75 countries to determine whether the formal character of a country's political constitution has a systematic impact on decentralization of public revenues. The following regression results were obtained:

$$\hat{y} = \quad 96 \; - 1.21x_1 - 0.004x_2 - 0.6x_3 - 15.9x_4,$$
$$\quad (12.1) \quad (-1.3) \quad (-2.3) \quad (-5.5) \quad (-4.7)$$
$$R^2 = 0.65$$

where

y is central government share of total public revenues, expressed as a percentage

x_1 is the natural logarithm of population size in thousands

x_2 is per-capita income in 1985 U.S. dollars

x_3 is Social Security contributions as a percentage of total public revenue

x_4 is 1 for countries with a federal constitution and 0 otherwise

The values in parentheses are t-ratios of the regression estimates to their standard errors.

a) Interpret the meaning of the coefficient of x_4 in descriptive terms.

b) Using a 1% level of significance, test the hypothesis that the formal character of a country's constitution affects the proportion of public revenue that the central government obtains against the hypothesis that it does not.

c) If the largest coefficient of determination, R_j^2, among all sets of explanatory variables is 0.44, explain whether or not multicollinearity may be a problem in this estimation.

d) If the computer program used for this problem gave a Durbin–Watson statistic of 1.17, what interpretation would you give to this information?

15.35 A time-series study has been done based on annual data for 26 years on the demand for money as a function of the current interest rate, last period's interest rate, and the change in the interest rate from year to year. Last period's interest rate reflects habit and inertia, and the change in interest rates reflects expectations of change based on recent changes. The Durbin–Watson statistic is 1.1, and $R^2 = 0.95$.

a) Using a 5% level of significance, test the hypothesis of no positive autocorrelation against the alternative of positive autocorrelation.

b) On the basis of your answer to part (a), explain if the analyst should proceed to test the hypothesis that the change in interest rate is useful in explaining variation in the demand for money.

15.36 Given the multiple-regression results in Table 15.14, where $n = 12$.

TABLE 15.14 Multiple Regression Results

Variable	Mean	Standard Deviation	
y	306.67	174.98	$r_{yx_1} = 0.9348$
x_1	12.58	9.31	$r_{yx_2} = 0.3501$
x_2	11.17	8.95	$r_{x_1x_2} = 0.0096$

Coefficient	Estimate	Standard Deviation	
b_1	17.61	0.623	$R_{y \cdot x_1 x_2} = 0.995$
b_2	6.70	0.647	$s_e = 19.220$
a	10.17	11.972	

Obs	Observed y	Residual
1	650	−1.63
2	80	11.99
3	120	−18.46
4	180	+32.34
5	360	17.79
6	140	−21.07
7	450	7.11
8	550	11.43
9	280	−14.37
10	300	−16.30
11	350	−17.43
12	220	

a) Which independent variable is most important in determining y?

b) Find the residual for the twelfth observation if the observed values for x_1 and x_2 are 8 and 9, respectively.

c) What are the degrees of freedom for the F-test on the multiple linear association represented by this estimated model?

d) What percentage of the total variation in y has been explained by this regression?

e) Using a plot, comment on the validity of the assumption of homoscedasticity in this model.

f) Using a plot, comment on the validity of the assumption of nonautocorrelation in this model.

g) Do you think multicollinearity is a problem in this estimation? Explain your answer.

15.37 Table 15.15 gives values of the observed and estimated values of imports for a country over time. The estimated values result from a sample regression equation of imports on GDP. Use the residuals from the table and do the following:

a) Plot e_t against $\widehat{y}_t$

b) Plot e_t against e_{t-1}

c) Determine the Durbin–Watson test result

d) Interpret the results of parts (a)–(c) in terms of possible violations of assumption 4 or 5.

TABLE 15.15 Regression Results for $y = $ imports

Obs	Observed	Estimated	Residual
1	7.2	7.2822	−0.0822
2	8.2	8.6568	−0.4568
3	10.3	10.1508	0.1491
4	9.7	10.0910	−0.3910
5	12.1	11.7046	0.3954
6	15.1	14.3342	0.7658
7	15.8	15.3501	0.4499
8	16.6	16.4856	0.1144
9	16.1	16.3661	−0.2661
10	17.9	18.3980	−0.4980
11	19.8	19.7128	0.0872
12	20.7	20.9678	−0.2678

15.38 Repeat Exercise 15.37 using Table 15.16 based on a model with $y = \ln$ (imports) and $x = \ln$(domestic price) for textiles over an eight-year period.

TABLE 15.16 Regression Results for $y = \ln$ (imports)

Obs	Observed	Estimated	Residual
1	7.96	7.7391	0.2209
2	7.79	7.9512	−0.1612
3	7.73	8.2718	−0.5418
4	8.33	8.2718	0.0582
5	8.94	8.7037	0.2363
6	8.96	8.8124	0.1476
7	9.98	9.5823	0.3977
8	10.16	10.4798	−0.3198

15.39 Repeat Exercise 15.37 using Table 15.17 based on a model with $y = $ annual corporate profit before taxes and $x = $ average monthly wholesale sales for a 16-year period.

TABLE 15.17 Regression Results for
                 y = corporate profit

Obs	Observed	Estimated	Residual
1	16.8	17.7977	−0.9977
2	15.3	17.3958	−2.0958
3	20.4	18.9900	1.4100
4	24.4	20.1957	4.2043
5	21.1	20.4368	0.6632
6	21.4	20.7986	0.6014
7	18.4	20.7182	−2.3182
8	25.0	21.9239	3.0761
9	23.5	22.7544	0.7456
10	22.9	22.7143	0.1857
11	18.3	22.4195	−4.1195
12	25.4	23.9601	1.4399
13	23.0	24.0003	−1.0003
14	21.7	24.2548	−2.5548
15	24.7	24.9649	−0.2649
16	26.7	25.6749	1.0251

15.40 Repeat Exercise 15.37 for Table 15.18 based on a model with y = net income earned from direct investment in Canada by U.S. firms and x = imports into the United States from Canada over a ten-year period.

TABLE 15.18 Regression Results for
                 y = foreign investment income

Obs	Observed	Estimated	Residual
1	24	20.4888	3.5112
2	22	22.8432	−0.8432
3	21	25.1976	−4.1976
4	24	24.0204	0.0204
5	29	31.0835	−2.0835
6	33	32.2607	0.7393
7	34	33.4379	0.5621
8	34	32.2607	1.7393
9	35	35.7923	−0.7923
10	36	34.6151	1.3849

15.41 Explain why the residuals in any of the Problems 15.37–15.40 were not used to detect a possible problem of non-normality of the disturbances.

15.42 Suppose the model of Problem 15.38 is reconsidered using bi-weekly rather than annual data with a total number of observations equal to $8(26) = 208$.

   a) If the distribution of the disturbances is normal, what would be the expected frequencies of values within the class intervals as defined in Example 15.5.

   b) If the calculated chi-square for this set of residuals is 21, what would be the p-value for the test of

normality of ϵ? Make a conclusion about the acceptability of assumption 2.

15.43 A model to explain the level of imports of a country over time uses 60 quarterly observations on imports and on these explanatory variables: disposable income, government expenditures, money stock, and interest rate. Analysis of the residuals gives a Durbin–Watson statistic of $d_c = 1.156$.

   a) Is autocorrelation a problem?

   b) Estimate a value of $\widehat{\rho}$ that could be used to transform the data for re-estimation.

   c) A second estimation using the transformed data provides a d-value of 1.813. Explain what improvement has been made.

15.44 Explain how to interpret the plot in Figure 15.19 with regard to a potential problem of heteroscedasticity.

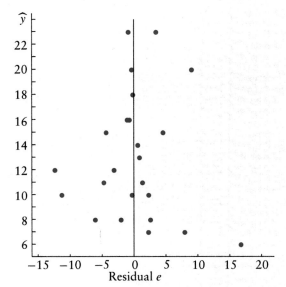

FIGURE 15.19 Plot of predicted values against residuals

15.45 Explain how to interpret the plot in Figure 15.20 with regard to a potential problem of autocorrelation.

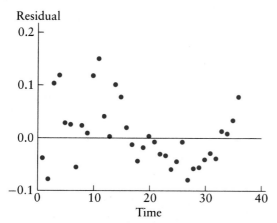

Residual

FIGURE 15.20 Plot of residuals over time

15.46 For the model of Problem 15.36, an auxiliary regression is calculated using the square of the residuals as the dependent variable and using the explanatory variables of x_1^2, x_2^2, and the product variable x_1x_2. The value of R^2 is 0.73.

a) Explain the purpose of this regression.

b) Perform a White test using the chi-square distribution. Specify the degrees of freedom and the critical value with a significance level of 0.05.

15.47 With regard to the model in Problem 15.34, there is a possibility that the variance of the disturbances may increase as the size of the per-capita income x_3 increases.

a) What grouping of observations would you recommend for doing a Goldfeld–Quandt test of this possibility?

b) Suppose regressions of the model using two appropriate subgroups of data result in sums of squares of errors of 2,823 for the high subgroup and 1,283 for the low subgroup. Interpret the result.

USING THE COMPUTER

15.48 Refer to the data for a model on job ratings in Problem 14.31(b). Use the residuals from regressions on two subgroups of this data to check for a violation of assumption 4 by making a Goldfeld–Quandt test. Order the observations according to the size of $\widehat{y}$.

15.49 Using the residuals from the import model in Problem 13.67, do an appropriate plot to detect possible heteroscedasticity. Order the observations by time and run two regressions on subgroups of the data to make a Goldfeld–Quandt test.

15.50 Repeat Problem 15.49 using the education–income data from Problem 13.37 and the equation income $= \alpha + \beta(\text{education})$. Order the observations by size of $\widehat{y}$.

15.51 Return to the data set in Table 14.2 and the results in Example 15.10 for the housing model. Order the data according to the variable *Vacant* and run two regressions on subgroups of data to make a Goldfeld–Quandt (G–Q) test. Interpret the results.

15.52 Run a computer program to obtain least squares regression results and a list of residuals for the data and model in Problem 14.43 for detergent sales.

a) Make a plot of e_t against $\widehat{y}$ and interpret.

b) Order the observations by size of population and perform a G–Q test.

15.53 Repeat Problem 15.52(b), ordering the observations by the size of advertising expense.

15.54 Answer parts (a) and (b).

a) Repeat Problem 15.52(a) using the top fifty firms in **Data Set 2** and the model in Problem 13.78 for sales.

b) Perform a White test for heteroscedasticity.

15.55 Using **Data Set 1** and the model in Problem 14.50 for sales, perform a White test for heteroscedasticity.

15.56 Refer to Table 15.6 for the original and transformed data used in the investment model.

a) Repeat steps 2–4 of the correction process for autocorrelation, beginning with an estimated value of $d = 1.106$.

b) Compare your regression results with those in Figure 15.13.

c) Examine the value of the d-statistic based on your regression. Does it show any improvement toward reducing autocorrelation?

15.57 Use **Data Set 5** and the multiple regression model in Problem 14.45 for imports.

a) Perform a Durbin–Watson test and interpret the result.

b) Have the computer make appropriate plots to examine for a possible violation of assumption 5. Interpret the results and compare with your conclusion in part (a).

15.58 Use **Data Set 5** and the model in Problem 13.83 for GDP.

a) Perform a Durbin–Watson test and interpet the result.

b) Use the d-value to estimate the autocorrelation coefficient. Make a transformation of variables as in Example 15.16 and re-estimate the model. Include the determination of the new D–W statistic.

c) Compare and interpret the results of the before-and-after regressions, including consideration of the properties of the estimators.

15.59 Use **Data Set 6**, excluding the outlier observation number 80, to regress income on years of education and on the number of persons in the household.

a) Find the OLS estimation and the OLS residuals.

b) Obtain three plots of residuals versus $\widehat{y}$, x_1, or x_2 in order to check for possible heteroscedasticity. Interpret.

c) Perform a White test for heteroscedasticity.

d) Using class groups as in Problem 15.14, sketch a histogram of the residuals and perform a chi-square test for normality.

15.60 For **Data Set 6**, including all observations, and the same model as in Problem 15.59, run a least squares regression. Then, do the following:

a) Divide the data into four groups by the variable REGION and run four separate regressions. Find s_e for the OLS regression on each region.

b) Perform a G–Q test between the pair of regions with the largest difference in the respective values of s_e. If heteroscedasticity is indicated, repeat the test for the pair of regions with the next largest difference in values of s_e. Continue examining pairs of regions until you are satisfied that you have identified any violations of assumption 4.

c) Make a transformation of variables by dividing each observation by the value of s_e for its respective region. Re-estimate the model using the transformed data to obtain a special case of generalized least squares estimation. Compare your results with the original estimation in terms of both the values and the properties of the estimates.

CASE PROBLEMS

15.61 Use the model and data in Problem 13.86 for highway deaths to do the following:

a) Obtain the least-squares regression results, including a list of residuals and a plot of residuals versus $\widehat{y}$.

b) Order the observations used in part (a) by the size of the population density given in Problem 14.54, and perform a G–Q test omitting the middle 20% of the

observations.

c) Include the variable *population density* in the model and repeat the residual analysis of parts (a) and (b).

15.62 Follow the steps for an empirical research project in Section 15.7 to develop your own model, find relevant data, estimate and test the model, and write a report on your findings.

CHAPTER 16

Time Series and Index Numbers

Introduction to Time Series

In Chapter 13, we studied methods for describing the nature of the relationship between two variables. In this chapter, we turn to a subset of this type of problem in which the independent variable under investigation is time.

Recording observations of a variable that is a function of time results in a set of numbers called a **time series**. We have used time series for variables in Chapters 13–15, such as the observations in **Data Set 5**. Most data in business and economic publications take the form of a time series — the monthly sales receipts in a retail store, the annual Gross Domestic Product (GDP) of a country, and indices of consumer and wholesale prices, to name just a few. The analysis of time-series data usually focuses on two types of problems:

1. attempting to estimate the components that produce the pattern in the series
2. forecasting the future behaviour of the series

Both these topics are interesting in themselves as statistical problems. Methods of analyzing time series can become quite complex. Forecasting future values can be an extension of multiple regression if the important factors that explain the variable of interest are very systematic. If not, it can be more of a random walk into successive periods. Sometimes, a forecasting model that works well may simply be a naive model where the next value is best predicted as a simple multiple of the current value. Other times, a rather complex mix of autoregressive structure of a variable on its previous values and a moving average pattern is determined to provide good forecasts. Such models fall under the heading of ARIMA models, with the *AR* representing auto-regressiveness and the *MA* referring to a moving average.

In this chapter, we shall concentrate our attention primarily on the meaning and identification of the components of a time series rather than the study of forecasting. There are entire courses and texts designed for time series analysis. The interested reader is well advised to pursue additional study for information about advanced methods of decomposition and forecasting with time series because of their central importance in the planning function performed by many businesses and government agencies.

Components of a Time Series

In general, the fluctuations in an economic time series are assumed to result from four different components: trend (T), seasonal variation (S), cyclical variation (C), and irregular or random variation (I). **Trend** is the long-term movement in a time series. Consumer debt, for example, has grown at a rate of approximately 3–4% a year over the past 20 years. The tendency toward a decreasing work week and increasing price levels over the past several decades also illustrates long-term movements or trends. **Seasonal variation** represents fluctuations that repeat themselves within a fixed period of one year. Many economic series have seasonal highs or lows due to changes in the supply of certain factors (youth employment in the summer, food harvests in the fall), in demand for certain factors (ski equipment in the winter, toys before Christmas, gardening supplies in the spring), or in marketing factors (seasonal changes in clothing, new car models in the fall). The **cyclical variation** of a time series represents a pattern repeated over time periods of differing length, usually longer than one year. Business cycles, with their stages of prosperity, recession, and recovery, are important examples of such cyclical movements.

The movements in a time series generated by trend, seasonal variation, and cyclical variation are assumed to be based on systematic causes that have a more or less regular influence. Exactly the opposite holds true for random or **irregular variation**, which is, by definition, fluctuation that is unpredictable or takes place at various points in time, by chance or randomly. Floods, strikes, and fads illustrate the irregular component of a time series. Figure 16.1 presents a graphical view of the four components of a time series. In each case, the dependent variable y is expressed as a function of the independent variable t (time).

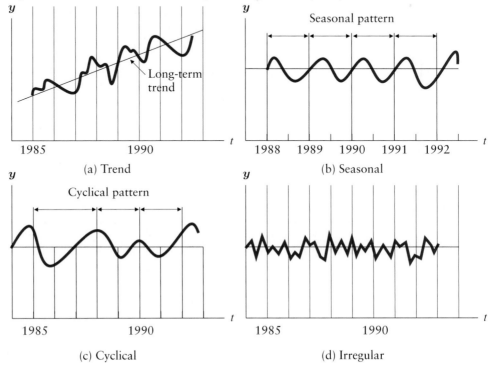

FIGURE 16.1   The four components of a time series

The Time-Series Model

Now that we have specified the components of a time series, the problem becomes one of estimating each of these components for a given series. In order to separate these components, we make some assumptions about how they are related in the population under investigation; these assumptions are referred to as the *time-series model*.

Time-series models usually fall into one of two categories, depending on whether their components are expressed as sums or products. The first of these, called the **additive model**, assumes that the value of y equals the *sum* of the four components, or that $y = T + S + C + I$. By assuming that the components of a time series are additive, we are, in effect, assuming that these components are independent of one another. Thus, for example, trend can affect neither seasonal nor cyclical variation, nor can these components affect trend. The other major type of relationship between the components expresses y in the form $y = T \times S \times C \times I$ and is called the **multiplicative model**. A model of this form assumes that the four components are related to one another, yet still allows for the components to result from different basic causes.

For the purpose of estimating each of the components of a time series, models normally treat S, C, and I as deviations from the trend. In other words, trend is usually estimated in units of y and the other components are measured in index form with values greater than 100 indicting a deviation above the trend value and values below 100 indicating a movement below the trend. Each of the components, T, S, and C of the time series can be isolated by statistical techniques. While some of these methods are excessively tedious, the basic concepts are similar to the simple methods to be discussed in this chapter.

The principles of *decomposition* of a time series into its components for a multiplicative model, $y = T \times S \times C \times I$, are presented in subsequent sections. The steps to be explained are:

1. Isolate the seasonal component S by the ratio-to-moving average (or ratio-to-trend) method. Determine the seasonal index with a base value of 100.
2. Divide the values of y by the seasonal index S and multiply by 100 to obtain $100\ y/S = T \times C \times I$.
3. Model the trend component by fitting an appropriate linear or non-linear function. Divide $T \times C \times I$ by the trend value $\hat{y}$ to obtain $(C \times I)$.
4. Eliminate I by finding a weighted moving average of the $C \times I$ values and obtain the cyclical component C.

Once all the components of a time series are identified, forecasts of the value of the time series at some future point in time can be made by first estimating the value of the trend component at that point and then modifying this trend value by an adjustment that takes into account the seasonal and cyclical components.

Some Purposes and Problems of Forecasts

The primary purpose of forecasting future values of a time series is to facilitate planning. A business manager wants to forecast the trend in sales in order to make long-range planning decisions about investment in more plant capacity and new equipment. Or there may be a need to forecast cyclical movements in order to take advantage of lower interest-rate periods to conduct a bond sale or of a period of high investor expectations to release a new issue of common stocks. Seasonal variation is important for short-run planning of inventories and employment levels, as the manager needs to be prepared for periods of high demand for certain products and services. As consumers, we recognize these seasonal components also and plan to make purchases at times of special sales when prices are lower. Of course, the marketing experts use the seasonal components to plan advertising campaigns to entice buyers to purchase during the high season when the product or service is most desirable. A salesperson would prefer selling ski equipment in the fall and winter and air conditioners in the spring and summer, rather than vice versa.

The most obvious problem inherent in forecasting future values of a time series is the potential size of the (unpredictable) irregular component. This component is a random variable whose size depends upon a large number of independent factors that affect the economic variable y. Psychological and sociological variables of individual and group behaviour, as well as other economic and business considerations, can affect the forecast. In addition, the irregular component may consist of one single occurrence in the time period being forecast, such as a flood, a major political event, or an energy crisis. Neither the size nor the direction of the irregular component can be predicted.

There is also an important problem in trying to forecast the more regular parts of the time series: the trend, cyclical, and seasonal components. In forecasting, it is necessary to assume that no change occurs in the fundamental causes underlying these regular patterns. For this reason, forecasts far beyond the range of presently observable values of the time series are always very dubious. In most cases, this means that the forecaster must not try to predict very far into the future, for fear of being greatly embarrassed.

Trend Functions

An important step in analyzing a time series is usually estimation of the trend component T. As was true in regression analysis, the first decision usually must be whether or not the model can be assumed to be linear. A plot of the relevant values against time serves as a guide to the appropriate trend function. Also, the graph can help detect atypical values. It may be advisable to eliminate one or two observations when calculating the mean value of y if these observations are clearly outliers from the rest of the series and if their inclusion will disturb the whole trend line.

The method of least squares, developed in Chapter 13, represents the most popular method of fitting a trend line to time-series data. The population trend equation is $y = \alpha + \beta x$ where x is units of time.

Scaling and Interpreting the Time Variable

In any time-series analysis, it is important to carefully define the units of the time variable x and the point of origin in time at which $x = 0$. Since time is continuous, it really makes little difference if the units used to express time are years, months, weeks, days, or any other desirable period. Also, because the point in time that is selected as $x = 0$ has no influence on the analysis, any point in time can be assigned this value. We will illustrate two short time series.

◻ EXAMPLE 16.1 Let $y =$ the number of days of sick leave taken monthly by all employees in a firm, measured over the six-month period shown in Table 16.1.

TABLE 16.1 Monthly Observations of Days of Sick Leave

$y =$ Days of Sick Leave	Time Period (1993)	Value of x
16	March	-5
17	April	-3
18	May	-1
20	June	$+1$
18	July	$+3$
24	August	$+5$

The units of x in Table 16.1 are expressed in units of half-months, with $x = 0$ corresponding to the date, midnight June 1, 1993. The values of x represent the number of half-months before or after the end of May 1993. For example, the value $x = 5$ represents August 15, 1993, which is five half-months after June 1. To forecast a trend value for November, the value $x = 11$ would be substituted into the trend equation. To forecast a trend value at the *end* of the year (December 31, 1993), the value $x = 14$ would be used.   ∎

☐ **EXAMPLE 16.2**   The data (*y*) in Table 16.2 are fees collected by an accountant who has begun using weekends and evenings for an income tax return service in her community. We use x measured in years with the origin $x = 0$ corresponding to July 1, 1992. The value $x = -1$ thus corresponds to July 1, 1991, and $x = 2$ is July 1, 1994.   ∎

TABLE 16.2   Income Tax Service Fees (thousands of dollars)

Year	x	y
1990	−2	$2
1991	−1	6
1992	0	10
1993	1	13
1994	2	16

Using Simple Regression to Find the Trend Line

The solutions for least square estimators a and b in the trend line $\widehat{y} = a + bx$ are identical to those for a simple regression in Formula 13.8 repeated in Formula 16.1.

Least squares regression formulas:

$$b = \frac{\text{SC}xy}{\text{SS}x} = \frac{\Sigma(x_i - \bar{x})(y_i - \bar{y})}{\Sigma(x_i - \bar{x})^2}$$
$$a = \bar{y} - b\bar{x}$$
(16.1)

At the origin point in time, $x = 0$, the value of the time series is a. For each advancing time period, the value of the trend for $\widehat{y}$ changes by the amount b. Although we recognize that estimation of a long-run trend cannot be achieved based on a small number of observations, we use the data in Table 16.2 to illustrate the linear trend line.

Applying least squares methodology with the data from Table 16.2 to find the trend line for income tax service fees, the value of a equals 9.4 and the value of b is 3.5. Hence, the line of best fit is as follows with x in units of a year:

$$\widehat{y} = 9.4 + 3.5x$$

Note that $x = 0$ is July 1, 1992, and $x = 2$ is July 1, 1994. An estimate of fees for 1997 ($x = 5$) based on trend factors only would be:

$$\widehat{y} = 9.4 + 3.5(5) = 26.9$$

In reporting any trend equation, it is very important to include the units for x and the point in time corresponding to the value $x = 0$.

The trend line based on the data of Table 16.2 is shown in Figure 16.2. Clearly, extrapolation along the trend line in either direction is dangerous. In earlier years before offering income tax service, no fees, not negative fees, were collected. As clientele have increased, so have fees, but there is a limit on the total number of returns that can be done. Continuing this upward trend into the future is dubious.

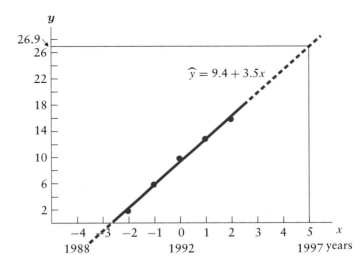

FIGURE 16.2   Trend line for data of Table 16.2 in which the forecast value of sales for mid-1997 is 26.9 thousand dollars

This simple illustration emphasizes the principle of caution in using trend equations for forecasts more than a few periods into the future. Underlying conditions may change so much that the same trend is not even appropriate. A good practice is to update the trend each time period as new data becomes available. Even then, recall that the forecasted value is only a point estimate. Confidence limits on the forecast would follow the same methodology as in Section 13.8. The limits become wider at a nonlinear rate as the value of x differs from its mean (Figure 13.14). In forecasting trend values, the measure of x in the future period necessarily gets farther and farther above the mean of x and uncertainty increases.

◻ STUDY QUESTION 16.1   **Trend Line for Days of Sick Leave**

Determine and graph the trend line for the data in Table 16.1.

● ANSWER   Using the method of least squares, we find $a = 18.83$ and $b = 0.643$. The trend equation in units of one-half month with origin at June 1, 1993, is as follows and is graphically illustrated in Figure 16.3:

$$\widehat{y} = 18.83 + 0.643x$$

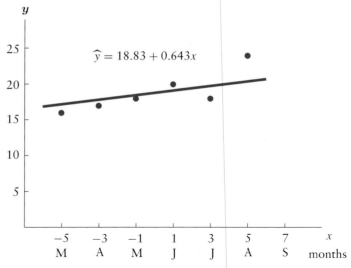

FIGURE 16.3   Trend line for the data of Table 16.1

Translations of Trend Lines

The x-values shown in Table 16.2 and represented by the regression line $\widehat{y} = 9.4 + 3.5x$ are based on yearly data. In many instances, it is necessary to compare or combine in one statistical analysis, time series which have different periodicities or magnitudes. One series may be in time periods of a year and another deseasonalized series may be in periods of quarters. Another may be monthly. The latter two could be in magnitudes of quarters or months, or they could be measured at an annual rate.

Also, when having a trend equation determined by a computer, the origin point is typically set at the middle of the period prior to the first observed one so that values of x for the observed periods are $1, 2, 3, \ldots T$. The origin of this trend equation would differ from another based on a set of values available for a shorter or longer number of periods, or from one with the origin at the mid-point of the observed time series. For these reasons, it is useful to know how to switch a trend line based on yearly data to a trend line based on quarterly, monthly, or even weekly time periods, or from annual magnitudes to quarterly magnitudes. For each of these situations, there will usually be different values plotted at a different point in time for the same data set. Consider, for example, Figure 16.4, in which the upper line represents the trend line for the yearly data in Table 16.2.

The lower line in Figure 16.4 represents the same data shown in quarterly magnitudes. That is, the values represented by circles are one-fourth the size of the values represented by squares. Note that these circle values are plotted at the middle of each quarter (Feb. 15, May 15, Aug. 15, and Nov. 15), and thus no quarterly value falls at the same point in time as do the yearly values (July 1).

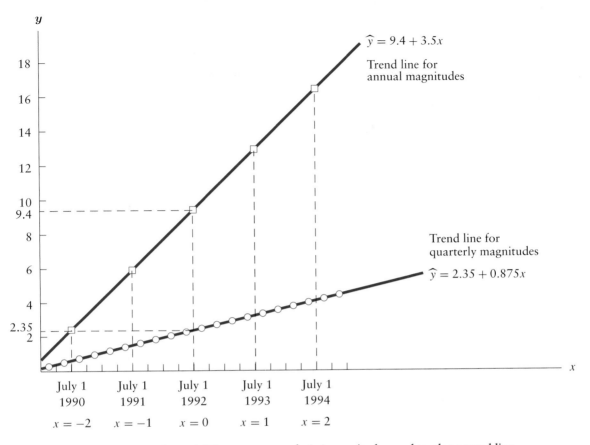

FIGURE 16.4   Annual (□) versus quarterly (○) magnitudes used to plot a trend line

There are three basic ways in which to translate one trend line into another, each following a simple rule.

Rule 1. *Changing magnitudes of the series (y):* Multiply both coefficients a and b by the ratio of the size of the new magnitude for y to the size of the old magnitude for y.

Rule 2. *Changing time units of (x):* Multiply the slope coefficient b by the ratio of the size of the new unit for x to the size of the original unit for x.

Rule 3. *Changing the origin point in time:* Substitute $x + t$ into the equation and solve for a new intercept, where t is the number of x-units desired (positive or negative) to move the origin (forward or backward in time).

We can illustrate these rules in translating the trend line for fees in Formula 16.1. In reducing annual magnitudes to quarterly magnitudes for the trend equation $\widehat{y} = a + bx = 9.4 + 3.5x$, where x is in years with origin at July 1, 1992, it is necessary to multiply both a and b by the ratio $\frac{1}{4}$. This follows Rule 1, since a quarter is one-fourth of a year. We obtain the following:

$$\widehat{y} = \tfrac{1}{4}(9.4 + 3.5x) = 2.35 + 0.875x$$

This equation gives quarterly magnitudes, but the values of x are still measured in years ($x = 1$ is one year), and the origin remains at July 1 as shown in the lower line of Figure 16.4.

To obtain quarterly magnitudes with x measured in quarters, we use Rule 2 and multiply the slope coefficient b by $\frac{1}{4}$. This yields the following line where $x = 0$ at July 1, 1992, and $x = 1$ is one quarter later, October 1, 1992.

$$\widehat{y} = 2.35 + \tfrac{1}{4}(0.875x) = 2.35 + 0.21875x$$

This line is the same as the lower line in Figure 16.4 with the scale for x changed so that each unit of x is one quarter (shown by the tick marks on the x-scale) rather than one year. If we wish to have the quarterly magnitudes centred at the middle of a quarter, we need to shift the origin of the line in quarterly units ($\widehat{y} = 2.35 + 0.21875x$) one-half quarter to the right from July 1 to August 16. Using Rule 3, we add $\frac{1}{2}$ to x in the equation above. The equation becomes:

$$\widehat{y} = 2.35 + 0.21875(x + \tfrac{1}{2}) = 2.46 + 0.21875x$$

This equation is again represented by the lower line in Figure 16.4 except that the integer values of x (in quarters) are now located exactly on the circles shown on the line. The coloured circle is now the origin point ($x = 0$ at August 15, 1992). Note that all three of these steps in converting the trend line could be combined if the latter equation is the desired one. The combined change beginning with the original trend line for annual magnitudes, $\widehat{y} = a + bx$, would be:

$$\widehat{y} = \left(\frac{a}{4}\right) + \left(\frac{b}{16}\right)\left(x + \frac{1}{2}\right) = \left(\frac{a}{4} + \frac{b}{32}\right) + \left(\frac{b}{16}\right)x$$

For our example, $a = 9.4$ and $b = 3.5$. Hence, the resulting equation is:

$$\widehat{y} = \frac{9.4}{4} + \frac{3.5}{32} + \left(\frac{3.5}{16}\right)x$$
$$= 2.46 + 0.21875x$$

Changes in trend equations from annual magnitudes to monthly, or from monthly to quarterly, can be done following the same logical processes.

☐ STUDY QUESTION 16.2 Quarterly Trend Line for Days of Sick Leave

Change the trend equation in Study Question 16.1 to one in quarterly magnitudes and quarterly time units with origin at mid–first quarter, 1993.

● **ANSWER** The trend equation in monthly units and magnitudes with origin at June 1, 1993, is:

$$\widehat{y} = 18.83 + 0.643x$$

To change to quarterly from monthly magnitudes, both coefficients must be multiplied by $\frac{3}{1}$. To change to quarterly from monthly units, the coefficient of x must be multiplied by $\frac{3}{1}$. To move the origin back 3.5 months to mid-February 1993, the term $(x - 3.5)$ is substituted for x in the trend equation. The revised trend line desired is:

$$\widehat{y} = 3[18.83 + 3(0.643)(x - 3.5)]$$
$$\widehat{y} = (56.490 - 20.255) + 5.79x$$
$$\widehat{y} = 36.235 + 5.79x$$

■

A special problem arises when data are analyzed for a product or service that is produced for only a fraction of a year in each year. For example, sugar beet–processing plants operate for about four months, starting in September of each year, and all sugar-refining processes shut down completely when the last beets are processed around the beginning of the following calendar year. When a trend line is being plotted for monthly production of sugar from sugar beets, the x-values must be expressed in months, but there will be only four nonzero values of x observed in each year. Problem 16.14 provides the reader with an opportunity to work an example of this type.

Nonlinear Trends

The problem of fitting a trend line to a nonlinear time series is essentially the same problem we mentioned in Section 15.6 concerning nonlinear regression—that of finding an equation that best describes the relationship between an independent variable (time, in this case) and the dependent variable (the time-series values). As is true in fitting a regression line, it is not sufficient merely to find an equation that provides a good fit to the data; it also is necessary to find a model that is justifiable in terms of the underlying economic nature of the series. In estimating the trend in a time series, there are a number of nonlinear equations that can be justified under a wide variety of circumstances. We will detail only one and suggest some other possibilities.

Exponential Curve

Time series are often used to describe data that increase or decrease at a constant proportion over time, such as population growth, the sales of a new product, or the spread of a highly communicable disease. Data taking this form can be approximated by an equation referred to as the **exponential trend**:

Exponential trend:
$$\widehat{y} = ab^x \tag{16.2}$$

The form of the exponential trend depends on the values of a and b. If b is between zero and one, then the value of $\widehat{y}$ will decrease as x increases. When b is larger than one, $\widehat{y}$ will increase as x increases. The value of a gives the y-intercept of the curve, as shown in Figure 16.5.

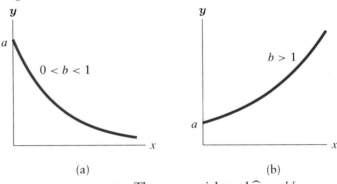

(a)   (b)

FIGURE 16.5   The exponential trend $\widehat{y} = ab^x$

As seen in Example 15.20, we can transform the exponential trend into a linear relationship by taking the logarithm of both sides of Formula 16.2:

$$\log y = \log(ab^x) = \log a + (\log b)x \qquad (16.3)$$

Our model is now linear, and the least-squares approach can be used to find the line of best fit with the values of the dependent variable being the logarithm of the time series values and the independent variable being time.

Consider the data given in Table 16.3 and graphed in Figure 16.6. We see that profits from 1988 to 1992 were not linear and that an equation of the type shown in Figure 16.5(b) might be reasonable. To use least-squares regression analysis to find the values of a and b in the equation $y = ab^x$, it is necessary to substitute $\log a$ for a, $\log b$ for b, and $\log y$ for y in Formula 16.1.

TABLE 16.3   Profits

Year	x	y
1988	−2	1
1989	−1	3
1990	0	6
1991	1	14
1992	2	41

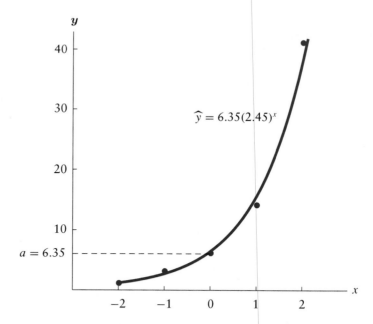

FIGURE 16.6   Profits from Table 16.3

Using base 10 logarithms, we obtain solutions as follows,

$$\log a = 0.8028, \quad \log b = 0.3895$$

Taking the antilog of these values yields the least-squares estimates $a = 6.35$ and $b = 2.45$. Thus, the exponential trend equation is:

$$\widehat{y} = (6.35)(2.45)^x$$

Using this equation to forecast profits for 1993 ($x = 3$) yields $(6.35)(2.45)^3$ = 93.38. The fit provided by this equation for all values of x from -2 to $+2$ is shown in Figure 16.6.

Other Nonlinear Trend Functions

Both the trend line and the exponential trend are determined from only two estimates, a and b. Sometimes, better fits can be obtained by more complex functions or functions with additional parameters to be estimated. One should be wary of two facts:

1. More complexity and estimation of more parameters is generally more costly and more difficult to interpret or to translate into different units of time or different magnitudes for comparison and use with other trends.

2. Trying to be too detailed about fitting a particular historical time series may result in fitting parts of the irregular component existing as shocks in the observed data. It is frequently better to estimate the general trend rather than to try to be too perfect in matching the observed data.

If it is desirable to allow for more flexibility in deciding on the position of the trend curve than is provided by the exponential curve, a constant c can be added to the equation. The resulting function is called the **modified exponential trend:**

Modified exponential trend:

$$\widehat{y} = c + ab^x \qquad (16.4)$$

The modified exponential, like the exponential itself, can assume many different forms, depending on the values of a, b, and c. Although the addition of the constant c merely serves to shift the exponential curve up or down by a constant amount, such a shift is convenient in describing a time series with values that approach an upper or lower limit, as shown in Figure 16.7.

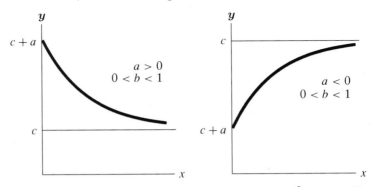

FIGURE 16.7   The modified exponential trend $\widehat{y} = c + ab^x$

If the linear trend described by $\widehat{y} = a + bx$ is too simplified because the observed data seem to reflect a decreasing slope as time advances, it is possible to use an extension to a quadratic equation.

Quadratic trend:

$$\widehat{y} = a + bx + cx^2 \tag{16.5}$$

This adds another parameter c which is the coefficient of the square of the value of the time period, such as 1, 4, 9, 16, …. A common application results in an upward trend component as given by a positive value of b, but one which is modified by a slowing growth as x increases due to a small but negative value of c. Again, this function tends to be accurate only in the immediately relevant range of x, for as x becomes too large, the third term begins to dominate the function and values of $\widehat{y}$ would hit a turning point and begin to decrease. One would have an upside-down U-shaped quadratic curve. Higher order polynomial functions with terms in x^3, x^4, et cetera, would allow for S-shaped functions or for multiple turning points, peaks, and troughs.

There are a number of additional curves used to estimate trend in a time series, two of which are relatively common. The first is known as a **logistic trend** and is defined by the following equation:

Logistic trend:

$$\widehat{y} = \frac{1}{c + ab^x} \tag{16.6}$$

Note that the logistic trend is just the reciprocal of the modified exponential curve. Its rate of growth or decline is relatively rapid at first but slows down in the later stages of the time series, as shown in Figure 16.8. Bacterial growth or sales increases for a new company sometimes exhibit such a pattern over time.

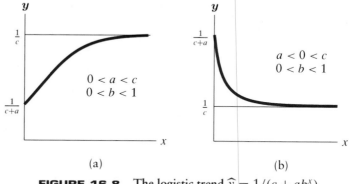

(a)   (b)

FIGURE 16.8 The logistic trend $\widehat{y} = 1/(c + ab^x)$

Another nonlinear trend equation is called the **Gompertz trend**, named after Benjamin Gompertz, who used the curve in the early 1800s in work concerning mortality tables. This curve is similar to the exponential curve, except that the constant b is raised to the power c^x instead of to the power x:

Gompertz trend:

$$\widehat{y} = ab^{c^x} \tag{16.7}$$

When the value of c in a Gompertz trend is between zero and one, the power to which b is raised will approach zero as x increases; hence, the value of $\hat{y}$ will become closer and closer to a, as shown in part (a) of Figure 16.9. When the value of c is greater than one, the trend will either increase without bound (when $b > 1$) or approach zero (when $0 < b < 1$) as x becomes larger and larger, as shown in part (b) of Figure 16.9. Thus, the Gompertz trend allows for various shapes of nonlinear curves in fitting a time series.

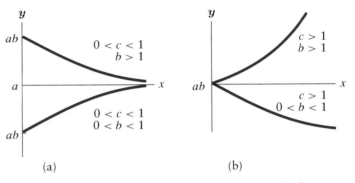

FIGURE 16.9   The Gompertz trend $\hat{y} = ab^{c^x}$

The problem of deciding which of the many available nonlinear equations to use in estimating trend in a given circumstance is often a difficult one. Commonly, the choice is a practical one determined by which type of curve is computed by one's computer software. It is not unusual, in fitting the commonly used mathematical curves to a set of time-series observations, to find that two or more equations provide approximately the same closeness of fit. For the purpose of merely describing the data, there is little to choose among these curves. The problem arises when such curves are used to predict future values of the time series (extrapolations) because the curves tend to diverge rather quickly. Unacceptably large divergences may result from even a small extrapolation. Thus, as we pointed out earlier in this chapter, it is not sufficient merely to find a trend function providing a *good fit* to the data. It is necessary to fit a curve that can be theoretically justified by a general assessment of the underlying nature of the series. You should also recognize that a good fit is not guaranteed by any of these functions. No curve may fit well because there may be no single persistent relationship between the dependent variable and time.

☐ STUDY QUESTION 16.3   Nonlinear Trends for Social Security Tax

Use the values in Table 16.4 for the maximum individual annual U. S. social security tax (employer and employee contributions) for the years 1959–1992 with x in units of 3 years. Plot the tax values. Suggest which trend function given in this section might best fit these data.

TABLE 16.4   Maximum Annual Social Security Tax

Year	Tax	Year	Tax
1959	288	1977	1,930
1962	300	1980	3,175
1965	348	1983	4,784
1968	686	1986	6,006
1971	811	1989	7,210
1974	1,544	1992	10,656

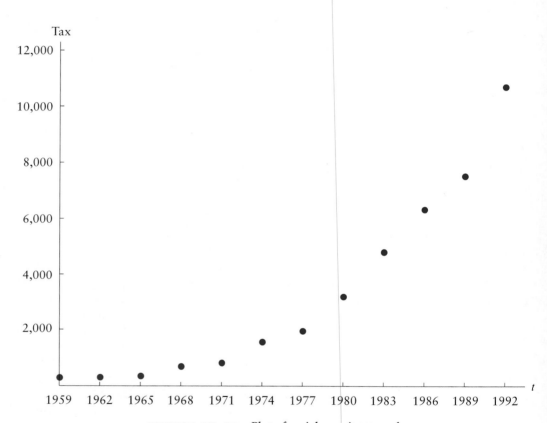

FIGURE 16.10   Plot of social security tax values

• ANSWER   A plot of the maximum social security tax values for these years is shown in Figure 16.10. The two nonlinear functions that might best fit these data are the exponential trend as in Formula 16.2 and Figure 16.5(b) and the Gompertz trend as in Figure 16.9(b) with $c > 1$ and $b > 1$.   ■

section 16.4   # Moving Averages

In the discussion thus far, we have assumed that a trend line can be calculated without first removing, or at least minimizing, the effect of seasonal, cyclical, and random movements in the series. However, it may be easier to estimate trend if the effects of these fluctuations are removed from the data. Methods for removing these effects are usually referred to as smoothing techniques.

The Method of Moving Averages

The most commonly used method of smoothing data is called the **method of moving averages.** A moving average is actually a series of averages, where each average is the mean value of the time series over a fixed interval of time and where all possible averages of this time length are included in the analysis. A 12-month moving average, for example, must include the mean value for each 12-month period in the series. These averages represent a new series that has been smoothed to eliminate fluctuations that occur within a 12-month period. Since a seasonal pattern will repeat itself every 12 months, a 12-month moving average will reduce fluctuations caused by the seasons of the year. Note that a 12-month moving average will also tend to eliminate any other fluctuations with a pattern that repeats itself over an interval of less than a year's duration, such as daily or weekly patterns. Similarly, a five-year moving average could be used to reduce a pattern or cycle that repeats itself every five years.

TABLE 16.5   Profits, 5 year Centred Moving Average

Year	y	Centred M.A	Year	y	Centred M.A.
1980	2		1988	13	11.4
1981	4		1989	14	12.6
1982	5	5.2	1990	11	14.0
1983	7	6.0	1991	14	15.4
1984	8	6.8	1992	18	17.2
1885	6	8.0	1993	20	
1986	8	9.2	1994	23	
1987	11	10.4			

To illustrate the process of calculating a moving average, we will use this approach to smooth the data in Table 16.5. These data appear to fluctuate in a cyclical pattern that repeats itself every five years. In calculating a five-year moving average, we first must determine the mean value for the initial five years, 1980–1984. This mean value, which equals $(1/5)(2 + 4 + 5 + 7 + 8) = 5.2$, is *centred* on (placed in the middle of) the five years being averaged, 1982. Similarly, the next moving average, 6.0, is computed from the values corresponding to 1981 through 1985 and centred in the year 1983. This process continues until the last observation is included; the last moving average is 17.2, and this value is centred at the year 1992. The moving average values, when compared with the original values, tend to reduce the variation and represent a smoothed version of the time series in which the cyclical component has been reduced. If the observation units were one quarter of a year or less, the moving average technique would smooth out seasonal variations also. The comparison between the original time series and its representation by the moving average values is shown in Figure 16.11.

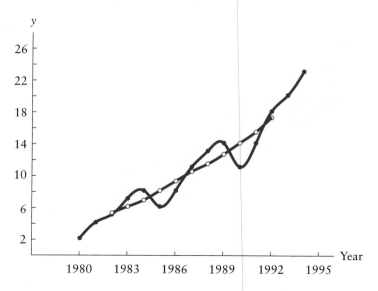

FIGURE 16.11 Values of annual profits (●) and five-period moving average values (○) from Table 16.5

This moving average procedure gives equal weights to all five observations in calculating each mean value. Sometimes, one may wish to increase the relative importance of one or more observations by using a **weighted moving average.** In a five-year weighted moving average, for example, the weights might be 1, 2, 3, 2, 1. The middle periods are usually weighted most and the outer values least. This scheme is based on the assumption that the middle value in a series of observations should have the largest emphasis since that is where the resulting moving average value will be centred. Using this weighting system on the data in Table 16.5, we obtain a weighted moving average centred at 1982 equal to the following:

$$\frac{1(2) + 2(4) + 3(5) + 2(7) + 1(8)}{1 + 2 + 3 + 2 + 1} = 5.22$$

The second weighted moving average would be centred in 1983 and equal to:

$$\frac{1(4) + 2(5) + 3(7) + 2(8) + 1(6)}{1 + 2 + 3 + 2 + 1} = 6.33$$

By continuing this process, we could derive the entire series for the weights 1, 2, 3, 2, 1. Had we used some other weighting system, an entirely different moving average would be determined. In general, the weights used depend on the degree to which the analyst wishes to emphasize particular values while still obtaining some smoothing of the data and elimination of part of the random or irregular movements.

The Use of Moving Averages for Smoothing

It is important to note that by smoothing a time series we have not solved the problem of estimating the trend component for that series. Smoothing the series merely serves to eliminate some of the variability not attributable to trend, in the hope that the trend component can be more easily identified.

A moving average method has several weaknesses as a smoothing device. First of all, this method is often only partially successful in removing all random or irregular fluctuations. In addition, the moving average method tends to introduce spurious cyclical movements into the data being smoothed, so that an analyst who tries to smooth data may, in fact, introduce a nonexistent cycle.

A final problem with the use of the moving average is the arbitrary choice of its length, denoted by h, which is the number of consecutive values used in the averages, and the selection of weights. Using no weights is really a choice of equal weights. The larger the value of h, the more the moving average smooths out the original data, but the greater is $(h - 1)$, the number of total observations at the beginning and end of the data for which no moving average value can be determined. Using the five-period moving average, we see in Table 16.5 that a total of four observations are lost in the moving-average series, two at the beginning and two at the end. The size of h must be large enough for smoothing purposes but small enough to retain sufficient observations. Also, to smooth cycles, the value of h should be selected to coincide with the length of the cycle (or an integer multiple of its length). If the cycle length varies, some complex moving-average techniques that use different values of h may be most appropriate.

☐ STUDY QUESTION 16.4 Moving-Average Smoothing of U.S.S.R. Industrial Production

Annual estimates are given in Table 16.6 for a component of industrial production in the Soviet Union for 25 years prior to its break-up in 1991. Find a seven-period moving average for these values.

TABLE 16.6   Annual Industrial Production in the Soviet Union

Observation	Value	Observation	Value
1	14	14	24
2	14	15	28
3	18	16	26
4	18	17	29
5	22	18	32
6	25	19	34
7	35	20	40
8	40	21	44
9	14	22	46
10	18	23	49
11	21	24	54
12	23	25	60
13	22		

• **ANSWER**   The average of the first seven observations gives the moving average value centred at observation 4. Averages of each successive seven observations give the M.A. values in Table 16.7. Six observations are lost in the smoothing. ■

TABLE 16.7 Seven-period Moving Average

Observation	M.A.	Observation	M.A.
1–3	—	14	24.71
4	20.86	15	26.29
5	24.57	16	27.86
6	24.57	17	30.43
7	24.57	18	33.29
8	25.00	19	35.86
9	25.14	20	39.14
10	24.71	21	42.71
11	23.14	22	46.71
12	21.43	23–25	—
13	23.14		

section 16.5

Decomposition of a Time Series

In estimating the components of a time series, emphasis naturally falls on estimating the trend. Often, however, it may be just as (or even more) important to be able to estimate the *seasonal* component in a time series. From a planning point of view, for example, it is often necessary for business managers to take fluctuations other than trend into consideration when financing future operations, purchasing materials or merchandise, establishing employment practices, et cetera. Many of these fluctuations are of a seasonal nature, caused by the weather, as in the increase in swimwear sales during the summer months, or by social customs, as in the increase of retail sales during the Christmas season.

Seasonal Index

The seasonal component of a time series is usually expressed by a number, called a **seasonal index**, which expresses the value of the seasonal fluctuation in each month (or quarter) as a percent of the trend value expected for that period. A seasonal index for June of 104 means that, because of seasonal factors, the time-series value is expected to be 4% above the trend value for June. If the seasonal index is 93 for the first quarter, then the time-series value is expected to be 7% less than the trend value during January through March.

Because of seasonal variation, special care must be taken in forecasting sales for any given month or in comparing sales between months. Such forecasts or comparisons are usually made by using a seasonal index to *deseasonalize* the data. Since the base value of a seasonal index is always 100, to deseasonalize a time-series, the original values are divided by the seasonal index and multiplied by 100 as follows:

Deseasonalized time series:

$$\text{Seasonally adjusted value} = \frac{\text{Original value} \times 100}{\text{Seasonal index}} \quad (16.8)$$

☐ **EXAMPLE 16.3**   We will assume that bicycle sales for a given manufacturer have averaged 50,000 units a month for the past five years. However, the average sales in each month are not always equal to 50,000. In February, for example, sales over the past five years have averaged 30,000 units. Similarly, May has averaged 50,000 units, and December, 80,000 units. Since February has averaged only 60% of the overall average sales of 50,000, the seasonal index for February is $S_{\text{Feb.}} = 60.0$. The indices for May and December would be $S_{\text{May}} = 100.0$ and $S_{\text{Dec.}} = 160$.

Formula 16.8 is used to seasonally adjust values of bicycle sales. Assume that the actual sales for February and December in a given year were 32,000 and 84,000, respectively. Adjusting these values, we obtain:

$$\text{Adjusted February sales } = \frac{32,000 \times 100}{60} = 53,333$$

$$\text{Adjusted December sales } = \frac{84,000 \times 100}{160} = 52,500$$

Note how this seasonal adjustment makes the comparison of sales between the two months very easy. Here we see that February sales were slightly better than December sales on a seasonally adjusted basis. Because the average seasonal index for these two months exceeds $100[(60 + 160)/2 = 110]$, their total adjusted value (105,833) is less than the total sales that actually occurred (116,000). If a seasonal index has been correctly formulated, the adjusted total for 12 months will always equal the actual total over all 12 months.   ■

Ratio-to-Trend Method

In order to determine seasonal index numbers, it is customary to proceed with step 1 of the four step decomposition suggested in Section 16.1. For the multiplicative model $y = T \times S \times C \times I$, one method for estimating the seasonal component in this model is called the **ratio-to-trend method**. We estimate S by removing trend from the series without attempting to remove cyclical and irregular variation. If a trend value has been calculated for each monthly value of y in the series, trend can be eliminated by dividing y by these monthly trend values, $y/T = S \times C \times I$; the remaining fluctuations are assumed to represent, primarily, seasonal variation.

Ratio-to-Moving-Average Method

The problem with the ratio-to-trend procedure is that it produces a seasonal index that still contains C and I. There is a way to calculate a seasonal index, called the **ratio-to-moving-average method**, in which these fluctuations have been removed. The first step in this approach is to smooth monthly data by using a 12-month moving average (or use a four-quarter moving average if the time series is quarterly). If we disregard the irregular component, the causes and occurrences of which are unknown, the smoothed series will contain only the components T and C, since a 12-month moving average will remove seasonal variations. The new series of $T \times C$ values can be divided into the *original* time-series values, y, to obtain the following equation:

$$(T \times S \times C)/(T \times C) = S$$

Thus, by a rather roundabout route, we have isolated S and determined a seasonal index in which the variations attributable to T and C have been removed. To illustrate how this process works, we use the data of Table 16.8, which represents monthly sales in an athletic shoe store over the three year period, 1991–1993.

TABLE 16.8 Monthly Sales in an Athletic Shoe Store

Year	J	F	M	A	M	J	J	A	S	O	N	D
1991	67	71	72	73	71	70	67	64	66	74	82	99
1992	80	86	89	89	84	83	79	76	77	87	98	114
1993	92	98	101	103	96	96	89	87	90	99	112	131

□ **EXAMPLE 16.4** To begin the process of determining the seasonal component, a 12-month moving average is taken over all months in the series. This moving average is shown in columns labelled (3) in Table 16.9. Now, to associate the moving-average values with the fifteenth rather than the first day of each month, these values are *centred* by taking the average of each two adjacent months. The centred moving-average values are shown in columns labelled (4) and represent $T \times C$ (and, probably, some parts of I which are ignored or assumed to be virtually the same as the component I in the original time series).

TABLE 16.9 Original and Moving Average (M.A.) Values for Athletic Shoe Store Sales

(1)	(2)	(3)	(4)	(2)	(3)	(4)	(2)	(3)	(4)
			Centred			Centred			Centred
	1991	12-month	12-month	1992	12-month	12-month	1993	12-month	12-month
Month	Sales	M.A.	M.A.	Sales	M.A.	M.A.	Sales	M.A.	M.A.
January	67			80	81.3	80.8	92	93.9	93.5
February	71			86	82.3	81.8	98	94.8	94.4
March	72			89	83.2	82.8	101	95.9	95.4
April	73			89	84.3	83.8	103	96.9	96.4
May	71			84	85.6	85.0	96	98.1	97.5
June	70	73.0		83	86.8	86.2	96	99.5	98.8
July	67	74.1	73.6	79	87.8	87.3	89		
August	64	75.3	74.7	76	88.8	88.3	87		
September	66	76.8	76.1	77	89.8	89.3	90		
October	74	78.1	77.5	87	91.0	90.4	99		
November	82	79.2	78.7	98	92.0	91.5	112		
December	99	80.3	79.8	114	93.1	92.6	131		

We have now eliminated S (and some remaining parts of I) from the series. To find a seasonal index, we divide the original time-series values (sales) in columns labelled (2) in Table 16.9 by the 12-month centred moving-average values in columns (4) and multiply by 100. The result of this computation, shown in Table 16.10, is two index numbers for each month of the year.

Since these index numbers may differ, some irregular component variation I is still included. By averaging the monthly $S \times I$ estimates for each calendar month, some more of the irregular component is eliminated. In a long time series with at least five values of $S \times I$ for each month, this averaging virtually eliminates all of the irregular component and isolates the pure seasonal index component S with $T, C,$ and I removed. The averages of these two values are the seasonal indices found in the bottom row of Table 16.10. ■

TABLE 16.10   Seasonal Average Index for Monthly Sales in an Athletic Shoe Store

Year	Jan.	Feb.	Mar.	Apr.	May	June	July	Aug.	Sept.	Oct.	Nov.	Dec.
1991							91.0	85.7	86.7	95.5	104.2	124.1
1992	99.0	105.1	107.5	106.2	98.8	96.3	90.5	86.1	86.2	96.2	107.1	123.1
1993	98.4	103.8	105.9	106.8	98.5	97.2						
Average	98.7	104.5	106.7	106.5	98.7	96.8	90.8	85.9	86.5	95.9	105.7	123.6

Levelling the Index

A final step that is sometimes necessary in the construction of seasonal indices is called *levelling the index*. The raw seasonal index values are obtained by averaging the ratios for each quarter or month as the case may be. This averaging process is done without regard to the fact that the average of these *averages* over the entire year must be 100 if deseasonalizing the series is to alter only the pattern but not the level of the raw data. (Refer to the last two sentences in Example 16.3.) For example, if the average over the year of the raw seasonal indices were 90, the use of the raw seasonal indices would raise the average level of the deseasonalized series by $100[(100/90) - 1]\%$ or about 11% above the average level of the raw data series. Clearly, this is an unintended result of deseasonalizing the series. The seasonal index in Table 16.10 averages 100.025 which is sufficiently close to 100 so that levelling is unnecessary in this case.

In order to level an index, one finds the average of the raw seasonal indices over the year and divides that average value into each raw seasonal index or average for each month or quarter and multiplies by 100. The effect of this computation is to increase or decrease all values of the raw seasonals in the same proportion and to make the levelled index average exactly 100 over the year.

Figure 16.12 will help summarize some of the material in this section. Figure 16.12(a) shows the original sales data and the moving average of these data from Table 16.9. It is apparent that a pattern of monthly changes exists, having a low point in August and a high point in December. This pattern is reflected in the seasonal index from Table 16.10 that is shown in Figure 16.12(b).

The second step in the decomposition of a time series is to use the seasonal index (after levelling, if needed) to deseasonalize the original observations. As discussed before, Formula 16.8 shows that dividing a time series by the appropriate seasonal index values *seasonally adjusts* it. The deseasonalized data can be more accurately examined for trend and cycles than the original data since any confusion of seasonal fluctuations is eliminated. Quarterly gross domestic product data, for example, are usually adjusted to remove seasonal fluctuations.

Step three of the decomposition is to use the methods discussed in Section 16.2 to determine the best linear or nonlinear trend in the deseasonalized time series. Obviously, if the time series involves annual data, there is no need to deseasonalize and the decomposition would begin with this step of finding the trend.

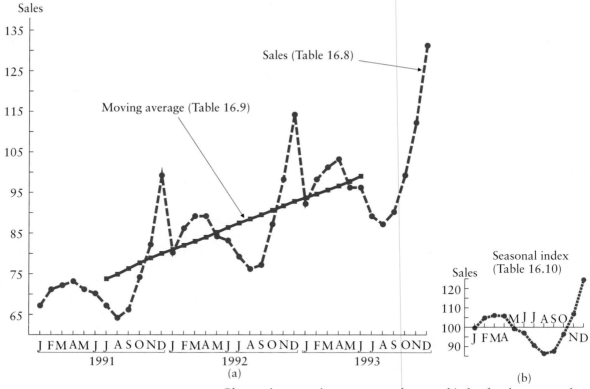

FIGURE 16.12   Observations, moving average, and seasonal index for shoe store sales

Determining the Cyclical Variation

Once the trend component T is isolated, such as by any of the estimations suggested in Section 16.2, we can divide the seasonally adjusted values, $(T \times C \times I)$ by T and obtain only the components $(C \times I)$. As pointed out earlier, if several years of data were involved so that months or quarters had already been averaged to get the raw seasonal index values, much of I, the irregular component, may have already been eliminated. However, one final step will remove any remaining parts of I.

We can use a roundabout method again, to isolate C in a simple way. In step four of the decomposition, a weighted moving average of three or five periods can be determined, using the $C \times I$ data. The greater the number of periods, the greater the probability of removing all of I. But in a longer moving average, the cycles might be smoothed out too much and partially eliminated also. To help avoid this smoothing, the best type of weights to use are large weights for the centre values and much smaller weights for the values farther away from the centre. If the weights are constructed so that their sum is equal to one, then no division by the sum of the weights is necessary. For example in a five-period moving average, the weights might be $-0.1, 0.3, 0.6, 0.3$, and -0.1. The advantage of this extra computation using weights is that it produces a smoother curve for the cycle component C, while it is also more sensitive to the original fluctuations because it preserves the amplitude of the cycles more faithfully. Using an odd-period moving average is convenient for centring the resulting values which constitute the component C. For example, based on the monthly data for our sales problem, the cyclical component for April would be as follows:

$$C_{April} = -0.1(C \times I)_{February} + 0.3(C \times I)_{March} + 0.6(C \times I)_{April}$$
$$+ 0.3(C \times I)_{May} - 0.1(C \times I)_{June}$$

Values of C for other months may be found in a similar way.

It is usually desirable to isolate the cyclical component of a time series so that turning points and peaks and troughs may be studied. If a stable cyclical pattern, such as a 3 to 4-year business cycle or a 20-year housing construction cycle could be isolated, it would greatly aid economists in determining the underlying causes and in forecasting future movements.

PROBLEMS

16.1 What is a time series? Why is it necessary to distinguish time-series analysis from regression analysis?

16.2 Personal food expenditures (y) for a given population during the years 1990–1994 are as shown in Table 16.11.

TABLE 16.11 Personal Food Expenditure for a Population (billions of dollars)

y	Years
370	1990
390	1991
395	1992
410	1993
435	1994

a) Fit a straight-line trend line for y by the method of least squares with origin of mid-1992.

b) Give the amount of total deviation, explained deviation, and unexplained deviation for the 1993 observation.

16.3 The trend line for average annual wages of members of a local electricians' union from 1974 to 1992 is $\hat{y} = 26,500 + 800x$, with origin at mid-1983 and x in units of one year.

a) What is the average annual increase in wages over this period?

b) Suppose a local nonunion electrician made $36,000 in 1993. How much did this person's income differ from the trend value in 1993 for union members?

16.4 A study is being made to determine the growth of annual honey production (y) over time (x) measured in years before and after 1990. The data are shown in Table 16.12 ($x = 0$ is 1990):

TABLE 16.12 Growth of Annual Honey Production (y) Over Time (x)

x	−2	−1	0	1	2
y	6	9	12	11	15

a) Find the regression equation of y on x.

b) Find the estimated value of honey production for 1993.

16.5 The value of building permits for historical renovation in a certain town over an eight-year period is given in Table 16.13.

TABLE 16.13 Value of Building Permits

(year)	Value	(year)	Value
1986	$300,000	1990	$310,000
1987	150,000	1991	490,000
1988	210,000	1992	380,000
1989	400,000	1993	400,000

a) Plot the above data and make a freehand estimate of the trend line.

b) Use the method of least squares to determine a trend line with x in years and origin in 1985.

c) What value would you estimate for 1994?

d) Find the least-squares regression line for quarterly magnitudes, with x measured in years. Shift the origin one-half quarter forward in time.

16.6 The values in Table 16.14 represent sales data for the years 1985–1990.

TABLE 16.14 Sales Data Over Time

Year	Sales (units)
1985	18,000
1986	19,000
1987	23,000
1988	24,000
1989	26,000
1990	28,000

a) Plot the values and then estimate a linear trend line by the freehand method.

b) Construct a least-squares regression line to estimate trend with $x = 0$ for 1984.

c) Find the least-squares regression line for quarterly magnitudes, with x measured in years. Shift the origin one-half year backward in time.

16.7 The sales of a new product had the growth pattern shown in Table 16.15:

TABLE 16.15 Sales of a New Product Over Time

x (year)	Sales	x (year)	Sales
1	1,600	4	4,600
2	2,700	5	5,100
3	3,900	6	5,400

a) Fit a straight line to these data.

b) Fit a quadratic trend.

c) Indicate which model appears to give the better fit.

16.8 Refer to the social security tax values in Table 16.4 and the plot in Figure 16.10. Fit an exponential trend to these data with origin in mid-1959 and x in units of three years.

16.9 Find a three-year moving average for the data in Table 16.16.

TABLE 16.16 Sales Over Time

Year	Sales
1982	$18,000
1983	20,000
1984	22,000
1985	19,000
1986	21,000
1987	24,000
1988	21,000
1989	23,000
1990	27,000

16.10 Table 16.17 gives the amounts of money (to the nearest thousand dollars) lost gambling each year by a certain entertainer during vacations in Nassau.

TABLE 16.17 Gambling Losses Over Time

Year	Amount	Year	Amount
1986	$ 2,000	1991	$23,000
1987	7,000	1992	29,000
1988	5,000	1993	68,000
1989	16,000	1994	2,000
1990	12,000		

Find the four-period moving average for the amounts lost.

16.11 Use Table 16.18 to answer parts (a) and (b).

a) Compute the trend equation by the method of least squares with $x = 0$ in mid-1988 and x in units of years.

b) Compare the trend value for 1990 with the three-period moving average value for 1990.

TABLE 16.18 Tonnage Trend Over Time

Year	Tons	year	Tons
1985	30	1989	51
1986	44	1990	68
1987	50	1991	65
1988	42		

16.12 Answer parts (a)–(e).

a) State two reasons for estimating the seasonal component of a time series.

b) State two reasons for estimating the trend equation for a time series.

c) State two disadvantages of the use of a (simple) moving average as a fit of trend.

d) Describe one advantage and one disadvantage of using a moving-average smoothing method in time-series analysis.

e) Explain the difference between cyclical and seasonal variations in a time series.

16.13 The trend line (annual total equation) for suits is $\widehat{y} = 3,600 + 480x$ with origin at October, 1991. The seasonal index for April is 80. Estimate the seasonally adjusted output for April, 1995.

16.14 The operating season for a certain tomato cannery is from June to October. The observations in Table 16.19 represent monthly sales, in thousands, for this cannery from 1989 to 1991.

TABLE 16.19 Tomato Cannery Sales (thousands of dollars)

Year	June	July	August	September	October
1989	$75	$86	$102	$105	$90
1990	83	89	110	115	92
1991	84	95	113	118	89

a) Find a seasonal index using the ratio-to-moving-average method, using a five-month moving average.

b) Assume that the multiplicative model $y = T \times S \times C \times I$ holds and that there is no irregular variation. Decompose the index for August of 1990 into the component parts T, S, and C, using your answer to part (a).

16.15 Explain how to find the cyclical component of a time series.

16.16 Find the cyclical component of the time series on industrial production in the Soviet Union given in Table 16.6.

16.17 The Business Research Department of the Carolina Corporation forecasts sales for next year of $12 million, based on a trend projection. It is expected that no sharp cyclical fluctuations will occur during the year, that the effect of trend *within* the year will be negligible, and that the past pattern of quarterly seasonal variation will continue. The pattern is as shown in Table 16.20.

TABLE 16.20 Carolina Corporation's Quarterly Seasonal Index

Quarter	1st	2nd	3rd	4th
Seasonal index	130	90	75	105

Prepare a forecast of quarterly sales from the above information for the first and second quarters of next year.

16.18 In finding the cyclical component of a time series, explain how to obtain C once the $(C \times I)$ component has been isolated.

◆ **16.19** The index for seasonal variation of railcar production for selected months is 60 for January, 70 for March, 120 for August, and 100 for December.

a) In which of these four months is railcar production most typical of the monthly average?

b) In which of these months is the production usually the greatest?

c) Production increased from 6 railcars in January to 10 in August. Determine the percentage change in railcar production allowing for seasonal variation.

16.20 The index of seasonal variation for cement production for selected months is 60 for January, 70 for April, 122 for August, and 100 for November.

a) In which of these months is cement production usually the greatest?

b) In which of these months is the production most typical of the monthly average?

c) Production in a certain region increased from 6,060,000 cubic yards of cement in January 1993 to 11,590,000 cubic yards of cement in August 1993. Determine the percentage change in cement production, allowing for seasonal variation.

16.21 Answer parts (a) and (b).

a) The unadjusted sales index of the C-B Company is 102 for January 1992. The seasonally adjusted index for the same month is 133. Find the seasonal index for January.

b) The annual sales for 1996 are forecast to be $240,000. The seasonal index for March is computed to be 90. Give a reasonable forecast of the sales for March 1996.

◆ **16.22** Consider the time series data in Table 16.21 for the annual sales of a company from year 1985 to 1995.

a) Smooth the time series by taking a five-year moving average.

b) What is the smoothed-series value corresponding to the year 1990?

c) What does this moving average achieve?

TABLE 16.21 Annual Sales

Year	Sales
1985	$190,000
1986	130,000
1987	210,000
1988	220,000
1989	330,000
1990	470,000
1991	400,000
1992	500,000
1993	570,000
1994	570,000
1995	620,000

◆ **16.23** The ratio-to-moving-average method was used to determine the seasonal indices for new building permits sought in north-western Ontario for each of the 12 months. They are shown in Table 16.22.

TABLE 16.22 Seasonal Indices for Building Permits

Month	Seasonal Index
January	36
February	42
March	60
April	97
May	135
June	156
July	171
August	169
September	136
October	113
November	56
December	29

It is expected that no sharp cyclical fluctuation will occur during the year, that the effect of the trend within the year will be negligible, and that the past pattern of monthly variation will continue.

a) In which month were the maximum building permits sought?

b) Due to an economic boom in the region, the building permits forecast for next year is estimated to be 30,000. Forecast the number of applications for building permits in July next year.

c) The number of building permits sought this year was 800 in January and 3,600 in June. Determine the percentage change in building permits when seasonal variation is accounted for.

16.24 Assume that you have been given the quarterly seasonal index as shown in Table 16.23.

TABLE 16.23 Quarterly Seasonal Index

Quarter	1st	2nd	3rd	4th
Seasonal index	90	115	95	108

Note that these seasonal values do not sum to 100. Prepare a new seasonal index by levelling these values so that the sum equals 100.

16.25 Consider the monthly data in Table 16.24 representing minority youth unemployment levels for the two-year period 1991–1992 (in millions).

TABLE 16.24 Minority Youth Unemployment Levels (millions)

	Year	
Month	1991	1992
January	22.1	22.9
February	21.9	22.3
March	22.6	23.0
April	23.4	23.9
May	24.5	25.0
June	26.0	26.5
July	26.0	26.6
August	25.9	25.7
September	25.7	25.9
October	25.4	25.7
November	24.6	24.1
December	24.1	24.6

a) Plot the above data, letting $x = 0$ represent January 1, 1992 and x in units of months so November 1991 is $x = -1.5$ and March 1992 is $x = +2.5$, and so forth.

b) Use the method of least squares to determine a trend line.

c) Construct a seasonal index using the ratio-to-trend method.

d) Find a seasonal index using the ratio-to-moving-average method, based on a five-month moving average.

---

section 16.6

Index Numbers

Our objective in the following discussion is to develop a measure that summarizes the characteristics of large masses of data and is useful for period to period comparisons. An index number accomplishes this purpose by aggregating information into a single measure without dimensions that permits comparisons to be easily made. Although index numbers are used in many areas of the behavioural and social sciences, their main application involves describing business and economic activity, such as changes in prices, production, wages, and employment, over a period of time.

An **index number** is simply the ratio of two numbers expressed as a percentage. The denominator is the value in a selected time period, known as the *base* period. The numerator is the value for the period (i) of interest. The ratio is multiplied by 100 to put it in percentage terms. Formula 16.9 provides the definition of an index number:

$$(\text{Index number})_i = 100 \left[\frac{\text{Value in period } i}{\text{Value in base period}} \right] \qquad (16.9)$$

☐ **EXAMPLE 16.5**   Consider the data given in Table 16.25 for the average price in cents of a litre of orange juice on February 1 in Saskatoon for six successive years. If the year 1988 is chosen as the base year, the index number for the price of juice in 1993 is 100(117/63) = 185.7. This indicates an 85.7% increase in price for 1993 relative to the base year 1988. Other values of the index are computed the same way and are shown in the third column of Table 16.5. If a different base year had been selected, say 1990, the index for each year would change to reflect the percentage change of a given year relative to 1990. As shown in the final column of Table 16.25, the index for 1993 with base year 1990 is 100(117/122) = 95.9. This indicates a 4.1% decrease in price for 1993 relative to 1990. When examining any reports or arguments using index numbers, it is important to know the base year so that appropriate comparative statements can be made.   ■

TABLE 16.25   Prices of Orange Juice (cents/litre)

Year	Price	Index (1988 = 100)	Index (1990 = 100)
1988	63	100.0	51.6
1989	78	123.8	63.9
1990	122	193.7	100.0
1991	139	220.6	113.9
1992	124	196.8	101.6
1993	117	185.7	95.9

Uses of Index Numbers

The primary purposes of an index number are to provide a value useful for comparing magnitudes of aggregates of related variables to each other and to measure the changes in these magnitudes over time. Consequently, many different index numbers have been developed for special uses. Let us briefly mention some of their common uses.

First, index numbers are useful summary measures for policy guides. The U.S. Federal Reserve Board may use index numbers on interest rates, employment, or consumer credit as inputs to discussions on appropriate open-market transactions. Government officials may use price and income indices to set minimum wage guidelines.

Second, many index numbers have been developed as indicators of business conditions, including the *Financial Times*, *Fortune*, or *Canadian Business* indices. Many banks and government agencies all publish various index numbers for this same purpose.

Also, some of these indices are commonly used for comparing changes among different sectors of the economy. Growth in the agricultural or mining sector might be compared with growth in the manufacturing sector. Levels of state and local government expenditures might be analyzed and compared among regions by using index numbers.

A fourth use of certain special indices, such as wage, productivity, and cost-of-living indices, is in wage contracts and labour–management bargaining. Management often likes to tie wage increases to productivity increases, while labour unions like to relate the need for wage increases to cost-of-living increases. Similar relations among indices are used in escalator clauses to adjust insurance coverage and change retirement or welfare benefits.

Finally, a fifth and very common use of an index number is as a deflator. Certain measures of economic activity are divided by price or cost indices and multiplied by 100 in order to obtain the *real* or constant dollar value of these measures. That is, an adjustment is made for the changing value of the dollar, so that more meaningful comparisons can be made over time.

Using an Index as a Deflator

The use of an index as a *deflator* is so common that it merits special attention. Since the base value of any index number is 100, the real value is obtained by the following rule:

$$\text{Real value} = \frac{(\text{Nominal value}) \times 100}{\text{Index number}} \qquad (16.10)$$

☐ **EXAMPLE 16.6**   Suppose that a person's retirement income increases from $10,000 to $15,000 over a given period, while the consumer price index (CPI) increases from 100 to 130. The *nominal* increase in income of $5,000 is offset by general inflation indicated by the 30% increase in the CPI. If this index is assumed to be relevant to the consumer purchases of the retiree, it could be used to *deflate* the income increase and to find the *real* increase in income.

The real income at the beginning and at the end of the period being studied, respectively, is:

$$\frac{10,000 \times 100}{100} = \$10,000 \quad \text{(Beginning real income)}$$

$$\frac{15,000 \times 100}{130} = \$11,538 \quad \text{(Ending real income)}$$

With the extra $5,000 income this retired person could buy only an extra $1,538 worth of goods and services because prices increased. ■

Real income is usually called the *purchasing power* of the money income. In comparing incomes, wages, or rents of individuals, or gross national product, or personal income per capita of different countries, the use of an appropriate deflator is common practice. In this way, the real value is more easily recognized.

◻ **EXAMPLE 16.7** A local government allocated $25 million for street repairs and improvements in 1988, when costs of labour, materials, land, equipment, et cetera, were measured by a construction cost index of 125 (relative to a base period equal to 100, in 1985). In 1993 the budget allocation for street repairs and improvements is $30 million. However, the index of costs in 1993 has risen to 180. We find the real value of the available money by deflating it in terms of constant base-year costs in each case, using the cost index:

$$\text{Real value in 1988} = \frac{\$25 \text{ million} \times 100}{125} = \$20 \text{ million}$$

$$\text{Real value in 1993} = \frac{\$30 \text{ million} \times 100}{180} = \$16.67 \text{ million}$$

The 1993 allocation of $30 million will support repairs of only $100(20/16.67) = 83\%$ as much as the 1988 allocation of $25 million would have permitted five years earlier. ■

Constructing an Index

Having discussed the nature and uses of index numbers, we turn in the next section to a discussion of constructing a price index. While this is only one type of index, it shares many problems of construction with indices of all other types. The reader should be ready to recognize the following usual considerations.

Each index number must have a base period for which the value of the index is 100.0. The selection of a typical base year is somewhat arbitrary but very important. If a particularly exceptional period were selected in which the values of the variables were quite extreme, then all other values of the index would be affected.

A second arbitrary choice involves the selection of the type of index to use (simple, relative, or weighted) and of the appropriate weights to use in combining the values of different items included in the aggregate measure. Incidentally, the choice of items to include is often very debatable. An attempt should be made to include the most common and representative items. An index for new car prices may not include prices for all possible cars that could be purchased, but it surely must include the most popular cars of the largest auto-makers. Similarly, an index of wages per person-hour in manufacturing must include a sample of *representative* types of workers across *representative* groups of industries selected to be *representative* of all regions of the country. The problems inherent in such selections are numerous. The final result may be some representative index number that does not suit anyone in particular.

The most compelling practical problem in constructing an index is obtaining sufficient and accurate data for all the items included. To obtain a consumer price index, one might sample consumers to find out how much they paid and what quantity they bought of a large list of products, or one might sample storekeepers to find out their sales and prices on all the different items. Once a set of quantities and prices is obtained, the calculation of the index is essentially a problem involving weighted averages.

Price Index Numbers

section 16.7

Since prices play a major role in every economy, there has been great interest in developing appropriate price indices. In this section, several simple price indices are defined, and some of the procedures for determining their value are outlined. Most of these use the simple *price relative* as a cornerstone. It is an index number for prices of a single item similar to the index number for juice prices in Table 16.25. A **price relative** is the ratio of the price of a certain commodity in a given period (p_i) to the price of that same commodity in some base period (p_0). If we let P_i represent the price index number for a given year relative to the base year, then $P_i = 100(p_i/p_0)$. Following this convention, the index for the base year is 100, since $P_0 = 100(p_0/p_0) = 100(1)$. In general, a price relative shows the percentage increase or decrease in the price of a commodity from the base period to a given period.

To illustrate the construction of a price relative, we will apply the concept to the price of eggs for the years from 1991 to 1993. In a selected market the price of eggs for these three years is 60, 68, and 80 cents a dozen, respectively. With 1991 as the base period or year (1991 = 100), the price relatives for the three years are as follows:

$$1991 \text{ price relative} = 100 \left(\frac{p_0}{p_0} \right) = 100 \frac{60}{60} = 100$$

$$1992 \text{ price relative} = 100 \left(\frac{p_1}{p_0} \right) = 100 \frac{68}{60} = 113$$

$$1993 \text{ price relative} = 100 \left(\frac{p_2}{p_0} \right) = 100 \frac{80}{60} = 133$$

Thus, the price of eggs increased 13% from 1991 to 1992 and 33% from 1991 to 1993.

Aggregate Indices

Rather than describe changes in a single commodity, one may wish to describe changes in the general price level. To do this, we combine a representative number of commodities, sometimes called a **market basket**, into an aggregate price index. The prices of these commodities in a given year are compared with the prices of the same market basket in a base year. One such index, called the *simple aggregate price index*, can be expressed as follows:

Simple aggregate price index:

$$P_i = 100 \left(\frac{\Sigma p_i}{\Sigma p_0} \right) \qquad (16.11)$$

☐ **EXAMPLE 16.8** Suppose we use the price data in the supermarket survey shown in Table 16.26 to compute a simple aggregate price index. We use prices on September 29, 1990, as the base period and compute the index for prices on September 13, 1992. The sum of the prices on September 13, 1992, is $\Sigma p_2 = \$2.03 + 1.85 + \cdots + 0.75 = \$15.61$. The subscript 2 indicates two years after the base period. The sum of the prices on September 29, 1990, is $\Sigma p_0 = \$1.89 + 1.86 + \cdots + 0.86 = \$15.31$. Substitution into Formula 16.11 gives a simple aggregate price index as follows:

$$P_2 = 100 \left(\frac{\Sigma p_2}{\Sigma p_0} \right) = 100 \left(\frac{15.61}{15.31} \right) = 102$$

This index indicates that prices in 1992 were 2.0% higher than in 1990. ■

TABLE 16.26 Supermarket Survey: Food Price Data

Item	Sept. 29, 1990 Prices	Sept. 14, 1991 Prices	Sept. 13, 1992 Prices
Meats: (one quarter kilogram)			
Bacon	1.89	2.68	2.03
Frankfurters	1.86	2.07	1.85
Pork loin chops	2.25	2.71	2.55
Ground beef	1.56	1.67	1.57
Sirloin steak	3.19	3.45	3.12
Boneless rump roast	3.07	3.09	2.91
Whole fryers	0.63	0.73	0.83
Fruit:			
3 kiwi	0.86	0.81	0.75
Sum	15.31	16.61	15.61

The simple aggregate price index has two main disadvantages. First, it is sensitive to the units of measurement for each commodity. For instance, suppose the kiwi price in Table 16.26 were changed to the equivalent price for one dozen kiwi rather than three kiwi. The price for one dozen would be four times greater, or $3.44 in 1990 and $3.00 in 1992. Since the price of kiwis decreased between 1990 and 1992, the result of giving kiwis more emphasis in the index will be a lower price index for P_2. Recomputing the index number for 1992 relative to 1990 would give the following simple aggregate price index:

$$P_2 = 100 \left(\frac{17.86}{17.89} \right) = 99.8$$

If this index were being used in a cost-of-living adjustment for welfare benefits, the decrease of 0.2% instead of an increase of 2.0% would be very significant to the total government budget and to welfare recipients as a whole.

Second, the index in Formula 16.11 fails to consider the relative importance of the commodities. That is, this price index is formulated under the assumption that each commodity is used equally as much. Thus, if persons typically use more than one kilogram of ground beef for every kilo of pork loin chops, or if persons use more than one kilo of whole fryers (chicken) for every kilo of sirloin steak, this index would be incorrect. The actual price aggregate that would be appropriate should take into account the differing quantities of the items used.

The first disadvantage can be overcome merely by changing to a *simple average of price relatives* index. As the name suggests, this index equals the average of all price relatives. Since $\Sigma(p_i/p_0)$ equals the sum of these price relatives and N equals the total number of commodities, we define the index as follows:

Simple average of price relatives:

$$P_i = \frac{100 \sum \left(\frac{p_i}{p_0} \right)}{N}. \tag{16.12}$$

◻ **EXAMPLE 16.9**   To find the simple price relative index for September 1991 or 1992 relative to September 1990 for the prices in Table 16.26, we first find the price relative, p_1/p_0 and p_2/p_0 for each item. These are shown in Table 16.27.

TABLE 16.27   Price Relatives for Prices in Table 16.26

Item	p_1/p_0	p_2/p_0
Bacon	1.10	1.07
Frankfurters	1.11	0.99
Pork loin chops	1.20	1.13
Ground beef	1.07	1.01
Sirloin steak	1.08	0.98
Rump roast	1.01	0.95
Fryers	1.16	1.32
Kiwi	0.94	0.87
Sum	8.67	8.32

The index computed by Formula 16.12 for these eight items for 1992 is:

$$P_2 = 100 \left(\frac{8.32}{8} \right) = 104.$$

This index would be unaffected by changes in units of measurement for a particular commodity, since the units cancel out in each calculation of the price relative prior to summing and computing the index. However, this index still equally weights each price relative. ∎

Weighted Price Indices

Weighted index numbers overcome the second disadvantage of the simple indices. They permit consideration of the relative importance of the commodities in the market basket, which is usually measured in terms of the total amount of money spent on each commodity during a specified time period. The product of the price of a commodity and the quantity purchased in a given year represents the total amount of money consumers spend on that particular commodity. If q_i represents the quantity purchased in year i, then $p_0 q_0$ equals the total amount spent on a particular commodity in the base year, and $p_i q_i$ represents the amount spent in some other year. A *weighted average of price relatives* index weights the various price relatives in a market basket by the total amount spent on that commodity. This index may take on two different forms, depending on whether base-year weights ($p_0 q_0$) or the weights of some given year ($p_i q_i$) are used in constructing the index. Whichever weighting system is applied, it must be used for all values of the index being constructed.

Weighted average of price relatives:

Base-year weights: $\quad P_i = \dfrac{100\sum\left[\dfrac{p_i}{p_0}\left(p_0 q_0\right)\right]}{\Sigma p_0 q_0}$

$\qquad\qquad\qquad\qquad\qquad\qquad\qquad\qquad$ (16.13)

Given-year weights: $\quad P_i = \dfrac{100\sum\left[\dfrac{p_i}{p_0}\left(p_i q_i\right)\right]}{\Sigma p_i q_i}$

A weighted average of price relatives index can be constructed from the data in Table 16.26 if the quantities purchased for each commodity are known. To illustrate the use of Formula 16.13, let us consider another subset of commodities with prices and quantities as shown in Table 16.28.

TABLE 16.28 Price and Quantity Data

Commodity	Quantities		Prices	
	1990	1993	1990	1993
Milk (litre)	30	35	0.60	0.75
Bread (half loaf)	25	20	0.60	0.80
Bananas (4)	20	30	0.40	0.45
Margarine (250 g)	10	5	0.55	0.65
Oranges (doz)	15	20	1.80	1.95

Consider 1990 as the base period indicated by the subscript zero. The weighted price relative for milk using base-year weights of $p_0 q_0 = 30(0.60) = \$18.00$ would be:

$$\frac{p_3}{p_0}\left(p_0 q_0\right) = \frac{0.75}{0.60}(\$18.00) = 1.25(\$18.00) = \$22.50$$

The weighted price relative values given in Table 16.29 are calculated in the same fashion.

TABLE 16.29 Weighted Price Relative Values for the Data in Table 16.28

Commodity	$p_0 q_0$	Base-Year Weights $\dfrac{p_3}{p_0}(p_0 q_0)$	$p_3 q_3$	Given Year Weights $\dfrac{p_3}{p_0}(p_3 q_3)$
Milk	18.00	$22.50	26.25	$32.81
Bread	15.00	20.00	16.00	21.33
Bananas	8.00	9.00	13.50	15.19
Margarine	5.50	6.50	3.25	3.84
Oranges	27.00	29.25	39.00	42.25
Total	73.50	$87.25	98.00	$115.42

We can now use this information to calculate the two types of weighted average of price relatives by using Formula 16.13. The base-year weights p_0q_0 are used first and then the given-year weights p_3q_3 are used:

$$\frac{100\sum\left[\frac{p_3}{p_0}\left(p_0q_0\right)\right]}{\sum p_0q_0} = 10\left(\frac{\$87.25}{\$73.50}\right) = 118.7$$

$$\frac{100\sum\left[\frac{p_3}{p_0}\left(p_3q_3\right)\right]}{\sum p_3q_3} = 100\left(\frac{\$115.42}{\$98.00}\right) = 117.8$$

In this example, the two methods give results that happen to be quite close together.

A popular means of constructing a weighted price index does not employ weighted price relatives, but rather, weights each price directly by multiplying it by the quantity of that commodity purchased in either the base year or some other year. The value p_iq_0, for example, represents the price of a commodity in year i weighted by the quantity of the commodity purchased in the base year. The total theoretical value of the commodities in year i is thus $\sum p_iq_0$. If we now take the ratio of this value to the actual value of these goods in the base year, $\sum p_0q_0$, the resulting index is called a **Laspeyres price index:**

Laspeyres price index:

$$LP_i = \frac{100\sum p_iq_0}{\sum p_0q_0} \qquad\qquad (16.14)$$

Note that the Laspeyres price index is equivalent to the weighted average of price relatives index using base-year weights:

$$\frac{100\sum\left[\frac{p_i}{p_0}(p_0q_0)\right]}{\sum p_0q_0} = \frac{100\sum p_iq_0}{\sum p_0q_0}$$

If, instead of q_0, the quantity q_i consumed in the given year i is used to weight prices, the resulting index is called a **Paasche price index:**

Paasche price index:

$$PP_i = \frac{100\sum p_iq_i}{\sum p_0q_i} \qquad\qquad (16.15)$$

☐ **EXAMPLE 16.10** The Laspeyres and Paasche price indices can be constructed from the totals in Table 16.30. A new column added from Table 16.29 gives $\sum p_0q_3$, the total theoretical value of commodities purchased in 1993 if they could have been bought at 1990 prices. Using Formulas 16.14 and 16.15, the price indices are:

Laspeyres price index: $\quad \dfrac{100\sum p_3q_0}{\sum p_0q_0} = 100\left(\dfrac{\$87.25}{\$73.50}\right) = 118.7$

Paasche price index: $\quad \dfrac{100\sum p_3q_3}{\sum p_0q_3} = 100\left(\dfrac{\$98.00}{\$83.75}\right) = 117.0 \qquad ■$

TABLE 16.30 Prices Weighted by Quantities as Given in Table 16.28

Commodity	Base Year Quantity Weights		Year 3 Quantity Weights	
	$p_0 q_0$	$p_3 q_0$	$p_0 q_3$	$p_3 q_3$
Milk	$18.00	$22.50	$21.00	$26.25
Bread	15.00	20.00	12.00	16.00
Bananas	8.00	9.00	12.00	13.50
Margarine	5.50	6.50	2.75	3.25
Oranges	27.00	29.25	36.00	39.00
Total	$73.50	$87.25	$83.75	$98.00

Since construction of the Paasche index requires determination of new weights each year, while the Laspeyres index does not, the Laspeyres index is used much more often. Furthermore, the Laspeyres index has the added advantage that indices obtained from this formula may be compared from year to year, while indices obtained by using the Paasche formula can be compared easily only with the base year. Both indices, however, tend to reflect a slight bias when reporting price changes. Under the usual conditions of a downward-sloping demand schedule, people tend to purchase more when items are lower priced and less when the price rises. Thus, the numerator of the Laspeyres index will be somewhat higher than it should be, resulting in an overestimation of price increases. At the same time, the numerator of the Paasche index will tend to be lower than it should be, resulting in an underestimation of price increases.

section 16.8

Economic Indices and Their Limitations

We have presented only an introduction to the topic of index numbers. In practice, the process of constructing and updating an index can become quite involved. Before leaving the subject, we shall briefly describe a few types of the more widely used indices and some of their limitations.

Many countries collect information and report a Consumer Price Index (CPI) and a Producer Price Index (PPI). These two indices represent excellent examples of attempts to summarize large masses of data in a single price index. In the U.S., the CPI is a modified Laspeyres index based primarily on 265 different items in 68 separate expenditure classes (foods, fuels, apparel, et cetera), which are priced throughout each month. It represents average changes in prices paid by consumers in retail markets for about 80% of the total noninstitutional civilian population of the United States. Half of these are wage-earners and clerical workers, but also included are salaried workers, self-employed, retired, and unemployed persons. It does not include farm families. It is compiled from a survey of such persons in 85 urban areas chosen to represent all towns with a population over 2,500. Persons are selected based on a probability sample from the Census of Population.

In Canada, the CPI was called the cost-of-living index prior to 1952. The base period is updated periodically, but not frequently, because such an updating is an expensive operation. When an index is updated, successive versions of the series are *linked* so that the new index will equal 100 in the new base period.

The Canadian CPI is based upon prices (including taxes) paid by consumers in private retail outlets, government stores, offices, and other consumer service establishments. Current index values are published by Statistics Canada and are available in holdings of many libraries, such as *Consumer Price Movements*. The data are available in digital form through CANSIM, the Statistics Canada Database. The primary subclassifications of the CPI are food, housing, recreation and education, clothing, health and personal care, tobacco and alcoholic beverages, and transportation. Measures are also calculated and published for a number of cities and regions on a monthly basis.

The Producer Price Index for the U.S. involves about 26,000 price quotations for that Tuesday during the week that contains the thirteenth day of the month. These prices are gathered by mail questionnaire for approximately 3,400 commodities. This index gives an indication of prices received in primary markets (not retail) of the United States by producers in all stages of processing. It includes components for price movements of goods in all mining and manufacturing categories and will eventually include 6,000 separate industries from beet sugar production and boat building to poultry dressing and pesticide manufacturing.

Various countries and international organizations such as the United Nations and World Bank produce economic *quantity indices* including an *Index of Industrial Production* (IIP) and Export and Import Indices. The latter calculate quantity changes in both exports and imports. The IIP measures changes in manufacturing output.

The limitations of economic indices follow directly from the problems suggested earlier in the construction of an index. Since the useful and meaningful application of an index often depends on what year is selected as the base, it is important to use as the base a period with *normal* or *average* economic activity. Sometimes the base-year value can be the average price or quantity of several years rather than a single year.

The base can be changed only when a major revision of the indices occurs, not more often than about every 15 years. The cost and time involved in such a major revision is quite significant. For example, since the CPI in the U.S. was first formulated in 1919, it has undergone major revisions in 1940, 1953, 1964, and 1978. The last three of these have taken three, five, and eight years and have cost $4 million, $6.5 million, and $50 million, respectively. The 1978 revision began in 1970 and used the base year 1967. Agencies try to do continuing sample surveys and partial updates of the information used in the CPI so that it is kept useful between major revisions. Because of the sampling error involved, about three years of consecutive data are needed before the updated market basket of goods can be determined with enough statistical accuracy.

Exactly what items are included in the index also has an important bearing on the validity of the index. In the case of the CPI, there are hundreds of specific items whose price and quantity need to be determined and updated. Census information is used to determine the geographic sample areas based on population shifts. Thus, as population growth occurs faster in one region over another, new spending patterns will emerge in the index as more persons from these areas will be included in the sample.

Periodic surveys help provide information on prices and quantities. To provide an accurate list of the marketplace to be sampled and to know where consumers buy items, surveys of stores can be conducted. Particular items selected in the market basket must conform to detailed specifications (variety, brand, size, special features, et cetera) that are basically the same across the country, although the final selection of items reported are store-specific and depend on local sales information. The reporting stores are selected based on a survey of families that are asked for information on the name, location, and amount spent in retail stores for many different categories of goods and services. To remain relevant, it is good practice to update this by a continuing survey of one-fifth of the sampling units each year. Thus, in a five-year cycle, the entire sample has been repeated.

The weights (quantities) used in the CPI are also based on information gained from surveys of families. In the U.S., the Consumer Expenditure Survey is a sample of 20,000 families in 216 geographic areas across the country using quarterly interviews. Since it is often difficult to recall expenditures on minor or everyday items, the survey also included a sample of 20,000 families who kept a one-week diary of all expenditures for each of two selected weeks. To update this information, the Continuing Survey covers 85 geographic sampling units and includes quarterly interviews for five consecutive quarters with 6,000 households. Also, 4,800 households are asked each year to keep and submit two one-week diaries of expenditures. These surveys help to keep the index current. For example, among the over 250 items in the *general* or *other* category (not food, apparel, transportation, housing, energy, or some other major category), the Continuing Surveys have allowed recent changes such as from the former item *piano lessons, organs* to the new item *fees for lessons – golf, swimming, tennis, piano, et cetera* and from *movie admissions* to *admissions to movies, concerts, theatres, et cetera*, new items that reflect current life-styles. Also, diesel fuel and gasohol were first included in the motor fuels component beginning in September 1981. An important revision in the treatment of housing prices occurred in January 1983, which treats costs of home ownership in terms of equivalent monthly costs (like rental housing) instead of as an investment-type expenditure.

For an accurate Producers Price Index, seasonal adjustment factors should be recalculated annually as new observations become available. The items and industries covered should also be revised as often as practicable. It is common in a revision for over 100 new items to be included and as many others to be dropped. In the U.S. revision of July 1982, 162 new commodities were added.

These price indices by countries are adjusted to try to take into account changes in quality as well. In October 1982 the PPI component for passenger cars, for example, for the U.S. was adjusted for quality change. Of the average producer price increase per car in 1983 of $215.55, it was determined that nearly half of this, $107.66, was due to quality improvements. The quality changes were split about evenly between those for fuel economy or emission controls and those for improved warranties or corrosion protection. More recent quality changes have involved safety items such as air bags and anti-lock brakes.

Even with such attention, the indices are still open to question because of rapid changes in technology, quality, and products. In 1985, most price indices still did not include the large amounts of expenditures on computers, printers, software, video games, and the like. Since, over a period of time, some items fall out of use completely, and others appear that had no earlier counterpart, it is difficult, if not impossible, to compare the prices of many of today's goods with those of an earlier period. For example, it is unrealistic to compare the price of an old icebox with the price of today's modern refrigerator, and the price of a portable video recorder cannot be compared with the price of an article that was not on the market 50 years ago.

This inability to compare goods, and consequently prices, over time has led to charges that price indices exaggerate the real increase in prices and that a CPI, in particular, exaggerates the change in the cost of living because the indices do not sufficiently take into account the improvement in the quality of goods and the worth of these quality increases to consumers. The economist Lloyd G. Reynolds suggested the following type of comparison to illustrate this problem. Give a family a 1975 Sears Catalog, a 1990 Sears Catalog, and $3,000 and allow them to make up an order list from either the 1975 or the 1990 catalog, but not mix items from both. Most families would probably use the 1990 catalog, which must mean that they consider the higher 1990 prices more than offset by new and improved quality of products. This implies that there was no real increase in consumer prices between 1975 and 1990, even though the CPI indicated a sizeable increase.

Both the consumer and the producer price indices are available in seasonally adjusted or unadjusted form. The seasonally adjusted indices reveal more clearly underlying cyclical trends and are most useful in regression analysis involving other quantities that are seasonally adjusted. Unadjusted data are of primary interest to users who need information on the actual dollar value of transactions, such as marketing specialists, purchasing agents, and commodity traders. Unadjusted indices are also used generally to escalate contracts such as purchase agreements and real-estate leases.

Because there are so many difficulties in constructing meaningful price indices, they should be used only as guides and indicators of price movements and should not be quoted as indisputable facts. Also, one should remember that they represent prices to some "average" person with "average" tastes and preferences. Whether or not they are relevant to a particular person or group must always be questioned before they are applied.

PROBLEMS

16.26 Go to a library and find the current value of the *Consumer Price Index* (CPI) and the *Producer Price Index* (PPI) in your country.

a) Determine how the value of these indices has changed over the past year, as well as over the past ten years. How has the composition of the items included in these indices changed over the past ten years?

b) Find as many examples as you can from the news media illustrating current uses of these indices, (labour–management negotiations, inflation reports, et cetera).

16.27 A budget request for a new university building was $3.5 million in 1990, and a similar request is $4.5 million in 1995. Also, an index of building and construction costs (assumed to be applicable to this situation) with base year 1992 = 100 is equal to 95 in 1990 and 140 in 1995. Compare the relative real value of the building that could have resulted from the two budget requests.

16.28 The Consumer Price Index for services increased from 107 to 115 during a certain period.

a) If a consumer budgeted $20 per month for services at the beginning of this period, how much should be budgeted for the same level of services at the end of the period?

b) A person's after tax salary increased from $800 to $852 per month during this period. What is the real change experienced in purchasing power for services?

16.29 In the past year, the GNP of a nation has risen from $200 billion to $212 billion, which represents a 6% growth rate. However, the price index used to calculate the national product has also risen from 125 to 130. What is the real growth rate of this nation's GNP after accounting for inflation?

16.30 If an index of money wages of workers (1982 = 100) was 250 in 1993 and an appropriate index of living costs (1982 = 100) was 200 in the same year, what has been the percent increase from 1982 to 1993 in these wages of workers?

    a) money wages

    b) real wages

16.31 The average beginning salary for accountants has increased from $42,000 to $45,000 over a period of years when the consumer price index increased from 100 to 120. What is the change in the *real* value of accountants' salaries?

16.32 Given in Table 16.31 are data for the average purchase price on new Yamaha baby-grand pianos.

TABLE 16.31   Average Expenditure for New Pianos

Year	Expenditure
1992	$9,963
1991	8,717
1990	7,526
1989	6,861
1988	6,382

    a) Convert the data to index numbers using 1988 as the base year.

    b) Repeat part (a) using 1990 as the base year.

    c) Using the index numbers from part (a), determine whether a buyer spending $7,000 in 1989 or a buyer spending $10,000 in 1992 got more piano for the money.

    d) Repeat part (c), using the index numbers from part (b). Compare the results of parts (c) and (d).

16.33 Table 16.32 gives the after tax salaries in 1983 and 1993 for selected city employees.

TABLE 16.32   After Tax Salaries for Selected City Employees

Employee	1983	1993
Secretary	$ 6,888	$11,004
Manager	11,376	17,880
Janitor	6,000	9,672
Teacher	13,120	21,088
Mayor	38,500	57,864

    a) If 1983 is chosen as the base period, the cost-of-living index for 1993 is 224. Determine the real value of the 1993 amounts in terms of 1983 dollars.

    b) If 1993 is chosen as the base period, what would be the value of the cost-of-living index for 1983?

16.34 The market basket values for 1990 and 1993 were observed as given in Table 16.33.

TABLE 16.33   Market Basket Values

Item	1990 (base) Price	Quantity	1993 Price	Quantity
Candy bar	0.30	100	0.50	50
Soft drink	1.00	25	1.40	30
T-shirts	10.00	4	15.00	3
Tennis balls	2.50	1	2.00	2

Construct the following:

    a) price relatives for each commodity

    b) a simple aggregate price index

    c) a simple average of price relatives index

    d) a weighted average of price relatives index, using both base-year and given-year weights

    e) a Laspeyres and a Paasche price index

16.35 Repeat Problem 16.34 for the market basket values in Table 16.34 that were observed in 1955 and 1956:

TABLE 16.34   Market Basket Values

Item	1955 (base) Price	Quantity	1956 Price	Quantity
Milk	15¢ qt.	25 qt	15¢ qt.	20 qt.
Eggs	50¢ doz.	10 doz.	45¢ doz.	15 doz.
Bread	15¢ loaf	30 loaves	20¢ loaf	35 loaves

16.36 The data in Table 16.35 for price (p) and quantity (q) for vegetables are given.

TABLE 16.35   Market Basket Values

Item	1992 (p)	1993 (p)	1992 (q)	1993 (q)
Lettuce (head)	0.57	0.86	8	9
Tomatoes (lb.)	0.59	0.70	12	14
Onions (3 lb.)	0.93	1.09	3	4
Potatoes (10 lb.)	1.88	2.67	4	2

    a) Find the simple index of price relatives for 1993 using 1992 as the base year.

    b) Construct a Laspeyres price index for 1993 vegetable prices.

    c) Construct a Paasche price index for 1993.

    d) Explain the difference between the index in part (a) and those in parts (b) and (c).

♦ **16.37** Unit energy consumption costs and use patterns during the late 1980s are summarized in Table 16.36.

TABLE 16.36 Energy Consumption Costs and Patterns

Energy Type	Unit Cost			Mean Monthly Consumption		
	1985	1987	1989	1985	1987	1989
Electric (kw-hrs)	$0.023	$0.024	$0.038	1,704	1,652	1,597
Oil (gallons)	0.44	0.48	0.82	257	260	230
Gas (million ft^3)	8.35	9.46	12.24	7.8	7.1	6.8

a) Compute the Laspeyres price indices for 1987 and 1989 using 1985 as the base year.

b) Compute the Paasche price indices for 1987 and 1989 using 1985 as the base year.

c) What are the advantages of using the Laspeyres price index over the Paasche price index?

d) If a household spent $5,000 for energy in 1987 and $6,000 in 1989, explain in which year they would have consumed more units of energy.

16.38 Given the historical data in Table 16.37 on monthly purchases by the average midwestern farm family:

TABLE 16.37 Monthly Purchases

Commodity	1950		1960	
	p	q	p	q
Eggs (doz.)	0.40	10	0.60	9
Sugar (lb.)	0.10	35	0.20	30
Butter (lb.)	0.50	5	0.40	6

a) Compute a weighted aggregate Laspeyres price index, using 1950 as the base year.

b) Assume that your index applied in general for all foods. Also assume that a certain family spends $1,200 for food in 1950 and $1,750 in 1960. In which year would they have had more to eat for their money?

16.39 Price and quantity data (in relevant units) for sales of major appliances are collected in order to construct a consumer durable-goods price index. From the data in Table 16.38, determine a Laspeyres price index for 1990 relative to the base period, 1993, and interpret its meaning.

TABLE 16.38 Major Appliance Sales

Commodity	1990		1993	
	p	q	p	q
Range	7.5	8	8	12
Refrigerator	8	10	8.8	12
Air conditioner	1	6	2	15

16.40 The data in Table 16.39 on student expenses was uncovered by the campus newspaper for an editorial on the *good old days*.

TABLE 16.39 Student Expenses

Item	Lunch	Gasoline	Movie
1960			
Price (cents)	30	25	50
Quantity	6	1	4
1964			
Price (cents)	50	30	90
Quantity	6	2	2
1966			
Price (cents)	60	35	100
Quantity	6	3	3

a) Compute the Laspeyres price index for the three years, using 1960 as the base.

b) Assuming that these data are representative of all commodities and all students, determine the real standard of living, relative to 1960, of students who spent $500 per semester in 1960, $600 in 1964, and $700 in 1966.

CHAPTER SUMMARY

KEY TERMS AND EXPRESSIONS

Time series: Periodic observations of a variable that is a function of time.

Trend (T) : Long-term movement in a time series.

Seasonal variation (S): Fluctuations repeated over a period of one year.

Cyclical variation (C): Pattern repeated over periods of varying lengths, usually longer than one year.

Irregular variation (I): Unpredictable or random fluctuations.

Additive model: $y = T + S + C + I$

Multiplicative model: $y = T \times S \times C \times I$

Exponential trend: $\widehat{y} = ab^x$

Modified exponential trend: $\widehat{y} = c + ab^x$

Logistic trend: $\widehat{y} = 1/(c + ab^x)$

Gompertz trend: $\widehat{y} = ab^{c^x}$

Method of moving averages: A series of averages in which each average is the mean value over an interval of time of fixed length centred at the midpoint of each interval.

Weighted moving average: A moving average in which each observation is given a weight that reflects its relative importance.

Seasonal index: A number that expresses the value of the seasonal fluctuation during a period of time.

Ratio-to-trend method: Method for estimating S by dividing both sides of $y = T \times S \times C \times I$ by T. Does not eliminate $C \times I$.

Ratio-to-moving average method: A method for estimating S by first isolating $T \times C$ and then dividing $T \times S \times C$ by $T \times C$.

Index number: A number that relates the values of a particular aggregate to its value in a selected base period.

Price relative: The ratio of the price of a certain commodity in a given period to the price of that commodity in some base year.

Market basket: The group of commodities selected to represent the typical purchases of an *average* person.

Laspeyres price index: A price index constructed by weighting each price by the quantity consumed in the base period.

Paasche price index: A price index constructed by weighting each price by the quantity consumed in the time period i of interest.

EXERCISES

16.41 Describe the additive and the multiplicative models used in time-series analysis. Which of these models do you think is more realistic for most economic time series? Explain why. Give examples where each model would be appropriate.

16.42 Assume that the sales volume in a certain industry can be described by the multiplicative model $y = T \times S \times C \times I$. One month last year, the trend estimate of sales was 44,000 units, and actual sales were 55,000 units. If we assume that the seasonal index was $S = 95$, and the index for cyclical movement was $C = 119$, what index value must be associated with the irregular movement, I?

16.43 The estimate of trend accounted for $180,000 of a department store's sales last October. Assuming a multiplicative model, no irregular variation, and a cyclical index of 110, find the seasonal index for this month. Actual sales were $210,000.

16.44 Given a trend equation, $\widehat{y} = 37.50 + 6x$ with origin at July 1, 1992, and x in units of one year, where y is truck sales in thousands, convert the equation to monthly units with origin at March 1, 1994.

16.45 The trend equation is $\widehat{y} = 137.50 + 8x$. Its origin is July 1, 1993; x is expressed in units of one year; y is fruit sales in thousands. Find the monthly trend value for February 15, 1995.

16.46 A producer of one-man portable helicopters had sales over the five years, 1988–1992, of 1, 2, 3, 5, and 9 units, respectively.

   a) Find the trend line for sales, letting $x = 0$ represent 1990.

   b) Find the standard error of estimate for this trend line, and explain its meaning.

   c) What is your estimate for sales in 1994?

16.47 A company has determined a seasonal index and a trend line for their monthly sales. The seasonal index for December is 140. The trend line for monthly sales is $\hat{y} = 163,250 + 4,520x$, with x in units of months, and origin at mid-April 1994. Forecast company sales for December 1996.

16.48 The data given in Table 16.40 is for sales of boating supplies.

TABLE 16.40 Boating Supplies Sales

1994 Quarter	Actual Sales	Trend Values`	Seasonal Index
1	100,000	90,000	80
2	150,000	95,000	130
3	120,000	100,000	110
4	110,000	105,000	80

a) Give one representation of the trend equation for sales of boating supplies.

b) Find seasonally adjusted sales for the four quarters of 1994.

c) Assuming no change in the trend or seasonal pattern and assuming that other factors remain constant, forecast second-quarter sales for 1996.

16.49 The data in Table 16.41 are the means of ratios of original data to the 12-month moving averages for the sales of a retail store. The data cover a period of ten years.

TABLE 16.41 Retail Store Sales

Month	Means of Ratios
January	56
February	60
March	100
April	110
May	105
June	102
July	80
August	72
September	88
October	105
November	120
December	145
Total	1,143

a) Compute the index of seasonal variation from these ratios for the months of March, April, and August. Be sure to level the index.

b) The total sales for next year are estimated in December of this year at 120 million. What would be the best estimate of sales for April and August?

16.50 Use the information in Table 16.42.

TABLE 16.42 Price and Quantity of Imported Goods

Year	Import Price, y	Quantity Imported, x
1983	2	6
1984	3	5
1985	6	4
1986	5	5
1987	4	7
1988	3	10
1989	5	9
1990	7	7
1991	8	8
1992	7	9

a) A trend line for import price is $\hat{y} = 2.8 + 0.5x$, where $x = 0$ for 1983. Is the import price for these years above or below the trend estimates?

b) Do you think it would be a good idea to remove seasonal variation from this data, as well as trend, before studying the cyclical relatives? Give a reason.

c) Find the values of the three-year moving average of quantity imported for the years 1985 and 1988.

16.51 The secular trend of sales for the Jones Department Store is accurately described by the equation $\hat{y} = 120,000 + 1,000x$, where x represents a period of one month and has a value of zero in December 1994. The seasonal indices for the company's sales are:

TABLE 16.43 Jones Department Seasonal Indices

Month	Index
January	100
February	80
March	90
April	120
May	115
June	95
July	75
August	70
September	90
October	95
November	120
December	150

a) Ignoring cyclical and random influences, forecast sales for February 1996, May 1999, and December 1997.

b) What factors could cause these estimates to be incorrect?

c) What may be done to compensate for inaccuracies as they become apparent?

16.52 In the library, find a ten-year time series on annual household income for Canada, a region, your province, or for some occupation, race, or sex subgroup. Find a time series on consumer prices that is relevant for this group of households. Calculate the adjusted annual household income, corrected for price changes, and interpret your results in terms of the growth of real income over the period.

16.53 Answer parts (a) and (b) about the Laspeyres price index.

a) Suggest two important practical difficulties in determining a Laspeyres price index.

b) Explain how a Laspeyres price index differs from a simple arithmetic average of price relatives.

USING THE COMPUTER

16.54 Use the annual values for imports in **Data Set 5**.

a) Find a trend line for imports.

b) Fit an exponential trend to the data for imports.

c) Which of the two trends gives the better approximation?

16.55 Repeat Problem 16.54 using the consumer price index in **Data Set 5**.

16.56 Repeat Problem 16.54 using the values of population in **Data Set 5**.

16.57 Use the data for unemployment in **Data Set 5**.

a) Plot the values of UNEM against time. Which type of trend function do you think would best fit this data?

b) Determine the quadratic trend equation.

16.58 Answer parts (a) and (b).

a) Write a computer program, using software of your choice, to determine seasonally adjusted monthly values for a time series. Follow the pattern as presented in conjunction with Tables 16.8 through 16.10. Include a check and process for levelling, if necessary.

b) Using a monthly series over at least five years, demonstrate how the program works.

16.59 Using the library, find the price and quantity sold of shares of ten selected stocks on the last day of the previous 40 weeks. Use one week as the base period and find the following:

a) simple price index of the stocks

b) Laspeyres price index of these stocks

c) Find the Dow-Jones stock index at week-end for these same weeks and, using the same base period, construct an index of the Dow-Jones index to compare with your index in part (b).

d) Use a computer to find a four-week moving average of your index.

CHAPTER 17

Statistical Decision Theory

Introduction To A Decision Problem

The focus of this chapter, as the title implies, is on the process of making decisions from a statistical point of view. Decision-making in this context is often referred to as *decision-making under uncertainty* because the consequences or payoffs resulting from each decision are assumed not to be known (in advance) with certainty. As you might suspect, there is also a set of techniques concerned with *decision-making under certainty*, in which consequences of a decision are assumed to be known (in advance) with certainty. Most real-world decisions generally involve some element of uncertainty; hence, it is convenient to have a formal procedure for analyzing each possible action a decision-maker might take in a given situation, and for selecting the best action.

The origins of statistical decision theory are relatively recent, dating back to the early 1950s. Since that time, this branch of statistics has grown rapidly in popularity, with a corresponding development of the theory and its applications. Because much of the analysis of statistical decision theory centres around a formula first published in 1763 by the Reverend Thomas Bayes (Bayes' rule), this approach is often referred to as the "Bayesian" approach. In fact, there is considerable debate among statisticians about the appropriateness of the Bayesian approach compared to the "classical" approach to statistics (traditional procedures for sampling, estimation, and hypothesis-testing). We will not enter into this debate here but instead will present both the advantages and disadvantages of statistical decision theory.

In analyzing a decision-making problem it is necessary to be able to specify exactly what **actions** (or alternatives) are available. We will label actions as a_1, a_2, a_3, ... In addition, we assume that each action yields a *payoff* or some type of consequence that depends on the value of a random variable called the **state of nature**. States of nature will be labeled as θ_1, θ_2, θ_3, ... (θ is the Greek letter "theta").

☐ **EXAMPLE 17.1** Suppose that you are considering buying 100 shares of one of four common stocks (actions a_1, a_2, a_3, or a_4), each of which costs $10 now. You intend to sell your stock at the end of one year. If you could somehow foresee the future and *know* that one year from now the prices of these stocks would be $15, $11, $8, and $10, respectively, then your decision would be an easy one — buy the first stock (action a_1). Action a_1 yields a profit of $500 ($5 profit on each of 100 shares); a_2 gives a payoff of $100; a_3 results in a profit of $200 (a loss); and a_4 produces zero profit. This situation represents decision-making under certainty, since there is no uncertainty about what state of nature (what set of prices) will occur a year from now.

Instead of knowing what prices will be in one year, you probably can only guess what the prices might be on the basis of your impression of the economy in general, your knowledge of various industries and firms within these industries, or perhaps merely a hot tip from a friend. There may be many different states of nature, each yielding a different set of payoffs for the various actions you could take. Thus, your problem is really one of decision-making under uncertainty. ■

A Decision Problem under Uncertainty

To extend the stock problem to include uncertainty, suppose that you decide that there are three possible states of nature (θ_1, θ_2, and θ_3). For instance, you might decide that stock prices one year hence are directly related to the stability of the economy during the year. In this case, θ_1 might correspond to a mild recession, θ_2

to a stable economy, and θ_3 to a mild expansion. [Other states are also possible (for example a depression), but for convenience we will assume that there are only three.] Suppose that for θ_1 the prices a year from now will be those given previously ($15, $11, $8, and $10); for θ_2 the prices will be $5, $12, $12, and $13; and for θ_3 they will be $17, $11, $15, and $15. The payoffs that these prices reflect can be expressed in what is called a **payoff table**, as shown in Table 17.1.

Dominated actions. No one action from this payoff table is obviously the "best" one. Action a_1 yields the largest payoff *if* θ_1 or θ_3 occurs, while a_4 is optimal if θ_2 occurs. Note that a_3 can never be the optimal action because a_4 always results in a payoff at least as large as, or larger than, a_3 no matter *what* state of nature occurs. When θ_1 occurs, a_4 yields $0 and a_3 yields only $200; for θ_2, a_4 results in a payoff of $300 compared with only $200 for a_3; in θ_3, both actions yield the same payoff, $500. An action such as a_3 in this case, which is no better than some other action no matter what state of nature occurs, is said to be a **dominated action**. Thus, a_3 could be dropped from the decision problem, since it can never be the optimal action.

TABLE 17.1   Payoff Table for Stock Example

		States of Nature		
		θ_1	θ_2	θ_3
Actions	a_1	$500	$-$500	$700
	a_2	100	200	100
	a_3	$-200	200	500
	a_4	0	300	500

Expected Monetary Value Criterion

section 17.2

We would like to establish a decision criterion that not only takes into account all of the values in the payoff table, but also considers their *relative likelihood*. Fortunately, there is a procedure for accomplishing this, called the **Expected Monetary Value criterion**.

In order to be able to use the Expected Monetary Value (EMV) criterion, it is necessary to know (or be able to determine) the probability of each state of nature. If there is considerable 'objective' evidence (for example, historical data) or a theoretical basis for assigning probabilities, then this task may be a fairly easy one. The difficulty in many real-world problems is that there may be little or no historical data and no theoretical basis to use in making probability assessments. The answer to the question of how to assign probabilities in these circumstances is not an easy one. Bayesian statisticians usually suggest that, in assessing the *subjective probability* of an event, the decision-maker should ask, "What odds would make me exactly indifferent between the two sides of an even bet?"[1]

---

[1] Odds represent the *ratio* of the probabilities representing two mutually exclusive events. In betting, odds represent an allowance for the differing risks assumed by the bettors — the greater the risk, the greater the odds.

◻ **EXAMPLE 17.2**   At what odds would you consider it a fair bet (you would be indifferent between the two sides of a bet) if you were asked to participate in a bet in which the two sides are (1) the prime interest rate will be less than 10% next January, or (2) the prime rate will equal or exceed 10% next January? Suppose you say that 4 : 1 odds against the rate's being less than 10% represents fair odds (that is, you would be willing to take either side of the bet at these odds). By definition, your subjective probability that the rate will be less than 10% is P, or 0.20. In a decision-making context, one could use this approach to assess the probability of each state of nature. One must be careful, of course, to see that the sum of these probabilities equals one.

You should recall from the material on expectations in Section 4.3 that an expected value is merely the mean (or arithmetic average) of a random variable. As we indicated previously, such an expectation calculated in decision theory is generally referred to as an *expected monetary value* (or *EMV*). To illustrate the calculation of EMVs, let us suppose that, in the stock example, the probabilities of our three states of nature are:

$$P(\theta_1) = 0.30 \qquad P(\theta_2) = 0.60 \qquad \text{and} \qquad P(\theta_3) = 0.10$$

The EMV of actions a_1, a_2, a_3, and a_4 is obtained by multiplying each payoff by its probability of occurrence and then summing these values:

$$\text{EMV}(a_1) = \$500(0.30) - \$500(0.60) + \$700(0.10) = -\$80$$
$$\text{EMV}(a_2) = \$100(0.30) + \$200(0.60) + \$100(0.10) = \$160$$
$$\text{EMV}(a_3) = -\$200(0.30) + \$200(0.60) + \$500(0.10) = \$110$$
$$\text{EMV}(a_4) = \$0(0.30) + \$300(0.60) + \$500(0.10) = \$230$$

> Under the EMV criterion, the decision-maker selects the alternative that will yield the highest expected monetary value.

For this example, action a_4 results in the highest EMV, with an average payoff of $230. However, if the three states of nature had been assigned probabilities other than 0.30, 0.60, and 0.10, then some other action might have been the optimal decision. For example, you should verify that 0.40, 0.20, and 0.40 lead to action a_1 as the optimal EMV. No matter what values $P(\theta_1)$, $P(\theta_2)$, and $P(\theta_3)$ take on, however, a_3 can never yield the largest EMV because it is a *dominated action*.   ◼

The Effect of Risk on the Optimal Decision

The EMV criterion itself suffers from one major weakness, namely, that it considers only the expected or mean profit and does not take into account the variance in the payoffs. If the variance is fairly constant across the relevant alternatives, this weakness probably will not cause any problems; but when the variability is large, the EMV criterion may indicate an action that will not be the most preferred for some people.

◻ **EXAMPLE 17.3**   Suppose that you must choose between two stocks (a_1 and a_2) and that there are only two possible states of nature (θ_1 and θ_2), each having the *same* probability as follows:

$$P(\theta_1) = 0.50 = P(\theta_2)$$

Table 17.2 indicates the relative payoffs for these data. Even though the EMV of a_2 is ten times as large as that of a_1, most people (including the authors) would select a_1 if forced to pick between the two stocks because they cannot afford to risk losing $10,000. Some people might prefer a_2 over a_1, which merely illustrates the fact that the value of a dollar is not necessarily the same for one person as for some other person; neither does the value of a dollar necessarily *remain the same* to one person over time. We will see later in this chapter (Section 17.7) that it is possible to take the *value* of money into account in decision-making situations by using the expected utility criterion.

TABLE 17.2 Example of Decision Affected by Risk

		States of Nature		
		θ_1	θ_2	EMV
Actions	a_1	−$50	$100	25
	a_2	10, 500	−10, 000	250
Probability		0.50	0.50	

∎

Our decision situations thus far have been based on the assumption that a single decision is to be made for the payoffs involved. This may not be the case for an executive who regularly makes decisions involving relatively large amounts of money or a stockbroker who is investing continually in the stock market. In such cases, a decision-maker may be less concerned about the variance in payoffs for any one decision because he or she knows that, over a large number of decisions, gains should offset losses.

Perkins Plastics — An Example

To illustrate the process involved in calculating EMVs in a more complicated setting, we present the following example involving a small plastics firm.

□ **EXAMPLE 17.4** Perkins Plastics has had adhesion problems in its experiments with chrome plating on a plastic butterfly-valve because of irregularities in the electric flow during the plating process. On the basis of historical data, management knows that approximately 70% of the time the current is fairly uniform, in which case 90% of each batch of 1,000 valves produced will be good and only 10% will be defective. The other 30% of the time, when the current is somewhat irregular, only 60% of the valves are good and 40% are defective.

Unfortunately, there is no way the engineers at Perkins Plastics can determine how good the current flow is without testing each item in the batch. All they know is that either 90% or 60% of the valves in each batch will be good.

Perkins Plastics has several alternative ways to handle each batch. One alternative is to send the batch directly to the next operation (assembly) and hope for the best; their records shows that when they do this they incur costs of delay and adjustment of about $1,000 for each batch in which 90% of the valves are good and $4,000 cost for those in which 60% are good. Another alternative for Perkins Plastics is to rework the entire batch. This process ensures that the batch will be sufficiently free from defects that no delay and adjustment costs occur; however, this reworking costs $2,000.

The decision facing Perkins Plastics at this point is whether they should send each batch directly to assembly or rework it. The relevant data are shown in Table 17.3. Note in Table 17.3 that the optimal decision is for Perkins to send each batch to assembly, as this action has a higher EMV than does the rework action.

Another way to systematically display the information in a decision problem is to use a **tree diagram** such as the one shown in Figure 17.1. Just as we explained in Section 3.2, the tree diagram shows the steps of the problem. The first set of "branches" of the tree represents the decision-maker's possible *actions*, and the second set represents the various *states of nature*. The circled value represents the EMV that results from the decision to send the batch directly to assembly. Nonoptimal branches on a decision tree are usually marked with the symbol ╪, as shown on the rework branch. The symbol □ on the decision tree indicates a point at which the decision-maker has to select between alternatives; the symbol ○ indicates a point at which selection between branches is made by "nature" (that is, in a probabilistic manner). The decision tree in Figure 17.1 shows the same optimal decision, "assembly," as does Table 17.3. ■

TABLE 17.3   Payoff Table for Perkins Plastics

		States of Nature			
		90% Good	60% Good	EMV	Optimal
Actions {	Assembly	−$1,000	−$4,000	−$1,900	←
	Rework	−$2,000	−$2,000	−$2,000	
Probability		0.70	0.30		

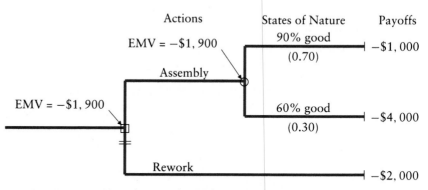

FIGURE 17.1   Tree diagram for Perkins Plastics, no sampling information

Thus far, we have assumed that a decision-maker arrives at a probability value for each state of nature via a personal assessment of the situation; this assessment can be based on a large variety of factors, such as available historical data, personal experience in similar situations, or just gut feelings. In many circumstances, however, it is desirable to have more information about the probability of each state of nature before attempting to make a decision. Most people gather information of this type almost daily: We ask our friends about places to eat, or live, or courses to take; we read consumer reports before making major purchases; and we study the stock market before investing. In a very real sense, you could say that we are *gathering sample evidence* about the relevant states of nature.

In our analysis of decisions, we would like to be able to formally incorporate additional (sample) information into the process. Additional information is usually not free; if nothing else, it takes time and effort merely to gather and interpret this information. Thus, our decision process should not only be able to incorporate new information, but it should also be able to indicate how *much* additional information it is worthwhile to collect.

Our first step in evaluating information will be to consider the effect of sample information on the decision-maker's evaluation of the relative likelihood of each state of nature. We will then turn to the more general question of *how much* information should be collected.

Formulating a Bayesian Problem

We will illustrate Bayes' rule by assuming that Perkins Plastics has recently learned that they can use a device in their plating operations that is capable of testing a sample of valves from each batch. Perkins is currently considering testing a *single valve* from the current batch (larger samples will be considered later). Perkins believes that determining whether one valve, randomly selected from a batch, is good or defective might help them estimate $P(90\%$ good$)$ and $P(60\%$ good$)$. Better estimates of these probabilities will, presumably, improve their ability to select between assembly and rework.

The description of the Perkins Plastics problem gave the following two probabilities:

$$P(90\% \text{ good}) = 0.70 \quad \text{and} \quad P(60\% \text{ good}) = 0.30$$

These two probabilities are called **prior probabilities**. They represent the probabilities of the two states of nature *before* any sample information is seen. The purpose of using Bayes' rule is to revise these prior probabilities in the light of (or given) the various possible sample outcomes. These revised probabilities are called **posterior probabilities**.

In the Perkins example, there are two possible sample outcomes: either one good valve is drawn (G) or one defective valve is drawn (D). The posterior probabilities for Perkins are thus:

$$P(90\% \text{ good} \mid G) \quad \text{and} \quad P(90\% \text{ good} \mid D)$$
$$P(60\% \text{ good} \mid G) \quad \text{and} \quad P(60\% \text{ good} \mid D)$$

Note that while we had *two* prior probabilities, there are *four* posterior probabilities. This occurs because each of the two prior probabilities must be re-evaluated in the light of both possible results, G and D.

☐ STUDY QUESTION 17.1   Cost Estimate of Sewage Treatment Facility

The city of Bedford is trying to estimate the cost of a new sewage treatment facility. A major factor in the cost is the amount of rock (limestone) found at the site. If the city estimates a normal amount of rock and the amount is found to be excessive, the penalty to the city in time lost, legal battles, et cetera, will be $20,000. The penalty for estimating an excessive amount when it is really normal will be $8,000. If they estimate correctly, there is no penalty. The city's prior probability of normal rock is 0.70; the prior probability of excessive rock is 0.30. What is the best decision to make based on this information? Draw the decision tree.

• **ANSWER** The optimal decision is to estimate excessive rock. The decision tree is shown in Figure 17.2.

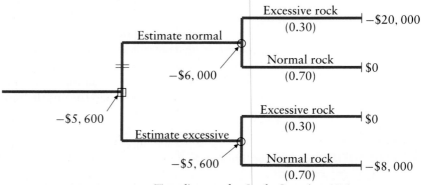

FIGURE 17.2 Tree diagram for Study Question 17.1

section 17.3 The Expected Value of Perfect Information (EVPI)

In Section 17.4 we will begin the process of indicating how statistical decision theory uses sample information to revise prior probabilities. A major goal of this revision of probabilities is to determine if sample information is worth purchasing. That is, because sample information almost always costs money, or at least time is lost before action can be taken, the decision needs to be made whether or not to collect the sample. In this section we determine an upper limit on the value of the sample information by determining the expected value of perfect information (EVPI).

EVPI is the expected value of having perfect information, relative to not having any sample information at all. To understand EVPI imagine you will repeat a decision over and over again. Perkins Plastics, for example, must repeatedly decide to rework or send to assembly not just one batch of valves, but many different batches (each batch of size 1000 valves). If Perkins had perfect information, they would know ahead of time whether each batch is 90% good, or 60% good. This perfect information will allow Perkins to always made the correct decision — i.e., send to assembly if the batch is 90% good, and rework if the batch is 60% good. EVPI measures how much better off Perkins is with this information. Because EVPI is the value of perfect information, it represents the maximum amount Perkins would pay for sample information.

To determine EVPI we first need to calculate another measure, the expected value with perfect information, which we abbreviate as EMV(PI). It is important to understand how EMV(PI) differs from EVPI. EMV(PI) is the average payoff assuming perfect information exists, and costs nothing. EMV(PI) is an absolute measure. EVPI, in contrast, is a relative measure — the amount the decision is better off with perfect information relative to without it. We calculate EMV(PI) by "flipping" the decision tree. That is, we put the state of nature first, and then the decisions. For Perkins plastics, the flip of Figure 17.1 is shown in Figure 17.3.

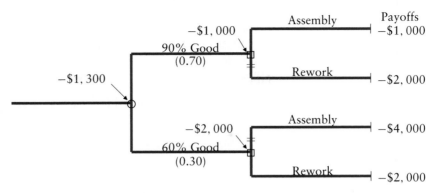

FIGURE 17.3   Flip of Figure 17.1

The tree above shows that assembly $(-\$1,000)$ is the best choice for the decision maker after learning that the batch is 90% good. Similarly, the rework branch $(-\$2,000)$ is the best choice after learning that the batch is 60% good. From the prior probabilities we know that a 90% batch will occur with probability 0.70, and a 60% batch with probability 0.30. Thus, under perfect information the expected cost to Perkins is:

$$EMV(PI) = 0.70(-\$1,000) + 0.30(-\$2,000)$$
$$= -\$1,300$$

This result says that, on the average, Perkins' payoff will be $-\$1,300$ if perfect information is available at no cost. To determine EVPI, which is how much better off Perkins is with perfect information relative to having no information, note in Figure 17.1 that EMV(no information) $= -\$1,900$. The difference between $-\$1,900$ and $-\$1,300$ is 600, which is EVPI. That is,

$$EVPI = EMV(PI) - EMV(\text{no information})$$
$$= -\$1,300 - (-\$1,900) = \$600$$

The upper limit on the value of sample information for Perkins is $600. Perkins knows now that any sample information, no matter how good, must be worth less than $600 (per batch).

The Revision of Probabilities

section 17.4

The general formula for **Bayes' rule** given in Chapter 3 is presented below, using the terminology of this chapter. The sums in these formulas include all possible states of nature.

Bayes' Rule:

$$P(\text{state of nature} \mid \text{sample}) = \frac{P(\text{state of nature})P(\text{sample} \mid \text{state of nature})}{\Sigma P(\text{state of nature})P(\text{sample} \mid \text{state of nature})}$$

or

$$\text{Posterior probability} = \frac{(\text{Prior probability})(\text{likelihood})}{\Sigma(\text{Prior probability})(\text{likelihood})} \qquad (17.1)$$

The second equation in Formula 17.1 clearly shows that the calculation of a posterior probability involves prior probabilities and likelihoods. A **likelihood** indicates how likely each sample outcome is, given the various states of nature. Thus, in this context, a likelihood is defined as follows:

Likelihood: P(sample | state of nature)

In our Perkins Plastics case, there are two possible sample results [good (G) or defective (D)] and two possible states of nature (90% good and 60% good). Thus, there are four likelihoods:

P(G | 90% good)   and P(D | 90% good)

P(G | 60% good)   and P(D | 60% good)

Since our sample involves drawing only a single valve from a large batch, it is not difficult to determine the value of each of the four likelihoods. For example, *given that* 90% of a batch is good, the probability of drawing a single good valve is 0.90. That is:

$$P(G \mid 90\% \text{ good}) = 0.90$$

The complement of this probability is the likelihood, given a batch that is 90% good, of drawing a single defective valve.

$$P(D \mid 90\% \text{ good}) = 0.10$$

By similar reasoning,

$$P(G \mid 60\% \text{ good}) = 0.60 \quad \text{and} \quad P(D \mid 60\% \text{ good}) = 0.40.$$

We now have all the information necessary to calculate the four posterior probabilities in our Perkins Plastics example. Suppose that we now assume that a sample of one of Perkins' valves resulted in a good valve. Thus, we want to use Bayes' rule to determine the two posteriors, P(90% good | G) and P(60% good | G). The first of these two values is calculated below, using Formula 17.1.

P(90% good | G)

$$= \frac{P(90\% \text{ good}) P(G \mid 90\% \text{ good})}{P(90\% \text{ good}) P(G \mid 90\% \text{ good}) + P(60\% \text{ good}) P(G \mid 60\% \text{ good})}$$

$$= \frac{(0.70)(0.90)}{(0.70)(0.90) + (0.30)(0.60)} = \frac{0.63}{0.81} = 0.7778$$

The posterior probability P(60% good | G) is the complement of this value — that is, P(60% good | G) = 1 − 0.7778 = 0.2222.

We have just calculated the two posteriors for the case in which the sample was a good valve. To complete our statistical decision theory analysis, we also need to calculate the two posteriors for the case in which the sample results in a defective valve. Rather than use Formula 17.1 explicitly to calculate these two posteriors, we now present a tabular procedure that is often a more convenient format for calculating posteriors. The reader should keep in mind that this process is exactly equivalent to using Formula 17.1. In the tabular approach, each possible sample result is treated separately. Hence, Table 17.4 is relevant only for the sample result — one defective.

TABLE 17.4 Sample Result — One Defective

(1)	(2)	(3)	(4)	(5)
States of Nature	Prior	One-Defective Likelihood	Joint Probability = (Prior)(Likelihood)	Posterior
90% good	0.70	0.10	0.07	$0.07/0.19 = 0.3684$
60% good	0.30	0.40	0.12	$0.12/0.19 = 0.6316$
Marginal probability	=	(Σ)(prior)(likelihood)	= 0.19	= P(1 Defective)

The first three columns in this table merely represent the information already known — namely, the states of nature, the priors, and the likelihoods. Each value in column (4) represents the numerator of the formula for Bayes' rule. This numerator is called a joint probability and is always the product (prior)(likelihood). The sum of column (4), which is Σ(prior)(likelihood), represents the denominator of the formula for Bayes' rule (called a marginal probability). Finally, dividing each value in column (4) by the sum of the values in column (4), we obtain the posterior probabilities given in column (5).

Marginal Probabilities. In the process of making decisions on the basis of posterior probabilities, we will need to determine how likely it is that each sample result will occur. In the Perkins Plastics case, we thus need to know $P(G)$ and $P(D)$. Marginal probabilities are always easy to calculate once Bayes' rule has been used, as each value of Σ(prior)(likelihood) is a marginal probability. Thus, from our two Bayesian calculations thus far, we can determine the following:

$$P(G) = \Sigma(\text{prior})(\text{likelihood}) = 0.81$$

and

$$P(D) = \Sigma(\text{prior})(\text{likelihood}) = 0.19$$

In other words, a good valve will be drawn 81% of the time, while a defective valve will be drawn 19% of the time.

Scheme for Revising Probabilities. Bayes' rule thus provides us with a means for revising probabilities in the light of sample information. The prior probabilities represent a state of uncertainty before any sample evidence is seen, while the posterior probabilities represent the state of uncertainty *after* a particular sample has been seen. It is important to emphasize that the terms prior, and posterior probabilities, relate only to a particular sample. A decision-maker may want to consider taking a second sample after observing the result of the first sample. The result of the first sample at that point represents historical data; hence, the posterior probabilities from the first sample become prior probabilities for the second sample. A diagram of this relationship appears in Figure 17.4.

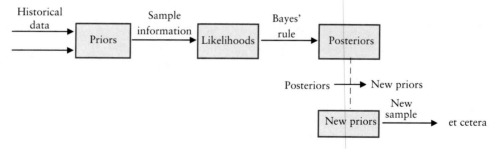

FIGURE 17.4   The revision of probabilities

The Value of Information ($n = 1$)

One of the most important decisions in all statistical decision theory problems is whether or not gathering sample information is worthwhile. The advantage of having sample information is that we can look at the results of the sample and, in light of this information, make the optimal decision. The disadvantage of gathering sample information is that the information is usually not free. Fortunately, the methods of statistical decision theory provide us with a procedure for determining whether the advantages of gathering sample information outweigh the disadvantages.

In our Perkins Plastics example, the decision about gathering sample information involves whether the company should rent the testing device. We will assume that the cost for this device, including its rent and all labour involved, is $5 for each valve tested. Our objective is to decide whether a sample of one valve ($n = 1$) is worth $5 (larger samples will be considered later). To make this decision, we will determine the EMV after both possible sample results (G and D), using the posterior probabilities calculated in Section 17.4. This type of analysis is referred to as *preposterior analysis*, since we are looking at the posterior probabilities before we have even decided to sample.

The Decision Tree

Recall that, in our original decision problem in Section 17.3, a tree diagram was useful. A tree diagram is also useful at this point, except that now we must expand the tree shown in Figure 17.1 to include a branch (a decision) that represents gathering a sample of size $n = 1$. The resulting decision tree is presented in Figure 17.5.

The sequence of actions and states of nature in a decision tree must always be arranged in exactly the same order in which they occur. In this case, the first decision is whether to send the valves to assembly, to rework them, or to sample ($n = 1$). *If the sample branch is followed, then the results of the sample must appear next on the decision tree.* Our sample results are either one good or one defective. Note that the probabilities presented below these results are the same marginal probabilities calculated in Section 17.4:

$$P(G) = 0.81 \quad \text{and} \quad P(D) = 0.19$$

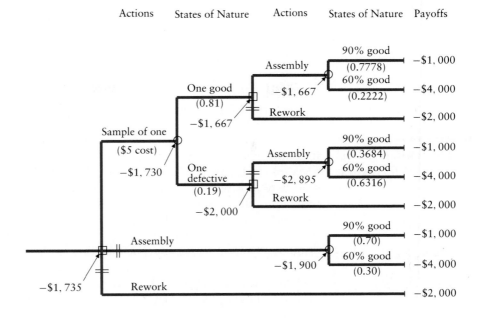

FIGURE 17.5 Tree diagram for sample of one ($n = 1$)

After observing a sample outcome, the decision-maker will have the alternative of deciding on the same actions that were outlined in the original statement of the problem. In Figure 17.5, the actions presented after the sample outcomes are the original choices: either send the valves to assembly or rework them. Finally, our decision tree indicates that if we send the batch to assembly, we will find that the state of nature is, in reality, either 90% good or 60% good. Note that the probabilities at the end of the tree (0.7778, 0.2222, 0.3684, and 0.6316) are the posterior probabilities calculated in Section 17.4. The payoffs (losses) given in the original problem are listed at the end of the tree, and the circled values are EMVs.

Calculation of the EMVs in a decision tree usually starts with the branches at the right-hand margin and proceeds toward the left. This is called **backwards induction**. For example, the expected value of $-\$1,667$ is derived from multiplying the posterior probability $P(90\% \text{ good} | G) = 0.7778$ times the cost of a 90% batch, $-\$1,000$, and adding this to $P(60\% \text{ good} | G) = 0.2222$ times the cost of a 60% batch, $-\$4,000$:

$$-\$1,667 = (0.7778)(-\$1,000) + (0.2222)(-\$4,000)$$

After a sample of one good valve, the optimal action is to send it directly to assembly (at an expected value of $-\$1,667$), rather than to rework, it (at a cost of $-\$2,000$). If the sample valve is *defective*, however, the best strategy is to rework them (at a cost of $-\$2,000$) rather than send them to assembly at an expected value of $-\$2,895$:

$$-\$2,895 = (0.3684)(-\$1,000) + (0.6316)(-\$4,000)$$

We now know what cost to expect after each possible sample result. We also know how often each possible result will occur; that is, $P(G) = 0.81$ and $P(D) = 0.19$. Putting this information together, we now can say that 81% of the time the cost will be $-\$1,667$, and 19% of the time the cost will be $-\$2,000$. Thus, the expected value of the sample branch equals the sum of these two expected values times the probability that they will occur:

$$(0.81)(-\$1,667) + (0.19)(-\$2,000) = -\$1,730 \;.$$

Subtract the $5 cost of sampling from this value, and the total EMV is $-\$1,735$.

Evaluating the Results

It is now evident, from our decision tree, that the sample-of-one branch with its EMV of $-\$1,735$ is a better choice than the next best alternative, which is to send it to assembly (EMV $= -\$1,900$). In statistical decision theory, there are two important measures that indicate by how much sample information increases expected profits or reduces expected costs. One of these measures is designed to *include* the cost of the sample itself, while the other *excludes* sampling costs. For instance, if sample costs are not included in the Perkins Plastics case, then the value of the sampling information (the testing device) is the difference between $-\$1,900$ (the optimal payoff before sampling) and $-\$1,730$ (the optimal payoff after sampling). This difference is called the *expected value of sample information* (**EVSI**), and is defined as follows:

$$
\begin{aligned}
\text{EVSI} = {}&\text{EMV(optimal after sample, excluding sampling costs)}\\
&-\text{EMV(optimal before sample)}
\end{aligned}
\tag{17.2}
$$

In the case of Perkins Plastics, the EVSI is as follows:

$$\text{EVSI} = -\$1,730 - (-\$1,900) = \$170$$

The value of EVSI can be thought of as the maximum amount the decision-maker should pay for the sample information. Thus, Perkins Plastics should pay no more than $170 for a sample of one, since they cannot expect to save more than this amount (on the average) from the single observation.

When the cost of sampling is known, it is useful in decision theory analysis to include this cost in calculating the *net* savings to the decision-maker. This value is called the *expected net gain from sampling* (**ENGS**), which can be defined as follows:

$$
\begin{aligned}
\text{ENGS} = {}&\text{EMV(optimal after sample, including sampling costs)}\\
&-\text{EMV(optimal before sample)}
\end{aligned}
\tag{17.3}
$$

For Perkins Plastics, the after-sample EMV is $-\$1,730$ less the $5 sampling cost, or $-\$1,735$. Hence:

$$\text{ENGS} = -\$1,735 - (-\$1,900) = \$165$$

It is not difficult to see that ENGS and EVSI differ by the cost of the sample, and EVSI is the larger of the two.

$$ENGS = EVSI - \text{cost of sampling} \qquad (17.4)$$

☐ STUDY QUESTION 17.2   A Study of the Cost of Testing for Rock

The city of Bedford (Study Question 17.1) is considering drilling a single hole to test for rock. The likelihood of this test indicating normal or excessive rock is given in the following table.

TABLE 17.5   Likelihood of Normal or Excessive Rock Using One Test Hole

		State of Nature	
		Normal	Excessive
Test results {	No rock	0.90	0.30
	Rock	0.10	0.70

Complete the decision tree begun in Study Question 17.1, assuming that the sample costs $1,000. Calculate ENGS and EVSI. What decision should Bedford make?

• **ANSWER**   The optimal decision is to take the sample of size $n = 1$. See Figure 17.6.

TABLE 17.6   Probabilities for Study Question 17.2

Sample Result	States of Nature	Prior	Likelihood	Joint	Posterior
Rock	excessive rock	0.30	0.70	0.21	0.75
	normal rock	0.70	0.10	0.07	0.25
				$P(\text{rock}) = 0.28$	
No rock	excessive rock	0.30	0.30	0.09	0.125
	normal rock	0.70	0.90	0.63	0.875
				$P(\text{no rock}) = 0.72$	

From Formula 17.2,

$$EVSI = -\$2,360 - (-\$5,600) = \$3,240$$

From Formula 17.3,

$$ENGS = -\$3,360 - (-\$5,600) = \$2,240$$

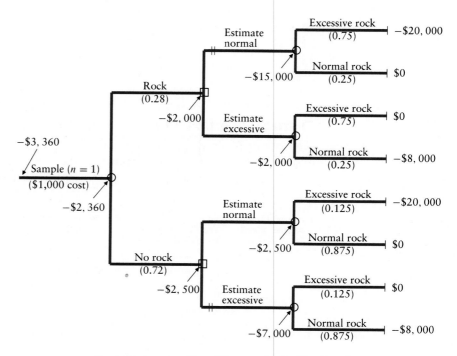

FIGURE 17.6 Tree Diagram for Bedford Rock

Analysis For Larger Sample Sizes

section 17.6

If a sample of size one saves $165, a logical question is whether or not we can do even better with a larger sample, perhaps $n = 2$, or $n = 3$ or more. Fortunately, the process of analyzing these larger samples is very similar to the one carried out for $n = 1$. We will complete the process for $n = 2$ below, assuming that testing this additional sample valve will cost Perkins another $5.

To begin our analysis, we first need to determine what sample outcomes are possible. When drawing two valves, we could receive: (**1**) two good [2G], (**2**) one good, one defective [1G, 1D] or (**3**) two defective [2D]. Since there are three different sample outcomes, we now have the following *six* posterior probabilities to calculate:

$$P(90\% \text{ good} \mid 2G), \quad P(90\% \text{ good} \mid 1G, \ 1D), \quad P(90\% \text{ good} \mid 2D)$$

and

$$P(60\% \text{ good} \mid 2G), \quad P(60\% \text{ good} \mid 1G, \ 1D), \quad P(60\% \text{ good} \mid 2D)$$

As before, we must determine the likelihood corresponding to each one of these posteriors. For example, the first likelihood, $P(2G \mid 90\% \text{ good})$ is determined by noting that if the two draws are independent and the probability of finding a good valve on each draw is 0.90,† then the probability of finding two good valves in two draws is (0.90)(0.90):

$$P(2G \mid 90\% \text{ good}) = (0.90)(0.90) = 0.81$$

The reader may recall a standard formula and a routine process for finding such probabilities. Indeed, when the samples are drawn independently and the probability of success is a constant (as we assumed here, $P(\text{good}) = 0.90$), the *binomial distribution* can be used to calculate the likelihoods. Thus, looking in Table I under $n = 2$ and $\pi = 0.90$, we find the following likelihoods:

$$P(2G \mid 90\% \text{ good}) = 0.81, \qquad P(1G, \ 1D \mid 90\% \text{ good}) = 0.18, \qquad \text{and}$$
$$P(2D \mid 90\% \text{ good}) = 0.01$$

To find the likelihoods for the batch in which 60% of the valves are good, we look in Table I under $n = 2$, $\pi = 0.60$:

$$P(2G \mid 60\% \text{ good}) = 0.36, \qquad P(1G, \ 1D \mid 60\% \text{ good}) = 0.48, \qquad \text{and}$$
$$P(2D \mid 60\% \text{ good}) = 0.16$$

It will be possible to calculate the likelihoods for all of the discrete Bayesian problems discussed in the remainder of this book by using Table I.

We are now ready to calculate the three marginal probabilities and the six posteriors, using the tabular format presented in Section 17.4. The values obtained are shown in Table 17.7.

Note that in Table 17.7 the three marginal probabilities sum to 1.0, as they must [$P(2G) = 0.675$, $P(1G, \ 1D) = 0.270$, $P(2D) = 0.055$]. The six posterior probabilities are shown in the last column.

Our next step in the decision analysis is to draw the decision tree. This tree should have four initial branches, corresponding to the four actions "assembly," "rework," "sample of one," and "sample of two." Because the first three of these branches were given in Figure 17.5, we present in Figure 17.7 only the new branch, that of "sample of two."

The reader should verify that the marginal and posterior probabilities given in Figure 17.7 correspond to those of Table 17.7. The EMVs are determined as before, by backwards induction. Note that the optimal decision is to send the valves to assembly only after a sample of two good valves — otherwise, the optimal decision is to rework the valves. The total EMV of this "sample of two" branch is $-\$1,649$, excluding the $10 cost. A summary of the EMVs is given in Table 17.8.

Our final step in the decision analysis is to calculate EVSI and ENGS. The value of EVSI indicates how much better $n = 2$ is than the optimal action before sampling (which was to send the valves to assembly at an expected value of $-\$1,900$).

$$\text{EVSI}(n = 2) = \text{EMV}(\text{optimal for } n = 2) - \text{EMV}(\text{optimal before sampling})$$
$$= -\$1,649 - (-\$1,900) = \$251$$

---

† We will assume that the number of valves per batch is large enough (1,000 items) so that the probability of finding a good valve changes very little from one draw to the next.

TABLE 17.7   Probabilities for the Perkins Plastics Example ($n = 2$)

Sample	State of Nature	Prior	Likelihood	Joint	Posterior
2 good	90% batch	0.70	0.81	0.567	$0.567/0.675 = 0.840$
	60% batch	0.30	0.36	0.108	$0.108/0.675 = 0.160$
		1.00		Marginal = 0.675	1.000
1 good, 1 defective	90% batch	0.70	0.18	0.126	$0.126/0.270 = 0.467$
	60% batch	0.30	0.48	0.144	$0.144/0.270 = 0.533$
		1.00		Marginal = 0.270	1.000
2 defective	90% batch	0.70	0.01	0.007	$0.007/0.055 = 0.127$
	60% batch	0.30	0.16	0.048	$0.048/0.055 = 0.873$
		1.00		Marginal = 0.055	1.000

The value \$251 represents the maximum amount Perkins Plastics should pay for a sample of size two. To calculate ENGS, we must subtract the \$10 sampling cost from \$251:

$$\text{ENGS}(n = 2) = \text{EVSI}(n = 2) - \text{cost of sample}(n = 2)$$
$$= \$251 - \$10 = \$241$$

Since ENGS($n = 1$) was \$165 and ENGS($n = 2$) is \$241, a sample of size two is better than a sample of size one.

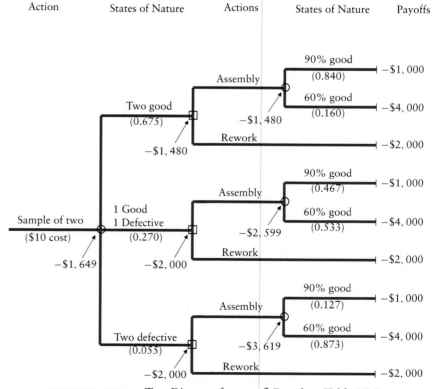

FIGURE 17.7   Tree Diagram for $n = 2$ Based on Table 17.7

Samples of Size $n > 2$. It should be clear by now that we can continue this process of analyzing larger and larger samples and that the best sample size is the one giving the largest ENGS. Although the calculations become increasingly tedious as the sample size gets larger, it is often relatively easy to program these calculations on a computer. If this is done, then computer costs must be added to the analysis. At this point, it would be feasible but tedious for the reader to calculate ENGS for the Perkins Plastics problem for $n = 3$. However, we do advise the reader to calculate the marginal and posterior probabilities for $n = 3$, which should be checked by referring to Table 17.9. The ENGS for $n = 3$ is $265.70.

TABLE 17.8   Summary of decision analysis for $n = 2$ from Figure 17.4

Sample Results	Marginal Probability	Optimal Action	EMV	(EMV) × (Marginal prob.)
2 good	0.675	Assembly	−$1,480	−$999
1 good, 1 defective	0.270	Rework	−$2,000	−$540
2 defective	0.055	Rework	−$2,000	−$110
			Total EMV = −$1,649	

In Table 17.10 the values of ENGS and EVSI for $n = 1, 2, \ldots, 26$ are given under the assumption that each additional sample observation costs an extra $5. From this table we see that $n = 20$ is the optimal sample for Perkins Plastics.[2] For other problems, the optimal size could be very large. Or it may be that all values of ENGS are negative, implying that the decision-maker should not sample at all. In other instances it may be better to take a sample, observe the results of this sample, and then decide whether or not to stop sampling or to continue with further observations. A discussion of such *stopping rules* is beyond the scope of this book.

TABLE 17.9   Probabilities for Perkins Plastics Example ($n = 3$)

Sample	State of Nature	Prior	Likelihood	Joint	Posterior
3G	90% good	0.70	0.729	0.5103	0.8873
	60% good	0.30	0.216	0.0648	0.1127
			Marginal = 0.5751		
2G, 1D	90% good	0.70	0.243	0.1701	0.5676
	60% good	0.30	0.432	0.1296	0.4324
			Marginal = 0.2997		
1G, 2D	90% good	0.70	0.027	0.0189	0.1795
	60% good	0.30	0.288	0.0864	0.8205
			Marginal = 0.1053		
3D	90% good	0.70	0.001	0.0007	0.0352
	60% good	0.30	0.064	0.0192	0.9648
			Marginal = 0.0199		

---

[2] The decision rule for $n = 20$ (which is not shown here) is to rework if the number of defectives is 5 or larger. Otherwise, the batch is sent to assembly.

TABLE 17.10 Values of EVSI and ENGS for Selected Sample Sizes

Sample Size	EVSI	Sample Cost	ENGS	Sample Size	EVSI	Sample Cost	ENGS
1	$170.00	$ 5	$165.00	14	$494.53	$ 70	$424.53
2	251.00	10	241.00	15	506.82	75	431.82
3	280.70	15	265.70	16	513.03	80	433.03
4	281.51	20	261.51	17	514.30	85	429.30
5	340.80	25	315.80	18	523.77	90	433.77
6	380.05	30	350.05	19	533.60	95	438.60
7	400.04	35	365.04	20	539.21	100	439.21
8	405.35	40	365.04	21	541.33	105	436.33
9	423.85	45	378.85	22	543.92	110	433.92
10	450.49	50	400.49	23	551.80	115	436.80
11	451.96	55	406.96	24	556.66	120	436.66
12	472.33	60	412.33	25	559.01	125	434.01
13	479.94	65	414.94	26	559.26	130	429.26

☐ **STUDY QUESTION 17.3** The Cost of Testing for Rock when $n = 2$

Extend Study Question 17.2 by assuming that the city now has the option to drill twice for rock. The two drillings are independent and will cost a total of $1,200. Determine whether $n = 2$ is better than $n = 1$, and calculate ENGS.

TABLE 17.11 Probabilities for Study Question 17.3

Sample Result	State of Nature	Prior	Likelihood	Joint	Posterior
Both rock	excessive	0.30	0.490	0.147	0.955
	normal	0.70	0.010	0.007	0.045
			P(both rock) = 0.154		
One rock, One no rock	excessive	0.30	0.420	0.126	0.500
	normal	0.70	0.180	0.126	0.500
			P(1 rock, 1 no rock) = 0.252		
Both no rock	excessive	0.30	0.090	0.027	0.045
	normal	0.70	0.810	0.567	0.955
			P(both no rock) = 0.594		

Decision Table:	Payoff if City Estimates	
Sample Results:	Excessive	Normal
Both rock	0.955(0)+ 0.045(−8,000) = −$360	0.955(−20,000)+ 0.045(0) = −$19,100
1 rock, 1 no rock	0.500(−8,000)+ 0.500(0) = −$4,000	0.500(0)+ 0.500(−20,000) = −$10,000
Both no rock	0.045(0)+ 0.955(−8,000) = −$7,640	0.045(−20,000)+ 0.955(0) = −$900

• **ANSWER**   A sample of $n = 2$ is better than $n = 1$. The problem is solved in tabular form in Table 17.11. The reader may wish to draw the decision tree. A summary of the EMVs is given in Table 17.12.

$$\text{EVSI}(n = 2) = -\$1,598 - (-\$5,600) = \$4,002$$

$$\text{ENGS}(n = 2) = \$4,002 - \$1,200 = \$2,802$$

TABLE 17.12   Summary of Decision Analysis for Study Question 17.3

Sample Results	Marginal Probability	Optimal Action	EMV	(EMV) × (Marginal Probability)
Both rock	0.154	Est. excessive	−360	−55.40
1 rock, 1 no rock	0.252	Est. excessive	−4,000	−1,008.00
Both no rock	0.594	Est. normal	−900	−534.60
				Total EMV = −1,598.00

PROBLEMS

17.1 What are the disadvantages of the EMV criterion?

17.2 The Koseman Company is considering adding a new boiler to its factory in an attempt to avoid costly delays in case one of the present boilers must shut down for repairs. The company has determined that the following payoff table is appropriate for its present time horizon (5 years).

TABLE 17.13   Payoff Table

		States of Nature		
		No Repairs	Minor Repairs	Major Repairs
Actions	Do not add boiler	$0	−$4,000	−$15,000
	Add new boiler	−$10,000	−$10,000	−$10,000
Probability		0.20	0.30	0.50

Find the optimal action using the EMV criterion.

17.3 Draw the decision tree for Problem 17.2, indicating the optimal action by EMV. Find the expected value of perfect information (EVPI).

17.4 A toy manufacturer is considering introducing a novelty item in time for the Christmas season. Because of a distribution agreement, the number of items produced must be either 1,000, 5,000, or 10,000 units. These units can be produced either by a labour-intensive process that involves a fixed cost of $2,000 plus a variable cost of

$1.50 per unit or by a capital-intensive process involving fixed costs of $5,000 and a variable cost of $1.00 per unit. The company sells this novelty item for $3.00 per unit. Their current estimates are that the probability of selling only 1000 units is 1/6, the probability of selling 5,000 units is $\frac{1}{2}$, and the probability of selling 10,000 units is $\frac{1}{3}$. Unsold units have no salvage value. The company is trying to decide whether to produce 1,000, 5,000, or 10,000 units.

a) Find the optimal action using the EMV criterion.

b) Draw the decision tree, indicating the optimal action under EMV.

17.5 A lab test for HIV has been shown to correctly identify the presence of this virus in 95% of all people who are HIV-positive. Five percent of the time, however, the test will indicate HIV in someone who does not have it. If 5% of a given population is HIV-positive, what is the probability that a person whose lab test indicates HIV actually has the virus? Does this result surprise you?

17.6 Professor Ward Edwards of the University of Southern California conducted an experiment in which he asked college students to estimate the probability that a given sample of green and red balls came from one of two urns. Urn 1 contained 70 red balls and 30 green, while Urn 2 contained 70 green and 30 red balls. At the beginning of the experiment, one of these urns was selected at random, and then samples were drawn from this urn by randomly selecting a ball, noting its colour, and then replacing the ball. The subjects did not know which urn had been selected.

a) Suppose that one red ball is drawn. Without working it out, what is your *guess* as to the posterior value $P(\text{Urn } 1 \mid \text{One red})$?

b) Suppose that a sample of ten balls is drawn, resulting in seven red and three green. Without working it out, what is your *guess* as to the value of $P(\text{Urn } 1 \mid 7R, 3G)$?

c) In Edwards' experiments, a typical subject guessed that the probability in part (a) was about 0.60, and most estimated that the probability in a question similar to part (b) was less than 0.80. Use Bayes' rule to calculate the actual posterior values for parts (a) and (b), and then assess how well you and Dr. Edwards' subjects did in estimating these probabilities. [*Hint:* Table I can be used to calculate the four likelihoods, $P(\text{One red} \mid \text{Urn } 1)$, $P(\text{One red} \mid \text{Urn } 2)$, $P(7 \text{ red}, 3 \text{ green} \mid \text{Urn } 1)$, and $P(7 \text{ red}, 3 \text{ green} \mid \text{Urn } 2)$.]

17.7 A company can ship some equipment either by sea or by air. There is a possibility of a strike affecting either type of shipment. The cost matrix, including shipment and delay costs, is given below.

TABLE 17.14 A Cost Matrix

	Strike (B_1)	No Strike (B_2)
Ship by air	4,000	3,000
Ship by sea	6,000	1,000

a) If the probability of a strike is 0.4, what are the expected costs of each method of shipment?

b) Suppose that some inside informer suggests that a strike will occur and that the accuracy of this rumour (R) is given by the following likelihoods:

$$P(R \mid B_1) = 0.8 \quad \text{and} \quad P(R \mid B_2) = 0.3$$

Find the revised probability of a strike, given this extra information. Find $P(B_1 \mid R)$.

c) Using the revised probability, find the best choice of shipment according to the expected monetary value criterion.

17.8 Suppose that we receive a concession to sell popcorn at football games. We must decide whether to build one booth on the "Home" side or to build two booths, one each on the "Home" and "Visitors" sides of the stadium. If the games attract large crowds of visitors, it would be better to have two booths, but their cost and the cost of equipment within them would be a considerable expense. The payoff matrix is determined to be:

TABLE 17.15 A Payoff Matrix

Action		Capacity Crowds	Regular "Home" Crowd
A_1	Build one booth	$350	$300
A_2	Build two booths	500	200

a) Suppose that we consider the probability of capacity crowds to be 0.4 and the probability of regular-sized "home" crowds to be 0.6. Which action is better? What is EVPI?

b) Suppose that a preseason forecast predicts a much improved team and preseason ticket sales are up by 30%. From previous experience, we determine that such situations have preceded games with capacity crowds four out of ten times and have preceded games with regular crowds in two out of ten cases – in other words, the likelihoods are $P(\text{up } 30\% \mid \text{capacity}) = \frac{4}{10}$ and $P(\text{up } 30\% \mid \text{regular}) = \frac{2}{10}$. Find the revised probability of the two different-sized crowds, and determine which action is better in light of the new information.

17.9 A corporation considers two levels of investment in a real-estate development, a low participation (A_1) or a high participation (A_2). Two states of nature are deemed possible, a partial success (B_1) or a complete success (B_2). The payoff matrix is estimated to be:

TABLE 17.16 A Payoff Matrix for Two Levels of Investments

	B_1	B_2
A_1	−200	400
A_2	−500	1,000

a) How large does the prior probability of B_1 have to be in order to make action A_1 the better choice?

b) Suppose that the states of nature are presumed initially to occur with probabilities $P(B_1) = 0.4$, $P(B_2) = 0.6$. Then a more careful study is made, which leads to the conclusion that the project will be only a partial success. In previous relevant studies, this same conclusion was obtained in eight out of ten cases when similar projects were partial successes. Also, this conclusion was obtained in four out of 12 cases when similar projects were *complete* successes. Thus, the likelihoods are $P(\text{study says partial} \mid B_1) = \frac{8}{10}$ and $P(\text{study says partial} \mid B_2) = \frac{4}{12}$. Find the revised probabilities of the states of nature, and determine which investment level is appropriate.

17.10 Suppose that you are trying to choose between these investments (a_1, a_2, a_3), where the payoff table (in dollars) is as follows.

TABLE 17.17   A Payoff Table

		States of Nature		
		θ_1	θ_2	θ_3
Actions	a_1	$0	$0	$1,400
	a_2	500	500	500
	a_3	400	100	900
Probability		0.30	0.30	0.40

What is the optimal action under EMV? What is EVPI?

17.11 Joe Doakes is considering flying from Montreal to Toronto in the hopes of making an important sale to P. J. Bety, president of NOCO, Inc. If Joe makes this sale, he will earn a commission of $1,100. Unfortunately, Joe figures that there is a 50–50 chance that Bety will be called out of town at the last moment and he will have no chance at a sale. Even if he goes to see Bety, Joe estimates that he has only one chance in five of making the sale. The trip will cost Joe $100, whether or not he gets to see Bety.

a) Draw the tree diagram for Joe, and determine whether Joe should fly to Toronto or not.

b) Joe was heard to remark, "I'd give my right arm to know if Bety will be in town." How much does he value his right arm?

c) Suppose an information service offers to tell Joe, before he decides to fly, whether or not they think Bety will be in town. The record of this company is such that if they say Bety will be in, the probability that she will, in fact, be in is 0.70; in other words, the posterior probability is $P(\text{in} \mid \text{say in}) = 0.70$. If they say she will be out, they will be correct 90% of the time; or $P(\text{out} \mid \text{say out}) = 0.90$. If this service costs $10, and Joe figures that the probability that they will say Bety is in is 0.50, should he buy the service? Draw the tree diagram. Find ENGS.

17.12 Answer parts (a) and (b).

a) Can EVSI ever assume a negative value? Explain.

b) What will be the value of EVSI if, no matter what sample result is observed, the same decision is optimal after sampling as was optimal before sampling?

17.13 The Dixon Corporation makes picture tubes for a large television manufacturer. Dixon is concerned because approximately 30% of their tubes have been defective. When the television manufacturer encounters a defective tube, Dixon is charged a $20 penalty cost to pay for repairs and lost time. One way Dixon can avoid this penalty cost is to re-examine and fix each defective

tube before shipping. This would cost an extra $7 per tube. Or they can rent a testing device that costs $1 for each tube tested. Since this device is not infallible, its effectiveness was tested by running a large number of tubes through it, some known to be good and others known to be defective. The results of this study determined the following likelihoods.

TABLE 17.18   The Likelihood of Good or Defective Picture Tubes

		State of Tube	
		Good	Defective
Test Results {	Positive	0.75	0.20
	Negative	0.25	0.80
		1.00	1.00

Draw the decision tree for Dixon, assuming that they must decide between shipping directly, re-examining each tube, or testing each tube. Calculate ENGS, EVPI, and EVSI.

17.14 The Techno Corporation is considering making either minor or major repairs to a malfunctioning production process. When the process is malfunctioning, the percentage of defective items produced seems to be a constant, with either $\pi = 0.10$ (indicating minor repairs necessary) or $\pi = 0.25$ (indicating major repairs necessary). Defective items are produced randomly, and there is no way Techno can tell for sure whether the machine needs minor or major repairs. If minor repairs are made when $\pi = 0.25$, the probability of a defective is reduced to 0.05. If minor repairs are made when $\pi = 0.10$ or major repairs are made when $\pi = 0.10$ or $\pi = 0.25$, then the proportion of defectives is reduced to zero. Techno has recently received an order for 1,000 items. This item yields them a profit of $0.50 per unit, except that they have to pay a $2.00 penalty cost for each item found to be defective. Major repairs to the process cost $100, while minor repairs cost $60. No adjustment can be made to the production process once a run has started. Prior to starting the run, however, Techno can sample items from a trial run, at a cost of $1.00 per item. The prior probabilities are $P(\text{major}) = 0.3$, $P(\text{minor}) = 0.7$.

a) Find the optimal action for Techno if they are trying to decide between not sampling at all, and sampling one item. Draw the decision tree. Find EVPI.

b) Find the optimal action for Techno if they are willing to consider a sample of either one or two items. Draw the decision tree. Calculate ENGS and EVSI.

17.15 Tennis balls produced by a certain company are considered defective if they do not bounce at least 42 inches when dropped from a height of six feet. In the past, about 40% of all balls shipped are later found to be defective. If the company ships a defective ball, they incur costs (lost goodwill, returns, et cetera) of $0.20 per ball. Instead of shipping directly, however, the company can vacuum-seal each ball at a cost of $0.10 per ball. This ensures that each ball will be good. The company is also considering testing each ball by dropping it *twice* from a height of six feet. A good ball will always bounce at least 42 inches; a defective will bounce 42 inches or more half of the time, with each bounce independent of all others. This testing procedure costs $0.02 per ball. Draw the decision tree for this company, calculate ENGS, EVPI, and EVSI, and indicate the optimal action for the company.

17.16 A university is trying to decide whether to schedule its June commencement indoors or outdoors. If they schedule it outdoors and it rains, the change of plans and move indoors will cost the university an extra $1,000. On the other hand, if the decision is to hold commencement indoors and it does not rain, the extra cost to the university will be $300 (mostly lighting and air conditioning). The probability of rain in June is 0.20.

a) Find the optimal action. Draw the decision tree, and find EVPI.

b) A local expert has promised to forecast the weather on commencement day (rain or no rain) for $100. This person is known to forecast according to the two likelihoods $P(\text{predicts rain} \mid \text{will rain}) = 0.70$ and $P(\text{predict no rain} \mid \text{will not rain}) = 0.80$. Draw the decision tree and calculate EVSI and ENGS.

◆ **17.17** A common problem in many businesses is making inventories of perishable items (perishable due to spoilage or obsolescence). In one such problem, a buyer of a toy store must decide on the quantity of a particular toy to order. The average life of such a toy is 3 months. During this period, it is believed, the demand will be between 4 and 7 toys. The cost of a toy is $10 and the selling price will be set at $20. Any toys left unsold at the end of the period will be sold quickly at $5 each. Assume that the demand distribution of the toys is given below:

TABLE 17.19

Toys sold	Probability
4	0.30
5	0.40
6	0.20
7	0.10

a) Construct the payoff table, stating clearly the decisions and the states of nature.

b) Determine the best action based on the expected monetary value criterion.

c) What is the expected value of perfect information?

17.18 One interesting property of Bayes' rule is that when $n > 1$, probabilities may be revised after *each observation* or after *each group* of observations. For example, in Section 17.6 we calculated the posterior probability $P(90\% \text{ good} \mid 1G, 1D) = 0.467$. This probability could have been calculated by assuming that the good valve was received on the first sample and the defective valve on the second sample. The posteriors $P(90\% \text{ good} \mid 1G)$ and $P(60\% \text{ good} \mid 1G)$ become the priors for calculating the new posteriors, which are determined after seeing the second valve (a defective).

a) Show that the two-phase method described above yields the same value as $P(90\% \text{ good} \mid 1G, 1D)$.

b) Show that the above posterior, when acting as the prior for a sample of one more valve (another good), yields the posterior for the sample (G, D, G) of $P(90\% \text{ good} \mid 2G, 1D) = 0.568$.

<table><tr><td>section 17.7</td><td></td></tr></table>

Utility Analysis[†]

As we pointed out earlier, the EMV criterion suffers from the weakness that it fails to take into account the variability in profits of a decision. As early as the eighteenth century, Daniel Bernoulli investigated the fact that, for most people, the value of a payoff does not always vary proportionally with its dollar amount. Bernoulli's work can be considered as perhaps the first stage in the development of a method permitting measurement of *relative* values in a decision-making context. This method was developed by the late John von Neumann, a mathematician, and Oskar Morgenstern, an economist, and was first published in 1944 in their now classic book, *The Theory of Games and Economic Behavior*. Their method measures relative values using an index or scale of utility, called a **utility function**.

[†] This section may be omitted without loss in continuity.

A Utility Scale

It is important to point out at this time that a utility scale is *unique to the individual* for whom it is constructed, and it is not meaningful to compare the values on one person's scale with the values on any other person's scale. We must mention also that, although the examples given below involve only monetary payoffs or consequences, nonmonetary factors can be taken into account as well.

A utility index, as determined by the von Neumann–Morgenstern approach, is measured on an **interval scale**. This type of scale is characterized by its lack of a predetermined zero-point (no specified origin) and the fact that the units of measurement can be selected arbitrarily. For example, Centigrade and Fahrenheit temperature scales both represent interval measurement. It is because of this arbitrary choice of origin and unit that one cannot make interpersonal comparisons of utility.

The von Neumann–Morgenstern approach to determining a utility function is to ascertain the utility for a number of points between two values, and then use these points as the basis for sketching a continuous function over the entire range. Finding the utility for given dollar values is accomplished by asking the decision-maker to indicate whether alternative I or II is more attractive for certain values of A, B, and C where A, B, and C are dollar values such that \$$A >$ \$$B >$ \$$C$:

Alternative I: Receive \$$B$ for certain.

Alternative II: Receive \$$A$ with probability π.

Receive \$$C$ with probability $1 - \pi$.

Alternative II is sometimes referred to as the **standard lottery**, while Alternative I is called the **certainty equivalent**. Suppose that we denote the utility of Alternative I to the decision-maker as $U(\$B)$ and denote the expected utility for Alternative II as $\pi U(\$A) + (1 - \pi)U(\$C)$. If the decision-maker is indifferent between these two alternatives, then

$$U(\$B) = \pi U(\$A) + (1 - \pi)U(\$C).$$

This equation is the basis from which a von Neumann–Morgenstern utility function is constructed.

Constructing a Utility Function

□ **EXAMPLE 17.5** Construct a utility function for the decision-maker in the Perkins Plastics example that will associate a utility value for profits ranging from −\$5,000 to \$5,000. In constructing a utility scale, two points must be assigned arbitrarily. Any dollar value can be assigned any utility value, as long as the higher dollar value is assigned the higher utility. We assume that everyone prefers more money to less. Let us rather arbitrarily set the following values:

$$U(\$0) = 0 \quad \text{and} \quad U(\$5,000) = 100$$

The unit of measurement in utility is called a **utile**, so \$0 has a value of 0 utiles, and \$5,000 has a value of 100 utiles.

There are a number of ways we can use these two values to determine additional points on the utility function. In one method, the value of B is the decision variable. For example, we might let $A = \$5,000$, $C = \$0$, and $\pi = \frac{1}{2}$ and ask the decision-maker what value of B makes the following two alternatives equally attractive:

Alternative I: Receive \$$B$ for certain.

Alternative II: Receive \$5,000 with probability $\pi = \frac{1}{2}$.

Receive \$0 with probability $1 - \pi = \frac{1}{2}$.

Assume that our decision-maker says that the two alternatives are equally attractive when $B = \$1,000$. The utility associated with $1,000 can now be calculated as follows:

$$U(\$1,000) = \frac{1}{2}U(\$5,000) + \frac{1}{2}U(\$0)$$

$$= \frac{1}{2}(100) + \frac{1}{2}(0)$$

$$= 50 \text{ utiles}$$

Now we have three points on the utility curve, counting the original two points.

To determine a fourth point, we can use a second method in which the value of C is the unknown value. Let $A = \$1,000$, $B = \$0$, and $\pi = \frac{1}{2}$, and ask the decision-maker to choose between the following alternatives:

> *Alternative I:*   Receive $0 for certain.
>
> *Alternative II:*   Receive $1,000 with probability $\pi = \frac{1}{2}$.
>
> Receive C with probability $1 - \pi = \frac{1}{2}$.

Assume that the decision-maker is indifferent when $C = -\$1,500$. Then

$$U(\$0) = \frac{1}{2}U(\$1,000) + \frac{1}{2}U(-\$1,500)$$

$$0 = \frac{1}{2}(50) + \frac{1}{2}U(-\$1,500)$$

$$U(-\$1,500) = -50 \text{ utiles}$$

This result gives a fourth point on the utility curve.

Although it is usually convenient to let either A, B, or C be the value the decision-maker must adjust to the point of indifference and to let $\pi = \frac{1}{2}$ (the subjective appraisal of Alternative II is easier with 50–50 odds), we can formulate a third method in which π is the decision variable. Let $A = \$0$, $B = -\$1,500$, and $C = -\$5,000$. The two alternatives are:

> *Alternative I:*   Lose $1,500 for certain.
>
> *Alternative II:*   Receive $0 with probability π.
>
> Lose $5,000 with probability $1 - \pi$.

Assume our decision-maker is indifferent when $\pi = 0.75$:

$$U(-\$1,500) = (0.75)U(\$0) + (0.25)U(-\$5,000)$$

$$-50 = (0.75)(0) + (0.25)U(-\$5,000)$$

$$U(-\$5,000) = -200$$

The preceding examples illustrate three variations on the process of determining points on a utility function. Once a sufficient number of such points have been calculated to ensure that the function is accurately represented, then the utility function can be drawn by sketching a line between the points. We show, in Figure 17.8, what the function for Perkins Plastics might look like when it is completed (the five points already calculated are marked with the symbol •).

The Effect of Risk on the Utility Function

Note several interesting characteristics about this function. First, the slope of the curve for most positive values is *concave* in shape, meaning that the decision-maker is a **risk-avoider** in this region. That is, if two alternatives have equal EMVs, then the decision-maker will prefer the alternative with the *lower* variability in payoff. This fact can be seen by our decision-maker's answer to the first set of alternatives presented. At that time, the decision-maker indicated indifference between receiving $1,000 for sure and gambling for stakes of $0 and $5,000 at 50–50 odds. Note that this gamble has an EMV of $2,500. The decision-maker's answer thus implies that any amount above $1,000, received with certainty, is preferable to the gamble. In other words, our decision-maker would rather have, say, $1,100 for sure than take the risk that the gamble might result in a payoff of only $0. Hence, for dollar values between $1,000 and $5,000 this decision-maker can be classified as a risk-avoider. Perhaps Figure 17.9, which is an enlarged view of the decision-maker's utility function between $0 and $5,000, will help explain why the function between $1,000 and $5000 represents risk avoidance.

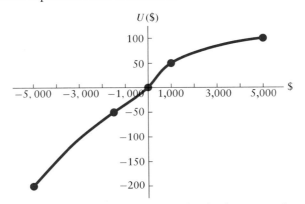

FIGURE 17.8   Utility function for the decision-maker of Perkins Plastics

The dashed line in Figure 17.9 (the "gamble line") represents a standard lottery where $A = \$5,000$ and $C = \$0$. When $\pi = \frac{1}{2}$, then the point a, which is halfway between the endpoints of the gamble line, represents the expected value of the gamble. We see that the EMV at point a is $2,500, and the expected utility is 50 utiles. Point b represents the utility received by the decision-maker for $1,000 received with certainty. Thus,

$$U(\$1,000) = U(\text{Gamble}) = 50 \text{ utiles,}$$

which is the answer that this person indicated in response to our first set of alternatives.

Note, from the diagram, that our decision-maker's utility for $2,500 received with certainty is 80 utiles (point c). One might ask, at this time, what value of π would make this decision-maker indifferent between the standard lottery and the certainty of receiving $2,500. As shown by point d on the gamble line, it requires a gamble with an EMV of $4,000 to yield the 80 utiles that the certainty of $2,500 yields. Thus, the value of π has to be 0.80, since

$$0.80(\$5,000) + 0.20(\$0) = \$4,000.$$

For payoffs from about −$1, 500 to $1,000 Figures 17.8 and 17.9 indicate that this decision-maker is a **risk-taker**, since the function is *convex* in shape in this region.[3] The answer to our second set of alternatives illustrates this fact. Recall that our second set of alternatives involved a gamble between −$1, 500 and $1,000, with $\pi = \frac{1}{2}$. The EMV of this gamble is thus −$250. Since the certainty equivalent is $0 in this case, the decision-maker is indicating a willingness to take the risk of the gamble whenever the amount received for certain is less than $0. For example, suppose that this person is given a choice between receiving −$100 for sure (a $100 loss) or taking a gamble between −$1, 500 and +$1, 000 at 50–50 odds. Our decision-maker is a risk-taker in this range and would prefer the gamble, even though its average loss of $\frac{1}{2}(−$1, 500) + \frac{1}{2}($1, 000) = −$250$ is worse than the certain loss of −$100. Finally we see that, for large losses, our decision-maker is again a *risk-avoider*, since the utility function is concave in shape in negative regions of the function. This fact is illustrated by the answers to our third set of alternatives.

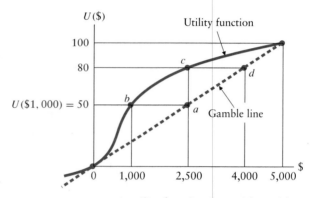

FIGURE 17.9 A utility function for a risk-avoider

Had our decision-maker's function been a straight line over part of its range (linear in shape), then this person would have been classified as **risk-neutral** in these portions of the utility function. That is, the gamble line and the utility function would be the same line; hence, this person would select the alternative yielding the highest EMV. Table 17.20 summarizes the three categories often used to distinguish decision-makers.

As indicated in Figure 17.9, most utility functions are not entirely convex, concave, or linear over the entire range of dollar values. Rather, a typical person might be a risk-avoider for certain dollar values, risk-neutral for other values, and perhaps a risk-taker for part of the curve. A utility function in which the decision-maker is willing to take risks for small amounts but avoids risks for large losses or gains is perhaps typical of many people. Most of us are willing to risk losing small amounts in poker games or by buying lottery tickets, but we avoid large losses by insuring our cars, homes, and businesses.

Maximizing Expected Utility

Constructing a utility function is not an easy task, as we have seen. For important decisions, however, it may be a very worthwhile task, in that the substitution of

---

[3] Concave from below means that the slope of the function is decreasing as the amount of dollars increases. That is, the second derivative of the function is negative. Its shape is rounded like a mountain top. A convex function has a second derivative that is positive; thus, its shape is more like a valley or a soup bowl. The slope of a convex function is increasing as the amount of dollars increases.

TABLE 17.20   Categories of Decision-Makers

Category	Utility Function Shape	Description
1. Risk-taker	Convex (slope increasing)	If a gamble has the same EMV as a dollar amount to be received with certainty, a *risk-taker* will always prefer the gamble.
2. Risk-neutral	Straight line (slope constant)	A person who is *risk-neutral* will always select that alternative (gamble or certainty) with the highest EMV.
3. Risk-avoider	Concave (slope decreasing)	If a gamble has the same EMV as a dollar amount to be received with certainty, a *risk-avoider* will always prefer the certainty.

utility values for monetary values may well change the optimal decision from one action to another.

□ **EXAMPLE 17.6**   We have reproduced, in Figure 17.10, the Perkins Plastics problem for $n = 1$. See Figures 17.1 and 17.5. The final number at the end of each branch is the appropriate utility value taken from Figure 17.8.

$$-\$4,000 = -150 \text{ utiles} \quad -\$2,000 = -60 \text{ utiles} \quad -\$1,000 = -40 \text{ utiles.}$$

The analysis is carried out in terms of expected utilities instead of the expected monetary values used in Figures 17.1 and 17.5.

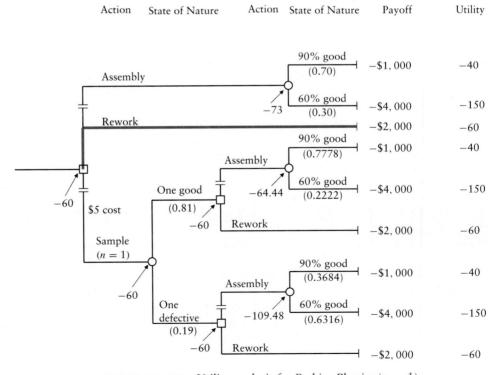

FIGURE 17.10   Utility analysis for Perkins Plastics ($n = 1$)

The tree diagram in Figure 17.10 indicates the effect of risk on the Perkins Plastics decision when $n = 1$. By looking at the sample branch, we see that *both* sample results lead to a decision to rework. Since this is the same decision that is optimal without taking the sample, the decision-maker need not bother taking the sample. In other words, the sample is worthless, and the value of EVSI must be zero. *EVSI will always equal zero if the sample branch cannot possibly lead to a different solution from that which was optimal before the sample.* Of course, the fact that a sample of size $n = 1$ is not advantageous does not mean that larger samples would also have no value. ◼

☐ **STUDY QUESTION 17.4**   Utility Analysis in Bedford Rock Case

Subtract the sample cost ($1,000) from each dollar value at the end of the decision tree in Study Question 17.2. Replace these dollar values with utilities, and then determine the optimal action. Use the following information about utilities, and indicate whether the person is a risk-taker, a risk-avoider, or risk-neutral.

$$U(\text{cost of } \$21,000) = -100 \qquad U(\text{cost of } \$20,000) = 0$$
$$U(\text{cost of } \$9,000) = 750 \qquad U(\text{cost of } \$1,000) = 950$$
$$U(\text{cost of } \$0) = 1000$$

The decision-maker is indifferent between I and II, where

> *Alternative I:* $8,000 cost for sure
>
> *Alternative II:* $20,000 cost at $\pi = 0.30$ and $0 at $1 - \pi = 0.70$

● **ANSWER**   Expected utilities are shown in the tree diagram in Figure 17.11. The sample costs are included in the payoffs on the right. Note that we have not put a minus sign in front of costs; a cost of $20,000 could have been denoted as $-\$20,000$. The utility of a cost of $\$8,000 = 0.70U(0) + 0.30U(\$20,000) = 0.70(1,000) + 0.30(0) = 700$. The optimal decision is to sample because the expected utility of the "sample branch" (841.5) is higher than the expected utility of the "do not sample" branch (700). The utility function, determined by graphing the points given above, is that of a risk avoider. (The curve is concave from below.) The indifference relationship given also indicates a risk-avoider. ◼

| section 17.8 | # Decision Analysis For Continuous Functions[†] |

Thus far, only discrete functions have been used in our decision-theory analysis. That is, the number of actions have been discrete sets, as have the states of nature, the prior probabilities, the sampling distribution, the likelihoods, and the posterior probabilities. Although most real-world problems involve only discrete functions, the number of alternatives in many cases is so large that a continuous function is much easier to handle. We will see in this section that decision analysis theory for continuous functions is a direct extension of the theory for discrete functions.

---

† This section may be omitted without loss of continuity.

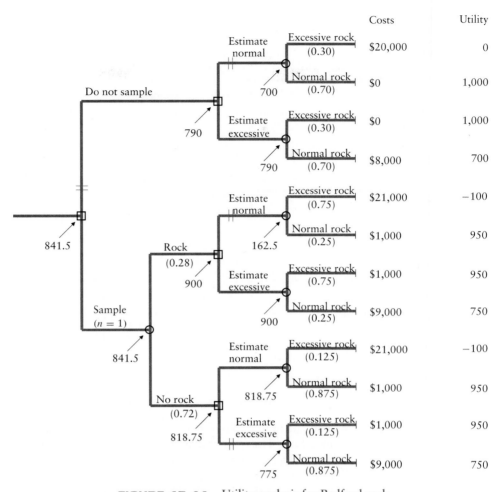

FIGURE 17.11   Utility analysis for Bedford rock

☐ **EXAMPLE 17.7**   A decision-maker is faced with a situation in which one of the variables is too large to handle in discrete form. Perhaps the president of a company is trying to estimate what sales might be for a new product under a number of different assumptions about its price. Or a book club might want to decide between acquiring the rights to a new book or paying royalties, by estimating the percent of its members who will purchase this book. In both of these examples it may be possible to collect sample information, and the result of the sample could be any one of a large number of outcomes. The tree diagram in Figure 17.12 represents what the book club's decision problem might look like. The fans in this diagram represent variables involving a large number of outcomes or alternatives.

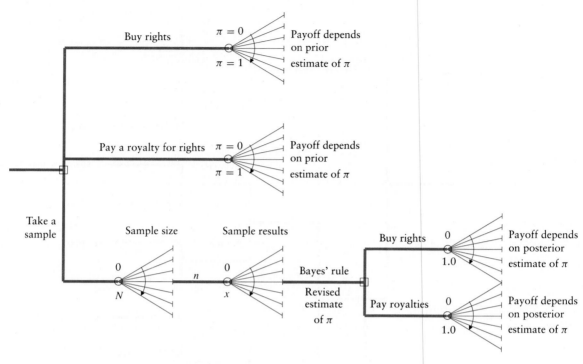

FIGURE 17.12   Tree diagram for book club

The bottom branch in Figure 17.12 represents a random sample of the book club's members. This potential action for the book club could be used if the club decided to conduct a sample to try to estimate how many members intend to purchase the book. Clearly, the sample size (n) must be less than or equal to the number of members in the club (N). The proportion of members in this sample who indicate that they would buy the book provides the basis for revising (via Bayes' rule) the decision-maker's prior probability distribution into a posterior distribution. The posterior distribution is then used (in the same manner as the prior) to decide whether to buy the rights or to pay royalties. Before taking the sample, the decision-maker will want to decide whether or not any sample size leads to a positive ENGS and, if more than one sample size does, which will be the optimal sample size. This is exactly the same process we carried out with the Perkins Plastics example. We will not attempt to exhaust all possible aspects of the analysis of our book-club example because doing so involves several concepts beyond the scope of this chapter. However, Exercise 17.30 at the end of this chapter encourages the reader to carry out several additional steps in the analysis of the book-club example.

To begin an analysis of a decision situation such as that shown in Figure 17.12, we must assume that the decision-maker can express the prior probabilities in the form of a probability density function. Although theoretically this density function can assume any shape, we will see that the process of revising these probabilities in light of the sample information becomes quite complicated unless the prior distribution either is normally distributed or follows the beta distribution.[4]

---

[4] The beta distribution is a continuous function that is closely related to the binomial distribution.

Limiting the prior distribution in this way is not as restrictive as it may seem, for these two distributions have been shown to be appropriate in many different situations. It is interesting to note that if a decision-maker's prior distribution is relatively flat, this means that the decision-maker has little or no knowledge about the relative likelihood of the various states of nature. Such a prior distribution is called a *diffuse* prior.

Let us illustrate the assessment of a prior probability by assuming that the decision-maker in our book-club example has indicated that a normal prior is appropriate. Let us assume also that the decision-maker is indifferent, at 50–50 odds, when betting that the proportion (π) of book club members who will order the book is either (1) less than or equal to 0.129 or (2) more than 0.129. In addition, this person says that there is only one chance in 20 that the proportion of sales will be larger than 0.162. These values are consistent with a prior normal distribution, having a mean of 0.129 and a standard deviation of $\sigma = 0.02$. This standard deviation was calculated by noting that the estimate of one chance in 20 corresponds to the ninety-fifth percentile, for which the standardized normal equivalent is $F(z) = 1.645$. See Table III. Solving

$$z = \frac{x - \mu}{\sigma},$$

where $x = 0.162$, $\mu = 0.129$, and $z = 1.645$, we obtain the value $\sigma = 0.02$. The decision-maker's prior distribution is thus normally distributed, with a mean of 0.129 and $\sigma = 0.02$, or $N(0.129, 0.02^2)$.

Our next step in analyzing the book-club tree diagram in Figure 17.12 is to incorporate payoffs into the analysis. For this example, suppose that buying the rights to the book costs $12,000; if royalties are paid, the company must pay $1,000 for each 1% of the membership that orders the book. The revenue to the company is $120,000\pi$ if they buy the rights and $20,000\pi$ if they pay royalties. Note that the difference in these revenues is the $1,000 royalty cost per 1%. Fixed costs to the company are $2,000 in either case. These costs and revenues, including the fixed cost of $2,000, are reflected in the following two payoff functions:

Action a_1:	Buy rights	$-\$14,000 + \$120,000\pi$
Action a_2:	Pay royalties	$-\$2,000 + \$20,000\pi$

By setting these two functions equal and solving for π, we can determine the breakeven value of π — that value at which the expected cost of the two actions is exactly equal. In our example, the breakeven value is $\pi_b = 0.12$, which means that if less than 12% order the book, action a_2 is better, while if more than 12% order, action a_1 is better. At 12%, the actions a_1 and a_2 have the same expected cost. Since our payoff functions are both linear, it is not difficult to prove that, in deciding between these two actions, we need only compare the mean of the decision-maker's prior distribution with π_b. Since the prior mean (0.129) exceeds $\pi_b(= 0.120)$, the optimal action is to buy the rights. The expected profit for this action is $-\$14,000 + 120,000(0.129) = \$1,480$. We might note at this point that our decision tree might have had a branch that said, "Do not print book." If this branch had an EMV = 0, the action "buy rights" is clearly better for the estimated $\pi = 0.129$, since its EMV = $1,480$. Had the estimated π been 0.10 or less, both actions a_1 and a_2 would have negative EMV's; hence, "Do not print" would have been better.

Let us assume that the decision-maker in Figure 17.12 has decided on the upper branch (buy the rights) and is now faced with the problem of deciding how many books to print on the initial production run, a decision that must be made before the orders begin coming in. Ideally, the company would like to print exactly enough books to cover the orders they will receive. If they overestimate or underestimate the number of orders, they will incur additional costs, as shown in Figure 17.13. The optimal value to estimate in this situation depends on the value of c_u (cost of underestimation) and c_o (cost of overestimation), as well as on the decision-maker's probability distribution of the anticipated orders. *The optimal estimate for minimizing expected costs is that value of the decision variable which corresponds to the following cumulative probability.*[5]

Value of cumulative probability that minimizes expected costs:

$$\frac{c_u}{c_u + c_o} \qquad\qquad (17.5)$$

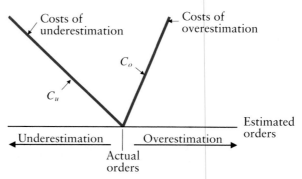

FIGURE 17.13 Cost of overestimating or underestimating orders

For our example, we will suppose that $c_u = \$0.50$ and $c_o = \$0.75$. Thus, the optimal value of the decision-maker's prior distribution of orders calculated from Formula 17.5 is as follows:

$$\frac{0.50}{0.50 + 0.75} = 0.40$$

This means that if we denote the optimal number of books to print as x^*, then we need to solve the expression $P(x \le x^*) = 0.40$ for x^*. To do this, first recall that the decision-maker's prior distribution was determined to be normally distributed, with $\mu = 0.129$ and $\mu = 0.02$. This information can be used to standardize $P(x \le x^*) = 0.40$ as follows:

$$P(x \le x^*) = P\left(\frac{x - \mu}{\sigma} \le \frac{x^* - 0.129}{0.02}\right) = 0.40$$

or

$$P\left(z \le \frac{x^* - 0.129}{0.02}\right) = 0.40$$

---

[5] Proof of this fact can be found in most operations research texts.

From Table III in Appendix C we know that

$$P(x \le -0.25) = 0.40$$

which means (from these two equations) that

$$-0.25 = \frac{x^* - 0.129}{0.02}$$
$$x^* = 0.129 + 0.02(-0.25) = 0.124$$

The optimal number for the decision-maker to print is thus 12.4% of the club's membership. ∎

<table>
<tr><td>**section 17.9**</td></tr>
</table>

Bayes' Rule for Continuous Functions†

If a decision-maker wants to gather additional (sample) information, then Bayes' rule is again the means for transforming prior probabilities into posterior probabilities. Bayes' rule for continuous functions follows the same form as for discrete functions, except that the continuous case involves integrating a continuous density function rather than summing a discrete probability function. Refer to Formula 17.1 in Section 17.4.[6] The random variables in the continuous case can, at least theoretically, be any proper probability distribution. However, integration of the denominator of Bayes' rule is quite difficult unless the likelihood function is a beta distribution and sampling is from a binomial distribution, or the likelihood function is normally distributed and sampling is from a normal distribution. When the prior is a beta distribution and the sampling is from a binomial distribution, the posterior distribution will also be a beta distribution. Since the beta distribution has not been discussed in this book, we will not attempt to illustrate how priors can be revised in this fashion, although the process is not a difficult one. Rather, we turn to a more thorough analysis of the case in which $f(\theta)$ and the sampling distribution are both normal.

> When the prior is normal and sampling is from a normal distribution, then the posterior distribution will also be normal.

Furthermore, if the prior distribution has a mean μ_0 and a variance σ_0^2, and a sample of size n with sample mean x is taken from a normal distribution with variance σ^2, then the posterior distribution will have a mean μ_1 and a variance σ_1^2, as follows:

---

† This section may be omitted without loss of continuity.

[6] If we let $f(\theta)$ be the prior density function, $f(x \mid \theta)$ represent the likelihood function, x be the sample result, and $f(\theta \mid x)$ be the posterior density function, then Bayes' rule is:

Bayes' rule for continuous random variables: $f(\theta \mid x) = \dfrac{f(\theta) f(x \mid \theta)}{\int f(\theta) f(x \mid \theta) \, d\theta}$

For normal distributions:

$$\text{Posterior mean:} \qquad \mu_1 = \frac{\mu_0 \sigma^2 + n \bar{x} \sigma_0^2}{\sigma^2 + n \sigma_0^2} \qquad\qquad (17.6)$$

$$\text{Posterior variance:} \quad \sigma_1^2 = \frac{\sigma^2 \sigma_0^2}{\sigma^2 + n \sigma_0^2} \qquad\qquad (17.7)$$

These formulas merely represent the process of taking a weighted average of the prior and sample evidence. The posterior mean μ_1 will always lie between the prior mean μ_0 and the sample mean $\bar{x}$. In addition, the posterior variance will always be smaller than the prior variance.[7] The more **diffuse** (flat) the decision-maker's **prior** distribution, the more the posterior distribution will depend on the sample data.

☐ **EXAMPLE 17.8**   Assume that a company is attempting to forecast sales of their product in a new area. The decision-maker's prior distribution for sales is normally distributed with a mean of $\mu_0 = 2,000$ and a variance of $\sigma_0^2 = 200^2$. We will assume that the decision-maker has taken a random sample from ten other (comparable) areas and found $\bar{x} = 1,800$. We will assume also that these ten samples came from a normally distributed population with variance $\sigma^2 = 400^2$. The posterior values are computed from Equations 17.6 and 17.7 to be:

Posterior mean:
$$\mu_1 = \frac{\mu_0 \sigma^2 + n \bar{x} \sigma_0^2}{\sigma^2 + n \sigma_0^2}$$
$$= \frac{2,000(400)^2 + 10(1,800)(200)^2}{(400)^2 + 10(200)^2} = 1857$$

Posterior variance:
$$\sigma_1^2 = \frac{\sigma^2 \sigma_0^2}{\sigma^2 + n \sigma_0^2}$$
$$= \frac{(400)^2 (200)^2}{(400)^2 + 10(200)^2} = 106.92^2$$

Note that the posterior mean (1857) lies between the prior mean (2,000) and the sample mean (1,800). The posterior variance $(106.9)^2$ is smaller than the prior variance (200^2) and smaller than the variance of the population from which the sample was drawn (400^2).

As in our book-club example, the decision-maker can now use the mean of the probability distribution (in this case the posterior rather than the prior distribution) to calculate the EMVs and to determine the breakeven value of the mean (μ_b) at which the expected costs are equal. The decision about which of two or more actions minimizes expected costs is similar to that of our prior analysis: If $\mu_1 > \mu_b$ one action is taken, while if $\mu_1 < \mu_b$ the other action is taken. When $\mu_1 = \mu_b$, the actions result in the same EMV.   ∎

---

[7] This result holds only for the normal process being discussed and not for revising a beta–prior by sampling from a binomial distribution.

Loss Functions

In many statistical decision theory problems, **loss functions** are somewhat more convenient for determining optimal actions than are the profit functions we have used thus far. In this context, a loss is generally defined to be an opportunity loss. Thus, we must specify, for each possible state of nature, a function that describes the loss a decision-maker incurs by not making the optimal decision. A loss function can have any form, although linear functions are often used because they are fairly easy to manipulate and because they are appropriate in many different situations. For example, we will see below that the linear payoff functions for our book-club example translate into the two linear loss functions graphed in Figure 17.14.

Let us determine the decision-maker's opportunity loss from Figure 17.12. If the true π is less than 0.12 and decision a_2 (pay royalties) is made, then there is no loss, since this is the correct decision. However, if $\pi > 0.12$, then decision a_2 is incorrect and the decision-maker incurs a loss that depends on the value of π. For instance, suppose that $\pi = 0.13$ as shown in Figure 17.14. The opportunity loss is the difference between the EMV of the optimal decision [EMV(a_1) = $1,600] and the EMV of the incorrect decision [EMV(a_2) = $600], which is $1,600 − $600 = $1,000. With a little knowledge of algebra the reader should be able to verify that the opportunity loss when $\pi = 0.11$ is also $1000, only this time a_2 is the better decision. Thus, in Figure 17.14, opportunity loss is given by the difference between the higher and the lower line (the shaded areas). Figure 17.15 presents the opportunity loss for this problem.

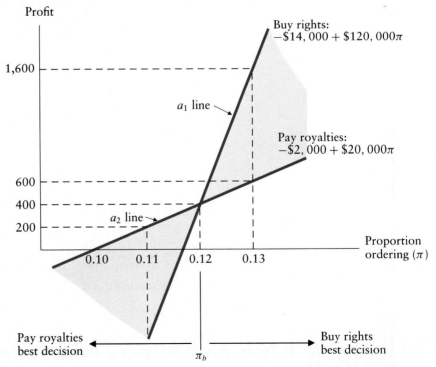

FIGURE 17.14   Payoff functions for book club

We will see shortly how the linear loss function can be especially helpful in decision-theory analysis. A quadratic loss function, which is another type of loss function used in decision-making problems, is diagrammed in Figure 17.16. There, the decision-maker's loss is given by the *square* of the difference between the estimated value (a) and the true value (θ). If we let $l(a, \theta)$ represent the loss incurred when $a \neq \theta$, then the quadratic loss function is $l(a, \theta) = (a - \theta)^2$. A quadratic loss function is popular not only because squared errors are appropriate in some circumstances, but because it is mathematically convenient — it can be differentiated easily using calculus.

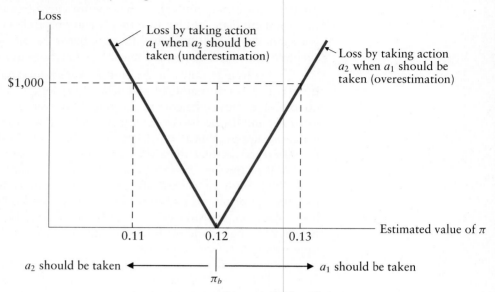

FIGURE 17.15   Opportunity loss function

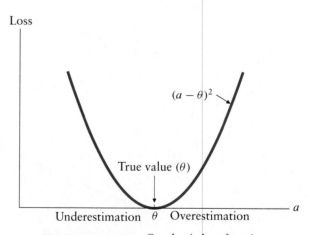

FIGURE 17.16   Quadratic loss function

<table>
<tr><td>section 17.10</td></tr>
</table>

Bayesian Analysis: Advantages and Disadvantages

Most procedures normally associated with classical statistics, such as point and interval estimation, hypothesis testing, and regression analysis also can be accomplished from a Bayesian point of view, although the two approaches differ considerably. The Bayesian approach is designed to result in optimal decisions for a given prior distribution and loss function. The major criticism of the Bayesian approach is that it requires a number of subjective evaluations, the validity of which is questioned by the classical statistician. For instance, how reasonable is it to ask a decision-maker to form a prior distribution for a set of events of which one has little or no prior knowledge? And even if one has prior knowledge, is it really valid to ascertain the prior probability distribution by asking questions about alternatives (gambles) that would never have to be faced in real life? Also, how is it possible for a decision-maker to formulate a loss function for events when he or she may have no idea of the consequences of a wrong decision or may not be able to express the losses in monetary terms? Consider the surgeon trying to decide on an operation that may cost the patient's life.

The Bayesian answer to these questions is that often a decision-maker is making a number of similar evaluations in classical statistics and may not even be aware of it. For example, in hypothesis-testing, the classical statistician is assuming, in effect, a flat (diffuse) prior and basing all decisions on the sample evidence and a *quite subjective* value of the risk of making a Type I error (α).

Despite the obvious advantages of statistical decision theory as an aid to the decision-making process, the number of businesses that have even experimented with its use remains quite small. Many companies simply have not been exposed to this new technique, while others have tried it and found it too time-consuming and/or costly to add to their decision-making process. On the other hand, a number of major companies, such as DuPont, Pillsbury, General Electric, and the Ford Motor Company, have tried decision-theory analysis, and most often the users are pleased with it. Just how great an impact this approach will have on decision-making in the future is a question that cannot be answered at this time.

PROBLEMS

17.19 Suppose that $U(\$500) = 100$ and $U(\$100) = 50$. If a decision-maker expresses indifference between a gamble when $500 occurs with probability $\frac{1}{2}$, $100 occurs with probability $\frac{1}{2}$, and $200 occurs for certain, find $U(\$200)$. Is this person risk-taking or risk-avoiding?

17.20 Suppose that a decision-maker has expressed an indifference between receiving B for sure and a 50–50 gamble between A and C for each of the following values.

TABLE 17.21 A Payoff Table

A	C	B
$ 10	−$5	$0
10	−10	−5
20	−5	10
50	−10	10
100	0	20

a) Let $U(\$10) = 10$ and $U(0) = 0$ and then find the utility for −$5, −$10, $20, $50, and $100.

b) Sketch this person's utility function. Can you classify this person as a risk-taker, risk-neutral, or a risk-avoider?

17.21 Sketch a utility function for a person who is, simultaneously, a risk-avoider for dollar values between $2,000 and $1,000 at $\pi = \frac{1}{2}$ and a risk-taker between $2,000 and $0 at $\pi = \frac{1}{2}$.

17.22 A business executive has asked your advice on the following decision. The executive can either take $50 for certain or participate in a venture that gives an equal chance of winning $100, $40, or $0.

a) What decision should you recommend (to participate in the venture or not) if the executive wants to maximize expected earnings?

b) What decision should you recommend if the executive wants to maximize expected utility and is indifferent between two cases of equal chances of A and C, or B for certain, as follows:

TABLE 17.22 A Payoff Table

	A	B	C
Case 1	100	40	0
Case 2	100	50	40

c) Sketch the utility function. Does the executive appear to be a risk-taker, risk-neutral, or a risk-avoider?

17.23 Attempt to construct your own utility function for money for dollar values between −$500 and +$1, 500.

17.24 A decision-maker considers the utility function $U(m) = m^{1/2}$, where m = money and $0 \leq m \leq 1,600$.

a) Sketch this function.

b) Does this function represent a risk-taker, risk-neutral, or a risk-avoider?

c) Use this utility function to find the action that maximizes expected utility in Exercise 17.10. Can you guess, before calculating EU, which action will be optimal? Explain.

d) Will your answer to part (c) change if the utility function $U(m) = 100 + 10m^{1/2}$? Explain.

17.25 Redo the Perkins Plastics problem from this chapter for $n = 2$. Use Figure 17.7, letting $U(-\$1,000) = -100$, $U(-\$2,000) = -300$, and $U(-\$4,000) = -1,000$, and find the action that maximizes expected utility.

17.26 Rework Problem 17.4, letting $U(m) = m^{1/2}$, where m = money, and find the optimal action by maximizing expected utility.

17.27 Suppose that the decision-maker for the problem represented by Figure 17.12 is attempting to assess the prior probability distribution of π_0, the proportion of customers who will buy the book. This person decides that the chances are only one out of four that π will be less than 0.10 and the chances are four out of five that π

will not be greater than 0.14. Assuming that the prior is normal, find its mean and variance.

17.28 A food manufacturer is trying to determine the mean weight of its boxes of breakfast cereal. The company considers the weight to be normally distributed with a standard deviation of 0.4, and its prior distribution is normal with a mean of 16.2 ounces and a standard deviation of 0.2. Find the posterior distribution if $n = 100$ and $\bar{x} = 16.0$.

17.29 The owner of a local fabric store is trying to prepare an order for a certain type of very expensive material, based on the mean number of yards sold during each six-month period. The owner can sell this material on consignment (action a_1) or purchase it outright (action a_2). The payoffs for these two actions are (x = number of yards sold) as follows:

$$\text{Action } a_1: \quad -\$100 + 5x$$
$$\text{Action } a_2: \quad -\$1290 + 15x$$

a) What is the breakeven value of μ? What action would you select if $\mu_0 = 120$ yards and $\sigma_0^2 = 25$ yards, and the prior is normally distributed?

b) The owner feels that the cost of overestimating the size of the order is four times as much as the cost of underestimating. What size order should be placed?

c) Assume that the owner takes a sample of the sales of four comparable fabric stores and finds that sales are 120, 112, 122, and 118 yards. If it is assumed that the sample came from a normal distribution with a variance of 20, what is the posterior distribution?

d) What action should be taken on the basis of the posterior distribution? What size order should be placed on the basis of the posterior distribution, assuming the same costs as in part (b)?

e) Construct two graphs, one showing the loss function if a_1 is taken incorrectly [$l(a_1, \mu)$] and the other showing the loss function if a_2 is taken incorrectly [$l(a_2, \mu)$].

CHAPTER SUMMARY

KEY TERMS AND EXPRESSIONS

Actions: The choices available to the decision-maker.

State of Nature: The possible condition or state that influences the choice of an action in a decision situation.

Payoff Table: A table that gives all the possible consequences or payoffs to the decision-maker that would

result from each combination of action and state of nature.

Dominated Action: An action with payoffs no better than the payoffs of some other action, no matter what state of nature occurs.

EMV Criterion: Maximization of expected monetary value.

Tree Diagram: A design for systematically presenting the important features of the decision problem.

Prior Probabilities: Probabilities determined before any sample information is seen.

Posterior Probabilities: Revised probabilities determined in light of sample information.

Bayes' Rule: A formula for transforming a prior probability into a posterior probability:

$$\text{Posterior} = \frac{(\text{prior})(\text{likelihood})}{\Sigma(\text{priors})(\text{likelihoods})}$$

Likelihood: The probability that a specified sample result will take place, given that a particular state of nature is true.

Backwards Induction: Process of determining expected values on a decision tree, proceeding from right to left.

EVSI: Expected value of sample information.

ENGS: Expected net gain from sampling.

Utility Function: A description of the relationship between various dollar amounts and the index used to measure the value to the decision-maker of these dollars.

Interval Scale: A measurement or index in which the origin and units are not predetermined, but the size of the interval must be constant.

Standard Lottery: A gamble between \$A with probability π and \$C with probability $1 - \pi$, in which \$A > \$C.

Certainty Equivalent: The amount of money (\$B) that leaves the decision-maker indifferent to a given standard lottery.

Utile: A unit used to measure utility.

Risk-Avoider: A decision-maker who, for certain gambles, will prefer a dollar amount received with certainty over a gamble, even though the latter has a higher EMV.

Risk-Taker: A decision-maker who, in certain circumstances, prefers a gamble with EMV lower than the alternative amount that could be received with certainty.

Risk-Neutral: A decision-maker who neither takes nor avoids risks — in other words, a person who maximizes EMV, since the utility function is a straight line.

Diffuse Prior: A relatively flat prior distribution.

Loss Function: A function $l(a, \theta)$ specifying the loss under action a when the actual state of nature is θ.

EXERCISES

17.30 Return to the book-club example of Section 17.8. Assume that the decision-maker has taken a sample of size $n = 10$ and four of these ten book-club members indicate that they would buy the book.

a) Use *discrete* decision analysis to revise the decision-maker's prior. To do this, you should graph the cumulative prior, then divide the horizontal axis into ten intervals so that each interval contains 10% of the area. Let the midpoints of the ten intervals be the π values used to calculate the likelihoods where each π value has a prior of 0.10. The sample result of four of ten and Table I in Appendix C will give you ten posterior values. Plot these posterior values and fit (sketch) the normal distribution they seem to approximate.

b) Find a reference on the use of the beta distribution as a prior and binomial sampling: then try to rework the entire problem using what you have learned.

17.31 A procedure for calculating EVSI, equivalent to that presented in Section 17.5, is to focus *only* on those sample results that lead to a decision *different* from the optimal decision without sample information. The expected value of the sample information depends only on how much additional profit (on the average) is earned because of this change in decision. Thus, one first must calculate how much more expected profit the new decision yields over the old (using the posterior probabilities), and then multiply this value by the (marginal) probability of observing the sample result(s) that lead to a new decision.

a) Note that for the data given in Figure 17.5, the previously optimal decision (shown in Figure 17.1 to be to *send the batch to assembly*) is changed to *rework* only after observance of a defective valve. Since the expected value of sending the batch to assembly after such a sample is $-\$2,895$ and reworking costs are only \$2,000, the decision to rework saves \$895. Verify that this savings, multiplied times the probability of observing one defective valve, equals the EVSI for $n = 1$.

b) Verify by the above method that the EVSI for Figure 17.6 is \$251.

17.32 Read enough of a reference on Bayesian analysis so that you can describe what is meant by a "natural conjugate prior."

17.33 As an exercise in assessing subjective probabilities, try to construct a probability distribution representing your estimate of the number of cheques processed each day by one of the major banks in Boston (this bank has six branch offices in the Boston area). For example, to find the mean of your distribution, you might ask yourself what value of x would make you indifferent between the following two bets at 50–50 odds:
Bet I: number of cheques $\geq x$ and
Bet II: number of cheques $< x$.
It might be interesting also to assess your 0.01 and 0.99 fractiles. The 0.01 fractile is the value of x that you think makes Bet I 99 times as likely to be correct as Bet II; for the 0.99 fractile, Bet II must be 99 times as likely as Bet I. Check your answers against the true value given in the back of the book to see how good your estimate is. Does the true value fall between your 0.01 and 0.99 fractiles?

◆ **17.34** Corporations may hire accounting firms to audit their corporate records in order to discover two kinds of problems: fraud by company employees and fairness of the financial statements. Upon completing any audit, the firm will either indicate that the financial statements are fair, or fail to indicate fairness and report any existing irregularities. Thus, the accounting firms are prone to making two types of errors. On the one hand, the auditor may indicate fairness of the financial statements when in fact there are irregularities. On the other hand, the auditor may refuse to indicate the financial statements are fair when in fact everything is in order. Both kinds of errors have financial implications for the accounting firms.

　　Suppose you have audited the financial records of a company and are faced with the problem of deciding whether or not the financial statements are fair. You have estimated the following costs for making the two kinds of errors mentioned above. If you report incorrectly that the financial statements are not fair when they are, then the estimated cost of this error is $20,000. If, on the other hand, you indicate the fairness of the financial statements when problems exist, your expected losses are estimated at $100,000.

a) Formulate the payoff table for this problem, stating clearly the actions and the states of nature.

b) Assume that the probability that the financial statements are fair is 0.9. What action should be taken?

c) What should the auditor be willing to pay for perfect information about the records?

◆ **17.35** Williams, marketing manager of Nano Computers, is faced with yet another problem. The manager must decide which one of three models of the micro (NC1, NC2, or NC3) the company should market. All of these models would be assembled in the People's Republic of China. The cost of assembling each model consists of a fixed cost and a variable cost per unit. The fixed cost, of course, does not depend on the number of units assembled. The cost for the three models are given below:

TABLE 17.23

Model	Fixed Cost	Variable cost/unit
NC1	$200,000	$400
NC2	$160,000	$430
NC3	$120,000	$455

The company has set four possible sales levels of 500 units, 1,000 units, 1,500 units, and 2,000 units based on demand forecasts.

a) Construct a payoff table stating clearly the actions and the states of nature.

b) Suppose the following probability distribution is given for the sales levels:

TABLE 17.24

Sales	Probability
500	0.40
1,000	0.30
1,500	0.20
2,000	1.10

Use EMV to determine the best possible solution.

c) Determine the value of perfect information, EVPI.

◆ **17.36** A company has $1 million dollars to invest in one of three possible investments for a period of three months. The three investments under consideration are Certificates of Deposit (X), Money Market Funds (Y), and Treasury Bills (Z). The expected return on these three investments depends upon the prevailing economic conditions labeled S_1 (expansionary), S_2 (stable), and S_3 (recessionary). The payoff table:

TABLE 17.25

		States of Nature		
		S_1	S_2	S_3
Actions	X	$40,000	$30,000	$20,000
	Y	$20,000	$30,000	$40,000
	Z	$30,000	$35,000	$15,000

The company associates the following likelihoods (probabilities) for the three states of nature.

$$P(S_1) = 0.30 \quad P(S_2) = 0.45 \quad P(S_3) = 0.25$$

a) Draw a decision tree for the above problem.

b) Obtain the optimal action based on the expected monetary value.

c) Determine the expected value of perfect information.

◆ **17.37** Helen Kopter, owner of High Tail Airfreight Company, is considering expanding her fleet size. She can expand by buying 5 more aircraft of type I or type II. Her payoff depends on the business activity in the coming months. She has classified three states of nature: Low Growth (S_1), Normal Growth (S_2), and Turbo Growth (S_3). The pay-off table below provides expected payoffs (in thousands of dollars) under different action-growth combinations.

TABLE 17.26

Actions	States of Nature		
	S_1	S_2	S_3
No change (A_1)	1,000	1,100	1,300
Expand type I (A_2)	−500	1,000	2,000
Expand type II (A_3)	−1,500	−500	4,000

The probability assessment of the three states of nature are given as:

$$P(S_1) = 0.25, \quad P(S_2) = 0.35, \quad P(S_3) = 0.40$$

a) What is the optimal strategy based on the expected monetary value criterion?

b) How much should she be willing to pay, prior to making a decision, to learn with complete reliability the true state of nature?

c) Suppose a market research firm has agreed to conduct a study to project the future growth pattern. From past records the firm's performance is stated in the following conditional probability table.

TABLE 17.27

	Firm's Projection		
	Low (L)	Normal (N)	Turbo (T)
True State			
Low (S_1)	0.80	0.15	0.05
Normal State (S_2)	0.10	0.80	0.10
Turbo State (S_3)	0.05	0.15	0.80

Thus, for example, if the true state of nature was going to be "Turbo", the firm would predict it accurately 80% of the time; 5% of the time it would predict "Low" and 15% of the time it would predict "Normal". Equivalently, $P(T \mid S_3) = 0.80$, $P(N \mid S_3) = 0.15$, and $P(L \mid S_3) = 0.05$.
    What would Ms. Kopter's optimal strategy be if the firm projects "Turbo" growth?

USING THE COMPUTER

17.38 Return to Problem 17.14.

a) Prepare a flowchart designed to find the optimal sample size for Techno. This flow chart should have a subroutine for generating binomial probabilities, and it should print out the action Techno should take (major or minor repairs) for each possible sample result using the optimal sample size.

b) Write and run the computer program for part (a).

17.39 For the Perkins Plastics problem in Table 17.9.

a) Draw the decision tree and find EVSI and ENGS for $n = 3$.

b) Prepare a flowchart for a computer program designed to solve the Perkins Plastics problem for $0 \le n \le 30$. See Table 17.10.

c) Write and run the computer program for part (b).

17.40 The values of ENGS in Table 17.10 were calculated on a computer by calculating first the value for $n = 1$, then the value for $n = 2$, and so forth, up to $n = 26$.

a) In writing a computer program to find the optimal sample size, why is it not possible to program the computer to stop as soon as ENGS begins to decrease? (*Hint:* See Table 17.10 for $n = 3$, $n = 4$.)

b) In Table 17.10, why does EVSI increase only a small amount for some values of n (for example, $n = 3$ to $n = 4$), while it increases a large amount for other values (for example, $n = 4$ to $n = 5$)?

c) Design a decision rule for stopping a computer program that is calculating ENGS for successive sample sizes (keeping in mind your answer to part (a)).

CASE PROBLEM

17.41 The Delaney-Bryce Corporation is a major manufacturer of specialized soap and detergent products. It currently controls 31 subsidiary companies that manufacture disinfecting detergent power primarily for use by hospitals, linen suppliers, diaper services, and other large institutional laundry facilities. Each of the 31 subsidiaries sells in its own region, and together they serve a large portion of the United States.

Delaney-Bryce established the Ohio Valley Detergent Corporation in Cincinnati last year. Since that time, Ohio Valley has captured a larger market share in each of the three quarters its plant has been in operation. The directors expect that the company will have reached maturity sometime in the next three years and that the rapid growth in sales it has been experiencing during the present start-up period will begin to level off. The warehouse that Ohio Valley has been using for the past year is rapidly becoming inadequate to serve the company's growing sales volume. The directors, knowing that such rapid changes in requirements would occur in the company's first stages, leased the present warehouse facilities for only 18 months. This lease will expire soon, and the director and officers now wish to negotiate another lease. Now that Ohio Valley is approaching maturity, they wish to acquire warehouse space for a period of three years. Leasing facilities on this long-term basis will save the company money both as a result of lower monthly rent payments and by avoiding the need to regularly renegotiate lease terms.

There are only two warehouse facilities in Cincinatti that the directors of Ohio Valley feel may be adequate. Both contain the necessary equipment and other features that the company's operation requires. The location of each warehouse is also suitable to the directors. But the sizes of the facilities differ, one being 16,500 square feet, the other being 21,000 square feet. The decision must be made, then, as to which of these two different-sized warehouses Ohio Valley Detergent Corporation should lease in order to minimize its expected cost. But before such a decision can be made, it will be necessary for the directors to have some reliable prediction of the level of sales the company can expect to maintain over the period covered by the lease. Kenneth Rein, a member of the board, has predicted that over the next three years Ohio Valley will sell about 10.83 million pounds of detergent annually and that this prediction of sales comes from a normal distribution with a standard deviation of 1.18 million pounds. The 16,500-square-foot warehouse will hold a maximum of 1,835,000 pounds of detergent. Likewise, the 21,000-square-foot warehouse can be used to store at most 2,300,000 pounds.

The company plans to keep on hand, at any one time, a two-month supply of its product. This means that if Ohio Valley should sell exactly the predicted amount of 10.83 million pounds, it would want always to keep in storage $(1/6)(10.83) = 1,805,000$ pounds of detergent. Note that, for this prediction for two months of sales, the standard deviation is 196,667 pounds, which is one-sixth of the error associated with the prediction of full-year sales (that is, $1/6 \times 1,180,000$).

In addition to this information on warehouse utilization, Rein has given you the following guidelines concerning the costs involved in leasing each of the two available warehouses. As Ohio Valley is most concerned with avoiding unnecessary expenses, Rein tells you to consider that, for this decision process, the cost will be zero if the company leases the smaller warehouse and, for the duration of the lease, requires no more than the space that the smaller warehouse can provide. The cost is also assumed to be zero if Ohio Valley leases the larger facility and requires more space over the years than the smaller warehouse could have provided. If the company leases the smaller warehouse and sales are at a higher level than can be supplied by this facility, high-cost short-term facilities will have to be leased to supplement the main warehouse. Rein estimates that this added cost, combined with costs of reduced efficiency due to the resulting lack of centralization, will be approximately $500,000 over the entire period of the lease. If the company leases the larger warehouse and sales over the lease years prove to be low enough that it actually needs only the smaller warehouse, the extra expense will be $325,000 over the life of the lease (lease terms prohibit subleasing of unused space).

Ohio Valley has recently learned that they can purchase a sample survey for $5,000. This survey's outcomes will be either favourable (meaning large sales) or unfavourable (meaning moderate sales). Judging from past records, Ohio Valley estimates that if sales less than or equal to 1,835,000 is the true state of nature, the survey will result in the unfavourable outcome about 77% of the time. Conversely, if sales greater than 1,835,000 is the true state of nature, the survey will result in the "favourable" outcome about 66% of the time. On the basis of this information, draw the decision tree, and calculate EVSI and ENGS.

CHAPTER 18

Nonparametric Statistics

Introduction

The statistical tests considered in Chapters 10–16 have specified certain properties of the parent population that must hold or be assumed true before these tests can be used. Although these tests are quite *robust*, in the sense that the tests are still useful when the assumptions about the parent population are not exactly fulfilled, there are still many circumstances when the researcher cannot or does not want to make such assumptions. The statistical methods appropriate in these circumstances are called *nonparametric tests* because they do not depend on any assumptions about the parameters of the distribution of the parent population.

Measurement

Nonparametric tests do not require assumptions about the parameters of the parent population, and often, they do not require a **level of measurement** as strong as that necessary for parametric tests. By measurement we mean the process of assigning numbers to objects or observations; the level of measurement depends on how the numbers are assigned. The measurement of quantifiable information usually takes place on one of four levels, depending on the strength of the underlying scaling procedure used. The four major levels of measurement are represented by nominal, ordinal, interval, and ratio scales.

The weakest type of measurement is given by a **nominal scale**, which merely sorts objects into categories according to some distinguishing characteristic and gives each category a name (hence nominal). Since classification on a nominal scale does not depend on the label or symbol assigned to each category, these symbols may be interchanged without affecting the information given by the scale. Classifying automobiles by brands constitutes a nominal scale, as does distinguishing Liberal from Conservative voters or smokers from non-smokers. In most nominal measurement, one is concerned with the number (or frequency) of observations falling in each of the categories.

An **ordinal scale** offers the next highest level of measurement and expresses the relationship of order. Objects in an ordinal scale are characterized by relative rank so that a typical relationship is expressed in terms such as higher, greater, or preferred to. Only the relations *greater than*, *less than*, or *equal to* have meaning in ordinal measurement. When a football team is ranked nationally, for example, the measurement used is an ordinal scale if it is impossible (or meaningless) to say how *much* better or worse this team is compared to others. Most subjective attributes of objects or persons (such as flavour or beauty) are difficult, if not impossible, to consider on a scale higher than the ordinal. Distinguishing armed-service personnel by rank (captain, major) is another example of ordinal measurement.

A third type of scale is given by **interval measurement**, sometimes called *cardinal measurement*. Measurement on an interval scale is based on the assumption of exact knowledge of the quantitative difference between objects being scaled. That is, it must be possible to assign a number to each object in such a manner that the difference between them is reflected by the difference in the numbers. Any size unit may be used in this type of measurement, and the choice of a zero-point (origin) for the data is arbitrary as long as a one-unit change on the scale always reflects the same change in the object being scaled. Temperature measured on either a centigrade or a Fahrenheit scale represents interval measurement, since the choice of origin and unit for these scales is arbitrary. Temperature measured on an absolute scale, however, does not represent interval measurement, since this scale has a natural origin, which is the zero-point, the point at which all molecular motion ceases. Most I.Q. measures also represent interval scales, since there is no natural origin (zero intelligence) and the choice of a unit can be made arbitrarily. The name, interval measurement, is used because this type of scale is concerned primarily with the distance *between* values, that is, the *interval* between them.

The strongest type of measurement is represented by **ratio scales** — scales that have all the properties of an interval scale *plus* a natural origin; only the *unit of measurement* is arbitrary. Fixing the origin (the zero-point) permits comparisons not only of the intervals between objects, but of the absolute value of the number assigned to these objects. Hence, in this type of scale, ratios have meaning, and statements can be made to the effect that *x is twice the value of y*. Weight, length, and mass are all measured by using a ratio scale. Expressions of distance, in terms of kilometres, miles, or feet, are examples of ratio measurements, since all these scales have a common origin (the zero-point, representing no distance). Value measures of goods or income are also ratio measurements. Whether the units are dollars, francs, D-marks, or yen, zero earnings is the same in all currencies.

Parametric versus Nonparametric Tests

Parametric statistical methods require, in addition to some knowledge about the characteristics of the parent population (for example, normality), that measurements be equivalent to at least an interval scale. That is, in order to find the means and variances necessary for these tests, one must be able to assume that it is meaningful to compare intervals. It makes no sense to add, subtract, divide, or multiply ordinal scale values because the numbers on an ordinal scale have no meaning except to indicate rank order. There is no way to find, for example, the average between a corporal and a major in terms of military rank.

The distinguishing characteristic of **nonparametric tests** is that usually no assumptions about the parameters of the parent population are necessary. To avoid the parametric assumptions normally required for tests based on interval or ratio scales, most nonparametric tests deal only with nominal or ordinal data. That is, such tests ignore any properties of a given scale except ordinality. This means that if the data are, in fact, measurable on an interval scale, nonparametric tests waste (by ignoring) this knowledge about intervals. By wasting data, such tests gain the advantage of not having to make parametric assumptions, but sacrifice power in terms of using all available information to reject a false null hypothesis. Nonparametric tests require more observations than **parametric tests** to achieve equal probabilities of Type I and Type II errors. For example, one nonparametric test using ranked data requires about 105 observations to be as powerful as a *t*-test based on 100 observations of interval measurement data.[1]

section 18.2   Tests Comparable to Parametric *t*-tests

There are numerous nonparametric tests that can be used in place of the parametric *t*-tests described in Chapters 10 and 11. Three such tests are presented in this section: the *Mann–Whitney U-test*, the *Wald–Wolfowitz runs test*, and the *sign test*.

---

[1] The tests referred to are the Wilcoxon matched-pairs, signed-ranks test and the matched-pairs *t*-test on differences between means.

The Mann–Whitney U-Test

The **Mann–Whitney U-test,** used to determine whether or not two independently drawn samples came from the same population, is one of the most powerful non-parametric tests. This test is designed to test the null hypothesis that two populations are identical against the alternative hypothesis that they are not. The Mann–Whitney test is an alternative to Formula 11.3, the two-sample t-test, when the researcher does not want to (or cannot) make the assumptions that the populations are characterized by normal distributions with equal variances.

The first step in the Mann–Whitney U-test is to consider all the values representing the two samples as a single set of observations and to rank this entire group from the lowest number to the highest number. If the null hypothesis that the two samples were drawn from the same population is true, the observations from the two samples will be scattered throughout this ranking of both groups. If the two samples do not come from identical populations, the observations of one sample will tend to be bunched together at the low end of the rankings, at the high end of the rankings, or in the middle of the rankings. Such patterns can be detected by calculating a value of U, which is the statistic for the Mann–Whitney test. The statistic U is calculated by counting the number of times the scores from one sample precede each score in the other sample. If the count is quite large or quite small in relation to the value expected under the null hypothesis, then the two samples may not be randomly interspersed. This result indicates that one sample may have come from a different population than the other.

To calculate the value of the statistic U for any data set, suppose we let T_1 represent the total number of times an observation in sample 1 precedes each value in sample 2. Similarly, let T_2 represent the total number of times an observation in sample 2 precedes each observation in sample 1. Because the process of calculating T_1 and T_2 can become quite tedious, there is a formula that makes the calculations much easier. If we let n_1 and n_2 be the two sample sizes, r_1 = the sum of the ranks of all values from sample 1, and r_2 = the sum of the ranks from sample 2, we use the following:

Mann–Whitney U-statistic = $\min\{T_1, T_2\}$ where

$$T_1 = n_1 n_2 + \frac{n_1(n_1 + 1)}{2} - r_1$$

and

$$T_2 = n_1 n_2 - T_1$$

(18.1)

We should point out that for these formulas it makes no difference which sample is labelled 1 and which is labelled 2.

The value of the Mann–Whitney statistic is defined to be the *minimum* of the two values, $\{T_1, T_2\}$. Defining it this way means that the more similar the two samples are, the higher will be the value of U. Hence, we reject H_0 when U is small. Since the value of U depends only on the ranks of the scores in the two groups, it is possible to determine the probability of various values of U. Critical values of the Mann–Whitney statistic for small samples are not given in this text but are available in specialized books on nonparametric statistics.

☐ **EXAMPLE 18.1**   To illustrate the Mann–Whitney U-test, we use the data on pulp brightness from Section 11.6. Recall from Table 11.5 (which is reproduced in Table 18.1 with the observations for each chemical ordered from lowest to highest) that a random sample of size $n_1 = 11$ is taken for chemical 1, and a random sample of size $n_2 = 10$ is taken for chemical 2.

TABLE 18.1   Sample of Ranked Pulp Brightness (Table 11.5, with ordered data)

Chemical 1	75.91, 77.15, 77.36, 77.39, 77.54, 77.55, 78.00, 78.04, 78.36, 78.36, 78.95
Chemical 2	74.47, 76.15, 76.21, 76.22, 76.39, 77.20, 78.05, 78.06, 82.75, 82.87

The null hypothesis is that the two samples were drawn from the same population in regard to pulp brightness. The alternative hypothesis is that they were drawn from different populations. To calculate T_1, focus on each observation for chemical 2 and count the number of observations from chemical 1 *lower than* this value. For example, the smallest observation for chemical 2 is 74.47, and no values of chemical 1 are lower than this number. If we focus on the next smallest chemical 2 value (76.15), we find one chemical 1 value (75.91) smaller than this number. The same result is true for the next three values of chemical 2. You may make the counts for observations 6 to 9. For the tenth chemical 2 value (82.87), there are 11 chemical 1 values smaller. The sum of these counts is the value of T_1:

$$T_1 = 0 + 1 + 1 + 1 + 1 + 2 + 8 + 8 + 11 + 11 = 44$$

To complete the Mann–Whitney Test, we also need to calculate T_2, which is the total number of times a value from sample 2 precedes each value in sample 1. A good exercise for the reader is to verify that

$$T_2 = 66.$$

For the pulp problem:

$$U = \min\{44, 66\} = 44$$

From tables for $n_1 = 11$ and $n_2 = 10$, the critical value for $\alpha = 0.05$ is $U = 26$. This means that for any value of U less than or equal to 26, the null hypothesis should be rejected. Our observed value of 44 is greater than 26. Hence, we do not reject H_0 and instead conclude that the samples could have come from the same population, or logically, from two populations with the same means.   ■

TABLE 18.2   Ranks Derived from Table 18.1

Value	74.47	75.91	76.15	76.21	76.22	76.39	77.15	77.20	77.36	77.39	77.54
Chemical	2	1	2	2	2	2	1	2	1	1	1
Rank	1	2	3	4	5	6	7	8	9	10	11
Value		77.55	78.00	78.04	78.05	78.06	78.36	78.36	78.95	82.75	82.87
Chemical		1	1	1	2	2	1	1	1	2	2
Rank		12	13	14	15	16	17	18	19	20	21

Suppose we use Formula 18.1 to determine T_1 and T_2. Table 18.2 gives the necessary ranks. The sum of the ranks associated with chemical 1 in Table 18.2 is:

$$r_1 = 2 + 7 + 9 + 10 + 11 + 12 + 13 + 14 + 17 + 18 + 19 = 132$$

Thus, T_1 and T_2 are calculated as follows:

$$T_1 = (11)(10) + \frac{(11)(11 + 1)}{2} - 132 = 110 + 66 - 132 = 44$$

$$T_2 = (11)(10) - 44 = 66$$

This verifies our earlier result.

Tables for U often stop at $n_1 = n_2 = 20$. When n_1 or n_2 is larger than 20 and the two sample sizes are not too different in size, the sampling distribution of U can be approximated with the following *normal* statistic:

Normal approximation for the Mann–Whitney test:

$$z = \frac{U - E[U]}{\sigma_U}$$

where

$$E[U] = \frac{n_1(n_2)}{2} \qquad (18.2)$$

and

$$\sigma_U = \sqrt{\frac{n_1 n_2 (n_1 + n_2 + 1)}{12}}$$

When ties occur across samples in the Mann–Whitney test, they are treated by assigning the *average* of the ranks of those observations that are tied. In the pulp brightness example the observations corresponding to ranks 17 and 18 are identical. In this case, both observations would be given a rank of 17.5, which is the average of the ranks 17 and 18.

The Wald–Wolfowitz Runs Test

Another test that can be used in place of the t-test for independent samples is the **Wald–Wolfowitz runs test**. Although this test is not as powerful as the Mann–Whitney U-test, it is useful in some situations for which that test may not be appropriate. The null hypothesis in this test is the same as in the Mann–Whitney test — namely that the two samples were drawn from the same population. The alternative hypothesis is that the populations differ in some respect.

To test for differences between two samples, the observations are placed in a single group and then ranked (just as they were in the Mann–Whitney test). The number of runs in this ranking can now be counted, where a run is a sequence of the ranked observations all of which came from the same sample. An indication of whether or not the two samples came from the same population is given by the total number of runs. If the number of runs is not particularly large, or not particularly small, this means that the ranks corresponding to the samples are randomly intermixed; hence, it is reasonable to accept H_0 that they came from the same population. If there is a systematic alternating pattern to the data, the number of runs will be large, indicating that the null hypothesis of randomness should be rejected. Also, a small number of runs will occur whenever there is some systematic difference between the two samples. For example, if the ranks corresponding to one sample are consistently lower than those for the other sample, this suggests that the central location of the two samples differs. Similarly, if one sample has a smaller *spread* than the other sample, the ranks corresponding to this sample will bunch in the centre of the array, resulting in a low number of runs.

When ties occur in this test, the usual procedure is to assign ranks so as to make the number of runs as large as possible. In other words, ranks are assigned in a manner least favourable to rejecting H_0.

Table XI in Appendix C presents critical values (r) for the Wald–Wolfowitz runs test. The values in Table XI are lower-tail critical values only, used when the number of runs is expected to be low. When the test is two-sided, the upper critical value is related to the lower critical value (r) by the following relationship:

Upper critical value:	$n_1 + n_2 - r$

As the examples that follow will illustrate, the Wald–Wolfowitz test can be used with two-sample data (Example 18.2) or with certain data representing only a single sample (Example 18.3).

□ **EXAMPLE 18.2**   As an illustration of a two-sample Wald–Wolfowitz runs test, consider once again the data in Example 18.1. As in Table 18.2, we arrange all 21 of the observations in order from the lowest number to the highest. The number of runs is shown in Table 18.3 to be 9. From Table XI we see that the critical region for $\alpha = 0.05$, when $n_1 = 11$ and $n_2 = 10$ is $r \leq 6$. (In this problem we are interested only in the lower critical value, since an alternating pattern to the data would have no meaning.) Because the sample result does not fall in the critical region, the null hypothesis that these two samples of pulp brightness were drawn from the same population cannot be rejected.   ■

TABLE 18.3   Number of Runs Derived from Table 18.1

Value	74.47	75.91	76.15	76.21	76.22	76.39	77.15	77.20	77.36	77.39	77.54
Chemical	2	1	2	2	2	2	1	2	1	1	1
Run	1	2		3			4	5		6	

Value		77.55	78.00	78.04	78.05	78.06	78.36	78.36	78.95	82.75	82.87
Chemical		1	1	1	2	2	1	1	1	2	2
Run			6 (continued)			7		8		9	

Sometimes the observations in a single sample can be classified into one of two categories. For example, a single sample of average (daily) price changes on the London Stock Exchange might result in each day's being classified as average price increases or average price does not increase. Similarly, in looking at a sequence of customers in a store, we might classify them as male or female. In using the Wald–Wolfowitz test for such *one-sample* problems, it is necessary for the sample to fall into some natural sequence such as day 1, day 2, et cetera, for the stock exchange and customer 1, customer 2, et cetera for people in a store.

☐ **EXAMPLE 18.3** In our discussion on regression analysis, we indicated that examining the residuals is one method for testing for autocorrelation. If successive residuals tend to have the same sign or systematically alternate in sign, this indicates that autocorrelation may be a problem. The null and alternative hypotheses in this situation are:

$$H_0: \text{residuals independent (random)}$$

$$H_a: \text{residuals autocorrelated (positively or negatively)}$$

A nonparametric way of examining the residuals for autocorrelation is to look at the list of residuals for runs of plus (+) and minus (−) signs. To do this, we repeat (in Table 18.4) the residuals for the model in Problem 15.28 (based on the data in Table 15.9).

TABLE 18.4 The Residuals from Problem 15.28

Observation	Residual	Sign	Run Number
1	−76.550	−	1
2	35.985	+	
3	9.990	+	2
4	107.309	+	
5	−78.740	−	3
6	44.392	+	4
7	−6.606	−	5
8	80.032	+	6
9	−144.722	−	7
10	24.667	+	
11	4.073	+	8
12	60.532	+	
13	−118.247	−	9
14	57.887	+	10

Let $n_1 = $ the number of positive signs and $n_2 = $ the number of negative signs. From Table 18.4, $n_1 = 9$ and $n_2 = 5$, and the number of runs is ten. The lower-tail critical value for positive autocorrelation from Table XI is $r = 3$, which means that the upper-tail critical value for negative autocorrelation is as follows:

$$n_1 + n_2 - r = 9 + 5 - 3 = 11$$

Thus, H_0 would be rejected whenever the number of runs is three or fewer or 11 or more. Our result, which was ten runs, means that we are just inside the critical value for negative autocorrelation. We cannot reject the null hypothesis that the pattern of positive or negative signs is random. This differs from the answer for Problem 15.28. The more powerful Durbin-Watson test using the actual values of residuals resulted in the conclusion that negative autocorrelation did exist. ∎

Table XI presents critical values only for small values of n_1 and n_2. When both sample sizes are fairly large (> 19), the following normal approximation can be used.

Standardization of r for runs test:

$$z = \frac{r - E[r]}{\sigma_r}$$

where

$$E[r] = \frac{2n_1 n_2}{n_1 + n_2} + 1 \tag{18.3}$$

and

$$\sigma_r = \sqrt{\frac{2n_1 n_2 (2n_1 n_2 - n_1 - n_2)}{(n_1 + n_2)^2 (n_1 + n_2 - 1)}}$$

The Matched-Pairs Sign Test

The **matched-pairs sign test** is an example of a nonparametric test that may be used instead of the t-test for matched-pairs samples (discussed in Section 11.4). It is designed to determine whether significant differences exist between two populations based on two samples that are related in such a manner that each observation from one sample can be matched with a specific observation from the other sample. For example, one may wish to study the behaviour of carefully matched workers under two wage-incentive plans. Or the attitudes of wives may be contrasted with the attitudes of their husbands. Another common example is the before-and-after effect of a treatment on individuals or objects. Consumers are asked to make before-and-after judgments, such as rating breakfast cereals before and after a change in the production recipe to reduce fat, salt or sugar. Another illustration would be measuring the productivity of an employee before and after a special training course.

In the sign test, the two values in each pair are compared. If the sample 1 value is larger than the sample 2 value, this pair is given a plus ($+$) sign. If the sample 1 value is smaller than the sample 2 value, this pair is given a minus sign ($-$). Usually, the null hypothesis is that the two samples were drawn from populations with the same central tendency as measured by the median. The alternative hypothesis is that they differ. These hypotheses can be tested via the binomial distribution with the binomial parameter $\pi = 0.5$, meaning that either sign is equally likely for any matched pair.

☐ **EXAMPLE 18.4** A questionnaire is administered to nine women working in executive positions and to their working husbands to determine whether differences exist in the typical number of hours they spend at work per week. The null hypothesis is that the sample was drawn from a population in which the median number of hours worked by a woman and her husband do not differ. This is equivalent to the null hypothesis $H_0: \pi = 0.50$. The alternative hypothesis is that either the husbands or the wives work more hours: $H_a: \pi \neq 0.50$. Table 18.5 gives the data appropriate for use in the sign test.

724 CHAPTER 18 • NONPARAMETRIC STATISTICS

TABLE 18.5 Number of Hours Worked in Matched-pairs Samples

Pair	Wife's Hours	Husband's Hours	Works Most	Sign
1	51	45	wife	+
2	56	44	wife	+
3	38	40	husband	−
4	44	41	wife	+
5	55	52	wife	+
6	40	35	wife	+
7	65	59	wife	+
8	48	42	wife	+
9	58	46	wife	+

In using the sign test, the only relevant fact about these matched hours is whether the wife's hours are higher or lower than the husband's hours. It may be that only column four in Table 18.5 is reported in the survey. The t-test from Chapter 11 cannot be used unless the hours are given (as they are in this case for expository purposes) and the additional assumption of normality of the populations is made.

If the null hypothesis is true, then $\pi = \frac{1}{2}$; that is, half of the signs should be positive in the entire population of couples. We must find the probability that the sample distribution of signs would occur if $\pi = \frac{1}{2}$ and compare this with a significance level, say, $\alpha = 0.05$. Since we are not hypothesizing whether the husbands or the wives will have the higher hours, this is an example of a two-sided test, and we must double the probability to get the p-value. If α is greater than the p-value, we *reject* the null hypothesis and conclude that there is a significant difference in the central location of the distributions of husbands' and wives' hours. Let $x =$ number of positive signs. For this example, $x = 8$. From Table I:

$$P(x \geq 8 \mid n = 9, \pi = 0.50) = 0.0196$$

Because H_a is two-sided, we double this value. Thus, the p-value is as follows:

$$2P(x \geq 8) = 2(0.0196) = 0.0392$$

Since $\alpha = 0.05 > 0.0392$, the null hypothesis is rejected. If the alternative hypothesis for this problem had been a one-sided test, for example, if it had been predicted that the wives would have higher hours, then H_0 could be rejected at the 0.0196 level of significance or higher. ∎

☐ **EXAMPLE 18.5** As in the binomial test, the null hypothesis in the sign test need not specify that $\pi = \frac{1}{2}$. Consider a problem in which product A is compared with product B, and suppose that we asked each of ten people interviewed to rate these two products on a scale of 100. We might hypothesize that the probability of A being preferred to B is not $\frac{1}{2}$, but some other value, say $\frac{3}{4}$ [that is, $P(A > B) = \frac{3}{4}$]. The alternative to this hypothesis may be that $P(A > B) < \frac{3}{4}$. The sample results of the ten interviews given in Table 18.6 show five positive signs. Since the values were assigned subjectively by different persons, we only use ordinal measurement for each pair to get the signs.

TABLE 18.6   Scaled Values of Preference for Two Products A and B

Consumer	Product A Score	Product B Score	Sign
1	75	58	+
2	85	92	−
3	61	69	−
4	55	50	+
5	82	71	+
6	88	84	+
7	45	78	−
8	90	79	+
9	63	69	−
10	71	80	−

Under the null hypothesis with $n = 10$ and $\pi = \frac{3}{4}$, the probability of five or fewer positives from Table I is:

$$P(x \leq 5) = 0.0781$$

It is not possible, on the basis of this sample, to reject the null hypothesis $H_0: \pi = \frac{3}{4}$ at conventional levels of significance such as $\alpha = 0.01$ or 0.05. We conclude that it remains an acceptable view that $\frac{3}{4}$ of the population prefer product A to B. Note that a t-test cannot be used here unless interval measurement is assumed and the individual scores are given. ■

Use of Normal Approximation for Large Samples

When the number of matched pairs n is large and the hypothesized value of π is not extremely close to zero or 1, then the normal approximation to the binomial may be applied to this sign test (as discussed in Section 6.6). The mean and variance of a binomial random variable are $\mu = n\pi$ and $\sigma^2 = n\pi(1-\pi)$. Thus, an approximately standardized normal variable may be determined when $n\pi(1 - \pi) \geq 3$ by

$$z = \frac{x - n\pi}{\sqrt{n\pi(1 - \pi)}},$$

where x is the number of positive signs.

☐ **EXAMPLE 18.6**   We test whether $\frac{3}{4}$ of the population prefers product A to B by asking $n = 180$ consumers to rate each product on a scale of 100. The hypotheses are $H_0: \pi = \frac{3}{4}$ and $H_a: \pi < \frac{3}{4}$ where π is the population proportion that prefers product A to product B. The comparative results contain 120 positive signs. Because $n\pi(1 - \pi) = 180\left(\frac{3}{4}\right)\left(\frac{1}{4}\right) = 33.75 > 3$, we may use the normal approximation. Substituting $n\pi = 180\left(\frac{3}{4}\right) = 135$, we calculate the standardized normal variable as follows:

$$z_c = \frac{x - n\pi}{\sqrt{n\pi(1 - \pi)}} = \frac{120 - 135}{\sqrt{33.75}} = -2.58$$

Since $\alpha = 0.01$ is greater than the p-value $= P(z \leq -2.58) = 0.0049$, we reject the null hypothesis and conclude on the basis of this larger sample that less than $\frac{3}{4}$ of the population prefer product A to B. ■

PROBLEMS

18.1 Identify the level of measurement required for the following tests:

a) the binomial test

b) the Mann–Whitney U-test

c) the sign test

18.2 What is the power of a test? Explain why nonparametric tests are generally less powerful than parametric tests.

18.3 Identify each of the following numbers as representing measurement on nominal, ordinal, interval, or ratio scales.

a) the number of shares traded on the TSE on a given day

b) the numbers on football players' jerseys

c) a listing of the top 300 companies in Canada according to total assets

d) worker identification numbers

e) the order in which five candidates finished in an election.

18.4 Using the Mann–Whitney U-test, test for significant differences between the populations represented by the sample data given for the tannery and university labs in **Data Set 3**. Let $\alpha = 0.05$. Be sure to specify your null and alternative hypotheses in advance. The critical value is $U = 64$.

18.5 From **Data Set 1**, draw a random sample of twenty cities, ten having a population greater than 100,000 and another ten having a population of less than 100,000. Use a Mann–Whitney U-test on the percent population change from these two samples to see whether the populations differ. State your null and alternative hypotheses and let $\alpha = 0.05$. The critical value is $U = 23$.

18.6 A stress test on a random sample of two different types of bolts made by International Farm Equipment resulted in the limits shown in Table 18.7 (in pounds) before a bolt bent or broke. Test to see whether these two types of bolts were drawn from the same population using a Mann–Whitney U-test. Specify H_0 and H_a and let $\alpha = 0.02$. The critical value is $U = 19$.

TABLE 18.7 Bolt Strength Limit in Pounds

Bolt A	Bolt B	Bolt A	Bolt B
1044	1219	893	1117
1382	1194	1246	1401
1147	1370	1455	1338
1091	1209	1073	1264
1285	1366	1313	1352

18.7 Answer the same questions posed in Problem 18.6, but now using a two-sample Wald–Wolfowitz runs test, with $\alpha = 0.05$.

18.8 Similarly to Example 18.3, use a one-sample Wald–Wolfowitz runs test on the residuals in Problem 15.36. State your hypotheses and let $\alpha = 0.05$.

18.9 As measured by the market index, prices on a stock exchange are hypothesized to increase or decrease in a random pattern. Prices were observed for 23 consecutive market days. An **I** was recorded if prices increased, and an **N** if prices did not increase.

I I N N I I I N N N I I I I I I N N N N I I I I

Use a one-sample runs test to determine whether this pattern suggests randomness. Let $\alpha = 0.05$.

18.10 Consider the data in Table 18.8, representing prices for the daily rental of an economy automobile.

TABLE 18.8 Daily Rental of an Economy Automobile

City	Hertz	Avis
1 Boston	$50	$45
2 Detroit	48	47
3 Kansas City	44	40
4 Los Angeles	42	41
5 Miami	35	32
6 Phoenix	39	40
7 Washington, D.C.	55	54

Use a sign test for matched pairs on the basis of this sample to see whether there is a significant difference between the rates charged by the two companies. State your null and alternative hypotheses and report a p-value.

18.11 Draw a matched-pairs sample from **Data Set 1**. You should pick ten cities from eastern Canada matched as closely as possible with ten cities from western Canada. Match cities according to households and sales. Use a matched-pairs sign test to determine whether there is a significant difference in taxes, letting $\alpha = 0.05$. State your null and alternative hypotheses.

18.12 Ten applicants for a computer programming position took a test to determine general computer knowledge as well as a test for logical thinking ability. Their scores on both tests are as shown in Table 18.9.

TABLE 18.9 Computer and Logical Thinking Test Scores

Applicant	Computer Test	Logical Thinking Test
1	25	38
2	30	36
3	42	50
4	44	45
5	58	30
6	59	78
7	75	77
8	79	85
9	87	65
10	90	76

a) Use a sign test to test the null hypothesis, at $\alpha = 0.05$, that an applicant's score on the computer test is not different from the score on the logical thinking test.

b) What p-value would you report?

18.13 Use a matched pairs sign test on the salary data shown in Table 18.10 (originally Table 11.3). Let $\alpha = 0.05$ and be sure to state H_0 and H_a.

TABLE 18.10 Comparative Starting Salaries for Ten Matched Pairs of People

Pair	Toronto	Montreal
1	$40,400	$40,000
2	39,800	39,900
3	39,700	40,000
4	40,500	40,400
5	40,600	40,600
6	40,100	39,900
7	40,300	40,400
8	39,900	39,700
9	40,400	40,300
10	40,700	40,200

Goodness-of-Fit Tests

section 18.3

The tests presented thus far represent nonparametric procedures designed to see how closely two samples correspond to one another in order to test the hypothesis that they come from the same population. In many statistical problems, the researcher is interested in another, similar problem, that of determining how closely sample observations fit a theoretical population. In this section, we will present two tests designed for this purpose, called *goodness-of-fit tests*.

The One-sample Chi-Square Test

Recall that if the set of outcomes in an experiment can be divided into two categories (such as a success or a failure, make a sale or not, male or female, own stock or not), the appropriate test statistic is the binomial variable. When more than two categories or classes of outcomes are involved, then the appropriate test is the **chi-square test**.

The chi-square variable is used in cases with more than two categories to test how closely a set of *observed* frequencies corresponds to a given set of *expected* frequencies. The expected frequencies can be thought of as the average number of values expected to fall in each category, based on some theoretical probability distribution. For example, one probability distribution that is often useful is the uniform distribution in which the expected frequencies in all categories will be equal. The observed frequencies can be thought of as a sample of values from some probability distribution. The chi-square variable can be used to test our hypotheses about the expected frequencies by determining whether the observed and expected frequencies are close enough for us to conclude that the sample came from the probability distribution. For this reason, the test is called a *goodness-of-fit* test.

Assume that there are k categories ($k > 1$) and that the *expected* frequency in each of these categories is denoted as $E_1, E_2, \ldots, E_k$, or equivalently, $E_i (i = 1, 2, \ldots, k)$. Similarly, the k *observed* frequencies will be denoted as $O_1, O_2, \ldots, O_k$, or $O_i (i = 1, 2, \ldots, k)$. To test the goodness of fit of the observed frequencies (O_i) to the expected frequencies (E_i), we use the following chi-square variable with $\nu = k - 1$ degrees of freedom.

Chi-square goodness-of-fit statistic:

$$\chi^2_{(k-1)} = \sum_{i=1}^{k} \frac{(O_i - E_i)^2}{E_i} \tag{18.4}$$

Formula 18.4 measures the goodness of fit between the values of O_i and E_i as follows: When the fit is good (that is, O_i and E_i are generally close), then the numerator of 18.4 will be relatively small, and hence the value of χ^2 will be small. Conversely, if O_i and E_i are not close, then the numerator of 18.4 will be relatively large, and the value of χ^2 will be large also. Note that this implies that the chi-square formula is always a one-sided test, using the right-hand tail of the distribution. In other words, since *both* positive and negative differences between E_i and O_i become positive when squared, the critical region for the goodness-of-fit test must lie in the upper (positive) tail of the χ^2-distribution. For example, suppose that in a particular problem involving 16 categories, the fit between the 16 values of O_i and E_i from Formula 18.4 yields $\chi^2 = 25.0$. From Table VII in the row corresponding to $k - 1 = 15$ d.f., we find that $P(\chi^2 \geq 25) = 0.05$. Thus, at any $\alpha > 0.05$ level of significance, we can reject the null hypothesis about the expected values.

☐ **EXAMPLE 18.7**   An automobile dealer trying to arrange vacations for the sales personnel decides to test the null hypothesis that sales of new cars were equally distributed over the first six months of last year. The expected frequency for this hypothesis thus specifies that $E_1 = E_2 = \cdots = E_6$. The alternative hypothesis is that sales were not equally distributed over the six months. If the dealer sold 150 new cars in this period, the expected frequency under the null hypothesis would be 25 cars sold in each month. The observed sales are given in Table 18.11.

The null and alternative hypotheses are:

$$H_0: E_1 = E_2 = \cdots = E_6 = 25$$

$$H_a: \text{the frequencies are not all equal.}$$

TABLE 18.11   Monthly New Car Sales

	Jan.	Feb.	Mar.	Apr.	May	June	Total
Expected sales (E_i)	25	25	25	25	25	25	150
Observed sales (O_i)	27	18	15	24	36	30	150

The chi-square statistic for this example has $k - 1 = 5$ degrees of freedom. If we arbitrarily let $\alpha = 0.025$, the appropriate critical region, shown in Figure 18.1, is obtained from Table VII in the row $\nu = 5$. From this figure, we see that the null hypothesis will be rejected in favour of the alternative hypothesis of unequal frequencies in monthly sales if the calculated value of χ^2 exceeds 12.8.

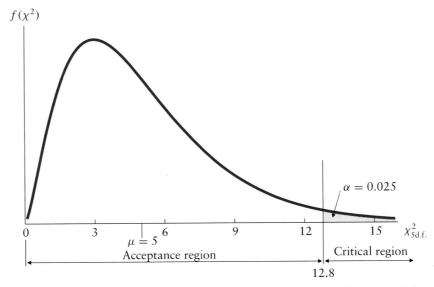

FIGURE 18.1   Critical region for a goodness-of-fit test, $\nu = 5, \alpha = 0.025$.

The value of χ^2 can be calculated as follows:

$$\chi_c^2 = \frac{(27 - 25)^2}{25} + \frac{(18 - 25)^2}{25} + \frac{(15 - 25)^2}{25}$$
$$+ \frac{(24 - 25)^2}{25} + \frac{(36 - 25)^2}{25} + \frac{(30 - 25)^2}{25}$$
$$= 12.0$$

Thus, at the significance level $\alpha = 0.025$, we fail to reject the null hypothesis of a uniform distribution that all monthly sales are equal and thus conclude that deviations from monthly sales of 25 are due to random occurrences. However, from Table VII, note that for $k - 1 = 5$ degrees of freedom and $\alpha = 0.05$, the critical value for the test would be 11.1. Therefore, if $\alpha = 0.05$ had been selected as the level of significance for rejecting H_0, the null hypothesis would have been rejected. Using a computer, the p-value is 0.0348.

In this case, the choice of the α-level is crucial to the decision. The costs of having too many or too few salespeople on hand in a given month should be given more consideration before α is set at an arbitrary level. Also, a larger number of past months may be sampled if the sales pattern is presumed not to have changed. For example, the sales for the past three years in the months of January, February, March, et cetera, might be used to test for equal monthly sales. ■

Two special properties of the chi-square goodness-of-fit test merit special attention. First, for this test the distinction between one-sided and two-sided alternatives is not relevant, since H_a merely specifies that the expected frequencies are not those under H_0. The chi-square goodness-of-fit test rejects H_0 only for large values of χ^2. Hence, in reporting a p-value, we always use the form $P(\chi^2 > \chi_c^2)$. A second property of this goodness-of-fit test is that $\Sigma(O_i - E_i)^2/E_i$ may not closely follow the χ^2 distribution if the expected frequency in any cell is less than 5. In problems where $E_i < 5$ for one or more cells, the usual procedure is to combine adjacent cells in such a manner that the new expected frequencies all exceed 5.

Use of χ^2 for Testing Normality

Because the assumption of normality for underlying probability distributions is so common, it is desirable to have a test for normality based on a set of sample values from that underlying population. For example, in residual analysis after a regression, you may wish to test if the residuals indicate that the original disturbances in the model were normally distributed. The observed residuals within any defined interval can be counted to obtain the observed frequencies E_i in Formula 18.4. The expected frequencies can be determined for any defined interval by using the normal probability table. A large computed chi-square would indicate significant discrepancies from a normal distribution and lead to rejection of the hypothesis that the disturbances are normally distributed.

The only question in applying the test is what intervals to define. Some analysts like to use intervals of half-standard deviations from the mean. They would compute the number of expected occurrences and count the number of observed frequencies in the intervals for the standardized normal z of $\{-3.5, -3.0\}$, $\{-3.0, -2.5\}$, $\{-2.5, -2.0\}$, ..., $\{-0.5, 0\}$, $\{0, 0.5\}$, ..., $\{2.5, 3.0\}$, $\{3.0, 3.5\}$. For example, in the third interval of $\{-2.5, -2.0\}$, the expected proportion of all values in the distribution would be $[0.9938 - 0.9772] = 0.0166$. The expected frequency E_i in this interval would be $(0.0166)n$ where n is the number of residuals in the regression. Using the mean and standard deviation of the sample under consideration, these z-values can be transformed into values that define corresponding intervals for the residuals. The count of residuals within each interval is straightforward. Obviously, these frequencies are greater for the half-unit intervals closer to zero and much less for those intervals near the tails of the distribution.

Other analysts prefer to use intervals on z that include the same number of expected frequencies in each interval so that the denominator in Formula 18.4 remains constant. This also has the advantage of balancing the observations across the intervals so that we avoid the problem of intervals with less than 5 frequencies. For example, the interval for z less than -1.645 should include 5% of the distribution. The interval between -1.645 and -1.28 should include 5% of the distribution. We could continue using the standard normal distribution table to define twenty intervals, each of which should include 5% of the distribution. The expected frequencies in this case would all be equal to $(0.05)n$. The observed frequencies within each corresponding interval would be determined in the same way as before. We should note that this χ^2 test for normality works best when the number of residuals is quite large, say over 100, so that the expected number in each category is at least five.

◻ **EXAMPLE 18.8** Consider a regression based on 500 observations. We wish to test H_0: errors are normally distributed, against H_a: they are not. We define twenty intervals, each expected to include 5% of the normal distribution, so the expected frequencies are $(0.05)500 = 25$ in each interval. Using the mean of the residuals, zero, and the standard deviation of the residuals, $\Sigma e^2/(n-1) = [s_e(n-m-1)/(n-1)]$, to define the twenty intervals in terms of standard deviation units for the residuals e_i, the observed frequencies for the 500 standardized residuals are found as shown in Table 18.12. Using $\alpha = 0.05$ for the test of hypotheses, the critical value of χ^2 for $(k-1) = 19$ degrees of freedom is 30.1 as found in Table VII. We find the computed value of χ^2 using Formula 18.4.

TABLE 18.12 Observed Frequencies O_i for Twenty Intervals

Intervals 1–10	27	25	20	29	27	25	18	19	27	21
Intervals 11–20	19	26	22	38	28	18	27	24	32	28

$$\chi_c^2 = \frac{(27-25)^2}{25} + 0 + \frac{(20-25)^2}{25} + \frac{(29-25)^2}{25} + \cdots$$
$$+ \frac{(32-25)^2}{25} + \frac{(28-25)^2}{25}$$
$$= \frac{(4+0+25+16+\cdots+49+9)}{25} = \left(\frac{490}{25}\right) = 19.6$$

Since this computed chi-square is less than the critical value (30.1) and the p-value is 0.419, we fail to reject the null hypothesis and can conclude that the sample of residuals come from a normal distribution. ∎

The Two-sample Chi-Square Test for Independence

In the chi-square test described above, a set of values was tested for goodness of fit using only a single attribute. At this time we extend that analysis by assuming that two attributes are under investigation and that we want to determine whether or not these attributes are independent. For example, instead of investigating car sales relative to the single attribute, month of the year, we may wish to construct a test to determine whether the attribute, car model (such as sedans versus hardtops), and the attribute, months of the year, are independent in their effect on sales. Similarly, in the supermarket example in Section 5.8, Table 5.7, we might have been interested in determining whether or not the pattern of arrivals is independent of the attribute, days of the week. For such examples, there is no general theory available to use in determining the expected frequency for each category. However, we can use the observed data to calculate expected frequencies under the assumption that the null hypothesis (of independence) is true.

The one-sample chi-square test illustrated above can be generalized to include problems involving any number of categories for the two attributes. Let us designate the two attributes as A and B, where attribute A is assumed to have r categories ($r > 1$) and attribute B is assumed to have k categories ($k > 1$). Furthermore, assume that the total number of observations in the problem is labelled n. A representation of these n observations in matrix form is shown in Figure 18.2, where O_{ij} represents the observation in the ith row and the jth column. A matrix in the form of Figure 18.2 is called a *contingency table*.

Attribute B

	1	2	3	$\cdots$	j	$\cdots$	k	Totals
1	O_{11}	O_{12}	O_{13}	$\cdots$	O_{1j}	$\cdots$	O_{1k}	$O_{1\bullet}$
2	O_{21}	O_{22}	O_{23}	$\cdots$	O_{2j}	$\cdots$	O_{2k}	$O_{2\bullet}$
3	O_{31}	O_{32}	O_{33}	$\cdots$	O_{3j}	$\cdots$	O_{3k}	$O_{3\bullet}$
$\vdots$	$\vdots$	$\vdots$	$\vdots$		$\vdots$		$\vdots$	$\vdots$
i	O_{i1}	O_{i2}	O_{i3}	$\cdots$	O_{ij}	$\cdots$	O_{ik}	$O_{i\bullet}$
$\vdots$	$\vdots$	$\vdots$	$\vdots$		$\vdots$		$\vdots$	$\vdots$
r	O_{r1}	O_{r2}	O_{r3}	$\cdots$	O_{rj}	$\cdots$	O_{rk}	$O_{r\bullet}$
Totals	$O_{\bullet 1}$	$O_{\bullet 2}$	$O_{\bullet 3}$	$\cdots$	$O_{\bullet j}$	$\cdots$	$O_{\bullet k}$	$O_{\bullet\bullet} = n$

Attribute A

FIGURE 18.2 Contingency table

The dots in the column and row totals in the matrix indicate that these numbers represent the sum of a particular set of values. For example, the number $O_{\bullet 1}$ represents the sum down the rows of all the observed values in the first column, while $O_{1\bullet}$ represents the sum across the columns of all the observed frequencies in the first row. The symbol $O_{\bullet\bullet}$ represents the sum over all rows and columns; hence, $O_{\bullet\bullet}$ must equal n, the total number of observations.

Calculating the expected frequency E_{ij} for each cell in a contingency table involves multiplying the *proportion* of the total number of observations falling in the jth category for attribute B (which is $O_{\bullet j}/n$) times the *number* of observations falling in the ith category of attribute A (which is $O_{i\bullet}$).†

Expected frequency in ith row, jth column:

$$E_{ij} = \left(\frac{O_{\bullet j}}{n}\right)(O_{i\bullet}) = \frac{O_{i\bullet}O_{\bullet j}}{n} \qquad (18.5)$$

As we mentioned earlier, the expected frequency should be five or more for each cell in a chi-square goodness-of-fit test. When this is not the case, adjacent cells should be combined.

Once the expected frequency for each of the cells in the contingency table is obtained, using Formula 18.5, the χ^2 statistic for testing independence between the effects of two attributes can be determined by the following formula:

---

† This expectation is a direct result of the relationship presented in Chapter 3, which says that two discrete events A_i and B_j are independent if and only if

$$P(A_i \cap B_j) = P(A_i)P(B_j).$$

Since our estimates of $P(A_i)$ and $P(B_j)$ are $O_{i\bullet}/n$ and $O_{\bullet j}/n$, respectively, the product $(O_{i\bullet}/n)(O_{\bullet j}/n)$ is our estimate of the joint probability. Multiplying this product by the total number of observations (n), we obtain Formula 18.5.

Two-attribute χ^2 statistic:

$$\chi^2_{(r-1)(k-1)} = \sum_{i=1}^{r}\sum_{j=1}^{k} \frac{(O_{ij} - E_{ij})^2}{E_{ij}} \qquad (18.6)$$

The number of degrees of freedom for this χ^2-statistic can be determined by noting that, in calculating the expected frequency for each cell, we must assume that the marginal totals ($O_{i\bullet}$ and $O_{\bullet j}$) are fixed quantities. This means that one degree of freedom is lost for each row and each column, so that the total number of degrees of freedom is the product, $(r-1)(k-1)$.

☐ **EXAMPLE 18.9** We apply Formula 18.6 to the problem of trying to determine whether the prices of certain stocks on the London stock exchange are independent of the industry to which they belong. Assume that four categories of industries are investigated (labelled I, II, III, and IV) and that stock prices in these industries are classified into one of three categories (high-priced, middle-priced, or low-priced). The data from such an analysis might look like the values shown in Table 18.13, where the expected values are in the upper left of each cell, and the observed values are in the lower right.

TABLE 18.13 Frequencies for the Stock Example

	E_{ij}		O_{ij}		
			Industry		
Stock Prices	I	II	III	IV	Total
High	13.8	10.4	8.7	12.1	45
	15	8	10	12	
Medium	18.5	13.8	11.5	16.2	60
	20	16	12	12	
Low	7.7	5.8	4.8	6.7	25
	5	6	3	11	
Total	40	30	25	35	130

To illustrate the calculation of expected frequencies, note that the expected frequency of high-priced stocks in industry I is found by multiplying the proportion of stock in industry I to the total number of observations, which is 40/130, by the number of observations in the high-priced category (45). The resulting product is

$$\frac{40}{130}(45) = 13.8$$

and is shown in the first cell. Similarly, the expected frequency for high-priced stocks in industry II is $(30/130)(45) = 10.4$. Note that, for each row and column, the sum of the expected frequencies must be the same as the sum of the observed frequencies. The number of degrees of freedom for this problem is $(r-1)(k-1) = (3)(2) = 6$, and the calculated value of χ^2_c is:

$$\chi^2_c = \frac{(15-13.8)^2}{13.8} + \frac{(8-10.4)^2}{10.4} + \cdots + \frac{(11-6.7)^2}{6.7} = 6.825$$

To be significant at the 0.05 level, the value of χ^2 has to be greater than 12.6 for 6 degrees of freedom. Since the computed value $\chi_c^2 = 6.825$ is less than this value, the null hypothesis cannot be rejected at the 0.05 level of significance. The p-value is 0.337. Thus, we conclude that the price of stocks is independent of the industry associated with that stock. ■

The Kolmogorov–Smirnov Test

We have shown how the chi-square test can be used to measure goodness of fit when the data are in nominal form (categories). When the data are in at least *ordinal* form, the **Kolmogorov–Smirnov test** can be used. This test has the advantage over the chi-square test in that it is generally more powerful, it is easier to compute, and it does not require a minimum expected frequency in each cell.

The Kolmogorov-Smirnov (K–S) test involves a comparison between the theoretical and sample *cumulative* relative frequency distributions. To make this comparison, the data are put into classes (or categories) that have been arrayed from the lowest to the highest class. This is the step that requires ranking or ordinal measurement. Suppose we use the symbol F_i to denote the cumulative relative frequency for each category of the theoretical distribution and S_i to denote the comparable value for the sample frequency. The K–S test is based on the maximum value of the absolute difference between F_i and S_i. Denoting this statistic as D, we have the following statistic:

Statistic for K–S test:	$D = \text{Max} \,\lvert F_i - S_i \rvert$. (18.7)

The decision to reject the null hypothesis (that the sample and theoretical distributions are equal) is based on the value of D. The larger the value of D, the more confidence we have that H_0 is false. Note that this is a one-tailed test, since the value of D is always positive, and we reject H_0 for large values of D. Table XIII in Appendix C gives the critical values for various probability values.

☐ **EXAMPLE 18.10**   Once again consider the supermarket data from Section 5.8. In Table 18.14 we repeat the data from Table 5.7, showing the relative frequencies for both the observed and theoretical Poisson distributions. Table 18.14 also shows the cumulative frequencies and $\lvert F_i - S_i \rvert$.

From the last column in Table 18.14, we see that the maximum value of $\lvert F_i - S_i \rvert$ is $D = 0.0365$. Since the sample size is $n = 100$, the last row of Table XIII in Appendix C gives the appropriate critical value of D. For $\alpha = 0.01$, the critical value is $1.63/\sqrt{n} = 1.63/\sqrt{100} = 0.163$. Because $D = 0.0365$ is less than the critical value, we do not reject H_0. That is, the agreement between the observed and the theoretical values is sufficiently close for us to believe that the sample came from a population with a Poisson distribution. ■

The K–S test uses the *ordinal* nature of the classes, while the chi-square test makes use of only *nominal* properties of the data. We should also point out that the K–S test can be used for testing goodness of fit between two *sample* cumulative relative frequency distributions. In this case, the procedure is exactly the same as before, except that the statistic D has a different distribution, which we do not present.

TABLE 18.14   Supermarket Data from Table 5.7 for K–S Test

Arrivals	Observed Relative Frequency	Cumulative Relative Frequency (S_i)	Theoretical Relative Frequency	Cumulative Relative Frequency (F_i)	$|F_i - S_i|$
0	0.010	0.010	0.0224	0.0224	0.0124
1	0.080	0.090	0.0850	0.1074	0.0174
2	0.190	0.280	0.1615	0.2689	0.0111
3	0.230	0.510	0.2046	0.4735	0.0365
4	0.170	0.680	0.1944	0.6679	0.0121
5	0.150	0.830	0.1477	0.8156	0.0144
6	0.080	0.910	0.0936	0.9092	0.0008
7	0.030	0.940	0.0508	0.9600	0.0200
8	0.030	0.970	0.0241	0.9841	0.0141
9	0.020	0.990	0.0102	0.9943	0.0043
10	0.010	1.000	0.0039	0.9982	0.0018
11	0.000	1.000	0.0013	0.9995	0.0005
12	0.000	1.000	0.0004	0.9999	0.0001
13	0.000	1.000	0.0001	1.0000	0.0000

section 18.4

Nonparametric Measures of Correlation

The correlation measures presented in Chapters 13 and 14 have been based on measurements of variables for which a mean, variance, and covariance can be determined. Sometimes, it is desirable to be able to calculate correlations among variables when such measures are not obtainable. In general, the determination of means, variances, and covariances requires *interval measurement*, which means that the difference (interval) between any two observations must be meaningful. Frequently, data may be observed that have only *ordinal measurement*. In such cases, only the *relative* ranking of any two observations has meaning. For example, a stock analyst may list a ranking of the ten best common stocks for purchase by investors interested primarily in safety and income. The rank of any two stocks in such a list has meaning, but the difference between ranks does not. For example, we know that stock 4 is ranked better than stock 7 and stock 2 is ranked higher than stock 5. However, we do *not* know whether the difference in desirability between stocks 4 and 7 is identical to the difference between stocks 2 and 5, even though this difference is three rank positions in both instances. Now, if one had two such rankings of stocks by different analysts, a measure of correlation between the two rank orderings might be desired. In such a situation, the previous correlation measures are not appropriate because of the ordinal nature of the data. Fortunately, there are nonparametric measures of correlation that can be used.

Spearman's Rank Correlation Coefficient

Research published by C. Spearman in 1904 led to the development of what is perhaps the most widely used nonparametric measure of correlation. This measure, usually denoted either by r_s or by the Greek word *rho*, has thus become known as **Spearman's rho**. Spearman's rank correlation coefficient r_s is very similar to the ordinary correlation coefficient we have studied thus far, except that now ranks are used as the data. A perfect positive correlation ($r_s = +1$) means that the two samples rank each object identically, while a perfect negative correlation ($r_s = -1$) means that the ranks of the two samples have an exactly *inverse* relationship. Values of r_s between -1 and $+1$ denote less than perfect correlation. To measure correlation by Spearman's method, we first take the difference between the rank of an object in one sample and its rank in the second sample, and we then square this difference. If this squared difference is denoted as d_i^2 for the ith pair of observations, then the sum of these squared differences over a set of n pairs of observations is:

$$\sum_{i=1}^{n} d_i^2$$

The value of r_s is derived from Σd_i^2 as follows:

Spearman's rank correlation coefficient:

$$r_s = 1 - \frac{6\sum_{i=1}^{n} d_i^2}{n^3 - n} \tag{18.8}$$

□ EXAMPLE 18.11   To illustrate Formula 18.8, suppose two investment services are asked to rate five different mutual (growth) funds. We label the growth funds A, B, C, D, E and assume that the first service rates the funds as A > B > C > D > E, while the second rates them as A > C > E > B > D, as shown in Table 18.15. We see in Table 18.15 that $\Sigma d_i^2 = 10$. Thus, the rank correlation between the ratings of the two investment services is:

$$r_s = 1 - \frac{6(10)}{5^3 - 5} = 1 - \frac{60}{120} = 0.50 \qquad ■$$

TABLE 18.15   Calculating Spearman's Rho

Fund	Service 1	Service 2	d_i	d_i^2
A	1	1	0	0
B	2	4	-2	4
C	3	2	1	1
D	4	5	-1	1
E	5	3	2	4
	$n = 5$			Sum $= 10$

In order to test the significance of a given value of r_s, it is necessary to determine the probability that this given value of r_s will occur under the null hypothesis. This probability depends on the number of permutations of the two variables that give rise to the particular value of r_s. Tables are available that give the critical values of r_s for small values of n. We will not present these tables in this text, but they are readily available in specialized texts on nonparametric statistics.

When n is large ($n \geq 10$), the significance of an obtained value of r_s under the null hypothesis can be determined from the following t-variable:

Test statistic for Spearman's rho:

$$t_{(n-2)} = \frac{r_s\sqrt{n-2}}{\sqrt{1-r_s^2}} \tag{18.9}$$

This statistic can be shown to follow the *t*-distribution with $(n-2)$ degrees of freedom. Formula 18.9 is similar to Formula 13.24 for the product moment correlation coefficient.

□ **EXAMPLE 18.12**   Suppose a company owns a large number of different McDonald's franchises. This company is interested in the rank correlation between sales and advertising for each franchise. A sample of size $n = 11$ is taken, and Spearman's rho is calculated to be $r_s = 0.755$. In this case the computed value t_c is:

$$t_c = \frac{0.755\sqrt{11-2}}{\sqrt{1-0.755^2}} = 3.454$$

From the *t*-table in Appendix C, this value is seen to be significant at the 0.005 level of significance. Using a computer, the *p*-value is 0.0036. We can, with a high degree of confidence, reject the null hypothesis that there is no correlation in the population — we can reject $H_0: \rho = 0$. Note that we have assumed that a one-tailed test is appropriate in this example. That is, the alternative hypothesis is $H_a: \rho \neq 0$. If a two-tailed test had been used ($H_a: \rho > 0$), the significance level and *p*-value would be doubled. ■

Kendall's Correlation Coefficient

An alternative to Spearman's rho for determining a rank correlation is to calculate Kendall's correlation coefficient. This statistic, developed by the statistician M. G. Kendall, is denoted by the Greek letter τ (tau) and called **Kendall's tau**. Although Kendall's tau is suitable for determining the rank correlation of the same type of data for which Spearman's rho is useful, the two methods employ different techniques for determining this correlation, so their values will not usually be the same. Spearman's rho is perhaps more widely used, but Kendall's tau has the advantage of being generalizable to a partial correlation coefficient, and the distribution of tau more rapidly approaches a normal distribution.

The rank correlation coefficient τ is determined by first calculating an index that indicates how the ranks of one set of observations, *taken two at a time*, differ from the ranks of the other set of observations. The easiest way to determine the value of this index is to arrange the two sets of rankings so that one of them, say the first sample, is in ascending order, from the lowest rank to the highest rank. The other set, representing the second sample, will not be in ascending order unless the ranks of the two samples agree perfectly. Now, consider all possible pairs of the n ranks in this second sample: assign a value of $+1$ to each pair in which the two ranks are in the same (ascending) *order* as they are in the first sample, and assign -1 to each pair in which the two ranks are *not* in the same order as they are in the first sample. The sum of these $+1$ and -1 values is an indication of how well the second set of rankings agrees with the first set. Since there are $_nC_2$ combinations of n objects taken two at a time, this sum (or index) can assume any value between

$+_nC_2$ and $-_nC_2$. Kendall's tau is defined as the ratio of the computed value of this index to the maximum value it can assume, which is $_nC_2$.

Kendall's rank correlation coefficient:

$$\tau = \frac{\text{Computed index}}{\text{Maximum index}} \qquad (18.10)$$

Note that when there is perfect positive correlation, τ will equal $+1$, since the computed index and the maximum index will both equal $_nC_2$. If there is a perfect negative correlation, the computed index will equal $-_nC_2$, and τ will equal -1.

◻ **EXAMPLE 18.13** The value of Kendall's tau can be determined for the set of data in Table 18.15, pertaining to the rank correlation between mutual funds rated by two investment services. Let us use the ratings by service 1 as the base for comparison, since these ranks are already in ascending order. Now the ratings for service 2 in Table 18.15 must be compared, two at a time, in order to determine the number of pairs in the same order ($+$) as in the first sample and the number not in the same order ($-$). First fund A is compared with each of the four other funds. Since fund A is ranked ahead of fund B by service 2, we score a $+1$ for the A–B comparison. Similarly, service 2 ranks fund A ahead of funds C, D, and E; hence, we score a $+1$ for each of the comparisons A–C, A–D, and A–E. Now we must compare fund B with the other three funds (C, D, and E). We see that B is after C in service 2 rankings, thus, the B–C comparison is given a -1 score. All such paired comparisons for this example are shown in Table 18.16.

The maximum index in this example is the number of paired comparisons, which is:

$$_nC_2 = {_5}C_2 = 10$$

TABLE 18.16 Computations for Kendall's Tau Using the Data in Table 18.15

Pair	Value	Pair	Value	Pair	Value	Pair	Value
A vs B	$+1$	B vs C	-1	C vs D	$+1$	D vs E	-1
A vs C	$+1$	B vs D	$+1$	C vs E	$+1$		
A vs D	$+1$	B vs E	-1				
A vs E	$+1$						

Computed index = Sum of values = 4

The computed index is the number of $+1$ scores (7) minus the number of -1 scores (3):

$$7 - 3 = 4$$

Thus, Kendall's tau is:

$$\tau = \frac{4}{10} = 0.40$$

■

Note that Kendall's tau (0.40) is less than the comparable value of Spearman's rho (0.50). Both coefficients, however, utilize the same amount of information about the association between two variables, and for a given set of observations both can be used to test the null hypothesis that two variables are unrelated in the population. For small samples, tables are available for determining the probability of a given value of τ or r_s under this null hypothesis. For large samples, methods of statistical inference involving r_s and τ can be constructed utilizing the t-distribution and the normal distribution, respectively. We presented the t-statistic for Spearman's rho earlier. The comparable statistic for Kendall's tau is the following standardized z-statistic,

---

Standardized z-value for Kendall's tau:

$$z = \frac{\tau - \mu_\tau}{s_\tau}$$

(18.11)

---

where μ_τ is assumed to be zero under the null hypothesis, and the standard deviation is as follows:

$$s_\tau = \sqrt{\frac{2(2n + 5)}{9n(n - 1)}}$$

☐ **EXAMPLE 18.14**   Consider once again the McDonald's franchises (Example 18.12) for which the calculated value of Kendall's tau is $\tau = 0.527$. The standard deviation for a sample of $n = 11$ is:

$$s_\tau = \sqrt{\frac{2(2 \times 11 + 5)}{9 \times 11(11 - 1)}} = 0.234$$

The computed standardized normal value is thus:

$$z_c = \frac{0.527}{0.234} = 2.252$$

Since $P(z \geq 2.252) = 0.0122$, we can reject $H_0: \rho = 0$ when $\alpha > 0.0122$ for a one-sided test and when $\alpha > 2(0.0122) = 0.0244$ for a two-sided test.   ∎

PROBLEMS

18.14 What is meant by the phrase *goodness-of-fit test*? How is the chi-square distribution used to make this test? How does a one-sample test differ from a two-sample test?

18.15 Certain industries are often criticized for having hired less than a proportional number of members of minority groups. Suppose you are interested in workers with an MBA degree, and you find that the recipients of MBAs are 20% females, 10% male minorities, and 70% white males. In one of the industries criticized, a random sample of 1000 executive positions resulted in the breakdown given in Table 18.17.

TABLE 18.17 Number of MBA Graduates Hired

White Males	Women	Minority Males
800	150	50

a) Calculate the expected frequency for each cell, using the population proportions 0.70, 0.20, and 0.10. Use the chi-square test to determine whether the observed and expected frequencies are close enough for the null hypothesis to be accepted. Use $\alpha = 0.01$. State your null and alternative hypotheses.

b) What p-value would you report?

18.16 At a Metro bus-subway transfer station, a motion engineer is studying the flow of passengers making transfers from the subway train to each of six adjoining bus platforms. In one group of 102 passengers, the observed frequencies of transfer to each bus platform are shown in Table 18.18.

TABLE 18.18 Transfers from Subway to Buses

Platform:	1	2	3	4	5	6
Frequency:	14	21	25	13	18	11

Use a χ^2 test with $\alpha = 0.025$ to determine if the null hypothesis of equal distribution of transfers to the six bus platforms can be rejected.

18.17 A store has four different entrances. The store manager is trying to determine whether there is a difference in the number of customers coming into the store through these entrances. The manager establishes the null hypothesis that one-fourth of all customers will use each entrance. A random sample of 200 customers resulted in the data in Table 18.19.

TABLE 18.19 Customer Flow Through a Store's Entrances

Entrance:	I	II	III	IV
Customers:	75	40	30	55

Use a chi-square test and $\alpha = 0.05$ to decide whether the null hypothesis should be accepted or rejected. State H_0 and H_a.

18.18 A cafeteria proposes to serve four main entrees. For planning purposes the manager expects that the proportions of each that will be selected by the customers will be those shown in Table 18.20. Of the first 50 customers, 15 select hot dogs and chili, 20 select roast beef, five select chicken, and ten select fish. The manager wonders whether to revise the preparation schedule or whether this deviation from expectations is merely chance variation. Make an appropriate test, at the 0.01 level of significance, on which to base your advice to this manager.

TABLE 18.20 Anticipated Proportions of Entree Selection

Selection	Hot Dogs and Chili	Roast Beef	Chicken	Fish
Proportion	0.20	0.50	0.20	0.10

18.19 In a regression analysis based on 500 observations, we wish to test if the errors are normally distributed (a key assumption for regression). Using defined intervals for the normal distribution which would each include five percent of the values, the residuals from the regression are categorized into corresponding intervals. Table 18.21 shows the count of residuals in each interval. Using $\alpha = 0.005$, test if these indicate that the assumption of normality should be rejected.

TABLE 18.21 Observed Frequencies O_i of Residuals for Twenty Intervals

Intervals 1–10	33 39 24 31 32 34 34 26 20 27
Intervals 11–20	16 22 24 36 17 14 23 14 17 17

♦ **18.20** In a gambling casino, a die is rolled 100 times with the results in Table 18.22.

TABLE 18.22 Die Rolling Results

Number of Dots	Observed Frequency
1	14
2	21
3	25
4	13
5	18
6	9

Use the chi-square goodness-of-fit test to determine if there is sufficient evidence to claim that the die is unfair. Use $\alpha = 0.05$.

18.21 A company making cardboard boxes of a variety of shapes has been working three shifts for the past four months. The plant manager is interested in determining whether the number of packaging errors that occur in a given week is related to the shift or to the sex of the worker. The plant has approximately the same number of male and female workers on each shift. The packaging errors shown in Table 18.23 were recorded over a two-week period.

TABLE 18.23 Packaging Errors

	7 A.M.–3 P.M.	3 P.M.–11 P.M.	11 P.M.–7 A.M.
Males	15	5	10
Females	5	10	15

a) Determine the expected frequency in each cell. What null and alternative hypotheses are being tested here?

b) Would you accept H_0 or H_a if $\alpha = 0.05$?

c) What p-value would you report?

18.22 A marketing advisor was asked to rate various brands of jeans on colour and style. Each brand was rated I, II, or III according to colour and rated A or B according to style. The frequencies of classifications were as shown in Table 18.24.

TABLE 18.24 Colour and Style Rating for Different Brands of Jeans

		Colour	
	I	II	III
Style A	20	15	5
Style B	10	20	10

a) Use a chi-square test to determine whether or not these data indicate independence between style and colour. Use $\alpha = 0.025$.

b) What p-value would you report?

18.23 Fifty apple trees were treated with one of two new types of insect spray. Each tree was rated at the end of the season as either having a normal amount of insects or being insect free. The results are given in Table 18.25.

TABLE 18.25 Tree Rating

	Normal	Insect Free
Spray I	9	16
Spray II	1	24

a) What null and alternative hypotheses should be tested here? What level of α would you recommend?

b) Can H_0 be rejected if $\alpha = 0.01$?

18.24 In an experiment on economic behaviour, the price decisions of various producers are observed. For each decision, the producer's profit position in the previous period is known. Consider the price decisions in Table 18.26 by 100 different producers compared to previous profit.

TABLE 18.26 Price Decisions of One Hundred Producers

	Profits Increased	Profits Same	Profits Decreased
Raise price	12	5	20
Price same	15	16	2
Lower price	8	4	18

Test at the $\alpha = 0.05$ level whether the price actions of these producers are independent of their previous profit positions.

18.25 In a study on new automobile purchases, it was suggested that the colour of car a person picks is not independent of the amount of optional equipment purchased. The data in Table 18.27 report on two colour selections (white and black) and three levels of optional equipment (I = none, II = \$1–\$1,600, and III = over \$1,600). Use these data and a chi-square test for the null hypothesis that colour is independent of the optional equipment selected.

TABLE 18.27 Comparison of Colour and Optional Equipment in New Automobile Purchases

Equipment	White	Black
I	14	26
II	14	6
III	30	10

18.26 Use the K–S test to measure the goodness of fit of the data in Problem 5.48 to a Poisson distribution with $\lambda = 0.7$. Is H_0 accepted or rejected if $\alpha = 0.05$?

18.27 A study was recently completed to determine whether or not the *order* in which a person's name appears on a political ballot has any influence on that person's chances of being elected. Ninety-two elections were observed, each having four candidates. The results are shown in Table 18.28.

TABLE 18.28   Number of Election Wins Compared With Position on Ballot

	Position				
	1	2	3	4	Total
Number of wins	29	21	17	25	92

a) Use the K–S test to examine the relationship between these data and the distribution one would expect if the probability of winning were equal for all four positions. Is H_0 accepted or rejected? Let $\alpha = 0.05$.

b) Use a chi-square test to accomplish the same purpose as in part (a).

18.28 One study by a commuter airline indicated that the number of passengers requesting window seats follows a binomial distribution with $\pi = 0.30$. The data from this study included a random sample of 50 passengers selected from each of 100 different flights and is given in Table 18.29.

TABLE 18.29   Number of Airline Window Seat Selection Requests

Number of People Requesting Window Seats	Frequency
9	5
10	5
11	6
12	10
13	12
14	11
15	13
16	12
17	8
18	6
19	6
20	3
21	2
22	1
	100

Use the K–S test to compare these data with the binomial distribution for $n = 50$ and $\pi = 0.30$. State H_0 and H_a and let $\alpha = 0.01$.

18.29 Five microcomputers have been rated by two different computer magazines as shown in Table 18.30. Each magazine rated the computers on a scale from 0 to 50. Compute and interpret Spearman's rho and Kendall's tau.

TABLE 18.30   Rating of Five Microcomputers

Microcomputer	Magazine I	Magazine II
1	25	15
2	39	22
3	21	30
4	48	12
5	8	10

18.30 Compute Spearman's rho and Kendall's tau for the correlation between percent elongation of leather between the Tannery lab and the University lab in **Data Set 3**.

18.31 Use the data in Table 18.5, for hours worked, to find the following.

a) Spearman's rho

b) Kendall's tau

18.32 Find the rank correlation for the data on car rental rates in Problem 18.10 using either Spearman's rho or Kendall's tau.

18.33 Use the aptitude test data in Problem 18.12 to calculate the following.

a) Kendall's tau

b) Spearman's rho

18.34 Determine Kendall's tau and Spearman's rho for the correlation of the salary data in Problem 18.13.

18.35 A group of workers are scored on their ability to perform two sets of tasks emphasizing strength and coordination.

a) Using the data in Table 18.31, compute and compare the values of Spearman's rho and Kendall's tau. Interpret your results.

b) Calculate the *t*-statistic for Spearman's rho. Can you reject H_0 on the basis of this statistic? Use a two-sided test and $\alpha = 0.05$.

TABLE 18.31 Workers' Ability to Perform Two
Different Tasks

Worker	Task 1	Task 2
1	32	25
2	37	31
3	49	45
4	51	40
5	65	33
6	66	73
7	82	72
8	86	80
9	94	60
10	95	69

TABLE 18.32

Professor of	Group I	Group II
Marketing	9	7
Economics	3	2
Statistics	1	1
Accounting	6	5
Finance	4	3
Law	11	11
Psychology	10	9
History	7	10
Mathematics	5	8
Biology	2	4
English	8	6

18.36 Two groups of students decided to rate 11 different professors. The two rankings are shown in Table 18.32.

a) Calculate Kendall's tau and Spearman's rho.

b) Test the significance of your results in part (a) by calculating t for Spearman's rho and z for Kendall's tau. Use a one-sided alternative and $\alpha = 0.01$.

CHAPTER SUMMARY

KEY TERMS AND EXPRESSIONS

Levels of measurement:

> **Nominal:** Categorize data by "names" only.
>
> **Ordinal:** Scale has the property of order.
>
> **Interval:** Scale has order plus a constant interval.
>
> **Ratio:** Scale has order, a constant interval, plus a unique zero-point (making ratio statements meaningful).

Parametric versus nonparametric tests: Parametric tests generally require a measurement level of at least an interval scale and some assumption about the underlying distribution, such as the normality of the parent population. Nonparametric tests require no such assumptions.

Mann–Whitney U-test: A nonparametric test to determine whether or not two samples were drawn from the same population.

Wald–Wolfowitz runs test: A nonparametric test to determine whether or not two samples were drawn from the same population.

Matched-pairs sign test: An ordinal test for population differences involving paired samples and information on whether an object's rating is larger (+) or smaller (−) than the rating of its paired object.

Chi-square test: A test to determine the goodness of fit between a single sample and a theoretical population (one-sample test) or to determine whether two attributes are dependent or independent (two-sample test).

Kolmorogov–Smirnov test: A goodness-of-fit test when the data are in at least ordinal form.

Spearman's rho (r_s): A nonparametric measure of correlation based on ranks.

Kendall's tau (τ): A nonparametric measure of correlation based on ranks.

EXERCISES

18.37 Return to the residuals in Table 18.4. Calculate a rank correlation measure using the following pairs of residuals: 1–2, 2–3, 3–4, ..., 13–14.

18.38 Consult a text that presents nonparametric statistics and read about the contingency coefficient C.

Describe how this measure differs from Spearman's rho and Kendall's tau.

18.39 Show that Spearman's rho is the rank–order equivalent of the Pearson product–moment correlation coefficient discussed in Section 13.6.

USING THE COMPUTER

18.40 Find a computer program that calculates nonparametric statistics. Solve the following problems using this program.

a) Problem 18.36.

b) Problem 18.23.

c) 18.22.

18.41 Use a computer program to determine Spearman's rho for the data in Problem 18.35.

CASE PROBLEM

18.42 In Chapter 11, Problem 11.48, the case problem was to consider **Data Set 1**, a sample of cities grouped into 4 regions of Canada. You were to run a series of parametric tests contrasting the regions and prepare a

report indicating key differences in these market regions. Redo that report now, using only nonparametric statistics. Use as many of the tests and statistics in this chapter as possible.

CHAPTER 19

Linear Programming

Introduction

Linear programming is an important method of solving a variety of problems in logistics, scheduling, and resource management. Since the 1950s, it has come to play an essential role in many fields. Large transportation companies, financial institutions, and engineering firms all use linear programming to solve problems that formerly were intractable. The technique has become so widespread that software companies have made linear programming the centrepiece of their Operations Research packages. Output from one of these packages, CMMS, is used in this chapter.

A linear-programming problem involves finding the optimal value of a quantity such as profit, cost, or risk when there are resource limitations or other restrictive requirements. The quantity to be optimized (maximized or minimized) is expressed algebraically as a linear function called the **objective function**. The restrictions are expressed as linear inequalities or equalities involving the same variables that appear in the objective function. A standard notation for a linear programming problem is

$$\text{optimize } Z = \Sigma c_j x_j$$

subject to
$$\Sigma a_{ij} x_j \leq b_i$$

$$x_j \geq 0$$

The constraints can have $\geq$ or $=$ signs instead of $\leq$ signs. The variables are all non-negative.

The best-known algorithm for solving these optimization problems is the **simplex method** created by George Dantzig. The simplex procedure will not be discussed in this chapter. For solutions, most companies rely on the computer, but it is difficult to understand the computer printout without some insight into the nature of solutions to linear-programming problems. For this reason, part of this chapter is devoted to solutions by graphical analysis.

The first three sections of this chapter deal with graphing techniques. Section 19.2 is a review of the basic facts about linear expressions and their graphs. Section 19.3 discusses how to use graphs to find the optimal solution to simple linear-programming problems. Section 19.4 discusses the sensitivity of the optimal solution to changes in the parameters of the problem. The final two sections of the chapter introduce the formulation of problems and their format for solution by computer.

Graphing Lines and Linear Inequalities

An equation of the form $y = mx + b$, where m and b are constants, is said to define y as a linear function of x. The reason for this terminology is that the graph of the function is a straight line.

◻ **EXAMPLE 19.1**   Draw the graph of $y = 3x + 2$.

● **SOLUTION**   An easy way of doing this is to construct a table of values. Give x a few simple values and calculate the corresponding y coordinates. For example, if $x = 2$, substitute this value into the right-hand side of the equation to get the following:

$$y = 3(2) + 2 = 8$$

TABLE 19.1 Table of Values for $y = 3x + 2$

Variable			Value		
x	1	2	3	4	5
y	5	8	11	14	17

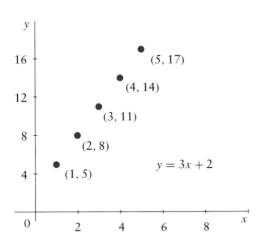 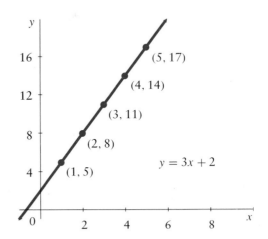

FIGURE 19.1 Selected points on the graph of $y = 3x + 2$ and the straight line that represents it

When plotted on the x and y axes, the points appear to lie in a straight line and the graph of the function is the straight line drawn through the points. The line extends infinitely far in each direction, a fact that is sometimes indicated by arrowheads on the line. Unless there is a chance of confusion, the arrowheads are usually omitted.

As can be seen in the table of values, every time x is increased by 1 unit, the value of y increases by 3 units. This number is called the **slope** of the line. All non-vertical lines have a slope. ■

> The slope of a non-vertical line is the amount by which y increases for a unit increase in x.

An alternative definition of the slope of the line joining two points (x_1, y_1) and (x_2, y_2) is given by the following formula.

$$\text{slope} = \frac{y_2 - y_1}{x_2 - x_1} = \frac{\text{change in } y}{\text{change in } x}$$

For example, the slope of the line joining the points $(2, 5)$ and $(7, 20)$ is

$$\frac{y_2 - y_1}{x_2 - x_1} = \frac{20 - 5}{7 - 2} = 3$$

The linear expression $y = mx + b$ is called the **slope-intercept** form of the equation of the line. When the equation of a line is given in this form, the coefficient of x is the slope of the line, and the constant term is the y-*intercept*, that is, the y coordinate of the point of intersection of the line and the y-axis. These statements may easily be verified algebraically.

To show that m is the slope, let (x_1, y_1) and (x_2, y_2) be two points on the line that has the equation $y = mx + b$. It is clear that $y_1 = mx_1 + b$ and $y_2 = mx_2 + b$, since both points must have coordinates satisfying the equation of the line. Use the alternative definition of the slope to obtain the following:

$$\text{slope} = \frac{y_2 - y_1}{x_2 - x_1} = \frac{(mx_2 + b) - (mx_1 + b)}{x_2 - x_1}$$

$$= \frac{mx_2 + b - mx_1 - b}{x_2 - x_1}$$

$$= \frac{mx_2 - mx_1}{x_2 - x_1}$$

$$= \frac{m(x_2 - x_1)}{x_2 - x_1}$$

$$= m$$

To show that b is the y-intercept, simply observe that any point on the y-axis has its x-coordinate equal to zero. The y-value on the line corresponding to $x = 0$ is $y = m(0) + b = b$. This statement leads to an important principle for graphs.

Intercept Principle

To find the x-intercepts of a graph, let $y = 0$, and solve the resulting expression to find x. To find the y-intercepts of a graph, let $x = 0$, and solve the resulting expression to find y. In the case of a straight line, there cannot be more than one x-intercept or y-intercept, unless the line is vertical or horizontal.

□ **EXAMPLE 19.2**   Find the slope and x and y intercepts of the following. What are the coordinates of the points where the graphs cross the axes? Sketch the graphs.
a) $y = 2x - 4$ b) $3x + 4y = 24$

● **SOLUTION**

a) The coefficient of x is 2. This is the slope. The constant term, -4, is the y-intercept. To find the x-intercept, set $y = 0$.

$$0 = 2x - 4$$

$$2x = 4$$

$$x = 2 \qquad\qquad \text{(The } x\text{-intercept is 2.)}$$

The line crosses the x-axis at $(2, 0)$, and the y-axis at $(0, -4)$. This is shown in Figure 19.2.

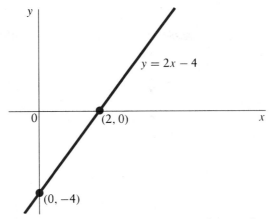

FIGURE 19.2   The x and y-intercepts for $y = 2x - 4$

b) $3x + 4y = 24$ may be algebraically transformed into the form $y = mx + b$.

$$4y = -3x + 24$$

$$y = -\frac{3}{4}x + 6$$

This is the equation of a line with slope $m = -3/4$ and y-intercept 6. The y-intercept could also have been found from the original equation by setting $x = 0$.

$$3(0) + 4y = 24$$

$$4y = 24$$

$$y = 6$$

The x-intercept can be found from the original equation in the same way by setting $y = 0$.

$$3x + 4(0) = 24$$

$$3x = 24$$

$$x = 8$$

The x-intercept is 8 and the y-intercept is 6. The line crosses the x-axis at $(8, 0)$ and crosses the y-axis at $(0, 6)$. The sketch is shown in Figure 19.3. ■

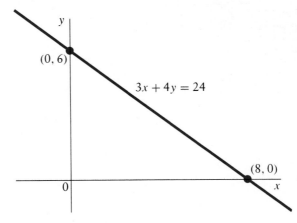

FIGURE 19.3   The intercepts for $3x + 4y = 24$

Note that the line in Figure 19.2 slopes upward from left to right, whereas the line in Figure 19.3 slopes downward. In the first case, $m = 2$, and in the second case $m = -3/4$. It is always the case that lines with positive slopes have increasing y values to the right (upward slope) and lines with negative slopes have decreasing y values to the right (downward slope). Lines with slope $m = 0$ are horizontal.

Horizontal and Vertical Lines

Horizontal lines have slope $m = 0$. The equation of such a line has the form $y = 0x + b$, which is $y = b$. Vertical lines do not have a defined slope. The equation of a vertical line can be written in the form $x = c$, where c is a constant. See Figure 19.4.

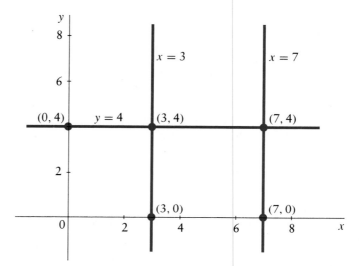

FIGURE 19.4 Examples of equations in the form $x = c$ and $y = b$

Other Equation Forms

In linear-programming applications, linear equations involving two variables usually have the form $c_1x + c_2y = K$, or $c_1x_1 + c_2x_2 = K$. Variable names are often chosen that are evocative of what the variables stand for rather than using x and y or x_1 and x_2. An example is $50C + 100L = 1{,}200{,}000$, where C and L stand for units of capital and labour.

Sometimes more complicated-looking algebraic expressions arise that can be put into linear form by manipulation, and it is important for computer solution that they be represented as $c_1x_1 + c_2x_2 = K$. If $c_2 \neq 0$, the expression $c_1x + c_2y = K$ can be transformed into slope-intercept form.

$$c_2 y = -c_1 x + K$$

$$y = -\frac{c_1}{c_2}x + \frac{K}{c_2}$$

The slope of the line is seen to be $m = -c_1/c_2$, and the y-intercept is K/c_2. According to the intercept principle, the x and y intercepts can be found by letting y and x in turn equal zero.

To find the x-intercept, let $y = 0$.

$$c_1 x + c_2 \cdot 0 = K$$

$$x = \frac{K}{c_1}$$

To find the y-intercept, let $x = 0$.

$$c_1 \cdot 0 + c_2 y = K$$

$$c_2 y = K$$

$$y = \frac{K}{c_2}$$

The x-intercept is K/c_1 and the y-intercept is K/c_2. It is convenient in many cases to sketch the graph of a line by locating the intercepts, and joining the points.

☐ **EXAMPLE 19.3**   Find the x and y intercepts and use them to help sketch the graph of each of the following equations. In each case, find the slope of the line.

a) $4x + 2y = 17$ b) $3x_1 - 4x_2 = 30$

● **SOLUTION**

a) To find the x-intercept, set $y = 0$.

$$4x = 17$$

$$x = \frac{17}{4} = 4.25$$

To find the y-intercept, set $x = 0$.

$$2y = 17$$

$$y = \frac{17}{2} = 8.5$$

$$m = -\frac{c_1}{c_2} = -\frac{4}{2} = -2$$

b) To find the x_1-intercept, set $x_2 = 0$.

$$3x_1 = 30$$

$$x_1 = 10$$

To find the x_2-intercept, set $x_1 = 0$.

$$-4x_2 = 30$$

$$x_2 = -\frac{30}{4} = -7.5$$

$$m = -\frac{c_1}{c_2} = \frac{-3}{-4} = \frac{3}{4}$$

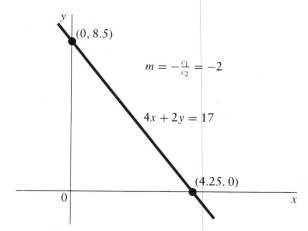

FIGURE 19.5   The slope and intercepts of $4x + 2y = 17$

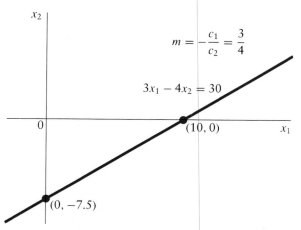

FIGURE 19.6   The slope and intercepts of
$3x_1 - 4x_2 = 30$

☐ **EXAMPLE 19.4**   Show that the following equation may be transformed into linear form. Find the intercepts and sketch the graph. What is the slope?

$$\frac{4A}{4A + 5B} = 0.60$$

● **SOLUTION**   Multiply both sides of the equation by $4A + 5B$.

$$4A = 0.60(4A + 5B)$$
$$4A = 2.40A + 3.00B$$
$$1.60A - 3.00B = 0$$

This is a linear expression of the form

$$c_1 A + c_2 B = K$$

To find the A-intercept, set $B = 0$.

$$1.60A = 0$$

$$A = 0$$

To find the B-intercept, set $A = 0$.

$$-3.00B = 0$$

$$B = 0$$

Both A and B intercepts are zero. The graph passes through the origin and the slope is $m = -\dfrac{c_1}{c_2} = \dfrac{-1.60}{-3.00} = 0.533$.

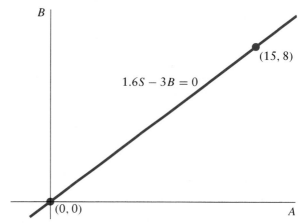

FIGURE 19.7   The intercept for an equation in the form $c_1 A + c_2 B = K$ where $K = 0$

To facilitate the sketching, a second point $(15, 8)$ has been used. Any other point could have been used — it is not necessary to find one with integer (whole-number) coordinates.   ◼

Intersections of Lines

The point of intersection of two non-parallel lines can be found by solving their equations simultaneously. If two different lines have the same slope they are parallel, and do not have a point of intersection.

CASE 1: If both line equations are in the slope-intercept form, the solution is quite easy. For example, if the point is the intersection of the lines with equations

$$y = 3x + 2$$

and

$$y = 8x - 7,$$

the solution is found by setting the right-hand sides equal to each other.

$$8x - 7 = 3x + 2$$

$$5x = 9$$

$$x = \frac{9}{5} = 1.8$$

The y-coordinate is then found by substituting the x value into either of the original equations.

$$y = 3(1.8) + 2 = 7.4$$

or

$$y = 8(1.8) - 7 = 7.4$$

The point of intersection is $(1.8, 7.4)$.

□ EXAMPLE 19.5   Show that the lines with the following equations

$$y = \frac{2}{3}x - 1$$

$$y = \frac{3}{2}x - \frac{7}{2}$$

$$y = -2x + 7$$

all have a point in common.

• SOLUTION   There are different ways of solving this problem. One way would be to solve each pair of equations simultaneously, and show that the point of intersection was the same for each pair. A simpler way will be followed here: the first pair of equations will be solved simultaneously, and then it will be shown that the coordinates of the point of intersection satisfy the equation of the third line. The coordinates of the point will satisfy all three equations, so it must be a point common to all three lines.

To solve the first pair of equations simultaneously, set their right-hand sides equal to each other.

$$\frac{3}{2}x - \frac{7}{2} = \frac{2}{3}x - 1$$

$$\frac{3}{2}x - \frac{2}{3}x = \frac{7}{2} - 1$$

$$\frac{9}{6}x - \frac{4}{6}x = \frac{7}{2} - \frac{2}{2}$$

$$\frac{5}{6}x = \frac{5}{2}$$

$$x = \frac{5}{2}\left(\frac{6}{5}\right) = 3$$

Substitute $x = 3$ into either of the equations.

$$y = \frac{3}{2}(3) - \frac{7}{2} = \frac{9}{2} - \frac{7}{2} = 1$$

The point $(3, 1)$ is the point of intersection of the first pair of lines.

The third line has equation $y = -2x + 7$. Substitute $(3, 1)$ into it. Since $1 = -2(3) + 7$, the point $(3, 1)$ satisfies the equation of the third line. It follows that the point $(3, 1)$ satisfies the equations of all three lines, and is a common intersection point.   ■

CASE 2: Usually in linear programming, lines have equations of the form $c_1x_1 + c_2x_2 = K$. There is a simple algebraic technique for solving two such equations simultaneously.

☐ **EXAMPLE 19.6**   Find the point of intersection of the lines with the following equations.

$$4x_1 + 3x_2 = 34$$
$$3x_1 + 2x_2 = 25$$

● **SOLUTION**

a) To solve for x_2, multiply the top equation by 3 and the bottom equation by 4, then subtract the new equations.

$$12x_1 + 9x_2 = 102$$
$$\underline{12x_1 + 8x_2 = 100}$$
$$x_2 = 2$$

b) To solve for x_1, multiply the original top equation by 2 and the original bottom equation by 3.

$$8x_1 + 6x_2 = 68$$
$$\underline{9x_1 + 6x_2 = 75}$$
$$-x_1 \qquad = -7 \quad \text{or} \quad x_1 = 7$$

The point of intersection is $(7, 2)$. ■

The above technique may be understood informally as multiplying the equations by appropriate numbers to make the coefficients of one of the variables the same in the two equations. If the new equations are then subtracted, it becomes very easy to solve for the other variable.

Formally, the technique may be described as follows:

$$a_1 x_1 + a_2 x_2 = K$$
$$c_1 x_1 + c_2 x_2 = L$$

a) To solve for x_2, multiply the top equation by c_1 and the bottom equation by a_1. This makes the coefficients of x_1 the same in the two new equations. Then subtract the new equations.

$$a_1 c_1 x_1 + a_2 c_1 x_2 = K c_1$$
$$\underline{a_1 c_1 x_1 + a_1 c_2 x_2 = a_1 L}$$
$$(a_2 c_1 - a_1 c_2) x_2 = K c_1 - a_1 L$$

It is now easy to solve for x_2.

b) To solve for x_1, multiply the original top equation by c_2 and the original bottom equation by a_2. This makes the coefficients of x_2 the same in the two new equations.

$$a_1 c_2 x_1 + a_2 c_2 x_2 = K c_2$$
$$\underline{a_2 c_1 x_1 + a_2 c_2 x_2 = a_2 L}$$
$$(a_1 c_2 - a_2 c_1) x_1 = K c_2 - a_2 L$$

It is now easy to solve for x_1. ■

☐ **EXAMPLE 19.7** Find the points of intersection of the lines with equations

a) $5x_1 + 17x_2 = 49$
$3x_1 + 12x_2 = 33$

b) $4x_1 - 5x_2 = 4$
$2x_1 + 7x_2 = 40$

• **SOLUTION**

a) To solve for x_2, multiply the top equation by 3 and the bottom equation by 5.

$$15x_1 + 51x_2 = 147$$
$$\underline{15x_1 + 60x_2 = 165}$$
$$-9x_2 = -18$$
$$x_2 = \frac{-18}{-9} = 2$$

To solve for x_1, multiply the original top equation by 12 and the original bottom equation by 17.

$$60x_1 + 204x_2 = 588$$
$$\underline{51x_1 + 204x_2 = 561}$$
$$9x_1 \qquad = 27$$
$$x_1 = 3$$

The point of intersection is $(3, 2)$.

b) To solve for x_2, multiply the top equation by 2 and the bottom equation by 4.

$$8x_1 - 10x_2 = 8$$
$$\underline{8x_1 + 28x_2 = 160}$$
$$-38x_2 = -152$$
$$x_2 = 4$$

To solve for x_1, multiply the original top equation by 7 and the original bottom equation by -5.

$$28x_1 - 35x_2 = 28$$
$$\underline{-10x_1 - 35x_2 = -200}$$
$$38x_1 \qquad = 228$$
$$x_1 = 6$$

The point of intersection is $(6,4)$.

Notice that in part b) following the recipe is not necessary. For example, to solve for x_2, it would have been sufficient to leave the top equation as is, and to multiply the bottom equation by 2.

$$4x_1 - 5x_2 = 4$$
$$\underline{4x_1 + 14x_2 = 80}$$
$$-19x_2 = -76$$
$$x_2 = 4$$

With experience and practice, such shortcuts become obvious. ∎

Specialized Topics for Linear Programming

Consider the following line equations, whose graphs are shown in Figure 19.8.

$$3x_1 + 4x_2 = 10$$
$$3x_1 + 4x_2 = 20$$
$$3x_1 + 4x_2 = 30$$

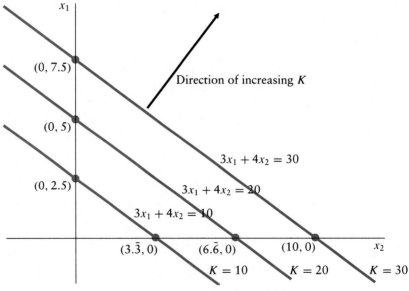

FIGURE 19.8   A family of parallel lines

The lines are parallel, since they all have the same slope, namely $-3/4$. All lines with equations of the form $3x_1 + 4x_2 = K$ have the same slope, and are said to form a **family** of parallel lines. Different values of K define different lines of the family. As K takes on larger positive values, the lines in the family cross the axes farther from the origin in the first quadrant. The arrow in Figure 19.8 is perpendicular to the lines in the family, and indicates the direction of increasing values of K.

☐ **EXAMPLE 19.8**   Sketch some representative lines for the families indicated, and draw an arrow showing the direction of increasing K.

a) $2x - 3y = K$ **b)** $-3x_1 + 4x_2 = K$

● **SOLUTION**

a) Three representative lines for $2x - 3y = K$ are sketched in Figure 19.9.

b) Three representative lines for $-3x_1 + 4x_2 = K$ are sketched in Figure 19.10.

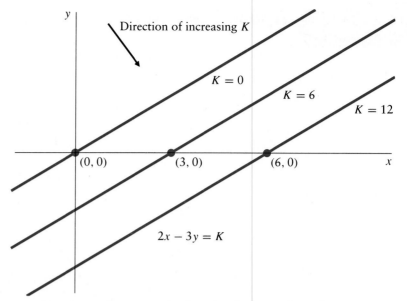

FIGURE 19.9 Representative lines for the family $2x - 3y = K$ when $K = 0$, $K = 6$, and $K = 12$

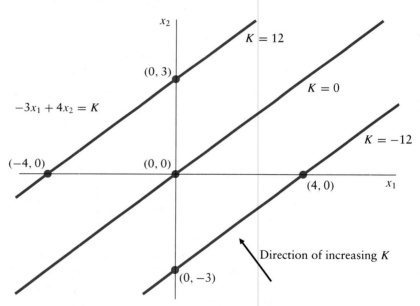

FIGURE 19.10 Representative lines for the family $-3x_1 + 4x_2 = K$ when $K = -12$, $K = 0$, and $K = 12$

It is clear from this solution and the discussion above that K can increase in any direction, depending on the values of c_1 and c_2. There is always a unique direction of increasing K for given values of c_1 and c_2. The direction opposite is the direction of decreasing K. ∎

In summary, it can be said that the equations $c_1x_1 + c_2x_2 = K$, for different values of K have graphs that form a family of parallel lines. There is a unique direction of increasing K, which can be represented by an arrow perpendicular to the lines of the family.

Graphs of Linear Inequalities

Expressions of the type

$$c_1x_1 + c_2x_2 \leq K \quad \text{or} \quad c_1x_1 + c_2x_2 \geq K$$

are linear inequalities. The graphs of these inequalities include a boundary line and all points on one side of the line.

☐ **EXAMPLE 19.9**   Sketch the region defined by the inequality

$$3x_1 + 4x_2 \leq 20$$

• **SOLUTION**   The boundary of the region is the line with the equation $3x_1 + 4x_2 = 20$. The best way to determine which side of the line is defined by the inequality is to choose a point not on the line, usually the origin, and see whether its coordinates satisfy the inequality. If they do, shade the same side as the check point, and if they do not, shade the opposite side. In this case, the origin is not on the line, and $3(0) + 4(0) = 0$, which is less than or equal to 20. The conclusion is that the origin is on the side of the line defined by the inequality. The sketch is shown in Figure 19.11. The shading shows the side of the line defined by the inequality.   ■

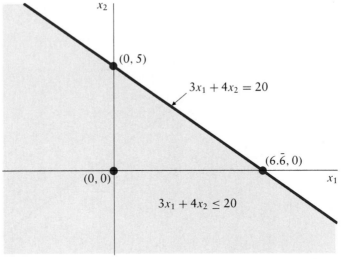

FIGURE 19.11   The shaded area represents the region defined by the inequality $3x_1 + 4x_2 \leq 20$

☐ **EXAMPLE 19.10**   Sketch the regions defined by the following inequalities.
a) $3x_1 - 4x_2 \leq 20$ b) $4x_1 + 5x_2 \geq 0$ c) $-4x_1 + 5x_2 \leq 0$

• **SOLUTION**

a) The boundary of the region is the line with equation $3x_1 - 4x_2 = 20$. The origin is not on the line, and $(0, 0)$ satisfies the inequality. The graph of the inequality is the boundary line shaded on the same side as the origin. See Figure 19.12.

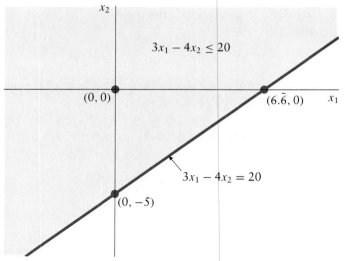

FIGURE 19.12   The region defined by the inequality
$3x_1 - 4x_2 \leq 20$

b) The boundary of the region is the line with equation $4x_1 + 5x_2 = 0$. The origin is on this line, so it is not a suitable check point for determining which side of the line to shade. Take $(1, 0)$, a point not on the line. Since $4(1) + 5(0) = 4 \geq 0$, the point $(1, 0)$ satisfies the inequality. It follows that the line should have shading on the same side as that on which $(1, 0)$ lies. See Figure 19.13.

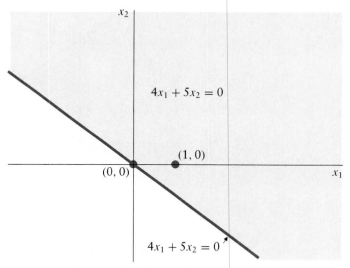

FIGURE 19.13   The region defined by the inequality
$4x_1 + 5x_2 \geq 0$

c) The boundary of the region is the line with equation $-4x_1 + 5x_2 = 0$. The origin is on this line, so it is not a suitable check point for determining which side of the line to shade. Take $(0, 1)$, a point not on the line. Since $-4(0) + 5(1) = 5 \geq 0$, the point $(0, 1)$ does not satisfy the inequality. It follows that the line should have shading on the side opposite to $(0, 1)$. See Figure 19.14. ∎

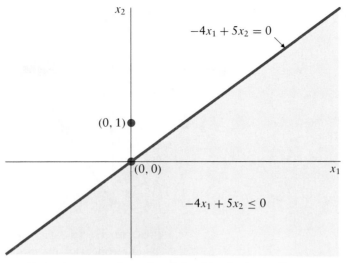

FIGURE 19.14   The region defined by the inequality $-4x_1 + 5x_2 \leq 0$

Be careful not to fall into the trap of shading the under side of the line for a less than or equal to inequality and the upper side of the line for a greater than or equal to inequality. The foregoing examples show that this does not always give the correct answer. The check-point method is the best way.

In linear-programming applications, it is almost always the case that more than one inequality is graphed on the same set of axes, and the intersection of the shaded regions is considered. The intersection of the shaded regions is called the **feasible region,** and it is always in the first quadrant.

◻ STUDY QUESTION 19.1

Find the feasible region defined by the intersection of these inequalities.

$$3x_1 + 4x_2 \leq 24$$
$$2x_1 - x_2 \leq 4$$
$$x_1 \geq 0, x_2 \geq 0 \quad \text{(defines the first quadrant)}$$

● **ANSWER**   The origin $(0, 0)$ satisfies both inequalities. Thus, the region to be shaded lies below $3x_1 + 4x_2 = 24$ and to the left of $2x_1 - x_2 = 4$. Since $x_1 \geq 0, x_2 \geq 0$, the feasible region is restricted to the area that is common to both inequalities in the first quadrant.   ▪

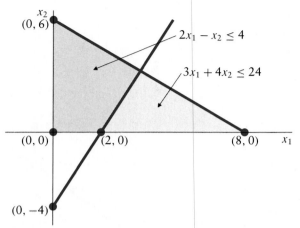

FIGURE 19.15 The double-shaded area shows the feasible region for the inequalities $3x_1 + 4x_2 \leq 24$, $2x_1 - x_2 \leq 4$, and $x \geq 0, y \geq 0$

PROBLEMS

19.1 Find equations for the lines given the following data.

a) passing through $(-2, 3)$ with slope 2.5

b) passing through the origin with slope -3

c) passing through $(-1, 4)$ with slope -3

d) joining the points $(2, 4)$ and $(6, -2)$

e) joining the points $(-1, 1)$ and $(2, 2)$

f) having x-intercept 2 and y-intercept -4

19.2 Show that $\frac{x}{h} + \frac{y}{k} = 1$ is an equation of a line with x-intercept h and y-intercept k.

19.3 Find the slopes and intercepts of the lines with the following equations.

a) $y = 3x - 7$ **b)** $2x + 4y = 16$
c) $\frac{x}{2} + \frac{y}{4} = 1$ **d)** $3x - 2y = 4$
e) $x = 4y - 2$

19.4 Find the equations of the sides of the triangle shown in Figure 19.16. What is the numerical value of y?

19.5 Find the point of intersection for each of the following pairs of lines.

a) $y = \frac{3}{2}x + \frac{5}{2}$ **b)** $y = 4x - 2$
$y = -2x - 1$ $y = 10x$

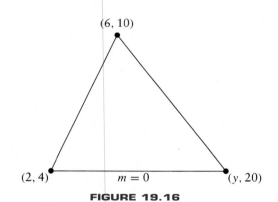

FIGURE 19.16

19.6 Find the point of intersection for each of the following pairs of lines.

a) $2x_1 - x_2 = 4$ **b)** $3A + 4B = 12$
$3x_1 + 4x_2 = 24$ $2A - 6B = 7$
c) $5x - 9y = 17$ **d)** $0.45x - 0.35y = 2.32$
$2x + 3y = -2$ $0.16x + 0.22y = 1.66$

19.7 Sketch the families of lines indicated by choosing four different values of K. Draw the four parallel lines and include the direction of increasing K in the sketch.

a) $5x_1 + 6x_2 = K$ **b)** $5x_1 - 6x_2 = K$
c) $-5x_1 + 6x_2 = K$ **d)** $2A - 3B = K$

19.8 Sketch the following inequalities.

a) $2A - 3B \leq 60$ **b)** $-2A + 3B \leq 60$
c) $4x_1 + x_2 \leq 10$ **d)** $2x_1 - 3x_2 \geq 0$

19.9 Determine the feasible region (in the first quadrant) defined by the following systems of inequalities. Shade the intersections of the inequalities.

a) $4x_1 + 8x_2 \leq 16$
$2x_1 + 5x_2 \leq 9$
$x_1 \geq 0, x_2 \geq 0$

b) $4x_1 + 8x_2 \leq 16$
$2x_1 + 5x_2 \geq 9$
$x_1 \geq 0, x_2 \geq 0$

c) $2A + 3B \leq 6$
$3A + 2B \leq 6$
$A \leq 2$
$A \geq 0, B \geq 0$

d) $2A + 3B \leq 6$
$3A + 2B \leq 6$
$A + B \geq 1$
$A \geq 0, B \geq 0$

19.10 Find and label all the vertices of the feasible regions in Problem 19.9.

section 19.4   Graphical Solution (two variables)

When a linear-programming problem involves only two variables, the constraints define a portion of the first quadrant that can be sketched using line-graphing techniques. The region determined is the *feasible region*. Values of the variables at points in the feasible region are the **only** allowable values.

In most cases the feasible region is an area, but occasionally it reduces to a line segment, a single point, or even the empty set. Feasible regions of these sorts are not typical, however.

All feasible regions are *convex*, which means that there are no indentations. The technical way of saying this is that the line segment joining any two points in the feasible region must lie entirely within the region. Refer to Figure 19.17.

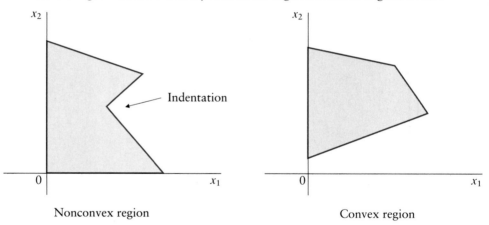

Nonconvex region   Convex region

FIGURE 19.17   Only a convex region can represent the feasible region of a linear-programming problem

Sketches of Feasible Regions

The non-negativity constraints ($x_1 \geq 0, x_2 \geq 0$) guarantee that the feasible region is in the first quadrant, as shown in the following examples.

☐ **EXAMPLE 19.11**   Find the area described by the following set of equations. Is the area a feasible region?

$$2x_1 + 3x_2 \leq 18$$
$$2x_1 + x_2 \leq 10$$
$$x_1 \geq 0, x_2 \geq 0$$

● **SOLUTION** Shade the same side as the origin for $2x_1 + 3x_2 \le 18$ and $2x_1 + x_2 \le 10$, since $(0, 0)$ satisfies both inequalities. The point of intersection of the boundary lines is shown in Figure 19.18 (b) and is the simultaneous solution of the first pair of equations.

$$2x_1 + 3x_2 = 18$$

$$2x_1 + x_2 = 10$$

The solution may be obtained in the standard ways: algebraic manipulation or substitution. The point of intersection is found to be $(3, 4)$.

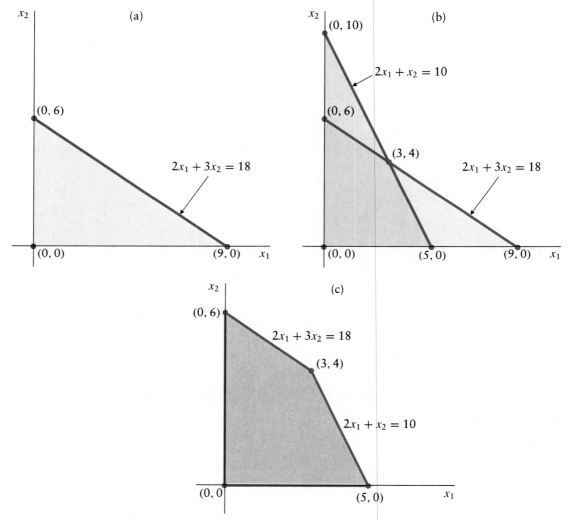

FIGURE 19.18 The double shaded area represents the feasible region for the inequalities $2x_1 + 3x_2 \le 18$, $2x_1 + x_2 \le 10$, and $x_1 \ge 0$, $x_2 \ge 0$

The boundary lines of the area form corners, or **vertices**, at $(0, 0)$, $(0, 6)$, $(3, 4)$, and $(5, 0)$. It is a feasible region because the area is a *convex* region of the plane. ■

☐ **EXAMPLE 19.12**   Is the area described by the following set of equations a feasible region?

$$4x_1 + 3x_2 \leq 27$$
$$-x_1 + x_2 \geq 2$$
$$x_1 \geq 0, x_2 \geq 0$$

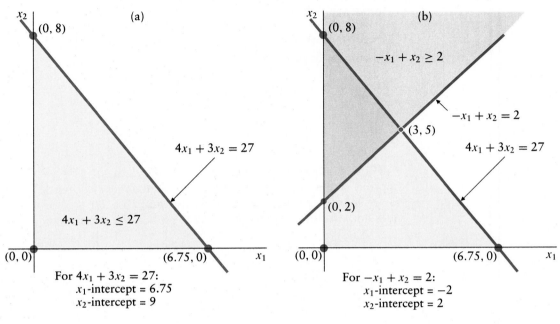

For $4x_1 + 3x_2 = 27$:
x_1-intercept = 6.75
x_2-intercept = 9

For $-x_1 + x_2 = 2$:
x_1-intercept = -2
x_2-intercept = 2

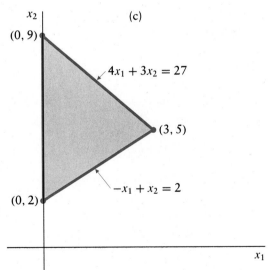

FIGURE 19.19   The double-shaded area represents the feasible region for the inequalities $4x_1 + 3x_2 \leq 27$, $-x_1 + x_2 \geq 2$, and $x_1 \geq 0$, $x_2 \geq 0$

• **SOLUTION**   Since $(0, 0)$ satisfies the inequality, shade the same side as the origin for $4x_1 + 3x_2 \leq 27$, as shown in Figure 19.19 a). Shade the side opposite to the origin for $-x_1 + x_2 \geq 2$, since $(0, 0)$ does not satisfy the inequality. The point of intersection of the boundary lines is shown in Figure 19.19 b) and is found by solving the following equations simultaneously.

$$4x_1 + 3x_2 = 27$$
$$-x_1 + x_2 = 2$$

The intersection point is $(3, 5)$. The area is a feasible region because the area is convex with vertices $(0, 2)$, $(0, 9)$, and $(3, 5)$.   ■

☐ EXAMPLE 19.13   Describe the shape of the feasible region specified by the following set of equations.

$$-3x_1 + x_2 \leq 2$$
$$-x_1 + 2x_2 \geq 4$$
$$x_1 + 2x_2 \geq 2$$
$$x_1 \geq 0, x_2 \geq 0$$

• SOLUTION   Shade the same side as the origin for $-3x_1 + x_2 \leq 2$. Shade the opposite side to the origin for $-x_1 + 2x_2 \geq 4$. Shade the opposite side to the origin for $x_1 + 2x_2 \geq 2$. Observe that the constraint $x_1 + 2x_2 \geq 2$ is superfluous, since it does not affect the region defined by the other two constraints.

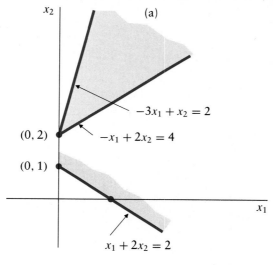 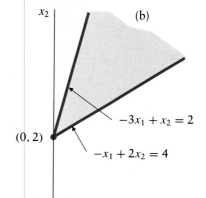

FIGURE 19.20   The shaded area is the feasible region for the inequalities $-3x_1 + x_2 \leq 2$, $-x_1 + 2x_2 \geq 4$, and $x_1 + 2x_2 \geq 2$

The feasible region is a wedge with vertex at $(0, 2)$. The wedge is unbounded in the sense that the feasible region has x_1 and x_2 values that are arbitrarily large.   ■

☐ EXAMPLE 19.14   Describe the feasible region.

$$5x_1 - 2x_2 \leq 3$$
$$-3x_1 + 4x_2 = 4$$
$$x_2 \leq 10$$
$$x_1 \geq 0, x_2 \geq 0$$

• **SOLUTION**   Shade $x_2 \le 10$ on the same side as the origin. Shade $5x_1 - 2x_2 \le 3$ on the same side as the origin. The equality constraint $-3x_1 + 4x_2 = 4$ defines a line, so neither side is shaded.

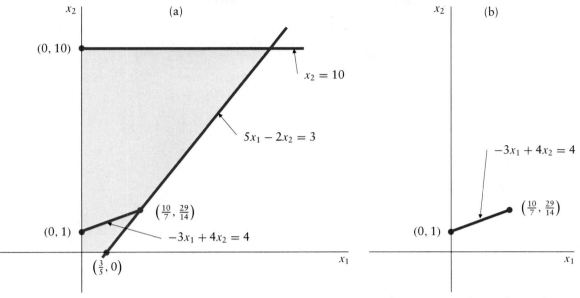

FIGURE 19.21   The feasible region is the line segment indicated by the equality $-3x_1 + 4x_2 = 4$

The feasible region is the line segment joining $(0, 1)$ to $\left(\frac{10}{7}, \frac{29}{14}\right)$, the intersection point of $5x_1 - 2x_2 = 3$ and $-3x_1 + 4x_2 = 4$.

The points $(0, 1)$ and $\left(\frac{10}{7}, \frac{29}{14}\right)$, are called the vertices of the feasible region in such a case and are shown in Figure 19.21 b). ∎

◻ **EXAMPLE 19.15**   Prove that the feasible region defined by the following inequalities is the null set.

$$x_1 + x_2 \ge 5$$
$$4x_1 - x_2 \le 0$$
$$x_1 - 4x_2 \ge 0$$
$$x_1 \ge 0, x_2 \ge 0$$

• **SOLUTION**   Shade the side opposite the origin for $x_1 + x_2 \ge 5$ since $(0, 0)$ does *not* satisfy the inequality. The boundary line for $4x_1 - x_2 \le 0$ passes through the origin, so use another check point. A suitable point is $(1, 0)$. Shade the side opposite $(1, 0)$ since $x_1 = 1, x_2 = 0$ does not satisfy the inequality. Shade the side opposite $(0, 1)$ for $x_1 - 4x_2 \ge 0$. As in the previous inequality, the origin is not a suitable check point.

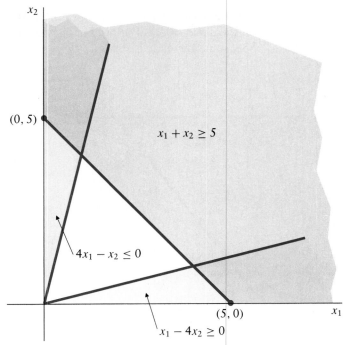

FIGURE 19.22   The intersection is the null set

There is no point common to all three shaded regions. The feasible region is the empty set. When this happens, the linear-programming problem is said to be **in-feasible**. If this happens in a real-life situation, it usually means that too many conditions have to be met, and the problem cannot be solved. ∎

The foregoing examples illustrate the usual types of feasible regions when two variables are involved. Completed feasible-region sketches should be checked to make sure that they lie in the first quadrant and are convex.

Incorporating the Objective Function

The objective function has the form $Z = c_1 x_1 + c_2 x_2$ when two variables are involved. If Z is given different numerical values, the graphs of the resulting equations will form a family of parallel straight lines. The numerical value of Z will increase on the same side for all the lines, and the numerical value of Z will decrease on the opposite side. This observation leads to the discovery of the most important fact in linear programming:

> The *optimal value* of Z corresponds to an *objective-function line* that passes *through a vertex* of the feasible region.

To see what this means, consider the feasible region outlined in Example 19.11. We want to maximize the value of Z, subject to certain conditions.

$$\max Z = x_1 + x_2$$

subject to

$$2x_1 + 3x_2 \leq 18$$

$$2x_1 + x_2 \leq 10$$

$$x_1 \geq 0, \ x_2 \geq 0$$

First, a sketch is made of the family of lines represented by $Z = x_1 + x_2$, by giving the values 1,2,3,4,...7 in turn to Z and sketching the lines. See Figure 19.23.

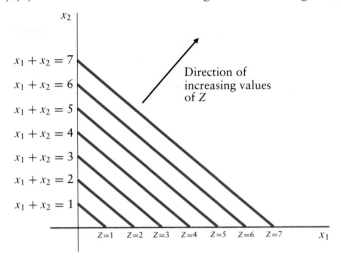

FIGURE 19.23   The family of lines represented by $Z = x_1 + x_2$ where $Z = 1$ to 7

When lines of the family are superimposed on a sketch of the feasible region, as in Figure 19.24, it becomes clear that the highest value for a point in the feasible region must occur at $(3, 4)$. Any higher value of Z gives an objective-function line that does not intersect the feasible region. Remember that the only values of the variables that are allowable come from points in the feasible region.

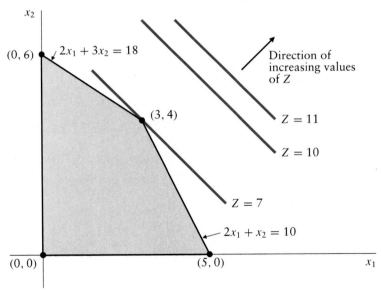

FIGURE 19.24   The optimal value for $Z = x_1 + x_2$ is $Z = 7$

The solution to the problem

$$\max Z = x_1 + x_2$$

subject to

$$2x_1 + 3x_2 \le 18$$
$$2x_1 + x_2 \le 10$$
$$x_1 \ge 0, \ x_2 \ge 0$$

is $x_1 = 3$, $x_2 = 4$, $Z = 7$.

□ **EXAMPLE 19.16**   Solve the following optimization problems.

a) max $Z = x_1 + 3x_2$
    s.t. $2x_1 + 3x_2 \le 18$
           $2x_1 + x_2 \le 10$
           $x_1 \ge 0, \ x_2 \ge 0$

b) max $Z = x_1 - x_2$
    s.t. $2x_1 + 3x_2 \le 18$
           $2x_1 + x_2 \le 10$
           $x_1 \ge 0, x_2 \ge 0$

• **SOLUTION**

a) Figure 19.25 provides the graphical solution. The objective-function line passing through the vertex $(0, 6)$ gives the highest possible value of Z in the feasible region. The solution is $x_1 = 0$, $x_2 = 6$, $Z = 18$.

b) Figure 19.26 provides a graphical solution. The objective-function line passing through the vertex $(5, 0)$ gives the highest possible value of Z in the feasible region. The solution is $x_1 = 5$, $x_2 = 0$, $Z = 5$. Notice that the direction of increasing Z is *downward*, not upward. It is important to check numerically which is the direction of increasing Z and not to rely on intuition. ■

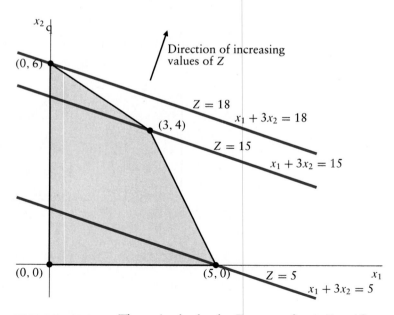

FIGURE 19.25   The optimal value for $Z = x_1 + 3x_2$ is $Z = 18$

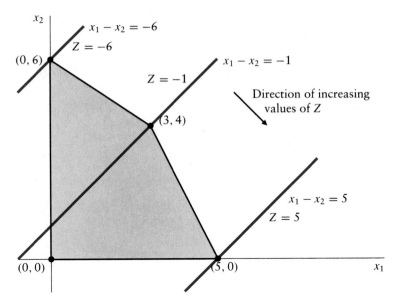

FIGURE 19.26   The optimal value for $Z = x_1 - x_2$ is $Z = 5$

☐ **EXAMPLE 19.17**   Solve the following problems, subject to the following set of constraints.

a) $\min Z = x_1 + x_2$ **b)** $\min Z = x_1 + 3x_2$ **c)** $\min Z = x_1 - x_2$

$$2x_1 + 3x_2 \leq 18$$

$$2x_1 + x_2 \leq 10$$

$$x_1 \geq 0, x_2 \geq 0$$

• **SOLUTION**   These minimization problems can be solved using Figures 19.24 to 19.26. The direction of *decreasing* Z must be taken, since it is the lowest value that is required for minimization.

The solutions are as follows:

a) $x_1 = 0, x_2 = 0, Z = 0$
b) $x_1 = 0, x_2 = 0, Z = 0$
c) $x_1 = 0, x_2 = 6, Z = -6$ ■

It can be seen that for either a maximization or a minimization problem, the optimal solution must occur at a vertex of the feasible region. One approach to solving a linear-programming problem is to find the coordinates of all the vertices, and evaluate the objective function at each one. The optimal solution can then be selected from the list of values.

☐ **EXAMPLE 19.18**   Find max Z and min Z, where $Z = 3x_1 - x_2$, subject to the following constraints:

$$-2x_1 + 5x_2 \leq 50$$

$$3x_1 + 2x_2 \leq 39$$

$$2x_1 - x_2 \leq 12$$

$$x_1 \geq 0, \ x_2 \geq 0$$

● **SOLUTION** As usual, the coordinates of the vertices can be found by solving the appropriate pairs of simultaneous linear equations. For example,

$$3x_1 + 2x_2 = 39$$
$$2x_1 - x_2 = 12$$

has intersection point $(9, 6)$. The graph of the feasible region is shown in Figure 19.27.

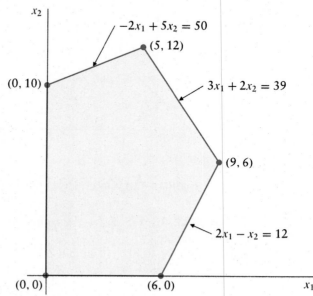

FIGURE 19.27 The feasible region for the inequalities $-2x_1 + 5x_2 \le 50$, $3x_1 + 2x_2 \le 39$, and $2x_1 - x_2 \le 12$

Substitution into $Z = 3x_1 - x_2$ yields the following values:

At $(0, 0)$, $Z = 3(0) - 0 = 0$
$(6, 0)$, $Z = 3(6) - 0 = 18$
$(9, 6)$, $Z = 3(9) - 6 = 21$
$(5, 12)$, $Z = 3(5) - 12 = 3$
$(0, 10)$, $Z = 3(0) - 10 = -10$

The solution is max $Z = 21$ when $x_1 = 9$ and $x_2 = 6$, and min $Z = -10$ when $x_1 = 0$ and $x_2 = 10$. ∎

Anomalies

The examples that have been given illustrate what can be expected in a straightforward situation where enough information is given for there to be one and only one solution to a linear-programming problem. There are, however, some problems that do not fit this pattern. They can be categorized as **alternative optimal, unbounded** or **infeasible problems**.

☐ **STUDY QUESTION 19.2** An Alternative Optimal Linear-Programming Problem

For the following situation, describe the optimal objective-function line. Does this contradict the fact that the optimal value must occur at a vertex of the feasible region?

$$\max Z = x_1 + 0.5x_2$$

$$\text{s.t.}\quad 2x_1 + 3x_2 \leq 18$$
$$2x_1 + x_2 \leq 10$$
$$x_1 \geq 0,\ x_2 \geq 0$$

● **ANSWER** The objective-function lines are parallel to one edge of the feasible region. The highest value of Z is 5 and the optimal objective-function line passes through an entire line segment in the feasible region. Every point on the line segment gives Z its optimal value of 5. This does not contradict the principle that the optimal value must occur at a vertex. There are, in fact, two vertices at which the objective function has its maximum value. Two solutions are

$$x_1 = 3,\ x_2 = 4,\ Z = 5 \quad\text{and}\quad x_1 = 5,\ x_2 = 0,\ Z = 5$$

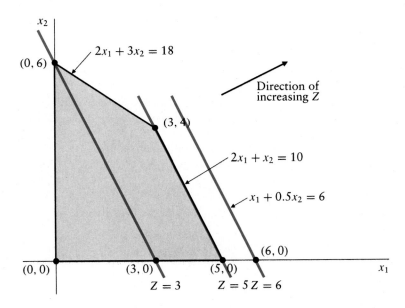

FIGURE 19.28   The optimal objective-function line is $x_1 + 0.5x_2 = 5$

Note that there are infinitely many other solutions as well, on the line segment joining the vertices. ■

☐ **STUDY QUESTION 19.3**   **An Unbounded Linear-Programming Problem**

Is there a maximum value of Z for the feasible region described in the following problem? Why?

$$\max Z = 2x_1 + 3x_2$$
$$\text{s.t.}\quad -3x_1 + x_2 \leq 2$$
$$-x_1 + 2x_2 \geq 4$$
$$x_1 + 2x_2 \geq 2$$
$$x_1 \geq 0,\ x_2 \geq 0$$

● **ANSWER** The feasible region is a wedge with vertex at $(0, 2)$, as shown in Figure 19.29. There is no maximum value of Z, since the objective function lines intersect the feasible region for any numerical value of Z, no matter how large.

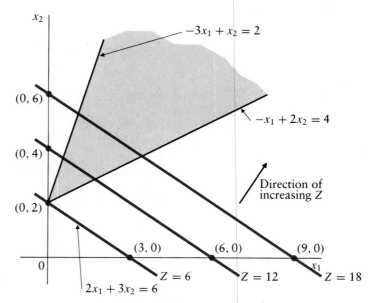

FIGURE 19.29   An optimal function value does not exist in an unbounded linear-programming problem

Note that the minimization problem

$$\min Z = 2x_1 + 3x_2$$

$$\text{s.t.}\quad -3x_1 + x_2 \le 2$$
$$-x_1 + 2x_2 \ge 4$$
$$x_1 + 2x_2 \ge 2$$
$$x_1 \ge 0, x_2 \ge 0$$

has a solution, namely $x_1 = 0$, $x_2 = 2$, $Z = 6$.   ■

□ **STUDY QUESTION 19.4**   **An Infeasible Linear-Programming Problem**
Describe the feasible region for this problem.

$$\max Z = 25.5x_1 - 31.9x_2$$

$$\text{s.t.}\quad x_1 + x_2 \ge 5$$
$$4x_1 - x_2 \le 0$$
$$x_1 - 4x_2 \ge 0$$
$$x_1 \ge 0, x_2 \ge 0$$

• **ANSWER**   The feasible region is the empty set. There are no values of x_1 and x_2 that simultaneously satisfy all the constraints. Thus, the problem is said to be *infeasible*.   ■

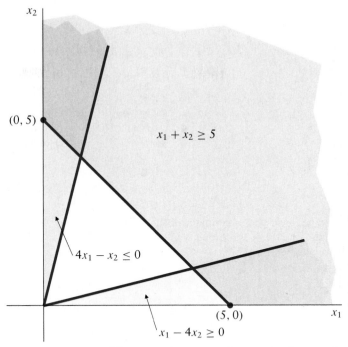

$x_1 + x_2 \geq 5$

$(0, 5)$

$4x_1 - x_2 \leq 0$

$(5, 0)$

$x_1 - 4x_2 \geq 0$

FIGURE 19.30   The constraints cannot be met simultaneously

PROBLEMS

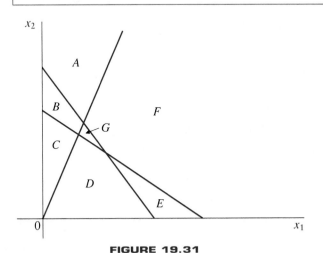

FIGURE 19.31

19.11 The lines with equations

$$9x_1 + 8x_2 = 72$$
$$3x_1 + 5x_2 = 30$$
$$x_1 - x_2 = 0$$

have been sketched in the first quadrant, creating regions A, B, C, D, E, F, and G in Figure 19.31. What are the regions defined by the following sets of constraints?

a) $9x_1 + 8x_2 \leq 72$
$3x_1 + 5x_2 \leq 30$
$x_1 - x_2 \geq 0$
$x_1 \geq 0, x_2 \geq 0$

b) $9x_1 + 8x_2 \leq 72$
$3x_1 + 5x_2 \geq 30$
$x_1 - x_2 \geq 0$
$x_1 \geq 0, x_2 \geq 0$

c) $9x_1 + 8x_2 \geq 72$
$3x_1 + 5x_2 \geq 30$
$x_1 - x_2 \leq 0$
$x_1 \geq 0, x_2 \geq 0$

d) $9x_1 + 8x_2 \leq 72$
$3x_1 + 5x_2 \leq 30$
$x_1 - x_2 \leq 0$
$x_1 \geq 0, x_2 \geq 0$

19.12 Using the information from the problem above, write the inequalities that would determine regions B, E, and F.

19.13 For each of the following linear-programming problems, sketch the feasible region and solve graphically. Label each vertex of the feasible region, giving its coordinates. Sketch the optimal objective-function line, showing it passing through the optimal vertex. State the solution, giving the values of the decision variables and the objective function.

a) $\max Z = 3x_1 + 4x_2$
s.t. $2x_1 + 3x_2 \le 36$
    $5x_1 + 2x_2 \le 35$
    $5x_1 + x_2 \le 30$
    $x_1 \ge 0, x_2 \ge 0$

b) $\min Z = 3x_1 - 2x_2$
s.t. $7x_1 + 5x_2 \le 35$
    $2x_1 + x_2 \ge 5$

    $x_1 \ge 0, x_2 \ge 0$

b) $\min Z = 2x_1 - 5x_2$

s.t. $-2x_1 + 3x_2 \le 18$
    $-x_1 + x_2 \le 4$
    $x_1 + x_2 \ge 4$
    $x_1 \ge 0, x_2 \ge 0$

c) $\max Z = 9A - 3B$
s.t. $A + B \le 5$
    $A + B \ge 3$
    $-A + B \le 1$
    $A - B \le 1$
    $A \ge 0, B \ge 0$

d) $\min Z = 1.5y - 2.5x$
s.t. $-2x + 3y \le 15$
    $2x - y \le 5$
    $y \ge 2$

    $x \ge 0, y \ge 0$

c) $\min Z = 2x_1 - 3x_2$

s.t. $-2x_1 + 3x_2 \le 18$
    $-x_1 + x_2 \le 4$
    $x_1 + x_2 \ge 4$
    $x_1 \ge 0, x_2 \ge 0$

19.14 The following linear-programming problems all involve an anomaly. Determine the anomaly in each case, and solve, if possible.

a) $\max Z = 2x_1 + 5x_2$

s.t. $-2x_1 + 3x_2 \le 18$

    $-x_1 + x_2 \le 4$

    $x_1 + x_2 \ge 4$

    $x_1 \ge 0, x_2 \ge 0$

d) $\max Z = 3x_1 + 4x_2$

s.t. $-x_1 - x_2 \le 25$

    $2x_1 + 3x_2 \le 10$

    $x_2 \ge 4$

    $x_1 \ge 0, x_2 \ge 0$

---

section 19.5

Graphical Sensitivity Analysis

In the standard linear-programming problem

$$\text{optimize } Z = \Sigma c_j x_j$$

$$\text{s.t.}\quad \Sigma a_{ij} x_j \overset{\le}{\underset{\ge}{=}} b_i$$

the constants c_j, a_{ij}, and b_i are called the **parameters** of the problem. If one of the parameters in a problem is changed, it is often important to know what effect the change has on the optimal solution.

❑ **EXAMPLE 19.19**   Find an optimal solution for each of the following:

a) $\max Z = 2x_1 + 3x_2$
s.t. $x_1 + x_2 \le 100$
    $2x_1 - x_2 \ge 40$
    $x_1 \ge 0, x_2 \ge 0$

b) $\max Z = 2x_1 + 2.9x_2$
s.t. $x_1 + x_2 \le 100$
    $2x_1 - x_2 \ge 40$
    $x_1 \ge 0, x_2 \ge 0$

c) $\max Z = 2x_1 + 3x_2$
s.t. $x_1 + x_2 \le 100.1$
    $2x_1 - x_2 \ge 40$
    $x_1 \ge 0, x_2 \ge 0$

• **SOLUTION**   The optimal solutions are as follows:

a) $x_1 = 46.67$, $x_2 = 53.33$, $Z = 253.33$

b) $x_1 = 46.67$, $x_2 = 53.33$, $Z = 248$

c) $x_1 = 46.70$, $x_2 = 53.40$, $Z = 253.60$

It is not surprising that the answers to the three problems are close in value since the only difference between (a) and (b) is the change in c_2 from 3 to 2.9, and the only difference between (a) and (c) is the change in b_1 from 100 to 100.1.   ■

Analysis shows that there is a technique for finding the solution to a new problem from the original solution if it has not been too seriously changed from the original. In the following computations, only one parameter will be changed at a time.

Changes in an Objective-Function Coefficient (c_j)

Consider the following problem:

$$\max Z = 2x_1 + 3x_2$$
$$\text{s.t.} \quad x_1 + 3x_2 \leq 15$$
$$4x_1 + x_2 \leq 16$$
$$x_1 \geq 0, x_2 \geq 0$$

The graphical solution is given in Figure 19.32.

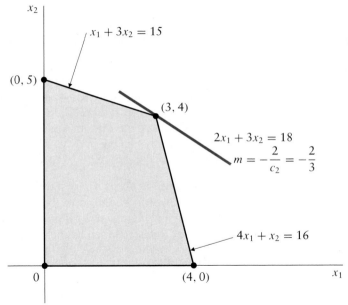

FIGURE 19.32   The slope of the objective-function line is $-2/3$

The optimal solution is $x_1 = 3$, $x_2 = 4$, $Z = 18$.

The slope of the objective function line is $-2/3$.

The slope of the boundary of the feasible region between $(0, 5)$ and $(3, 4)$ is $-1/3$ and the slope of the boundary between $(3, 4)$ and $(4, 0)$ is -4. One reason that $(3, 4)$ is the optimal vertex is that the slope of the objective-function line lies between the values -4 and $-1/3$.

If $c_1 = 2$ were to be left at its current value and c_2 were changed, then the slope of the objective-function line would change. So long as the change kept the slope of the line at a value between -4 and $-1/3$, the vertex $(3, 4)$ would still be optimal. See Figure 19.33.

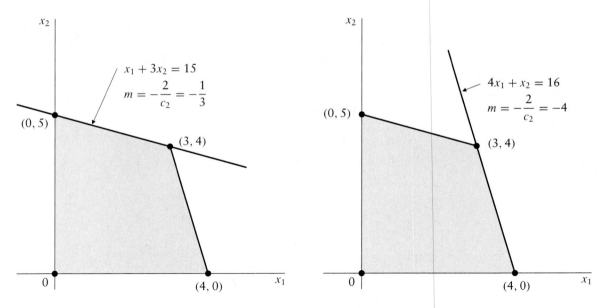

FIGURE 19.33 $(3, 4)$ is the optimal vertex because the objective-line slope lies between $-1/3$ and -4

The slope of the objective-function line is $-c_1/c_2 = -2/c_2$. If $-2/c_2 = -1/3$, it follows that $c_2 = 6$. If $-2/c_2 = -4$, it follows that $c_2 = 1/2$. Since $c_1 = 2$, then for any value of c_2 between $1/2$ and 6, $(3, 4)$ would be the optimal vertex. The optimal value of Z would depend on the value of c_2, since $Z = c_1 x_1 + c_2 x_2 = 2(3) + c_2(4) = 6 + 4c_2$. Clearly any change in c_2 would be accompanied by a change four times as great in the optimal Z value.

The **range analysis** for c_2 states that the smallest value of c_2 for the current optimal vertex would be 0.5, and the largest value would be 6. The sensitivity of the solution to any change in c_2 is given by the x_2 value of 4. The optimal value of Z changes four times as much as the change in c_2.

Remember that this analysis is valid only so long as all the other parameters remain unchanged. If the value of c_2 is changed to less than 0.5 or greater than 6, another vertex will be optimal.

☐ **EXAMPLE 19.20**   If possible, use range analysis to solve the following:

a) $\max Z = 2x_1 + x_2$
   s.t. $x_1 + 3x_2 \leq 15$
   $4x_1 + x_2 \leq 16$
   $x_1 \geq 0, x_2 \geq 0$

b) $\max Z = 2x_1 + 6.5x_2$
   s.t. $x_1 + 3x_2 \leq 15$
   $4x_1 + x_2 \leq 16$
   $x_1 \geq 0, x_2 \geq 00$

● **SOLUTION**

a) $c_2 = 1$ is a value in the range $0.5 \leq c_2 \leq 6$. Therefore, the optimal solution is $x_1 = 3, x_2 = 4, Z = 10$. Note that the change in c_2 is -2 and the corresponding change in the optimal Z value is $4(-2) = -8$.

b) $c_2 = 6.5$ is not a value in the range $0.5 \leq c_2 \leq 6$. The optimal solution cannot be determined using the sensitivity factor of 4.   ∎

❑ **EXAMPLE 19.21**   Perform a range analysis for c_1 based on the following problem.

$$\max Z = 2x_1 + 3x_2$$

$$\text{s.t.} \quad x_1 + 3x_2 \leq 15$$

$$4x_1 + x_2 \leq 16$$

$$x_1 \geq 0, x_2 \geq 0$$

• **SOLUTION**   The slope of the objective function line is $-c_1/c_2 = -c_1/3$. Refer to Figure 19.32. The current optimal vertex is the optimal vertex for objective function slopes between -4 and $-1/3$.

If $-c_1/3 = -4$, it follows that $c_1 = 12$.

If $-c_1/3 = -1/3$, it follows that $c_1 = 1$.

As long as $1 \leq c_1 \leq 12$, the optimal vertex is $(3, 4)$, and the optimal solution is $x_1 = 3, x_2 = 4, Z = 3c_1 + 12$.

The sensitivity factor for c_1 is 3. Any change in c_1 leads to a change three times as great in the optimal Z value.   ∎

The range and sensitivity analysis for an objective-function coefficient may always be written in the form:

> If all other parameters remain the same, so long as $\ell \leq c_j \leq u$, the *current optimal vertex* remains optimal. Within this range, a change in c_j results in a change in the optimal value of Z that is x_j times as great.

The lower limit ℓ in the range analysis could be anything from $-\infty$ (negative infinity) to the current value of c_j, and the upper limit u could be anything from the current value of c_j to $+\infty$ (positive infinity).

❑ **EXAMPLE 19.22**   Do the range and sensitivity analysis for c_2 in the following linear-programming problem.

$$\max Z = 2x_1 + 3x_2$$

$$\text{s.t.} \quad -2x_1 + 3x_2 \leq 15$$

$$2x_1 - x_2 \geq 5$$

$$x_1 \geq 0, x_2 \geq 0$$

• **SOLUTION**   The graphical solution is shown in Figure 19.34.

The optimal solution is $x_1 = 7.5, x_2 = 10, Z = 45$. The effect of increasing c_2 from its current value of 3 is to make the objective-function line more nearly horizontal. No amount of increase will make the slope positive, since $-c_1/c_2 < 0$. This means that the range for c_2 includes all values greater than or equal to the current value of 3.

A decrease in c_2 can be made until the slope of the objective-function line equals the slope of the boundary line joining $(2.5, 0)$ to $(7.5, 10)$. The slope of this line is 2.

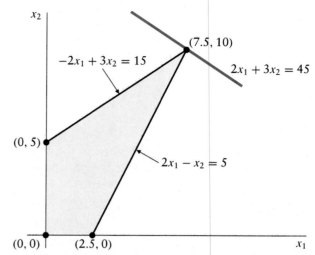

FIGURE 19.34   The optimal objective-function line is $2x_1 + 3x_2 = 45$

If the objective-function line has slope 2, then

$$-\frac{c_1}{c_2} = \frac{-2}{c_2} = 2$$

This is true for $c_2 = -1$.

The range analysis reveals that so long as $-1 \leq c_2$, the current optimal vertex remains optimal. That is, the optimal solution is $x_1 = 7.5$, $x_2 = 10$, $Z = 15 + 10c_2$. Clearly any change in c_2 leads to a change ten times as great in the optimal value of Z.

Note that it is not necessary to write $-1 \leq c_2 < +\infty$, since $-1 \leq c_2$ means the same thing. ■

Changes in a Right-hand-Side Constant (b_i)

If all the other parameters in a linear-programming problem are kept the same, and b_i, one of the right-hand-side constants is changed, analysis shows that for a range of values, the change in the optimal Z value is proportional to the change in b_i. This phenomenon is similar to what happens when an objective-function coefficient is changed, but there is a major difference. The optimal values of the decision variables do not stay the same. Consider the following situation, which is shown graphically in Figure 19.35.

$$\max Z = x_1 + 3x_2$$
$$\text{s.t.} \quad 2x_1 + x_2 \leq 13$$
$$x_1 - x_2 \leq 2$$
$$-x_1 + x_2 \leq 3$$
$$x_2 \leq 5$$
$$x_1 \geq 0, x_2 \geq 0$$

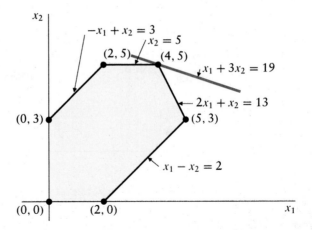

FIGURE 19.35   The optimal Z value is 19

The optimal solution is $x_1 = 4, x_2 = 5, Z = 19$. Figures 19.36 a) to d) illustrate what happens if b_1 is changed from its current value of 13 to various values between 9 and 19. Some of the information in Figures 19.36 a) to d) is summarized in Table 19.2.

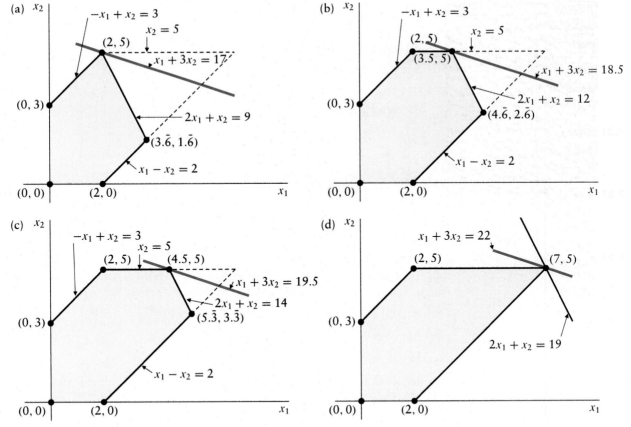

FIGURE 19.36   The effect on the optimal solution when $b_1 = 9, b_1 = 12, b_1 = 14$, and $b_1 = 19$

In each case, the change in the optimal Z value is exactly half the change in b_1. This sensitivity factor of 0.5 applies between the points $(2, 5)$ and $(7, 5)$. At the point

TABLE 19.2   The Effect of Changing b_1 on the Optimal Z Value

b_1 Current Value	b_1 New Value	Change in b_1	Current Optimal Z	New Optimal Z	Change in Optimal Z
13	9	−4	19	17.0	−2.0
13	12	−1	19	18.5	−0.5
13	14	+1	19	19.5	+0.5
13	19	+6	19	22.0	+3

(2, 5) the value of b_1 is 9, and at the point (7, 5) the value of b_1 is 19. These values of b_1 are simply determined by finding $2x_1 + x_2$ at the respective vertices.

If b_1 is increased to more than 19, the constraint $2x_1 + x_2 \leq b_1$ becomes superfluous, since it does not restrict the feasible region as determined by the rest of the constraints. See Figure 19.37.

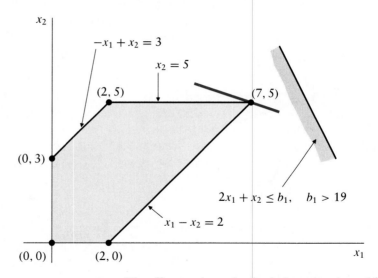

FIGURE 19.37   The effect on the optimal solution when $b_1 > 19$

If b_1 is decreased to less than 9, the constraint $2x_1 + x_2 \leq b_1$ may restrict the feasible region, but the sensitivity factor of 0.5 no longer applies. See Figure 19.38.

The optimal solution is $x_1 = 0.\overline{6}$, $x_2 = 3.\overline{6}$, $Z = 11.\overline{6}$.

The change in b_1 is $5 - 13 = -8$.

The change in optimal Z is $11.\overline{6} - 19 = 7.\overline{3}$.

The change in the optimal value of Z is not one half of the change in b_1.

The range and sensitivity analysis for a right-hand-side constant may always be written in the following form.

> If all other parameters remain the same, so long as $l \leq b_i \leq u$, the change in the optimal Z value is proportional to the change in b_i.

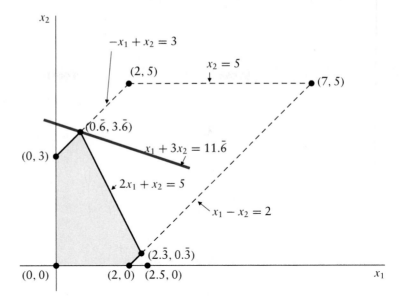

FIGURE 19.38 The effect on the optimal solution when $b_1 = 5$

The sensitivity factor for right-hand-side constant changes is called the **shadow price**. The lower limit ℓ in the range analysis could be anything from $-\infty$ to the current value of b_i, and the upper limit u could be anything from the current value of b_i to $+\infty$. If a change causes b_i to be negative, it is customary to multiply the constraint by -1 to make it positive. Do not forget that the direction of an inequality is reversed when both sides are multiplied by -1.

☐ **EXAMPLE 19.23** Complete the range and sensitivity analysis for the second constraint (b_2) in the following problem. Then find the shadow price in Table 19.3.

$$\max Z = 4x_1 + 3x_2$$
$$\text{s.t.} \quad x_1 + 2x_2 \leq 10$$
$$5x_1 + 6x_2 \leq 34$$
$$3x_1 + 2x_2 \leq 18$$
$$x_1 \geq 0, x_2 \geq 0$$

Figures 19.39 a) to c) show the optimal value for each of three situations.

The highest value b_2 that can be given before the constraint becomes superfluous is 38, as shown in Figure 19.39 b). If b_2 is given a value less than 30, the optimal vertex is more than one corner away from the optimal vertex in the original problem. The range for b_2 is $30 \leq b_2 \leq 38$.

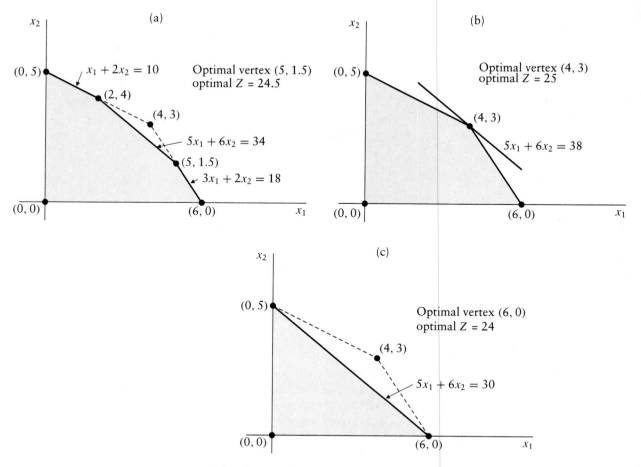

FIGURE 19.39 The effect on the objective-function line when $b_2 = 34$, $b_2 = 38$, and $b_2 = 30$

TABLE 19.3 Calculation of the Shadow Price

Change in b_2	Change in Optimal Z	Shadow Price
+4	+0.5	$\dfrac{0.5}{4} = 0.125$
−4	−0.5	$\dfrac{-0.5}{-4} = 0.125$

From the table above the shadow price is 0.125.

The range and sensitivity analysis may be stated in the standard way: if all the other parameters remain the same, so long as $30 \leq b_2 \leq 38$, the change in the optimal Z value is 0.125 times the change in b_2. ■

☐ **EXAMPLE 19.24** Based on the results of the previous example, solve the following linear-programming problems.

a) $\max Z = 4x_1 + 3x_2$
s.t. $\quad x_1 + 2x_2 \leq 10$
$\quad\quad 5x_1 + 6x_2 \leq 37$
$\quad\quad 3x_1 + 2x_2 \leq 18$
$\quad\quad x_1 \geq 0, x_2 \geq 0$

b) $\max Z = 4x_1 + 3x_2$
s.t. $\quad x_1 + 2x_2 \leq 10$
$\quad\quad 5x_1 + 6x_2 \leq 32.5$
$\quad\quad 3x_1 + 2x_2 \leq 18$
$\quad\quad x_1 \geq 0, x_2 \geq 0$

• SOLUTION

a) 37 is in the allowable range $30 \leq b_2 \leq 38$. The change in b_2 is $37 - 34 = 3$. Therefore, the change in optimal Z is $(0.125)(3) = 0.375$ and the optimal Z value is $24.5 + 0.375 = 24.875$. Note that without further analysis, the optimal values of x_1 and x_2 are unknown.

b) 32.5 is in the allowable range $30 \leq b_2 \leq 38$. The change in b_2 is $32.5 - 34 = -1.5$. Therefore, the change in optimal Z is $(0.125)(-1.5) = -0.1875$ and the optimal Z value is $24.5 + (-0.1875) = 24.3125$. As noted earlier, the optimal values of x_1 and x_2 are unknown. They could, of course, be found graphically. ■

The Sign of the Shadow Price

The two examples just given had shadow prices of 0.5 and 0.125, both positive numbers. However, shadow prices are not always positive. For example, if a constraint in a maximization problem is of the greater-than-or-equal-to type, then the shadow price is negative or zero. Still, it is possible to predict the sign of the shadow price using the following principle.

> The maximum value of any expression increases as the feasible region is made larger and decreases as the feasible region is made smaller. More technically, if A is a subset of B, then the maximum value of Z in A is less than or equal to the maximum value of Z in B.

This principle is easy to understand once it is realized that B has more points than A, so that the highest value in A could be less than some other value at one of the extra points.

There is a corresponding principle for minimization problems: the minimum value of any expression decreases as the feasible region is made larger and increases as the feasible region is made smaller. The two statements may be expressed as one.

> The optimal value of Z improves as the feasible region is made larger and worsens as the feasible region is made smaller.

This principle is used in developing Table 19.4.

TABLE 19.4 The Sign of the Shadow Price for Maximum and Minimum Problems

Type of Constraint	Type of Problem	Shadow Price
$\leq$	max	≥ 0
$\leq$	min	≤ 0
$\geq$	max	≤ 0
$\geq$	min	≥ 0
$=$	max or min	not easily predictable

It is worth noting that if a constraint is not *binding*, then the shadow price is zero. A constraint is called **binding** if the optimal values of the decision variables make the left-hand side of the constraint equal to the right-hand side. Consider the following linear-programming problems:

a) $\max Z = x_1 + 2x_2$
s.t. $x_1 + x_2 \leq 100$
$2x_1 + 3x_2 \leq 250$

$x_1 \geq 0, x_2 \geq 0$

b) $\min Z = x_1 + 2x_2$
s.t. $3x_1 + 4x_2 \leq 24$
$2x_1 + x_2 \geq 4$
$x_1 + 6x_2 \geq 6$
$x_1 \geq 0, x_2 \geq 0$

The optimal solution to (a) is $x_1 = 0$, $x_2 = 83.33$, $Z = 166.67$. The first constraint is not binding since $x_1 + x_2 = 83.33$, which is less than 100. It follows that the shadow price is zero. The second constraint is binding, since $2x_1 + 3x_2 = 250$. The shadow price is greater than or equal to zero.

The optimal solution to (b) is $x_1 = 1.636$, $x_2 = 0.727$. The first constraint is not binding, since $3x_1 + 4x_2 = 7.816$, which is less than 24. The shadow price is therefore 0. The second constraint is binding, since $2x_1 + x_2 = 4$. The shadow price is greater than or equal to zero. The third constraint is binding, since $x_1 + 6x_2 = 6$. The shadow price is greater than or equal to zero.

PROBLEMS

(*Note:* In the following problems, only one parameter changes.)

19.15 a) In Example 19.19, the optimal solution to

$$\max Z = 2x_1 + 3x_2$$
$$\text{s.t.}\quad x_1 + x_2 \leq 100$$
$$2x_1 - x_2 \geq 40$$
$$x_1 \geq 0, x_2 \geq 0$$

was given as $x_1 = 46.67$, $x_2 = 53.33$, $Z = 253.33$, and the optimal solution to

$$\max Z = 2x_1 + 3x_2$$
$$\text{s.t.}\quad x_1 + x_2 \leq 100.1$$
$$2x_1 - x_2 \geq 40$$
$$x_1 \geq 0, x_2 \geq 0$$

was given as $x_1 = 46.70$, $x_2 = 53.40$, $Z = 253.60$. The change in b_1 from 100 to 100.1 is within the permissible range. What is the shadow price for the first constraint?

b) Is the shadow price for the second constraint ≥ 0 or ≤ 0? Derive the answer from Table 19.4, rather than working it out.

19.16 Consider the following linear-programming problem.

$$\max Z = 6x_1 + 7x_2$$
$$\text{s.t.}\quad x_1 + 3x_2 \leq 30$$
$$4x_1 + x_2 \leq 32$$
$$x_1 \geq 0, x_2 \geq 0$$

Optimal solution: $x_1 = 6$, $x_2 = 8$, $Z = 92$

a) Verify that the range and sensitivity analysis for c_1 yields the result that so long as $2.33 \leq c_1 \leq 28$, the optimal values of the decision variables will be $x_1 = 6$, $x_2 = 8$, and the change in the optimal value of Z will be 6 times the change in c_1.

b) Perform the range and sensitivity analysis for c_2.

c) Verify that so long as $8 \leq b_1 \leq 96$, the change in the optimal value of Z will be twice the change in b_1, that is, the shadow price is 2.

d) Perform the range analysis for b_2 and find the shadow price for the second constraint.

19.17 If possible, use the results of Problem 19.16 to solve the following linear-programming problems. If a problem cannot be solved without further analysis, state why not. It is not necessary to carry out the analysis.

a) $\max Z = 25x_1 + 7x_2$

$$\text{s.t.} \quad x_1 + 3x_2 \leq 30$$
$$4x_1 + x_2 \leq 32$$
$$x_1 \geq 0, x_2 \geq 0$$

b) $\max Z = 6x_1 + 1.75x_2$

$$\text{s.t.} \quad x_1 + 3x_2 \leq 30$$
$$4x_1 + x_2 \leq 32$$
$$x_1 \geq 0, x_2 \geq 0$$

c) $\max Z = 6x_1 + 7x_2$

$$\text{s.t.} \quad x_1 + 3x_2 \leq 100$$
$$4x_1 + x_2 \leq 32$$
$$x_1 \geq 0, x_2 \geq 0$$

d) $\max Z = 6x_1 + 7x_2$

$$\text{s.t.} \quad x_1 + 3x_2 \leq 30$$
$$4x_1 + x_2 \leq 16$$
$$x_1 \geq 0, x_2 \geq 0$$

19.18 Do a range and sensitivity analysis for c_1, c_2, b_1, and b_2 for the following:

$$\max Z = 2x_1 + 3x_2$$

$$\text{s.t.} \quad x_1 + x_2 \leq 100$$
$$4x_1 + x_2 \geq 40$$
$$x_1 \geq 0, x_2 \geq 0$$

19.19 Use the results of Problem 19.18 to solve the following problems.

a) $\max Z = 2x_1 + 10x_2$

$$\text{s.t.} \quad x_1 + x_2 \leq 100$$
$$4x_1 + x_2 \geq 40$$
$$x_1 \geq 0, x_2 \geq 0$$

b) $\max Z = 2x_1 + 3x_2$

$$\text{s.t.} \quad x_1 + x_2 \leq 100$$
$$4x_1 + x_2 \geq 45$$
$$x_1 \geq 0, x_2 \geq 0$$

Formulations

section 19.6

In general, linear-programming problems in practical situations involve more than two variables. Sometimes hundreds of variables are used. A complex problem cannot be solved using the graphical approach outlined in the foregoing sections, so an algebraic procedure called the **simplex method** is applied.

The simplex method is an approach that is quite efficient, but is tedious to work through for a problem of any size. It is so important as a technique, however, that many software packages have been created to perform the work, once the formulation of the problem has been done. In view of the easy availability of computer solutions, the most important skill to develop is accuracy in formulating the problem. Several standard scenarios will be given in this section, along with their formulations.

◻ **EXAMPLE 19.25** Montreal Cereal Products sells three types of mixes that it advertizes as health snacks. The recipes for 300 g containers of the mixes are shown in Table 19.5.

The company has on hand 500 kg of cereal products, 110 kg of peanuts, 100 kg of flaked almonds and hazelnuts, and 150 kg of shredded coconut. Formulate this mixture problem so that the number of containers of each mix that should be made to maximize the total profit can be determined, assuming that all boxes can be sold.

TABLE 19.5   Recipes for Montreal Cereal Products Health Snacks

Ingredient	Mix 1 (g)	Mix 2(g)	Mix 3 (g)
Cereal products	150	200	175
Whole peanuts	50	25	25
Flaked almonds and hazelnuts	50	50	25
Shredded coconut	50	25	75
	300 g	300 g	300 g
Profit per container	$2.45	$2.00	$3.05

● **SOLUTION**   Let x_1 be the number of boxes of Mix 1, x_2 be the number of boxes of Mix 2, x_3 be the number of boxes of Mix 3.

$$\max Z = 2.45x_1 + 2.00x_2 + 3.05x_3$$
$$\begin{aligned}
\text{s.t.} \quad 150x_1 + 200x_2 + 175x_3 &\leq 500,000 \\
50x_1 + 25x_2 + 25x_3 &\leq 110,000 \\
50x_1 + 50x_2 + 25x_3 &\leq 100,000 \\
50x_1 + 25x_2 + 75x_3 &\leq 150,000 \\
x_1, x_2, x_3 &\geq 0
\end{aligned}$$

Note the change in units for the b_i values from kilograms to grams. Units must match between left-hand sides and right-hand sides. ■

Example 19.25 could have a further requirement that some of the variables have whole number (integer) values. It would not make sense to specify the production of a fraction of a box, so in Example 19.25, x_1, x_2, and x_3 can be specified as being integer valued. When specifications like these are included, the linear-programming problem is called an **integer-programming** problem. It is possible for the solution of an integer-programming problem to be quite different from the solution to the same problem without the integer requirements, but in most practical questions, the answers are about the same.

❏ **EXAMPLE 19.26**   R.B. James is in charge of the investment funds of the Halifax Resource Group. He has $250,000 to invest, and has narrowed the investment choices to five possibilities, listed in Table 19.6 along with some performance estimates.

TABLE 19.6   Investment Possibilities for the Halifax Resource Group

Details	1	2	3	4	5
Share Price	$90	$45	$160	$60	$125
Growth Rate	0.11	0.16	0.07	0.08	0.12
Annual Dividend	$1.50	$0.80	$1.50	$0.95	$1.20
Risk	0.09	0.12	0.05	0.08	0.28

He must invest all of the $250,000 in these five choices according to the following guidelines:

1. No more than $75,000 should be invested, in total, in investments 2 and 5.

2. At least 50 percent of the money invested should be placed in investments 1 and 3.
3. Total return on investment should be at least 8 percent. Return includes growth and dividends.
4. The total amount received in dividends should be at least $3000.
5. The average risk, weighted by the number of dollars in each investment, should be kept to no more than 0.10.

    a) Formulate this investment problem in order to maximize the return.
    b) Formulate the problem in order to minimize the weighted risk.

• SOLUTION

a) Let x_j be the number of shares of investment J, where $J = 1, 2, 3, 4, 5$. The objective function is

$$Z = 0.11(90x_1) + 0.16(45x_2) + 0.07(160x_3) + 0.08(60x_4) + 0.12(125x_5)$$
$$+ 1.50x_1 + 0.80x_2 + 1.50x_3 + 0.95x_4 + 1.20x_5$$
$$= 9.90x_1 + 7.20x_2 + 11.20x_3 + 4.80x_4 + 15.00x_5 + 1.50x_1 + 0.80x_2$$
$$+ 1.50x_3 + 0.95x_4 + 1.20x_5$$
$$= 11.40x_1 + 8.00x_2 + 12.70x_3 + 5.75x_4 + 16.20x_5$$

$$\text{Max } Z = 11.40x_1 + 8.00x_2 + 12.70x_3 + 5.75x_4 + 16.20x_5$$
$$\text{s.t.} \quad 45x_2 + 125x_5 \leq 75,000$$
$$90x_1 + 45x_2 + 160x_3 + 60x_4 + 125x_5 = 250,000$$
$$90x_1 + 160x_3 \geq 0.50(250,000)$$
$$11.40x_1 + 8.00x_2 + 12.70x_3 + 5.75x_4 + 16.20x_5 \geq 0.08(250,000)$$
$$1.50x_1 + 0.80x_2 + 1.50x_3 + 0.95x_4 + 1.20x_5 \geq 3000$$

$$0.09\left(\frac{90x_1}{250,000}\right) + 0.12\left(\frac{45x_2}{250,000}\right) + 0.05\left(\frac{160x_3}{250,000}\right) + 0.08\left(\frac{60x_4}{250,000}\right)$$
$$+ 0.28\left(\frac{125x_5}{250,000}\right) \leq 0.10$$

This formulation should be simplified and rewritten as follows to maximize the return.

$$\text{Max } Z = 11.40x_1 + 8.00x_2 + 12.70x_3 + 5.75x_4 + 16.20x_5$$
$$\text{s.t.} \quad 45x_2 + 125x_5 \leq 75,000$$
$$90x_1 + 45x_2 + 160x_3 + 60x_4 + 125x_5 = 250,000$$
$$90x_1 + 160x_3 \geq 125,000$$
$$11.40x_1 + 8.00x_2 + 12.70x_3 + 5.75x_4 + 16.20x_5 \geq 20,000$$
$$1.50x_1 + 0.80x_2 + 1.50x_3 + 0.95x_4 + 1.20x_5 \geq 3000$$
$$8.10x_1 + 5.40x_2 + 8.00x_3 + 4.80x_4 + 35.00x_5 \leq 25,000$$
$$x_1, x_2, x_3, x_4, x_5 \geq 0$$

b) With the same constraints as part (a), the formulation should be written as follows to minimize the weighted risk.

$$\min Z = 0.09\left(\frac{90x_1}{250,000}\right) + 0.12\left(\frac{45x_2}{250,000}\right) + 0.05\left(\frac{160x_3}{250,000}\right)$$
$$+ 0.08\left(\frac{60x_4}{250,000}\right) + 0.28\left(\frac{125x_5}{250,000}\right)$$

Alternatively, multiplying this expression by 250,000 will give an expression that is minimized for the same values of x_1, x_2, x_3, x_4 and x_5.

$$\text{Min } Z = 8.10x_1 + 5.40x_2 + 8.00x_3 + 4.80x_4 + 35x_5$$

Of course, after the problem is solved , the weighted return would be found by dividing the optimal Z value by 250,000. Both parts (a) and (b) can be formulated as integer-programming problems, since it is not possible to buy a fraction of a share. ∎

☐ **EXAMPLE 19.27** Willie's safety equipment has two factories in western Canada and retail outlets in Vancouver, Calgary, and Edmonton. The demand for specialized goggles in the three cities is such that the outlet in Vancouver needs 800, Calgary needs 1200, and Edmonton needs 1100. Factory 1 can deliver 1500 goggles, and Factory 2 can deliver 2000. Willie's accounting department has calculated the unit cost of delivery from each factory to each city. Formulate the problem to determine how many goggles should be sent from each factory to each city in order to minimize the total delivery (transportation) cost.

TABLE 19.7   Goggle Delivery Cost from Factory to City

	Vancouver	Calgary	Edmonton
Factory 1	$0.65	$0.53	$0.58
Factory 2	0.61	0.58	0.56

• **SOLUTION**

Let x_{1v} be the number of goggles sent from Factory 1 to Vancouver,
x_{2v} be the number of goggles sent from Factory 2 to Vancouver,
x_{1c} be the number of goggles sent from Factory 1 to Calgary,
x_{2c} be the number of goggles sent from Factory 2 to Calgary,
x_{1e} be the number of goggles sent from Factory 1 to Edmonton,
x_{2e} be the number of goggles sent from Factory 2 to Edmonton.

$$\text{Min } Z = 65x_{1v} + 53x_{1c} + 58x_{1e} + 61x_{2v} + 58x_{2c} + 56x_{2e}$$
$$\text{s.t.}\quad x_{1v} + x_{1c} + x_{1e} \leq 1500$$
$$x_{2v} + x_{2c} + x_{2e} \leq 2000$$
$$x_{1v} + x_{2v} \geq 800$$
$$x_{1c} + x_{2c} \geq 1200$$
$$x_{1e} + x_{2e} \geq 1100$$
$$x_{1j} \geq 0 \text{ for all } i, j$$

This problem seems to call for integer-programming formulation but it can be proven that transportation problems of this type always have integer answers anyway, so there is no need to specify integer values. Since there are enough goggles available, it could be argued that the last three constraints should read as follows.

$$x_{1v} + x_{2v} = 800$$

$$x_{1c} + x_{2c} = 1200$$

$$x_{1e} + x_{2e} = 1100$$

Both formulations will give the same solution. ■

☐ **EXAMPLE 19.28** TO-TABLE, a trendy Toronto store, uses wood blocks cut into shapes to make a line of chunky furniture. The blocks can be cut in two patterns to make long blocks for legs and arms and square blocks for seats and backs of chairs. One pattern produces 6 long blocks and 3 square blocks. The other pattern produces 8 long blocks and 4 square blocks. The first pattern can be cut quickly, so that the labour and machine costs come to $6, but the second pattern needs a more complicated sequence of cuts, and the labour and machine costs are $10. Excess wood from both patterns can be put to other use, so waste is not a consideration.

For the coming month, TO-TABLE needs at least 70 office chairs and 90 dining-room chairs. Office chairs use 6 long blocks and 4 square blocks, and dining-room chairs use 4 long blocks and 2 square blocks each. Formulate the problem to determine how many blocks should be cut in each pattern to satisfy the demand at the lowest possible labour and machine costs.

• **SOLUTION** Let p_1 be the number of blocks cut in pattern 1, and p_2 be the number of blocks cut in pattern 2.

$$\min Z = 6p_1 + 10p_2$$
$$\text{s.t.} \quad 6p_1 + 8p_2 \geq (70)(6) + (90)(4) = 180$$
$$3p_1 + 4p_2 \geq (70)(4) + (90)(2) = 460$$
$$p_1 \geq 0, p_2 \geq 0$$

☐ **EXAMPLE 19.29** An institution in St John's requires staff 24 hours a day, with peak and slow periods at the same times every day. The day is divided into 6 eight-hour shifts, staggered so that they start four hours apart. Employees always work eight hours straight, with no overtime. The minimum personnel requirements are given in Table 19.8 for each four-hour period during the day.

TABLE 19.8 Minimum Personnel Requirements

Time Period	Minimum Personnel Required
Midnight – 4 a.m.	18
4 a.m. – 8 a.m.	26
8 a.m. – Noon	32
Noon – 4 p.m.	29
4 p.m. – 8 p.m.	36
8 p.m. – Midnight	25

Formulate this personnel-scheduling problem to determine the minimum number of persons needed in a day.

• SOLUTION

Let x_1 be the number of employees starting work at midnight.

x_2 be the number of employees starting work at 4 a.m.

x_3 be the number of employees starting work at 8 a.m.

x_4 be the number of employees starting work at noon.

x_5 be the number of employees starting work at 4 p.m.

x_6 be the number of employees starting work at 8 p.m.

$$\min Z = x_1 + x_2 + x_3 + x_4 + x_5 + x_6$$

$$\begin{aligned} \text{s.t.} \quad x_6 + x_1 &\geq 18 \\ x_1 + x_2 &\geq 26 \\ x_2 + x_3 &\geq 32 \\ x_3 + x_4 &\geq 29 \\ x_4 + x_5 &\geq 36 \\ x_5 + x_6 &\geq 25 \\ x_1, x_2, x_3, x_4, x_5, x_6 &\geq 0 \end{aligned}$$

This is clearly an integer-programming problem. ■

☐ **EXAMPLE 19.30**   Consider the situation of Example 19.29 once more. Suppose employees are paid \$16 an hour for regular shifts starting at 8 a.m., noon, and 4 p.m. and \$20 an hour for regular shifts starting at 8 p.m., midnight, or 4 a.m. It is possible to extend a regular shift by 4 hours, but the overtime rate is time and one-half. The overtime hours must be worked starting at the end of the regular shift, so that the employee works 12 consecutive hours, and union regulation states that no more than one-third of the employees working at any given time may be on overtime.

Formulate the problem to determine the personnel schedule that should be adopted to minimize the salary budget for the day. It may be assumed that there are always employees willing to work overtime.

• SOLUTION

Let $x_1, x_2, x_3, x_4, x_5, x_6$ be the number of employees starting at different shift times who do not work overtime.

$y_1, y_2, y_3, y_4, y_5, y_6$ be the number of employees starting at different shift times who do work overtime.

For the x_1 workers starting at midnight with no overtime, the pay is \$20 × 8 = \$160. For the x_2 and x_6 workers the pay is also \$160, but for the x_3, x_4, and x_5 workers the pay is \$16 × 8 = 128.

For the y_1 workers starting at midnight, with overtime, the pay is \$20 × 8 + \$30 × 4 = 280. For the y_2 and y_6 workers the pay is also \$280, but for the y_3, y_4, and y_5 workers the pay is \$16 × 8 + 24 × 4 = \$224.

$$\min Z = 160x_1 + 160x_2 + 128x_3 + 128x_4 + 128x_5 + 160x_6 + 280y_1 + 280y_2$$
$$+ 224y_3 + 224y_4 + 224y_5 + 280y_6.$$

s.t.

Personnel Requirements

$$y_5 + x_6 + y_6 + x_1 + y_1 \geq 18$$
$$y_6 + x_1 + y_1 + x_2 + y_2 \geq 26$$
$$y_1 + x_2 + y_2 + x_3 + y_3 \geq 32$$
$$y_2 + x_3 + y_3 + x_4 + y_4 \geq 29$$
$$y_3 + x_4 + y_4 + x_5 + y_5 \geq 36$$
$$y_4 + x_5 + y_5 + x_6 + y_6 \geq 25$$

Union Regulation Constraints

$$y_5 \leq \tfrac{1}{3}(y_5 + x_6 + y_6 + x_1 + y_1)$$
$$y_6 \leq \tfrac{1}{3}(y_6 + x_1 + y_1 + x_2 + y_2)$$
$$y_1 \leq \tfrac{1}{3}(y_1 + x_2 + y_2 + x_3 + y_3)$$
$$y_2 \leq \tfrac{1}{3}(y_2 + x_3 + y_3 + x_4 + y_4)$$
$$y_3 \leq \tfrac{1}{3}(y_3 + x_4 + y_4 + x_5 + y_5)$$
$$y_4 \leq \tfrac{1}{3}(y_4 + x_5 + y_5 + x_6 + y_6)$$
$$x_1, x_2, x_3, x_4, x_5, x_6, y_1, y_2, y_3, y_4, y_5, y_6 \geq 0$$

The union-regulation constraints should be rewritten as follows:

$$2y_5 - x_6 - y_6 - x_1 - y_1 \leq 0$$
$$2y_6 - x_1 - y_1 - x_2 - y_2 \leq 0$$
$$2y_1 - x_2 - y_2 - x_3 - y_3 \leq 0$$
$$2y_2 - x_3 - y_3 - x_4 - y_4 \leq 0$$
$$2y_3 - x_4 - y_4 - x_5 - y_5 \leq 0$$
$$2y_4 - x_5 - y_5 - x_6 - y_6 \leq 0$$

□ EXAMPLE 19.31   A Winnipeg fuel company uses three ingredients, A, B, and C, to mix a variety of fuels. Ingredient A is extremely volatile, and fuels with a high percentage of it are called premium fuels. Ingredient B is moderately volatile, whereas ingredient C is practically inert, and is used to combat the tendency of fuel mixtures to explode. The company is going to produce three types of fuel this year: premium 1, premium 2, and standard. The proportion of ingredient A in premium 1 fuel must be at least 50 percent, and in premium 2 fuel must be at least 40 percent. At least 20 percent of each type of fuel must be ingredient C, and government regulations prohibit any fuel with more than 70 percent ingredient A content. Standard fuel has at least a 35 percent ingredient C content and fuel with more than 55 percent of ingredient C will not burn, and so is useless. Price and cost data for the fuels are given in Tables 19.9 and 19.10.

TABLE 19.9   Fuel Type Cost and Demand

Fuel Type	Price per Litre	Expected Demand/(litre)
Premium 1	$2.00	2,000,000
Premium 2	$1.50	5,000,000
Standard	$0.90	8,000,000

TABLE 19.10 Fuel Type Cost and Availability

Ingredient	Cost per Litre	Availability/(litre)
A	$0.90	4,000,000
B	$0.65	3,500,000
C	$0.35	9,000,000

How should premium 1, premium 2, and standard fuel be blended, and how much of each type of fuel should be produced in order for the fuel company to maximize its profit? It may be assumed that there are competing companies, so it is not essential to meet the expected demand. Assume also that any fuel produced can be sold up to the level of demand.

● **SOLUTION** It is convenient to use variables for the blending and for the numbers of litres of each type of fuel to formulate this blending problem.

Let A_1 be number of litres of ingredient A used to produce premium 1 fuel.

A_2 be the number of litres of ingredient A used to produce premium 2 fuel.

A_s be the number of litres of ingredient A used to produce standard fuel.

$B_1, B_2, B_s, C_1, C_2, C_s$ are defined similarly.

Let L_1 be the number of litres of premium 1 fuel produced.

L_2 be the number of litres of premium 2 fuel produced.

L_s be the number of litres of standard fuel produced.

$$\text{Max } Z = 2.00L_1 + 1.50L_2 + 0.90L_s - 0.90(A_1 + A_2 + A_s)$$
$$- 0.65(B_1 + B_2 + B_s) - 0.35(C_1 + C_2 + C_s)$$
$$= 2.00L_1 + 1.50L_2 + 0.90L_s - 0.90A_1 - 0.90A_2 - 0.90A_s - 0.65B_1$$
$$- 0.65B_2 - 0.65B_s - 0.35C_1 - 0.35C_2 - 0.35C_s$$

s.t.

$A_1 \geq 0.50L_1$	$C_1 \geq 0.20L_1$	$A_1 \leq 0.70L_1$
$A_2 \geq 0.40L_2$	$C_2 \geq 0.20L_2$	$A_2 \leq 0.70L_2$
	$C_s \geq 0.20L_s$	$A_s \leq 0.70L_s$

$C_s \geq 0.35L_s$	$L_1 = A_1 + B_1 + C_1$	$L_1 \leq 2,000,000$
$C_1 \leq 0.55L_1$	$L_2 = A_2 + B_2 + C_2$	$L_2 \leq 5,000,000$
$C_2 \leq 0.55L_2$	$L_s = A_s + B_s + C_s$	$L_s \leq 8,000,000$
$C_s \leq 0.55L_s$		

$A_1 + A_2 + A_s \leq 4\ 000\ 000$

$B_1 + B_2 + B_s \leq 3\ 500\ 000$ All variables ≥ 0

$C_1 + C_2 + C_s \leq 9\ 000\ 000$

It may be observed that some of the constraints listed above are unneccessary to write down. For example, $C_s \geq 0.20L_s$ is implied by the later constraint $C_s \geq 0.35L_s$, so it is possible to omit $C_s \geq 0.20L_s$ without changing the question. It does not hurt to leave it in, however: redundant constraints do not lead to sub-optimal answers. Not including crucial constraints really affects linear-programming problems. It is better to err on the side of too many rather than too few. ∎

Linear-programming problems all require the properties of *proportionality*, *divisibility*, and *additivity*.

Proportionality is the property that guarantees the linearity of the objective function and constraints. For any individual variable, a unit increase in its value always adds the same amount to the objective function and the same amount to the left-hand side of a constraint.

Divisibility is the property that variables can have any value, integer or non-integer, in the feasible region. In some real-life situations this property does not hold, but in most circumstances a simple roundoff gives the correct answer if an integer value is required.

Additivity is the property that resources cannot be shared. If one activity requires A resource units and another activity requires B resource units, then the two activities will require $A + B$ resource units.

PROBLEMS

◆ **19.20** Canadian Trust Company carries an investment portfolio consisting of a variety of stocks and bonds. Due to policy renewals, $1,000,000 is available for use in investment in new opportunities. Relevant data about the four investment opportunities are given in the table.

TABLE 19.11 Investment Opportunities

	A	B	C	D
Price per share	$120.00	$60.00	$80.00	$100.00
Expected return per share	$7.20	$3.00	$7.20	$4.00
Risk per share	0.020	0.015	0.030	0.008

The risk measure indicates the relative uncertainty associated with the stock in terms of realizing returns. The management must determine an optimal portfolio — a portfolio that maximizes the total expected return, subject to the following guidelines.

a) The total amount of risk should be no more than 1,500.

b) No one stock can account for more than 40% of the total investment.

c) The amount invested in the blue chip stock D should be at least two times as much as the investment in the risky security C.

Formulate the problem as a linear programming model, defining clearly the decision variables, objective function, and constraints.

◆ **19.21** Olson Gregarian Brewery must determine how many TV spots and magazine ads to purchase with an advertising budget of $100,000. Each TV spot is expected to increase sales by 30,000 cans, whereas each magazine ad will increase sales by 100,000 cans. Olson's gross profit on sales is $0.10 per can. One TV spot costs $2,000, whereas each magazine ad requires an expenditure of $5,000. To have a balanced marketing program, the advertising budget must allocate no more than $70,000 in magazine ads and no more than $50,000 in TV spots.

a) Determine the net increase in beer profits for each TV spot and magazine ad that reflects the respective costs.

b) Assuming that Olson's management wishes to maximize the net increase in beer profits, formulate the marketing manager's decision as a linear programming model.

c) Solve the linear-programming model graphically and state the optimal advertising campaign.

◆ **19.22** The ABC Company is interested in determining an optimal production mix for four products W, X, Y, and Z that it manufactures. The controller has determined the following price and cost information per unit of each product.

TABLE 19.12 Price and Cost Information

	W	X	Y	Z
Selling price	$41	$50	$58	$71
Direct labour	15	20	25	30
Direct material	18	20	22	24
Variable overhead	3	4	4	8
Fixed overhead	1	1	1	1

All four products use the same direct material which costs $3 per kilogram. Direct labour rate is $20 per hour. Monthly capacities are 5000 direct labour hours and 30,000 kilograms of direct material. Fixed overhead is assumed to be the same for each product. The company wants to make sure that total overhead expenses do not exceed $17,000. The company would like to determine the monthly production schedule of these four products in order to maximize the net profit. Formulate this problem as a linear-programming problem.

♦ **19.23** Ace Widgets, Incorporated, makes two models of widgets — standard and deluxe. Both models are assembled from an identical frame. The standard model differs from the deluxe model only in terms of the finish work, which takes 5 hours of labour on the standard version and 8 hours on the deluxe model. In planning the current month's production, Ace's foreman finds that only 12 frames and 80 hours of finishing are available. The supply of all other required material is unlimited. Any number of widgets can be sold at a profit: $10 for a standard widget and $5 for a deluxe widget. The foreman wants to produce quantities of the two models that will maximize company profit.

a) Formulate the foreman's problem as a linear-programming model.

b) Solve the linear program graphically, and state the optimal production plan.

♦ **19.24** A firm produces three products X, Y, and Z. These products sell for $30, $50, and $60 per unit, respectively. The sales agent is paid a monthly allowance of $1000 and 10% of the value of the goods sold.

Each product is processed on two machines: a grinding machine and a finishing machine. One unit of product X requires two hours of grinding, product Y requires 3 hours, and product Z requires 4 hours of grinding. The grinding machine operates 8 hours a day and 25 days a month.

Finishing requirements per unit of products X, Y, and Z are 2 hours, 4 hours, and 3 hours, respectively. Though the finishing machine can theoretically operate 8 hours a day for 25 days, frequent breakdowns actually consume 20% of the time.

Final assembly of the product is done by hand. Four units of X can be assembled by one worker in an hour; it takes one worker-hour to put together one unit of Y; and 30 minutes to assemble one unit of Z. One unit of product X requires 3 pounds of raw material. Similar requirements for product Y and Z are 5 pounds and 8 pounds. Labour is paid at the rate of $7 per hour, and raw material costs $3 per pound.

The firm uses the following equation to estimate the overhead.

$$\text{Overhead} = \$500 + \$3 \text{ per direct labour hour}$$

Formulate this problem as a linear programming model, defining each variable and constraint.

| section 19.7 | # Computer Solutions |

Computer software for solving linear-programming problems has been marketed by several companies. One of the easier disks to use is *Computer Models for Management Science* by Erikson and Hall. The LINP option of the CMMS package enables the programmer to enter the data once the problem is formulated, and to calculate the solution by pressing a function key. The output includes range and sensitivity analysis.

To see the information given by the computer, consider the problem formulated previously in Example 19.23.

$$\text{Max } Z = 4x_1 + 3x_2$$

$$\text{s.t. } x_1 + 2x_2 \le 10$$
$$5x_1 + 6x_2 \le 34$$
$$3x_1 + 2x_2 \le 18$$

$$x_1 \ge 0, \ x_2 \ge 0$$

INFORMATION ENTERED

```
NUMBER OF VARIABLES         :   2
NUMBER OF <= CONSTRAINTS    :   3
NUMBER OF = CONSTRAINTS     :   0
NUMBER OF >= CONSTRAINTS    :   0
```

MAX $Z = 4x_1 + 3x_2$

SUBJECT TO:

$1x_1 + 2x_2 <=$ 10
$5x_1 + 6x_2 <=$ 34
$3x_1 + 2x_2 <=$ 18

RESULTS

VARIABLE	VARIABLE VALUE	ORIGINAL COEFFICIENT	COEFFICIENT SENSITIVITY
X1	5	4	0
X2	1.5	3	0

CONSTRAINT NUMBER	ORIGINAL RIGHT-HAND VALUE	SLACK OR SURPLUS	SHADOW PRICE
1	10	2	0
2	34	0	.125
3	18	0	1.125

OBJECTIVE FUNCTION VALUE: 24.5

SENSITIVITY ANALYSIS
OBJECTIVE FUNCTION COEFFICIENTS

VARIABLE	LOWER LIMIT	ORIGINAL COEFFICIENT	UPPER LIMIT
X1	2.5	4	4.5
X2	2.667	3	4.8

RIGHT-HAND-SIDE VALUES

CONSTRAINT NUMBER	LOWER LIMIT	ORIGINAL VALUE	UPPER LIMIT
1	8	10	NO LIMIT
2	30	34	38
3	14	18	20.4

END OF ANALYSIS

FIGURE 19.40   The computer printout, including the range and sensitivity analysis of the objective function

The printout indicates that the optimal solution is $x_1 = 5$, $x_2 = 1.5$, $Z = 24.5$. These are the variable value and objective function value entries in the results section of the computer solution. The second part of the results section deals with constraints and shadow prices. If a constraint has non-zero slack or surplus, it is not a binding constraint, and the shadow price is zero. In this example, the first constraint is non-binding, so the shadow price is zero, but the other two constraints have shadow prices 0.125 and 1.125.

The range analyses are given in the sensitivity analysis portion of the printout. They can be expressed in the usual way:

c_j **ranges**

a) So long as $2.5 \leq c_1 \leq 4.5$, the optimal solution is $x_1 = 5$ and $x_2 = 1.5$. The change in the optimal Z value is 5 times the change in c_1.

b) So long as $2.667 \leq c_2 \leq 4.8$, the optimal solution is $x_1 = 5$ and $x_2 = 1.5$. The change in the optimal Z value is 1.5 times the change in c_1.

b_i **ranges**

a) So long as $8 \leq b_1 \leq \infty$, the shadow price is zero. There will be no change in the optimal Z value for $b_1 \geq 8$.

b) So long as $30 \leq b_2 \leq 38$, the shadow price is 0.125. The change in the optimal Z value will be 0.125 times the change in b_2.

c) So long as $14 \leq b_3 \leq 20.4$, the shadow price is 1.125. The change in the optimal Z value will be 1.125 times the change in b_3.

The coefficient sensitivity column will not be used in this chapter. It indicates the cost of introducing one unit of a variable into the solution, and is zero unless the optimal value of that variable is zero.

In the next examples, the printout will be used to help answer practical questions based on the formulation. It is important to develop skill in translating the questions into terms that can be answered by referring to the computer solution.

☐ **EXAMPLE 19.32**   This is the mixture problem of Example 19.25 in the section on formulation. The formulation is reproduced, and the computer solution is given. Answer these questions.

1. How many boxes of each mix should be produced?
2. What is the total profit?
3. Which of the available ingredients is not all used? How much is left over?
4. How much would the profit on a container of Mix 1 have to be before it became worthwhile to produce more than 250 containers of it?
5. What would the total profit be if the profit on a container of Mix 2 were only $1.60?
6. How much would the total profit be if 510 kg of cereal products were available?
7. How much would the total profit be if only 80 kg of whole peanuts were available?

To review: Montreal Cereal Products sells three types of mixes that it advertizes as health snacks. The recipes for 300 g containers of the mixes are given in Table 19.13.

TABLE 19.13   Recipes for Montreal Cereal Products Health Snacks

Ingredient	Mix 1	Mix 2	Mix 3
Cereal products	150	200	175
Whole peanuts	50	25	25
Flaked almonds and hazelnuts	50	50	25
Shredded coconut	50	25	75
	300 g	300 g	300 g
Profit per container	$2.45	$2.00	$3.05

The company has on hand 500 kg of cereal products, 110 kg of peanuts, 100 kg of flaked almonds and hazelnuts, and 150 kg of shredded coconut.

● SOLUTION

Let x_1 be the number of boxes of Mix 1,
   x_2 be the number of boxes of Mix 2,
   x_3 be the number of boxes of Mix 3.

$$\max Z = 2.45x_1 + 2.00x_2 + 3.05x_3$$
$$\text{s.t.} \quad 150x_1 + 200x_2 + 175x_3 \le 500,000$$
$$50x_1 + 25x_2 + 25x_3 \le 110,000$$
$$50x_1 + 50x_2 + 25x_3 \le 100,000$$
$$50x_1 + 25x_2 + 75x_3 \le 150,000$$
$$x_1, \ x_2, \ x_3 \ge 0$$

RESULTS

VARIABLE	VARIABLE VALUE	ORIGINAL COEFFICIENT	COEFFICIENT SENSITIVITY
X1	250	2.45	0
X2	1000	2	0
X3	1500	3.05	0

CONSTRAINT NUMBER	ORIGINAL RIGHT-HAND VALUE	SLACK OR SURPLUS	SHADOW PRICE
1	500000	0	.005
2	110000	35000	0
3	100000	0	.008
4	150000	0	.027

OBJECTIVE FUNCTION VALUE: 7187.5

SENSITIVITY ANALYSIS
OBJECTIVE FUNCTION COEFFICIENTS

VARIABLE	LOWER LIMIT	ORIGINAL COEFFICIENT	UPPER LIMIT
X1	2.265	2.45	2.82
X2	1.538	2	2.787
X3	2.125	3.05	3.365

RIGHT-HAND-SIDE VALUES

CONSTRAINT NUMBER	LOWER LIMIT	ORIGINAL VALUE	UPPER LIMIT
1	400000	500000	520000
2	75000	110000	NO LIMIT
3	94117.648	100000	128000
3	133333.344	150000	200000

FIGURE 19.41   The computer printout for the mixture problem in Example 19.32

1. The numbers of boxes of each mix that should be produced are $x_1 = 250$, $x_2 = 1000$, $x_3 = 1500$. This means that 250 containers of Mix 1, 1000 containers of Mix 2, and 1500 containers of Mix 3 should be produced.

2. The total profit is $7,187.50.

3. The slack value of 35,000 indicates that the ingredient in constraint 2 is not all used. There are 35 kg of whole peanuts left over. (1000 g = 1 kg)

4. The profit is $2.45. This appears as the original coefficient of x_1 in the objective function. The upper limit is given as $2.82, so that any level of profit above $2.82 for Mix 1 would result in a changed optimal solution. Since the profit on Mix 1 is the only one to increase under such circumstances, clearly more of Mix 1 would be produced.

5. $1.60 is within the range $1.538 \leq c_2 \leq 2.787$. Therefore the change in the optimal Z value is 1000 times the change in c_2. The sensitivity factor 1000 is the current optimal value of x_2. Thus the new optimal Z value and new total profit would be $\$7187.50 + 1000(-0.40) = \$6787.50$

6. $510 \text{ kg} = 510,000 \text{ g}$, which is within the allowable range $400,000 \leq b_1 \leq 520,000$. The shadow price is $(0.005)(1000) = \$5/\text{kg}$. Thus the new optimal profit would be $\$7187.50 + (10 \text{ kg})(\$5/\text{kg}) = \$7237.50$

7. $80 \text{ kg} = 80,000 \text{ g}$, which is within the allowable range $75,000 \leq b_2 < \infty$. Since the shadow price is zero, the total profit would be unchanged at $\$7187.50$. ∎

☐ **EXAMPLE 19.33**   This is the personnel scheduling problem with overtime formulated in Example 19.29 of the section on formulation. The computer solution is given. Answer these questions.

1. What is the cost of 24 hours of operation?
2. Which shift has no workers starting on it?
3. Which shift requires overtime workers, according to the schedule given in the solution?
4. What would the cost be if the hourly rate for the shift starting at 8 a.m. were increased to $18?
5. What would happen if the hourly rate for the shift starting at noon were increased to $18?
6. If a new contract were signed with the union requiring the institution to increase the minimum personnel requirements of one of its shifts by 3 workers, which shifts would be considered? What would the added cost be?

To review: Suppose employees are paid $16 an hour for regular shifts starting from 8 a.m, noon, and 4 p.m, and $20 an hour for regular shifts starting at 8 p.m, midnight, or 4 a.m. It is possible to extend a regular shift by 4 hours, but the overtime rate is time and one-half. The overtime hours must be worked starting at the end of the regular shift, so that employee works 12 consecutive hours, and union regulations state that no more than one-third of the employees working at any given time may be on overtime.

● **SOLUTION**   Let x_1, x_2, x_3, x_4, x_5, x_6 be the number of employees starting at different shift times who do not work overtime. Let y_1, y_2, y_3, y_4, y_5, y_6 be the number of employees starting at different shift times who do work overtime.

For the x_1 workers starting at midnight with no overtime, the pay is $\$20 \times 8 = \$160$. For the x_2 and x_6 workers the pay is also $160, but for the x_3, x_4, and x_5 workers the pay is $\$16 \times 8 = 128$.

For the y_1 workers starting at midnight, with overtime, the pay is $\$20 \times 8 + \$30 \times 4 = 280$. For the y_2 and y_6 workers the pay is also $280, but for the y_3, y_4, and y_5 workers the pay is $\$16 \times 8 + 24 \times 4 = \$224$.

$$\min Z = 160x_1 + 160x_2 + 128x_3 + 128x_4 + 128x_5 + 160x_6$$
$$+ 280y_1 + 280y_2 + 224y_3 + 224y_4 + 224y_5 + 280y_6.$$

s.t.

Union Regulation Constraints

$$y_5 \leq \tfrac{1}{3}(y_5 + x_6 + y_6 + x_1 + y_1)$$
$$y_6 \leq \tfrac{1}{3}(y_6 + x_1 + y_1 + x_2 + y_2)$$
$$y_1 \leq \tfrac{1}{3}(y_1 + x_2 + y_2 + x_3 + y_3)$$
$$y_2 \leq \tfrac{1}{3}(y_2 + x_3 + y_3 + x_4 + y_4)$$
$$y_3 \leq \tfrac{1}{3}(y_3 + x_4 + y_4 + x_5 + y_5)$$
$$y_4 \leq \tfrac{1}{3}(y_4 + x_5 + y_5 + x_6 + y_6)$$
$$x_1, x_2, x_3, x_4, x_5, x_6, y_1, y_2, y_3, y_4, y_5, y_6 \geq 0$$

The union-regulation constraints should be rewritten as follows for proper computer format:

$$2y_5 - x_6 - y_6 - x_1 - y_1 \leq 0$$
$$2y_6 - x_1 - y_1 - x_2 - y_2 \leq 0$$
$$2y_1 - x_2 - y_2 - x_3 - y_3 \leq 0$$
$$2y_2 - x_3 - y_3 - x_4 - y_4 \leq 0$$
$$2y_3 - x_4 - y_4 - x_5 - y_5 \leq 0$$
$$2y_4 - x_5 - y_5 - x_6 - y_6 \leq 0$$

Personnel Requirements

$$y_5 + x_6 + y_6 + x_1 + y_1 \geq 18$$
$$y_6 + x_1 + y_1 + x_2 + y_2 \geq 26$$
$$y_1 + x_2 + y_2 + x_3 + y_3 \geq 32$$
$$y_2 + x_3 + y_3 + x_4 + y_4 \geq 29$$
$$y_3 + x_4 + y_4 + x_5 + y_5 \geq 36$$
$$y_4 + x_5 + y_5 + x_6 + y_6 \geq 25$$

Note that the order of constraints has been changed. The *CMMS* instructions require that $\leq$ constraints be listed first, $=$ constraints next, and finally $\geq$ constraints.

RESULTS

VARIABLE	VARIABLE VALUE	ORIGINAL COEFFICIENT	COEFFICIENT SENSITIVITY
X1	12	160	0
X2	14	160	0
X3	18	128	0
X4	11	128	0
X5	19	128	0
X6	0	160	32
Y1	0	280	24
Y2	0	280	88
Y3	0	224	0
Y4	0	224	64
Y5	6	224	0
Y6	0	280	88

CONSTRAINT NUMBER	ORIGINAL RIGHT-HAND VALUE	SLACK OR SURPLUS	SHADOW PRICE
1	0	0	0
2	0	26	0
3	0	32	0
4	0	29	0
5	0	36	0
6	0	25	0
7	18	0	96
8	26	0	64
9	32	0	96
10	29	0	32
11	36	0	96
12	25	0	32

OBJECTIVE FUNCTION VALUE: 11647.999

SENSITIVITY ANALYSIS
OBJECTIVE FUNCTION COEFFICIENTS

VARIABLE	LOWER LIMIT	ORIGINAL COEFFICIENT	UPPER LIMIT
X1	160	160	192
X2	128	160	160
X3	96	128	160
X4	96	128	128
X5	128	128	160
X6	128	160	NO LIMIT
Y1	256	280	NO LIMIT
Y2	192	280	NO LIMIT
Y3	224	224	NO LIMIT
Y4	160	224	NO LIMIT
Y5	160	224	224
Y6	192	280	NO LIMIT

RIGHT-HAND-SIDE VALUES

CONSTRAINT NUMBER	LOWER LIMIT	ORIGINAL VALUE	UPPER LIMIT
1	0	0	NO LIMIT
2	-26	0	NO LIMIT
3	-32	0	NO LIMIT
4	-29	0	NO LIMIT
5	-36	0	NO LIMIT
6	-25	0	NO LIMIT
7	12	18	18
8	26	26	32
9	26	32	32
10	29	29	35
11	30	36	36
12	25	25	31

FIGURE 19.42 The computer printout for the personnel scheduling problem in Example 19.33

1. The cost of 24 hours of operation is $11,648. The figure 11,647.999 is created by a rounding process in the computer. Clearly, since the x_j and y_j values are whole numbers, and the rates are whole numbers, the answer must be a whole number.

2. Since $x_6 = 0$ and $y_6 = 0$, no workers start on the 8 p.m shift.

3. Since $y_5 = 6$, the shift employing overtime workers must occur 8 hours later than 4:00 p.m., namely at midnight.

4. If the hourly rate for the shift starting at 8:00 a.m. were increased to $18, the coefficient of x_3 in the objective function would increase from 128 to 144. This is in the allowable range $96 \le c_3 \le 160$, so the optimal solution would retain the current x_j and y_j values. The new optimal Z value would be $11,648 + 16(18) = $11,936$.

5. If the hourly rate for the shift starting at noon were increased to $18, the coefficient of x_4 in the objective function would increase from 128 to 144. This does not lie in the allowable range $96 \le c_4 \le 128$. It is impossible to tell what would happen from this printout alone. It would be necessary to rerun the problem with the new coefficient.

6. The smallest shadow price of increasing the right-hand side of a minimum-personnel constraint is 32, which is y_2 or y_4 in the personnel constraints, and is either the shift starting at noon or the shift starting at 8 p.m. One of these shifts would be considered, since the shadow price is higher for all the other shifts.

■

Incidentally, there is an alternative optimal solution to this problem, namely $x_1 = 18$, $x_2 = 8$, $x_3 = 18$, $x_4 = 5$, $x_5 = 25$, $x_6 = 0$, $y_3 = 6$, $y_1 = y_2 = y_4 = y_5 = y_6 = 0$.

The existence of an alternative optimal solution can be detected by finding a decision variable with value zero that has a coefficient sensitivity of zero. In this problem, $y_3 = 0$ and has coefficient sensitivity zero.

□ **EXAMPLE 19.34** This is the investment problem formulated in Example 19.26 of the section on formulation. The objective is to maximize return. The computer solution is given. Answer these questions.

1. What is the optimal investment policy for R.B. James?
2. How high would the growth rate for investment 4 have to be before R.B. James would buy its shares?
3. If R.B. James could invest $80,000 in total in investments 2 and 5, what would be the optimal return?
4. If R.B. James invested $80,000 in total in investments 2 and 5, by how much would the rate of return increase?
5. If the weighted risk were to be lowered to 0.095, would the same investment plan be followed?

To review: R.B. James is in charge of the investments funds of the Halifax Resource Group. He has $250,000 to invest and has narrowed the choices to five possibilities, listed in Table 19.14 along with some performance estimates.

TABLE 19.14 Investment Possibilities for the Halifax Resource Group

Details	1	2	3	4	5
Share Price	$90	$45	$160	$60	$125
Growth Rate	0.11	0.16	0.07	0.08	0.12
Annual Dividend	$1.50	$0.80	$1.50	$0.95	$1.20
Risk	0.09	0.12	0.05	0.08	0.28

He must invest all of the $250,000 in these five and he has these guidelines to follow:

1. No more than $75,000 should be invested in total in investments 2 and 5.
2. At least 50 percent of the money invested should be placed in investments 1 and 3.
3. Total return on investment should be at least 8 percent. Return includes growth and dividends.
4. The total amount received in dividends should be at least $3000.
5. The average risk, weighted by the number of dollars in each investment, should be kept to no more than 0.10.

• **SOLUTION**

a) Let x_j be the number of shares of investment J.

$$J = 1, 2, 3, 4, 5.$$

The objective function is

$$Z = 0.11(90x_1) + 0.16(45x_2) + 0.07(160x_3) + 0.08(60x_4) + 0.12(125x_5)$$
$$+ 1.50x_1 + 0.80x_2 + 1.50x_3 + 0.95x_4 + 1.20x_5$$
$$= 9.90x_1 + 7.20x_2 + 11.20x_3 + 4.80x_4 + 15.00x_5 + 1.50x_1 + 0.80x_2$$
$$+ 1.50x_3 + 0.95x_4 + 1.20x_5$$
$$= 11.40x_1 + 8.00x_2 + 12.70x_3 + 5.75x_4 + 16.20x_5$$

$$\text{Max } Z = 11.40x_1 + 8.00x_2 + 12.70x_3 + 5.75x_4 + 16.20x_5$$

s.t.
$$90x_1 + 45x_2 + 160x_3 + 60x_4 + 125x_5 = 250,000$$
$$45x_2 + 125x_5 \le 75,000$$
$$90x_1 + 160x_3 \ge 0.50(250,000)$$
$$11.40x_1 + 8.00x_2 + 12.70x_3 + 5.75x_4 + 16.20x_5 \ge 0.08(250,000)$$
$$1.50x_1 + 0.80x_2 + 1.50x_3 + 0.95x_4 + 1.20x_5 \ge 3000$$

$$0.09\left(\frac{90x_1}{250,000}\right) + 0.12\left(\frac{45x_2}{250,000}\right) + 0.05\left(\frac{160x_3}{250,000}\right)$$
$$+ 0.08\left(\frac{60x_4}{250,000}\right) + 0.28\left(\frac{125x_5}{250,000}\right) \le 0.1$$

This formulation should be rewritten as follows to maximize the return:

$$\text{Max } Z = 11.40x_1 + 8.00x_2 + 12.70x_3 + 5.75x_4 + 16.20x_5$$

s.t.
$$45x_2 + 125x_5 \le 75,000$$
$$8.10x_1 + 5.40x_2 + 8.00x_3 + 4.80x_4 + 35.00x_5 \le 25,000$$
$$90x_1 + 45x_2 + 160x_3 + 60x_4 + 125x_5 = 250,000$$
$$90x_1 + 160x_3 \ge 125,000$$
$$11.40x_1 + 8.00x_2 + 12.70x_3 + 5.75x_4 + 16.20x_5 \ge 20,000$$
$$1.50x_1 + 0.80x_2 + 1.50x_3 + 0.95x_4 + 1.20x_5 \ge 3000$$
$$x_1, x_2, x_3, x_4, x_5 \ge 0$$

Note again that the order of the constraints has been changed. The second constraint is an algebraically simplified version of the original requirement that the average risk should be no more than 0.10.

RESULTS

VARIABLE	VARIABLE VALUE	ORIGINAL COEFFICIENT	COEFFICIENT SENSITIVITY
X1	1944.444	11.4	0
X2	1666.667	8	0
X3	0	12.7	7.567
X4	0	5.75	1.85
X5	0	16.2	6.022

CONSTRAINT NUMBER	ORIGINAL RIGHT-HAND VALUE	SLACK OR SURPLUS	SHADOW PRICE
1	75000	0	.051
2	25000	250	0
3	250000	0	.127
4	125000	49999.996	0
5	20000	15499.999	0
6	3000	1250	0

OBJECTIVE FUNCTION VALUE: 35500

SENSITIVITY ANALYSIS
OBJECTIVE FUNCTION COEFFICIENTS

VARIABLE	LOWER LIMIT	ORIGINAL COEFFICIENT	UPPER LIMIT
X1	8.625	11.4	16
X2	5.832	8	NO LIMIT
X3	NO LIMIT	12.7	20.267
X4	NO LIMIT	5.75	7.6
X5	NO LIMIT	16.2	22.222

RIGHT-HAND-SIDE VALUES

CONSTRAINT NUMBER	LOWER LIMIT	ORIGINAL VALUE	UPPER LIMIT
1	0	75000	83333.344
2	24750	25000	NO LIMIT
3	200000	250000	252777.781
4	NO LIMIT	125000	175000
5	NO LIMIT	20000	35500
6	NO LIMIT	3000	4250

FIGURE 19.43   The computer printout for the investment problem in Example 19.34

1. James is to buy 1944.444 shares of investment 1 and 1666.667 shares of investment 2. Since fractions of a share cannot be bought, an integer solution should be sought, so strictly speaking, integer programming should be performed. The third constraint would have to be relaxed to:

$$90x_1 + 45x_2 + 160x_3 + 60x_4 + 125x_5 \le 250000.$$

The best integer solution is 1944 shares of investment 1 and 1666 shares of investment 2.

2. The return would have to be greater than the upper limit of $7.60 for investment before R.B. James would buy its shares. The current value of $5.75 is made up of growth of $4.80 and dividend $0.95. To exceed $7.60, the growth would have to be greater than $7.60 − $0.95 = $6.65. In other words, the growth rate would have to be greater than $\left(\frac{6.65}{60}\right)(100\%)$ or 11.083%.

3. An investment of $80,000 is within the range $0 \leq b_1 \leq 83333.344$, so the shadow price is 0.051. The optimal return would be $35,500 + (80,000 - 75,000)(0.051) = \$35,755.$

4. The current rate of return is $\left(\frac{35,500}{250,000}\right)(100\%) = 14.2\%$. The new rate of return would be $\left(\frac{35,755}{250,000}\right)(100\%) = 14.302\%$. The increase in the rate of return would be about one tenth of 1% (0.00102 to be precise).

5. If the weighted risk were to be lowered to 0.095, the right-hand side of the second constraint would become $(0.095)(25,000) = 23,750$. This is less than the lower limit of 24,750, so the optimal value of at least one of the decision variables would change. The problem can be solved by running the question with the new right-hand value of 23,750. ∎

◻ **EXAMPLE 19.35**   This is the computer solution to the blending problem from Example 19.31 of the formulation section. Answer the following questions.

1. What is the optimal profit?
2. Give the optimal recipes for one litre of each of the types of fuel.
3. What is the cost of a litre of premium 1 fuel?
4. How much would the selling price for a litre of premium 1 fuel have to be lowered before no premium 1 fuel would be produced? What does this mean in terms of profit on premium 1 fuel?
5. If more of one of the ingredients were available, the profit could be improved. Which ingredient is it? What would the value of a litre of the ingredient be?

To review: A Winnipeg fuel company uses three ingredients, A, B, and C, to mix a variety of fuels. Ingredient A is extremely volatile, and fuels with a high percentage of it are called premium fuels. Ingredient B is moderately volatile, whereas ingredient C is pratically inert, and is used to combat the tendency of fuel mixtures to explode. The company is going to produce three types of fuel this year: premium 1, premium 2, and standard. The proportion of ingredient A in premium 1 fuel must be at least 50 percent, and in premium 2 fuel must be at least 40 percent. At least 20 percent of each type of fuel must be ingredient C, and goverment regulations prohibit any fuel with more than 70 percent ingredient A content. Standard fuel has at least a 35 percent ingredient C content and fuel with more than 55 percent of ingredient C will not burn, and so is useless. Price and cost data for the fuels are given in the following two tables.

TABLE 19.15   Fuel Type Cost and Demand

Fuel Type	Price per Litre	Expected Demand
Premium 1	$2.00	2,000,000 L
Premium 2	1.50	5,000,000 L
Standard	0.90	8,000,000 L

TABLE 19.16 Fuel Ingredient and Cost

Ingredient	Cost per Litre	Availability
A	$0.90	4,000,000 L
B	0.65	3,500,000 L
C	0.35	9,000,000 L

• **SOLUTION**

Let A_1 be the number of litres of ingredient A used to produce premium 1 fuel.

Let A_2 be the number of litres of ingredient A used to produce premium 2 fuel.

Let A_s be the number of litres of ingredient A used to produce standard fuel.

B_1, B_2, B_s, C_1, C_2, C_s are defined similarly.

Let L_1 be the number of litres of premium 1 fuel produced.

L_2 be the number of litres of premium 2 fuel produced.

L_s be the number of litres of standard fuel produced.

RESULTS

VARIABLE	VARIABLE VALUE	ORIGINAL COEFFICIENT	COEFFICIENT SENSITIVITY
A1	999999.812	− .9	0
A2	2250000	− .9	0
AS	99999.937	− .9	0
B1	0	− .65	.55
B2	0	− .65	0
BS	3500000	− .65	0
C1	999999.812	− .35	0
C2	2750000	− .35	0
Cs	4400001	− .35	0
L1	1999999.875	2	0
L2	5000000	1.5	0
LS	8000000	.9	0

CONSTRAINT NUMBER	ORIGINAL RIGHT-HAND VALUE	SLACK OR SURPLUS	SHADOW PRICE
10	4000000	650000	0
11	3500000 .	0	.25
12	9000000	850000	0

OBJECTIVE FUNCTION VALUE: 10557500

SENSITIVITY ANALYSIS
OBJECTIVE FUNCTION COEFFICIENTS

VARIABLE	LOWER LIMIT	ORIGINAL COEFFICIENT	UPPER LIMIT
A1	−3.65	− .9	−.35
A2	− .9	− .9	−.35
AS	−1.572	− .9	−.9
B1	NO LIMIT	− .65	−.1
B2	NO LIMIT	− .65	−.65
BS	− .65	− .65	NO LIMIT
C1	− .9	− .35	NO LIMIT
C2	− .9	− .35	NO LIMIT
CS	− .9	− .35	NO LIMIT
L1	.625	2	NO LIMIT
L2	.597	1.5	NO LIMIT
Ls	.597	.9	NO LIMIT

FIGURE 19.46   The computer printout for the blending problem in Example 19.35

1. The optimal profit is $10,557,500.

2. The optimal recipes for one litre of each type of fuel are as follows:
   Premium 1 fuel: $A_1 = 1,000,000$, $B_1 = 0$, $C_1 = 1,000,000$. Therefore, each litre of premium 1 fuel is an equal mixture of ingredients A and C.
   Premium 2 fuel: $A_2 = 2,250,000$, $B_2 = 0$, $C_2 = 2,750,000$. Therefore, each litre of premium 2 fuel contains $\frac{2,250,000}{5,000,000}(1000) = 450$ mL of ingredient A, and $\frac{2,750,000}{5,000,000}(1000) = 550$ mL of ingredient C.
   Standard fuel: $A_s = 100,000$, $B_s = 3,500,000$, $C_s = 4,400,000$. Therefore, each litre of standard fuel contains $\frac{100,000}{8,000,000}(1000) = 12.5$ mL of ingredient A, $\frac{3,500,000}{8,000,000}(1000) = 437.5$ mL of ingredient B, and $\frac{4,400,000}{8,000,000}(1000) = 550$ mL of ingredient C.

3. Each litre of premium 1 fuel costs 62.5 cents $((0.5)(0.90)+(0.5)(0.35) = 0.625)$.

4. The lower limit for the coefficient of L_1 in the objective-function coefficient range is 0.625. The current solution remains optimal so long as the selling price of premium fuel does not go below 62.5 cents. Since the cost of a litre is 62.5 cents, this means that so long as there is no actual loss on premium 1 fuel, it will be optimal to meet the demand for it.

5. The only ingredient with a positive shadow price is B (constraint 11). It follows that greater availability of ingredient B would lead to a larger profit. The value of a litre of ingredient B is $0.65 + 0.25$, or 0.90, since its cost has been deducted in the objective function. ■

PROBLEMS

19.25 For the linear-programming problem
$$\text{Max } Z = 3x_1 + 2x_2 + 5x_3$$
$$\text{s.t.} \quad 2x_1 + x_2 \le 100$$
$$x_1 - 2x_2 + x_3 \le 250$$
$$x_1 + x_2 + 2x_3 \ge 25$$
$$x_1, x_2, x_3 \ge 0$$

use the LINP printout to answer the following questions, if possible. If the printout does not provide enough information to answer a question, state why not.

a) What is the optimal solution?

b) How high would the coefficient of x_1 have to be in order to have x_1 enter the solution? How low would the coefficient of x_2 have to be before the optimal value of x_2 became zero?

c) What is the optimal solution to the following problem?

$$\text{Max } Z = 3x_1 + 5x_2 + 5x_3$$
$$\text{s.t.} \quad 2x_1 + x_2 \leq 100$$
$$x_1 - 2x_2 + x_3 \leq 250$$
$$x_1 + x_2 + 2x_3 \geq 25$$
$$x_1, x_2, x_3 \geq 0$$

d) What is the optimal value of Z for the problem shown here?

$$\text{Max } Z = 3x_1 + 2x_2 + 5x_3$$
$$\text{s.t.} \quad 2x_1 + x_2 \leq 125$$
$$x_1 - 2x_2 + x_3 \leq 250$$
$$x_1 + x_2 + 2x_3 \geq 25$$
$$x_1, x_2, x_3 \geq 0$$

e) What are the optimal values of x_1, x_2, and x_3 for part d)?

f) What is the optimal solution for the following problem?

$$\text{Max } Z = 3x_1 + 2x_2 + 5x_3$$
$$\text{s.t.} \quad 2x_1 + x_2 \leq 100$$
$$x_1 - 2x_2 + x_3 \leq 250$$
$$x_1 + x_2 + 2x_3 \geq 250$$
$$x_1, x_2, x_3 \geq 0$$

g) What is the optimal solution for the problem shown here?

$$\text{Max } Z = 3x_1 + 2x_2 + 5x_3$$
$$\text{s.t.} \quad 2x_1 + x_2 \leq 100$$
$$-x_1 + 2x_2 - x_3 \geq 150$$
$$x_1 + x_2 + 2x_3 \geq 25$$
$$x_1, x_2, x_3 \geq 0$$

RESULTS

VARIABLE	VARIABLE VALUE	ORIGINAL COEFFICIENT	COEFFICIENT SENSITIVITY
X1	0	3	26
X2	100	2	0
X3	450	5	0

CONSTRAINT NUMBER	ORIGINAL RIGHT-HAND VALUE	SLACK OR SURPLUS	SHADOW PRICE
1	100	0	12
2	250	0	5
3	25	975	0

OBJECTIVE FUNCTION VALUE: 2450

SENSITIVITY ANALYSIS
OBJECTIVE FUNCTION COEFFICIENTS

VARIABLE	LOWER LIMIT	ORIGINAL COEFFICIENT	UPPER LIMIT
X1	NO LIMIT	3	29
X2	-10	2	NO LIMIT
X3	0	5	NO LIMIT

RIGHT-HAND-SIDE VALUES

CONSTRAINT NUMBER	LOWER LIMIT	ORIGINAL VALUE	UPPER LIMIT
1	0	100	NO LIMIT
2	-200	250	NO LIMIT
3	NO LIMIT	25	1000

FIGURE 19.47 The computer printout for Problem 19.25

19.26 R.B. James is in charge of the investment funds of the Halifax Resource Group. He has $250,000 to invest, and has narrowed the choices to five possibilities, listed in Table 19.17 below along with some performance estimates.

He must invest all of the $250,000 in these five and he has some guidelines to follow:

1. No more than $75,000 should be invested in total in investments 2 and 5.
2. At least 50 percent of the money invested should be placed in investments 1 and 3.

TABLE 19.17 Investment Possibilities

Investment	1	2	3	4	5
Share Price	$90.00	$45.00	$160.00	$60.00	$125.00
Growth Rate	0.11	0.16	0.07	0.08	0.12
Annual Dividend	$1.50	$0.80	$1.50	$0.95	$1.20
Risk	0.09	0.12	0.05	0.08	0.28

3. Total return on investment should be at least 8%. Return includes growth and dividends.

4. The total amount received in dividends should be at least $3000.
5. The average risk, weighted by the number of dollars in each investment, should be kept to no more than 0.10.

Formulate the problem in order to minimize the weighted risk.

$$\min Z = 0.09 \left(\frac{90x_1}{250,000} \right) + 0.12 \left(\frac{45x_2}{250,000} \right)$$
$$+ 0.05 \left(\frac{160x_3}{250,000} \right) + 0.08 \left(\frac{60x_4}{250,000} \right)$$
$$+ 0.28 \left(\frac{125x_5}{250,000} \right)$$

or, since multiplying by 250,000 will give an expression that will be minimized for the same values of x_1, x_2, x_3, x_4, and x_5,

$$\text{Min } Z = 8.10x_1 + 5.40x_2 + 8.00x_3 + 4.80x_4 + 35x_5$$

s.t. $45x_2 + 125x_5 \leq 75,000$

$8.10x_1 + 5.40x_2 + 8.00x_3 + 4.80x_4 + 35.00x_5$
$\leq 25,000$

$90x_1 + 45x_2 + 160x_3 + 60x_4 + 125x_5$
$= 250,000$

$90x_1 + 160x_3 \geq 125,000$

$11.40x_1 + 8.00x_2 + 12.70x_3 + 5.75x_4$
$+ 16.20x_5 \geq 20,000$

$1.50x_1 + 0.80x_2 + 1.50x_3 + 0.95x_4 + 1.20x_5$
≥ 3000

$x_1, x_2, x_3, x_4, x_5 \geq 0$

a) What is the best investment plan subject to R.B.'s constraints? What do you think the best plan is if only whole shares can be bought? How much worse is the return if only whole numbers of shares can bought?

b) What is the total rate of return on investment?

c) If the risk factor for investment 1 were reduced to 0.085, what would be the best investment plan? To what value would the risk factor have to be reduced before R.B. James should consider buying shares of investment 1?

d) If the total amount invested in dividends had to be at least $3,150, would the optimal weighted risk increase or decrease? What would be the new weighted risk?

e) If at least 60 percent of the money invested had to be placed in investments 1 and 3, what would be the optimal investment plan?

RESULTS

VARIABLE	VARIABLE VALUE	ORIGINAL COEFFICIENT	COEFFICIENT SENSITIVITY
X1	0	8.1	.552
X2	0	5.4	1.394
X3	927.419	8	0
X4	1693.548	4.8	0
X5	0	35	28.619

CONSTRAINT NUMBER	ORIGINAL RIGHT-HAND VALUE	SLACK OR SURPLUS	SHADOW PRICE
1	75000	75000	0
2	25000	9451.613	0
3	250000	0	.006
4	125000	23387.109	0
5	20000	1516.13	0
6	3000	0	4.645

OBJECTIVE FUNCTION VALUE: 15548.388

SENSITIVITY ANALYSIS
OBJECTIVE FUNCTION COEFFICIENTS

VARIABLE	LOWER LIMIT	ORIGINAL COEFFICIENT	UPPER LIMIT
X1	7.548	8.1	NO LIMIT
X2	4.006	5.4	NO LIMIT
X3	.4	8	12.8
X4	3	4.8	5.126
X5	6.381	35	NO LIMIT

RIGHT-HAND-SIDE VALUES

CONSTRAINT NUMBER	LOWER LIMIT	ORIGINAL VALUE	UPPER LIMIT
1	0	75000	NO LIMIT
2	15548.387	25000	NO LIMIT
3	240460.531	250000	319999.969
4	NO LIMIT	125000	148387.109
5	NO LIMIT	20000	21516.129
6	2405.063	3000	3151.042

FIGURE 19.48 The computer printout for Problem 19.26

♦ **19.27** A firm manufactures three products, A, B, and C. Each one of these products uses resources from each of the three departments X, Y, and Z. In order to determine the best product mix within the constraints of the availability of resources in person-hours in the three departments, the following formulation is given by the resident managerial accountant.

$$\text{Max } 15.5A + 20B + 16C$$

s.t. $2A + 3B + 6C \leq 200$ (Department X)

$3A + 4B + 2C \leq 160$ (Department Y)

$3A + 3B + 4C \leq 210$ (Department Z)

$A, B, C \geq 0$

Note that the profits per unit of products A, B, and C are $15.50, $20, and $16 respectively. Department X has 200 person-hours available, whereas Departments Y and Z have only 160 and 210 person-hours available.

The following partial computer output is obtained by using LINP. On the basis of the information given, provide your responses to the following:

a) Specify the optimal product mix.

b) Which resources are fully utilized and which ones have slack?

c) Interpret the meaning of the shadow prices.

d) Suppose the net profit per unit of product B is increased from $20 to $22. Would it change your optimal product-mix? Explain.

RESULTS

VARIABLE	VARIABLE VALUE	ORIGINAL COEFFICIENT	COEFFICIENT SENSITIVITY
A	40	15.5	0
B	0	20	1.071
C	20	16	0

CONSTRAINT NUMBER	ORIGINAL RIGHT-HAND VALUE	SLACK OR SURPLUS	SHADOW PRICE
1	200	0	1.214
2	160	0	4.357
3	210	10	0

OBJECTIVE FUNCTION VALUE: 940

SENSITIVITY ANALYSIS
OBJECTIVE FUNCTION COEFFICIENTS

VARIABLE	LOWER LIMIT	ORIGINAL COEFFICIENT	UPPER LIMIT
A	14.667	15.5	24
B	NO LIMIT	20	21.071
C	10.333	16	46.5

RIGHT-HAND-SIDE VALUES

CONSTRAINT NUMBER	LOWER LIMIT	ORIGINAL VALUE	UPPER LIMIT
1	106.667	200	223.333
2	66.667	160	174
3	200	210	NO LIMIT

FIGURE 19.49 The computer printout for Problem 19.27

CHAPTER SUMMARY

KEY TERMS AND EXPRESSIONS

Linear expression: An algebraic expression of the form $\sum a_{ij}x_j$.

Slope: The amount by which y increases for a unit increase in x.

Intercept: The value of a variable where a line crosses an axis.

Family of lines: The set of all lines of the form $ax + by = K$, for different values of K.

Feasible region: The set of points satisfying all the constraints in a linear-programming problem.

Objective function: The expression for which the maximum or minimum value is sought.

Formulation: The act of expressing a described optimization problem in terms of a linear objective function and constraints.

Constraint: An expression of the form
$\Sigma a_{ij}x_j = b_i$, $\Sigma a_{ij}x_j \leq b_i$ or $\Sigma a_{ij}x_j \geq b_i$
that expresses a condition or restriction on the values of the variables.

Graphical solution: A method of solving a linear- programming problem involving a sketch of the feasible region and evaluation of the objective function at vertices.

Anomalies: Non-standard linear programming situations involving alternative optimal solutions, unbounded problems, or infeasible problems.

Alternative optimal solutions: A situation in which more than one set of values of the variables gives an optimal solution.

Unbounded problem: A situation in which there is no upper limit in a maximization problem, or no lower limit in a minimization problem.

Infeasible problem: A situation in which there are no values that satisfy every constraint, so that the feasible region is the empty set.

Sensitivity analysis: The study of the effect of changing one of the objective-function coefficients or one of the right-hand-side values of a constraint.

Shadow price: The amount by which the optimal value of Z changes for a unit change in the right-hand-side of a constraint.

Integer programming: Linear programming when some or all of the variables are specified as having integer values.

Computer solutions: The use of commercial software packages to solve linear-programming problems.

EXERCISES

19.28 Sketch the feasible regions determined by the following systems of inequalities:

a) $4x_1 + 3x_2 \le 37$
   $3x_1 - 7x_2 \le 0$
   $-x_1 + 2x_2 \le 10$
   $x_1 \ge 0, x_2 \ge 0$

b) $-2x_1 + x_2 \le 1$
   $2x_1 + 3x_2 \ge 11$
   $6x_1 + x_2 \le 25$
   $x_1 \ge 0, x_2 \ge 0$

c) $-2x_1 + x_2 \le 1$
   $2x_1 + 3x_2 \ge 11$
   $6x_1 + x_2 \ge 25$
   $x_1 \ge 0, x_2 \ge 0$

d) $-2x_1 + x_2 \le 1$
   $2x_1 + 3x_2 \le 11$
   $6x_1 + x_2 \le 25$
   $x_1 \ge 0, x_2 \ge 0$

19.29 Solve the following linear-programming problems graphically:

a) max $z = 3x_1 - 2x_2$

s.t. $4x_1 + 3x_2 \le 37$
   $3x_1 - 7x_2 \le 0$
   $-x_1 + 2x_2 \le 10$
   $x_1 \ge 0, x_2 \ge 0$

b) min $z = 4x_1 + 3x_2$

s.t. $-2x_1 + x_2 \le 1$
   $2x_1 + 3x_2 \ge 11$
   $6x_1 + x_2 \le 25$
   $x_1 \ge 0, x_2 \ge 0$

c) Show that $-5 \le x_1 - x_2 \le 4$ on the feasible region defined by:

$$2x_1 + 3x_2 \le 15$$
$$3x_1 + x_2 \le 12$$
$$x_1 \ge 0, x_2 \ge 0$$

19.30 Consider the following linear-programming problem.

$$\max z = 4x_1 + 11x_2$$

s.t. $x_1 + 3x_2 \le 21$
$$2x_1 + 5x_2 \le 36$$
$$2x_1 + x_2 \le 20$$
$$x_1 \ge 0, x_2 \ge 0$$

a) Show that the optimal solution is $x_1 = 3$, $x_2 = 6$, $z = 78$.

b) Find the range of values of c_1 for which $(3, 6)$ is the optimal vertex. Do the same for c_2.

c) Find the shadow prices for each of the three constraints. For what ranges of values of b_1, b_2, and b_3 are the shadow prices valid?

d) Based on the solution to the original problem, what is the maximum value of $z = 4x_1 + 10.5x_2$ in the feasible region?

e) Use a shadow price found in c) to solve the following:

$$\max z = 4x_1 + 11x_2$$

s.t. $x_1 + 3x_2 \le 21$
$$2x_1 + 5x_2 \le 37.5$$
$$2x_1 + x_2 \le 20$$
$$x_1 \ge 0, x_2 \ge 0$$

♦ **19.31** Cougar Incorporated, a small but well-known sports equipment firm, manufactures three brands of jogging shoes: Colt, Puma, and Bullet. Each one of these shoes goes through three departments: cutting and sewing, finishing, and quality inspection. The following table provides the hours of labour required per pair of shoes for each brand in the three departments.

TABLE 19.18   Breakdown of Labour

	Cutting and sewing Department	Finishing Department	Quality Inspection Department
Colt	0.30 hours	0.20 hours	0.10 hours
Puma	0.35	0.30	0.15
Bullet	0.40	0.35	0.20

Due to the nature of work in the different departments, and also because of certain clauses in the union contract, it is not possible to move labour from one department to another. Labour is paid at the hourly rate of $25, on the average, in all the departments.

Direct material costs for a pair of Colt, Puma, and Bullet jogging shoes are $20, $25, and $30 respectively. Variable overheads have been estimated at $10 per labour hour. Selling prices of the three brands are $55, $72, and $85 per pair respectively.

The company has no problem selling every pair of shoes it can manufacture. Production, however, is limited due to the availability of workers in each department. On a daily basis, the cutting and sewing department has 100 hours of labour available, finishing has 50 hours, and quality inspection has only 30 hours of labour available. The company would like to determine a daily production plan that maximizes the profit.

Formulate the above problem as a linear-programming model, clearly defining all the decision variables, the objective function, and the constraints.

19.32 A small airline is considering running a service from Thunder Bay, with flights to Toronto, Winnipeg, and Regina. The route under consideration is a loop, leaving Thunder Bay, visiting Regina, Winnipeg, and Toronto, in that order, and returning to Thunder Bay.

Fuel has different costs at the different airports, so a major consideration is the plan for buying and carrying fuel. If there were no additional costs associated with carrying fuel, it would be advisable to buy it all at the lowest price. Unfortunately, the airplanes have a limited capacity for carrying fuel, and, in any case, the amount used with the extra weight of stockpiled fuel would be substantially increased —it takes fuel to carry fuel. The minimum requirement is the amount of fuel used when no additional fuel is carried. The right-most column in the table below, labelled Carrying Cost, indicates how much fuel is required to carry each litre in excess of the minimum requirement.

TABLE 19.19 Fuel Purchasing Consideration

Airport	Cost per Litre	Min. Requirement	Max. Capacity	Carrying Cost
Thunder Bay	1.80	8000	25,000	0.10
Regina	1.55	6000	25,000	0.16
Winnipeg	1.95	12,000	25,000	0.13
Toronto	1.75	9000	25,000	0.17

What is the optimal plan for buying fuel for this loop? This problem may be formulated by letting THB, REG, WPG, and TOR be the number of litres bought at the respective airports, and XTH, XRE, XWP, and XTO be the fuel left over on arrival at the airports. The relationship between these last 4 variables can be exemplified by the connection between XTH and XTO. The number of litres left on arrival in Thunder Bay equals the number of litres left on arrival in Toronto plus the number of litres bought in Toronto minus the 9000-litre minimum requirement and the fuel needed to carry the excess fuel.

$$XTH = TOR + XTO - 9000 - 0.17(TOR + XTO - 9000).$$

This reduces to $0.83TOR + 0.83XTO - XTH = 7470$
The formulation is

$$Min\ Z = 1.80THB + 1.55REG + 1.95WPG + 1.75TOR$$

s.t
$$THB + XTH \le 25,000$$
$$REG + XRE \le 25,000$$
$$WPG + XWP \le 25,000$$
$$TOR + XTO \le 25,000$$
$$0.83TOR + 0.83XTO - XTH = 7470$$
$$0.90THB + 0.90XTH - XRE = 7200$$
$$0.84REG + 0.84XRE - XWP = 5040$$
$$0.82WPG + 0.82XWP - XTO = 9840$$
$$THB + XTH \ge 8000$$
$$REG + XRE \ge 6000$$
$$WPG + XWP \ge 12,000$$
$$TOR + XTO \ge 9000$$
all variables ≥ 0

a) What is the optimal solution?

b) How low would the price of fuel have to be in Winnipeg before it would be worthwhile to buy some in that city?

c) What would the total fuel cost for the loop be if fuel in Regina cost $1.60?

d) What would the total fuel cost for the loop be if the airline had a route change that meant a minimum fuel requirement of 8750 litres from Thunder Bay to Regina?

e) The airplanes have a maximum capacity of 25,000 litres. Could this capacity be reduced without a cost penalty, and if so, by how much could it be reduced?

RESULTS

VARIABLE	VARIABLE VALUE	ORIGINAL COEFFICIENT	COEFFICIENT SENSITIVITY
THB	8000	1.8	0
REG	20285.715	1.55	0
WPG	0	1.95	.105
TOR	9000	1.75	0
XTH	0	0	0
XRE	0	0	0
XWP	12000	0	0
XTO	0	0	0

CONSTRAINT NUMBER	ORIGINAL RIGHT-HAND VALUE	SLACK OR SURPLUS	SHADOW PRICE
1	25000	17000	0
2	25000	4714.286	0
3	25000	13000	0
4	25000	16000	0
5	7470	0	1.8
6	7200	0	1.55
7	5040	0	1.845
8	9840	0	1.75
9	8000	0	.405
10	6000	14285.714	0
11	12000	0	.41
12	9000	0	.256

OBJECTIVE FUNCTION VALUE: 61592.855

SENSITIVITY ANALYSIS
OBJECTIVE FUNCTION COEFFICIENTS

VARIABLE	LOWER LIMIT	ORIGINAL COEFFICIENT	UPPER LIMIT
THB	1.395	1.8	2.108
REG	1.205	1.55	1.638
WPG	1.845	1.95	NO LIMIT
TOR	1.494	1.75	2.25
XTH	−.308	0	NO LIMIT
XRE	−.45	0	NO LIMIT
XWP	−.41	0	.105
XTO	−.5	0	NO LIMIT

RIGHT-HAND-SIDE VALUES

CONSTRAINT NUMBER	LOWER LIMIT	ORIGINAL VALUE	UPPER LIMIT
1	8000	25000	NO LIMIT
2	20285.715	25000	NO LIMIT
3	12000	25000	NO LIMIT
4	9000	25000	NO LIMIT
5	−530	7470	7470
6	−13085.715	7200	7200
7	−6960	5040	9000
8	840	9840	9840
9	8000	8000	25000
10	NO LIMIT	6000	20285.715
11	12000	12000	15960
12	9000	9000	18638.555

FIGURE 19.50   The computer printout for Problem 19.32

CASE PROBLEMS

The following problems should be formulated and run on a computer.

19.33 Montreal Cereal Products has decided that the recipes for different mixes of health snacks can be varied to some extent. The new recipe requirements for 300g containers are as follows:

TABLE 19.20   Recipe Variations

	Mix 1 (g)	Mix 2 (g)	Mix 3 (g)
Cereal products	at most 150	at most 200	at most 200
Whole peanuts	at least 50	at most 25	at most 50
Flaked almonds and hazelnuts	at least 50	at least 75	at most 25
Shredded coconut	at least 25	at least 50	—
	300 g	300 g	300 g
Revenue per 300g container	$3.00	$2.50	$3.50

TABLE 19.21

	Cost of Ingredients
Cereal products	$0.15/100 g (500 kg available)
Whole peanuts	$0.20/100 g (110 kg available)
Flaked almonds/hazelnuts	$0.25/100 g (100 kg available)
Shredded coconut	$0.20/100 g (150 kg available)

a) How many containers of each mix should be produced? What is the optimal profit?

b) Give the recipes for 300 g containers of mix 1 and mix 3.

c) What would the optimal profit be if mix 1 sold for $3.20 a container?

d) What would the revenue have to be for a container of mix 2 in order for it to be reasonable to produce some?

e) If Montreal Cereal Products can obtain more of one of the ingredients, which one would it be most interested in getting?

f) What would the optimal profit be if Montreal Cereal Products decided to buy an extra 50 kg of shredded coconut to use in the mixture?

19.34 P.B Charles is going to receive a windfall of $10,000 in May and has decided to become involved in commodity speculation. He has 35 m^2 (350, 000 cm^2) of floor area available in a warehouse, and has chosen to buy and sell fish and corn meal during the summer months.

The prices of these commodities will be set at the beginning of each month this summer, and the price will hold for the entire month. The two kinds of meal may be freely bought and sold during the month in any quantity at the set price. The prices are not known in advance, of course, but Charles's knowledge of the field leads him to make the predictions shown in Table 19.22.

TABLE 19.22   Monthly Meal Prices

	Fish	Corn
June	$1.80/kg	$1.60/kg
July	2.40	2.15
August	2.00	1.95

At the end of August, any leftover meal will be sold for an estimated $2.10 per kilogram. Charles's profit is the difference between the price he pays for the meal and the price for which he sells the meal.

Each kilogram of fish meal requires 100 cm^2 of floor space in the warehouse, and each kilogram of corn requires 50 cm^2. Storage costs amount to $0.05 per kilogram per month, and are incurred even if the storage is only for a part of the month. The monthly storage charges must be paid in advance at the beginning of the month. For his own convenience, Charles will buy or sell certain amounts of each meal at the beginning of each month. Any money not tied up will be kept in a non-interest-bearing chequing account. For speculative reasons, Charles has personally decided to ensure that at least 40 percent of the weight of the meal in storage is to be fish meal at all times.

Formulate a linear programming model to help Charles get the best return over the three-month period.

a) What is P.B. Charles's optimal plan, and what profit will he make?

b) Would it be useful for P.B. Charles to have more storage space in the warehouse? How much would the profit be if he had 40 m^2 of floor area?

c) How much would the profit be if he had 41 m^2 of floor area?

d) If P.B. Charles wanted to, he could make the same profit starting with less money. How little money could he have started with?

APPENDIX A
Data Sets

Column headings match the names of the associated ASCII files that appear on the CGA-prepared data diskette.

DATA SET 1 The Canadian People, Markets, 1991
         OBS1   = Observation number (alphabetical)
         POP1   = Total population by city (000's)
         POPCHG = Population change 1981 to 1991
         HSHOLDS = Number of households (000's)
         INCOME = Personal income total (million $)
         SALES1   = Retail sales (million $)
         Note: blank spaces indicate missing data.

OBS1	CITY	POP1	POPCHG	HSHOLDS	INCOME1	SALES1
1	Alma	30.3		10.6	449.7	218.7
2	Baie-Comeau	32.9	−2.29	11.4	596.3	306.1
3	Barrie	88.1	44.18	30.4	1666.3	703.9
4	Bathurst	35.7	1.51	11.8	473.7	249.3
5	Belleville	92.3	7.95	33.9	1683.4	654.8
6	Bonnyville	11.2	24.39	3.3	163.0	75.3
7	Bracebridge	12.7	39.91	4.5	237.4	97.3
8	Brandon	42.0	15.57	16.0	669.8	585.6
9	Brantford	93.6	5.98	34.3	1622.4	622.2
10	Brock	12.7	36.87	4.3	197.7	80.5
11	Brockville	39.9	11.98	14.7	770.5	303.0
12	Calgary	727.3	16.16	274.6	15174.0	6428.0
13	Campbell River	28.3	10.35	10.6	493.6	227.4
14	Campbelton	17.0	−5.82	5.8	218.2	109.8
15	Camrose	13.2	5.13	5.0	201.4	76.9
16	Capital, Subd. A	10.1	25.99	4.3	159.9	64.2
17	Carbonear	13.7	4.99	4.1	136.3	67.4
18	Central Kootenay, Subd. B	12.5	−0.82	4.7	168.4	69.2
19	Charlottetown	58.9	15.59	20.1	854.7	427.9
20	Chatham	43.9	6.50	16.1	814.4	317.8
21	Chester	10.7	6.85	4.0	147.2	68.1
22	Chicoutimi-Jonquière	158.9	0.43	55.2	2476.8	1230.4
23	Chilliwack	52.0	6.35	19.7	771.1	336.4
24	Clearwater No. 99	10.3	11.73	3.5	157.5	66.9
25	Cobourg	16.0	22.25	6.0	307.8	121.8
26	Colbeau	15.5	0.42	5.2	210.7	102.5
27	Collingwood	12.8	6.05	4.7	219.8	83.4
28	Columbia-Shuswap, Subd. C	12.7	3.14	4.9	169.0	67.8
29	Corner Brook	34.5	−1.81	10.6	444.7	233.3
30	Cornwall	52.9	1.61	19.5	893.2	337.5
31	Courtenay	40.5	14.85	15.6	615.8	239.1
32	Cowansville	11.8	−7.03	4.4	167.9	72.0

OBS1	CITY	POP1	POPCHG	HSHOLDS	INCOME1	SALES1
33	Cranbrook	16.1	0.79	6.0	263.5	118.4
34	Dawson Creek	10.2	−10.81	3.9	146.6	60.0
35	Delhi	15.1	−0.18	5.5	244.4	91.5
36	Drummondville	59.0	7.82	22.6	849.8	379.0
37	Duncan	24.9	1.98	9.5	387.5	170.3
38	Dunnville	12.2	7.37	4.2	191.0	74.3
39	East Hants	18.9	27.11	6.2	273.9	144.6
40	Edmonton	816.0	10.13	301.4	15173.9	6347.7
41	Edmundston	23.6	5.64	8.1	330.5	167.4
42	Elliot Lake	18.1	1.15	5.8	360.7	151.2
43	Essa	16.8	23.32	5.1	254.8	109.5
44	Estevan	10.6	15.13	3.9	206.4	106.8
45	Fort McMurray	52.8	22.42	17.0	1165.2	554.1
46	Fort St. John	13.2	−4.91	4.8	209.0	92.9
47	Fraser-Fort George, Subd.	13.1	12.25	4.4	221.1	110.1
48	Fredericton	68.4	10.22	24.8	1192.3	639.4
49	Gander	11.2	1.26	3.5	170.5	95.1
50	Gaspé	17.9	3.81	5.7	234.9	119.1
51	Granby	55.2	14.15	21.2	872.1	402.8
52	Grand Falls	26.3	0.72	7.9	327.6	177.5
53	Grande Prairie	28.7	18.24	10.0	503.1	214.9
54	Grande Prairie County No.	12.0	−0.23	3.8	185.0	81.5
55	Gravenhurst	11.0	28.99	3.8	164.9	64.9
56	Guelph	104.5	33.22	37.1	2006.6	827.0
57	Haileybury	14.7	−4.28	5.2	238.9	85.0
58	Haldimand	18.9	11.89	6.3	353.8	147.7
59	Halifax	312.5	12.47	113.2	5662.1	2960.8
60	Hamilton	600.3	10.73	219.1	12158.5	4937.7
61	Hawkesbury	11.4	1.13	4.2	166.5	62.8
62	Huntsville	14.5	26.75	5.2	225.4	86.7
63	Improvement District No.	13.2	13.92	4.1	153.8	64.7
64	Joliette	36.2	4.66	13.8	554.0	254.7
65	Kamloops	61.1	−5.98	22.8	1020.5	461.3
66	Kapuskasing	11.3	−5.54	4.1	221.5	87.6
67	Kelowna	95.6	12.20	37.3	1525.4	672.0
68	Kenora	15.9	2.13	5.8	313.9	119.0
69	Kingston	135.9	18.31	48.9	2587.6	1047.1
70	Kings, Subd. A	21.1	12.44	7.1	268.9	133.1
71	Kings, Subd. B	10.9	8.21	3.7	139.7	68.0
72	Kirkland Lake	11.7	−4.33	4.8	187.9	63.2
73	Kitchener	350.2	21.67	125.6	6795.5	2753.5
74	Kitimat	10.7	−16.26	3.6	224.8	116.2
75	La Tuque	12.9	−7.54	5.0	212.0	97.7
76	Labrador City	11.1	−24.70	3.3	185.1	110.5
77	Lachute	12.0	2.38	4.7	173.8	76.1
78	Leamington	13.6	7.87	4.9	224.0	86.4
79	Lethbridge	61.5	12.60	23.4	1045.4	415.4
80	Lindsay	21.8	29.27	8.1	358.9	137.3
81	Lloydminster	18.6	23.28	6.6	323.7	146.7

OBS1	CITY	POP1	POPCHG	HSHOLDS	INCOME1	SALES1
82	London	371.5	13.75	141.0	7388.3	2885.3
83	Lunenburg	25.8	4.45	9.1	349.7	168.5
84	Magog	19.6	7.91	7.7	290.5	128.9
85	Matane	15.3	−2.03	5.8	222.4	100.5
86	Matsqui	103.8	37.97	35.6	1532.6	728.1
87	Medicine Hat	51.2	3.28	19.3	825.1	323.4
88	Midland	36.9	8.04	13.3	606.7	228.6
89	Moncton	105.3	7.26	37.1	1707.8	916.9
90	Montmagny	11.8	−4.64	4.2	159.0	73.1
91	Montreal	3084.1	7.76	1222.6	57773.3	27803.5
92	Moose Jaw	38.0	5.72	14.5	586.5	276.4
93	Nanaimo	64.8	12.25	25.6	1028.7	440.1
94	Nanaimo, Subd. B	13.7	21.32	5.4	218.9	94.1
95	Nanticoke	21.1	6.39	7.4	348.2	136.1
96	New Glasgow	38.6	−1.95	13.5	527.9	258.8
97	Norfolk	11.0	−1.75	3.8	152.8	57.3
98	North Battleford	19.4	10.38	7.1	298.9	146.6
99	North Bay	57.2	−1.17	20.6	976.9	375.1
100	Orillia	32.3	4.59	12.0	247.0	206.0
101	Oromocto	10.3	13.72	3.1	129.3	73.4
102	Oshawa	249.9	34.05	84.0	5232.3	2270.3
103	Ottawa-Hull	885.3	19.00	330.9	19827.7	8545.4
104	Owen Sound	28.2	3.23	10.5	489.4	172.3
105	Pembroke	23.3	3.01	8.4	375.6	140.3
106	Penticton	40.8	9.36	16.6	627.4	260.2
107	Peterborough	90.5	5.62	33.2	1641.3	627.7
108	Port Alberni	25.0	−11.78	9.5	423.2	188.4
109	Port Hope	13.2	31.87	4.8	238.9	94.6
110	Portage la Prairie	13.5	2.93	4.9	201.0	85.1
111	Powell River	18.0	−7.00	7.1	276.5	116.5
112	Prince Albert	42.7	12.44	15.0	612.8	305.8
113	Prince George	69.4	2.77	24.4	1204.3	576.5
114	Prince Rupert	17.4	−5.24	6.1	314.0	152.9
115	Québèc	622.0	6.51	237.3	10880.1	5249.7
116	Quesnel	24.7	7.99	8.6	366.6	169.6
117	Red Deer	61.2	31.85	22.3	1060.8	439.8
118	Red Deer County No. 23	14.4	6.47	4.8	238.9	104.8
119	Regina	192.7	10.94	71.7	3458.0	1756.3
120	Rimouski	47.9	6.53	17.4	780.3	378.4
121	Rivière-du-Loup	22.9	2.10	8.2	335.1	159.7
122	Roberva	11.7	2.83	3.8	152.7	75.8
123	Rouyn	37.9	6.91	14.3	586.7	269.3
124	Saint Georges	23.3	20.52	8.4	313.5	144.1
125	Saint Jerome	46.5	8.58	18.2	712.5	321.8
126	Saint John	123.6	2.05	44.1	1882.6	986.8
127	Sainte-Marie	10.4	16.26	3.6	154.3	76.4
128	Saint-Hyacinthe	50.2	5.62	19.3	800.2	369.2
129	Saint-Jean-sur-Richelieu	63.3	9.04	24.3	986.7	454.6
130	Salaberry-de-Valleyfield	39.0	−1.28	15.3	601.5	268.8

OBS1	CITY	POP1	POPCHG	HSHOLDS	INCOME1	SALES1
131	Salmon Arm	12.0	11.22	4.6	167.6	70.4
132	Sarnia	95.8	14.07	34.7	2051.9	847.3
133	Saskatoon	207.3	18.36	77.9	3460.7	1708.9
134	Sault Ste. Marie	83.7	−3.70	30.3	1510.7	582.2
135	Scugog	21.5	59.18	6.9	432.5	194.5
136	Selkirk	10.1	0.94	3.5	155.6	70.5
137	Sept-iles	25.0	−23.10	9.1	386.4	180.0
138	Shawinigan	62.3	−1.91	24.6	902.9	395.6
139	Sherbrooke	136.0	8.49	53.2	2172.0	995.5
140	Simcoe	14.9	4.23	5.6	285.9	111.0
141	Sorel	46.4	−1.37	17.3	721.4	342.7
142	Squamish	10.3	0.22	3.7	174.7	81.4
143	Stratford	27.5	4.72	10.7	529.8	200.2
144	St. Catharines-Niagara	358.5	4.61	132.2	6639.9	2595.3
145	St. Johns	164.0	6.03	51.1	2496.9	1412.2
146	Sudbury	149.7	−4.12	53.8	2611.9	1018.4
147	Summerside	17.4	20.47	5.9	238.9	119.6
148	Sunshine Coast, Subd. A	13.6	20.35	5.6	233.4	99.9
149	Swift Current	16.0	8.77	6.4	266.2	125.1
150	Sydney	120.6	−1.95	39.9	1481.1	734.6
151	Terrace	17.8	−0.08	6.0	281.8	136.5
152	Thetford Mines	30.9	−9.53	11.6	446.0	203.8
153	Thompson	15.9	11.16	5.2	289.8	141.6
154	Thunder Bay	122.9	0.76	45.0	2401.0	949.3
155	Tilsonburg	11.6	10.60	4.6	210.2	76.9
156	Timmins	47.7	3.43	16.9	835.7	328.0
157	Toronto	3822.4	22.10	1343.6	87322.3	37455.5
158	Trail	19.1	−17.18	7.6	336.6	149.9
159	Trois-Rivières	131.9	5.23	50.9	2076.8	954.1
160	Truro	42.4	9.35	15.5	612.6	295.5
161	Val-d'Or	29.0	11.64	10.9	475.0	223.6
162	Vancouver	1586.6	25.12	610.2	30454.5	14352.9
163	Vernon	44.6	5.91	17.2	681.6	299.9
164	Victoria	283.4	17.39	115.5	5078.8	2247.1
165	Victoriaville	40.3	10.71	14.9	595.4	277.1
166	Wallaceburg	11.6	0.76	4.3	210.2	80.2
167	West Hants	13.7	9.69	4.6	182.3	91.3
168	West Lincoln	10.5	6.35	3.3	182.7	78.9
169	Wetaskiwin	10.4	8.35	4.0	155.9	58.8
170	Weyburn	10.2	7.53	4.0	175.1	84.9
171	Whitehorse	17.4	17.73	6.1	355.8	148.8
172	Williams Lake	35.5	7.09	12.4	533.9	250.3
173	Wilmot	11.8	8.39	3.9	223.0	95.0
174	Windsor	260.2	3.71	96.1	5229.1	2084.3
175	Winnipeg	648.5	9.52	247.3	11554.2	5030.6
176	Woodstock	26.9	1.03	10.2	491.2	186.0
177	Yarmouth	10.5	6.79	3.7	146.3	72.0
178	Yellowknife	12.6	33.08	4.1	302.8	138.1
179	Yorkton	18.7	2.05	7.1	273.9	129.8

DATA SET 2   Canadian Companies
Companies 1–50 and 451–500 out of top 500
SALES2   = 1990 sales (000's)
INCOME2 = 1990 net income (000's)
RATIO   = 1990 debt/equity ratio
EMPLOY = 1990 number of employees
RANK   = 1990 ranking by sales
Note: blank spaces indicate missing data.

RANK	COMPANY (ACTIVITY)	SALES2	INCOME2	RATIO	EMPLOY
1	General Motors Canada (autos)	18458171	45526	0.16	42555
2	BCE (telecommunications)	18373000	1147000	0.77	119000
3	Ford Motor of Canada (autos)	13706200	−57100	0.32	28000
4	Imperial Oil (oil and gas)	11226000	493000	0.38	14702
5	George Weston (foods & stores)	10856000	125000	0.65	55818
6	Canadian Pacific (diversified)	10499700	355300	0.76	72200
7	Brascan (diversified)	10275000	80300	0.58	
8	Alcan Aluminum (aluminum)	10217667	633572	0.53	57000
9	Noranda (integrated forest)	9434000	120000	1.09	56000
10	Seagram (beverages)	7148984	882101	0.65	17700
11	Chrysler Canada (autos)	7067000	16100	0.08	13100
12	Provigo (food stores)	6525700	60700	1.87	14000
13	Ontario Hydro (electric utility)	6484000	129000	4.68	26821
14	Thompson (publishing & travel)	6258715	449218	0.48	44800
15	Petro-Canada (oil & gas)	5873000	181000	0.84	6353
16	Hydro-Quebec (electric utility)	5822988	404000		20067
17	Shell Canada (integrated oil)	5444000	312000	0.32	7136
18	John Labatt (brewing, food)	5274000	169000	0.45	16500
19	Imasco (consumer products)	5234000	295100	0.79	27940
20	Hudson's Bay (department stores)	4970000	158000	1.06	
21	NOVA Corp. of Alberta (nat. gas)	4736000	185000	1.46	10000
22	Oshawa Group (food stores)	4598798	60353	0.30	
23	IBM Canada (information tech.)	4578000	316000		12741
24	Sears Canada (retail & catalogue)	4571100	21300	1.76	48000
25	Amoco Canada Petroleum (oil)	4461000	−53000	5.84	4200
26	Canada Safeway (food stores)	4317951	73918	7.70	29000
27	Varity (auto parts & machinery)	4159759	118430	0.97	18731
28	Canadian Wheat Board (grain)	4110944			466
29	Canadian National Railway	4077800	7734	0.56	39091
30	Air Canada (int'l air carrier)	3939000	−74000	1.39	23100
31	Canada Packers (food processing)	3821873	41102	0.28	12000
32	Canada Post (postal service)	3698110	148800	0.05	50522
33	Inco (nickel, alloys)	3626678	514812	0.61	19387
34	Socanav (diversified)	3271368	−12131	119.30	
35	Horsham (gold mining, oil)	3252810	67858	0.84	5500
36	Dofasco (steel)	3250300	−679200	0.56	19200
37	Moore (business forms)	3231565	140750	0.06	25021
38	Total Petroleum (NA)(oil)	3185448	49090	0.28	
39	Abitibi-Price (newsprint, paper)	3088000	−44600	0.45	14300
40	Canadian Tire (auto/household)	3060125	144366	0.44	25000

RANK	COMPANY (ACTIVITY)	SALES2	INCOME2	RATIO	EMPLOY
41	TransCanada PipeLines (pipelines)	3033178	214900	1.81	1757
42	Bombardier (transport equipment)	2836300	100100	0.58	24775
43	PWA (airlines)	2745600	−14600	2.02	16548
44	Mitsui & Co. (Cda) (import/export)	2680009	3952	1.48	123
45	United Westburne (elect/plumbing)	2563522	18197	1.46	7071
46	Molson (diversified)	2538219	106696	0.47	13900
47	Jim Pattiso Group (diversified)	2535000			13000
48	Honda Canada (auto wholesale)	2454476			2000
49	Carena (real estate development)	2447440	42052	4.29	6
50	Quebecor (publishing & printing)	2433726	35831	2.85	17100
451	Scotsburn Co-operative (dairy)	145256			515
452	CTV Television Network (broadcast)	145147		21.31	
453	Rhone-Poulenc Canada (chemicals)	145081	3062	0.00	147
454	Canadian Oxygen (gases)	145049	2973	5.59	808
455	Commonwealth Plywood (plywood)	145006	−176		1150
456	LOF Glass of Canada (auto glass)	144933	10536	3.00	
457	Federal Express (package delivery)	144000			
458	Gesco Ind. (floor coverings)	143984	49	0.96	350
459	Canstar Sports (sporting goods)	143829	8412	1.32	1410
460	Consolidated Carma (real estate)	143608	35643	0.78	85
461	Cosmair Canada (cosmetic & hair)	143172	2438		661
462	Parkland Industries (oil/gas)	142535	−231	1.41	125
463	Cognos (data management & software)	141161	6676	0.11	1046
464	Goodfellow (lumber wholesalers)	139595	−809	0.72	341
465	Electrohome (electronics)	139497	−3313	3.16	1002
466	VIA Rail Canada (passenger rail)	139000			4517
467	Cambior (gold producer)	138820	23991	0.04	667
468	Procor (rail cars)	138546	20767	2.60	585
469	Cabano Transportation (hwy. trans.)	137906	3956	2.03	2100
470	Tomen Canada (import/export)	137221	552	7.26	
471	Ontario Northland (tranport./tele.)	137090	3889	0.16	1400
472	Livingston Group (customs brokers)	137086			2200
473	V.K. Mason (construction)	137049			125
474	Bennett & Wright (construction)	136500			1900
475	Loewen Group (funeral services)	136500	12864	1.34	2362
476	Liquid Carbonic (industrial gases)	136171	13861	0.74	619
477	Sandwell (eng. & computer systems)	135717	5307	0.05	1500
478	Group Laperrière & Verreault	134574	2089	0.72	1043
479	Western Co-operative Fertilizers	134307	4782		
480	Intermetco (metals recycling, pipe)	134273	1021	0.20	300
481	Hitachi Cda (household appliances)	133000			300
482	Sandoz Canada (pharmaceuticals)	132100	3700	0.53	550
483	GDO Ward Mallette (business advis.)	132000			1959
484	Ideal Metal (non-ferrous metals)	131320	989	0.29	378
485	Armstrong World Indus. Canada	130605	4351	0.06	612
486	Babcock Canada (industrial)	130418	−4068	0.01	
487	Consolidated NBS (computer systems)	129891	−45602		
488	Control Data Cda (computer systems)	129879	−1554	0.24	1200

RANK	COMPANY (ACTIVITY)	SALES2	INCOME2	RATIO	EMPLOY
489	Monenco (engineering)	129679	1885	1.26	2000
490	Hamilton Group (computer leasing)	129231	4823	0.84	295
491	Linamar Machines (defense/auto)	128559	3262	1.19	1300
492	North Canadian Oils (oil & gas)	128300	31200	0.34	435
493	Princeton Mining (copper/asbestos)	126416	10808		700
494	Chateau Stores (fashion retailing)	126325	2914	0.38	
495	BC Transit (urban transit)	125843	2799	5.00	3656
496	United Grain Growers (agriculture)	125171	690	2.05	1473
497	Hammond Manufacturing (transform)	125029	85	1.93	1400
498	Unican Security Systems (security)	124494	1374	1.20	1650
499	Champion Road Machinery (graders)	124356			700
500	Atcor Resources (oil & gas)	123762	5258	0.24	75

DATA SET 3 Leather Elongation Study–Percent Elongation of Leather
(A random sample of $n = 45$, 15 from each of three labs)
OBS3 = Observation number
TN = Tannery lab
UN = University lab
IND = Industrial lab

OBS3	TN	UN	IND
1	21	23	25
2	20	25	33
3	22	25	30
4	20	29	31
5	23	24	27
6	21	28	33
7	22	22	25
8	15	20	29
9	10	10	14
10	19	14	26
11	18	19	25
12	15	20	28
13	18	16	22
14	18	19	28
15	20	22	24

DATA SET 4 Financial Information on Physicians
OBS4 = Number of doctor in survey
HRS = Reported weekly hours worked
INC = Reported annual net income of doctor
FEE = Average fee charged by doctor for office visit
EXPS = Average annual operating expense

OBS4	HRS	INC	FEE	EXPS
1	48.2	124000	40.86	111400
2	48.4	115800	44.30	102000
3	47.6	115800	34.80	90400
4	46.7	151400	62.60	52800
5	44.4	100400	37.54	68400
6	47.8	99800	47.05	74600
7	47.7	124400	38.84	115800
8	47.6	132800	37.90	103400
9	46.6	114800	44.48	94600
10	45.2	103600	43.56	70000
11	45.3	113200	52.24	109600
12	47.9	189400	87.80	158600
13	52.0	192000	66.14	138600
14	50.4	183600	64.06	124000
15	50.4	92600	37.02	66600
16	50.8	156200	66.14	115000
17	51.3	188800	74.04	116800
18	52.5	186400	64.80	125400
19	50.6	191800	52.78	117800
20	50.1	195600	60.20	162800
21	53.0	134600	32.76	125200
22	54.4	197200	44.72	122600
23	49.0	125800	40.12	97800
24	56.8	194600	58.46	122400
25	49.5	133800	43.78	110000
26	52.2	192800	61.76	140800
27	49.4	174200	65.14	127400
28	51.9	154200	36.98	115800
29	56.2	212000	45.96	184400
30	53.3	143600	40.94	173000
31	55.6	183000	55.42	88200
32	50.7	143600	37.02	143600
33	51.2	199000	60.20	132800
34	51.0	142600	44.00	126800
35	49.3	179200	59.88	119200
36	50.5	125600	43.08	125400
37	56.9	172200	55.18	135000
38	55.3	190200	55.42	143000
39	50.4	202400	80.18	178800
40	49.1	128200	53.74	124400

DATA SET 5 Annual Aggregate Economic Data for Canada
POP5 = Population of Canada (in 000's)
GDP = Gross domestic product (in $MIL)
EXPTS = Total exports (in $MIL)
IMPT = Total imports (in $MIL)
R123 = Interest rate on government bonds
CPIA = Consumer price index (1981 = 100)
UNEM5 = Unemployment rate in Canada
Note: blank spaces indicate missing data

YEAR5	POP5	GDP	EXPTS	IMPT	R123	CPIA	UNEM5
1950	13703.50	104821	16634	14542	1.8042	25.2083	
1951	14005.00	109492	18230	16901	2.4150	27.8667	
1952	14436.75	118627	20140	17650	2.8125	28.5167	
1953	14833.00	124526	19873	19247	3.2083	28.2833	
1954	15269.50	123163	19166	18140	2.1825	28.4583	
1955	15681.25	134889	20607	20652	2.1908	28.5000	
1956	16070.25	146523	22259	24115	3.6017	28.9250	
1957	16579.50	150179	22445	23396	4.4625	29.8333	
1958	17062.25	153439	22248	21578	3.2767	30.6083	
1959	17467.50	159484	23086	23795	5.0267	30.9583	
1960	17855.25	164126	24114	23738	3.9633	31.3500	
1961	18224.50	169271	25755	23798	3.5908	31.6500	
1962	18570.75	181264	26944	24350	4.2833	32.0333	
1963	18919.00	190672	29428	24999	4.2100	32.5667	
1964	19277.25	203382	33144	28284	4.4058	33.1583	
1965	19633.50	216802	34659	31861	4.5200	33.9750	
1966	19997.50	231519	39510	36234	5.3775	35.2417	3.3750
1967	20363.75	238306	43607	38129	5.2908	36.5250	3.8333
1968	20692.00	251064	49112	41877	6.3708	37.9917	4.5250
1969	20994.25	264508	53055	47346	7.4900	39.7000	4.4250
1970	21287.50	271372	57661	46534	6.5733	41.0417	5.6750
1971	21559.25	286998	60664	49866	4.9308	42.1917	6.2000
1972	21793.10	303447	65414	56754	5.5442	44.2250	6.2333
1973	22039.52	326848	72319	65078	6.5358	47.5917	5.5667
1974	22357.12	341235	70884	72290	8.0325	52.7750	5.3333
1975	22687.67	350113	66088	69921	7.5367	58.4667	6.9167
1976	22985.47	371688	73090	75959	8.2733	62.8583	7.1167
1977	23259.77	385122	79573	77286	7.4600	67.8917	8.0917
1978	23503.22	402737	90429	83008	8.7733	73.9333	8.3750
1979	23737.95	418328	94976	92471	10.7658	80.7000	7.4750
1980	24029.57	424537	97564	97035	12.4400	88.9083	7.4833
1981	24324.50	440127	101853	105313	15.9667	100.0000	7.5417
1982	24571.02	425970	99637	89343	13.9483	110.7833	10.9583
1983	24777.52	439448	106017	97395	10.1800	117.2250	11.8583
1984	24969.52	467167	124785	114058	11.6700	122.3167	11.2500
1985	25158.14	489437	132218	123935	10.1167	127.1500	10.4833
1986	25348.42	505666	138119	133369	9.0867	132.4500	9.5500
1987	25604.17	526123	142288	142286	9.1883	138.2417	8.8583
1988	25899.27	549237	154950	160607	9.6742	143.8250	7.7750
1989	26218.65	565657	156076	168838	10.7133	150.9750	7.5000
1990	26440.00	570743	161582	169385	11.6520	158.2590	8.1000

DATA SET 6	Survey on Food Consumption for the Elderly					
	(Sample of $n = 166$)					
	OBS6	= Observation number				
	REGION	= One of four regions (1, 2, 3, 4)				
	AGEYRS	= Age in years of head of household				
	NUMINHSE	= Number of people living in the household				
	MONINC	= Monthly income of household				
	SEX	= Sex of the head of household (1 = male, 0 = female)				
	EDUCYRS	= Years of education of head of household				

OBS6	REGION	AGEYRS	NUMINHSE	MONINC	SEX	EDUCYRS
1	1	73	2	608	1	8
2	1	64	2	1369	1	9
3	3	64	1	508	0	7
4	2	73	1	218	0	9
5	3	77	1	164	0	4
6	1	86	1	200	0	4
7	1	60	2	4034	1	12
8	1	62	3	400	1	8
9	2	64	1	187	0	10
10	2	63	1	238	0	12
11	4	71	1	648	0	12
12	3	77	1	117	0	7
13	3	77	1	390	0	13
14	3	77	1	264	0	14
15	2	68	2	801	1	16
16	1	67	1	272	0	8
17	3	57	3	600	1	8
18	3	67	2	858	1	12
19	1	59	2	1325	1	12
20	3	56	2	1465	1	12
21	2	65	5	1910	1	12
22	3	79	2	555	1	3
23	4	57	5	5400	1	12
24	2	79	1	187	0	8
25	2	57	2	667	0	13
26	3	78	1	304	1	7
27	4	56	2	1070	1	12
28	3	73	1	344	0	8
29	2	68	1	762	1	12
30	2	60	2	474	0	10
31	1	56	1	456	0	6
32	2	59	2	320	0	10
33	2	68	2	725	1	8
34	1	56	2	445	0	14
35	1	64	2	1429	0	12
36	3	59	3	1412	1	12
37	1	84	1	245	0	12
38	1	67	1	319	0	8
39	3	55	3	302	0	11
40	2	56	1	2042	0	16

OBS6	REGION	AGEYRS	NUMINHSE	MONINC	SEX	EDUCYRS
41	4	62	2	556	1	12
42	3	74	2	300	1	7
43	1	79	2	387	1	7
44	3	69	1	204	0	12
45	1	56	3	825	1	12
46	2	69	2	318	1	7
47	3	72	2	394	1	8
48	4	74	2	970	1	9
49	3	68	1	270	1	8
50	1	72	2	606	1	12
51	3	63	1	185	0	8
52	2	70	1	179	1	8
53	3	72	2	500	0	10
54	4	76	1	302	0	14
55	2	64	4	1618	1	8
56	1	68	1	248	1	14
57	3	62	2	2500	1	17
58	1	64	2	462	0	8
59	3	60	2	1376	1	17
60	3	68	2	668	1	11
61	2	55	1	933	0	12
62	3	72	2	675	1	4
63	3	56	2	1332	0	5
64	1	63	1	220	0	10
65	2	68	2	830	1	12
66	3	56	2	466	0	8
67	4	61	2	1908	1	14
68	4	71	1	370	1	14
69	1	88	2	1280	1	12
70	2	64	2	225	1	12
71	3	73	1	359	0	12
72	4	60	2	542	1	12
73	3	74	2	600	1	6
74	2	65	3	628	1	7
75	1	75	2	490	0	9
76	1	83	1	468	0	16
77	1	69	2	546	1	6
78	1	70	1	355	0	10
79	1	69	1	412	1	8
80	2	56	1	9900	0	12
81	2	58	4	2167	1	12
82	2	55	3	1695	1	12
83	2	63	3	375	1	8
84	2	69	1	404	0	7
85	3	64	2	1011	1	9
86	3	66	1	184	1	8
87	3	73	3	905	1	9
88	1	85	1	276	0	6

OBS6	REGION	AGEYRS	NUMINHSE	MONINC	SEX	EDUCYRS
89	3	62	2	833	1	12
90	2	61	2	1000	1	8
91	1	77	1	316	0	3
92	2	68	1	2300	1	17
93	2	70	1	238	0	10
94	3	56	1	159	0	4
95	4	55	3	141	1	17
96	2	82	2	353	1	12
97	4	75	2	554	1	14
98	2	64	2	517	1	7
99	2	75	1	223	0	8
100	2	56	2	1700	1	12
101	2	55	2	1218	1	12
102	4	63	1	850	0	12
103	1	59	4	1110	1	12
104	3	79	2	207	1	6
105	4	65	1	575	0	11
106	4	65	2	1344	0	17
107	1	67	7	942	1	8
108	1	59	2	1100	1	12
109	2	66	1	481	1	8
110	2	58	2	252	1	8
111	3	70	2	344	1	8
112	3	66	1	150	1	8
113	3	90	2	200	1	6
114	2	62	2	505	1	10
115	3	64	2	349	1	4
116	1	61	1	192	0	9
117	4	65	2	797	1	9
118	3	57	3	3400	1	17
119	1	63	2	902	1	12
120	1	63	2	801	1	12
121	1	83	1	198	0	8
122	1	72	1	427	1	6
123	2	63	2	1330	1	12
124	3	85	2	1539	1	14
125	4	57	4	3035	1	12
126	3	59	2	320	1	7
127	1	56	1	1250	1	12
128	2	58	1	575	0	12
129	4	73	2	359	1	12
130	1	56	1	3186	1	14
131	1	59	4	2004	0	9
132	1	56	2	2100	1	12
133	3	55	2	260	1	12
134	2	56	1	521	0	12
135	2	61	2	750	1	8
136	4	62	1	0	0	14

OBS6	REGION	AGEYRS	NUMINHSE	MONINC	SEX	EDUCYRS
137	1	56	5	1310	1	17
138	2	63	1	311	1	12
139	2	75	2	211	0	8
140	2	75	3	814	0	12
141	1	80	2	419	1	8
142	2	75	2	1043	1	8
143	4	68	2	549	1	10
144	1	79	2	422	1	7
145	1	58	2	1541	1	10
146	1	86	1	268	0	8
147	3	69	2	697	1	12
148	3	56	8	672	1	6
149	2	59	2	336	1	11
150	1	71	1	427	0	6
151	2	77	2	882	0	6
152	2	57	2	2085	1	16
153	4	73	1	265	0	11
154	3	67	3	973	1	12
155	2	73	2	478	1	8
156	4	74	1	677	0	11
157	3	74	2	367	0	6
158	1	83	2	370	1	0
159	1	70	2	271	1	12
160	2	62	2	1905	1	11
161	2	55	3	616	1	3
162	2	80	2	450	1	9
163	2	55	5	2225	1	12
164	3	57	2	537	0	12
165	2	58	3	1200	1	12
166	2	65	2	720	1	12

DATA SET 7 Canadian Mutual Fund Performance
Sample of 10 years of Canadian equity funds
OBS7 = Observation number (alphabetical)
ASSETS = Assets in 1000's of dollars
TENYR = Rate of return (%) for 10 years
FIVEYR = Rate of return (%) for 5 years
ONEYR = Rate of return (%) for 1 year
RISK = Measure of volatility (6 is highest, 1 is lowest)
CLASS = Size of fund
VS = Very small (0 to 10 million)
S = Small (10.1 to 50 million)
M = Medium (50.1 to 150 million)
L = Large (150.1 to 500 million)
VL = Very large (over 500 million)

OBS7	FUND	ASSETS	TENYR	RATE FIVEYR	ONEYR	RISK	CLASS
1	All Can Div. fund	13774	8.20	3.02	1.15	2	S
2	Altamira Equity Fund	6664	8.43	4.61	7.24	4	VS
3	Associate Investors	7988	8.12	5.51	10.59	4	VS
4	AGF Can. Equity	275020	8.49	0.61	3.29	5	L
5	AGF Growth Equity	108060	3.49	0.68	7.52	5	M
6	Bolton Tremblay Can. Cum.	71213	5.68	2.83	4.69	5	M
7	Bullock Growth	5159	0.88	0.62	6.69	5	VS
8	Cambridge Growth	22542	12.97	9.26	7.97	3	S
9	Can. Life Can Equity	190849	9.55	4.66	6.99	5	L
10	Can. Anaeth.	57908	9.36	5.84	10.08	4	M
11	Can. Inv. Fund	68073	7.95	3.07	5.24	5	M
12	Coop. Trust Gr.	4045	7.12	1.87	9.47	5	VS
13	Confed. Growth Fund	6837	8.64	3.80	4.50	4	VS
14	Corporate Investors	9027	8.25	5.29	6.76	4	VS
15	Corp. Inv. Stock Fund	9461	1.00	−6.62	1.78	4	VS
16	Cundill Sec.	16508	8.32	5.83	−2.36	4	S
17	Dynamic Fund	158175	7.62	7.05	7.78	4	L
18	Elliot and Page Gr. Fund	185631	10.89	6.88	9.41	5	L
19	Emp. Equity Growth Fund	18215	9.44	1.44	3.05	4	S
20	Gen. Tr. Can. Can. Eq.	29964	5.59	2.14	6.16	5	S
21	Guard. Can. Equity	25036	7.10	1.67	0.96	4	S
22	Guar. Enterprise	13225	9.65	3.56	6.97	5	S
23	Imp. Growth Can. Equity	80538	13.89	14.02	9.50	5	M
24	Industrial Equity	65538	6.00	−0.28	−14.41	5	M
25	Ind. Growth Fund	1408725	11.68	6.83	2.23	4	VL
26	Ind. Pension Fund	78990	9.76	2.42	−5.74	5	M
27	Inv. Ret. Mutual Fund	956400	8.51	6.93	8.28	5	VL
28	Jones Heward Fund	42837	6.86	2.06	9.66	5	S
29	Keltic Investment Gr. Trust	540	−0.20	−1.06	7.34	6	VS
30	Laur. Viking Can.	178236	7.49	2.61	5.60	4	L
31	London Life Can. Eq.	160885	9.73	4.95	13.73	5	L
32	Mackenzie Eq.	59929	8.70	3.25	−4.51	5	M
33	ManuLi Vista 1 Eq. Fund	227843	7.44	4.54	9.09	5	L
34	ManuLi Vista 2 Eq. Fund	227843	6.64	3.75	8.84	5	L

OBS7	FUND	ASSETS	TENYR	FIVEYR	ONEYR	RISK	CLASS
35	Mar. Life Gr. Fund	166310	8.11	2.55	8.45	5	L
36	Montreal Trust Eq.	17310	7.26	6.06	13.11	4	S
37	Montreal Trust Eq. Rsp.	64596	7.89	5.61	10.63	4	M
38	Nat. Trust Eq. Fund	104618	8.56	4.62	14.25	5	M
39	Phillips Hager & North Can.	53650	9.66	7.12	9.23	5	M
40	Prudential Growth Fund	62495	6.92	3.87	3.60	4	M
41	Royal Trust Can. St. Fund	233871	6.43	4.56	9.44	5	L
42	Royfund Eq.	678649	7.73	1.47	−0.60	4	VL
43	Talvest Gr.	61624	8.63	8.17	15.04	4	M
44	Trans--Can. Eq. Fund	15504	11.89	7.25	7.03	4	S
45	Trust Pret. & Rev. Can.	12743	4.40	2.03	10.06	4	S
46	United Accum.	143944	9.51	4.73	13.35	4	M
47	United Venture Ret. Fund	41291	5.20	0.92	3.78	5	S
48	Universal Can. Equity Fund	171617	10.41	4.16	−2.99	5	L

Source: *The Globe and Mail*, "Report on Business," May 16, 1991, page B22.
Prepared by Eric Kirzner.

DATA SET 8 59 Months of Returns for 4 Companies and a "Market"

MONTH = Month number (1–59) starting with 1 = January
IBM = Monthly returns for IBM
EXXON = Monthly returns for EXXON
G.E. = Monthly returns for General Electric
G.M. = Monthly returns for General Motors
MKT = Market returns: the average return for 40 companies, equally weighted (including the four above)

MONTH	IBM	EXXON	G.E.	G.M.	MKT
1	0.03	0.04	0.02	0.05	0.04
2	−0.02	−0.02	−0.03	−0.03	−0.04
3	0.05	0.07	0.04	0.06	0.05
4	0.00	0.01	0.02	0.03	0.00
5	−0.02	−0.05	0.01	0.02	−0.02
6	−0.03	0.08	0.02	0.03	0.03
7	−0.05	0.02	0.04	−0.03	0.00
8	0.02	0.04	0.03	0.05	0.08
9	−0.03	0.05	−0.03	0.04	−0.01
10	−0.08	−0.03	−0.05	−0.12	−0.06
11	0.06	0.03	−0.03	−0.06	0.05

MONTH	IBM	EXXON	G.E.	G.M.	MKT
12	−0.01	−0.05	0.10	−0.01	0.01
13	0.07	0.10	0.09	0.10	0.04
14	−0.06	0.09	−0.07	−0.06	−0.02
15	−0.12	−0.11	−0.04	−0.09	−0.06
16	−0.02	0.05	−0.01	−0.01	0.05
17	0.02	0.07	0.06	0.00	0.05
18	0.06	0.04	0.04	0.04	0.02
19	0.11	0.05	0.09	0.13	0.08
20	0.02	0.03	−0.03	0.03	0.00
21	−0.02	0.00	−0.02	−0.01	0.02
22	0.04	0.09	0.03	−0.07	−0.01
23	0.04	0.17	0.14	−0.08	0.07
24	0.00	−0.08	0.00	0.01	−0.01
25	−0.05	−0.04	0.00	0.02	−0.02
26	0.01	−0.05	0.09	0.10	0.03
27	−0.03	−0.05	0.01	0.05	0.05
28	−0.06	0.00	−0.02	0.02	0.00
29	0.02	−0.03	0.00	0.04	0.03
30	−0.01	0.06	−0.05	−0.05	−0.01
31	−0.03	0.02	−0.01	−0.03	−0.02
32	0.00	−0.05	−0.08	−0.09	−0.06
33	−0.02	−0.04	0.00	−0.04	−0.02
34	−0.05	−0.02	−0.01	−0.18	0.04
35	0.07	0.10	0.11	0.03	0.04
36	0.04	−0.05	−0.04	0.04	−0.03
37	0.19	−0.02	0.09	−0.01	0.01
38	−0.01	−0.04	0.01	−0.01	−0.04
39	−0.03	−0.02	0.02	0.11	0.01
40	0.08	0.00	0.01	0.02	0.05
41	−0.03	0.02	−0.04	0.04	−0.03
42	−0.01	−0.01	0.04	0.04	−0.01
43	0.08	−0.06	0.03	−0.04	−0.01
44	0.09	0.13	0.14	0.15	0.16
45	0.04	−0.02	0.00	−0.04	0.00
46	0.09	0.06	0.15	0.22	0.12
47	0.09	−0.03	0.09	0.07	0.06
48	0.11	0.06	0.03	0.04	0.01
49	0.03	0.01	0.09	0.01	0.05
50	0.01	0.00	0.05	−0.02	0.03
51	0.03	0.06	−0.02	−0.03	0.04
52	0.15	0.15	0.07	0.15	0.11
53	−0.04	−0.02	−0.08	−0.03	−0.03
54	0.08	0.00	0.07	0.11	0.06
55	0.00	0.06	−0.09	0.01	−0.02
56	0.00	0.08	0.03	−0.04	0.02
57	0.06	−0.04	0.04	0.05	0.02
58	0.00	0.05	−0.02	0.05	−0.02
59	−0.07	0.01	0.11	−0.05	0.04

APPENDIX B
The Algebra
of Statistics

Elements of Algebra

Even though the reader may have previously studied algebra, this appendix provides a good review and practice to ensure a familiarity with the algebra inherent in statistics. Because statistics is concerned with numbers, our discussion begins with the number system.

The Number System

Numbers are classified into numerous categories. The **natural numbers**, or **integers**, are those used for counting $(1, 2, 3, \ldots)$. [†] Integers are further divided as to whether they are prime or composite or even or odd. **Prime numbers** are integers exactly divisible only by 1 or themselves (1 is, by convention, not a prime number); **composite numbers** can be written as the product of two or more other integers called factors. Integers which are divisible by 2 are said to be **even numbers**, while numbers not exactly divisible by 2 are **odd numbers**.

❏ **EXAMPLE B.1**   The numbers 2, 3, 5, 7, 11, 12, 13, 17, 18, 19, and 21 are all integers. Which numbers are prime and which are composite? Explain.

● **SOLUTION**   The numbers 2, 3, 5, 7, 11, 13, 17, and 19 are prime numbers. The numbers 12 and 18 are both even, composite numbers because they can be expressed as a product of prime factors: $12 = (2)(2)(3)$; $18 = (2)(3)(3)$. The number 21 is odd, and is a composite number, whose prime factors are 3 and 7.

Finding the prime factors of a number is perhaps best accomplished by trial and error, trying only prime numbers as divisors. To find the prime factorization of 165, for example, divide by 3. Then divide the larger factor, 55, by 5. This results in the following prime factorization.

$$(3)(5)(11) = 165$$

Similarly, the prime factors of 318, which are 2, 3, and 53, are derived by dividing 318 first by 2, and then dividing 159 by 3.

$$(2)(3)(53) = 318$$

[†] The three dots, $\ldots$, are read as *and so forth*.

Inequalities and Absolute Values

A useful device for representing the relative position of numbers is the *number line*, which is illustrated in Figure B.1.

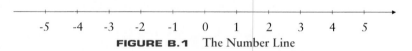

$$-5 \quad -4 \quad -3 \quad -2 \quad -1 \quad 0 \quad 1 \quad 2 \quad 3 \quad 4 \quad 5$$

FIGURE B.1   The Number Line

Numbers falling to the left of zero on the number line are called **negative numbers**. All numbers to the right of zero are called **positive numbers**. Zero is considered to be neither positive nor negative. If a number a falls to the right of a number b, then a is greater than b, which is written as $a > b$, or $b < a$. For instance, the numbers -2 and -4 are both negative numbers, and $-2 > -4$. If a number a must be greater than or equal to b, this is written as $a \geq b$, or $b \leq a$. The set of all positive numbers a is defined as $a > 0$.

Ratios of two integers, such as $\frac{1}{2}$, or $\frac{1}{4}$, or $\frac{3}{11}$, are called fractions. Any fraction can be divided out to obtain its decimal equivalent. For example, the fraction $\frac{1}{125}$ is equivalent to the decimal 0.008. Some decimals, such as this one, divide evenly and are finite (or terminating). Others do not divide evenly and are infinite (nonterminating), but repeat certain digits in a specific pattern, such as $\frac{1}{3} = 0.3333\ldots$ or $\frac{3}{11} = 0.272727\ldots$.

There is a special category of fractions in which the decimal is nonterminating and nonrepeating. There are two important nonterminating, nonrepeating constants (decimals) used in statistics, namely π and e. You may be familiar with the first, π, from your studies of geometry. Recall that the area of a circle is π times the square of the radius. The value of $\pi = 3.14159\ldots$ (the decimal continues, but with no pattern). A second important nonrepeating, nonterminating constant (decimal) is e, where $e = 2.71828\ldots$.

The **absolute value** of a number is the distance from that number to zero on the number line. When determining the absolute value, this distance is always positive. The absolute value of the number a is written as $|a|$. The absolute value of $-a$ has the same value: $|-a| = |a|$. For example, $|-12| = |12| = 12$; similarly, $|5 - 10| = |-5| = 5$ and $\left|\left(-\frac{1}{2}\right)\left(\frac{1}{2}\right)\right| = \left|-\frac{1}{4}\right| = \frac{1}{4}$.

❑ EXAMPLE B.2   Use symbolic notation to write the following expressions as inequalities.
a) the number 2 is greater than the number -4
b) -6 is less than -3
c) c is more than or equal to d.

● SOLUTION   a) $2 > -4$ b) $-6 < -3$ c) $c \geq d$ ■

Constants and Their Exponents

Letters at the beginning of the alphabet, such as a, b, and c, are often used to represent a number whose value does not change. This type of number is called a **constant**. Thus, the letter a could represent a constant, the value of which is unknown at this time. The expression $2a$ means to multiply the value of the constant a by two, and a^2 (a-squared) means to multiply the constant a by itself. For example, if $a = 5$, then $2a = 10$, and $a^2 = (5)(5) = 25$. Expressions of the form a^n are read as *a to the nth power*. The number a is called the **base** of the expression, and n is called the **exponent**.

The interpretation of a^n depends on whether n is positive or negative, and whether it is an integer or a fraction. If n is a positive number, then a is multiplied by itself n times as follows:

Exponential power rule:

$$a^n = \overbrace{(a)(a)(a)\cdots(a)}^{n \text{ terms}}$$

(B.1)

For example, if $a = 4$, then 4^3 (four to the third power, or four cubed) is

$$4^3 = (4)(4)(4) = 64$$

If $a = \frac{1}{5}$, then

$$a^3 = \left(\frac{1}{5}\right)^3 = \left(\frac{1}{5}\right)\left(\frac{1}{5}\right)\left(\frac{1}{5}\right) = \frac{1}{125}$$

Suppose the exponent of a is a negative number, as in the expression a^{-n}. In this case, we could rewrite the expression as $\left(\frac{1}{a}\right)^n$. To illustrate, if $a = 3$ and the exponent is -2, then

$$3^{-2} = \left(\frac{1}{3}\right)^2 = \frac{1}{9}$$

If the exponent in a^n is a fraction, then we write the expression as $a^{(1/n)}$. This expression is called the *nth root of a*. For example, $a^{(1/2)}$ is the square root of a, which is usually written as $\sqrt{a}$. Similarly, $a^{(1/3)}$ is the cube root of a, and is sometimes written as $\sqrt[3]{a}$. Finally, $a^{(1/4)}$ is the 4th root of a and can be written as $\sqrt[4]{a}$.

□ **EXAMPLE B.3**   Evaluate and explain the following exppressions:
a) $64^{(1/2)} = ?$
b) $64^{(1/3)} = ?$
c) $(1/81)^{(-1/4)} = ?$

• **SOLUTION**   a) $\sqrt{64} = \sqrt{(8)(8)} = 8$; square root of 64 is 8.
b) $\sqrt[3]{64} = \sqrt[3]{(4)(4)(4)} = 4$; cube root of 64 is 4
c) $(1/81)^{-1/4} = (81)^{(1/4)} = \sqrt[4]{81} = \sqrt[4]{(3)(3)(3)(3)} = 3$ ■

Logarithms

Logarithms were invented in the sixteenth century as an aid to calculations involving multiplication, division, powers, and roots. Logarithms use some of the rules of exponents to simplify calculations. Although calculators and computers have made logarithms unnecessary for most calculations, they are still useful in statistics for representing relationships.

The logarithm of a number is simply the power (exponent) to which the base is raised. In working with logarithms (called *logs*), it is necessary to select a base (b). The base can be any positive number, although 10 is often used because it is relatively convenient to use. The logarithm of some number x, using the base 10 is written as $\log_{10}(x)$. For example, the log of 100 to the base 10 is written as $\log_{10}(100)$. Similarly, the log of 500 to the base 10 is written as $\log_{10}(500)$.

The log of a number is simply the appropriate power (or exponent) of the base. For example, the $\log_{10}(100) = 2$ because 2 is the exponent of 10 which yields 100 ($10^2 = 100$). Similarly, the $\log_{10}(1000) = 3$ because 3 is the exponent of 10 which yields 1000 ($10^3 = 1000$). If we let y equal the log, then a general expression for a logarithm with base 10 is shown as follows:

General logarithmic expression for base 10:

$$\log_{10}(x) = y \qquad (B.2)$$

An equivalent way of writing the expression in (B.2) is $10^y = x$. Using either of these two forms, we can find the following logarithms, using the base 10.

> 0 is the logarithm of **1**
> 1 is the logarithm of **10**
> 2 is the logarithm of **100**
> 3 is the logarithm of **1000**
> 4 is the logarithm of **10,000**

Notice the advantage of these logarithms. The numbers on the right increase by a constant *proportion*, as each number is 10 times the previous number (1, 10, 100, 1000, 10,000). The logarithms on the left, on the other hand, increase by a constant *amount*, one unit at a time (0, 1, 2, 3, 4). In many problems, this latter set of values is much easier to work with than the former.

We can find the logarithm for any positive number. Consider a number between 100 and 1000, such as 500. We know that the logarithm of 100 is 2 (using the base 10), and the logarithm of 1000 is 3; hence the logarithm of 500 to the base 10, written as $\log_{10}(500)$, must be a decimal number between 2 and 3. The reader might reflect at this point on the fact that $\log_{10}(500)$ is a number *larger* than 2.5 even though 500 is closer to 100 than 1000. [The actual value of $\log_{10}(500) = 2.70$.] The next section demonstrates the process of finding the logarithm of numbers such as 500. For now, we note that most calculators and computers make this process quite simple.

An antilog, written **antilog(x)**, reverses the process of taking a logarithm. For example, the antilog of 2, using the base 10, is the number 100. Similarly, the antilog of the number 3 is 1000. Thus, an antilog is the original number shown as follows:

General antilogarithmic expression:

$$\text{antilog}\big[\log(x)\big] = x \qquad (B.3)$$

Any base can be used to define a system of logarithms. If we choose 3 as the base we find the following:

> $3^0 = 1$ (0 is the logarithm of 1, base 3) or $\log_3(1) = 0$
> $3^1 = 3$ (1 is the logarithm of 3, base 3) or $\log_3(3) = 1$
> $3^2 = 9$ (2 is the logarithm of 9, base 3) or $\log_3(9) = 2$

In this system, the logarithm of 5, for example, will be some number between 1 and 2 because 5 is between 3 and 9. This logarithm is written as $\log_3(5)$. The antilog of 2, using the base 3, is the number 9.

Two systems of logarithms are used most frequently, common logs and natural logs. Logarithms to the base 10, or $\log_{10}(x)$, are called *common logarithms*. This system is convenient because we are used to working in units of 10. Logarithms to the base e, or $\log_e(x)$, are convenient in many scientific applications. They are called *natural logarithms*. Natural logarithms are usually abbreviated as $\ln(x)$. Hence $\ln(100)$ is *the logarithm of 100 to the base e.*

General logarithmic expression for base e:

$$\log_e(x) = y \quad \text{or} \quad \ln(x) = y \qquad\qquad \text{(B.4)}$$

Finding natural logarithms usually requires a table of ln values, a calculator, or a computer. A calculator was used to compute the natural logs below.

$$\log_e(1) = \ln(1) = 0$$
$$\log_e(2) = \ln(2) = 0.6931$$
$$\log_e(4) = \ln(4) = 1.3863$$
$$\log_e(8) = \ln(8) = 2.0794$$

Notice in the natural logarithm calculations that while the original numbers are doubling $(1, 2, 4, 8)$, the natural logs are increasing by a constant amount (0.6931). Thus, we have again changed a set of numbers that are increasing by a constant proportion into a set increasing by a constant amount. For problems in business and economics, it generally makes no difference if natural or common logs are used. The next section illustrates calculation of both types using a hand calculator.

Logarithms can be used to make certain calculations easier, using the following two rules:

Rule 1. $\qquad\qquad\qquad \log(ab) = \log(a) + \log(b)$

The logarithm of a product is the sum of the logarithms.

Rule 2. $\qquad\qquad\qquad \log(a^b) = b\log(a)$

The log of a^b is b times the log of a.

☐ **EXAMPLE B.4**[†] Use common logs to evaluate the following.
a) $(10)(10,000)$ $\qquad\qquad\qquad\qquad\qquad$ **b)** $(1000)(1000^2)$

● **SOLUTION**
a) Apply Rule 1.

$$\log[(10)(10,000)] = \log(10) + \log(10,000)$$
$$= 1 + 4 = 5$$

[†] The two logarithmic rules illustrated in Example B.4 apply to both common and natural logs. For example, for natural logs, $\ln(e) = 1$, just as $\log_{10}(10) = 1$.

The antilog of 5 is 100,000; thus $(10)(10,000) = 10^5 = 100,000$.

b) Apply Rule 1 and then Rule 2.

$$\log(1000)(1000^2) = \log(1000) + \log(1000^2)$$
$$= 3 + 2\log(1000)$$
$$= 3 + 2(3) = 9$$

Thus, $(1000)(1000^2) = 10^9 = 1,000,000,000$. In *scientific notation*, the number 1,000,000,000 is written as $1.0E + 9$. The symbol $E + 9$ says to move the decimal point nine places to the *right*. As another example, consider $4.23E - 5$. In this case, the decimal is moved five places to the *left*, which means that $4.23E - 5 = 0.0000423$. ∎

Calculating Logarithms

It is possible to calculate logarithms by hand or with tabled values. However, using a computer or a calculator is much easier. Computers represent the easiest approach, but here we demonstrate the process of determining logarithms using calculators since this method is convenient when the number of values is small. Many calculators have function keys on them with the following labels: log, 10^x, ln, and e^x. The first two calculate logarithms to the base 10 and their antilogs respectively. The latter two calculate logarithms to the base e and their antilogs respectively.

Table B.1 presents five numbers (labelled as x), showing both the common and natural log values for each number as found with a calculator. For example, $\log_{10}(50) = 1.699$ was determined by using the log function. To do this, enter 50 and then press the log function key. In a similar way, $\ln(50) = 3.912$ was determined using the ln function key.

DATA SET 1   Calculating Logarithms

x	$\log(x)$	$\ln(x)$
10	1.000	2.303
50	1.699	3.912
100	2.000	4.605
500	2.699	6.215
1000	3.000	6.908

To show how antilogs work, Table B.2 gives the logarithm values from Table B.1, and then takes the antilog of each number. The antilog values shown in the second column are found by using the function 10^x on the calculator; the antilog values for the fourth column are found using the e^x key. Since an antilog reverses the logarithmic process, it is not surprising that the values in columns two and four of Table B.2 are exactly the same values we started with in column 1 of Table B.1 (*Note*: the log values in both Tables B.1 and B.2 are rounded, creating small rounding errors).

DATA SET 2   Logs and Antilogs

Log(x)	Antilog $= 10^x$	Ln(x)	Antilog $= e^x$
1.000	10	2.303	10
1.699	50	3.912	50
2.000	100	4.605	100
2.699	500	6.215	500
3.000	1000	6.908	1000

PROBLEMS

B.1 Indicate whether the following numbers are prime or composite, even or odd. If composite, give the prime factorization.

$$17, \ 20, \ 23, \ 24, \ 29, \ 30$$

◆ **B.2** Find the prime factors of the following numbers.
a) 177   b) 204   c) 1558

B.3 a) Find the absolute value of each of the following.
i) -2 ii) 5 iii) $(-3-5)$
iv) -3^2 v) $(-3)^2$

b) Calculate the value of each expression.
i) $\left(\frac{1}{3}\right)^3$ ii) 5^{-2} iii) $16^{\frac{1}{2}}$
iv) $125^{\frac{1}{3}}$ v) $\left(\frac{1}{4}\right)^{-0.5}$

B.4 Indicate the meaning of the following expressions in words, and specify which of the five are not always correct statements.
a) $-3 < -1$ b) $10 > -5$ c) $a > b$
d) $a \le a^2$ e) $|b| \ge b$

B.5 Find the common logarithm of the following numbers, using a calculator or a computer. How are the three logs related?
a) 150   b) 1500   c) 15,000

B.6 Find the antilog, base 10, of each of the following numbers. How are the three antilogs related?
a) 2.7118   b) 3.7118   c) 4.7118

B.7 Repeat Problem B.5 using natural logarithms.

B.8 Repeat Problem B.6 using natural logarithms.

B.9 How are the answers to Problem B.7 related to the answers to Problem B.5?

B.10 Use common logarithms to solve. Write each answer in conventional format and in scientific notation.
a) $(100)(1000)$ b) $(100^{\frac{1}{2}})(10,000)$
c) $(1000)^{\frac{1}{3}}(100)^{-\frac{1}{2}}$

B.11 Use natural logs to solve the following.
a) $(e^2)(e^{-\frac{1}{2}})(e^{1.5})$ b) $(700)(e^{4.6})(e^{-1})$

section B.2

Variables and Variable Notation

A **variable** is a quantity that may assume any one of a set of values. For example, we might describe the worth of a common stock by the variable *current price on the stock market*. The values of this variable are the prices that the stock can assume. Or, we might be interested in evaluating the inventory of a company for tax purposes by defining the variable as *the value of the inventory on October 15th*. A variable is the opposite of a constant, whose value is fixed in advance. Variables are often denoted by letters at the end of the alphabet, such as x and y.

Operations Involving Variables and Constants

When variables and constants are combined by the basic operations of addition, subtraction, multiplication, and division, we obtain algebraic expressions. For example,

$$10 - 3y + y^2$$

is an expression involving a single variable, y. This expression contains three terms: the constant 10, the coefficient 3 times the variable y raised to the first power, and the variable y raised to the power of 2. Note that if a term has no coefficient, such as y^2 in this expression, the coefficient is assumed to be 1. Thus, the expression

$$a + bx + cy^2$$

involves three constants (a, b, and c) and two variables (x and y). If $a = -5$, $b = 4$, and $c = -\frac{1}{2}$, then the expression becomes

$$-5 + 4x - \frac{1}{2}y^2$$

To find the **degree** of an expression take the highest value of any of the exponents, or the sum of the exponents of a term involving the product of variables, whichever is larger. For instance, the expression $ax^2 + bx + cy^3$ is degree 3 because the highest exponent is the third power. In the expression $bxy + y^2 + x^2y$, the degree is found by examining the term x^2y. In this term the sum of the exponents of the variables is 3, and hence the degree of the expression is 3.

Expressions of degree 2 are called **quadratic expressions**. An nth degree **polynomial** (many terms) involving only one variable (x) is written as follows:

General expression for a single variable nth degree polynomial:

$$a_0 + a_1x + a_2x^2 + \cdots + a_nx^n \qquad \text{(B.5)}$$

where n is a positive integer and a_0, a_1, ..., a_n are all constants.

▢ EXAMPLE B.5

a) What is the degree of the polynomial $7 - x + 3x^2 - 5x^3$?

b) What are the values of a_0, a_1, a_2, and a_3 in part a) above?

c) What degree is the expression $3x^2y^2 + y^3$?

• SOLUTION

a) The expression $7 - x + 3x^2 - 5x^3$ is a polynomial of degree 3 because x^3 is the term with the highest power.

b) The values of the constants are as follows:

$$a_0 = 7, \ a_1 = -1, \ a_2 = 3, \ \text{and } a_3 = -5.$$

c) The degree is 4 because x^2y^2 has exponents that sum to 4.   ∎

Example B.5 illustrates the use of superscripts and subscripts. As usual, superscripts denote successive powers, such as $x^2 = (x)(x)$ and $x^3 = (x)(x)(x)$. The subscripts in the nth degree polynomial (see Formula B.5) were used to distinguish the coefficients from one another. The next section covers subscripts more extensively.

Subscripts Used to Represent Variables

section B.3

Subscripts are used to distinguish between values of a particular variable or to indicate distinct variables. Thus, x_1 typically represents the first value of the variable x; x_2 represents the second value of the variable x, and x_i represents the ith variable in the sequence.

For example, if the symbol x_i represents the variable *sales in month i of the West Company* then x_1 represents sales in the first month of the year [x_1 = January sales], x_2 = sales in the second month of the year (February), and so forth, with x_{12} = December sales. Thus, sales for the entire year can be shown as

$$x_1, \ x_2, \ \ldots, \ x_{12} \qquad \text{or} \qquad x_i \ (i = 1, 2, \ldots, 12)$$

The sum of sales for all 12 months in a year can then be written as follows:

$$x_1 + x_2 + \cdots + x_{12}$$

Another way of writing this sum is to use the Greek letter epsilon (Σ). This symbol is read as *take the sum of*. Thus, Σx_i says to take the sum of the values of the variable x. At the bottom of the sum sign, we usually indicate the first value of x_i that is to be summed. The last value of x_i to be summed is usually indicated at the top of the sum sign. Hence, to sum the values of x starting at $i = 1$ and ending with $i = 12$, we write

$$\sum_{i=1}^{i=12} x_i = x_1 + x_2 + \cdots + x_{12}$$

which is read as *take the sum of x starting with x_1 and ending with x_{12}*. Often the "i equals" part of the summation notation is omitted. In such cases, the sum sign appears as follows:

$$\sum_{1}^{12} x_i$$

☐ **STUDY QUESTION B.1** Using Summation Notation

Write the sum of the monthly sales, assuming that a company is only interested in summing sales over the last six months of the year.

● **ANSWER**

$$\sum_{7}^{12} x_i = x_7 + x_8 + \cdots + x_{12}$$ ■

In statistics, we often do not know in advance what the final value of a summation process will be. That is, we may wish to sum a set of sales values, but we do not know how many values are to be summed. The usual approach in this situation is to let the symbol n represent the last number in the sum, where n can be any integer value, such as 2 or 6 or 12. The summation is thus written as follows:

General expression for the summation notation:

$$\sum_{1}^{n} x_i = x_1 + x_2 + \cdots + x_n \qquad \text{(B.6)}$$

This summation is thus read as *the sum of n numbers, where the first number is x_1, the second is x_2, and the last is x_n.* In summing monthly sales over a year, we would thus let $n = 12$, so that $\sum_{i=1}^{n} x_i = \sum_{i=1}^{12} x_i$.

Perhaps we should mention that in certain chapters of this book we have sometimes omitted the limits of summation and simply written Σx_i. This notation should be interpreted to mean *sum all relevant values of x_i.* In these instances, we have made sure that the reader always knows what the relevant values of x_i are. Also, we might point out that the choice of symbols in designating a sum of numbers is often quite arbitrary. For example, we might have used the letter y to denote monthly sales (instead of x) and used the letter j as a subscript (instead of i). In this case, $\sum_{j=1}^{12} y_j$ would denote the sum of the twelve monthly values.

Double Summations

In a number of chapters in this book, we have found it convenient to use *two* subscripts instead of just one. In these instances, the first subscript indicates one characteristic under study, and the second subscript indicates some other characteristic. For example, suppose that we let $x_{ij} =$ sales in the ith month by the jth sales representative. The notation $x_{6,2} = 15$ would indicate that in the sixth month ($i = 6$), sales representative number 2 ($j = 2$) sold 15 units. Using the same procedure previously described, we can denote the total sales over 12 months by the jth sales representative as the sum of x_{1j} (sales in the 1st month by the jth sales representative) plus $x_{2j}, \ldots$, plus $x_{12,j}$ (sales in the 12th month by the jth sales representative). That is,

Total sales by sales representative j:
$$\sum_{i=1}^{12} x_{ij} = x_{1j} + x_{2j} + \cdots + x_{12,j}$$

Another example of a similar type of sum is the sum of sales in the ith month (where i is some number between 1 and 12) over all the sales representatives in the company. If we let $k =$ total number of sales representatives, then this sum is x_{i1} (sales in month i by sales representative 1) plus $x_{i2}, \ldots$, plus x_{ik} (sales in month i by sales representative k). That is,

Total sales in month i:
$$\sum_{j=1}^{k} x_{ij} = x_{i1} + x_{i2} + \cdots + x_{ik}$$

Finally, we might wish to sum over all months ($i = 1, 2, \ldots, 12$) and all sales representatives ($j = 1, 2, \ldots, k$). This sum could be written as:

Total sales over all months and all sales representatives:
$$\sum_{\text{All } j}\sum_{\text{All } i} x_{ij} = \left\{ \begin{array}{llll} x_{11} & + x_{12} + \cdots + x_{1k} \\ +x_{21} & + x_{22} + \cdots + x_{2k} \\ \vdots & \\ +x_{12,1} & + x_{12,2} + \cdots + x_{12,k} \end{array} \right\}$$

Equations and Their Graphs

Variables and the relationship between variables represent an important part of analyzing many business and economic problems. To analyze such problems in business and economics, it is important to be able to describe relationships mathematically, and to know how to graph (or plot) them. Equations are the typical means for describing such relationships mathematically. The graph of an equation may indeed be the picture that is *worth a thousand words* in communicating the nature of the relationship between variables.

Because graphing equations is important for the understanding of many business and economic models, it is essential to know how to graph **linear** equations, as well as several simple, **nonlinear** equations.

☐ **EXAMPLE B.6**   To illustrate a linear equation, suppose the value of a piece of equipment depreciates (decreases in value) each year by 20 percent of its original value (assuming the equipment has a useful life of 5 years). Assume also that the original cost of the equipment is $2000. If x is the variable representing time (in years) and y represents the depreciated value, then the following equation represents the relationship between x and y:

$$y = -400x + 2000 \qquad 0 \leq x \leq 5$$

Note the restriction on the value of x, $0 \leq x \leq 5$, which is read as x is larger than or equal to 0, and also less than or equal to 5. This restriction represents the equipment's useful life of five years. Figure B.2 shows a graph of this equation. Find the x- and y-intercepts of this graph, and the value of the slope. What does the value of the slope mean?

• **SOLUTION**

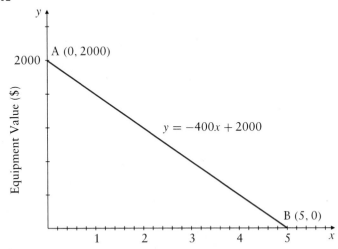

FIGURE B.2   The graph of the linear equation $y = -400x + 2000$

The horizontal axis is the x-axis (time), and the vertical axis is the y-axis (value). The equation $y = -400x + 2000$ is a straight line since the exponent of x is 1. To graph a straight line, we need only find two points on the line and then connect these points. Although any two points can be used, it is usually easiest to take the point where $x = 0$, the y-intercept, and the point where $y = 0$, the x-intercept. To do this, substitute $x = 0$ into the equation $y = -400x + 2000$. Then

$$y = -400(0) + 2000 = 2000$$

Thus, when $x = 0$, $y = 2000$ is a point on the line and also the y-intercept. This point is $(0, 2000)$ and is shown as point A in Figure B.2. Next, find the value of x when $y = 0$ by substituting $y = 0$ into the equation.

$$0 = -400x + 2000$$

$$400x = 2000$$

$$x = 5$$

Our second point, labelled point B in Figure B.2, is $x = 5$, $y = 0$, or $(5, 0)$ which is the x-intercept. Connecting these two points gives the desired straight line.

The coefficient of x is called the *slope* of the line. The slope is the rate of change, or how much y changes for each one unit change in x. For this example, the slope is -400, which means that as the year (x) increases by 1, the value of the equipment decreases by \$400. ∎

A linear equation written in **slope-intercept** form is shown as follows:

The slope-intercept form of a linear equation:

$$y = mx + b \qquad\qquad\qquad \text{(B.7)}$$

This means that the y-intercept equals the value of b, and the slope equals the value of m. For the equation $y = -400x + 2000$, $m = -400$ and $b = 2000$.

◻ STUDY QUESTION B.2   Plotting Total Cost and Volume of Production

The total cost of producing 10 units of a product is \$80 and the cost of producing 20 units of the same product is \$130. The cost for each additional unit of production is the same and does not depend on the current production level. Plot the linear equation of total cost (y) to volume (x), and find the formula relating x and y.

● **ANSWER**   Let x = the volume of production and y = total cost. The problem provides two points on the straight line, namely $x = 10$ and $y = 80$, or $(10, 80)$, and $x = 20$, $y = 130$, or $(20, 130)$. Connecting these points gives the line shown in Figure B.3. To determine the equation $y = mx + b$ for Figure B.3, first note that for 10 additional units ($x = 10$ to $x = 20$), the increase in cost is \$50 ($= \$130 - \$80$). The slope is thus $\frac{50}{10} = 5$, so $m = 5$. To determine the value of the intercept b, substitute either of the two points, plus $m = 5$, into $y = mx + b$, and solve for b. We pick the point $(10, 80)$.

$$y = mx + b$$

$$80 = 5(10) + b$$

$$b = 30$$

The equation shown in Figure B.3 is thus $y = 5x + 30$. In this case, the y-intercept, \$30 is the fixed or set-up cost of production, and \$5 is the variable cost of production.

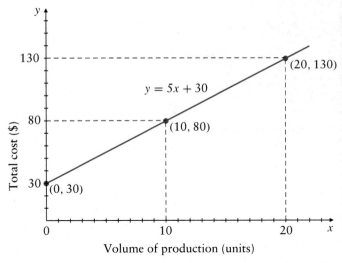

y

130 ⌐ ‐ ● (20, 130)

$y = 5x + 30$

Total cost ($)

80 ⌐ ‐ ‐ ‐ ‐ ‐ ‐ ‐ ‐ ● (10, 80)

30 ● (0, 30)

0   10   20   x

Volume of production (units)

FIGURE B.3   The graph of the linear equation $y = 5x + 30$

Linear Inequalities

section B.5

In some modelling problems, particularly linear programming, inequality signs are used rather than equalities. For example, the inequality $y \leq 500$ states that y is less than or equal to 500. Similarly, $x \geq 0$ says that x must be greater than or equal to zero. The inequality $x > 0$ specifies that x is greater than zero (and may not equal zero).

To illustrate the graphing of an inequality relationship, consider a problem where the material costs of producing a litre of paint are divided into two parts, x = amount of material 1, and y = amount of material 2. Each unit of x costs $4, while each unit of y costs $2. Thus, the total cost per litre is as follows:

$$4x + 2y$$

Suppose the materials budget for each litre is $10; then the fact that the total cost per litre cannot exceed $10 is given by the following linear inequality:

$$4x + 2y \leq 10 \qquad x \geq 0, \ y \geq 0$$

Inequalities such as this one can be graphed. To do so, we first change the inequality to an equality.

$$4x + 2y = 10$$

Then rearrange the equation into slope-intercept form.

$$2y = -4x + 10$$
$$y = -2x + 5$$

This equation can be plotted in the same manner as discussed in Study Question B.2. Its graph is shown in Figure B.4, where the y-intercept is $b = 5$, the slope is $m = -2$ and the x- intercept is 2.5.

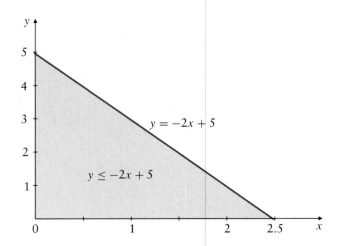

FIGURE B.4 The feasible region for the linear inequality $y \le -2x + 5$

The shaded portion of Figure B.4 is called the **feasible region**, which means all points in this region and on the line $4x + 2y = 10$ satisfy the inequality $4x + 2y \le 10$. In other words, the shaded region represents all possible points where the materials cost per litre of paint does not exceed the $10 budget. Also notice the two constraints, $x \ge 0$ and $y \ge 0$. These constraints restrict the values of x and y to the first quadrant. They are required because the amount of material $1(x)$ and the amount of material $2(y)$ can never be negative. ■

PROBLEMS

B.12 For the following expressions, indicate the degree of the expression and the constants and/or variables involved.

a) $a^2 + \left(\frac{1}{b}\right)x^2 - cz^{\frac{3}{2}}$

b) $c^{\frac{1}{2}}y^3 + 10xy + 5^4x^2$

c) $10\left(\frac{1}{y}\right)^{-3} + \pi r^2 - \left(\frac{1}{2}\right)x$

B.13 Give the summation notation for the following.

a) $x_{12} + x_{13} + x_{14}$ (for x_{1j})

b) the sum of the sales of four representatives ($i = 1, 2, 3, 4$) who work in three regions ($j = 1, 2, 3$)

B.14 Write the following in expanded form.

a) Σx_i for $i = 5, 6, \ldots, 10$

b) $\Sigma\Sigma y_{ij}$ for $i = 2, 3, 4$ and $j = 1, 2$

B.15 a) Write the general polynomial formula having degree four, using a single variable x.

b) Complete the polynomial from part (a) assuming that $a_0 = 3$, $a_1 = -2$, $a_2 = 1/3$, $a_3 = 0.01$, and $a_4 = 1/2$.

♦ **B.16** A young investor has saved $200 towards the purchase of a computer costing $1200. This person intends to save $100 per month for the computer. Find the equation relating $x =$ months and $y =$ dollars saved. Graph this function, showing when the amount saved will be sufficient to purchase the computer.

B.17 a) Graph the equation $y = \frac{1}{2}x - 100$ for $0 \le x \le 500$.

b) Graph the equation $y = -5x$ for $-5 \le x \le 5$.

c) Change the equal sign in parts (a) and (b) to $\le$, and shade the (two) resulting feasible regions. Assume $y \ge 0$.

♦ **B.18** A manufacturer markets a product at $5 per unit. The fixed costs are $5000 per month and the variable costs are $3 per unit. The product sells for $5, and all the units manufactured are sold. Construct a formula for total costs and total revenue. Plot both equations on a single graph and show the breakeven point (total cost = total revenue).

♦ **B.19** An investor has $12,000 divided between security A and security B. Security A returns 6% while security B returns 7%. Let $x =$ amount invested in A, and $y =$ total return. Plot the relationship between x and y. How much was invested in A and B if the return last year was $800?

♦ **B.20** The amount of money for home mortgages is a function of interest rates, among other things. Assume that the following equations represent the annual supply and demand schedules for home mortgage money in Canada, where p represents the interest rate in percentage terms and q represents the amount of mortgage money available in billions of dollars.

$$p = 4 + 0.25q$$
$$p = 10 - 0.75q$$

Plot these functions and find the equilibrium (demand = supply) mortgage rate and the supply at this rate.

B.21 On a single graph, shade the area satisfied by all of these linear inequalities.

a) $y \leq -x + 5$ b) $y \geq 2$
c) $x \leq 3$ d) $x + y \leq 0$

section B.6

Nonlinear Equations

Nonlinear equations are more difficult to graph. If the equation is fairly simple, a convenient approach is to plot a few points on a graph, and then connect the points with a smooth free-hand curve. This procedure is illustrated using a second degree equation in the following scenario.

The Santax Company needs to purchase 1000 units of plastic molding to fulfill an order they have for product A-431 (a small truck part) over the next year. Santax can purchase all the plastic at the beginning of the year and store it until needed, or buy the plastic in smaller amounts, closer to the time it is needed. Buying all the plastic at once has the advantage that it reduces handling costs because only one order is placed, processed, and received, but the disadvantage that carrying costs (storage, insurance, et cetera) are increased. Buying the plastic as it is required decreases storage costs but increases handling costs. Santax wants to know how many orders to place, the maximum equalling 1000, the minimum being one.

To develop a model for Santax, let $x =$ number of units ordered each time an order is placed. Thus, the number of orders placed will be $\frac{1000}{x}$. Since it costs $10 to place an order, ordering costs are as follows:

$$\text{Ordering costs} = \$10 \left(\frac{1000}{x} \right) = \frac{\$10,000}{x}$$

Santax has determined that carrying costs are, on the average, $2 per unit, or $2x$. Thus, if

$$y = \text{total costs} = \text{ordering costs} + \text{carrying costs}$$

then

$$y = \frac{10,000}{x} + 2x \quad \text{or} \quad 2x^2 - xy + 10,000 = 0 \quad \text{for } x > 0$$

This is a nonlinear, quadratic equation in x. The reader familiar with calculus can plot this equation fairly easily, including finding the optimal order point. Note that the value of x must be positive ($x > 0$), for a negative number of units ordered makes no sense, and $x = 0$ is not possible because $\frac{10,000}{0}$ is undefined.

The quadratic equation $2x^2 - xy + 10,000 = 0$ can be graphed by first constructing a table of values that satisfy it, and then connecting the points. Table B.3 is the table that results by substituting selected values of x into the equation $y = 10,000/x + 2x$. For example, if $x = 100$, then

$$y = \frac{10,000}{100} + 2(100) = 300$$

Table B.3 uses x-values most of which fall between 50 and 80, because it soon becomes clear in constructing the table that the optimal order point is in that range. Plotting a few points provides a reasonable graph of this function, as shown in Figure B.5.

TABLE B.3   Costs for Santax Problem

Quantity Ordered (x)	Ordering Cost $\left(\frac{10,000}{x}\right)$	Carrying Cost ($2x$)	Total Cost (y)
10	$1000.00	$ 20	$1020.00
40	250.00	80	330.00
50	200.00	100	300.00
60	166.67	120	286.67
70	142.86	140	282.86
80	125.00	160	285.00
100	100.00	200	300.00
200	50.00	400	450.00

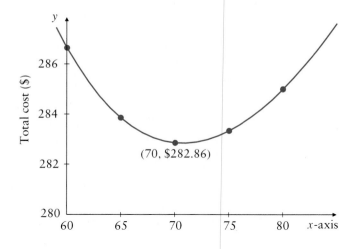

FIGURE B.5   The optimal order point is the minimum point on the curve of the quadratic equation $2x^2 - xy + 10,000 = 0$

An *eyeball* estimate of the minimum cost in Figure B.5 or from Table B.3 suggests ordering 70 units at a time, and thus placing about $\frac{10,000}{70} = 14.3$ orders per year. Using calculus, it can be shown that the exact minimum is $x = 70.71$, with a total cost of exactly $282.84. Thus, $x = 70$ is very close to the optimal number of orders that should be placed per year.

section B.7   Functions and Their Notation

Variables are often classified according to whether their values are *discrete* or *continuous*. The values of a discrete variable are individually distinct; that is, they are separable from one another. The price of a common stock, for instance, represents a discrete variable because the prices a stock can assume are separable values, distinguishable from one another. The following examples all represent discrete variables:

1. the number of defectives in a production lot
2. the amount of advertising expenditure a certain company plans to spend for next year
3. the amount of tax owed by a company

Most **discrete variables** represent some quality that can be counted. For example, one can count the number of errors discovered by an accounting audit. Hence, this variable is discrete. The number of values a discrete variable may assume can be either finite or infinite. In an accounting audit, the number of errors is infinite as there is no upper limit on the number of errors. Another example of a discrete variable is the cost of a unit of production. If one unit costs $50, then two units cost $100. There are no cost values between $50 and $100.

The values of a continuous variable are not separable from one another; each value is immediately adjacent to and indistinguishable from the next, and there are always an infinite number of values. Measured quantities are usually **continuous variables**. Therefore, time, weight, length, and area typically represent continuous variables. For example, the time it takes an alkaline battery to fail represents a continuous variable, as do the following:

1. the percentage increase in the consumer price index last month
2. the amount of oil shipped by Saudi Arabia next year
3. the amount of land (in acres) used for growing wheat in North America this year

One of the practical difficulties with continuous variables is that the devices used to measure such variables usually are read only in a discrete manner. For example, the variable *amount of gasoline needed to fill a car* is clearly a continuous variable, since this amount may be any value between zero and the capacity of the gas tank. From a practical point of view, however, this variable is discrete because most gas pumps cannot be read (at least accurately) beyond a few decimal points (usually $\frac{1}{10}$ of a litre). For most statistical analysis, it makes little difference if we treat such variables as discrete or continuous, although a continuous variable is often easier to manipulate than is a discrete variable with many different values.

If a unique value of some variable y is associated with every possible value of another variable x, then the variable y is said to be a **function** of the variable x. As will be demonstrated in the material that follows, functional relationships may be linear (straightline) or nonlinear (curved), and may involve discrete or continuous variables. The standard notation in working with functions is shown in Equation B.8, and is read *y is a function of x*.

General expression for function notation:

$$y = f(x) \tag{B.8}$$

There are three commonly used methods for describing a functional relationship: (1) a table, (2) a graph, and (3) an equation. All three of these methods work well for discrete functions, while the latter two work well for continuous functions.

Discrete Functions

By a discrete function, we mean the function in any situation where x is a discrete variable. It is important to understand the symbolic notation in writing functions. The notation $y = f(2)$, for example, represents the value of the variable y when $x = 2$. Thus, if $f(2) = 1200$, this means that when $x = 2$, the value of y is 1200. Similarly, if $f(4) = 400$, then $y = 400$ when $x = 4$. Values of $f(x)$ are typically determined by substituting x into the appropriate equation, as will be demonstrated in Example B.7.

□ **EXAMPLE B.7**   Consider once again the straightline depreciation problem of Example B.6. Now, however, assume interest is in depreciated values only at the *end* of each year; this means that only five values of x are of interest: $x = 1, 2, \ldots, 5$. Because $y = f(x)$ the relationship between x and y for this situation is now expressed as either:

$$y = -400x + 2000 \quad \text{or} \quad f(x) = -400x + 2000 \qquad \text{for } x = 1, 2, \ldots, 5$$

a) Are the variables x and y discrete or continuous? Explain.
b) Construct a table of values for $f(1)$ to $f(5)$.
c) Graph the function.

● **SOLUTION**

a) The variable x is discrete because all values of this variable are distinguishable from one another. Thus, the variable y is also discrete.

b) To construct a table of values, begin by substituting $x = 1$ into $f(x) = -400x + 2000$. Therefore,

$$f(1) = -400(1) + 2000$$
$$= 1600$$

TABLE B.4   Discrete Straightline Depreciation over Five Years

Year (x)	Depreciated Value at Year's End (y)
1	$y = f(1) = 1600$
2	$y = f(2) = 1200$
3	$y = f(3) = 800$
4	$y = f(4) = 400$
5	$y = f(5) = 0$

c) Figure B.6 is a graph of the function relating years (x) and depreciated value (y). The temptation to connect the points with a line must be resisted, since such a line might incorrectly lead a viewer to assume that the function is defined for values of x other than $x = \{1, 2, 3, 4, 5\}$.

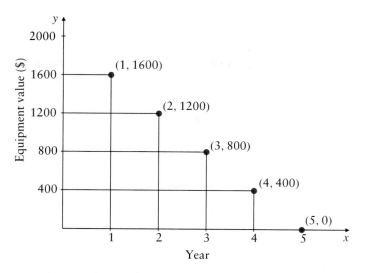

FIGURE B.6   A graphic representation of the discrete straight-line depreciation described by $f(x) = -400x + 2000$

The discrete relationship between x and y has now been expressed in three different ways --- Table B.4, a graph in Figure B.5, and a formula.

Continuous Functions

When the variable x is continuous, then the functional relationship between x and y must be expressed as a formula or a graph (but generally not in a table). The equation presented earlier,

$$y = -400x + 2000 \quad \text{for } 0 \le x \le 5$$

is a continuous function because the values of x are indistinguishable. There are many types of continuous functions, some linear and others nonlinear, only a few of which will be illustrated here.

☐ STUDY QUESTION B.3   Estimating Costs in a Ledger Account

An accountant is estimating ledger accounts to determine if there are factors other than costs influencing output in a production operation. The accountant determines the (average) relationship between machine-time (x, in hours) and cost (y, in dollars) to be the following:

$$y = 0.867x + 55,293 \quad \text{for } 0 \le x \le 50,000$$

a) Is this function linear or nonlinear?
b) Graph the function, finding in the process, $f(0)$, $f(10,000)$, $f(20,000)$, $f(30,000)$, $f(40,000)$, and $f(50,000)$.
c) How can the values a and b be interpreted in this specific situation?

• ANSWER

a) The function is linear, as the exponent of x is 1.
b) Table B.5 provides the values of the function for $x = 0$, 10,000, 20,000, 30,000, 40,000, and 50,000. The graph is shown in Figure B.7.

TABLE B.5 Values of the Function for Study Question B.3

Hours (x)	Cost (y)
0	$f(0) = \$55,293$
10,000	$f(10,000) = 63,963$
20,000	$f(20,000) = 72,633$
30,000	$f(30,000) = 81,303$
40,000	$f(40,000) = 89,973$
50,000	$f(50,000) = 98,643$

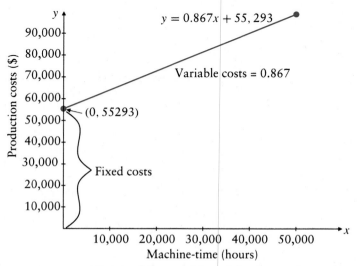

FIGURE B.7 Graph of the variable and fixed costs for Study Question B.3

c) The value of the intercept $b = \$55,293$ can be interpreted as a fixed cost, while the value of the slope $m = 0.867$ is the variable cost (per hour). ∎

Exponential functions are those involving a variable as an exponent. For example, a^{2x} and e^{-y} are both exponential functions (x and y are variables, a and e are constants). In order to practice with exponential functions, the reader may wish to plot the function $y = f(x) = 2^x$ for $0 \leq x \leq 5$. Study Question B.4 illustrates exponential functions using the constant e (recall $e = 2.71828\ldots$). That example demonstrates a calculation important to strategic problems in accounting and finance, that of determining the current value of a sum of money to be received in the future. In these cases, the dollar value from the future is discounted back to the present using some interest rate. The current value of the future money is called its *present value*.

☐ STUDY QUESTION B.4 Exponential Functions and Net Present Value

To illustrate how the value of money changes over time, suppose we want to know how much $10,000 is worth *now* if we do not receive the money until one year, two years, or ten years from now. The present value (labelled P) is the current value of the $10,000 dollars, received n periods from now, assuming some interest rate (i), such as 0.05 (5%).

For this problem, we assume that money earns interest at a constant rate i and that interest is compounded (the interest earns interest). Typically, interest is compounded monthly or weekly, or even daily. We assume, for the convenience of the mathematics, that interest is compounded *continuously*.

A general formula for the present value (P) of an amount S to be received in n periods (assuming continuous discounting) is

$$P = Se^{-in} \tag{B.9}$$

where i is the interest rate. A proof of this relationship is found in numerous mathematics and finance texts.

The equation to find the present value of \$10,000 received n years from now, assuming an interest rate of 5%, is shown as follows:

$$P = 10,000e^{-0.05n} \quad \text{for } n \geq 0$$

a) Determine P for integer values of n starting with zero and ending with 10. That is, find $f(0)$, $f(1)$, $f(2)$, ..., $f(10)$.

b) Interpret the value of $f(2)$.

c) Graph the function as a continuous function for $0 \leq n \leq 10$.

• **ANSWER** a) The P values are shown in Table B.6. They were determined using a calculator with an e^x function key. To perform this type of function on the calculator, we use the results for $f(1)$ in Table B.6 as an example. Enter 0.05 and press the $+/-$ key to produce the negative exponent -0.05. Then, as is true on most scientific calculators, press the 2nd F key followed by the e^x key, which is the $\ln x$ key. Multiply this result by 10,000. The result is 9,512.

TABLE B.6   Values for the Function in Study Question B.4

n	$P = f(n) = 10,000e^{-0.05n}$
0	$f(0) = 10,000e^0 = \$10,000$
1	$f(1) = 10,000e^{-0.05} = 9,512$ (using a calculator)
2	$f(2) = 10,000e^{-0.10} = 9,048$
3	$f(3) = 10,000e^{-0.15} = 8,607$
4	$f(4) = 10,000e^{-0.20} = 8,187$
5	$f(5) = 10,000e^{-0.25} = 7,788$
6	$f(6) = 10,000e^{-0.30} = 7,408$
7	$f(7) = 10,000e^{-0.35} = 7,047$
8	$f(8) = 10,000e^{-0.40} = 6,703$
9	$f(9) = 10,000e^{-0.45} = 6,376$
10	$f(10) = 10,000e^{-0.50} = 6,065$

b) In Table B.6, $f(2) = \$9{,}048$; thus, the present value of $10,000 received 2 periods from now is $9,048 (continuously discounted back to the present at a 5% interest rate). Similarly, the present value of $10,000 received 10 years from now is $6,065.

c) The graph of this function is shown in Figure B.8. It is important to recognize that Figure B.8 is a *curved* line, not a straight line.

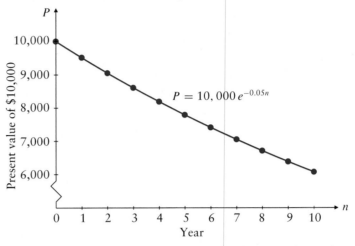

FIGURE B.8   Graph of the present value of $10,000 for Study Question B.4

Transforming Variables

section B.8

In some problems, it is convenient to transform a variable into another form in order to make it easier to manipulate, or to graph. In many business and economic situations, logarithmic transformations are especially helpful because the effect is to change a nonlinear function into a linear function. Natural logs $[\ln(x)]$ and common logarithms (logs) are both used frequently, and for many problems it makes no difference which base is used. We now summarize the two rules for logarithms in Section B.1, using the notation of variables.

> Logarithm rule: If $y = (a)(b^x)$, then
> $$\ln(y) = \ln(a) + \ln(b^x)$$
> $$= \ln(a) + x\ln(b)$$
> (B.10)

Logarithmic transformations are demonstrated in Examples B.8 and B.9, the first using a ln transformation on the function in Study Question B.4, the second using a log transformation on what we will call *learning curve data*.

☐ EXAMPLE B.8

a) Transform the exponential function

$$P = 10{,}000e^{-0.05n}$$

shown in Study Question B.4 into a linear function by taking natural logs.

b) Graph the function.

● **SOLUTION**

a) Take the natural logarithm of both sides of the equation as follows:

$$P = 10,000e^{-0.05n}$$
$$\ln(P) = \ln(10,000e^{-0.05n})$$
$$= \ln(10,000) + \ln(e^{-0.05n})$$
$$= 9.21 - 0.05n(\ln e)$$
$$= 9.21 - 0.05n$$

Use the linear function $y = -0.05n + 9.21$ for values of $n = 1$ to 10 in Table B.7 to produce the points on the graph shown in Figure B.9.

TABLE B.7 Finding the Natural Logarithm of a Function

n	$P = f(n) = 10,000e^{-0.05n}$	$\ln(P)$
0	$f(0) = 10,000e^0 = \$10,000$	9.21
1	$f(1) = 10,000e^{-0.05} = 9,512$	9.16
2	$f(2) = 10,000e^{-0.10} = 9,048$	9.11
3	$f(3) = 10,000e^{-0.15} = 8,607$	9.06
4	$f(4) = 10,000e^{-0.20} = 8,187$	9.01
5	$f(5) = 10,000e^{-0.25} = 7,788$	8.96
6	$f(6) = 10,000e^{-0.30} = 7,408$	8.91
7	$f(7) = 10,000e^{-0.35} = 7,047$	8.86
8	$f(8) = 10,000e^{-0.40} = 6,703$	8.81
9	$f(9) = 10,000e^{-0.45} = 6,376$	8.76
10	$f(10) = 10,000e^{-0.50} = 6,065$	8.71

b) Figure B.9, a plot of the values of n and $\ln(P)$, shows that the ln transformation has resulted in a straight line relationship.

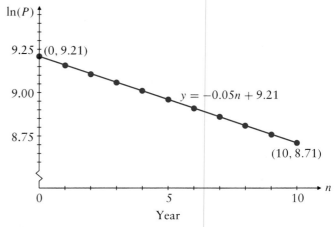

FIGURE B.9   The logarithmic transformation of the
exponential function $f(n) = 10,000e^{-0.05n}$

In Examples B.8 and Figure B.9, we illustrated the process of straightening the
relationship between two variables (n and P) by taking the natural logarithm of one
of the two variables (P). The following example illustrates a comparable process,
but this time straightening the relationship between two variables by taking the
logarithm of *both* variables, using common logs. We do not attempt to answer the
difficult question of how to know when to take the log of one variable, or more
than one.

When the costs were estimated in Study Question B.3, the relationship
between input and output (cost) was found to be linear. In many business situations,
the relationship between inputs and outputs may not be linear because of a "learning
curve," where a person becomes more efficient as he or she gains experience with a
task. Thus, with experience, production line workers become more proficient over
time, as do typists, clerks, lawyers, and even professors. The learning curve model
is based on the assumption that over time (an input) the efficiency of a process (an
output) may increase at a *proportional* rate rather than at a constant rate. Consider
for example, the data in Table B.8, where x is the input (time, in hours to perform
a task) and y is the output (a measure of employee productivity). In this case, the
x-values selected are $x = 1, 2, 4, 8, 16$, and 32.

TABLE B.8   Values to Demonstrate a Learning Curve

$x =$ hours to perform	$y =$ productivity
1	5.01
2	6.31
4	7.76
8	10.00
16	12.59
32	16.60

These data, graphed in Figure B.10, indicate a nonlinear (curved) relationship between $x =$ hours to perform and $y =$ productivity.

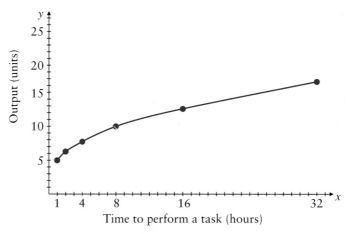

FIGURE B.10   The shape of a learning curve

A log transformation on *both* variables in Figure B.10 straightens the relationship. This is called a log-log or a double log transformation, indicating both variables are transformed. Although common logs were used here, any base could be used. A calculator was used to find the logs in Table B.9.

TABLE B.9   Calculating a Log-log Transformation

x = Hours	Log(x)	y = Productivity	Log(y)
1	0.00	5.01	0.70
2	0.30	6.31	0.80
4	0.60	7.76	0.89
8	0.90	10.00	1.00
16	1.20	12.59	1.10
32	1.51	16.60	1.22

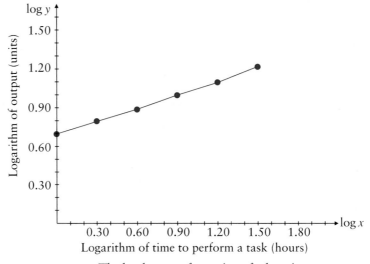

FIGURE B.11   The log-log transformation of a learning curve

Figure B.11 shows that the relationship between $\log(x)$ and $\log(y)$ is now approximately linear.

■

<table>
<tr><td>**section B.9**</td></tr>
</table>

More Complicated Equations

Numerous other functional relationships are used in statistics, some of which are more complicated and cannot easily be graphed. In certain cases, we merely want to evaluate such a function for certain values of x. To illustrate such a relationship, consider a fairly well-known bankruptcy function from accounting, called the *Altman z-score*, involving the following six variables:

z = bankruptcy score predictor
x_1 = net liquid assets/total assets
x_2 = retained earnings/total assets
x_3 = (earnings + interest)/total assets
x_4 = market equity value/total liability
x_5 = net sales/total assets

The **Altman function** is:

$$z = 1.2x_1 + 1.4x_2 + 3.3x_3 + 0.6x_4 + 1.0x_5$$

This z-score is interpreted as shown in Table B.10.

DATA SET 10   Altman z-score Interpretation

z-score	Interpretation
> 3.0	low danger of bankruptcy
2.7--3.0	some danger of bankruptcy (gray area)
1.8 --2.7	bankruptcy likely in two years
< 1.8	high danger of bankruptcy

☐ **EXAMPLE B.9**   A company, the West Company, has calculated the following values:

$$x_1 = 0.672, \ x_2 = 0.284, \ x_3 = 0.400, \ x_4 = 3.08, \ x_5 = 4.00$$

Determine and interpret the Altman z-score.

● **SOLUTION**   Substituting these values into the Altman function yields:

$$z = 1.2(0.672) + 1.4(0.284) + 3.3(0.400) + 0.6(3.08) + 1.0(4.00) = 8.372$$

Since the z-score for this company exceeds 3.0 (by a large amount), the company appears to be in good financial health.   ■

PROBLEMS

B.22 The relationship between a principal deposit of P and the balance at the end of n years $[P(n)]$ are given by the following formula, where $i =$ interest rate expressed as a percent (compounded annually).

$$P(n) = \left(1 + \frac{i}{100}\right)^n P \quad \text{for } n \geq 0$$

a) Assume $P = \$1,000$, and $i = 10\%$. Interpret the value of $P(0)$.

b) Find $P(1), P(2), P(3), \ldots, P(10)$. Plot this equation for $n = 1, 2, 3, \ldots, 10$ on the x-axis and $P(n)$ on the y-axis. Is the relationship between $P(n)$ and n linear or nonlinear?

c) Take the natural logarithm of the ten values of $P(n)$ from part (b), and plot the new relationship. Does this transformation make the relationship appear more or less linear?

B.23 The cost (y) of producing a product (x) is defined as follows:

$$y = x^2 - 12x + 40 \quad \text{for } 0 \leq x \leq 15$$

Find $f(0)$, $f(5)$, $f(7)$, $f(10)$, and $f(15)$, and then plot this function. Estimate the point where costs are at a minimum.

◆ **B.24** Economic problems sometimes involve solving supply and demand functions. Consider the following functions, where $p =$ price (in dollars) and $q =$ demand units per day.

$$p = \frac{q}{40} + 1.9 \quad \text{(supply function)}$$

$$p = \frac{8}{q} \quad \text{(demand function)}$$

a) Find $f(1)$, $f(2)$, $f(4)$, and $f(8)$ for both functions, and then plot both functions for $0 < q < 8$. Are they linear or nonlinear functions?

b) Use your graph to find the point where supply equals demand.

◆ **B.25** Consider the following information about the relationship between total revenue (TR) and quantity Q, and total cost (TC) and quantity Q.

$$TR = 50,000 + 200Q - Q^2,$$

$$TC = 4Q^2 - 1,000Q + 90,000$$

Graph both functions, for $0 < Q < 140$. What level of output represents the breakeven point ($TR = TC$)?

◆ **B.26** A real estate company owns an office complex containing 50 suites. At $400 per month, every suite can be rented. However, for each $10 per month increase in rent, it is estimated that there will be one vacant suite.

a) Explain why the following expression represents the revenue (R) collected from the (rented) suites when x is the rent.

$$R = x\left\{50 - \left[\frac{(x - 400)}{10}\right]\right\}$$

b) Plot this nonlinear function for $400 \leq x \leq 500$.

c) What value of x maximizes revenue?

d) What value of x yields $20,240 in rents?

◆ **B.27** The following function relates average cost (AC) to the quantity produced.

$$AC = \frac{432}{Q} + 3Q + 10$$

Plot this function for $0 < Q \leq 20$. Approximate the value of Q which minimizes average cost.

◆ **B.28** The equation for a company's demand curve is given as

$$Q = 700P^{-2.5}Y^{1.6}$$

where Q is the quantity demanded, P is the price, and Y is the real disposable income.

a) Express this equation as a linear relationship. (*Hint:* The use of logarithms is helpful.)

b) Evaluate the logarithm expression in part (a) assuming that $P = 50$ and $Y = 100$.

CHAPTER SUMMARY

KEY TERMS AND EXPRESSIONS

Natural numbers (integers): Used to count with $(1, 2, 3, \ldots)$.

Prime numbers: Integers that are exactly divisible only by 1 or themselves.

Composite numbers: An integer that can be expressed as a product of two or more prime numbers.

Even numbers: Integers that are exactly divisible by 2.

Odd numbers: Integers that are not exactly divisible by 2.

Negative numbers: Integers that are less than zero.

Positive numbers: Integers that are greater than zero.

Absolute value of a or $|a|$: The distance from a to 0.

Constant: A number whose value is fixed.

Base: The constant in an exponential expression.

Exponent: The power of a number (called the *base*).

Nontermination, nonrepeating decimals: (π, e)

Antilog(x): The number a in the expression $\log(n) = a$.

Log$_{10}(x)$: (Common) log of x to the base 10.

Log$_e(x)$: (Natural) log of x to the base e, $\ln e$.

Variable: A quantity that may assume any one of a number of values.

Nonlinear: A curved relationship.

Linear: A straightline relationship.

Degree: The highest exponent in a polynomial.

Quadratic expressions: Expressions of degree two.

Polynomial: An expression involving many terms, of the form

$$a_0 + a_1 x + a_2 x^2 + \cdots + a_n x^n.$$

Slope-intercept form: The form $y = mx + b$, where $b =$ intercept and $m =$ slope.

Feasible region: The values satisfying an inequality such as:

$$a_1 x_1 + a_2 x_2 + \cdots + a_n x_n \leq a_0.$$

Discrete variables: Variables whose values are individually separable from one another and most often are represented by some quality that can be counted.

Continuous variables: Variables with an infinite number of values that are *not* individually separable from one another and usually are measured quantities.

Function: A relationship between two or more variables.

Exponential functions: Functions involving a constant (often e) used as the base, with a variable as the exponent.

APPENDIX C
Tables of Functions

Table I gives values of the binomial mass function defined by

$$P(x) = {}_nC_x\pi^x(1-\pi)^{n-x}$$

$$= \frac{n!}{x!(n-x)!}\pi^x(1-\pi)^{n-x}.$$

This is the probability of exactly x successes in n independent Bernoulli trials with probability of success on a single trial equal to π. The values of x at the left of any section are to be used in conjunction with the values of π at the top of that section; the values of x at the right of any section are to be used in conjunction with the values of π at the bottom of that section.

☐ **EXAMPLE**   To evaluate $P(x)$ for $n = 5$, $x = 3$, and $\pi = 0.83$, locate the section of the table for $n = 5$, the column for $\pi = 0.83$, and the row for $x = 3$, and read

$$P(x) = 0.1652.$$

TABLE I   Binomial distribution ($n = 1$, $n = 2$)

$n = 1$

x	π	01	02	03	04	05	06	07	08	09	10		
0		9900	9800	9700	9600	9500	9400	9300	9200	9100	9000		1
1		0100	0200	0300	0400	0500	0600	0700	0800	0900	1000		0
		99	98	97	96	95	94	93	92	91	90	π	x
x	π	11	12	13	14	15	16	17	18	19	20		
0		8900	8800	8700	8600	8500	8400	8300	8200	8100	8000		1
1		1100	1200	1300	1400	1500	1600	1700	1800	1900	2000		0
		89	88	87	86	85	84	83	82	81	80	π	x
x	π	21	22	23	24	25	26	27	28	29	30		
0		7900	7800	7700	7600	7500	7400	7300	7200	7100	7000		1
1		2100	2200	2300	2400	2500	2600	2700	2800	2900	3000		0
		79	78	77	76	75	74	73	72	71	70	π	x
x	π	31	32	33	34	35	36	37	38	39	40		
0		6900	6800	6700	6600	6500	6400	6300	6200	6100	6000		1
1		3100	3200	3300	3400	3500	3600	3700	3800	3900	4000		0
		69	68	67	66	65	64	63	62	61	60	π	x
x	π	41	42	43	44	45	46	47	48	49	50		
0		5900	5800	5700	5600	5500	5400	5300	5200	5100	5000		1
1		4100	4200	4300	4400	4500	4600	4700	4800	4900	5000		0
		59	58	57	56	55	54	53	52	51	50	π	x

								$n = 2$					
x	π	01	02	03	04	05	06	07	08	09	10		
0		9801	9604	9409	9216	9025	8836	8649	8464	8281	8100		2
1		0198	0392	0582	0768	0950	1128	1302	1472	1638	1800		1
2		0001	0004	0009	0016	0025	0036	0049	0064	0081	0100		0
		99	98	97	96	95	94	93	92	91	90	π	x
x	π	11	12	13	14	15	16	17	18	19	20		
0		7921	7744	7569	7396	7225	7056	6889	6724	6561	6400		2
1		1958	2112	2262	2408	2550	2688	2822	2952	3078	3200		1
2		0121	0144	0169	0196	0225	0256	0289	0324	0361	0400		0
		89	88	87	86	85	84	83	82	81	80	π	x
x	π	21	22	23	24	25	26	27	28	29	30		
0		6241	6084	5929	5776	5625	5476	5329	5184	5041	4900		2
1		3318	3432	3542	3648	3750	3848	3942	4032	4118	4200		1
2		0441	0484	0529	0576	0625	0676	0729	0784	0841	0900		0
		79	78	77	76	75	74	73	72	71	70	π	x
x	π	31	32	33	34	35	36	37	38	39	40		
0		4761	4624	4489	4356	4225	4096	3969	3844	3721	3600		2
1		4278	4352	4422	4488	4550	4608	4662	4712	4758	4800		1
2		0961	1024	1089	1156	1225	1296	1369	1444	1521	1600		0
		69	68	67	66	65	64	63	62	61	60	π	x
x	π	41	42	43	44	45	46	47	48	49	50		
0		3481	3364	3249	3136	3025	2916	2809	2704	2601	2500		2
1		4838	4872	4902	4928	4950	4968	4982	4992	4998	5000		1
2		1681	1764	1849	1936	2025	2116	2209	2304	2401	2500		0
		59	58	57	56	55	54	53	52	51	50	π	x

TABLE I   Binomial distribution ($n = 3$, $n = 4$)

							$n = 3$							
x	π	01	02	03	04	05	06	07	08	09	10			
0		9703	9412	9127	8847	8574	8306	8044	7787	7536	7290			3
1		0294	0576	0847	1106	1354	1590	1816	2031	2236	2430			2
2		0003	0012	0026	0046	0071	0102	0137	0177	0221	0270			1
3		0000	0000	0000	0001	0001	0002	0003	0005	0007	0010			0
		99	98	97	96	95	94	93	92	91	90		π	x
x	π	11	12	13	14	15	16	17	18	19	20			
0		7050	6815	6585	6361	6141	5927	5718	5514	5314	5120			3
1		2614	2788	2952	3106	3251	3387	3513	3631	3740	3840			2
2		0323	0380	0441	0506	0574	0645	0720	0797	0877	0960			1
3		0013	0017	0022	0027	0034	0041	0049	0058	0069	0080			0
		89	88	87	86	85	84	83	82	81	80		π	x
x	π	21	22	23	24	25	26	27	28	29	30			
0		4930	4746	4565	4390	4219	4052	3890	3732	3579	3430			3
1		3932	4014	4091	4159	4219	4271	4316	4355	4386	4410			2
2		1045	1133	1222	1313	1406	1501	1597	1693	1791	1890			1
3		0093	0106	0122	0138	0156	0176	0197	0220	0244	0270			0
		79	78	77	76	75	74	73	72	71	70		π	x
x	π	31	32	33	34	35	36	37	38	39	40			
0		3285	3144	3008	2875	2746	2621	2500	2383	2270	2160			3
1		4428	4439	4444	4443	4436	4424	4406	4382	4354	4320			2
2		1989	2089	2189	2289	2389	2488	2587	2686	2783	2880			1
3		0298	0328	0359	0393	0429	0467	0507	0549	0593	0640			0
		69	68	67	66	65	64	63	62	61	60		π	x
x	π	41	42	43	44	45	46	47	48	49	50			
0		2054	1951	1852	1756	1664	1575	1489	1406	1327	1250			3
1		4282	4239	4191	4140	4084	4024	3961	3894	3823	3750			2
2		2975	3069	3162	3252	3341	3428	3512	3594	3674	3750			1
3		0689	0741	0795	0852	0911	0973	1038	1106	1176	1250			0
		59	58	57	56	55	54	53	52	51	50		π	x

		$n = 4$											
x	π	01	02	03	04	05	06	07	08	09	10		
0		9606	9224	8853	8493	8145	7807	7481	7164	6857	6561		4
1		0388	0753	1095	1416	1715	1993	2252	2492	2713	2916		3
2		0006	0023	0051	0088	0135	0191	0254	0325	0402	0486		2
3		0000	0000	0001	0002	0005	0008	0013	0019	0027	0036		1
4		0000	0000	0000	0000	0000	0000	0000	0000	0001	0001		0
		99	98	97	96	95	94	93	92	91	90	π	x

x	π	11	12	13	14	15	16	17	18	19	20		
0		6274	5997	5729	5470	5220	4979	4746	4521	4305	4096		4
1		3102	3271	3424	3562	3685	3793	3888	3970	4039	4096		3
2		0575	0669	0767	0870	0975	1084	1195	1307	1421	1536		2
3		0047	0061	0076	0094	0115	0138	0163	0191	0222	0256		1
4		0001	0002	0003	0004	0005	0007	0008	0010	0013	0016		0
		89	88	87	86	85	84	83	82	81	80	π	x

x	π	21	22	23	24	25	26	27	28	29	30		
0		3895	3702	3515	3336	3164	2999	2840	2687	2541	2401		4
1		4142	4176	4200	4214	4219	4214	4201	4180	4152	4116		3
2		1651	1767	1882	1996	2109	2221	2331	2439	2544	2646		2
3		0293	0332	0375	0420	0469	0520	0575	0632	0693	0756		1
4		0019	0023	0028	0033	0039	0046	0053	0061	0071	0081		0
		79	78	77	76	75	74	73	72	71	70	π	x

x	π	31	32	33	34	35	36	37	38	39	40		
0		2267	2138	2015	1897	1785	1678	1575	1478	1385	1296		4
1		4074	4025	3970	3910	3845	3775	3701	3623	3541	3456		3
2		2745	2841	2933	3021	3105	3185	3260	3330	3396	3456		2
3		0822	0891	0963	1038	1115	1194	1276	1361	1447	1536		1
4		0092	0105	0119	0134	0150	0168	0187	0209	0231	0256		0
		69	68	67	66	65	64	63	62	61	60	π	x

x	π	41	42	43	44	45	46	47	48	49	50		
0		1212	1132	1056	0983	0915	0850	0789	0731	0677	0625		4
1		3368	3278	3185	3091	2995	2897	2799	2700	2600	2500		3
2		3511	3560	3604	3643	3675	3702	3723	3738	3747	3750		2
3		1627	1719	1813	1908	2005	2102	2201	2300	2400	2500		1
4		0283	0311	0342	0375	0410	0448	0488	0531	0576	0625		0
		59	58	57	56	55	54	53	52	51	50	π	x

TABLE I Binomial distribution ($n = 5$, $n = 6$)

$n = 5$

x	π	01	02	03	04	05	06	07	08	09	10		
0		9510	9039	8587	8154	7738	7339	6957	6591	6240	5905		5
1		0480	0922	1328	1699	2036	2342	2618	2866	3086	3280		4
2		0010	0038	0082	0142	0214	0299	0394	0498	0610	0729		3
3		0000	0001	0003	0006	0011	0019	0030	0043	0060	0081		2
4		0000	0000	0000	0000	0000	0001	0001	0002	0003	0004		1
		99	98	97	96	95	94	93	92	91	90	π	x

x	π	11	12	13	14	15	16	17	18	19	20		
0		5584	5277	4984	4704	4437	4182	3939	3707	3487	3277		5
1		3451	3598	3724	3829	3915	3983	4034	4069	4089	4096		4
2		0853	0981	1113	1247	1382	1517	1652	1786	1919	2048		3
3		0105	0134	0166	0203	0244	0289	0338	0392	0450	0512		2
4		0007	0009	0012	0017	0022	0028	0035	0043	0053	0064		1
5		0000	0000	0000	0001	0001	0001	0001	0002	0002	0003		0
		89	88	87	86	85	84	83	82	81	80	π	x

x	π	21	22	23	24	25	26	27	28	29	30		
0		3077	2887	2707	2536	2373	2219	2073	1935	1804	1681		5
1		4090	4072	4043	4003	3955	3898	3834	3762	3685	3601		4
2		2174	2297	2415	2529	2637	2739	2836	2926	3010	3087		3
3		0578	0648	0721	0798	0879	0962	1049	1138	1229	1323		2
4		0077	0091	0108	0126	0146	0169	0194	0221	0251	0283		1
5		0004	0005	0006	0008	0010	0012	0014	0017	0021	0024		0
		79	78	77	76	75	74	73	72	71	70	π	x

x	π	31	32	33	34	35	36	37	38	39	40		
0		1564	1454	1350	1252	1160	1074	0992	0916	0845	0778		5
1		3513	3421	3325	3226	3124	3020	2914	2808	2700	2592		4
2		3157	3220	3275	3323	3364	3397	3423	3441	3452	3456		3
3		1418	1515	1613	1712	1811	1911	2010	2109	2207	2304		2
4		0319	0357	0397	0441	0488	0537	0590	0646	0706	0768		1
5		0029	0034	0039	0045	0053	0060	0069	0079	0090	0102		0
		69	68	67	66	65	64	63	62	61	60	π	x

x	π	41	42	43	44	45	46	47	48	49	50		
0		0715	0656	0602	0551	0503	0459	0418	0380	0345	0313		5
1		2484	2376	2270	2164	2059	1956	1854	1755	1657	1562		4
2		3452	3442	3424	3400	3369	3332	3289	3240	3185	3125		3
3		2399	2492	2583	2671	2757	2838	2916	2990	3060	3125		2
4		0834	0902	0974	1049	1128	1209	1293	1380	1470	1562		1
5		0116	0131	0147	0165	0185	0206	0229	0255	0282	0312		0
		59	58	57	56	55	54	53	52	51	50	π	x

						$n = 6$						
x	π	01	02	03	04	05	06	07	08	09	10	
0		9415	8858	8330	7828	7351	6899	6470	6064	5679	5314	6
1		0571	1085	1546	1957	2321	2642	2922	3164	3370	3543	5
2		0014	0055	0120	0204	0305	0422	0550	0688	0833	0984	4
3		0000	0002	0005	0011	0021	0036	0055	0080	0110	0146	3
4		0000	0000	0000	0000	0001	0002	0003	0005	0008	0012	2
5		0000	0000	0000	0000	0000	0000	0000	0000	0000	0001	1
		99	98	97	96	95	94	93	92	91	90	π x
x	π	11	12	13	14	15	16	17	18	19	20	
0		4970	4644	4336	4046	3771	3513	3269	3040	2824	2621	6
1		3685	3800	3888	3952	3993	4015	4018	4004	3975	3932	5
2		1139	1295	1452	1608	1762	1912	2057	2197	2331	2458	4
3		0188	0236	0289	0349	0415	0486	0562	0643	0729	0819	3
4		0017	0024	0032	0043	0055	0069	0086	0106	0128	0154	2
5		0001	0001	0002	0003	0004	0005	0007	0009	0012	0015	1
6		0000	0000	0000	0000	0000	0000	0000	0000	0000	0001	0
		89	88	87	86	85	84	83	82	81	80	π x
x	π	21	22	23	24	25	26	27	28	29	30	
0		2431	2252	2084	1927	1780	1642	1513	1393	1281	1176	6
1		3877	3811	3735	3651	3560	3462	3358	3251	3139	3025	5
2		2577	2687	2789	2882	2966	3041	3105	3160	3206	3241	4
3		0913	1011	1111	1214	1318	1424	1531	1639	1746	1852	3
4		0182	0214	0249	0287	0330	0375	0425	0478	0535	0595	2
5		0019	0024	0030	0036	0044	0053	0063	0074	0087	0102	1
6		0001	0001	0001	0002	0002	0003	0004	0005	0006	0007	0
		79	78	77	76	75	74	73	72	71	70	π x
x	π	31	32	33	34	35	36	37	38	39	40	
0		1079	0989	0905	0827	0754	0687	0625	0568	0515	0467	6
1		2909	2792	2673	2555	2437	2319	2203	2089	1976	1866	5
2		3267	3284	3292	3290	3280	3261	3235	3201	3159	3110	4
3		1957	2061	2162	2260	2355	2446	2533	2616	2693	2765	3
4		0660	0727	0799	0873	0951	1032	1116	1202	1291	1382	2
5		0119	0137	0157	0180	0205	0232	0262	0295	0330	0369	1
6		0009	0011	0013	0015	0018	0022	0026	0030	0035	0041	0
		69	68	67	66	65	64	63	62	61	60	π x
x	π	41	42	43	44	45	46	47	48	49	50	
0		0422	0381	0343	0308	0277	0248	0222	0198	0176	0156	6
1		1759	1654	1552	1454	1359	1267	1179	1095	1014	0937	5
2		3055	2994	2928	2856	2780	2699	2615	2527	2436	2344	4
3		2831	2891	2945	2992	3032	3065	3091	3110	3121	3125	3
4		1475	1570	1666	1763	1861	1958	2056	2153	2249	2344	2
5		0410	0455	0503	0554	0609	0667	0729	0795	0864	0937	1
6		0048	0055	0063	0073	0083	0095	0108	0122	0138	0156	0
		59	58	57	56	55	54	53	52	51	50	π x

TABLE I Binomial distribution ($n = 7$, $n = 8$)

$n = 7$

x	π	01	02	03	04	05	06	07	08	09	10		
0		9321	8681	8080	7514	6983	6485	6017	5578	5168	4783		7
1		0659	1240	1749	2192	2573	2897	3170	3396	3578	3720		6
2		0020	0076	0162	0274	0406	0555	0716	0886	1061	1240		5
3		0000	0003	0008	0019	0036	0059	0090	0128	0175	0230		4
4		0000	0000	0000	0001	0002	0004	0007	0011	0017	0026		3
5		0000	0000	0000	0000	0000	0000	0000	0001	0001	0002		2
		99	98	97	96	95	94	93	92	91	90	π	x

x	π	11	12	13	14	15	16	17	18	19	20		
0		4423	4087	3773	3479	3206	2951	2714	2493	2288	2097		7
1		3827	3901	3946	3965	3960	3935	3891	3830	3756	3670		6
2		1419	1596	1769	1936	2097	2248	2391	2523	2643	2753		5
3		0292	0363	0441	0525	0617	0714	0816	0923	1033	1147		4
4		0036	0049	0066	0086	0109	0136	0167	0203	0242	0287		3
5		0003	0004	0006	0008	0012	0016	0021	0027	0034	0043		2
6		0000	0000	0000	0000	0001	0001	0001	0002	0003	0004		1
		89	88	87	86	85	84	83	82	81	80	π	x

x	π	21	22	23	24	25	26	27	28	29	30		
0		1920	1757	1605	1465	1335	1215	1105	1003	0910	0824		7
1		3573	3468	3356	3237	3115	2989	2860	2731	2600	2471		6
2		2850	2935	3007	3067	3115	3150	3174	3186	3186	3177		5
3		1263	1379	1497	1614	1730	1845	1956	2065	2169	2269		4
4		0336	0389	0447	0510	0577	0648	0724	0803	0886	0972		3
5		0054	0066	0080	0097	0115	0137	0161	0187	0217	0250		2
6		0005	0006	0008	0010	0013	0016	0020	0024	0030	0036		1
7		0000	0000	0000	0000	0001	0001	0001	0001	0002	0002		0
		79	78	77	76	75	74	73	72	71	70	π	x

x	π	31	32	33	34	35	36	37	38	39	40		
0		0745	0672	0606	0546	0490	0440	0394	0352	0314	0280		7
1		2342	2215	2090	1967	1848	1732	1619	1511	1407	1306		6
2		3156	3127	3088	3040	2985	2922	2853	2778	2698	2613		5
3		2363	2452	2535	2610	2679	2740	2793	2838	2875	2903		4
4		1062	1154	1248	1345	1442	1541	1640	1739	1838	1935		3
5		0286	0326	0369	0416	0466	0520	0578	0640	0705	0774		2
6		0043	0051	0061	0071	0084	0098	0113	0131	0150	0172		1
7		0003	0003	0004	0005	0006	0008	0009	0011	0014	0016		0
		69	68	67	66	65	64	63	62	61	60	π	x

x	π	41	42	43	44	45	46	47	48	49	50		
0		0249	0221	0195	0173	0152	0134	0117	0103	0090	0078		7
1		1211	1119	1032	0950	0872	0798	0729	0664	0604	0547		6
2		2524	2431	2336	2239	2140	2040	1940	1840	1740	1641		5
3		2923	2934	2937	2932	2918	2897	2867	2830	2786	2734		4
4		2031	2125	2216	2304	2388	2468	2543	2612	2676	2734		3
5		0847	0923	1003	1086	1172	1261	1353	1447	1543	1641		2
6		0196	0223	0252	0284	0320	0358	0400	0445	0494	0547		1
7		0019	0023	0027	0032	0037	0044	0051	0059	0068	0078		0
		59	58	57	56	55	54	53	52	51	50	π	x

$n = 8$

x	π	01	02	03	04	05	06	07	08	09	10		
0		9227	8508	7837	7214	6634	6096	5596	5132	4703	4305		8
1		0746	1389	1939	2405	2793	3113	3370	3570	3721	3826		7
2		0026	0099	0210	0351	0515	0695	0888	1087	1288	1488		6
3		0001	0004	0013	0029	0054	0089	0134	0189	0255	0331		5
4		0000	0000	0001	0002	0004	0007	0013	0021	0031	0046		4
5		0000	0000	0000	0000	0000	0000	0001	0001	0002	0004		3
		99	98	97	96	95	94	93	92	91	90	π	x

x	π	11	12	13	14	15	16	17	18	19	20		
0		3937	3596	3282	2992	2725	2479	2252	2044	1853	1678		8
1		3892	3923	3923	3897	3847	3777	3691	3590	3477	3355		7
2		1684	1872	2052	2220	2376	2518	2646	2758	2855	2936		6
3		0416	0511	0613	0723	0839	0959	1084	1211	1339	1468		5
4		0064	0087	0115	0147	0185	0228	0277	0332	0393	0459		4
5		0006	0009	0014	0019	0026	0035	0045	0058	0074	0092		3
6		0000	0001	0001	0002	0002	0003	0005	0006	0009	0011		2
7		0000	0000	0000	0000	0000	0000	0000	0000	0001	0001		1
		89	88	87	86	85	84	83	82	81	80	π	x

x	π	21	22	23	24	25	26	27	28	29	30		
0		1517	1370	1236	1113	1001	0899	0806	0722	0646	0576		8
1		3226	3092	2953	2812	2670	2527	2386	2247	2110	1977		7
2		3002	3052	3087	3108	3115	3108	3089	3058	3017	2965		6
3		1596	1722	1844	1963	2076	2184	2285	2379	2464	2541		5
4		0530	0607	0689	0775	0865	0959	1056	1156	1258	1361		4
5		0113	0137	0165	0196	0231	0270	0313	0360	0411	0467		3
6		0015	0019	0025	0031	0038	0047	0058	0070	0084	0100		2
7		0001	0002	0002	0003	0004	0005	0006	0008	0010	0012		1
8		0000	0000	0000	0000	0000	0000	0000	0000	0001	0001		0
		79	78	77	76	75	74	73	72	71	70	π	x

x	π	31	32	33	34	35	36	37	38	39	40		
0		0514	0457	0406	0360	0319	0281	0248	0218	0192	0168		8
1		1847	1721	1600	1484	1373	1267	1166	1071	0981	0896		7
2		2904	2835	2758	2675	2587	2494	2397	2297	2194	2090		6
3		2609	2668	2717	2756	2786	2805	2815	2815	2806	2787		5
4		1465	1569	1673	1775	1875	1973	2067	2157	2242	2322		4
5		0527	0591	0659	0732	0808	0888	0971	1058	1147	1239		3
6		0118	0139	0162	0188	0217	0250	0285	0324	0367	0413		2
7		0015	0019	0023	0028	0033	0040	0048	0057	0067	0079		1
8		0001	0001	0001	0002	0002	0003	0004	0004	0005	0007		0
		69	68	67	66	65	64	63	62	61	60	π	x

x	π	41	42	43	44	45	46	47	48	49	50		
0		0147	0128	0111	0097	0084	0072	0062	0053	0046	0039		8
1		0816	0742	0672	0608	0548	0493	0442	0395	0352	0312		7
2		1985	1880	1776	1672	1569	1469	1371	1275	1183	1094		6
3		2759	2723	2679	2627	2568	2503	2431	2355	2273	2187		5
4		2397	2465	2526	2580	2627	2665	2695	2717	2730	2734		4
5		1332	1428	1525	1622	1719	1816	1912	2006	2098	2187		3
6		0463	0517	0575	0637	0703	0774	0848	0926	1008	1094		2
7		0092	0107	0124	0143	0164	0188	0215	0244	0277	0312		1
8		0008	0010	0012	0014	0017	0020	0024	0028	0033	0039		0
		59	58	57	56	55	54	53	52	51	50	π	x

TABLE I   Binomial distribution ($n = 9$, $n = 10$)

$n = 9$

x	π	01	02	03	04	05	06	07	08	09	10		
0		9135	8337	7602	6925	6302	5730	5204	4722	4279	3874		9
1		0830	1531	2116	2597	2985	3292	3525	3695	3809	3874		8
2		0034	0125	0262	0433	0629	0840	1061	1285	1507	1722		7
3		0001	0006	0019	0042	0077	0125	0186	0261	0348	0446		6
4		0000	0000	0001	0003	0006	0012	0021	0034	0052	0074		5
5		0000	0000	0000	0000	0000	0001	0002	0003	0005	0008		4
6		0000	0000	0000	0000	0000	0000	0000	0000	0000	0001		3
		99	98	97	96	95	94	93	92	91	90	π	x

x	π	11	12	13	14	15	16	17	18	19	20		
0		3504	3165	2855	2573	2316	2082	1869	1676	1501	1342		9
1		3897	3884	3840	3770	3679	3569	3446	3312	2169	3020		8
2		1927	2119	2295	2455	2597	2720	2823	2908	2973	3020		7
3		0556	0674	0800	0933	1069	1209	1349	1489	1627	1762		6
4		0103	0138	0179	0228	0283	0345	0415	0490	0573	0661		5
5		0013	0019	0027	0037	0050	0066	0085	0108	0134	0165		4
6		0001	0002	0003	0004	0006	0008	0012	0016	0021	0028		3
7		0000	0000	0000	0000	0000	0001	0001	0001	0002	0003		2
		89	88	87	86	85	84	83	82	81	80	π	x

x	π	21	22	23	24	25	26	27	28	29	30		
0		1199	1069	0952	0846	0751	0665	0589	0520	0458	0404		9
1		2867	2713	2558	2404	2253	2104	1960	1820	1685	1556		8
2		3049	3061	3056	3037	3003	2957	2899	2831	2754	2668		7
3		1891	2014	2130	2238	2336	2424	2502	2569	2624	2668		6
4		0754	0852	0954	1060	1168	1278	1388	1499	1608	1715		5
5		0200	0240	0285	0335	0389	0449	0513	0583	0657	0735		4
6		0036	0045	0057	0070	0087	0105	0127	0151	0179	0210		3
7		0004	0005	0007	0010	0012	0016	0020	0025	0031	0039		2
8		0000	0000	0001	0001	0001	0001	0002	0002	0003	0004		1
		79	78	77	76	75	74	73	72	71	70	π	x

x	π	31	32	33	34	35	36	37	38	39	40		
0		0355	0311	0272	0238	0207	0180	0156	0135	0117	0101		9
1		1433	1317	1206	1102	1004	0912	0826	0747	0673	0605		8
2		2576	2478	2376	2270	2162	2052	1941	1831	1721	1612		7
3		2701	2721	2731	2729	2716	2693	2660	2618	2567	2508		6
4		1820	1921	2017	2109	2194	2272	2344	2407	2462	2508		5
5		0818	0904	0994	1086	1181	1278	1376	1475	1574	1672		4
6		0245	0284	0326	0373	0424	0479	0539	0603	0671	0743		3
7		0047	0057	0069	0082	0098	0116	0136	0158	0184	0212		2
8		0005	0007	0008	0011	0013	0016	0020	0024	0029	0035		1
9		0000	0000	0000	0001	0001	0001	0001	0002	0002	0003		0
		69	68	67	66	65	64	63	62	61	60	π	x

x	π	41	42	43	44	45	46	47	48	49	50		
0		0087	0074	0064	0054	0046	0039	0033	0028	0023	0020		9
1		0542	0484	0431	0383	0339	0299	0263	0231	0202	0176		8
2		1506	1402	1301	1204	1110	1020	0934	0853	0776	0703		7
3		2442	2369	2291	2207	2119	2027	1933	1837	1739	1641		6
4		2545	2573	2592	2601	2600	2590	2571	2543	2506	2461		5
5		1769	1863	1955	2044	2128	2207	2280	2347	2408	2461		4
6		0819	0900	0983	1070	1160	1253	1348	1445	1542	1641		3
7		0244	0279	0318	0360	0407	0458	0512	0571	0635	0703		2
8		0042	0051	0060	0071	0083	0097	0014	0132	0153	0176		1
9		0003	0004	0005	0006	0008	0009	0011	0014	0016	0020		0
		59	58	57	56	55	54	53	52	51	50	π	x

					$n = 10$							

x	π	01	02	03	04	05	06	07	08	09	10		
0		9044	8171	7374	6648	5987	5386	4840	4344	3894	3487		10
1		0914	1667	2281	2770	3151	3438	3643	3777	3851	3874		9
2		0042	0153	0317	0519	0746	0988	1234	1478	1714	1937		8
3		0001	0008	0026	0058	0105	0168	0248	0343	0452	0574		7
4		0000	0000	0001	0004	0010	0019	0033	0052	0078	0112		6
5		0000	0000	0000	0000	0001	0001	0003	0005	0009	0015		5
6		0000	0000	0000	0000	0000	0000	0000	0000	0001	0001		4
		99	98	97	96	95	94	93	92	91	90	π	x

x	π	11	12	13	14	15	16	17	18	19	20		
0		3118	2785	2484	2213	1969	1749	1552	1374	1216	1074		10
1		3854	3798	3712	3603	3474	3331	3178	3017	2852	2684		9
2		2143	2330	2496	2639	2759	2856	2929	2980	3010	3020		8
3		0706	0847	0995	1146	1298	1450	1600	1745	1883	2013		7
4		0153	0202	0260	0326	0401	0483	0573	0670	0773	0881		6
5		0023	0033	0047	0064	0085	0111	0141	0177	0218	0264		5
6		0002	0004	0006	0009	0012	0018	0024	0032	0043	0055		4
7		0000	0000	0000	0001	0001	0002	0003	0004	0006	0008		3
8		0000	0000	0000	0000	0000	0000	0000	0000	0001	0001		2
		89	88	87	86	85	84	83	82	81	80	π	x

x	π	21	22	23	24	25	26	27	28	29	30		
0		0947	0834	0733	0643	0563	0492	0430	0374	0326	0282		10
1		2517	2351	2188	2030	1877	1730	1590	1456	1330	1211		9
2		3011	2984	2942	2885	2816	2735	2646	2548	2444	2335		8
3		2134	2244	2343	2429	2503	2563	2609	2642	2662	2668		7
4		0993	1108	1225	1343	1460	1576	1689	1798	1903	2001		6
5		0317	0375	0439	0509	0584	0664	0750	0839	0933	1029		5
6		0070	0088	0109	0134	0162	0195	0231	0272	0317	0368		4
7		0011	0014	0019	0024	0031	0039	0049	0060	0074	0090		3
8		0001	0002	0002	0003	0004	0005	0007	0009	0011	0014		2
9		0000	0000	0000	0000	0000	0000	0001	0001	0001	0001		1
		79	78	77	76	75	74	73	72	71	70	π	x

x	π	31	32	33	34	35	36	37	38	39	40		
0		0245	0211	0182	0157	0135	0115	0098	0084	0071	0060		10
1		1099	0995	0898	0808	0725	0649	0578	0514	0456	0430		9
2		2222	2107	1990	1873	1757	1642	1529	1419	1312	1209		8
3		2662	2644	2614	2573	2522	2462	2394	2319	2237	2150		7
4		2093	2177	2253	2320	2377	2424	2461	2487	2503	2508		6
5		1128	1229	1332	1434	1536	1636	1734	1829	1920	2007		5
6		0422	0482	0547	0616	0689	0767	0849	0934	1023	1115		4
7		0108	0130	0154	0181	0212	0247	0285	0327	0374	0425		3
8		0018	0023	0028	0035	0043	0052	0063	0075	0090	0106		2
9		0002	0002	0003	0004	0005	0006	0008	0010	0013	0016		1
10		0000	0000	0000	0000	0000	0000	0000	0001	0001	0001		0
		69	68	67	66	65	64	63	62	61	60	π	x

x	π	41	42	43	44	45	46	47	48	49	50		
0		0051	0043	0036	0030	0025	0021	0017	0014	0012	0010		10
1		0355	0312	0273	0238	0207	0180	0155	0133	0114	0098		9
2		1111	1017	0927	0843	0763	0688	0619	0554	0494	0439		8
3		2058	1963	1865	1765	1665	1654	1464	1364	1267	1172		7
4		2503	2488	2462	2427	2384	2331	2271	2204	2130	2051		6
5		2087	2162	2229	2289	2340	2383	2417	2441	2456	2461		5
6		1209	1304	1401	1499	1596	1692	1786	1878	1966	2051		4
7		0480	0540	0604	0673	0746	0824	0905	0991	1080	1172		3
8		0125	0147	0171	0198	0229	0263	0301	0343	0389	0439		2
9		0019	0024	0029	0035	0042	0050	0059	0070	0083	0098		1
10		0001	0002	0002	0003	0003	0004	0005	0006	0008	0010		0
		59	58	57	56	55	54	53	52	51	50	π	x

TABLE I Binomial distribution ($n = 20$)

$n = 20$

x	π	01	02	03	04	05	06	07	08	09	10	
0		8179	6676	5438	4420	3585	2901	2342	1887	1516	1216	20
1		1652	2725	3364	3683	3774	3703	3526	3282	3000	2702	19
2		0159	0528	0988	1458	1887	2246	2521	2711	2828	2852	18
3		0010	0065	0183	0364	0596	0860	1139	1414	1672	1901	17
4		0000	0006	0024	0065	0133	0233	0364	0523	0703	0898	16
5		0000	0000	0002	0009	0022	0048	0088	0145	0222	0319	15
6		0000	0000	0000	0001	0003	0008	0017	0032	0055	0089	14
7		0000	0000	0000	0000	0000	0001	0002	0005	0011	0020	13
8		0000	0000	0000	0000	0000	0000	0000	0001	0002	0004	12
9		0000	0000	0000	0000	0000	0000	0000	0000	0000	0001	11
		99	98	97	96	95	94	93	92	91	90	π	x

x	π	11	12	13	14	15	16	17	18	19	20	
0		0972	0776	0617	0490	0388	0306	0241	0189	0148	0115	20
1		2403	2115	1844	1595	1368	1165	0986	0829	0693	0576	19
2		2822	2740	2618	2466	2293	2109	1919	1730	1545	1369	18
3		2093	2242	2347	2409	2428	2410	2358	2278	2175	2054	17
4		1099	1299	1491	1666	1821	1951	2053	2125	2168	2182	16
5		0435	0567	0713	0868	1028	1189	1345	1493	1627	1746	15
6		0134	0193	0266	0353	0454	0566	0689	0819	0954	1091	14
7		0033	0053	0080	0115	0160	0216	0282	0360	0448	0545	13
8		0007	0012	0019	0030	0046	0067	0094	0128	0171	0222	12
9		0001	0002	0004	0007	0011	0017	0026	0038	0053	0074	11
10		0000	0000	0001	0001	0002	0004	0006	0009	0014	0020	10
11		0000	0000	0000	0000	0000	0001	0001	0002	0003	0005	9
12		0000	0000	0000	0000	0000	0000	0000	0000	0001	0001	8
		89	88	87	86	85	84	83	82	81	80	π	x

x	π	21	22	23	24	25	26	27	28	29	30	
0		0090	0069	0054	0041	0032	0024	0016	0014	0011	0008	20
1		0477	0392	0321	0261	0211	0170	0137	0109	0087	0068	19
2		1204	1050	0910	0783	0669	0569	0480	0403	0336	0278	18
3		1920	1777	1631	1484	1339	1199	1065	0940	0823	0716	17
4		2169	2131	2070	1991	1897	1790	1675	1553	1429	1304	16
5		1845	1923	1979	2012	2023	2013	1982	1933	1868	1789	15
6		1226	1356	1478	1589	1686	1768	1833	1879	1907	1916	14
7		0652	0765	0883	1003	1124	1242	1356	1462	1558	1643	13
8		0282	0351	0429	0515	0609	0709	0815	0924	1034	1144	12
9		0100	0132	0171	0217	0271	0332	0402	0479	0563	0654	11
10		0029	0041	0056	0075	0099	0128	0163	0205	0253	0308	10
11		0007	0010	0015	0022	0030	0041	0055	0072	0094	0120	9
12		0001	0002	0003	0005	0008	0011	0015	0021	0029	0039	8
13		0000	0000	0001	0001	0002	0002	0003	0005	0007	0010	7
14		0000	0000	0000	0000	0000	0000	0001	0001	0001	0002	6
		79	78	77	76	75	74	73	72	71	70	π	x

						$n = 20$						

x	π	31	32	33	34	35	36	37	38	39	40	
0		0006	0004	0003	0002	0002	0001	0001	0001	0001	0000	20
1		0054	0042	0033	0025	0020	0015	0011	0009	0007	0005	19
2		0229	0188	0153	0124	0100	0080	0064	0050	0040	0031	18
3		0619	0531	0453	0383	0323	0270	0224	0185	0152	0123	17
4		1181	1062	0947	0839	0738	0645	0559	0482	0412	0350	16
5		1698	1599	1493	1384	1272	1161	1051	0945	0843	0746	15
6		1907	1881	1839	1782	1712	1632	1543	1447	1347	1244	14
7		1714	1770	1811	1836	1844	1836	1812	1774	1722	1659	13
8		1251	1354	1450	1537	1614	1678	1730	1767	1790	1797	12
9		0750	0849	0952	1056	1158	1259	1354	1444	1526	1597	11
10		0370	0440	0516	0598	0686	0779	0875	0974	1073	1171	10
11		0151	1188	0231	0280	0336	0398	0467	0542	0624	0710	9
12		0051	0066	0085	0108	0136	0168	0206	0249	0299	0355	8
13		0014	0019	0026	0034	0045	0058	0074	0094	0118	0146	7
14		0003	0005	0006	0009	0012	0016	0022	0029	0038	0049	6
15		0001	0001	0001	0002	0003	0004	0005	0007	0010	0013	5
16		0000	0000	0000	0000	0000	0001	0001	0001	0002	0003	4
		69	68	67	66	65	64	63	62	61	60	π x

x	π	41	42	43	44	45	46	47	48	49	50	
1		0004	0003	0002	0001	0001	0001	0001	0000	0000	0000	19
2		0024	0018	0014	0011	0008	0006	0005	0003	0002	0002	18
3		0100	0080	0064	0051	0040	0031	0024	0019	0014	0011	17
4		0295	0247	0206	0170	0139	0113	0092	0074	0059	0046	16
5		0656	0573	0496	0427	0365	0309	0260	0217	0180	0148	15
6		1140	1037	0936	0839	0746	0658	0577	0501	0432	0370	14
7		1585	1502	1413	1318	1221	1122	1023	0925	0830	0739	13
8		1790	1768	1732	1683	1623	1553	1474	1388	1296	1201	12
9		1658	1707	1742	1763	1771	1763	1742	1708	1661	1602	11
10		1268	1359	1446	1524	1593	1652	1700	1734	1755	1762	10
11		0801	0895	0991	1089	1185	1280	1370	1455	1533	1602	9
12		0417	0486	0561	0642	0727	0818	0911	1007	1105	1201	8
13		0178	0217	0260	0310	0366	0429	0497	0572	0653	0739	7
14		0062	0078	0098	0122	0150	0183	0221	0264	0314	0370	6
15		0017	0023	0030	0038	0049	0062	0078	0098	0121	0148	5
16		0004	0005	0007	0009	0013	0017	0022	0028	0036	0046	4
17		0001	0001	0001	0002	0002	0003	0005	0006	0008	0011	3
18		0000	0000	0000	0000	0000	0000	0001	0001	0001	0002	2
		59	58	57	56	55	54	53	52	51	50	π x

TABLE I Binomial distribution ($n = 50$)

x	π	01	02	03	04	05	06	07	08	09	10		
0		6050	3642	2181	1299	0769	0453	0266	0155	0090	0052		50
1		3056	3716	3372	2706	2025	1447	0999	0672	0443	0286		49
2		0756	1858	2555	2762	2611	2262	1843	1433	1073	0779		48
3		0122	0607	1264	1842	2199	2311	2219	1993	1698	1386		47
4		0015	0145	0459	0902	1360	1733	1963	2037	1973	1809		46
5		0001	0027	0131	0346	0658	1018	1359	1629	1795	1849		45
6		0000	0004	0030	0108	0260	0487	0767	1063	1332	1541		44
7		0000	0001	0006	0028	0086	0195	0363	0581	0828	1076		43
8		0000	0000	0001	0006	0024	0067	0147	0271	0440	0643		42
9		0000	0000	0000	0001	0006	0020	0052	0110	0203	0333		41
10		0000	0000	0000	0000	0001	0005	0016	0039	0082	0152		40
11		0000	0000	0000	0000	0000	0001	0004	0012	0030	0061		39
12		0000	0000	0000	0000	0000	0000	0001	0004	0010	0022		38
13		0000	0000	0000	0000	0000	0000	0000	0001	0003	0007		37
14		0000	0000	0000	0000	0000	0000	0000	0000	0001	0002		36
15		0000	0000	0000	0000	0000	0000	0000	0000	0000	0001		35
		99	98	97	96	95	94	93	92	91	90	π	x

x	π	11	12	13	14	15	16	17	18	19	20		
0		0029	0017	0009	0005	0003	0002	0001	0000	0000	0000		50
1		0182	0114	0071	0043	0026	0016	0009	0005	0003	0002		49
2		0552	0382	0259	0172	0113	0073	0046	0029	0018	0011		48
3		1091	0833	0619	0449	0319	0222	0151	0102	0067	0044		47
4		1584	1334	1086	0858	0661	0496	0364	0262	0185	0128		46
5		1801	1674	1493	1286	1072	0869	0687	0530	0400	0295		45
6		1670	1712	1674	1570	1419	1242	1055	0872	0703	0554		44
7		1297	1467	1572	1606	1575	1487	1358	1203	1037	0870		43
8		0862	1075	1262	1406	1493	1523	1495	1420	1307	1169		42
9		0497	0684	0880	1068	1230	1353	1429	1454	1431	1364		41
10		0252	0383	0539	0713	0890	1057	1200	1309	1376	1398		40
11		0113	0190	0293	0422	0571	0732	0894	1045	1174	1271		39
12		0045	0084	0142	0223	0328	0453	0595	0745	0895	1033		38
13		0016	0034	0062	0106	0169	0252	0356	0478	0613	0755		37
14		0005	0012	0025	0046	0079	0127	0193	0277	0380	0499		36
15		0002	0004	0009	0018	0033	0058	0095	0146	0214	0299		35
16		0000	0001	0003	0006	0013	0024	0042	0070	0110	0164		34
17		0000	0000	0001	0002	0005	0009	0017	0031	0052	0082		33
18		0000	0000	0000	0001	0001	0003	0007	0012	0022	0037		32
19		0000	0000	0000	0000	0000	0001	0002	0005	0009	0016		31
20		0000	0000	0000	0000	0000	0000	0001	0002	0003	0006		30
21		0000	0000	0000	0000	0000	0000	0000	0000	0001	0002		29
22		0000	0000	0000	0000	0000	0000	0000	0000	0000	0001		28
		89	88	87	86	85	84	83	82	81	80	π	x

						$n = 50$							
x	π	21	22	23	24	25	26	27	28	29	30		
1		0001	0001	0000	0000	0000	0000	0000	0000	0000	0000		49
2		0007	0004	0002	0001	0001	0000	0000	0000	0000	0000		48
3		0028	0018	0011	0007	0004	0002	0001	0001	0000	0000		47
4		0088	0059	0039	0025	0016	0010	0006	0004	0002	0001		46
5		0214	0152	0106	0073	0049	0033	0021	0014	0009	0006		45
6		0427	0322	0238	0173	0123	0087	0060	0040	0027	0018		44
7		0713	0571	0447	0344	0259	0191	0139	0099	0069	0048		43
8		1019	0865	0718	0583	0463	0361	0276	0207	0152	0110		42
9		1263	1139	1001	0859	0721	0592	0476	0375	0290	0220		41
10		1377	1317	1226	1113	0985	0852	0721	0598	0485	0386		40
11		1331	1351	1332	1278	1194	1089	0970	0845	0721	0602		39
12		1150	1238	1293	1311	1294	1244	1166	1068	0957	0838		38
13		0894	1021	1129	1210	1261	1277	1261	1215	1142	1050		37
14		0628	0761	0891	1010	1110	1186	1233	1248	1233	1189		36
15		0400	0515	0639	0766	0888	1000	1094	1165	1209	1223		35
16		0233	0318	0417	0529	0648	0769	0885	0991	1080	1147		34
17		0124	0179	0249	0334	0432	0540	0655	0771	0882	0983		33
18		0060	0093	0137	0193	0264	0348	0444	0550	0661	0772		32
19		0027	0044	0069	0103	0148	0206	0277	0360	0454	0558		31
20		0011	0019	0032	0050	0077	0112	0159	0217	0288	0370		30
21		0004	0008	0014	0023	0036	0056	0084	0121	0168	0227		29
22		0001	0003	0005	0009	0016	0026	0041	0062	0090	0128		28
23		0000	0001	0002	0004	0006	0011	0018	0029	0045	0067		27
24		0000	0000	0001	0001	0002	0004	0008	0013	0021	0032		26
25		0000	0000	0000	0000	0001	0002	0003	0005	0009	0014		25
26		0000	0000	0000	0000	0000	0001	0001	0002	0003	0006		24
27		0000	0000	0000	0000	0000	0000	0000	0001	0001	0002		23
28		0000	0000	0000	0000	0000	0000	0000	0000	0000	0001		22
		79	78	77	76	75	74	73	72	71	70	π	x

TABLE I Binomial distribution ($n = 50$, cont.)

		31	32	33	34	35	36	37	38	39	40		
x	π												
4		0001	0000	0000	0000	0000	0000	0000	0000	0000	0000	46	
5		0003	0002	0001	0001	0000	0000	0000	0000	0000	0000	45	
6		0011	0007	0005	0003	0002	0001	0001	0000	0000	0000	44	
7		0032	0022	0014	0009	0006	0004	0002	0001	0001	0000	43	
8		0078	0055	0037	0025	0017	0011	0007	0004	0003	0002	42	
9		0164	0120	0086	0061	0042	0029	0019	0013	0008	0005	41	
10		0301	0231	0174	0128	0093	0066	0046	0032	0022	0014	40	
11		0493	0395	0311	0240	0182	0136	0099	0071	0050	0035	39	
12		0719	0604	0498	0402	0319	0248	0189	0142	0105	0076	38	
13		0944	0831	0717	0606	0502	0408	0325	0255	0195	0147	37	
14		1121	1034	0933	0825	0714	0607	0505	0412	0330	0260	36	
15		1209	1168	1103	1020	0923	0819	0712	0606	0507	0415	35	
16		1188	1202	1189	1149	1088	1008	0914	0813	0709	0606	34	
17		1068	1132	1171	1184	1171	1133	1074	0997	0906	0808	33	
18		0880	0976	1057	1118	1156	1169	1156	1120	1062	0987	32	
19		0666	0774	0877	0970	1048	1107	1144	1156	1144	1109	31	
20		0463	0564	0670	0775	0875	0956	1041	1098	1134	1146	30	
21		0297	0379	0471	0570	0673	0776	0874	0962	1035	1091	29	
22		0176	0235	0306	0387	0478	0575	0676	0777	0873	0959	28	
23		0096	0135	0183	0243	0313	0394	0484	0580	0679	0778	27	
24		0049	0071	0102	0141	0190	0249	0319	0400	0489	0584	26	
25		0023	0035	0052	0075	0106	0146	0195	0255	0325	0405	25	
26		0010	0016	0025	0037	0055	0079	0110	0150	0200	0259	24	
27		0004	0007	0011	0017	0026	0039	0058	0082	0113	0154	23	
28		0001	0003	0004	0007	0012	0018	0028	0041	0060	0084	22	
29		0000	0001	0002	0003	0005	0008	0012	0019	0029	0043	21	
30		0000	0000	0001	0001	0002	0003	0005	0008	0013	0020	20	
31		0000	0000	0000	0000	0001	0001	0002	0003	0005	0009	19	
32		0000	0000	0000	0000	0000	0000	0001	0001	0002	0003	18	
33		0000	0000	0000	0000	0000	0000	0000	0000	0001	0001	17	
		69	68	67	66	65	64	63	62	61	60	π	x

x	π	41	42	43	44	45	46	47	48	49	50		
						$n = 50$							
8		0001	0001	0000	0000	0000	0000	0000	0000	0000	0000		42
9		0003	0002	0001	0001	0000	0000	0000	0000	0000	0000		41
10		0009	0006	0004	0002	0001	0001	0001	0000	0000	0000		40
11		0024	0016	0010	0007	0004	0003	0002	0001	0001	0000		39
12		0054	0037	0026	0017	0011	0007	0005	0003	0002	0001		38
13		0109	0079	0057	0040	0027	0018	0012	0008	0005	0003		37
14		0200	0152	0113	0082	0059	0041	0029	0019	0013	0008		36
15		0334	0264	0204	0155	0116	0085	0061	0043	0030	0020		35
16		0508	0418	0337	0267	0207	0158	0118	0086	0062	0044		34
17		0706	0605	0508	0419	0339	0269	0209	0159	0119	0087		33
18		0899	0803	0703	0604	0508	0420	0340	0270	0210	0160		32
19		1053	0979	0893	0799	0700	0602	0507	0419	0340	0270		31
20		1134	1099	1044	0973	0588	0795	0697	0600	0506	0419		30
21		1126	1137	1126	1092	1030	0967	0884	0791	0695	0598		29
22		1031	1086	1119	1131	1119	1086	1033	0963	0880	0788		28
23		0872	0957	1028	1082	1115	1126	1115	1082	1029	0960		27
24		0682	0780	0872	0956	1026	1079	1112	1124	1112	1080		26
25		0493	0587	0684	0781	0873	0956	1026	1079	1112	1123		25
26		0329	0409	0497	0590	0687	0783	0875	0957	1027	1080		24
27		0203	0263	0333	0412	0500	0593	0690	0786	0877	0960		23
28		0116	0157	0206	0266	0336	0415	0502	0596	0692	0788		22
29		0061	0086	0118	0159	0208	0268	0338	0417	0504	0598		21
30		0030	0044	0062	0087	0119	0160	0210	0270	0339	0419		20
31		0013	0020	0030	0044	0063	0088	0120	0161	0210	0270		19
32		0006	0009	0014	0021	0031	0044	0063	0088	0120	0160		18
33		0002	0003	0006	0009	0014	0021	0031	0044	0063	0087		17
34		0001	0001	0002	0003	0006	0009	0014	0020	0030	0044		16
35		0000	0000	0001	0001	0002	0003	0005	0009	0013	0020		15
36		0000	0000	0000	0000	0001	0001	0002	0003	0005	0008		14
37		0000	0000	0000	0000	0000	0000	0001	0001	0002	0003		13
38		0000	0000	0000	0000	0000	0000	0000	0000	0001	0001		12
		59	58	57	56	55	54	53	52	51	50	π	x

TABLE I Binomial distribution ($n = 100$)

						$n = 100$						
x \ π	01	02	03	04	05	06	07	08	09	10		
0	3660	1326	0476	0169	0059	0021	0007	0002	0001	0000		100
1	3697	2707	1471	0703	0312	0131	0053	0021	0008	0003		99
2	1849	2734	2252	1450	0812	0414	0198	0090	0039	0016		98
3	0610	1823	2275	1973	1396	0864	0486	0254	0125	0059		97
4	0149	0902	1706	1994	1781	1338	0888	0536	0301	0159		96
5	0029	0353	1013	1595	1800	1639	1283	0895	0571	0339		95
6	0005	0114	0496	1052	1500	1657	1529	1233	0895	0596		94
7	0001	0031	0206	0589	1060	1420	1545	1440	1188	0889		93
8	0000	0007	0074	0285	0649	1054	1352	1455	1366	1148		92
9	0000	0002	0023	0121	0349	0687	1040	1293	1381	1304		91
10	0000	0000	0007	0046	0167	0399	0712	1024	1243	1319		90
11	0000	0000	0002	0016	0072	0209	0439	0728	1006	1199		89
12	0000	0000	0000	0005	0028	0099	0245	0470	0738	0988		88
13	0000	0000	0000	0001	0010	0043	0125	0276	0494	0743		87
14	0000	0000	0000	0000	0003	0017	0058	0149	0304	0513		86
15	0000	0000	0000	0000	0001	0006	0025	0074	0172	0327		85
16	0000	0000	0000	0000	0000	0002	0010	0034	0090	0193		84
17	0000	0000	0000	0000	0000	0001	0004	0015	0044	0106		83
18	0000	0000	0000	0000	0000	0000	0001	0006	0020	0054		82
19	0000	0000	0000	0000	0000	0000	0000	0002	0009	0026		81
20	0000	0000	0000	0000	0000	0000	0000	0001	0003	0012		80
21	0000	0000	0000	0000	0000	0000	0000	0000	0001	0005		79
22	0000	0000	0000	0000	0000	0000	0000	0000	0000	0002		78
23	0000	0000	0000	0000	0000	0000	0000	0000	0000	0001		77
	99	98	97	96	95	94	93	92	91	90	π	x

		$n = 100$											
x	π	11	12	13	14	15	16	17	18	19	20		
1		0001	0000	0000	0000	0000	0000	0000	0000	0000	0000		99
2		0007	0003	0001	0000	0000	0000	0000	0000	0000	0000		98
3		0027	0012	0005	0002	0001	0000	0000	0000	0000	0000		97
4		0080	0038	0018	0008	0003	0001	0001	0000	0000	0000		96
5		0189	0100	0050	0024	0011	0005	0002	0001	0000	0000		95
6		0369	0215	0119	0063	0031	0015	0007	0003	0001	0001		94
7		0613	0394	0238	0137	0075	0039	0020	0009	0004	0002		93
8		0881	0625	0414	0259	0153	0086	0047	0024	0012	0006		92
9		1112	0871	0632	0430	0276	0168	0098	0054	0029	0015		91
10		1251	1080	0860	0637	0444	0292	0182	0108	0062	0034		90
11		1265	1205	1051	0849	0640	0454	0305	0194	0118	0069		89
12		1160	1219	1165	1025	0838	0642	0463	0316	0206	0128		88
13		0970	1125	1179	1130	1001	0827	0642	0470	0327	0216		87
14		0745	0954	1094	1143	1098	0979	0817	0641	0476	0335		86
15		0528	0745	0938	1067	1111	1070	0960	0807	0640	0481		85
16		0347	0540	0744	0922	1041	1082	1044	0941	0798	0638		84
17		1212	0364	0549	0742	0908	1019	1057	1021	0924	0789		83
18		0121	0229	0379	0557	0739	0895	0998	1033	1000	0909		82
19		0064	0135	0244	0391	0563	0736	0882	0979	1012	0981		81
20		0032	0074	0148	0258	0402	0567	0732	0870	0962	0993		80
21		0015	0039	0084	0160	0270	0412	0571	0728	0859	0946		79
22		0007	0019	0045	0094	0171	0282	0420	0574	0724	0849		78
23		0003	0009	0023	0052	0103	0182	0292	0427	0576	0720		77
24		0001	0004	0011	0027	0058	0111	0192	0301	0433	0577		76
25		0000	0002	0005	0013	0031	0064	0119	0201	0309	0439		75
26		0000	0001	0002	0006	0016	0035	0071	0127	0209	0317		74
27		0000	0000	0001	0003	0008	0018	0040	0076	0134	0217		73
28		0000	0000	0000	0001	0004	0009	0021	0044	0082	0141		72
29		0000	0000	0000	0000	0002	0004	0011	0024	0048	0088		71
30		0000	0000	0000	0000	0001	0002	0005	0012	0027	0052		70
31		0000	0000	0000	0000	0000	0001	0002	0006	0014	0029		69
32		0000	0000	0000	0000	0000	0000	0001	0003	0007	0016		68
33		0000	0000	0000	0000	0000	0000	0000	0001	0003	0008		67
34		0000	0000	0000	0000	0000	0000	0000	0001	0002	0004		66
35		0000	0000	0000	0000	0000	0000	0000	0000	0001	0002		65
36		0000	0000	0000	0000	0000	0000	0000	0000	0000	0001		64
		89	88	87	86	85	84	83	82	81	80	π	x

TABLE I   Binomial distribution ($n = 100$, cont.)

						$n = 100$							
x	π	21	22	23	24	25	26	27	28	29	30		
7		0001	0000	0000	0000	0000	0000	0000	0000	0000	0000		93
8		0003	0001	0001	0000	0000	0000	0000	0000	0000	0000		92
9		0007	0003	0002	0001	0000	0000	0000	0000	0000	0000		91
10		0018	0009	0004	0002	0001	0000	0000	0000	0000	0000		90
11		0038	0021	0011	0005	0003	0001	0001	0000	0000	0000		89
12		0076	0043	0024	0012	0006	0003	0001	0001	0000	0000		88
13		0136	0082	0048	0027	0014	0007	0004	0002	0001	0000		87
14		0225	0144	0089	0052	0030	0016	0009	0004	0002	0001		86
15		1343	0233	0152	0095	0057	0033	0018	0010	0005	0002		85
16		0484	0350	0241	0159	0100	0061	0035	0020	0011	0006		84
17		0636	0487	0356	0248	0165	0106	0065	0038	0022	0012		83
18		0780	0634	0490	0361	0254	0171	0111	0069	0041	0024		82
19		0895	0772	0631	0492	0365	0259	0177	0115	0072	0044		81
20		0963	0881	0764	0629	0493	0369	0264	0182	0120	0076		80
21		0975	0947	0869	0756	0626	0494	0373	0269	0186	0124		79
22		0931	0959	0932	0858	0749	0623	0495	0376	0273	0190		78
23		0839	0917	0944	0919	0847	0743	0621	0495	0378	0277		77
24		0716	0830	0905	0931	0906	0837	0736	0618	0496	0380		76
25		0578	0712	0822	0893	0918	0894	0828	0731	0615	0496		75
26		0444	0579	0708	0814	0883	0906	0883	0819	0725	0613		74
27		0323	0448	0580	0704	0806	0873	0896	0873	0812	0720		73
28		0224	0329	0451	0580	0701	0799	0864	0886	0864	0804		72
29		0148	0231	0335	0455	0580	0697	0793	0855	0876	0856		71
30		0093	0154	0237	0340	0458	0580	0694	0787	0847	0868		70
31		0056	0098	0160	0242	0344	0460	0580	0691	0781	0840		69
32		0032	0060	0103	0165	0248	0349	0462	0579	0688	0776		68
33		0018	0035	0063	0107	0170	0252	0352	0464	0579	0685		67
34		0009	0019	0037	0067	0112	0175	0257	0356	0466	0579		66
35		0005	0010	0021	0040	0070	0116	0179	0261	0359	0468		65
36		0002	0005	0011	0023	0042	0073	0120	0183	0265	0362		64
37		0001	0003	0006	0012	0024	0045	0077	0123	0187	0268		63
38		0000	0001	0003	0006	0013	0026	0047	0079	0127	0191		62
39		0000	0001	0001	0003	0007	0015	0028	0049	0082	0130		61
40		0000	0000	0001	0002	0004	0008	0016	0029	0051	0085		60
41		0000	0000	0000	0001	0002	0004	0008	0017	0031	0053		59
42		0000	0000	0000	0000	0001	0002	0004	0009	0018	0032		58
43		0000	0000	0000	0000	0000	0001	0002	0005	0010	0019		57
44		0000	0000	0000	0000	0000	0000	0001	0002	0005	0010		56
45		0000	0000	0000	0000	0000	0000	0000	0001	0003	0005		55
46		0000	0000	0000	0000	0000	0000	0000	0001	0001	0003		54
47		0000	0000	0000	0000	0000	0000	0000	0000	0001	0001		53
48		0000	0000	0000	0000	0000	0000	0000	0000	0000	0001		52
		79	78	77	76	75	74	73	72	71	70	π	x

						$n = 100$						
x	π	41	42	43	44	45	46	47	48	49	50	
48		0293	0383	0480	0577	0665	0735	0781	0797	0781	0735	52
49		0216	0295	0384	0481	0577	0664	0735	0780	0796	0780	51
50		0153	0218	0296	0385	0482	0577	0665	0735	0780	0796	50
51		0104	0155	0219	0297	0386	0482	0578	0665	0735	0780	49
52		0068	0105	0156	0220	0298	0387	0483	0578	0665	0735	48
53		0043	0069	0106	0156	0221	0299	0388	0483	0579	0666	47
54		0026	0044	0070	0107	0157	0221	0299	0388	0484	0580	46
55		0015	0026	0044	0070	0108	0158	0222	0300	0389	0485	45
56		0008	0015	0027	0044	0071	0108	0158	0222	0300	0390	44
57		0005	0009	0016	0027	0045	0071	0108	0158	0223	0301	43
58		0002	0005	0009	0016	0027	0045	0071	0108	0159	0223	42
59		0001	0002	0005	0009	0016	0027	0045	0071	0109	0159	41
60		0001	0001	0002	0005	0009	0016	0027	0045	0071	0108	40
61		0000	0001	0001	0002	0005	0009	0016	0027	0045	0071	39
62		0000	0000	0001	0001	0002	0005	0009	0016	0027	0045	38
63		0000	0000	0000	0001	0001	0002	0005	0009	0016	0027	37
64		0000	0000	0000	0000	0001	0001	0002	0005	0009	0016	36
65		0000	0000	0000	0000	0000	0001	0001	0002	0005	0009	35
66		0000	0000	0000	0000	0000	0000	0001	0001	0002	0005	34
67		0000	0000	0000	0000	0000	0000	0000	0001	0001	0002	33
68		0000	0000	0000	0000	0000	0000	0000	0000	0001	0001	32
69		0000	0000	0000	0000	0000	0000	0000	0000	0000	0001	31
		59	58	57	56	55	54	53	52	51	50	π x

From Robert O. Schlaifer, *Analysis of Decisions Under Uncertainty* (Preliminary Edition, Volume II). New York: McGraw-Hill Book Company, 1967. Reprinted by permission of the Harvard Business School. Copyright © 1967 by the President and Fellows of Harvard College.

Table II gives the probability of exactly x successes, for various values of λ, as defined by the Poisson mass function.

$$P(x) = \frac{e^{-\lambda}\lambda^x}{x!}$$

◻ **EXAMPLES**   If $\lambda = 1.5$, then $P(2) = 0.2510$, $P(3) = 0.1255$.

TABLE II   Poisson distribution ($\lambda = 0.1$ to $\lambda = 4.0$)

Poisson Probabilities

x	0.1	0.2	0.3	0.4	0.5	0.6	0.7	0.8	0.9	1.0
0	.9048	.8187	.7408	.6703	.6065	.5488	.4966	.4493	.4066	.3679
1	.0905	.1637	.2222	.2681	.3033	.3293	.3476	.3595	.3659	.3679
2	.0045	.0164	.0333	.0536	.0758	.0988	.1217	.1438	.1647	.1839
3	.0002	.0011	.0033	.0072	.0126	.0198	.0284	.0383	.0494	.0613
4	.0000	.0001	.0002	.0007	.0016	.0030	.0050	.0077	.0111	.0153
5	.0000	.0000	.0000	.0001	.0002	.0004	.0007	.0012	.0020	.0031
6	.0000	.0000	.0000	.0000	.0000	.0000	.0001	.0002	.0003	.0005
7	.0000	.0000	.0000	.0000	.0000	.0000	.0000	.0000	.0000	.0001

λ

x	1.1	1.2	1.3	1.4	1.5	1.6	1.7	1.8	1.9	2.0
0	.3329	.3012	.2725	.2466	.2231	.2019	.1827	.1653	.1496	.1353
1	.3662	.3614	.3543	.3452	.3347	.3230	.3106	.2975	.2842	.2707
2	.2014	.2169	.2303	.2417	.2510	.2584	.2640	.2678	.2700	.2707
3	.0738	.0867	.0998	.1128	.1255	.1378	.1496	.1607	.1710	.1804
4	.0203	.0260	.0324	.0395	.0471	.0551	.0636	.0723	.0812	.0902
5	.0045	.0062	.0084	.0111	.0141	.0176	.0216	.0260	.0309	.0361
6	.0008	.0012	.0018	.0026	.0035	.0047	.0061	.0078	.0098	.0120
7	.0001	.0002	.0003	.0005	.0008	.0011	.0015	.0020	.0027	.0034
8	.0000	.0000	.0001	.0001	.0001	.0002	.0003	.0005	.0006	.0009
9	.0000	.0000	.0000	.0000	.0000	.0000	.0001	.0001	.0001	.0002

					λ					
x	2.1	2.2	2.3	2.4	2.5	2.6	2.7	2.8	2.9	3.0
0	.1225	.1108	.1003	.0907	.0821	.0743	.0672	.0608	.0550	.0498
1	.2572	.2438	.2306	.2177	.2052	.1931	.1815	.1703	.1596	.1494
2	.2700	.2681	.2652	.2613	.2565	.2510	.2450	.2384	.2314	.2240
3	.1890	.1966	.2033	.2090	.2138	.2176	.2205	.2225	.2237	.2240
4	.0992	.1082	.1169	.1254	.1336	.1414	.1488	.1557	.1622	.1680
5	.0417	.0476	.0538	.0602	.0668	.0735	.0804	.0872	.0940	.1008
6	.0146	.0174	.0206	.0241	.0278	.0319	.0362	.0407	.0455	.0504
7	.0044	.0055	.0068	.0083	.0099	.0118	.0139	.0163	.0188	.0216
8	.0011	.0015	.0019	.0025	.0031	.0038	.0047	.0057	.0068	.0081
9	.0003	.0004	.0005	.0007	.0009	.0011	.0014	.0018	.0022	.0027
10	.0001	.0001	.0001	.0002	.0002	.0003	.0004	.0005	.0006	.0008
11	.0000	.0000	.0000	.0000	.0000	.0001	.0001	.0001	.0002	.0002
12	.0000	.0000	.0000	.0000	.0000	.0000	.0000	.0000	.0000	.0001

					λ					
x	3.1	3.2	3.3	3.4	3.5	3.6	3.7	3.8	3.9	4.0
0	.0450	.0408	.0369	.0334	.0302	.0273	.0247	.0224	.0202	.0183
1	.1397	.1304	.1217	.1135	.1057	.0984	.0915	.0850	.0789	.0733
2	.2165	.2087	.2008	.1929	.1850	.1771	.1692	.1615	.1539	.1465
3	.2237	.2226	.2209	.2186	.2158	.2125	.2087	.2046	.2001	.1954
4	.1734	.1781	.1823	.1858	.1888	.1912	.1931	.1944	.1951	.1954
5	.1075	.1140	.1203	.1264	.1322	.1377	.1429	.1477	.1522	.1563
6	.0555	.0608	.0662	.0716	.0771	.0826	.0881	.0936	.0989	.1042
7	.0246	.0278	.0312	.0348	.0385	.0425	.0466	.0508	.0551	.0595
8	.0095	.0111	.0129	.0148	.0169	.0191	.0215	.0241	.0269	.0298
9	.0033	.0040	.0047	.0056	.0066	.0076	.0089	.0102	.0116	.0132
10	.0010	.0013	.0016	.0019	.0023	.0028	.0033	.0039	.0045	.0053
11	.0003	.0004	.0005	.0006	.0007	.0009	.0011	.0013	.0016	.0019
12	.0001	.0001	.0001	.0002	.0002	.0003	.0003	.0004	.0005	.0006
13	.0000	.0000	.0000	.0000	.0001	.0001	.0001	.0001	.0002	.0002
14	.0000	.0000	.0000	.0000	.0000	.0000	.0000	.0000	.0000	.0001

TABLE II   Poisson distribution ($\lambda = 4.1$ to $\lambda = 8.0$)

					λ					
x	4.1	4.2	4.3	4.4	4.5	4.6	4.7	4.8	4.9	5.0
0	.0166	.0150	.0136	.0123	.0111	.0101	.0091	.0082	.0074	.0067
1	.0679	.0630	.0583	.0540	.0500	.0462	.0427	.0395	.0365	.0337
2	.1393	.1323	.1254	.1188	.1125	.1063	.1005	.0948	.0894	.0842
3	.1904	.1852	.1798	.1743	.1687	.1631	.1574	.1517	.1460	.1404
4	.1951	.1944	.1933	.1917	.1898	.1875	.1849	.1820	.1789	.1755
5	.1600	.1633	.1662	.1687	.1708	.1725	.1738	.1747	.1753	.1755
6	.1093	.1143	.1191	.1237	.1281	.1323	.1362	.1398	.1432	.1462
7	.0640	.0686	.0732	.0778	.0824	.0869	.0914	.0959	.1002	.1044
8	.0328	.0360	.0393	.0428	.0463	.0500	.0537	.0575	.0614	.0653
9	.0150	.0168	.0188	.0209	.0232	.0255	.0280	.0307	.0334	.0363
10	.0061	.0071	.0081	.0092	.0104	.0118	.0132	.0147	.0164	.0181
11	.0023	.0027	.0032	.0037	.0043	.0049	.0056	.0064	.0073	.0082
12	.0008	.0009	.0011	.0014	.0016	.0019	.0022	.0026	.0030	.0034
13	.0002	.0003	.0004	.0005	.0006	.0007	.0008	.0009	.0011	.0013
14	.0001	.0001	.0001	.0001	.0002	.0002	.0003	.0003	.0004	.0005
15	.0000	.0000	.0000	.0000	.0001	.0001	.0001	.0001	.0001	.0002

					λ					
x	5.1	5.2	5.3	5.4	5.5	5.6	5.7	5.8	5.9	6.0
0	.0061	.0055	.0050	.0045	.0041	.0037	.0033	.0030	.0027	.0025
1	.0311	.0287	.0265	.0244	.0225	.0207	.0191	.0176	.0162	.0149
2	.0793	.0746	.0701	.0659	.0618	.0580	.0544	.0509	.0477	.0446
3	.1348	.1293	.1239	.1185	.1133	.1082	.1033	.0985	.0938	.0892
4	.1719	.1681	.1641	.1600	.1558	.1515	.1472	.1428	.1383	.1339
5	.1753	.1748	.1740	.1728	.1714	.1697	.1678	.1620	.1632	.1606
6	.1490	.1515	.1537	.1555	.1571	.1584	.1594	.1656	.1605	.1606
7	.1086	.1125	.1163	.1200	.1234	.1267	.1298	.1301	.1353	.1377
8	.0692	.0731	.0771	.0810	.0849	.0887	.0925	.0926	.0998	.1033
9	.0392	.0423	.0454	.0486	.0519	.0552	.0586	.0662	.0654	.0688
10	.0200	.0220	.0241	.0262	.0285	.0309	.0334	.0359	.0386	.0413
11	.0093	.0104	.0116	.0129	.0143	.0157	.0173	.0190	.0207	.0225
12	.0039	.0045	.0051	.0058	.0065	.0073	.0082	.0092	.0102	.0113
13	.0015	.0018	.0021	.0024	.0028	.0032	.0036	.0041	.0046	.0052
14	.0006	.0007	.0008	.0009	.0011	.0013	.0015	.0017	.0019	.0022
15	.0002	.0002	.0003	.0003	.0004	.0005	.0006	.0007	.0008	.0009
16	.0001	.0001	.0001	.0001	.0001	.0002	.0002	.0002	.0003	.0003
17	.0000	.0000	.0000	.0000	.0000	.0001	.0001	.0001	.0001	.0001

	λ									
x	6.1	6.2	6.3	6.4	6.5	6.6	6.7	6.8	6.9	7.0
0	.0022	.0020	.0018	.0017	.0015	.0014	.0012	.0011	.0010	.0009
1	.0137	.0126	.0116	.0106	.0098	.0090	.0082	.0076	.0070	.0064
2	.0417	.0390	.0364	.0340	.0318	.0296	.0276	.0258	.0240	.0223
3	.0848	.0806	.0765	.0726	.0688	.0652	.0617	.0584	.0552	.0521
4	.1294	.1249	.1205	.1162	.1118	.1076	.1034	.0992	.0952	.0912
5	.1579	.1549	.1519	.1487	.1454	.1420	.1385	.1349	.1314	.1277
6	.1605	.1601	.1595	.1586	.1575	.1562	.1546	.1529	.1511	.1490
7	.1399	.1418	.1435	.1450	.1462	.1472	.1480	.1486	.1489	.1490
8	.1066	.1099	.1130	.1160	.1188	.1215	.1240	.1263	.1284	.1304
9	.0723	.0757	.0791	.0825	.0858	.0891	.0923	.0954	.0985	.1014
10	.0441	.0469	.0498	.0528	.0558	.0588	.0618	.0649	.0679	.0710
11	.0245	.0265	.0285	.0307	.0330	.0353	.0377	.0401	.0426	.0452
12	.0124	.0137	.0150	.0164	.0179	.0194	.0210	.0227	.0245	.0264
13	.0058	.0065	.0073	.0081	.0089	.0098	.0108	.0119	.0130	.0142
14	.0025	.0029	.0033	.0037	.0041	.0046	.0052	.0058	.0064	.0071
15	.0010	.0012	.0014	.0016	.0018	.0020	.0023	.0026	.0029	.0033
16	.0004	.0005	.0005	.0006	.0007	.0008	.0010	.0011	.0013	.0014
17	.0001	.0002	.0002	.0002	.0003	.0003	.0004	.0004	.0005	.0006
18	.0000	.0001	.0001	.0001	.0001	.0001	.0001	.0002	.0002	.0002
19	.0000	.0000	.0000	.0000	.0000	.0000	.0000	.0001	.0001	.0001

	λ									
x	7.1	7.2	7.3	7.4	7.5	7.6	7.7	7.8	7.9	8.0
0	.0008	.0007	.0007	.0006	.0006	.0005	.0005	.0004	.0004	.0003
1	.0059	.0054	.0049	.0045	.0041	.0038	.0035	.0032	.0029	.0027
2	.0208	.0194	.0180	.0167	.0156	.0145	.0134	.0125	.0116	.0107
3	.0492	.0464	.0438	.0413	.0389	.0366	.0345	.0324	.0305	.0286
4	.0874	.0836	.0799	.0764	.0729	.0696	.0663	.0632	.0602	.0573
5	.1241	.1204	.1167	.1130	.1094	.1057	.1021	.0986	.0951	.0916
6	.1468	.1445	.1420	.1394	.1367	.1339	.1311	.1282	.1252	.1221
7	.1489	.1486	.1481	.1474	.1465	.1454	.1442	.1428	.1413	.1396
8	.1321	.1337	.1351	.1363	.1373	.1382	.1388	.1392	.1395	.1396
9	.1042	.1070	.1096	.1121	.1144	.1167	.1187	.1207	.1224	.1241
10	.0740	.0770	.0800	.0829	.0858	.0887	.0914	.0941	.0967	.0993
11	.0478	.0504	.0531	.0558	.0585	.0613	.0640	.0667	.0695	.0722
12	0.283	.0303	.0323	.0344	.0366	.0388	.0411	.0434	.0457	.0481
13	.0154	.0168	.0181	.0196	.0211	.0227	.0243	.0260	.0278	.0296
14	.0078	.0086	.0095	.0104	.0113	.0123	.0134	.0145	.0157	.0169
15	.0037	.0041	.0046	.0051	.0057	.0062	.0069	.0075	.0083	.0090
16	.0016	.0019	.0021	.0024	.0026	.0030	.0033	.0037	.0041	.0045
17	.0007	.0008	.0009	.0010	.0012	.0013	.0015	.0017	.0119	.0021
18	.0003	.0003	.0004	.0004	.0005	.0006	.0006	.0007	.0008	.0009
19	.0001	.0001	.0001	.0002	.0002	.0002	.0003	.0003	.0003	.0004
20	.0000	.0000	.0001	.0001	.0001	.0001	.0001	.0001	.0001	.0002
21	.0000	.0000	.0000	.0000	.0000	.0000	.0000	.0000	.0001	.0001

TABLE II   Poisson distribution ($\lambda = 8.1$ to $\lambda = 20$)

					λ					
x	8.1	8.2	8.3	8.4	8.5	8.6	8.7	8.8	8.9	9.0
0	.0003	.0003	.0002	.0002	.0002	.0002	.0002	.0002	.0001	.0001
1	.0025	.0023	.0021	.0019	.0017	.0016	.0014	.0013	.0012	.0011
2	.0100	.0092	.0086	.0079	.0074	.0068	.0063	.0058	.0054	.0050
3	.0269	.0252	.0237	.0222	.0208	.0195	.0183	.0171	.0160	.0150
4	.0544	.0517	.0491	.0466	.0443	.0420	.0398	.0377	.0357	.0337
5	.0882	.0849	.0816	.0784	.0752	.0722	.0692	.0663	.0635	.0607
6	.1191	.1160	.1128	.1097	.1066	.1034	.1003	.0972	.0941	.0911
7	.1378	.1358	.1338	.1317	.1294	.1271	.1247	.1222	.1197	.1171
8	.1395	.1392	.1388	.1382	.1375	.1366	.1356	.1344	.1332	.1318
9	.1256	.1269	.1280	.1290	.1299	.1306	.1311	.1315	.1317	.1318
10	.1017	.1040	.1063	.1084	.1104	.1123	.1140	.1157	.1172	.1186
11	.0749	.0776	.0802	.0828	.0853	.0878	.0902	.0925	.0948	.0970
12	.0505	.0530	.0555	.0579	.0604	.0629	.0654	.0679	.0703	.0728
13	.0315	.0334	.0354	.0374	.0395	.0416	.0438	.0459	.0481	.0504
14	.0182	.0196	.0210	.0225	.0240	.0256	.0272	.0289	.0306	.0324
15	.0098	.0107	.0116	.0126	.0136	.0147	.0158	.0169	.0182	.0194
16	.0050	.0055	.0060	.0066	.0072	.0079	.0086	.0093	.0101	.0109
17	.0024	.0026	.0029	.0033	.0036	.0040	.0044	.0048	.0053	.0058
18	.0011	.0012	.0014	.0015	.0017	.0019	.0021	.0024	.0026	.0029
19	.0005	.0005	.0006	.0007	.0008	.0009	.0010	.0011	.0012	.0014
20	.0002	.0002	.0002	.0003	.0003	.0004	.0004	.0005	.0005	.0006
21	.0001	.0001	.0001	.0001	.0001	.0002	.0002	.0002	.0002	.0003
22	.0000	.0000	.0000	.0000	.0001	.0001	.0001	.0001	.0001	.0001

					λ					
x	9.1	9.2	9.3	9.4	9.5	9.6	9.7	9.8	9.9	10
0	.0001	.0001	.0001	.0001	.0001	.0001	.0001	.0001	.0001	.0000
1	.0010	.0009	.0009	.0008	.0007	.0007	.0006	.0005	.0005	.0005
2	.0046	.0043	.0040	.0037	.0034	.0031	.0029	.0027	.0025	.0023
3	.0140	.0131	.0123	.0115	.0107	.0100	.0093	.0087	.0081	.0076
4	.0319	.0302	.0285	.0269	.0254	.0240	.0226	.0213	.0201	.0189
5	.0581	.0555	.0530	.0506	.0483	.0460	.0439	.0418	.0398	.0378
6	.0881	.0851	.0822	.0793	.0764	.0736	.0709	.0682	.0656	.0631
7	.1145	.1118	.1091	.1064	.1037	.1010	.0982	.0955	.0928	.0901
8	.1302	.1286	.1269	.1251	.1232	.1212	.1191	.1170	.1148	.1126
9	.1317	.1315	.1311	.1306	.1300	.1293	.1284	.1274	.1263	.1251
10	.1198	.1210	.1219	.1228	.1235	.1241	.1245	.1249	.1250	.1251
11	.0991	.1012	.1031	.1049	.1067	.1083	.1098	.1112	.1125	.1137
12	.0752	.0776	.0799	.0822	.0844	.0866	.0888	.0908	.0928	.0948
13	.0526	.0549	.0572	.0594	.0617	.0640	.0662	.0685	.0707	.0729
14	.0342	.0361	.0380	.0399	.0419	.0439	.0459	.0479	.0500	.0521
15	.0208	.0221	.0235	.0250	.0265	.0281	.0297	.0313	.0330	.0347
16	.0118	.0127	.0137	.0147	.0157	.0168	.0180	.0192	.0204	.0217
17	.0063	.0069	.0075	.0081	.0088	.0095	.0103	.0111	.0119	.0128
18	.0032	.0035	.0039	.0042	.0046	.0051	.0055	.0060	.0065	.0071
19	.0015	.0017	.0019	.0021	.0023	.0026	.0028	.0031	.0034	.0037
20	.0007	.0008	.0009	.0010	.0011	.0012	.0014	.0015	.0017	.0019
21	.0003	.0003	.0004	.0004	.0005	.0006	.0006	.0007	.0008	.0009
22	.0001	.0001	.0002	.0002	.0002	.0002	.0003	.0003	.0004	.0004
23	.0000	.0001	.0001	.0001	.0001	.0001	.0001	.0001	.0002	.0002
24	.0000	.0000	.0000	.0000	.0000	.0000	.0000	.0001	.0001	.0001

x	11	12	13	14	15	16	17	18	19	20
0	.0000	.0000	.0000	.0000	.0000	.0000	.0000	.0000	.0000	.0000
1	.0002	.0001	.0000	.0000	.0000	.0000	.0000	.0000	.0000	.0000
2	.0010	.0004	.0002	.0001	.0000	.0000	.0000	.0000	.0000	.0000
3	.0037	.0018	.0008	.0004	.0002	.0001	.0000	.0000	.0000	.0000
4	.0102	.0053	.0027	.0013	.0006	.0003	.0001	.0001	.0000	.0000
5	.0224	.0127	.0070	.0037	.0019	.0010	.0005	.0002	.0001	.0001
6	.0411	.0255	.0152	.0087	.0048	.0026	.0014	.0007	.0004	.0002
7	.0646	.0437	.0281	.0174	.0104	.0060	.0034	.0018	.0010	.0005
8	.0888	.0655	.0457	.0304	.0194	.0120	.0072	.0042	.0024	.0013
9	.1085	.0874	.0661	.0473	.0324	.0213	.0135	.0083	.0050	.0029
10	.1194	.1048	.0859	.0063	.0486	.0341	.0230	.0150	.0095	.0058
11	.1194	.1144	.1015	.0844	.0663	.0496	.0355	.0245	.0164	.0106
12	.1094	.1144	.1099	.0984	.0829	.0661	.0504	.0368	.0259	.0176
13	.0926	.1056	.1099	.1060	.0956	.0814	.0658	.0509	.0378	.0271
14	.0728	.0905	.1021	.1060	.1024	.0930	.0800	.0655	.0514	.0387
15	.0534	.0724	.0885	.0989	.1024	.0992	.0906	.0786	.0650	.0516
16	.0367	.0543	.0719	.0866	.0960	.0992	.0963	.0884	.0772	.0646
17	.0237	.0383	.0550	.0713	.0847	.0934	.0963	.0936	.0863	.0760
18	.0145	.0256	.0397	.0554	.0706	.0830	.0909	.0936	.0911	.0844
19	.0084	.0161	.0272	.0409	.0557	.0699	.0814	.0887	.0911	.0888
20	.0046	.0097	.0177	.0286	.0418	.0559	.0692	.0798	.0866	.0888
21	.0024	.0055	.0109	.0191	.0299	.0426	.0560	.0684	.0783	.0846
22	.0012	.0030	.0065	.0121	.0204	.0310	.0433	.0560	.0676	.0769
23	.0006	.0016	.0037	.0074	.0133	.0216	.0320	.0438	.0559	.0669
24	.0003	.0008	.0020	.0043	.0083	.0144	.0226	.0328	.0442	.0557
25	.0001	.0004	.0010	.0024	.0050	.0092	.0154	.0237	.0336	.0446
26	.0000	.0002	.0005	.0013	.0029	.0057	.0101	.0164	.0246	.0343
27	.0000	.0001	.0002	.0007	.0016	.0034	.0063	.0109	.0173	.0254
28	.0000	.0000	.0001	.0003	.0009	.0019	.0038	.0070	.0117	.0181
29	.0000	.0000	.0001	.0002	.0004	.0011	.0023	.0044	.0077	.0125
30	.0000	.0000	.0000	.0001	.0002	.0006	.0013	.0026	.0049	.0083
31	.0000	.0000	.0000	.0000	.0001	.0003	.0007	.0015	.0030	.0054
32	.0000	.0000	.0000	.0000	.0001	.0001	.0004	.0009	.0018	.0034
33	.0000	.0000	.0000	.0000	.0000	.0001	.0002	.0005	.0010	.0020
34	.0000	.0000	.0000	.0000	.0000	.0000	.0001	.0002	.0006	.0012
35	.0000	.0000	.0000	.0000	.0000	.0000	.0000	.0001	.0003	.0007
36	.0000	.0000	.0000	.0000	.0000	.0000	.0000	.0001	.0002	.0004
37	.0000	.0000	.0000	.0000	.0000	.0000	.0000	.0000	.0001	.0002
38	.0000	.0000	.0000	.0000	.0000	.0000	.0000	.0000	.0000	.0001
39	.0000	.0000	.0000	.0000	.0000	.0000	.0000	.0000	.0000	.0001

From *Handbook of Probability and Statistics* by R. S. Burington and D. C. May, Jr. Copyright 1953 by McGraw-Hill, Inc. Used with permission of McGraw-Hill Book Company.

TABLE III   Cumulative standardized normal distribution $F(z)$

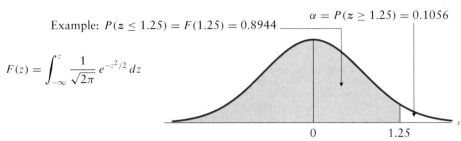

Example: $P(z \leq 1.25) = F(1.25) = 0.8944$

$\alpha = P(z \geq 1.25) = 0.1056$

$$F(z) = \int_{-\infty}^{z} \frac{1}{\sqrt{2\pi}} e^{-z^2/2} \, dz$$

z	.00	.01	.02	.03	.04	.05	.06	.07	.08	.09
.0	.5000	.5040	.5080	.5120	.5160	.5199	.5239	.5279	.5319	.5359
.1	.5398	.5438	.5478	.5517	.5557	.5596	.5636	.5675	.5714	.5753
.2	.5793	.5832	.5871	.5910	.5948	.5987	.6026	.6064	.6103	.6141
.3	.6179	.6217	.6255	.6293	.6331	.6368	.6406	.6443	.6480	.6517
.4	.6554	.6591	.6628	.6664	.6700	.6736	.6772	.6808	.6844	.6879
.5	.6915	.6950	.6985	.7019	.7054	.7088	.7123	.7157	.7190	.7224
.6	.7257	.7291	.7324	.7357	.7389	.7422	.7454	.7486	.7517	.7549
.7	.7580	.7611	.7642	.7673	.7704	.7734	.7764	.7794	.7823	.7852
.8	.7881	.7910	.7939	.7967	.7995	.8023	.8051	.8078	.8106	.8133
.9	.8159	.8186	.8212	.8238	.8264	.8289	.8315	.8340	.8365	.8389
1.0	.8413	.8438	.8461	.8485	.8508	.8531	.8554	.8577	.8599	.8621
1.1	.8643	.8665	.8686	.8708	.8729	.8749	.8770	.8790	.8810	.8830
1.2	.8849	.8869	.8888	.8907	.8925	.8944	.8962	.8980	.8997	.9015
1.3	.9032	.9049	.9066	.9082	.9099	.9115	.9131	.9147	.9162	.9177
1.4	.9192	.9207	.9222	.9236	.9251	.9265	.9279	.9292	.9306	.9319
1.5	.9332	.9345	.9357	.9370	.9382	.9394	.9406	.9418	.9429	.9441
1.6	.9452	.9463	.9474	.9484	.9495	.9505	.9515	.9525	.9535	.9545
1.7	.9554	.9564	.9573	.9582	.9591	.9599	.9608	.9616	.9625	.9633
1.8	.9641	.9649	.9656	.9664	.9671	.9678	.9686	.9693	.9699	.9706
1.9	.9713	.9719	.9726	.9732	.9738	.9744	.9750	.9756	.9761	.9767
2.0	.9772	.9778	.9783	.9788	.9793	.9798	.9803	.9808	.9812	.9817
2.1	.9821	.9826	.9830	.9834	.9838	.9842	.9846	.9850	.9854	.9857
2.2	.9861	.9864	.9868	.9871	.9875	.9878	.9881	.9884	.9887	.9890
2.3	.9893	.9896	.9898	.9901	.9904	.9906	.9909	.9911	.9913	.9916
2.4	.9918	.9920	.9922	.9925	.9927	.9929	.9931	.9932	.9934	.9936
2.5	.9938	.9940	.9941	.9943	.9945	.9946	.9948	.9949	.9951	.9952
2.6	.9953	.9955	.9956	.9957	.9959	.9960	.9961	.9962	.9963	.9964
2.7	.9965	.9966	.9967	.9968	.9969	.9970	.9971	.9972	.9973	.9974
2.8	.9974	.9975	.9976	.9977	.9977	.9978	.9979	.9979	.9980	.9981
2.9	.9981	.9982	.9982	.9983	.9984	.9984	.9985	.9985	.9986	.9986
3.0	.9987	.9987	.9987	.9988	.9988	.9989	.9989	.9989	.9990	.9990
3.1	.9990	.9991	.9991	.9991	.9992	.9992	.9992	.9992	.9993	.9993
3.2	.9993	.9993	.9994	.9994	.9994	.9994	.9994	.9995	.9995	.9995
3.3	.9995	.9995	.9995	.9996	.9996	.9996	.9996	.9996	.9996	.9997
3.4	.9997	.9997	.9997	.9997	.9997	.9997	.9997	.9997	.9997	.9998

TABLE IV   Cumulative exponential distribution, $F(T) = 1 - e^{-\lambda T}$

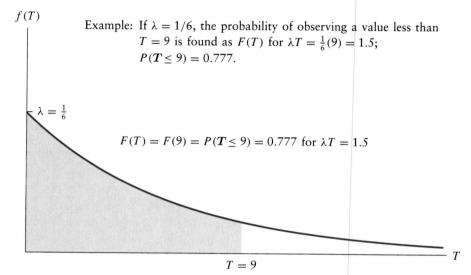

$f(T)$

Example: If $\lambda = 1/6$, the probability of observing a value less than $T = 9$ is found as $F(T)$ for $\lambda T = \frac{1}{6}(9) = 1.5$; $P(\boldsymbol{T} \leq 9) = 0.777$.

$\lambda = \frac{1}{6}$

$F(T) = F(9) = P(\boldsymbol{T} \leq 9) = 0.777$ for $\lambda T = 1.5$

$T = 9$

λT	$F(T)$	λT	$F(T)$	λT	$F(T)$	λT	$F(T)$
0.0	0.000	2.5	0.918	5.0	0.9933	7.5	0.99945
0.1	0.095	2.6	0.926	5.1	0.9939	7.6	0.99950
0.2	0.181	2.7	0.933	5.2	0.9945	7.7	0.99955
0.3	0.259	2.8	0.939	5.3	0.9950	7.8	0.99959
0.4	0.330	2.9	0.945	5.4	0.9955	7.9	0.99963
0.5	0.393	3.0	0.950	5.5	0.9959	8.0	0.99966
0.6	0.451	3.1	0.955	5.6	0.9963	8.1	0.99970
0.7	0.503	3.2	0.959	5.7	0.9967	8.2	0.99972
0.8	0.551	3.3	0.963	5.8	0.9970	8.3	0.99975
0.9	0.593	3.4	0.967	5.9	0.9973	8.4	0.99978
1.0	0.632	3.5	0.970	6.0	0.9975	8.5	0.99980
1.1	0.667	3.6	0.973	6.1	0.9978	8.6	0.99982
1.2	0.699	3.7	0.975	6.2	0.9980	8.7	0.99983
1.3	0.727	3.8	0.978	6.3	0.9982	8.8	0.99985
1.4	0.753	3.9	0.980	6.4	0.9983	8.9	0.99986
1.5	0.777	4.0	0.982	6.5	0.9985	9.0	0.99989
1.6	0.798	4.1	0.983	6.6	0.9986	9.1	0.99989
1.7	0.817	4.2	0.985	6.7	0.9988	9.2	0.99990
1.8	0.835	4.3	0.986	6.8	0.9989	9.3	0.99991
1.9	0.850	4.4	0.988	6.9	0.9990	9.4	0.99992
2.0	0.865	4.5	0.989	7.0	0.9991	9.5	0.99992
2.1	0.878	4.6	0.990	7.1	0.9992	9.6	0.99993
2.2	0.889	4.7	0.991	7.2	0.9993	9.7	0.99994
2.3	0.900	4.8	0.992	7.3	0.9993	9.8	0.99994
2.4	0.909	4.9	0.993	7.4	0.9993	9.9	0.99995

TABLE V Random digits

07018	31172	12572	23968	55216	85366	56223	09300	94564	18172
52444	65625	97918	46794	62370	59344	20149	17596	51669	47429
72161	57299	87521	44351	99981	55008	93371	60620	66662	27036
17918	75071	91057	46829	47992	26797	64423	42379	91676	75127
13623	76165	43195	50205	75736	77473	07268	31330	07337	55901
27426	97534	89707	97453	90836	78967	00704	85734	21776	85764
96039	21338	88169	69530	53300	29895	71507	28517	77761	17244
68282	98888	25545	69406	29470	46476	54562	79373	72993	98998
54262	21477	33097	48125	92982	98382	11265	25366	06636	25349
66290	27544	72780	91384	47296	54892	59168	83951	91075	04724
53348	39044	04072	62210	01209	43999	54952	68699	31912	09317
34482	42758	40128	48436	30254	50029	19016	56837	05206	33851
99268	98715	07545	27317	52459	75366	43688	27460	65145	65429
95342	97178	10401	31615	95784	77026	33087	65961	10056	72834
38556	60373	77935	64608	28949	94764	45312	71171	15400	72182
39159	04795	51163	84475	60722	35268	05044	56420	39214	89822
41786	18169	96649	92406	42773	23672	37333	85734	99886	81200
95627	30768	30607	89023	60730	31519	53462	90489	81693	17849
98738	15548	42263	79489	85118	97073	01574	57310	59375	54417
75214	61575	27805	21930	94726	39454	19616	72239	93791	22610
73904	89123	19271	15792	72675	62175	48746	56084	54029	22296
33329	08896	94662	05781	59187	53284	28024	45421	37956	14252
66364	94799	62211	37539	80172	43269	91133	05562	82385	91760
68349	16984	86532	96186	53893	48268	82821	19526	63257	14288
19193	99621	66899	12351	72438	99839	24228	32079	53517	18558
09237	23489	19172	80439	76263	98918	59330	20121	89779	58862
11007	77008	27646	82072	28048	41589	70883	72035	81800	50296
60622	25875	26446	25738	32962	24266	26814	01194	48587	93319
79973	26895	65304	34978	43053	28951	22676	05303	39725	60054
71080	74487	83196	61939	05045	20405	69324	80823	20905	68727
09923	36773	21247	54735	68996	16937	18134	51873	10973	77090
63094	85087	94186	67793	18178	82224	17069	87880	54945	73489
34968	76028	54285	90845	35464	68076	15868	70063	26794	81386
99696	78454	21700	12301	88832	96796	59341	16136	01803	17537
55282	61051	97260	89829	69121	86547	62195	72492	33536	60137

From RAND Corporation, *A Million Random Digits*. By permission.

TABLE VI   Cumulative t-distribution $F(t)$

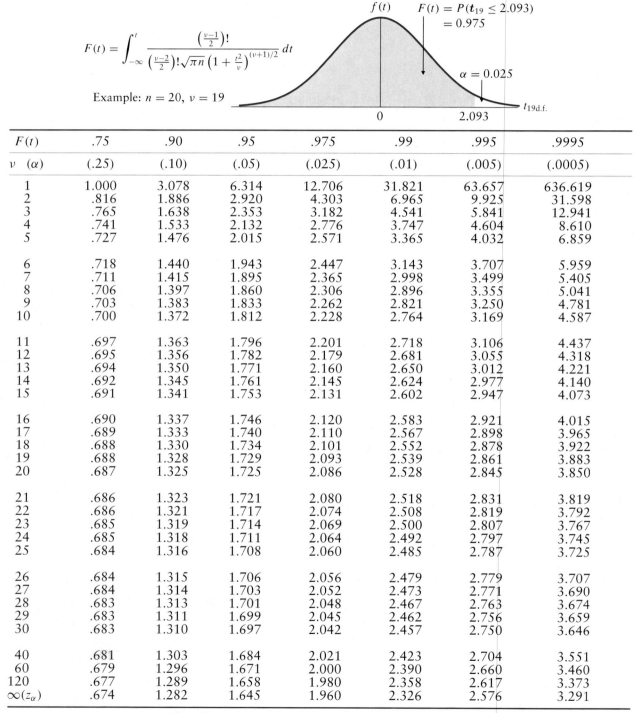

$$F(t) = \int_{-\infty}^{t} \frac{\left(\frac{v-1}{2}\right)!}{\left(\frac{v-2}{2}\right)!\sqrt{\pi n}\left(1 + \frac{t^2}{v}\right)^{(v+1)/2}}\, dt$$

Example: $n = 20$, $v = 19$

$f(t)$ $F(t) = P(t_{19} \leq 2.093)$ $= 0.975$

$\alpha = 0.025$

0 2.093 $t_{19\text{d.f.}}$

$F(t)$	.75	.90	.95	.975	.99	.995	.9995
v (α)	(.25)	(.10)	(.05)	(.025)	(.01)	(.005)	(.0005)
1	1.000	3.078	6.314	12.706	31.821	63.657	636.619
2	.816	1.886	2.920	4.303	6.965	9.925	31.598
3	.765	1.638	2.353	3.182	4.541	5.841	12.941
4	.741	1.533	2.132	2.776	3.747	4.604	8.610
5	.727	1.476	2.015	2.571	3.365	4.032	6.859
6	.718	1.440	1.943	2.447	3.143	3.707	5.959
7	.711	1.415	1.895	2.365	2.998	3.499	5.405
8	.706	1.397	1.860	2.306	2.896	3.355	5.041
9	.703	1.383	1.833	2.262	2.821	3.250	4.781
10	.700	1.372	1.812	2.228	2.764	3.169	4.587
11	.697	1.363	1.796	2.201	2.718	3.106	4.437
12	.695	1.356	1.782	2.179	2.681	3.055	4.318
13	.694	1.350	1.771	2.160	2.650	3.012	4.221
14	.692	1.345	1.761	2.145	2.624	2.977	4.140
15	.691	1.341	1.753	2.131	2.602	2.947	4.073
16	.690	1.337	1.746	2.120	2.583	2.921	4.015
17	.689	1.333	1.740	2.110	2.567	2.898	3.965
18	.688	1.330	1.734	2.101	2.552	2.878	3.922
19	.688	1.328	1.729	2.093	2.539	2.861	3.883
20	.687	1.325	1.725	2.086	2.528	2.845	3.850
21	.686	1.323	1.721	2.080	2.518	2.831	3.819
22	.686	1.321	1.717	2.074	2.508	2.819	3.792
23	.685	1.319	1.714	2.069	2.500	2.807	3.767
24	.685	1.318	1.711	2.064	2.492	2.797	3.745
25	.684	1.316	1.708	2.060	2.485	2.787	3.725
26	.684	1.315	1.706	2.056	2.479	2.779	3.707
27	.684	1.314	1.703	2.052	2.473	2.771	3.690
28	.683	1.313	1.701	2.048	2.467	2.763	3.674
29	.683	1.311	1.699	2.045	2.462	2.756	3.659
30	.683	1.310	1.697	2.042	2.457	2.750	3.646
40	.681	1.303	1.684	2.021	2.423	2.704	3.551
60	.679	1.296	1.671	2.000	2.390	2.660	3.460
120	.677	1.289	1.658	1.980	2.358	2.617	3.373
$\infty(z_\alpha)$	.674	1.282	1.645	1.960	2.326	2.576	3.291

* This table is abridged from the "Statistical Tables" of R. A. Fisher and Frank Yates published by Oliver & Boyd, Ltd., Edinburgh and London, 1938. It is here published with the kind permission of the authors and their publishers.

TABLE VII Cumulative chi-square distribution

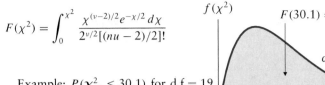

$$F(\chi^2) = \int_0^{\chi^2} \frac{\chi^{(\nu-2)/2} e^{-\chi/2} \, d\chi}{2^{\nu/2} [(nu-2)/2]!}$$

$f(\chi^2)$

$F(30.1) = 0.950$

$\alpha = P(\chi_{19}^2 \geq 30.1) = 0.05$

Example: $P(\chi_{19}^2 \leq 30.1)$ for d.f.= 19
$P(\chi^2 \leq 30.1) = F(30.1) = 0.950$

30.1 $\chi_{19\text{d.f.}}^2$

$F(\chi^2)$	.005	.010	.025	.050	.100	.900	.950	.975	.990	.995
ν (α)	(.995)	(.990)	(.975)	(.950)	(.900)	(.100)	(.050)	(.025)	(.010)	(.005)
1	$.0^4 393$	$.0^3 157$	$.0^3 982$	$.0^2 393$	0.158	2.71	3.84	5.02	6.63	7.88
2	.0100	.0201	.0506	.103	.211	4.61	5.99	7.38	9.21	10.6
3	.0717	.115	.216	.352	.584	6.25	7.81	9.35	11.3	12.8
4	.207	.297	.484	.711	1.06	7.78	9.49	11.1	13.3	14.9
5	.412	.554	.831	1.15	1.61	9.24	11.1	12.8	15.1	16.7
6	.676	.872	1.24	1.64	2.20	10.6	12.6	14.4	16.8	18.5
7	.989	1.24	1.69	2.17	2.83	12.0	14.1	16.0	18.5	20.3
8	1.34	1.65	2.18	2.73	3.49	13.4	15.5	17.5	20.1	22.0
9	1.73	2.09	2.70	3.33	4.17	14.7	16.9	19.0	21.7	23.6
10	2.16	2.56	3.25	3.94	4.87	16.0	18.3	20.5	23.2	25.2
11	2.60	3.05	3.82	4.57	5.58	17.3	19.7	21.9	24.7	26.8
12	3.07	3.57	4.40	5.23	6.30	18.5	21.0	23.3	26.2	28.3
13	3.57	4.11	5.01	5.89	7.04	19.8	22.4	24.7	27.7	29.8
14	4.07	4.66	5.63	6.57	7.79	21.1	23.7	26.1	29.1	31.3
15	4.60	5.23	6.26	7.26	8.55	22.3	25.0	27.5	30.6	32.8
16	5.14	5.81	6.91	7.96	9.31	23.5	26.3	28.8	32.0	34.3
17	5.70	6.41	7.56	8.67	10.1	24.8	27.6	30.2	33.4	35.7
18	6.26	7.01	8.23	9.39	10.9	26.0	28.9	31.5	34.8	37.2
19	6.84	7.63	8.91	10.1	11.7	27.2	30.1	32.9	36.2	38.6
20	7.43	8.26	9.59	10.9	12.4	28.4	31.4	34.2	37.6	40.0
21	8.03	8.90	10.3	11.6	13.2	29.6	32.7	35.5	38.9	41.4
22	8.64	9.54	11.0	12.3	14.0	30.8	33.9	36.8	40.3	42.8
23	9.26	10.2	11.7	13.1	14.8	32.0	35.2	38.1	41.6	44.2
24	9.89	10.9	12.4	13.8	15.7	33.2	36.4	39.4	43.0	45.6
25	10.5	11.5	13.1	14.6	16.5	34.4	37.7	40.6	44.3	46.9
26	11.2	12.2	13.8	15.4	17.3	35.6	38.9	41.9	45.6	48.3
27	11.8	12.9	14.6	16.2	18.1	36.7	40.1	43.2	47.0	49.6
28	12.5	13.6	15.3	16.9	18.9	37.9	41.3	44.5	48.3	51.0
29	13.1	14.3	16.0	17.7	19.8	39.1	42.6	45.7	49.6	52.3
30	13.8	15.0	16.8	18.5	20.6	40.3	43.8	47.0	50.9	53.7
z_α	−2.576	−2.326	−1.960	−1.645	−1.282	+1.282	+1.645	+1.960	+2.326	+2.576

NOTE: For $\nu > 30$ (i.e., for more than 30 degrees of freedom) take

$$\chi^2 = \nu \left[1 - \frac{2}{9\nu} + z_x \sqrt{\frac{2}{9\nu}} \right]^2 \quad \text{or} \quad \chi^2 = \tfrac{1}{2} \left[z_x + \sqrt{(2\nu - 1)} \right]^2$$

according to the degree of accuracy required. z_α is the standardized normal deviate corresponding to the α level of significance, and is shown in the bottom line of the table.

This table is abridged from "Tables of percentage points of the incomplete beta function and of the chi-square distribution," *Biometrika*. Vol. 32 (1941). Reprinted with permission of its author, Catherine M. Thompson, and the editor of *Biometrika*.

Table VIII(a) gives the critical values of the F distribution for a cumulative probability of 0.95 ($\alpha = 0.05$). The probability (α) represents the area exceeding the value of $F_{0.05, v_1, v_2}$, as shown by the shaded area in the figure below.

◻ **EXAMPLE** If $v_1 = 15$ (d.f. for the numerator), and $v_2 = 20$, then the critical value cutting off 0.05 is 2.20. $P(F \geq 2.20) = 0.05$, $P(F \leq 2.20) = 0.95$.

TABLE VIII(a) Cumulative F-distribution of 0.95 ($\alpha = 0.05$)

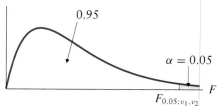

v_2 = Degrees of freedom for denominator	\multicolumn{9}{c}{v_1 = Degrees of freedom for numerator}								
	1	2	3	4	5	6	7	8	9
1	161	200	216	225	230	234	237	239	241
2	18.5	19.0	19.2	19.2	19.3	19.3	19.4	19.4	19.4
3	10.1	9.55	9.28	9.12	9.01	8.94	8.89	8.85	8.81
4	7.71	6.94	6.59	6.39	6.26	6.16	6.09	6.04	6.00
5	6.61	5.79	5.41	5.19	5.05	4.95	4.88	4.82	4.77
6	5.99	5.14	4.76	4.53	4.39	4.28	4.21	4.15	4.10
7	5.59	4.74	4.35	4.12	3.97	3.87	3.79	3.73	3.68
8	5.32	4.46	4.07	3.84	3.69	3.58	3.50	3.44	3.39
9	5.12	4.26	3.86	3.63	3.48	3.37	3.29	3.23	3.18
10	4.96	4.10	3.71	3.48	3.33	3.22	3.14	3.07	3.02
11	4.84	3.98	3.59	3.36	3.20	3.09	3.01	2.95	2.90
12	4.75	3.89	3.49	3.26	3.11	3.00	2.91	2.85	2.80
13	4.67	3.81	3.41	3.18	3.03	2.92	2.83	2.77	2.71
14	4.60	3.74	3.34	3.11	2.96	2.85	2.76	2.70	2.65
15	4.54	3.68	3.29	3.06	2.90	2.79	2.71	2.64	2.59
16	4.49	3.63	3.24	3.01	2.85	2.74	2.66	2.59	2.54
17	4.45	3.59	3.20	2.96	2.81	2.70	2.61	2.55	2.49
18	4.41	3.55	3.16	2.93	2.77	2.66	2.58	2.51	2.46
19	4.38	3.52	3.13	2.90	2.74	2.63	2.54	2.48	2.42
20	4.35	3.49	3.10	2.87	2.71	2.60	2.51	2.45	2.39
21	4.32	3.47	3.07	2.84	2.68	2.57	2.49	2.42	2.37
22	4.30	3.44	3.05	2.82	2.66	2.55	2.46	2.40	2.34
23	4.28	3.42	3.03	2.80	2.64	2.53	2.44	2.37	2.32
24	4.26	3.40	3.01	2.78	2.62	2.51	2.42	2.36	2.30
25	4.24	3.39	2.99	2.76	2.60	2.49	2.40	2.34	2.28
30	4.17	3.32	2.92	2.69	2.53	2.42	2.33	2.27	2.21
40	4.08	3.23	2.84	2.61	2.45	2.34	2.25	2.18	2.12
60	4.00	3.15	2.76	2.53	2.37	2.25	2.17	2.10	2.04
120	3.92	3.07	2.68	2.45	2.29	2.18	2.09	2.02	1.96
∞	3.84	3.00	2.60	2.37	2.21	2.10	2.01	1.94	1.88

Values of $F_{0.05; v_1, v_2}$

	v_1 = Degrees of freedom for numerator									
	10	12	15	20	24	30	40	60	120	∞
1	242	244	246	248	249	250	251	252	253	254
2	19.4	19.4	19.4	19.4	19.5	19.5	19.5	19.5	19.5	19.5
3	8.79	8.74	8.70	8.66	8.64	8.62	8.59	8.57	8.55	8.53
4	5.96	5.91	5.86	5.80	5.77	5.75	5.72	5.69	5.66	5.63
5	4.74	4.68	4.62	4.56	4.53	4.50	4.46	4.43	4.40	4.37
6	4.06	4.00	3.94	3.87	3.84	3.81	3.77	3.74	3.70	3.67
7	3.64	3.57	3.51	3.44	3.41	3.38	3.34	3.30	3.27	3.23
8	3.35	3.28	3.22	3.15	3.12	3.08	3.04	3.01	2.97	2.93
9	3.14	3.07	3.01	2.94	2.90	2.86	2.83	2.79	2.75	2.71
10	2.98	2.91	2.85	2.77	2.74	2.70	2.66	2.62	2.58	2.54
11	2.85	2.79	2.72	2.65	2.61	2.57	2.53	2.49	2.45	2.40
12	2.75	2.69	2.62	2.54	2.51	2.47	2.43	2.38	2.34	2.30
13	2.67	2.60	2.53	2.46	2.42	2.38	2.34	2.30	2.25	2.21
14	2.60	2.53	2.46	2.39	2.35	2.31	2.27	2.22	2.18	2.13
15	2.54	2.48	2.40	2.33	2.29	2.25	2.20	2.16	2.11	2.07
16	2.49	2.42	2.35	2.28	2.24	2.19	2.15	2.11	2.06	2.01
17	2.45	2.38	2.31	2.23	2.19	2.15	2.10	2.06	2.01	1.96
18	2.41	2.34	2.27	2.19	2.15	2.11	2.06	2.02	1.97	1.92
19	2.38	2.31	2.23	2.16	2.11	2.07	2.03	1.98	1.93	1.88
20	2.35	2.28	2.20	2.12	2.08	2.04	1.99	1.95	1.90	1.84
21	2.32	2.25	2.18	2.10	2.05	2.01	1.96	1.92	1.87	1.81
22	2.30	2.23	2.15	2.07	2.03	1.98	1.94	1.89	1.84	1.78
23	2.27	2.20	2.13	2.05	2.01	1.96	1.91	1.86	1.81	1.76
24	2.25	2.18	2.11	2.03	1.98	1.94	1.89	1.84	1.79	1.73
25	2.24	2.16	2.09	2.01	1.96	1.92	1.87	1.82	1.77	1.71
30	2.16	2.09	2.01	1.93	1.89	1.84	1.79	1.74	1.68	1.62
40	2.08	2.00	1.92	1.84	1.79	1.74	1.69	1.64	1.58	1.51
60	1.99	1.92	1.84	1.75	1.70	1.65	1.59	1.53	1.47	1.39
120	1.91	1.83	1.75	1.66	1.61	1.55	1.50	1.43	1.35	1.25
∞	1.83	1.75	1.67	1.57	1.52	1.46	1.39	1.32	1.22	1.00

v_2 = Degrees of freedom for denominator

Table VIII(b) gives the critical values of the **F** distribution for a cumulative probability of 0.99 ($\alpha = 0.01$). The probability (α) represents the area exceeding the value of $F_{0.01, v_1, v_2}$, as shown by the shaded area in the figure below.

◻ **EXAMPLES** If $v_1 = 15$ (representing the greater mean square), and $v_2 = 20$, then the critical value for $\alpha = 0.01$ is 3.09. $P(F \geq 3.09) = 0.01$, $P(F \leq 3.09) = 0.99$.

TABLE VIII(b)   Cumulative *F*-distribution of 0.99 ($\alpha = 0.01$)

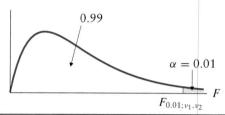

Values of $F_{0.01; v_1. v_2}$

$\alpha = 0.01$

$F_{0.01; v_1. v_2}$

v_1 = Degrees of freedom for numerator

v_2	1	2	3	4	5	6	7	8	9
1	4,052	5,000	5,403	5,625	5,764	5,859	5,928	5,982	6,023
2	98.5	99.0	99.2	99.2	99.3	99.3	99.4	99.4	99.4
3	34.1	30.8	29.5	28.7	28.2	27.9	27.7	27.5	27.3
4	21.2	18.0	16.7	16.0	15.5	15.2	15.0	14.8	14.7
5	16.3	13.3	12.1	11.4	11.0	10.7	10.5	10.3	10.2
6	13.7	10.9	9.78	9.15	8.75	8.47	8.26	8.10	7.98
7	12.2	9.55	8.45	7.85	7.46	7.19	6.99	6.84	6.72
8	11.3	8.65	7.59	7.01	6.63	6.37	6.18	6.03	5.91
9	10.6	8.02	6.99	6.42	6.06	5.80	5.61	5.47	5.35
10	10.0	7.56	6.55	5.99	5.64	5.39	5.20	5.06	4.94
11	9.65	7.21	6.22	5.67	5.32	5.07	4.89	4.74	4.63
12	9.33	6.93	5.95	5.41	5.06	4.82	4.64	4.50	4.39
13	9.07	6.70	5.74	5.21	4.86	4.62	4.44	4.30	4.19
14	8.86	6.51	5.56	5.04	4.70	4.46	4.28	4.14	4.03
15	8.68	6.36	5.42	4.89	4.56	4.32	4.14	4.00	3.89
16	8.53	6.23	5.29	4.77	4.44	4.20	4.03	3.89	3.78
17	8.40	6.11	5.19	4.67	4.34	4.10	3.93	3.79	3.68
18	8.29	6.01	5.09	4.58	4.25	4.01	3.84	3.71	3.60
19	8.19	5.93	5.01	4.50	4.17	3.94	3.77	3.63	3.52
20	8.10	5.85	4.94	4.43	4.10	3.87	3.70	3.56	3.46
21	8.02	5.78	4.87	3.37	4.04	3.81	3.64	3.51	3.40
22	7.95	5.72	4.82	4.31	3.99	3.76	3.59	3.45	3.35
23	7.88	5.66	4.76	4.26	3.94	3.71	3.54	3.41	3.30
24	7.82	5.61	4.72	4.22	3.90	3.67	3.50	3.36	3.26
25	7.77	5.57	4.68	4.18	3.86	3.63	3.46	3.32	3.22
30	7.56	5.39	4.51	4.02	3.70	3.47	3.30	3.17	3.07
40	7.31	5.18	4.31	3.83	3.51	3.29	3.12	2.99	2.89
60	7.08	4.98	4.13	3.65	3.34	3.12	2.95	2.82	2.72
120	6.85	4.79	3.95	3.48	3.17	2.96	2.79	2.66	2.56
∞	6.63	4.61	3.78	3.32	3.02	2.80	2.64	2.51	2.41

v_2 = Degrees of freedom for denominator

		ν_1 = Degrees of freedom for numerator								
		10	12	15	20	24	30	40	60	120	∞
	1	6,056	6,106	6,157	6,209	6,235	6,261	6,287	6,313	6,339	6,366
	2	99.4	99.4	99.4	99.4	99.5	99.5	99.5	99.5	99.5	99.5
	3	27.2	27.1	26.9	26.7	26.6	26.5	26.4	26.3	26.2	26.1
	4	14.5	14.4	14.2	14.0	13.9	13.8	13.7	13.7	13.6	13.5
	5	10.1	9.89	9.72	9.55	9.47	9.38	9.29	9.20	9.11	9.02
	6	7.87	7.72	7.56	7.40	7.31	7.23	7.14	7.06	6.97	6.88
	7	6.62	6.47	6.31	6.16	6.07	5.99	5.91	5.82	5.74	5.65
	8	5.81	5.67	5.52	5.36	5.28	5.20	5.12	5.03	4.95	4.86
	9	5.26	5.11	4.96	4.81	4.73	4.65	4.57	4.48	4.40	4.31
	10	4.85	4.71	4.56	4.41	4.33	4.25	4.17	4.08	4.00	3.91
ν_2 = Degrees of freedom for denominator	11	4.54	4.40	4.25	4.10	4.02	3.94	3.86	3.78	3.69	3.60
	12	4.30	4.16	4.01	3.86	3.78	3.70	3.62	3.54	3.45	3.36
	13	4.10	3.96	3.82	3.66	3.59	3.51	3.43	3.34	3.25	3.17
	14	3.94	3.80	3.66	3.51	3.43	3.35	3.27	3.18	3.09	3.00
	15	3.80	3.67	3.52	3.37	3.29	3.21	3.13	3.05	2.96	2.87
	16	3.69	3.55	3.41	3.26	3.18	3.10	3.02	2.93	2.84	2.75
	17	3.59	3.46	3.31	3.16	3.08	3.00	2.92	2.83	2.75	2.65
	18	3.51	3.37	3.23	3.08	3.00	2.92	2.84	2.75	2.66	2.57
	19	3.43	3.30	3.15	3.00	2.92	2.84	2.76	2.67	2.58	2.49
	20	3.37	3.23	3.09	2.94	2.86	2.78	2.69	2.61	2.52	2.42
	21	3.31	3.17	3.03	2.88	2.80	2.72	2.64	2.55	2.46	2.36
	22	3.26	3.12	2.98	2.83	2.75	2.67	2.58	2.50	2.40	2.31
	23	3.21	3.07	2.93	2.78	2.70	2.62	2.54	2.45	2.35	2.26
	24	3.17	3.03	2.89	2.74	2.66	2.58	2.49	2.40	2.31	2.21
	25	3.13	2.99	2.85	2.70	2.62	2.53	2.45	2.36	2.27	2.17
	30	2.98	2.84	2.70	2.55	2.47	2.39	2.30	2.21	2.11	2.01
	40	2.80	2.66	2.52	2.37	2.29	2.20	2.11	2.02	1.92	1.80
	60	2.63	2.50	2.35	2.20	2.12	2.03	1.94	1.84	1.73	1.60
	120	2.47	2.34	2.19	2.03	1.95	1.86	1.76	1.66	1.53	1.38
	∞	2.32	2.18	2.04	1.88	1.79	1.70	1.59	1.47	1.32	1.00

TABLE IX Table of Constants for Control Charts

Number of observations in sample n	Chart for averages	Chart for ranges			
	Constants for control limits	Constants for central line		Constants for control limits	
	A_2	d_2	$1/d_2$	D_3	D_4
2	1.880	1.128	0.8865	0	3.276
3	1.023	1.693	0.5907	0	2.575
4	0.729	2.059	0.4857	0	2.282
5	0.577	2.326	0.4299	0	2.115
6	0.483	2.534	0.3946	0	2.004
7	0.419	2.704	0.3698	0.076	1.924
8	0.373	2.847	0.3512	0.136	1.864
9	0.337	2.970	0.3367	0.184	1.816
10	0.308	3.078	0.3249	0.223	1.777
11	0.285	3.173	0.3152	0.256	1.744
12	0.266	3.258	0.3069	0.284	1.719
13	0.249	3.336	0.2998	0.308	1.692
14	0.235	3.407	0.2935	0.329	1.671
15	0.223	3.472	0.2880	0.348	1.652
16	0.212	3.532	0.2831	0.364	1.636
17	0.203	3.588	0.2787	0.379	1.621
18	0.194	3.640	0.2747	0.392	1.608
19	0.187	3.689	0.2711	0.404	1.596
20	0.180	3.735	0.2677	0.414	1.586
21	0.173	3.778	0.2647	0.425	1.575
22	0.167	3.819	0.2617	0.434	1.566
23	0.162	3.858	0.2592	0.443	1.557
24	0.157	3.895	0.2567	0.452	1.548
25	0.153	3.931	0.2544	0.459	1.541

Source: Reproduced by permission from ASTM Manual on Quality Control of Materials, American Society for Testing Materials, Philadelphia, PA, 1951.

TABLE X The Durbin–Watson d-statistic
Significance points of d_L and d_U: $\alpha = 0.05$

n	$m=1$ d_L	d_U	$m=2$ d_L	d_U	$m=3$ d_L	d_U	$m=4$ d_L	d_U	$m=5$ d_L	d_U
15	1.08	1.36	0.95	1.54	0.82	1.75	0.69	1.97	0.56	2.21
16	1.10	1.37	0.98	1.54	0.86	1.73	0.74	1.93	0.62	2.15
17	1.13	1.38	1.02	1.54	0.90	1.71	0.78	1.90	0.67	2.10
18	1.16	1.39	1.05	1.53	0.93	1.69	0.82	1.87	0.71	2.06
19	1.18	1.40	1.08	1.53	0.97	1.68	0.86	1.85	0.75	2.02
20	1.20	1.41	1.10	1.54	1.00	1.68	0.90	1.83	0.79	1.99
21	1.22	1.42	1.13	1.54	1.03	1.67	0.93	1.81	0.83	1.96
22	1.24	1.43	1.15	1.54	1.05	1.66	0.96	1.80	0.86	1.94
23	1.26	1.44	1.17	1.54	1.08	1.66	0.99	1.79	0.90	1.92
24	1.27	1.45	1.19	1.55	1.10	1.66	1.01	1.78	0.93	1.90
25	1.29	1.45	1.21	1.55	1.12	1.66	1.04	1.77	0.95	1.89
26	1.30	1.46	1.22	1.55	1.14	1.65	1.06	1.76	0.98	1.88
27	1.32	1.47	1.24	1.56	1.16	1.65	1.08	1.76	1.01	1.86
28	1.33	1.48	1.26	1.56	1.18	1.65	1.10	1.75	1.03	1.85
29	1.34	1.48	1.27	1.56	1.20	1.65	1.12	1.74	1.05	1.84
30	1.35	1.49	1.28	1.57	1.21	1.65	1.14	1.74	1.07	1.83
31	1.36	1.50	1.30	1.57	1.23	1.65	1.16	1.74	1.09	1.83
32	1.37	1.50	1.31	1.57	1.24	1.65	1.18	1.73	1.11	1.82
33	1.38	1.51	1.32	1.58	1.26	1.65	1.19	1.73	1.13	1.81
34	1.39	1.51	1.33	1.58	1.27	1.65	1.21	1.73	1.15	1.81
35	1.40	1.52	1.34	1.58	1.28	1.65	1.22	1.73	1.16	1.80
36	1.41	1.52	1.35	1.59	1.29	1.65	1.24	1.73	1.18	1.80
37	1.42	1.53	1.36	1.59	1.31	1.66	1.25	1.72	1.19	1.80
38	1.43	1.54	1.37	1.59	1.32	1.66	1.26	1.72	1.21	1.79
39	1.43	1.54	1.38	1.60	1.33	1.66	1.27	1.72	1.22	1.79
40	1.44	1.54	1.39	1.60	1.34	1.66	1.29	1.72	1.23	1.79
45	1.48	1.57	1.43	1.62	1.38	1.67	1.34	1.72	1.29	1.78
50	1.50	1.59	1.46	1.63	1.42	1.67	1.38	1.72	1.34	1.77
55	1.53	1.60	1.49	1.64	1.45	1.68	1.41	1.72	1.38	1.77
60	1.55	1.62	1.51	1.65	1.48	1.69	1.44	1.73	1.41	1.77
65	1.57	1.63	1.54	1.66	1.50	1.70	1.47	1.73	1.44	1.77
70	1.58	1.64	1.55	1.67	1.52	1.70	1.49	1.74	1.46	1.77
75	1.60	1.65	1.57	1.68	1.54	1.71	1.51	1.74	1.49	1.77
80	1.61	1.66	1.59	1.69	1.56	1.72	1.53	1.74	1.51	1.77
85	1.62	1.67	1.60	1.70	1.57	1.72	1.55	1.75	1.52	1.77
90	1.63	1.68	1.61	1.70	1.59	1.73	1.57	1.75	1.54	1.78
95	1.64	1.69	1.62	1.71	1.60	1.73	1.58	1.75	1.56	1.78
100	1.65	1.69	1.63	1.72	1.61	1.74	1.59	1.76	1.57	1.78

Significance points of d_L and d_U: $\alpha = 0.01$

n	m = 1		m = 2		m = 3		m = 4		m = 5	
	d_L	d_U	d_L	d_U	d_L	d_U	d_L	d_U	d_L	d_U
15	0.81	1.07	0.70	1.25	0.59	1.46	0.49	1.70	0.39	1.96
16	0.84	1.09	0.74	1.25	0.63	1.44	0.53	1.66	0.44	1.90
17	0.87	1.10	0.77	1.25	0.67	1.43	0.57	1.63	0.48	1.85
18	0.90	1.12	0.80	1.26	0.71	1.42	0.61	1.60	0.52	1.80
19	0.93	1.13	0.83	1.26	0.74	1.41	0.65	1.58	0.56	1.77
20	0.95	1.15	0.86	1.27	0.77	1.41	0.68	1.57	0.60	1.74
21	0.97	1.16	0.89	1.27	0.80	1.41	0.72	1.55	0.63	1.71
22	1.00	1.17	0.91	1.28	0.83	1.40	0.75	1.54	0.66	1.69
23	1.02	1.19	0.94	1.29	0.86	1.40	0.77	1.53	0.70	1.67
24	1.04	1.20	0.96	1.30	0.88	1.41	0.80	1.53	0.72	1.66
25	1.05	1.21	0.98	1.30	0.90	1.41	0.83	1.52	0.75	1.65
26	1.07	1.22	1.00	1.31	0.93	1.41	0.85	1.52	0.78	1.64
27	1.09	1.23	1.02	1.32	0.95	1.41	0.88	1.51	0.81	1.63
28	1.10	1.24	1.04	1.32	0.97	1.41	0.90	1.51	0.83	1.62
29	1.12	1.25	1.05	1.33	0.99	1.42	0.92	1.51	0.85	1.61
30	1.13	1.26	1.07	1.34	1.01	1.42	0.94	1.51	0.88	1.61
31	1.15	1.27	1.08	1.34	1.02	1.42	0.96	1.51	0.90	1.60
32	1.16	1.28	1.10	1.35	1.04	1.43	0.98	1.51	0.92	1.60
33	1.17	1.29	1.11	1.36	1.05	1.43	1.00	1.51	0.94	1.59
34	1.18	1.30	1.13	1.36	1.07	1.43	1.01	1.51	0.95	1.59
35	1.19	1.31	1.14	1.37	1.08	1.44	1.03	1.51	0.97	1.59
36	1.21	1.32	1.15	1.38	1.10	1.44	1.04	1.51	0.99	1.59
37	1.22	1.32	1.16	1.38	1.11	1.45	1.06	1.51	1.00	1.59
38	1.23	1.33	1.18	1.39	1.12	1.45	1.07	1.52	1.02	1.58
39	1.24	1.34	1.19	1.39	1.14	1.45	1.09	1.52	1.03	1.58
40	1.25	1.34	1.20	1.40	1.15	1.46	1.10	1.52	1.05	1.58
45	1.29	1.38	1.24	1.42	1.20	1.48	1.16	1.53	1.11	1.58
50	1.32	1.40	1.28	1.45	1.24	1.49	1.20	1.54	1.16	1.59
55	1.36	1.43	1.32	1.47	1.28	1.51	1.25	1.55	1.21	1.59
60	1.38	1.45	1.35	1.48	1.32	1.52	1.28	1.56	1.25	1.60
65	1.41	1.47	1.38	1.50	1.35	1.53	1.31	1.57	1.28	1.61
70	1.43	1.49	1.40	1.52	1.37	1.55	1.34	1.58	1.31	1.61
75	1.45	1.50	1.42	1.53	1.39	1.56	1.37	1.59	1.34	1.62
80	1.47	1.52	1.44	1.54	1.42	1.57	1.39	1.60	1.36	1.62
85	1.48	1.53	1.46	1.55	1.43	1.58	1.41	1.60	1.39	1.63
90	1.50	1.54	1.47	1.56	1.45	1.59	1.43	1.61	1.41	1.64
95	1.51	1.55	1.49	1.57	1.47	1.60	1.45	1.62	1.42	1.64
100	1.52	1.56	1.50	1.58	1.48	1.60	1.46	1.63	1.44	1.65

SOURCE: Reproduced by permission of the editor and authors, from J. Durbin and G. S. Watson, "Testing for serial correlation in least squares regression, (II)," *Biometrika*, 38, 1951, pp. 159--178.

TABLE XI   Critical values of r in the runs test

Given in the body of Table XI are various critical values of r for various values of n_1 and n_2. For the Wald–Wolfowitz two-sample runs test, any value of r that is equal to or smaller than that shown in Table XI is significant at the 0.05 level.

n_1 \ n_2	2	3	4	5	6	7	8	9	10	11	12	13	14	15	16	17	18	19	20
2											2	2	2	2	2	2	2	2	2
3					2	2	2	2	2	2	2	2	2	3	3	3	3	3	3
4				2	2	2	3	3	3	3	3	3	3	3	4	4	4	4	4
5			2	2	3	3	3	3	3	4	4	4	4	4	4	4	5	5	5
6		2	2	3	3	3	3	4	4	4	4	5	5	5	5	5	5	6	6
7		2	2	3	3	3	4	4	5	5	5	5	5	6	6	6	6	6	6
8		2	3	3	3	4	4	5	5	5	6	6	6	6	6	7	7	7	7
9		2	3	3	4	4	5	5	5	6	6	6	7	7	7	7	8	8	8
10		2	3	3	4	5	5	5	6	6	7	7	7	7	8	8	8	8	9
11		2	3	4	4	5	5	6	6	7	7	7	8	8	8	9	9	9	9
12	2	2	3	4	4	5	6	6	7	7	7	8	8	8	9	9	9	10	10
13	2	2	3	4	5	5	6	6	7	7	8	8	9	9	9	10	10	10	10
14	2	2	3	4	5	5	6	7	7	8	8	9	9	9	10	10	10	11	11
15	2	3	3	4	5	6	6	7	7	8	8	9	9	10	10	11	11	11	12
16	2	3	4	4	5	6	6	7	8	8	9	9	10	10	11	11	11	12	12
17	2	3	4	4	5	6	7	7	8	9	9	10	10	11	11	11	12	12	13
18	2	3	4	5	5	6	7	8	8	9	9	10	10	11	11	12	12	13	13
19	2	3	4	5	6	6	7	8	8	9	10	10	11	11	12	12	13	13	13
20	2	3	4	5	6	6	7	8	9	9	10	10	11	12	12	13	13	13	14

Adapted from Frieda S. Swed and C. Eisenhart, "Tables for testing randomness of grouping in a sequence of alternatives." *Ann. Math. Statist.*, Vol. 14 (1943), pp. 83--86, with the kind permission of the authors and publisher.

TABLE XII   Critical values of T for the Wilcoxon matched-pairs signed-ranks test

	Level of Significance for One-Tailed Test		
	.025	.01	.005
n	Level of Significance for Two-Tailed Test		
	.05	.02	.01
6	0	---	---
7	2	0	---
8	4	2	0
9	6	3	2
10	8	5	3
11	11	7	5
12	14	10	7
13	17	13	10
14	21	16	13
15	25	20	16
16	30	24	20
17	35	28	23
18	40	33	28
19	46	38	32
20	52	43	38
21	59	49	43
22	66	56	49
23	73	62	55
24	81	69	61
25	89	77	68

Adapted from Table I of F. Wilcoxon, *Some Rapid Approximate Statistical Procedures.* New York: American Cyanamid Company, 1949, p. 13. Reproduced with the permission of the American Cyanamid Company.

TABLE XIII   Critical values of D in the Kolmogorov–Smirnov one-sample test

Sample Size (n)	Level of Significance for $D = $ Maximum $\mid F_1 - S_1 \mid$				
	.20	.15	.10	.05	.01
1	.900	.925	.950	.975	.995
2	.684	.726	.776	.842	.929
3	.565	.597	.642	.708	.828
4	.494	.525	.564	.624	.733
5	.446	.474	.510	.565	.669
6	.410	.436	.470	.521	.618
7	.381	.405	.438	.486	.577
8	.358	.381	.411	.457	.543
9	.339	.360	.388	.432	.514
10	.322	.342	.368	.410	.490
11	.307	.326	.352	.391	.468
12	.295	.313	.338	.375	.450
13	.284	.302	.325	.361	.433
14	.274	.292	.314	.349	.418
15	.266	.283	.304	.338	.404
16	.258	.274	.295	.328	.392
17	.250	.266	.286	.318	.381
18	.244	.259	.278	.309	.371
19	.237	.252	.272	.301	.363
20	.231	.246	.264	.294	.356
25	.21	.22	.24	.27	.32
30	.19	.20	.22	.24	.29
25	.18	.19	.21	.23	.27
Over 35	$\dfrac{1.07}{\sqrt{n}}$	$\dfrac{1.14}{\sqrt{n}}$	$\dfrac{1.22}{\sqrt{n}}$	$\dfrac{1.36}{\sqrt{n}}$	$\dfrac{1.63}{\sqrt{n}}$

Adapted from F. J. Massey, Jr., "The Kolmogorov--Smirnov test for goodness of fit." *J. Amer. Statist. Ass.*, Vol. 46 (1951), p. 70, with the kind permission of the author and publisher.

Answers to Odd-Numbered Problems

Chapter One

1.1 A set of numbers could be either a population or a sample. However, if Greek letters (such as μ or π or σ) are used, the data set is a population.

1.5 a) $\mu = 2,892,212$. $\pi = 32/81 = 0.395$

b) $\bar{x} = 5,516,041$; mean for first 50 companies $= 5,649,044.48$

1.7 a)

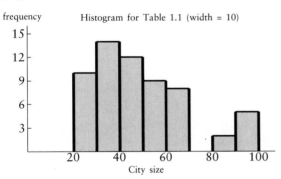

b)

1.9

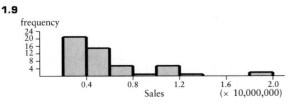

1.11

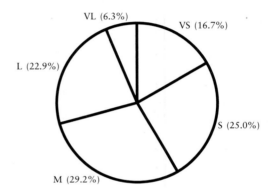

1.13

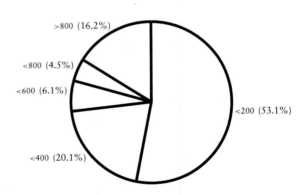

Chapter Two

2.3 The amount of price decrease is $45 - 35 = \$10$ for the sweater and $85 - 60 = \$25$ for the coat. Using a weighted average, the average percent decrease is $100[5(10) + 3(25)]/[5(45) + 3(85)] = 26.04\%$.

2.5 a) A guess for the median might be 1/5th of the way between 27.5 and 32.5, which is approximately 29.

b) The mode is the midpoint of the 2nd interval (midpoint = 25.5).

c) $\mu = (1/N)\Sigma f_i x_i = 31.17$.

2.7 a) Median = 1.0 [since $(N + 1)/2 = (100 + 1)/2 = 50.5$]. Mode = 0.

b) $\mu = (1/N)\Sigma x_i f_i = 0.80$.

2.9 For the values of x_i use the midpoints of the vacancy rate intervals, 5, 10, and 15 respectively. $\mu = \Sigma x_i (f_i/N) = 8.5$.

2.11 a) The median is $120,800.
$\mu = (1/N)\Sigma x_i = 118,880$.
The distribution has negative skewness.

b) $\mu = \$118,500$

2.13 The prospective employee knows nothing about the distribution of that company's data over the stated range. Ninety-nine workers at the lower end-point of the range and only one at the upper end-point would give a much different picture of the company than ninety-nine at the upper end and only one at the lower end. At least the average of this distribution should be given.

2.15 $\mu = 30.67$ (from Problem 2.5)

x (midpoints)	f	$(x - \mu)$	$(x - \mu)^2$	$(x - \mu)^2 f/N$
20	60	-10.67	113.85	22.77
25	80	-5.67	32.15	8.57
30	50	-0.67	0.45	0.08
35	40	4.33	18.75	2.50
40	30	9.33	87.05	8.71
45	20	14.33	205.35	13.69
50	20	19.33	373.65	24.91
	300			81.23

$\sigma^2 = 81.23$ (depends on how you round)

2.17 a) $\sigma^2 = \dfrac{\Sigma(x_1 - \mu)^2 f_i}{N} =$
$\dfrac{8(-2)^2 + 9(-1)^2 + 7(+1)^2 + 6(+3)^2}{30} = \dfrac{102}{30} = 3.4$
Standard deviation: $\sigma = \sqrt{3.4} = 1.844$

b) $\mu + \sigma = 27 + 1.844 = 28.844$; $\mu - \sigma = 25.156$. The mileage values of 26 and 28 are included; $\mu \pm 1\sigma$ thus includes $(16/30)100$ or 53% of the population.
$\mu \pm 2\sigma = 27 \pm 2(1.844)$ is the interval 23.312 to 30.688.
Thus $\mu \pm 2\sigma$ includes 100% of the distribution.

c) $(1.544/27)100 = 6.8\%$

2.19 $\sigma^2 = \Sigma(x_i - \mu)^2(f_i/N) = [(-3.5)^2(0.5) + (1.5)^2(0.3) + (6.5)^2(0.2)] = 15.25$

2.21 a) $\sigma^2 = (1/N)\Sigma(x_i - \mu)^2 = 0.443/6 = 0.0738$

b) $\sigma = \sqrt{0.0738} = 0.272$; $\mu \pm 1\sigma = 1.07 \pm 0.272 = [0.798, 1.342]$
There are three years (3, 5, 6) that had prices within one standard deviation of the mean.
Proportion = 0.50.

c) CV = $(0.272/1.07)100 = 25.4$ percent

2.23 a) $\mu = \Sigma x_i/N = 20/5 = 4$;
$\sigma^2 = (1/N)\Sigma(x_i - \mu)^2 = (1/5)(1 + 1 + 9 + 16 + 1) = 28/5 = 5.6$
$\sigma = \sqrt{5.6} = 2.37$

b) $\mu = (20 + 2 + 6)/7 = 28/7 = 4.0$
$\sigma^2 = (1/7)[28 + (2 - 4)^2 + (6 - 4)^2] = 36/7 = 5.14$
$\sigma = \sqrt{5.14} = 2.27 < 2.37$

c) $\mu = 4$, $\sigma^2 = \Sigma(x_i - \mu)^2/N = 60/7 = 8.6$, $\sigma = 2.93$
The standard deviation is larger because the new data that have been included in part c) are farther away from the mean than one standard deviation of the old data.

2.25 $\mu = 166/10 = 16.6$; mode = 14; median = 14; 60% mid-range excludes values (6, 7, 27, 35); 60% mid-range is $19 - 12 = 7$.
$\sigma^2 = 70.04$; $\sigma = \sqrt{70.04} = 8.37$

2.27 a) 85% of all math scores are below this one.

b) Between 50% and 75% of all college grades are below yours.

c) 70% to 80% of all franchises have lower sales growth.

2.29 $\mu = (1/32)[4(98) + 5(93) + 6(88) + 5(83) + 1(78) + 4(73) + 2(68) + 5(63)]$
$\mu = (2621)/32 = 81.91$.
Using formula (2.5), $\sigma^2 = (1/32)4,386.719 = 137.085$

2.31 a) Mode is $36,400, which appears twice. Median is halfway between the 8th and 9th values, which is $(1/2)(35,800 + 36,000) = \$35,900$.

b) Using the mid-point of each class as the value of x_i, $\mu = 35,781.25$.
The difference between this mean and the one calculated in 1.10(b) is that some of the individual observational detail is lost and grouping error is introduced.

2.33 a) $\mu = (1/10)(289,865) = \$28,986.50$
$\sigma^2 = 23,214,515.25$; $\sigma = \$4,818.14$
Median = $(1/2)(26,600 + 29,170) = \$27,885$

2.39 We assume "under 20" means 0--19, and "50 and over" means 50--90. We use class mid-points. For those who liked the movie, the mean is $\mu = (1/N)\Sigma(f_i x_i) = 24$; $\sigma^2 = 267$
For those who disliked the movie: $\mu = 31.9$; $\sigma^2 = 370$
The movie seems to appeal more to young people than to older people.

2.41 a)

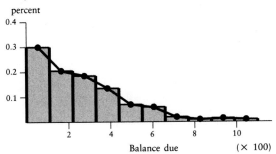

percent
Balance due   ($\times$ 100)

b) The open-ended class of "$1,000 and over" is not a good statistical procedure.

c) $\mu = (1/N)\Sigma f_i x_i = 225.25$

d) $\sigma^2 = 31,370.44$; $\sigma = \sqrt{31,370.44} = 177.12$
$\mu \pm 1\sigma = 225.25 \pm 177.12 = 48.13$ to 402.37.
This includes about 70% of the population (interpolating).
$\mu \pm 2\sigma = 225.25 \pm 2(177.12) = 0$ to 579.49.
This includes about 95.5% of the population.

e) The mean exceeds the median (225.25 > 190.02) so this distribution is positively skewed (skewed to the right).

2.43

Mean	100.125
Mode	98
Variance	10.3594
Std. Deviation	3.21860
Interquartile range	5

2.45 Mean fee = $51.80; $\sigma = 12.99
Plus or minus 1σ is $38.81 to $64.79.
Includes 26/40 doctors, or 65%.

2.47 mean = $\mu = (1/N)\Sigma f_i x_i = 396.2381$;
$\sigma^2 = 245.134$; $\sigma = 15.66$

2.49 $N = 300$, $\mu = 13.51833$
$\sigma^2 = 45.50$; $\sigma = \sqrt{45.50} = 6.745$
About 2/3 of the time, the total return is within 13.518 ± 6.745 or [6.733 to 20.263].

Chapter Three

3.1 a) Discrete and finite

b) $P(A) = P(B) = P(C) = 0.1666$, $P(D) = 0.50$. Subjective probabilities.

c) All probabilities between 0 and 1, and sum = 1.000.

3.3 a) Finite, discrete   **b)** Infinite, discrete

c) Finite, discrete   **d)** Infinite, continuous

e) Infinite, continuous

3.5 number of winners: $= 1 + 500 + 1000 = 1501$
$P(\text{win}) = (1501/50,000) = 0.03002$.

3.7 $P(> 30,000 \text{ and sales} > 800 \text{ million}) = 29/179 = 0.1620$

3.9 a) 360 workers   **b)** $70/360 = 0.1944$

c) $95/360 = 0.2639$

3.11 a) We need to determine how many different orderings are possible, where each switch (step) has two possible positions. Using Formula 2.1, where $n_1 = 2$, $n_2 = 2, \ldots, n_9 = 2$.
$n = (n_1)(n_2)(n_3)\ldots(n_9) = 2^9 = 512$. Person would have to try 512 codes: $P(\text{correct on 1 try}) = 1/512$.

b) There are only 9 different places the one "$-$" could be. Hence, $P(\text{correct on 1 try}) = 1/9$.

3.13 We must determine the value of $(2)(2)(2)\ldots(2)$ $= 2^k$ where $k = 8$, or $2^8 = 256$ different possibilities.

3.15 ABC, ACB, BCA, BAC, CAB, CBA, or 6 orderings.

3.17 a) $10^P 10 = \dfrac{10!}{(10-10)!} =$
$10 \cdot 9 \cdot 8 \cdot 7 \cdot 6 \cdot 5 \cdot 4 \cdot 3 \cdot 2 \cdot 1 = 3,628,800$

b) $10^C 3 = \dfrac{10!}{3!(10-3)!} =$
$\dfrac{10 \cdot 9 \cdot 8 \cdot 7 \cdot 6 \cdot 5 \cdot 4 \cdot 3 \cdot 2 \cdot 1}{(3 \cdot 2 \cdot 1)7 \cdot 6 \cdot 5 \cdot 4 \cdot 3 \cdot 2 \cdot 1} = 120$

3.19 a) $50! = 3.04140932(10^{64})$

b) $2.425192812(10^{23})$

c) $3.96845541(10^{22})$

3.23 a) $P(30 \text{ and } f) = P(\leq 30)P(f| \leq 30) = (1/2)(1/2) = (1/4)$

b) Indicates dependence, since $P(\text{female})$ changes depending on age.

c) $P(\text{female and age} \leq 30) = 1/4$
$P(\text{age} \leq 50) = 1 - P(\text{age} > 50) = 3/4$
$P(\text{age} \leq 30 \mid \text{female}) = \dfrac{1/4}{7/16} = 4/7$

d) $P(\text{female or} > 50) = P(f) + P(> 50) -$
$P(f \text{ and} > 50) = (7/16) + (1/4) - (1/8) = 9/16$

3.25 a) $P(G \text{ and } M) = P(G)P(M \mid G) = (0.60)(0.20) = 0.12$

b) $P(G \text{ or } M) = P(G) + P(M) - P(G \text{ and } M) = 0.60 + 0.30 - 0.12 = 0.78$

c)

	M	N	C	
G	0.12	0.30	0.18	0.60
E	0.18	0.10	0.12	0.40
	0.30	0.40	0.30	

d) Not independent since $P(M \mid G) = 0.20 \neq P(M) = 0.30$.

3.27 a) $P(6_f \text{ and } 6_m) = (1/6)(1/6) = 1/36$

b) $P(6_f \text{ or } 6_m) = P(6_m) + P(6_m) - P(6_f \text{ and } 6_m) = (1/6) + (1/6) - (1/36) = 11/36$

c) $P(\text{not alike}) = 1 - P(\text{alike})$
$P(\text{alike}) = P(1,1) + P(2,2) + \ldots + P(6,6) = (1/6)(1/6) + (1/6)(1/6) + \ldots + (1/6)(1/6) = 6/36 = 1/6$
$P(\text{not alike}) = 1 - (1/6) = 5/6$

3.29 a) $P(\text{male}) = 150/250 = 3/5$

b) $P(> 150) = 130/250 = 0.52$

c) $P(> 67 \text{ in.}) = 170/250 = 17/25 = 0.68$

d) $P(\leq 67 \text{ and male}) = P(\text{male})P(\leq 67 \mid \text{male}) = (150/250)(10/150) = 0.04$

e) $P(\text{female} \mid > 67) = \dfrac{P(\text{female and} > 67)}{P(> 67)} = \dfrac{30/250}{170/250} = 3/17$

3.31 a) $P(G \mid M) = \dfrac{P(M \mid G)P(G)}{P(M \mid G)P(G) + P(M \mid E)P(E)} = \dfrac{(.12/.6)(.6)}{(.12/.6)(.6) + (.18/.37)(.37)} = 0.12/0.30 = 0.40$

b) $P(f \mid \leq 30) = \dfrac{P(\leq 30 \mid f)P(f)}{P(\leq 30 \mid f)P(f) + P(\leq 30 \mid m)P(m)} = \dfrac{1/4}{(1/4) + (1/4)} = \dfrac{1}{2}$

3.35 $P(\text{pass} \mid \text{selected correctly}) = 0.90$;
$P(\text{selected correctly}) = 1/5$
$P(\text{pass} \mid \text{not correct}) = 0.30$; $P(\text{not correct}) = 4/5$

a) $P(\text{pass}) =$
$P(\text{Pass} \mid \text{selected correctly})P(\text{selected correctly}) +$
$P(\text{pass} \mid \text{not correct})P(\text{not correct}) = (1/5)(0.90) + (4/5)(0.30) = 0.42$

b) $P(\text{selected correctly} \mid \text{pass}) =$
$\dfrac{P(\text{selected correctly})P(\text{pass} \mid \text{selected correctly})}{P(\text{pass})} =$
$\dfrac{(1/5)(0.90)}{0.42} = \dfrac{0.18}{0.42} = \dfrac{3}{7}$

3.37 a) $P(\geq 60 \mid \text{large}) = \dfrac{46 + 18}{6 + 30 + 46 + 18} = 0.64$

b) $P(\text{small} \mid \geq 70) =$

$$\dfrac{P(\geq 70 \mid \text{small})P(\text{small})}{P(\geq 70 \mid \text{S})P(\text{small}) + P(\geq 70 \mid \text{med})P(\text{med}) + P(\geq 70 \mid \text{large})P(\text{large})}$$

$= \dfrac{0.06}{0.06 + 0.04 + 0.09} = 0.3158$

3.39 $P(\text{fiscal correct}) = 0.80$,
$P(\text{monetary correct}) = 0.80$

a) $P(\text{neither})$
$= P(\text{fiscal incorrect})P(\text{monetary incorrect}) = (0.20)(0.20) = 0.04$
$P(\text{both}) = P(\text{fiscal correct})P(\text{monetary correct}) = (0.80)(0.80) = 0.64$
$P(\text{only 1}) = P(\text{fiscal correct})P(\text{monetary incorrect}) + P(\text{fiscal incorrect})P(\text{monetary correct}) = (0.80)(0.20) + (0.20(0.80) = 0.32$

b) $P(\text{only 1} \mid \text{stable}) =$

$$\dfrac{P(\text{only1})P(\text{stable} \mid \text{only1})}{P(1)P(\text{stable} \mid 1) + P(\text{both})P(\text{stable} \mid \text{both}) + P(\text{neither})P(\text{stable} \mid \text{neither})}$$

$= \dfrac{(.32)(.70)}{(0.32)(.70) + (.64)(.99) + (.04)(.40)} =$
$\dfrac{.224}{.224 + .6336 + .016} = \dfrac{0.224}{0.8736} = 0.2564$
$P(\text{both} \mid \text{stable}) = \dfrac{(0.64)(0.99)}{0.8736} = \dfrac{0.6336}{0.8736} = 0.7253$
$P(\text{neither} \mid \text{stable}) = \dfrac{(0.04)(0.04)}{0.8736} = \dfrac{0.016}{0.8736} = 0.0183$
They do sum to one: $0.2564 + 0.7253 + 0.0183 = 1.0000$

3.43 a) Solving the following equation for $P(\text{above 90 and woman})$, $P(\text{above 90 or woman}) = P(\text{woman}) + P(\text{above 90}) - P(\text{above 90 and woman})$, we obtain
$P(\text{above 90 and woman}) = P(\text{woman}) + P(\text{above 90}) - P(\text{above 90 or woman}) = (2/4) + (3/4) - (4/4) = 1/4$

b) $P(\text{above 90} \mid \text{woman}) = \dfrac{P(\text{above 90 and woman})}{P(\text{woman})}$
$= \dfrac{(1/4)}{(2/4)} = \dfrac{1}{2}$

c) $P(\text{woman} \mid \text{above 90}) = \dfrac{P(\text{above 90 and woman})}{P(\text{above 90})}$
$= \dfrac{(1/4)}{(3/4)} = \dfrac{1}{3}$

3.45 Ave = \$370.33; 2 of the 6 are less than \$370.33;
P(at least 1) = P(only 1 lower) + P(both lower);
P(both lower) = P(1st lower)P(2nd lower) = (2/6)(1/5) = 1/15;
P(only 1 lower) = P(1st larger)P(2nd smaller) + P(1st smaller)P(2nd larger) = (4/6)(2/5) + (2/6)(4/5) = 8/15;
P(at least 1 lower) = 8/15 + 1/15 = 9/15 = 3/5
or $1 - \left(\dfrac{4}{6} * \dfrac{3}{5}\right) = \dfrac{18}{30} = \dfrac{3}{5}$

3.47 a) P(S and $\leq$ 1) = P(S)P($\leq$ 1 | S) = 0.02

b) P($\leq$ 1 | ISF) = 0.20

c) P(ISF| $\leq$ 1) = 0.05 $\neq$ P(ISF) = 0.01 $\rightarrow$ not independent.
P($\leq$ 1 | student) = (1/3) $\neq$ P($\leq$ 1) = 0.04 $\rightarrow$ not independent.

3.49 P(same, not 0) + P($\geq$ 1 has O) = P(both A) + P(both B) + P(both AB) + P(both O) + P(O_1 and A_2) + P(A_1 and O_2) + P(B_1 and O_2) + P(O_1 and B_2) + P(AB_1 and O_2) + P(O_1 and AB_2)
= 0.16 + 0.01 + 0.0025 + 0.2025 + 0.18 + 0.18 + 0.045 + 0.045 + 0.0225 + 0.0225 = 0.87

3.53 a) P(> \$1,000 income or > 20 households) = 50/179

b) P(> \$1,000 income and > 20 households) = 43/179

c) 43/49

e) Not independent, since P(> \$1,000| > 20) = 43/49 $\neq$ P(> \$1,000) = 44/179

3.55 Net Revenue from selling phones = \$1,000,000
Expected costs:

Returned def. phones = \$500,000
[= 0.50(0.05)1,000,000(\$20)]

Returned non def. phones = \$28,500
[= 0.01(0.95)(1,000,000)(\$3)]

P(return) = 0.50(0.05) + 0.01(0.95) = 0.0345

P(defective | returned) = 0.025/0.0345 = 0.7246

Profit = \$1,000,000 − 500,000 − \$28,500 = \$471,500.

Chapter Four

4.1

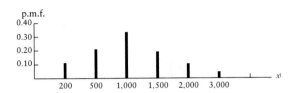

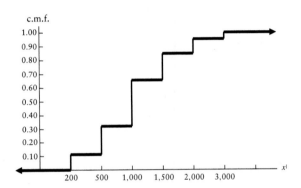

4.3 a) $E[x] = \Sigma x P(x) = 10.25$

b) $V[x] = (2 - 10.25)^2(2/12) + (7 - 10.25)^2(4/12) + (8 - 10.25)^2(1/12) + (16 - 10.25)^2(2/12) + (17 - 10.25)^2(1/12) = 32.1875$

4.5 a)

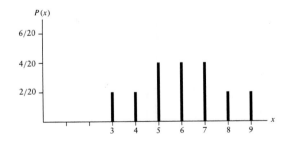

b) $E[x] = \Sigma x P(x) = 6.00$

c) $V[x] = E[(x - \mu)^2] = 3.0$
$\sigma_x = \sqrt{3} = 1.732$

d) Add samples (1, 1), (2, 2), (3, 3), (4, 4), and (5, 5)

to part a)

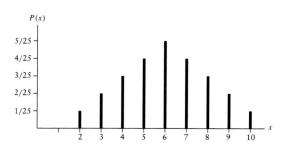

4.7 a) $E[x] = \Sigma x P(x) = \Sigma x (1/2)^x = 1.875$. [This answer, and $V[x]$ below, are only approximations because we limited x to be ≤ 6.]

b) By Formula (4.4):
$V[x] = \Sigma (x - 1.875)^2 (1/2)^x = (-0.875)^2 (1/2) + (0.125)^2 (1/4) + \cdots + (4.125)^2 (1/64) = 1.398$.

4.9 a) $E[x] = 1950/10 = 195$

b) $V[x] = E[(x - 195)^2] = (20^2 + 7^2 + 1^2 + 7^2 + 1^2 + 20^2 + 7^2 + 1^2 + 1^2 + 7^2)(1/10) = 100$
$\sigma = \sqrt{100} = 10$.

c) Between 185 and 205 are 8 of the 10 values (80%). All values lie between 175 and 215.

4.11 a)

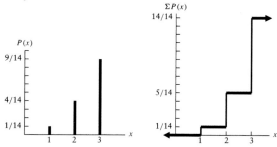

b) $1 \geq P(x) \geq 0$ since 1/14, 4/14, 9/14 are all between 1 and 0.
$\Sigma P(x) = 1/14 + 4/14 + 9/14 = 1.0$

c) $E[x] = \Sigma x P(x) = 1(1/14) + 2(4/14) + 3(9/14) = 36/14 = 2.571$
$V[x] = (1 - 2.571)^2 (1/14) + (2 - 2.571)^2 (4/14) + (3 - 2.571)^2 (4/14) = 0.39$

4.13 a)

b) $E[x] = 4(3/4) + 12(1/4) = 6.0$
$V[x] = \Sigma (x - 6.0)^2 P(x) = 2^2 (3/4) + 6^2 (1/4) = 3 + 9 = 12.0$

4.15 a) Any number $>$ \$2.00 is acceptable.

b) The student will earn \$65 or less if the number of consecutive sales is less than or equal to 5.
$P(\text{sales} \leq 5) = 31/32$

c) $E[x] = 2(1/2) + 4(1/4) + 8(1/8) + 16(1/16) + \cdots = 1 + 1 + 1 + 1 + \cdots = \text{infinity}$

4.17 a)

x	$P(x)$	y	$P(y)$
40,000	.25	30,000	1/3
20,000	.50	20,000	1/3
0	.25	10,000	1/3
$E[x] = 20,000$		$E[y] = 20,000$	

b) $E[x] = 10,000[4(1/4) + 2(1/2) + 0(1/4)] = 20,000$
$E[y] = 10,000[(3 + 2 + 1)(1/3)] = 20,000$

c) $V[x] = E[(x - 20,000)^2] = 200,000,000$;
$V[y] = 66,666,666$
$V[x/10,000] = \Sigma[(x/10,000) - 2]^2 P(x) = 2$
$V[x]/10,000 = 200,000,000/10,000 = 20,000$
Thus, $V[x/10,000] = \dfrac{1}{(10,000)^2} V[x]$

4.19 b) $\mu = \Sigma x P(x) = 47,675$
$\sigma^2 = 983,719,375$; $\sigma = 31,364$

4.23 a) Let $y = -2,500 + (.001)(x)$; y values are -17, $+19$, $+11$, -5.
$E[y] = (-17 + 19 + 11 - 5)(1/4) = 2$

b) $E[x] = \dfrac{E[y] - (-2,500)}{.001} = (2 + 2,500)(1000) = 2,502,000$

c) $V[y] = E[(y - 2)^2] = (19^2 + 17^2 + 9^2 + 7^2)(1/4) = 780/4 = 195$
$V[x] = V[y](1,000)^2 = 195 + 10^6 = 195,000,000$

4.25 a) $E[x] = 5$; $E[y] = 14$

b) $C[x, y] = 1.6 - 2.4 - 2.0 + 1.8 = -1$

c) $V[x] = 3.2 + 0.8 = 4.0$; $V[y] = 9.6 + 14.4 = 24.0$

d) $V[3x - 4y] = 3^2 (4.0) + (-4)^2 (24.0) + 2(3)(-4)(-1) = 444$

4.27

x	$P(x)$	y	$P(y)$	$x+y$	$P(x+y)$
1	0.4	4	0.6	5	0.24
2	0.2	9	0.4	10	0.16
4	0.4			6	0.12
				11	0.08
				8	0.24
				13	0.16
				sum	1.00

$(x+y)P(x+y)$	$[(x+y)-8.4]^2P(x+y)$
1.2	2.7744
1.6	0.4096
0.72	0.6912
0.88	0.5408
1.92	0.0384
2.08	3.3856
sum 8.40	7.8400

a) $E[x]+E[y]=2.4+6.0=8.4$
$E[x+y]=\Sigma(x+y)P(x+y)=8.4$

b) $V[x]=1.84;\ V[y]=6.0$
$V[x]+V[y]=1.84+6.0=7.84$
$V[x+y]=7.84$

4.29 a) $E[x\cdot y]=\Sigma(x\cdot y)P(x,y)=205/20=10.25$

b) $E[x+y]=E[x]+E[y]=(107/20)+(41/20)=$
$148/20=7.4$
$E[x-y]=(107/20)-(41/20)=66/20=3.3$

c) $C[x,y]=E[x\cdot y]-E[x]E[y]=-0.72$

d) $V[x]=14.23;\ V[y]=0.65$
$V[x+y]=14.23+0.65+2(-0.72)=13.44$
$V[x-y]=14.23+0.65-2(-0.72)=16.32$

4.31 b) $E[x]=\Sigma xP(x)=2.0;\ V[x]=1.0$

c) $E[y]=-4(1/16)-2(4/16)+0+2(4/16)+4(1/16)=$
0
$V[y]=4.0$

d) $E[y]=E[2x-4]=2E[x]-E[4]=4.0-4=0$
$V[y]=V[2x-4]=V[2x]+V[4]=4V[x]=4(1)=4$
Answers are the same.

4.33 a)

x	1	2	3	4	5	6	$g(y)$
1	1/36	0	0	0	0	0	$1/36=.0278$
2	1/36	1/30	0	0	0	0	.0611
y 3	1/36	1/30	1/24	0	0	0	.1028
4	1/36	1/30	1/24	1/18	0	0	.1584
5	1/36	1/30	1/24	1/18	1/12	0	.2416
6	1/36	1/30	1/24	1/18	1/12	1/6	.4083

b) $P(y=0\mid x=3)=P(y=1\mid x=3)=$
$P(y=2\mid x=3)=0$
$P(y=3\mid x=3)=P(y=4\mid x=3)=$
$P(y=5\mid x=3)=P(y=6\mid x=3)=$
$(1/24)/(4/24)=(1/24)/(4/24)=1/4$

c) $\Sigma yP(y)=1(.0278)+2(.0611)+3(.1028)+$
$4(.1584)+5(.2416)+6(.4083)=4.75$

4.39 The new data are 0, 13, 21, 27, 19, 40, 13, 19, 21, 27.
$\mu=\Sigma x_i/N=200/10=20$, which is 175 less than the mean in 4.9
$\sigma^2=100$, which is the same variance as 4.9.

4.41 Profit $=0.03x$, so $E[\text{profit}]=E[0.03x]=$
$0.03E[x]$.
Since $E[x]=5.64,\ E[\text{profit}]=0.1692$ cents per sale.
$V[\text{profit}]=0.01306$
Standard deviation of profit $=\sqrt{0.01306}=0.1143$
cents

4.43 $\mu=\Sigma xP(x)=0.35(1)+0.30(2)+0.10(3)+$
$0.15(4)+0.08(5)+0.02(6)=2.37$
$\sigma^2=1.95;\ \sigma=1.4$ (for one car, not two)

4.45 a) $E[x]=1.87;\ V[x]=0.71$
$E[y]=2.59;\ V[y]=1.04$

b) $E[x,y]=5.08$
$C[x,y]=5.08-(1.87)(2.59)=5.08-4.84=0.24$

c) Jobs and promotions are not independent because the covariance $\neq 0$.

4.47 From 4.13, expected sales of boxes of spark plugs is 6.0 and the variance is 12.0. Therefore, expected profit is $10(6)=\$60$, and the variance of expected profit is $(\$10)^2 12=1,200$ (dollars squared).

Chapter Five

5.1 a) Skewed right

b) $E[x]=n\pi=6(.4)=2.4$
$V[x]=n(\pi)(1-\pi)=6(.4)(.6)=1.44.$

c) $n=6,\ \pi=0.4.$ From Table I, $P(x\geq 4)=0.1792$

5.3 $n=4,\ \pi=0.2;\ P(x=2)=0.1536.$ Each project bid cannot depend on bid or success/failure in previous projects.

5.5 a)

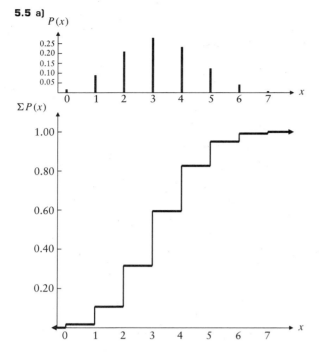

b) $P(x = 7) = 0.0079$; $P(x \geq 7) = 0.0086$

c) $\mu = n\pi = 3.2$; $\sigma^2 = n\pi(1 - \pi) = 8(.4)(.6) = 1.92$

5.7 a) $28/165 = 0.1697$; $15/165 = 0.0909$
$(28/165)22,395 \cong 3,800$; $(15/165)22,395 \cong 2,036$

b) $\$10.20(28/165)(22,395) - (1.81)(15/165)(22,395)$
$= \$35,078.71$

5.9 a) $P(x \geq 5 \mid n = 37, \pi = 0.60) = 0.0884$

b) $P(x \geq 25) = 0.2217$
$P(x < 25) = 0.7783$

c) $P(x \geq 133) = 0.0872$

d) $P(x = 10) + P(x < 5) = 0.0976 + 0.0696$
$= 0.1672$

5.11 $n = 6$, $\pi = 0.25$, using Table I:

a) $P(x = 3) = 0.1318$ **b)** $P(x \geq 3) = 0.1694$

c) $P(x \leq 3) = 0.9620$ **d)** $P(2 \leq x \leq 4) = 0.4614$

e) $\mu = n\pi = 6(1/4) = 1.5$
$\sigma^2 = n\pi(1 - \pi) = 6(1/4)(3/4) = 1.125$

5.13 $n = 20$, $\pi = 0.8$; $P(x \leq 13) = 0.0867$
Using the arbitrary rule of 0.05 mentioned in the text, this probability is *not* low enough to dispute the company's claim.

5.15 $n = 100$, $\pi = 0.5$

a) $P(x \geq 67) = 0.0004$. This probability is so low it would be difficult to support the bakery's claim.

b) Using the 5% arbitrary rule, find y such that $P(x \geq y) = 0.05$. Since $P(x \geq 59) = 0.0444$, suspect any value 59 or larger.

5.17 $n = 4$, $\pi = 0.25$, using Table I
$P(x = 0) = 0.3164$, $P(x = 1) = 0.4219$, $P(x = 2) = 0.2109$, $P(x = 3) = 0.0469$, $P(x = 4) = 0.0039$

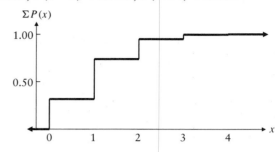

b) $P(x \geq 2) = 0.2617$

5.19 $n = 20$, $\pi = 0.67$

a) $P(x \leq 12 \mid n = 20, \pi = 0.67) = 0.3267$; conclude not different.

b) $P(x \leq 8 \mid n = 20, \pi = 0.67) = 0.0118$; surprising.

5.21 a) $\dfrac{_4C_3 \cdot {}_4C_2}{_{52}C_5} = \dfrac{\frac{4!}{3!1!}\frac{4!}{2!2!}}{\frac{52!}{5!47!}} = .00000923$

b) $\dfrac{_4C_4 \cdot {}_4C_1}{_{52}C_5} = \dfrac{\frac{4!}{0!4!}\frac{4!}{1!3!}}{\frac{52!}{5!47!}} = .00000154$

c) $\dfrac{_4C_4 \cdot {}_{48}C_1}{_{52}C_5} = \dfrac{\frac{4!}{0!4!}\frac{48!}{1!47!}}{\frac{52!}{5!47!}} = .000018$

5.23 a) $\dfrac{_5C_3 \cdot {}_5C_3}{_{10}C_6} = \dfrac{\frac{5!}{3!2!}\frac{5!}{3!2!}}{\frac{10!}{6!4!}} = 100/200 = .47619$

b) $P(\geq 4 \ NDP) = \dfrac{_5C_4 \cdot {}_5C_2}{_{10}C_6} + \dfrac{_5C_5 \cdot {}_5C_1}{_{10}C_6}$
$= \dfrac{50}{210} + \dfrac{5}{210} = \dfrac{55}{210} = .2619$

5.29 $n = 3$, $\pi = 0.4$; $P(x = 1) = {}_3C_1(.4)^1(.6)^2 = (3)(.4)(.36) = 0.4320$
Compares favourably with 5.20 answer of 0.4437

5.31 $P(x = 3 \mid n = 6, \pi = 0.50) = 0.3125$. This is not a good approximation because sampling is not with replacement, and $n = 6$ is very large relative to $N = 10$.

5.33 From Table II, $\lambda = 8.5$, $P(x = 10) = 0.1104$

5.35 $\lambda = 2.3$, $P(x = 2) = 0.2652$

5.37 a) When $\lambda = 1$, $\mu = 1$, and $\sigma = 1$
Hence, $\mu \pm 1\sigma = 1 \pm 1 = 0$ to 2 and $\mu \pm 2\sigma = 1 \pm 2(1) = 0$ to 3
$P(0 \leq x \leq 2) = 0.9197$; higher than 68%
$P(0 \leq x \leq 3) = 0.9801$; higher than 95%.

b) When $\lambda = 4$, $\mu \pm 1\sigma = 4 \pm 2 = 2$ to 6: $\mu \pm 2\sigma = 4 \pm 2(2) = 0$ to 8
$P(2 \leq x \leq 6) = 0.7978$; $P(0 \leq x \leq 8) = 0.9787$ (from Table II)
When $\lambda = 9$, $\mu \pm 1\sigma = 9 \pm 3 = 6$ to 12; $\mu + 2\sigma = 9 \pm 2(3) = 3$ to 15
$P(6 \leq x \leq 12) = 0.7602$; $P(3 \leq x \leq 15) = 0.9718$ (from Table II)
Probabilities are becoming closer to 0.68 and 0.95 because distribution becomes more symmetrical as λ increases.

5.39 a) $P(x = 3) = 0.2240$; Using Table II, $\lambda = 3$

b) $P(x = 6) = 0.1606$

c) The longer the time period, the longer will be the list of events which could take place.

5.41 a) $E[x] = n\pi = 380(.75) = 285$ claimed

b) $\pi = 0.75$ claimed
$P[x > (.75)(380)] = P(x > 285 \mid n = 380, \pi = 0.75) = 0.4803$

c) $P(\leq 300 \mid n = 380, \pi = 0.75) = 0.9687$

5.43 a) $\dfrac{7!}{2!4!1!}(20/35)^2(10/35)^4(5/35)^1 = 0.0326$

b) $\dfrac{6!}{3!2!0!1!}(.45)^3(.40)^2(.10)^0(.05)^1 = 0.04374$

5.45 $P(x \geq 1 \mid n = 4, \pi = 1/12) = 1 - P(x = 0) = 1 - 0.7061 = 0.2939$

5.49

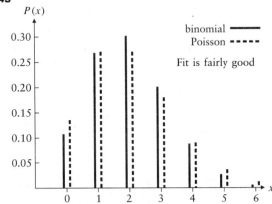

binomial ———
Poisson ------

Fit is fairly good

5.51 a)

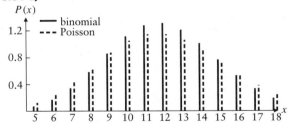

binomial ———
Poisson ------

b) $\pi = 0.24$, $\mu = n\pi = 12$, $\sigma^2 = n\pi(1 - \pi) = 9.12$

5.53 From Table I, $n = 10$; $P(x = 5) = 0.0005$
Poisson: $\lambda = n\pi = 10(.08) = 0.8$; $P(x = 5) = 0.0012$
$V[\text{binomial}] = n\pi(1 - \pi) = 10(0.08)(0.92) = 0.736$
$V[\text{Poisson}] = \lambda = 0.08$; variances compare quite well.

5.57 $P(x \geq 5 \mid n = 2,000, \pi = 0.001) = 0.05256$ (using a computer)

5.59 $P(65 \text{ or more}) = 0.00105$

Chapter Six

6.1 a)

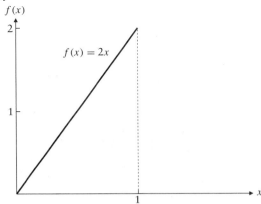

b) $A = (1/2)(\text{base})(\text{height}) = (1/2)(1)(2) = 1$

c) $P(0 \leq x \leq 1/2) = $ Area under $f(x)$ between $x = 0$ and $x = 1/2$.
Again, the area is a triangle, $A = (1/2)(1/2)(1) = 1/4$

6.3 $F(0) = 0$; $F(1/2) = 1/4$; $F(.707) = 1/2$;
$F(1) = F(3.7) = 1$

6.5 a)

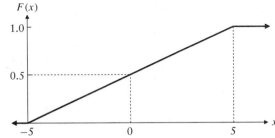

$F(-5) = (1/10)(-5) + (1/2) = 0$; $F(5) = (1/10)(5) + (1/2) = 1$

b) $F(-2) = (1/10)(-2) + (1/2) = 3/10 = 0.30$.

c) $F(3) = (1/10)(3) + (1/2) = 8/10 = 0.80$. Complement $= 1 - 0.80 = 0.20$.

6.7 a)

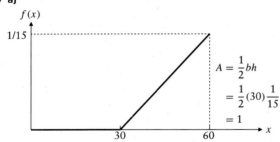

b) Mean is 2/3 of way from 30 to 60;
$\mu = E[d] = 50 \; (= \$50,000)$
Expected net profit is \$500,000.

c) $P(\text{inventory of} > 10,000) = P(d < 50)$
$A = (1/2)(20)(2/45) = 20/45 = 4/9$

d) $V[10d] = 10^2 V[d] = 100(50) = 5,000.$ Hence,
$V[\text{net profit}] = 1,000^2[10d] = 10^6(5,000) = 5 \times 10^9;$
$\sigma \cong \$70,111$
$\mu \pm 2\sigma = \$500,000 \pm 2(70,111) = \$358,578$ to
\$641,422

6.9 a)

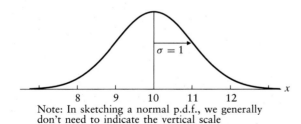

Note: In sketching a normal p.d.f., we generally
don't need to indicate the vertical scale

b)

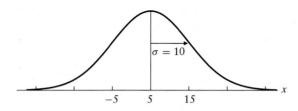

6.11 a) Normalize variable x:
$P(5 \le x \le 25) = 0.6826$

b) $P(-5 \le x \le 35) = 0.9544$

c) $P(-10 \le x \le 35) = 0.9710$

d) $P(x \ge 35) = 0.0228; \; P(x \le -5) = 0.0228$
$P(x \le -5 \text{ or } x \ge 35) = 0.0456$

6.13 a) $P(x \ge 85) = P\left(\dfrac{x-\mu}{\sigma} \ge \dfrac{85-60}{15}\right) =$
$P(z \ge 1.67) = 0.0475$

b) $P(45 \le x \le 55) =$
$P\left(\dfrac{45-60}{15} \le \dfrac{x-\mu}{\sigma} \le \dfrac{55-40}{5}\right) = 0.2120$

c) $P(x = 60) = 0$

6.15 $P(45 \le x \le 55) =$
$P\left(\dfrac{45-40}{5} \le \dfrac{x-\mu}{\sigma} \le \dfrac{55-40}{5}\right) = P(1 \le z \le 3) =$
$F(3) - F(1) = 0.1574$

6.17 $P(-1.28 \le z \le 1.65) = F(1.65) - F(-1.28) =$
0.8502

6.19 $P(x \le a) = 0.90; \; P\left(\dfrac{x-\mu}{\sigma} \le \dfrac{a-19,000}{2,000}\right) =$
0.90
$a = \$21,564, \; b = \$20,350$

6.21 a) $P(x \ge 140) = P\left(\dfrac{x-\mu}{\sigma} \ge \dfrac{140-100}{16}\right) =$
$P(z \ge 2.50) = 0.0062$

b) $P(x \le 80) = P\left(\dfrac{x-\mu}{\sigma} \le \dfrac{80-100}{16}\right) =$
$P(z \le -1.25) = 0.1056$

6.23 $n = 400, \; \pi = 0.60; \; n\pi = 240;$
$\sigma = \sqrt{n\pi(1-\pi)} = \sqrt{400(.60)(.40)} = 9.80$
$P(240 \le x \le 260) =$
$P\left(\dfrac{240-240}{9.80} \le \dfrac{x-n\pi}{\sqrt{n\pi(1-\pi)}} \le \dfrac{260-240}{9.80}\right) = P(0 \le$
$z \le 2.04) = 0.4793$

6.25 $n = 50, \; \pi = .75;$
$\sqrt{\pi(1-\pi)/n} = \sqrt{(.75)(.25)/50} = 0.061$
Using the normal approximation:
$P(p \le 0.50) = P(z \le -4.10)$
Since $P(z \le -4.10) \cong 0$, we would doubt the senator's
claim.

6.27 a)

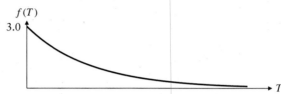

b) $\mu = 1/\lambda = 1/3, \; V[T] = 1/\lambda^2 = 1/9, \; \sigma = 1/3$

c) $\mu \pm 1\sigma$ is $P(0 \le T \le 2/3) = 0.865$ using
$\lambda T = 3(2/3) = 2$
$\mu \pm 2\sigma$ is $P(0 \le T \le 1.0) = F(1) = 0.950$ using
$\lambda T = 3(1) = 3$

6.29 a) $\lambda = 4$ per 6 min.; $P(x \geq 6) = 0.2148$ from Table II.

b) $P(T \geq 3) = 1 - F(3)$, where $\lambda = 2/3$ per min. $F(3) = 0.865$ $P(T \geq 3) = 1 - 0.865 = 0.135$

c) $P(2 \leq T \leq 4) = F(4) - F(2) = 0.933 - 0.727 = 0.206$ (using Table IV), 0.195 using the formula.

6.31 $\lambda = 2$ per hour; 15 min = 1/4 hour.

a) $P(T \leq 1/4) = 0.393$ **b)** $P(T \geq 3/4) = 0.223$

6.33 a) $P(0 \leq T \leq 1.0) = 0.865$

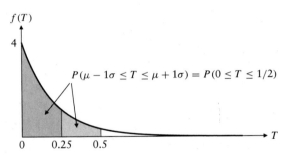

b) $P(0 \leq T \leq 1/2) = F(1/2) - F(0) = 0.865 - 0 = 0.865$

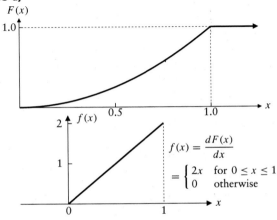

c) Yes, $P(0 \leq T \leq \mu + \lambda) = 0.865$ for any $\lambda > 0$. This probability exceeds 68% because the distribution is skewed.

d) For *any* λ: $P(\mu - 2\sigma \leq T \leq \mu + 2\sigma) = P(0 \leq T \leq 3/\sigma) = 0.950$

6.35 a)

b) $F(1/2) = (1/2)^2 = 1/4$. Yes.

c) $E[x] = \mu = 2/3$

d) $E[x^2]_0^1 = \int_0^1 2x^3 dx = \left[\frac{x^4}{2}\right]_0^1 = 1/2$; $V[x] = 1/18$

6.39 a) $\frac{dF(x)}{dx} = d\frac{\left(\frac{x}{b-a} - \frac{a}{b-a}\right)}{dx} = \frac{1}{b-a}$

b)

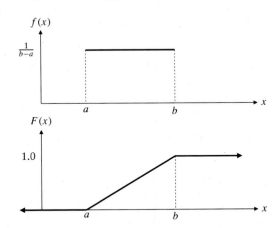

d) $E[x] = (b+a)/2$

6.41 a)

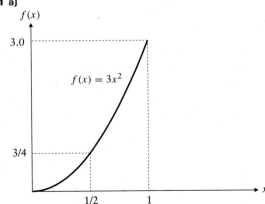

c) $F(x) = x^3$; $P(x \leq 1/4) = 1/64$

d) $E[x] = 3/4$

6.45 a)

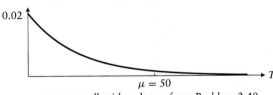

compares well with polygon from Problem 2.40

b) All are consistent with Problem 3.50.

c) $\mu = 1/\lambda = 50$; $\sigma = 1/\lambda = 50$; median = $0.7/0.02 = 35$. This is consistent with Problem 2.40.

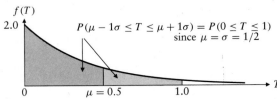

6.47 Using a computer, $P(x \leq 5/6(900) \mid n = 900,$
$\pi = .852) = 0.0647$

6.49 $P(x \geq 70) = 0.9505$

6.51 $P(x_{\text{binom}} \leq 230 \mid n = 1,000, \pi = 0.25) = 0.0763$
(using a computer), could be random.

6.53 a) $\pi = 0.133, n = 80$
$P(x \geq 10 \mid n = 80, \pi = 0.113) = 0.4180$ (using a
computer)

 b) $\pi = 0.227; P(x \leq 15 \mid n = 80, \pi = 0.227) =$
0.2428 (using a computer)

 c) $\pi = 0.10; P(x \leq 4 \mid n = 80, \pi = 0.10) = 0.0880$
(using a computer)

6.55 a) Find $P[p < 0.18] = P[z < (.18 -$
$\pi)/\sqrt{\pi(1 - \pi)/n}] = P(z < -1.12) = 0.1314$

 b) Upper limit $= 118.37$; lower limit $= 81.63$

Chapter Seven

7.11 a) $\bar{x} = 44.71, s^2 = 46.571, s = 6.824$

 b) These prices are for major cities only.

7.13 $\bar{x} = (1/n)\Sigma x f = (1/100)(80) = 0.80$
$s^2 = [1/(n - 1)]\Sigma(x - \bar{x})^2 f = 0.8687; s = 0.932$

7.15 $\bar{x} = (1/n)\Sigma x f = 422.75$

7.17 a) $\bar{x} = 105;$

 b) $s^2 = [1/(n - 1)]\Sigma(x - \bar{x})^2 = (1/3)(20) = 6.667;$
$s = 2.582$

 c) more suspicious since $\bar{x} = 105$ is large relative to
$\mu = 96$

 d) range $= |108 - 102| = 6$

 e) range only considers highest and lowest values.

7.21 a) $P(x \geq 5) = P\left(\dfrac{x - \mu}{\sigma/\sqrt{n}} \geq \dfrac{5 - 4.833}{.75/\sqrt{121}}\right) =$
$P(z \geq 2.44) = 1 - 0.9927 = 0.0073$
[45 seconds is 0.75 of a minute]
$P(\bar{x} \leq 5) = P\left(z \leq \dfrac{5 - 5.2}{.75/11}\right)$
$= P(z \leq -2.93) = 0.0017.$

 b) Answers do not depend on any assumptions about
the parent population because n is large enough for
the C.L.T.

7.23 a) $P(x \geq 35) = P(z \geq (35 - 30)/3) =$
$P(z \geq 1.67) = 0.0475$
$P(25 \leq x \leq 35) = P(-1.67 \leq z \leq 1.67) = 0.9050$

 b) $P(\bar{x} \geq 31) = P(z \geq (31 - 30)/(3/\sqrt{36})) =$
$P(z \geq 2) = 1 - F(2) = 0.0228$
$P(\bar{x} \leq 30.5) = P(z \leq 1) = 0.8413$
$P(29 \leq \bar{x} \leq 31) = P(-2 \leq z \leq 2) =$
$F(2) - [1 - F(2)] = 0.9544$

 c) In part (a) must assume normal population; in part
(b), no, since C.L.T. applies.

7.25 b) $\mu = 1/10[0 + 1 + 2 + \cdots + 9] = (1/10)(45) = 4.5$
$\sigma^2 = 8.25$

 c) $\sigma_{\bar{x}} = \sigma^2/\sqrt{3} = \sqrt{8.25/3} = 1.66.$

7.27 a) $E[\bar{x}] = \mu$ remains the same; $V[\bar{x}] = \sigma^2/n$ becomes smaller as n changes from 3 to 100. Interpreta-
tion of reasonably close differs.

 b) $\sigma_{\bar{x}} = \sigma/\sqrt{n} = \sqrt{8.25}/\sqrt{100} = 0.2872$

 c) Due to the CLT, z-values now should approximate
a normal distribution since n is large.

7.29 a) Factor: $\sqrt{(N - n)/(N - 1)}$; used to adjust standard deviation when sampling without replacement and
$n > 0.10N.$

 b) $\sigma_{\bar{x}} = \sqrt{\dfrac{\sigma_x^2}{n}\left(\dfrac{N - n}{N - 1}\right)} = \sqrt{[2,500/25][75/99]} =$
$\sqrt{75.8}$ so $\sigma_{\bar{x}} = 8.706$

7.31 a) $N = 400, n = 64, \bar{x} = 19.95.$ Given $\mu = 20,$
$\sigma = 0.10,$
$\sigma_{\bar{x}} = (0.10/8)\sqrt{\dfrac{400 - 64}{399}} = 0.0115$
$P(\bar{x} \leq 19.95) = P\left(z \leq \dfrac{19.95 - 20}{0.0115}\right) = P(z \leq -4.35).$
This probability is close to zero.

 b) The standard error would be
$\sigma_{\bar{x}} = 0.10/8 = 0.0125$

7.33 $\bar{x} = 196; s^2 = 684/3; s = 15.1$

 a) $P(\bar{x} \leq 196 \mid \mu = 210) = P(t \leq -1.85) = 0.0807,$
using a computer.
$P(\bar{x} \geq 196 \mid \mu = 180) = P\left(t \geq \dfrac{196 - 180}{(15.1)/2}\right) = P(t \geq$
$2.12) = 0.0621,$ using a computer.

 b) $P(\bar{x} \leq 196 \mid \mu = 210) = P\left(z \leq \dfrac{196 - 210}{14/2}\right) =$
$P(z \leq -2.00) = 0.0228$
$P(\bar{x} \leq 196 \mid \mu = 200) = P\left(z \leq \dfrac{196 - 200}{10/2}\right) =$
$P(z \leq -0.80) = 0.2119$

7.35 a) $\bar{x} = 119.25, s^2 = 1,513.32, s = 38.90$

b) $n = 100$, $s = 38.90$, $\mu = 110$,
$P(\bar{x} \geq 119.25) = P(t \geq (119.25 - 100)/3.890) = P(t \geq 2.378) = 0.0097$, using a computer.

c) Yes, the sample result is unexpected if $\mu_x = 110$.

7.37 a) With $s = 6$, $n = 9$, d.f. $= 8$ for $t = (\bar{x} - \mu)/(s/\sqrt{n})$
$P(\bar{x} \geq 54) = P(t \geq (54-50)/6/3) = P(t \geq 2) = 0.0403$, using a computer.
$P(\bar{x} \leq 44) = P(t \leq (44 - 50)/6/3) = P(t \leq -3) = 0.0085$, using a computer.
$P(45 \leq \bar{x} \leq 55) = P(-2.5 \leq t \leq 2.5) = 0.9631$, using a computer.

b) All t values are doubled as the sample size is 4 times larger.
$P(t \geq 4) \cong 0$; $P(t \leq -6) \cong 0$, $P(-5 \leq t \leq 5) = 1$ (approximately).

7.41 a) $E[\chi^2] = v = n - 1 = 24$; $V[\chi^2] = 2v = 48$

b) $P(\chi^2 \geq 43.0) = 1 - F(43.0) = 0.01$
$P(\chi^2 \geq 33.2) = 1 - F(33.2) = 0.10$
$P(\chi^2 \geq 9.89) = 1 - F(9.89) = 0.995$

7.43 $P(\chi^2_{14} \geq 14(800)/400) = P(\chi^2_{14} \geq 28.0) = 0.0142$, using a computer. Would be considered unusually high.

7.45 Point estimate is $\bar{x} = 1,600/900 = 1.78$
Sample standard deviation is $s = \sqrt{3,679.18/899} = 2.023$

7.47 a) $\bar{x} = \$40,200$, $s = 31,681.9$

b) $\sigma^2_{\bar{x}} = \sigma^2/n = 100,000,000/5 = 20,000,000$
$\sigma_{\bar{x}} = \sqrt{20,000,000} = 4,472.136$

c) $P(\bar{x} \geq 40,380) = P\left(z \geq \dfrac{40,380 - 30,000}{\sqrt{81,000,000/5}}\right) = P(z \geq 2.58) = 0.0049$

7.49 The correct answer is d) nonsampling error

7.51 The correct answer is b) each stratum differs as much as possible with respect to expected shrinkage but the shrinkage expected for items within each stratum are as close as possible.

7.53 The correct answer is d) the square root of the average determined in (c).

7.57 a) $P(z \leq 1.734) = 0.9585$

b) $P(t \leq 2.661) = 0.9946$

c) $P(\chi^2 \leq 50.00) = 0.9519$

Chapter Eight

8.3 The detection approach inspects the final product for defects while the prevention approach monitors the product throughout the process to identify potential problems.

8.5 Variation in Line (a) is due to common causes whereas the variation in Line (b) appears to be due to assignable causes. Line (a) is in control, (b) is not.

8.7 Both processes appear to be in control. Process (a), however, has part of the distribution outside the specification limits, hence it is not meeting specifications.

8.9 Process (a) appears to be in control. Both Processes (b) and (c) are out of control. In Process (b) two points fall outside the control limits. In Process (c) eight points in a row fall on one side of the centreline.

8.11 Both the processes need to be re-evaluated since they appear to violate the normality assumptions. The first one appears to have too much variability, the second too little variability.

8.13 a) $UCL_R = D_4\bar{R} = 2.115(10.9) = 23.0535$;
$LCL_R = D_3\bar{R} = 0$

c) The R chart provides a picture of the ranges over time. The R chart is acceptable if the ranges follow a random pattern and fall within the 3-sigma limits.

8.15 The process appears to be in control.

8.17 a) $\bar{R} = 0.0062$, $\bar{\bar{x}} = 0.751$

b) $UCL_R = D_4\bar{R} = 2.575(0.0062) = 0.0160$; $LCL_R = D_3\bar{R} = 0$

c) $UCL_{\bar{x}} = \bar{\bar{x}} + A_2\bar{R} = 0.7573$; $LCL_{\bar{x}} = 0.7447$

d) Both charts appear to be in statistical control.

e) The control limits lie within the specification limits.

8.19 a) $\bar{R} = 9.60$, $\bar{\bar{x}} = 17.18$

b) $UCL_R = D_4\bar{R} = 2.115(9.60) = 20.304$
$LCL_R = D_3\bar{R} = 0$

c) $UCL_{\bar{x}} = \bar{\bar{x}} + A_2\bar{R} = 22.604$
$LCL_{\bar{x}} = \bar{\bar{x}} - A_2\bar{R} = 11.756$

d) Both charts appear to be in statistical control.

8.21 $UCL_R = D_4\bar{R} = 0.00317$
$LCL_R = D_3\bar{R} = 0(0.0015) = 0$
$UCL_{\bar{x}} = \bar{\bar{x}} + A_2\bar{R} = 0.05287$;
$LCL_{\bar{x}} = \bar{\bar{x}} - A_2\bar{R} = 0.05113$
The range and mean for the third sample exceed the UCL, suggesting the process is out of control.

8.23 $UCL_R = 0.2115(0.0036) = 0.0076$
$LCL_R = 0(0.0036) = 0$
$UCL_{\bar{x}} = 0.1277$; $LCL_{\bar{x}} = 0.1235$
Upwards patterns suggest control problems.
We calculate the C_{pk} index, remembering that because of the control problem, this index may not have much meaning.
Estimate of $\sigma_x = \bar{R}/d_2 = 0.0036/2.326 = 0.00155$
$C_{pk} = 0.5161$; the process is clearly not capable.

8.25 The control limits for machines 4 and 5 lie outside the specification limits.
Machine 1: $C_{pk} = 3.333$; Machine 2: $C_{pk} = 1.666$; Machine 3: $C_{pk} = 1.33$; Machine 4: $C_{pk} = 0.952$; Machine 5: $C_{pk} = 0.833$

8.27 $C_p = 1.139$; $C_{pk} = 1.025$
The process is capable of meeting its specifications.

8.29 $C_p = 0.910$; $C_{pk} = 0.819$. Both the C_p and C_{pk} indexes are less than 1; process is not capable of meeting its specifications.

8.31 $UCL_p = 0.133$, $LCL_p = 0$

8.33 $\bar{c} = 7.4$, $UCL_c = 15.561$, $LCL_c = 0$

8.35 Average number of defectives per day = 33.55;
$\bar{p} = 0.03355$
$UCL_p = 0.0506$; $LCL_p = 0.0165$
The process does not appear to be in control because both samples 7 and 15 lie outside the control limits.

8.37 a) $\bar{c} = 9.35$; $UCL_c = 18.52$; $LCL_c = 0.18$

b) The process still appears to be in control.

8.43 a) Sample 26 lies outside the range limits. Not in control.

b) Means for samples 24, 26 and 27 all lie outside the control limits.

8.45 b) Average number rejected per day = 9.6;
$\bar{p} = 0.0096$
$UCL_p = 0.01885$; $LCL_p = 0.00035$

c) The process appears to be in control.

d) The proportion of cheques rejected for day 37 lies outside the control limits. The process is no longer in control.

e) All these points lie within control limits.

Chapter Nine

9.3 Each of the estimators is unbiased except b) maximum sample value.

9.5 $V[\text{med}] = 25$; $V[\bar{x}] = 8.34$

9.9 a) $E[p] = \pi = 0.4$, demonstrating that p is unbiased

b) $V[p] = E[p^2] - (E[p])^2 = 0.06$
The same result is obtained by the formula,
$V[p] = \dfrac{\pi(1-\pi)}{n} = \dfrac{0.4(0.6)}{4} = 0.06$
For $n = 5$ and $\pi = 0.4$,

$$V[p] = \frac{0.4(0.6)}{5} = 0.048.$$

9.13 a) $\bar{x}$ is best estimate of μ, $\bar{x} = 2.0$

b) 90% C.I. for μ is $-1.47 \le \mu \le 5.47$

9.15 a) 95% CI for μ is $8,748 \pm 1.96(970/\sqrt{36})$ or $\$8,431.13 \le \mu \le \$9,064.87$

9.17 90% C.I. for μ is $24.3 \pm 1.645(6/\sqrt{16})$ or $21.833 \le \mu \le 26.768$

9.19 a) $\bar{x} = 36/9 = 4$ is the best point estimate of μ.

b) $\bar{x} \pm t_{(\alpha/2, n-1)}s/\sqrt{n} = 4 \pm 1.86(4/\sqrt{9})$
90% confidence interval is $1.52 \le \mu \le 6.48$

9.21 90% C.I. for μ is $184 \pm 1.753(20/\sqrt{16})$ or $175.235 \le \mu \le 192.765$

9.23 95% C.I. for μ is $49.701 \le \mu \le 52.299$ (changes by more than $\frac{1}{2}$ second at each end].

9.25 a) $\bar{x} = 1,600/900 = 1.778$

b) 99% C.I. for μ is $1.778 \pm 2.576(2.023/\sqrt{900})$ or $1.604 \le \mu \le 1.952$

9.27 99% C.I. for π is $0.40 \pm 2.576\sqrt{0.4(0.6)/900}$ or $0.358 < \pi < 0.442$

9.29 95% C.I. for π is $0.60 \pm 1.96\sqrt{0.6(0.4)/100}$ or $0.504 \le \pi \le 0.696$

9.31 $n = (1.96)^2(1,000)^2/50^2 = 1,536.64$; a sample of 1,537 is necessary.

9.33 a) $\bar{x} \pm z_{\alpha/2}\sigma/\sqrt{n} = 29,000 \pm 1.96(3,000)/\sqrt{25}$
$\$27,824 \le \mu \le \$30,176$

b) decrease; decrease; decrease; remain unchanged

9.35 166 observations are necessary since $[2.576(2.5)/0.5]^2 = 165.89$

9.37 a) $34,000 \pm 2.326(6,000/\sqrt{16})$ or $\$30,511 \le \mu \le \$37,489$

b) $n = [2.33(6,000/600]^2 = 542.89$, so need $n = 543$

9.39 $(58/166) \pm 2.576\sqrt{0.35(0.65)/166}$ or $0.254 \leq \pi \leq 0.444$

9.41 $p = 32/40 = 0.80$ and $n = 40$. A 90% CI for π is $0.80 \pm 1.645\sqrt{0.80(0.20)/40}$; $0.696 \leq \pi \leq 0.904$

9.43 $5.32 \leq \sigma^2 \leq 19.17$ using Formula 9.8

9.45 $4.114 \leq \sigma^2 \leq 33.027$

9.47 $[30(0.94)/47] \leq \sigma^2 \leq [30(0.94)/16.80]$ $0.60 \leq \sigma^2 \leq 1.67$

9.49 A 90% CI for μ using $t_{0.05,23} = 1.714$ is $36.26 \pm 1.714(2.80/\sqrt{24})$ or $\$35.28 \leq \mu \leq \$37.24$. A 90% CI for σ^2 is $23(2.80)^2/35.2 \leq \sigma^2 \leq 23(2.80)^2/13.1$. Using square roots of each term, $2.26 \leq \sigma \leq 3.71$

9.57 Answer is item (d).

9.59 Answer is item (a).

9.61 Answer is item (d) using $z_{0.025} \cong 2$

9.63 Interpolating within Table VI, $t_{0.005,49} = 2.683$. A 99% CI for μ is $2.55 \pm 2.683(0.30/\sqrt{50})$ or $2.44 \leq \mu \leq 2.66$.

9.65 Use a planning value of $p = \frac{1}{2}$ and $z_{0.025} = 1.96$; $$n = \frac{(1.96)^2\left(\frac{1}{2}\right)\left(\frac{1}{2}\right)}{(0.05)^2} = 384.16$$ Use $n = 385$ at a cost of $385(\$0.35) = \$134.75$

9.67 Use the approximation in the footnote for Table VII with $n = 59$. $\chi^2 = 0.5[\pm 1.96 + \sqrt{2(58) - 1}]^2 = 80.4$ and 38.4 Use Formula 9.8 in each part:

a) $0.00245 \leq \sigma^2 \leq 0.00512$ for IBM

b) $0.00244 \leq \sigma^2 \leq 0.00511$ for Exxon

c) $0.00236 \leq \sigma^2 \leq 0.00494$ for GE

d) $0.00350 \leq \sigma^2 \leq 0.00733$ for GM

9.69

Lower Prob.	Upper Prob.	Interval Width
0.050	0.050	38.38
0.045	0.055	38.43
0.040	0.060	38.57
0.035	0.065	38.79
0.030	0.070	39.16
0.025	0.075	39.66
0.020	0.080	40.35
0.015	0.085	41.33
0.010	0.090	42.77
0.005	0.095	45.32

Chapter Ten

10.3 a) $H_0 : \mu = 110,000$, $H_a : \mu > 110,000$

c) $z_c = (118,800 - 110,000)/(30,000/\sqrt{40}) = 1.85$ p-value $= P(z \geq 1.85) = 0.0322$.

10.5 a) $H_0 : \mu = \$5,000$ vs. $H_a : \mu < \$5,000$
Type I: reject $\mu = \$5,000$ when μ is, in fact, equal to $\$5,000$.
Type II: accept $\mu = \$5,000$ when μ is, in fact, less than $\$5,000$.

b) Use $z = \dfrac{\bar{x} - \mu_0}{\sigma/\sqrt{n}}$

c) $\bar{x} \leq \$4,588$ is acceptance region

d) Accept $H_0 : P\left(z \leq \dfrac{4,650 - 5,000}{500/2}\right) = 0.0808$

e) $2P(z \leq -1.40) = 2(0.0808) = 0.1616$

10.7 $H_0: \mu = \$22,000$ vs. $H_a: \mu < \$22,000$; $z \leq -1.645$ is the critical region. Since $z_c = -2.50$ is less than -1.645, we reject H_0 and conclude that the average income in this rural county does seem to be less than $\$22,000$.

10.9 $z_c = -2.71$; $P(z \leq -2.71) = 0.0034$; $2P(z \leq -2.71) = 2(0.0034) = 0.0068$

10.11 b) $\bar{x} \leq \$24,467.10$ is the critical region.

c) Reject H_0.

d) $P(\bar{x} \leq 24,300) = P(z \leq -10) \cong 0$

10.13 a) $H_0 : \mu \leq 50$ vs. $H_a : \mu > 50$

b) $z_c = 1.333$; $z_{0.05} = 1.645$; accept H_0.

c) $\bar{x} = 1.645(3/8) + 50 = 50.617$ hours

10.15 a) $H_0 : \mu = 5,000$ vs. $H_a : \mu < 5,000$

b) $t = \dfrac{\bar{x} - \mu_0}{s/\sqrt{n}}$

c) Critical region: $t \leq -2.353$; $\bar{x} = \$4,650$; $s^2 = 196,666$; $t_c = -1.578$

d) Accept H_0.

e) $0.25 > P(t \leq -1.578) > 0.10$

10.17 $H_0 : \mu = 31.5$ vs. $H_a : \mu < 31.5$; $t_{0.01} = -2.492$; $t_c = -3.667$; reject H_0.

10.19 a) $H_0 : \mu = 500$, $H_a : \mu > 500$

c) $t_c = (520 - 500)/(50/\sqrt{100}) = 4$
$t_{0.01,99} = 2.36$. Reject H_0.

10.21 $H_0 : \mu = 18$ vs. $H_a : \mu < 18$; $t_{0.05,15} = -1.753$; $t_c = -2.00$; reject H_0.

10.23 a) $H_0 : \mu = 180$, $H_a : \mu > 180$

b) $z_c = (184 - 180)/(22.45/\sqrt{100}) = 1.782$
$z_{0.05} = 1.645$

d) $\bar{x} = 184$

e) $184 \pm 1.96(2.245)$ or $179.6 \leq \mu \leq 188.4$

10.25 The acceptance region is $\bar{x} \geq 23.88$,
$\beta = P(\bar{x} \geq 23.88 \mid \mu_a = 23.90) = 0.6480$
Power $= 1 - \beta = 0.3520$

10.27 $\beta(0.90) = 0.0075$, $\beta(0.95) = 0.1200$, $\beta(1.000) = 0.5319$, $\beta(1.05) = 0.9082$,
$\beta(1.20) = 0.5319$

10.29 a) $\alpha = 0.0114$; $\beta = 0.7171$

b) $E[\text{cost} \mid \pi = 0.10]$ is $0.0114(500) = \$5.70$
$E[\text{cost} \mid \pi = 0.25]$ is $0.7171(200) = \$143.42$

c) TEC $= \$43.03$ d) $x \geq 5$ is best C.R.

10.31 $H_0 : \pi = 0.80$ vs. $H_a : \pi < 0.80$
$P(x \leq 30 \mid n = 50, \ \pi = 0.80) = 0.0009$
Using a normal approximation, $z_c = -3.53$;
$P(z \leq -3.53) \cong 0$

10.33 a) $H_0 : \pi = 0.05$, $H_a : \pi \neq 0.05$

c) $z_{0.015} = 2.17$

d) $z_c = (0.08 - 0.05)/\sqrt{0.05(0.95)/50} = 0.97$

e) p-value $= 2P(z \geq 0.97) = 0.332$.

10.35 a) $H_a : \pi > 0.50$ vs. $H_0 : \pi = 0.50$ (use conservative H_0)

b) $p = 0.646$; $x = 42$ customers

10.37 a) $H_0 : \sigma^2 = 4$ vs. $H_a : \sigma^2 \neq 4$;

b) Acceptance region is $12.4 \leq \chi^2 \leq 39.4$

c) $\chi^2 = 18$; do not reject H_0

10.39 a) $H_0 : \sigma^2 = 1$ vs. $H_a : \sigma^2 > 1$

c) Critical region is $\chi_4^2 \geq 9.49$

d) $\chi_c^2 = 23.26$; Reject H_0.

e) $P(\chi_4^2 \geq 23.26) < 0.005$

10.41 $\sqrt{n} = 1.645(5,000)/100 = 6,765.06$
The firm must survey 6,766 people.

10.43 a) $P(x = 0 \text{ or } x = 2 \mid n = 2, \ \pi = 0.5) =$
$(1/4) + (1/4) = 1/2$.

x	true π	$\beta = P(x = 1)$
1	1/6	10/36
2	2/6	16/36
4	4/6	16/36
5	5/6	10/36

b) $P(\text{Type I}) = (3/6)(2/5) + (3/6)(2/5) = 2/5$

x	$\beta = P(x = 1)$
1	2/6
2	8/15
4	8/15
5	2/6

10.45 a) $H_0 : \pi = 0.50$, $H_a : \pi > 0.50$
$P(x \geq 60 \mid n = 100, \ \pi = 0.50) = 0.0285$
Reject H_0.

10.47 $H_0 : \mu = 1$, $H_a : \mu > 1$, $n = 45$ as five values are missing.

n	mean	std. error	t	Prob > |t|
45	2.8727	2.6336	1.0908	0.2813

Accept H_0.

10.49 a) $H_0 : \mu = 50$, $H_a : \mu > 50$
$t_c = (51.80 - 50)/(13.15/\sqrt{40}) = 0.87$
Accept H_0.

b) $H_0 : \sigma^2 = 144$, $H_a : \sigma^2 > 144$
$\chi_c^2 = 39(13.15)^2/144 = 46.8$
Using the approximation note to Table VII, the critical value is $0.5(10.42)^2 = 54.3$. Accept H_0.

10.51 a) $H_0 : \mu = 8$, $H_a : \mu < 8$. For fiveyr returns, $\bar{x} = 3.7$, $t_c = -7.30$, p-value < 0.00005; Reject H_0.

b) For tenyr returns, $\bar{x} = 7.8$, $t_c = -0.37$, p-value $= 0.358$. Accept H_0.

c) $H_0 : \sigma^2 = 4$, $H_a : \sigma^2 > 4$
For fiveyr returns, $\chi_c^2 = 52.08$
For tenyr returns, $\chi_c^2 = 40.98$
Both exceed the critical value of 39.4. Reject H_0.

Chapter Eleven

11.3 a) $H_0 : \mu_1 \geq \mu_2$ vs. $H_a : \mu_1 < \mu_2$. We must adjust H_0 to $H_0 : \mu_1 - \mu_2 = 0$

b) Use z for the difference between two sample means.

c) $z_{0.02} = -2.06$ **d)** $z_c = -3$; reject H_0.

11.5 a) $H_0 : \mu_1 - \mu_2 = 0$, $H_a : \mu_1 - \mu_2 > 0$

b) $z_{0.01} = 2.33$, $z_c = 2/0.775 = 2.58$. Reject H_0.

11.7 $t_c = 2.677$; since 2.677 exceeds critical value of 2.583, we reject H_0.

11.9 $\bar{x}_1 = 31.025$; $s_1^2 = 0.0758$; $\bar{x}_2 = 31.325$; $s_2^2 = 0.0492$; $t_c = -1.695$; since $t_c > t_{0.005,6} = -3.707$, accept $H_0 : \mu_1 - \mu_2 = 0$

11.11 $H_0 : \Delta = 0$, $H_a : \Delta \neq 0$; $\bar{D} = 11.833$, $s_D = 15.38$
$t_c = \dfrac{11.833 - 0}{15.38/\sqrt{6}} = 1.88$; Critical value is $t_{0.025,5} = 2.571$. Accept H_0.

11.13 μ_2 represents mean for new machine
$\bar{D} = 9.1$, $s_D = 4.4$, $n = 6$, $t_{0.05,5} = 2.015$
$t_c = (9.1 - 0)/(4.4/\sqrt{6}) = 5.065$. Reject H_0.
Should switch to the new machine.

11.15 $H_0 : \mu_m - \mu_F = 0$, $H_a : \mu_m - \mu_F \neq 0$

a) $\bar{D} = 2.0$, $s_D^2 = 322/9 = 35.78$, $s_D = 5.98$
$t_c = 2.0/(5.98/\sqrt{10}) = 1.06$
$t_{0.025,9} = 2.262$. Accept H_0.

b) $\bar{x}_m = 12.9$, $\bar{x}_F = 10.9$
$s_m^2 = 44.94$, $s_F^2 = 15.7$
$t_c = \dfrac{2}{\sqrt{6.064}} = 0.81$

c) $2P(t_9 \geq 1.06) = 0.3168$
$2P(t_{18} \geq 0.81) = 0.4286$

11.17 $H_0 : \pi_1 - \pi_2 = 0$ vs. $H_a : \pi_1 - \pi_2 \neq 0$
$z_{0.005} = \pm 2.575$; $t_c = 1.715$; do not reject H_0.

11.19 $H_0 : \pi_1 - \pi_2 = 0.10$ vs. $H_a : \pi_1 - \pi_2 > 0.10$
$z_c = 0.384$; $z_{0.01} = 2.33$; do not reject H_0.

11.21 a) $H_0 : \Delta \leq 0$, $H_a : \Delta = \mu_1 - \mu_2 > 0$

b) $\bar{D} = 1$, $s_D^2 = 2$, $t_c = 1.732$
$t_{0.05,5} = 2.015$ so do not reject H_0.

11.25 $F_c = s_A^2/s_B^2 = 110.25/174 = 0.634$
Accept $H_0 : \sigma_A^2 = \sigma_B^2$, since $F_c = 0.634$ exceeds lower critical value of 0.132.
Report $2P(F \leq 0.634) > 0.10$ or p-value $= 2(0.2692) = 0.5384$ using a computer.

11.27 Using Formula 11.8, we find 0.474 and 0.346 as the two lower critical values.

11.29 a) $H_0 : \sigma_1^2 = \sigma_2^2$, $H_a : \sigma_1^2 \neq \sigma_2^2$
$F_c = s_1^2/s_2^2 = 6^2/4^2 = 2.25$
p-value $= 2(0.004) = 0.008$ so reject H_0.

b) Since the variances are not equal, do not use t-test assuming equal variances. Use normal statistic in Formula 11.2.
$H_0 : \mu_1 - \mu_2 = 0$, $H_a : \mu_1 - \mu_2 < 0$
$z_{0.01} = 2.326$, $z_c = -2$. Accept H_0 of equal means.

11.35 $n_1 = 60$, $n_2 = 105$, $s_1^2 = 569,421$, $s_2^2 = 563,550$
$F_c = 1.01$. Conclude that variances are equal.
$\bar{x}_1 = 483.92$ for females and $\bar{x}_2 = 975.91$ for males.
$t_c = -4.14$, p-value $= 0.0001$. The means differ.

11.39 For H_0 : variances are equal, $F_c = 1.80$ with 148 and 29 d.f.
Accept H_0 if $\alpha = 0.05$ since p-value $= 0.064$.
For a two-sided test on means, $t_c = 1.21$ with p-value $= 0.227$
There is not a significant difference in means.

11.47 $n = 25$ matched pairs with $\bar{D} = 4.11$ and $s_D = 2.027$
$t_c = 10.13$ so reject the hypothesis of equal means.

Chapter Twelve

12.3

Source of Variation	Sum of Squares	D.F.	Mean Square	F-Ratio	P Value
II	5,601.6	4	1,400.4	5.37375	0.0142
Error	2,606	10	260.6		
Total	8,207.6	14			

Conclude the five industries differ because $p = 0.0142$ is lower than $\alpha = 0.05$.

12.5

Source of Variation	Sum of Squares	D.F.	Mean Square	F-Ratio	P Value
Code	7,123.5	3	2,374.5	3.64122	0.0304
Error	13,042.3	20	652.117		
Total	20,165.8	23			

Do not conclude that hours worked differ across the four industries because $p = 0.0304$ is higher than $\alpha = 0.01$.

12.7 SST = 4472; SSB = 420.33

SSW = 4051.67;

$F_c = [(SSB/2)/(SSW/15)] = [210.17/270.11] = 0.78$.

This is less than $F_{(.05,2,15)} = 3.68$.

Accept no difference in average rating scores among inspectors.

12.9

SOURCE	SUM OF SQUARES	D.F.	MEAN SQUARE	F RATIO	PROB.
BETWEEN	65.883	3	21.961	7.191	6.657E-04
WITHIN	109.941	36	3.054		
TOTAL	175.824	39			

The p-value of $p = 0.0006657$ indicates that H_0 should be rejected, hence we conclude the average brightness values are significantly different.

12.15 If an F for main effects is zero, we conclude that the sum of squares columns (or rows) equals zero, which implies that the means for those columns (rows) are all equal. If the F for interaction is zero, then SSI = 0, which implies that the differences in cell means are completely explained by the main effects.

12.17

SOURCE	SUM OF SQUARES	D.F.	MEAN SQUARE	F RATIO	PROB.
COLS	58.619	3	19.540	4.681	.0103
ROWS	.284	2	.142	.034	.9666
INTERACTION	8.234	6	1.372	0.329	.9150
ERROR	100.180	24	4.174		
TOTAL	167.316	35			

The p-value for columns ($p = 0.0103$) is quite low, but not less than the α-value of 0.01. The remaining two p-values (0.9666) and (0.9150) are very high. Thus, the null hypothesis cannot be rejected for either main effect, nor can it be rejected for the interaction effect.

12.19

SOURCE	SUM OF SQUARES	D.F.	MEAN SQUARE	F RATIO	PROB.
COLS	.018	2	9.1194E-03	1.593	.2218
ROWS	.146	2	.073	12.798	1.232E-04
INTERACTION	.012	4	2.9111E-03	.5087	.7298
ERROR	.155	27	5.7231E-03		
TOTAL	.331	35			

Brand (column) effect is not significant ($p = 0.2218$) The interaction effect is not significant ($p = 0.7298$). Type (row) effect is significant ($p = 0.0001232$). The estimated type effects are:

$\hat{\lambda}_1 = 0.664 - 0.695 = -0.031$

$\hat{\lambda}_2 = 0.638 - 0.695 = -0.057$;

$\hat{\lambda}_3 = 0.784 - 0.695 = 0.089$

12.21

SOURCE	SUM OF SQUARES	D.F.	MEAN SQUARE	F RATIO	PROB.
COLS	210.389	2	105.194	23.620	1.175E-06
ROWS	260.056	2	130.028	29.195	1.776E-07
INTERACTION	218.944	4	54.736	12.289	8.082E-06
ERROR	120.250	27	4.454		
TOTAL	809.639	35			

The ANOVA table above indicates (for $\alpha = 0.01$) significant main effect for tires ($p = 0.000001175$), a significant main effect for temperature ($p = 0.0000001776$), and a significant interaction effect ($p = 0.000008082$). The best tire thus depends on the temperature.

12.27 Guess significant main A effects because the A-values for level 1 are larger than for 2 or 3. B-values for level 1 appear larger than level 2, so guess B main effects. Finally, there could be interaction because the lines cross, but such an effect may not be significant.

12.29

Source of Variation	Sum of Squares	D.F.	Mean Square	F-Ratio	P Value
Cities	497.383	3	165.794	0.175	0.9130
Error	53,111.600	56	948.421		
Total	53,608.983	59			

Conclude the four cities do not differ because $p = 0.9130$ is larger than $\alpha = 0.05$.

12.31 a) There are three age categories ($n - 1 = 2$ d.f.). There are three brand categories ($n - 1 = 2$ d.f.). There are 27 replications total ($n - 1 = 26$ d.f.). There are three replications per cell 3(3)(3) = 27.

b) The main effect for age is not significant ($p = 0.266$).

The main effect for brands is significant at $\alpha > 0.001$. The interaction effect is not significant ($p = 0.974$).

Chapter Thirteen

13.3 50 is the rate of change of y with respect to x (the slope). That is, a one-unit change in x will result in 50 units of change in the same direction.

$\hat{y} = 320 + 50(5) = 570$.

13.5 a) A linear approximation seems appropriate.

b) $\hat{y} = -920 + 0.03x$

c) $\hat{y} = 8{,}080$ for $x = 300{,}000$

13.7 a) Relationship does not appear to be linear.

b) $\hat{y} = -21.175 + 11.56x$

c)

$y - \hat{y}$
-14.625
11.615
23.255
-10.185
-10.065

The sign of the deviations seems to be alternating somewhat.

d) For $x = 8$, $\hat{y} = -21.175 + 11.56(8) = 71.305$

13.9 $\hat{y} = 21.0 + 0.01x$

13.11 a) $\hat{y} = 7{,}500 + 3x$

b) $\hat{y} = 7{,}500 + 3(500) = \$9{,}000$

13.13 a) $\hat{y} = 6.39 + 0.9x$ when 6.39 is the estimate of the fixed cost per store and 0.9 is the estimate of the variable cost per employee.

b) $a = 6.39$ is constant regardless of the number of employees.

13.15 a) $SSE = 7{,}000$

b) $r^2 = 0.64$; 36% is unexplained.

c) $SST = 19{,}444.4$

13.17 $\hat{y} = 20 + 2x$; $r^2 = 0.826$

13.19 a) $b = -3{,}400/7{,}750 = -0.439$; $a = 30 - (-0.439)65 = 58.535$; $\hat{y} = 58.535 - 0.439x$

b) α is the intercept on the dependent variable axis. β is the slope of the demand function, dQ/dP.

c) $\hat{y} = 58.535 - 0.439(25) = 47.56$ (thousand calculators)

d) $SSR = (-0.439)(-3{,}400) = 1{,}492.6$; proportion of variation explained is $R^2 = 1{,}492.6/1{,}600 = 0.933$

e) C.V. residual $= 100(s_e/\bar{y}) = 100\sqrt{107.4/4}/30 = 17.3$

13.21 a) $R^2 = SSR/SST = 0.9(2{,}366.2)/2{,}391.6 = 0.89$

b) Use Formula 13.20, $r = 2{,}366.2/\sqrt{2{,}628.9}\sqrt{2{,}391.6} = 0.94$ r is the square root of R^2.

13.23 $SSE = 14.58$; $SST = 36.45$; $SSR = 21.87$

13.25 $s_e = 1.195$

13.29 a) $\hat{y} = 0.83 + 1.37x$

b) $SST = 26.83$, $r = SCxy/\sqrt{SSx}\sqrt{SSy} = 0.87$

13.31 a) $s_x = 21.6304 = \sqrt{SSx/(n-1)}$, so $SSx = 11{,}228.98$

b) $R^2 = (r)^2 = (0.6938)^2 = 0.48$

c) PCRIME $= 830.78 + 12.06$ URBAN

13.33 a) $\hat{y} = -2.464 + 2.26x$

b) $r = 0.960$

c) $SSE = \Sigma(y-\hat{y})^2 = 9.52$; $SSR = \Sigma(\hat{y}-\bar{y})^2 = 108.48$; $SST = SSE + SSR = 118$

d) $R^2 = SSR/SST = 0.919$; 91.9% of the variation is explained.

e) $r = \sqrt{0.919} = 0.9586$ from part (d) $r = \dfrac{b\sqrt{SSx}}{\sqrt{SSy}} = \dfrac{2.26\sqrt{21.2}}{\sqrt{118}} = 0.958$

13.35 a) $r_{y,\text{DLH}} = 0.785$; $r_{y,\text{NOU}} = 0.95$

b) $\hat{y} = -2.512 + 0.25928$ NOU For NOU $= 120$, $\hat{y} = 28.60$

13.37 a) $r = \dfrac{119{,}000}{\sqrt{90}\sqrt{1.84 \times 10^8}} = 0.925$

b) $t_c = \dfrac{0.925\sqrt{8}}{\sqrt{0.145}} = 6.87$. Since $t_{0.05,8} = 1.860$, reject H_0.

13.39 $H_0 : \rho = 0$ vs. $H_a : \rho > 0$; $t_c = 4.5$; reject H_0.

13.41 a) $t_c = 12.062/2.611 = 4.62$; $t_{0.05,23} = 1.714$ Reject H_0.

b) $(\hat{y} \mid x = 15.1) = 1{,}012.92$

c) $1{,}012.92 \pm 1.714(309.19) = 1{,}012.92 \pm 529.95$

13.43 a) $\hat{y} = -7.41 + 8.505(10) = \$77.64$ million in sales

b) 90.25% of variation in sales is explained by variation in income.

c) Demand theory would suggest that higher income implies higher sales, rather than the other way around.

13.45 a) $n = 40$; $SST = 486$

b) $F_c = 16$. Since F_c exceeds $F_{0.05;1.40} = 4.08$, we reject H_0.

c) $s_e = 3$; $s_b = 2.4$

13.47 $s_x = 223.60$, $s_y = 1{,}581.14$, $s_{xy} = 325{,}000$, $r = 0.92$

13.49 a) $s_f = 3.376$; $18.723 \le y_g \le 32.227$

b)

x	$\hat{y}$	Interval
8	26.70	20.31 to 33.07
9	27.925	21.79 to 34.06
10	29.15	23.10 to 35.20
11	30.375	24.24 to 36.51
12	31.60	25.21 to 37.99

c)

x	$s_{\bar{y}\cdot x}$	Interval
7	1.548	22.38 to 28.57
8	1.070	24.56 to 28.84
9	0.629	26.67 to 29.18
10	0.381	28.38 to 29.91
11	0.629	29.12 to 31.63
12	1.070	30.38 to 33.74

13.51 a) $t_c = 3/1.25 = 2.4$; $t_{0.1,28} = 1.313$, Reject H_0.

b) $\hat{y}_g = \$9,000$ from Problem 13.11
90% forecast interval is $\$9,000 \pm 1.701(140)$ or
$\$8,761.86 \leq \hat{y}_g \leq \$9,238.14$

13.53 The F-values are the squares of the t-values.

13.55 $b = \dfrac{\sum y x^3}{\sum x^6}$

13.57 SSE would be greater and r^2 less for any method other than OLS.

13.59 One should be very careful in making "cause-and-effect" inferences; the causal relation is part of the specification.

13.61 $1.12 \leq \beta \leq 3.88$

13.65 Would expect precision of forecast when $x = 40$ to be better than precision when $x = 100$ because the former value of x is closer to the mean of $\bar{x} = 50$.

13.67 a) $\hat{y} = -0.841 + 0.03853x$

b) $r^2 = 78.012/81.065 = 0.962$; 96.2% of variation explained; $s_e = \sqrt{3.053/9} = 0.58$

c) Comparing $t_{0.01,9} = 2.821$ with
$$t_c = \frac{0.981\sqrt{9}}{\sqrt{1-0.962}} = 15.1,$$ we reject H_0 in favour of $\rho > 0$.

d) For $H_a : \beta \geq 0.02$, $t_c = 7.28$; for $H_a : \beta \leq 0.05$, $t_c = -4.53$. Each H_a holds, so $0.02 \leq \beta \leq 0.05$

e) $\hat{y} = -0.841 + 0.03853(280) = 9.94$; $s_f = 0.5825\sqrt{1.49} = 0.71$. Comparing $t_{0.025,9} = 2.262$ with $t_c = \dfrac{9.94 - 10.5}{0.71} = -0.79$, we accept H_0 that the 1951 observation is consistent with the model.

13.69 a) $\hat{y} = 5.635 + 2.143x$

b) Comparing $t_{0.05,8} = 1.860$ with
$$t_c = \frac{2.143 - 1.5}{0.2827} = 2.27,$$ we reject H_0 and conclude that the slope exceeds 1.5.

c) Using retained earnings, $R^2 = 0.878$. Using stock price, $R^2 = 0.834$.
Not enough difference to argue for one model over the other.

13.75 a) $MSI = 32.967 + 0.78024$ NIO

b) $t_c = 4.554 > t_{0.05,17} = 1.74$. Reject H_0.

c) $R^2 = 0.55$

d) $t_c = 0.7413\sqrt{17}/\sqrt{1 - (0.7413)^2} = 4.554$, same as part (b).
$t_{0.025,17} = 2.11$ so reject H_0.

e) $0.78024 \pm 2.11(0.17135) = 0.78 \pm 0.36$

f) $\hat{y}_{40} = 32.96727 + 0.78024(40) = 64.1769$
$$s_{\bar{y}\cdot x} = 17.82748\sqrt{(1/19) + (40 - 44.15789)^2/10,824.52} = 4.1515$$
95% C.I. for $\mu_{y\cdot x}$ is $64.1769 \pm 2.11(4.1515)$ or $25.56 \leq \mu_{y\cdot x} \leq 102.80$

13.77 The number of residuals smaller than $|10.28|$ is 13.

13.79 a) $SALES = 10.243 + 0.425$ INCOME

b) $F_c = 18,885.45$ which far exceeds the critical value. Reject H_0.

c) Using $t_{0.01,20} = 2.528$, 98 C.I. on β has limits $0.425 \pm 2.528(0.003)$, $0.417 \leq \beta \leq 0.433$

13.81 a) $SALES = 34.486 + 0.419$ INCOME

b) $F_c = 823.41$ so reject H_0.

c) Using $t_{0.01,25} = 2.485$, $0.382 \leq \beta \leq 0.456$

13.83 a) $GDP = 89.36 + 3.186$(exports)

b) Comparing $t_{0.025,39} = 2022$ with
$t_c = (3.186 - 4)/0.084 = -9.7$, we reject H_0.
The slope is less than 4.

13.85 a) income $= -212.042 + 105.562$(educ)

b) $F_c = 19.92$

c) $t_c = 105.562/23.654 = 4.46$; conclude that $\beta > 0$

d) F_c in part (b) is the square of t_c in part (c).

13.87 a) IBM: $\hat{y} = 0.002 + 0.752$ MKT
EXXON: $\hat{y} = 0.004 + 0.713$ MKT
GE: $\hat{y} = 0.005 + 0.930$ MKT
GM: $\hat{y} = -0.003 + 0.893$ MKT

b) For the portfolio of $(GE + GM)/2$,
$\hat{y} = 0.0009 + 0.912$ MKT

Chapter Fourteen

14.3 a–b)

	Simple	Multiple
R^2	0.42	0.80
s_e	27.3	16.3
b_2	7.37	5.2
R^2_{adj}	0.408	0.788

Both goodness of fit measures show an improvement. Partial impact is less than simple impact when no other factors are included.

c) $r^2_{yx_2x_3 \cdot x_1} = (28,338.4 - 9,619.1)/28,338.4 = 0.661$

14.5 a) $\hat{y} = 4 + 0.6(6) + 0.3(35) = \$8.65$

b) $\Delta\hat{y} = 1(0.6) + 20(0.3) = \$6.60$

14.7 Intercept has no useful meaning.
$\dfrac{d(\text{burglary})}{d(\text{urban})} = 12$; $\dfrac{\partial(\text{burglary})}{\partial(\text{urban})} = 14.1$
$\dfrac{\partial(\text{burglary})}{\partial(\text{divorce})}$ divorce $=$ constant $= 83.8$.
urban $=$ constant

14.9 $R^2_{y \cdot x_1 x_2 x_3} = 0.68$; $r^2_{yx_3 \cdot x_1 x_2} = 0.333$

14.11 $r^2_{yx_3 \cdot x_1 x_2} = (4,586.3 - 4,574.8)/885.5 = 0.013$

14.13 a) True

b) False; all remaining variation is always explained.

c) True   d) True

e) False; true only if $r_{x_1 x_2} = 0$; in general, $r^2_{yx_1} + r^2_{yx_2} \geq R^2_{y \cdot x_1 x_2}$

14.15 a) $R^2 = 0.80$ b) $r^2_{yx_3 \cdot x_1 x_2} = 0.571$

c) $R^2_{adj} = 1 - (1 - 0.8)(23/20) = 0.77$

14.17 a) $\hat{y} = 6 + 3(-1) + 10(3) - 4(2) = 25$

b) $t_1 = 1.5, t_2 = 2.5, t_3 = -5$

c) x_3 most and x_1 least important

d) 60

14.19 a) $F_c = 49.3$. Model is useful.

b) $t_{0.025,36} = 2.03$; 95% C.I. is $-5.22 \pm 2.03(0.98)$
$\$ - 3,230 \geq b_2 \geq \$ - 7,210$

14.21 a) $r^2_{yx_4 \cdot x_1 x_2 x_3} = 30/200 = 0.15$

b) $F_c = (230/4)/(170/7) = 2.368$; $F_{(0.05;4,7)} = 4.12$
Accept H_0 that relation overall is not significant.

14.23 a) $\hat{y} = 6,000$

b) Compare $t_c = 6/2 = 3$ with $t_{(0.025,28)} = 2.048$, reject H_0 on β_1
$t_c = -10/4 = -2.5$. Reject H_0 on β_2
$t_c = 4/0.8 = 5$. Reject H_0 on β_3

14.25 $\hat{y} = 10.16 + 17.6x_1 + 4.3x_2$
$R^2 = 0.92$ so 92% of variation is explained by the model.
$s_e = 3$ compared to the average learning score of 306, so the model has low error of prediction.
School expenditures has a significant coefficient ($t_1 = 28.3$) but socioeconomic status does not ($t_2 = 1.48$). The sample group has a higher average learning score and socioeconomic status than overall population of 12th grade students. Its variance of socioeconomic status is very high (8.75) compared to the national average (2).

14.29 a) Solving yields $b_1 = 4$, $b_2 = 6$, and $a = -26$

c) $R_2 = 0.909$

d) $t_1 = (b_1 - \beta_1)/s_{b1} = 4/0.302 = 13.25$; reject $H_0 : \beta_1 = 0$
$t_2 = (b_2 - \beta_2)/s_{b2} = 6/0.427 = 14.05$; reject $H_0 : \beta_2 = 0$

e) $\dfrac{22(9.12)}{33.9} \leq \sigma^2_\epsilon \leq \dfrac{22(9.12)}{12.3}$
$5.92 \leq \sigma^2_\epsilon \leq 16.31$ (hours)^2

14.31 a) $b_1 = 0.7905$; $b_2 = 0.5323$; $a = 5.39$;
$\hat{y} = 5.39 + 0.7905x_1 + 0.5323x_2$

c) SSR $= 700.37$; SST $= 770.4$; SSE $= 70.03$

d) $F_c(700.37/2)/(70.03/7) = 35.0$. This exceeds $F_{0.05;2,7} = 4.74$, so conclude that x_1 and x_2 are linearly related to y.

e) SSE$/14.1 \leq \sigma^2_\epsilon \leq$ SSE$/2.17$
$4.97 \leq \sigma^2_\epsilon \leq 32.27$
C.V. residual is 2.6 to 6.8% using $2.22 \leq \sigma_\epsilon \leq 5.68$

14.33 Use four dummy variables with values of 0, except let $x_1 = 1$ for high school graduates, $x_2 = 1$ for college graduates, $x_3 = 1$ for master's degree, and $x_4 = 1$ for doctoral level.

14.35 a) Use three dummy variables with values of 0 except $Q_1 = 1$ for 1st quarter, $Q_2 = 1$ for 2nd quarter, and $Q_3 = 1$ for 3rd quarter

b) $y = \alpha + \beta_1 x + \beta_2 Q_1 + \beta_3 Q_2 + \beta_4 Q_3 + \epsilon$

c) Intercept represents 4th quarter.

d) β_2 gives change in sales for 1st quarter compared to 4th quarter.

14.37 a) $R^2 = 300/400 = 0.75$
$R^2_{adj} = 0.71$ which corrects for degrees of freedom

b) $F_c = $ MSR/MSE $= 150/8.33 = 18.01$

14.39 a) $\hat{y} = 131.9243 + 2.7261x_1 + 0.0472x_2 - 2.5874x_3$

b) $F_c = 17.87 > F_{(0.01;3,16)} = 5.29$ so reject H_0.

c) $t_c = 0.5075 > t_{(0.05,16)} = 1.746$ so accept H_0. Conclude $\beta_2 = 0$.

d) $R^2 = 0.77$

e) Δ cost $= -2.5874(7.5) = \$ - 19.40$.

14.41 74.6% of variation explained, but C.V. residual $= 72.2\%$, so model shows some useful relation but would not predict accurately. Jointly, the two explanatory variables help explain variation in y but neither has a significant coefficient. See Section 15.3 on multicollinearity.

14.43 a) Sales $= -1.791 + 0.365(\text{Pop}) + 0.540(\text{Unem}) + 0.022(\text{Adex}) + 0.612(\text{Comp})$

b) $t_1 = 4.18$; $t_2 = 2.67$; $t_3 = 1.77$; $t_4 = 1.78$; b_1 and b_2 are significant

c) $25(1.39)/37.7 \le \sigma_\epsilon^2 \le 34.75/14.6$
$0.92 \le \sigma_\epsilon^2 \le 2.38$

d) $\hat{y} = \$7.186$ million

14.45 b) R^2 increased slightly from 0.96 to 0.99 s_e decreases from 9.7 to 5.1 and C.V. residuals decreases from 15.2% to 8.0%.
The coefficient of GDP remains significant with a small increase from 0.31 to 0.39.

c) $F_{(0.05;2,37)} = 3.25$, $F_c = 51.9$ so the extra two variables are jointly useful in the model.

14.47 a) $F_{(0.05;2,42)} = 3.20$. Using Formula 14.10, $F_c = 19.04$
The addition of the two variables is useful.

b) $R^2_{y \cdot \text{Hsholds,Income}} = 0.79$ with $F_c = 82.7$ so these two variables only in the model would be significant.

c) $F_c = 12.1$. The addition of Pop and Sales is also jointly useful in the model.

d) Similar to (b). Pop and Sales in the model give a significant fit.

14.49 a) Let $R = 1$ if Risk $= 5$ or 6, otherwise $R = 0$.
$y = \alpha + \beta_1(\text{Assets}) + \beta_2 R + \beta_3 R(\text{Assets}) + \epsilon$

b) $\hat{y} = 4.20 + 0.00098(\text{Assets}) - 1.366R + 0.0039R(\text{Assets})$
Overall, $F_c = 1.03$ which is not significant.
None of the t-ratios show significant coefficients.

14.51 $\hat{y} = -21.096 + 0.166$ Income $+ 14.345$ Hsholds $- 0.489$ Popchg
$s_e = 30.6$, C.V. residuals $= 6.19\%$, $R^2 = 0.9996$. Fit is quite good with large proportion of variation explained and typical error in prediction with this data of about 6%. Coefficients on Income and Hsholds, but not on Popchg are significant.

14.53 a) $y = \alpha + \beta_1 x_1 + \beta_2 x_2 + \beta_3 G_1 + \beta_4 G_2 + \beta_5 G_3 + \epsilon$

b) 28.3% of the variation is explained. $t_{0.05,73} = 1.668$ (interpolating within Table VI) compared to $t_1 = 8.136$ (significant), $t_2 = 0.957$ (not significant), $t_3 = 2.577$ (significant), $t_4 = 3.049$ (significant), and $t_5 = 2.363$ (significant). $F_{(0.05;5,73)} = 2.35$ (by interpolation) compared to

$$F_c = \frac{\text{SSR}/5}{\text{SSE}/73} = \frac{4,181.375}{780.397} = 5.358$$

The joint linear relation is significant.

c) The intercept for development status 1 is 16.67; for status 3, the intercept is 4.867.
The difference is 11.803% more literacy within status 1 countries.

Chapter Fifteen

15.1 Specification and measurement error and changes in behaviour

15.3 a) Assumptions 1 and 4 **b)** Assumption 5

c) Assumption 5

15.11 a) Not a linear relationship.

b) $r_{xw} = -11.50/17.97 = -0.640$

15.13 a) $360(1 - 0.9772) = 8.2$

b) $360(0.8413 - 0.6915) = 53.9$

c) $\chi_c^2 = 18$ compared to $\chi_{0.05,9}^2 = 16.9$. Reject H_0. Assumption of normality is suspect.

15.15 a) $E_i = \{11.45, 67.95, 74.9, 95.8, 95.8, 74.9, 67.95, 11.45\}$

b) $\chi_{(0.01,7)}^2 = 18.5$; $\chi_c^2 = 32.7$. Assumption 2 seems violated.

15.17 Since $R^2_{x_1 x_2} = 0.9962 > R^2_{y \cdot x_1 x_2} = 0.7460$, multicollinearity is a problem.

15.19 a) Multicollinearity causes inaccurate measurement of the impact coefficient associated with individual explanatory variables.

b) If $R_1^2 = 0.75 > R^2 = 0.56$, multicollinearity is indicated.

15.21 a) 1.0 on the diagonal and symmetrical.

b) The highest pairwise r^2 value is 0.64 which is more serious in a model with R^2 only 0.35, and not too problematic in a model with $R^2 = 0.95$ (in terms of multicollinearity effects).

15.23 Use the lowest size n in Table X. Critical values for $\alpha = 0.01$ are $d_L = 0.81$ and $d_U = 1.07$.
$d = 4.50/3.88 = 1.16$, giving an indication of possible positive autocorrelation.

15.25 a) Plot shows similar spread in accord with Assumption 4.

$d = 0.785$ lies below d_L and indicates positive autocorrelation.

15.29 Let log and ln indicate logarithm to base 10 and natural logarithm respectively.

  a) $\log T = \log \alpha + (\beta + 1) \log I + \epsilon$

  b) $\ln E = \ln \alpha + \beta \ln I + \ln \epsilon$

15.31 a) $\log \hat{y} = \log a + (\log b)x$; $\log b = 0.1735$; $\log a = -0.2861$. Using antilogs, $\hat{y} = 0.517(1.491)^x$

  b) $\{y - \hat{y}\} = \{0.03, -0.05, -0.01, 0.05, -0.01, 0.02, 0.03\}$

15.33 a) The relationship is roughly parabolic.

  b) $b = -262.5/82.5 = -3.18$; $a = 70.5 - (-3.18)(5.5) = 88$; $\hat{y} = 88 - 3.18x$

  c) The first two residuals are positive, the next five negative, and the last three positive, indicating positive autocorrelation.

15.35 a) Since $d = 1.1$, which is less than $d_L = 1.14$ for $n = 26$, $m = 3$, and $\alpha = 0.05$, we conclude that positive autocorrelation is present.

  b) In the presence of autocorrelation the usual t and F tests are suspect and not reliable.

15.37 c) $d = 1.39$, which is near the value for d_U for $n = 15$.

  d) Autocorrelation is probably not a serious problem. Plots in parts (a) and (b) also suggest that Assumptions 4 and 5 are acceptable.

15.39 c) $d = 2.06$, indicating no autocorrelation.

  d) Plots in (a) and (b) suggest that Assumptions 4 and 5 are acceptable.

15.41 Sample size was too small.

15.43 a) Since $d_L = 1.28$ for $n = 60$, $m = 4$, and $\alpha = 0.01$, the d-value of 1.156 indicates positive autocorrelation.

  b) $\hat{p} = \frac{1}{2}(2 - d) = 0.42$

  c) $d = 1.813$ indicates that the problem of autocorrelation has probably been corrected.

15.45 Look for a few long runs of similar signs (positive autocorrelation) or frequent oscillation of different successive signs (negative autocorrelation).

15.47 a) Order cases by the size of income x_3. Group the lower 40% of the cases and group the upper 40% of the cases, omitting cases now numbered 31 through 45.

b) $F_c = 2,823/1,283 = 2.2$. $F_{(0.05;25,25)} = 1.95$ Reject H_0. Heteroscedasticity is indicated.

15.49 Use $n_A = 5$ and $n_B = 4$ with group A being the more recent time periods. $SSE_A = 0.271$ and $SSE_B = 0.071$. Comparing $F_{(0.05;3,2)} = 19.2$ with $F_c = 2.534$, we accept H_0 that there is no heteroscedasticity.

15.51 Group A has observations 1--10, and group B has observations 16--25.
Comparing $F_{(0.05;6,6)} = 4.28$ with $F_c = 151.7/107.5 = 1.4$, we conclude that there is no heteroscedasticity.

15.53 For ordering by advertising expense let Group A be observations 19--30 and Group B be observations 1--12. We obtain $SSE_A = 11.217$ and $SSE_B = 7.680$.

$$F_c = \frac{11.217/7}{7.680/7} = 1.460$$

Again, no heteroscedasticity is indicated.

15.55 Regress e^2 on the squares and cross-products of x's, giving 6 variables in the model. $\chi_c^2 = nR^2 = 178(0.145) = 25.81$
Heteroscedasticity is indicated.

15.57 a) $d = 0.397 < d_L$ which indicates positive autocorrelation.

  b) Plots show a grouping of points in the first and third quadrants, and four primary runs of residuals with the same sign.

15.59 a) Income $= -661.53 + 90.65$ Educyrs $+ 280.71$ Numinhse

  b) Plot of $\hat{y}$ with e shows some increasing spread as $\hat{y}$ increases.
Plot of e with Educyrs is somewhat similar.
Plot of e with Numinhse has roughly parallel bounding lines.

  c) Model regresses e^2 on x_1^2, x_2^2, and $(x_1 x_2)$. $R^2 = 0.127$
$\chi_c^2 = 165(0.127) = 20.96$ indicating heteroscedasticity (d.f. $= 3$)

  d) $E_i = \{3.8, 22.4, 24.7, 31.6, 31.6, 24.7, 22.4, 3.8\}$
$O_i = \{2, 9, 31, 58, 31, 17, 12, 5\}$
$\chi_c^2 = 40.2 > \chi_{(0.01,7)}^2 = 18.5$
The assumption of normality is suspect.

15.61 a) Order the observations by density;
deaths $= 107.029 + 4.306$(drivers)

  b) Let observations 31--50 be group A and items 1--20 be group B:
$$F_{(0.05;18,18)} = 2.22 \text{ and } F_c = \frac{2,305,701/18}{122,800/18} = 18.78$$
Heteroscedasticity exists.

c) Deaths $= 117.71 + 4.29$(drivers) $- 0.0205$(density). Using the same groupings of observations as in part (b), $F_{(0.05;17,17)} = 2.28$ and

$$F_c = \frac{2,278,093/17}{106,203/17} = 21.45$$

Heteroscedasticity exists in the multiple model as well, with $V[\epsilon_t]$ possibly related to (density)^2.

Chapter Sixteen

16.3 a) $800/year

b) $x = 10$; $\hat{y}_{1993} = 34,500$; income is $1,500 above trend.

16.5 b) $\hat{y} = 190.77 + 30.94x$

c) $\hat{y}_{1994(x=9)} = 190.77 + 30.94(9) = 469.23$

d) $\hat{y} = 190.77(1/4) + 30.94(1/4)[x + (1/8)]$
$\hat{y} = 48.66 + 7.735x$

16.7 a) Sales $= 1.19 + 0.769x$

b) Sales $= 0.06 + 1.62x - 0.12x^2$

c) Quadratic shows better fit with $R^2_{adj} = 0.99$ and C.V. residuals $= 2.1$ compared to 0.935 and 9.7 for the linear.

16.9

Year	Sales	M.A.
1982	18	
1983	20	20
1984	22	20.33
1985	19	20.67
1986	21	21.33
1987	24	22
1988	21	22.67
1989	23	23.67
1990	27	

16.11 $\hat{y} = 50 + 5.5x$
$\hat{y}_{1990} = 50 + 5.5(2) = 61.0$
M.A.$_{1990} = (51 + 68 + 65)/3 = 184/3 = 61.33$

16.13 Since $\hat{y} = 3,600 + 480x$ is for annual trend, to get equation for months, divide b by 12 $\rightarrow$ $\hat{y} = 3,600 + 40x$. Since $x = 0$ for October 1991, $x = 42$ for April 1995, and $\hat{y} = 3,600 + 40(42) = 5,280$ is trend value for April 1995. Seasonally adjusted figure is $5,280(0.80) = 4,224$

16.17 Quarterly average = $3 million; 1st quarter = $3.9 million; 2nd quarter = $2.7 million

16.19 a) December

b) August

c) $6/0.6 = 10$ for January; $10/1.2 = 8.33$ for August. Percentage decrease is $100(10 - 8.33)/10 = -16.7$

16.21 a) $S_{Jan} = 133/102 = 130.4$

b) Monthly average sales $= \$240,000/12 = \$20,000$
Adjusted sales for March $= 20,000(0.9) = \$18,000$

16.23 a) July

b) $(30,000/12)1.71 = 4,275$

c) For January, $80/0.36 = 2,222.22$
For June, $3,600/1.56 = 2,307.69$
Percentage increase is
$100(2,307.69 - 2,222.22)/2,222.22 = 3.8$

16.25 b) $\hat{y} = 24.52 - 0.085x$

c) Trend values (where $x = 0$ is Jan. 1, 1992)

	1991	1992
Jan	23.54	24.56
Feb	23.63	24.65
Mar	23.71	24.73
Apr	23.80	24.82
May	23.88	24.90
June	23.97	24.99
July	24.05	25.07
Aug	24.14	25.16
Sept	24.22	25.24
Oct	24.31	25.33
Nov	24.39	25.41
Dec	24.48	25.50

Seasonal index numbers

	Ave.	
Jan	0.936	
Feb	0.916	
Mar	0.942	
Apr	0.973	
May	1.015	
June	1.073	
July	1.071	
Aug	1.047	
Sept	1.043	
Oct	1.030	
Nov	0.979	
Dec	0.975	

d) Dividing original data by the 5-month M.A.

	Ave.
Jan	0.979
Feb	0.961
Mar	0.970
Apr	0.990
May	1.000
June	1.036
July	1.022
Aug	0.995
Sept	1.016
Oct	1.012
Nov	0.944
Dec	1.004

16.27 Using 1987 dollars, get $3.68 million building in 1990 and $3.21 million in 1995. Get $0.47 million more building in 1990.

16.29 First year real value is 160. Next year is 163.1. Percent change in real value is $100(3.1/160) = 1.94\%$ increase.

16.31 Decrease in real income is $37,500 - 42,000 = -\$4,500$

16.33 a) All employees had a real decline in income.

Employee	Real Value
Secretary	$ 4,913
Manager	7,982
Janitor	4,318
Teacher	9,414
Governor	25,832

b) $100(100/224) = 44.6$

16.35 a) Price relatives are 1.0 for milk, 0.9 for eggs, and 1.33 for bread.

b) $I = 100 \left(\dfrac{15 + 45 + 20}{15 + 50 + 15} \right) = 100$

c) $I = 100 \left(\dfrac{1.0 + 0.9 + 1.33}{3} \right) = 107.67$

d) Using 1955 weights, $I_n = 100(14.25/13.25) = 107.5$
Using 1956 weights, $I_n = 100(18.405/16.75) = 109.9$

e) $LP_{56} = 100(14.25/13.25) = 107.5$
$PP_{56} = 100(16.75/15.75) = 106.3$

16.37 a) $LP_{87} = 100(238.044/217.402) = 109.49$
$LP_{89} = 10(370.964/217.402) = 107.64$

b) $PP_{87} = 100(231.614/211.681) = 109.42$
$PP_{89} = 100(332.518/194.711) = 170.78$

d) Using the Laspayres index to obtain real energy value shows more used in 1987.

1987:	$100(5,000/109.5) = \$4,566$
1989:	$100(6,000/170.6) = \$3,517$

16.39 $LP = 100(201/231.6) = 86.79$. Prices in 1990 were 13.21% lower than in 1993.

16.43 Using a multiplicative model, $Y = 210,000 = 180,000(S)(1.10)$; $S = 1.06$

16.45 $\hat{y} = 137.50 + (8/12)x$ with $x = 0$ at July 1, 1993. For February 15, 1995, set $x = 19.5$; $\hat{y} = 150.5$

16.47 For December 1996, set $x = 32$; $\hat{y} = 307,890$. Seasonally adjusted value is $307,890(140/100) = \$431,046$.

16.49 a) Average monthly ratio is $1,143/12 = 95.25$. $S_{March} = 105$; $S_{April} = 115.5$; $S_{August} = 75.6$.

b) $10 million average per month; seasonally adjusted values are April = $11.55 million and August = $7.56 million.

16.51 a) February 1996 $= \hat{y} = 120,000 + 1,000(14)$ seasonally adjusted value is $134,000(80/100) = 107,200$
May 1989 forecast $(x = 53) = 173,000(115/100) = 198,950$
December 1997 forecast $(x = 36) = 234,000$

16.55 a) CPIA $= -77.16 + 5.57t$ with t in years and $t = 0$ at mid-1949

b) $\ln$ CPIA $= 2.27 + 0.07t$ or CPIA $= 9.68(1.07)^t$

c) Both models fit well with R^2 values of 0.96 and 0.98. C.V. residuals is smaller in the exponential trend equation, 1.54 compared to 9.8 for the linear case.

16.57 a) Linear trend seems to be appropriate.

b) Quadratic trend is $\hat{y} = 2.17 + 0.70t - 0.0175t^2$ where $t = 0$ at mid-1965.

Chapter Seventeen

17.3

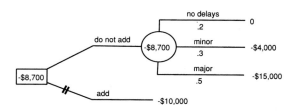

17.5 $P(\text{HIV} \mid \text{test}+) =$

$$\frac{P(\text{test} + \mid \text{HIV})P(\text{HIV})}{P(\text{test} + \mid \text{HIV})P(\text{HIV}) + P(\text{test} + \mid \text{NO HIV})P(\text{NO HIV})}$$

$$= \frac{(.95)(.05)}{(.95)(.05) + (.05)(.95)} = 0.50$$

17.7 a) $E[\text{air}] = \$3,400$, $E[\text{sea}] = \$3,000$

b) $P(B_1 \mid R) = \dfrac{P(R \mid B_1)P(B_1)}{P(R \mid B_1)P(B_1) + P(R \mid B_2)P(B_2)}$

$$= \frac{(.8)(.4)}{(.8)(.4) + (.3)(.6)} = .64$$

c) Best choice air: EMV[air] = $3,640;
EMV[sea] = $4,200

17.9 a) To be indifferent $-200P(B_1) +$
$400(1 - P(B_1)) = -500P(B_1) + 1,000(1 - P(B_1))$
$\rightarrow P(B_1) = 2/3$
Hence any value of $P(B_1) > 2/3$ will make A_1 better.

b) $P(\text{partial} \mid x) =$

$$\frac{P(x \mid \text{partial})P(\text{partial})}{P(x \mid \text{partial})P(\text{partial}) + P(x \mid \text{complete})P(\text{complete})}$$

$$= \frac{(.8)(.4)}{(.8)(.4) + (1/3)(.6)} = 0.615$$

EMV$(A_1) = \$31.00$; EMV$(A_2) = \$77.50$;
A_2 is better.

17.11 a)

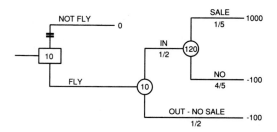

b) Values his right arm at $50.00

c)

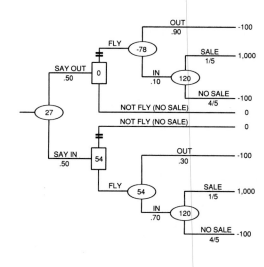

17.13

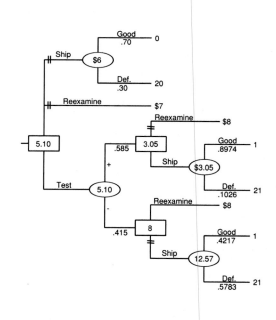

$P(\text{GOOD} \mid +) =$

$$\frac{P(+ \mid \text{GOOD})P(\text{GOOD})}{P(+ \mid \text{GOOD})P(\text{GOOD}) + P(+ \mid \text{DEF})P(\text{DEF})}$$

$$= \frac{(.75)(.7)}{(.75)(.7) + (.20)(.3)} = .8974$$

$$P(\text{GOOD} \mid -) = \frac{(.25)(.7)}{(.25)(.7) + (.80)(.3)} = .4217$$

ENGS = $0.90; EVSI = $1.90; EVPI = $3.90

17.15

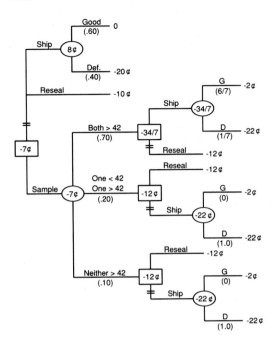

$P(G \mid \text{both} > 42) =$
$$\frac{P(\text{both} > 42 \mid G)P(G)}{P(\text{both} > 42 \mid G)P(G) + P(\text{both} > 42 \mid \text{def})P(\text{def})}$$
$$= \frac{(1.0)(0.60)}{(1.0)(0.60) + (0.50)(0.50)(0.40)} = 6/7$$
$P(\text{def} \mid \text{both} > 42) = 1/7$; ENGS = \$0.01; EVSI = \$0.03
Optimal action is to sample. EVPI = 4 cents

17.17 a) and **b)**

	States of Nature				
	S_1	S_2	S_3	S_4	EMV
D_1	40*	40	40	40	40
D_2	35	50*	50	50	45.5*
D_3	30	45	60*	60	45
D_4	25	40	55	70*	41.5

* = optimal decision for each state of nature

The optimal action is to buy 5 toys.

c) EMV(PI) = 51; EVPI = \$5.50
\$5.50 is the maximum to pay for perfect information.

17.19 U(200) = (1/2)U(500) + (1/2)U(100) = (1/2)(100) + (1/2)(50) = 75
Person is risk avoiding since EMV(gamble) = \$300, which exceeds the \$200 for certain.

17.21

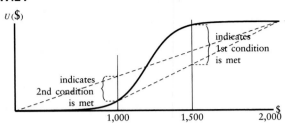

17.25 EU(Assembly) = −370; EU(Rework) = −300; EU(Sample) = −262.20
Using EU leads to the same decision assuming EMV in this case, ignoring the costs of sampling.

17.27 $P(\pi < .10) = 0.25$; $P(\pi < .14) = 0.80$
From Table III, $P(z \le -0.675) = 0.25$ and $P(z \le .84) = 0.80$ Hence,

$$\frac{.10 - \mu}{\sigma} = -.675 \text{ and } \frac{.14 - \mu}{\sigma} = .84$$

Solving simultaneously yields $\sigma = .0264$, $\mu = 0.11782$

17.29 a) The breakeven value μ_b is found by solving the payoff functions simultaneously; i.e., $-100 + 5x = -1,290 + 15x$ yields $x^* = 119$.
Since $\mu_0 = 120$, $\mu_b = 119$, optimal action is a_2

b) $x^* = 115.8$ is optimal order.

c) $\bar{x} = 118$; $\mu = 118\frac{1}{3}$; $\sigma_1^2 = 4.167$

d) Since $\mu_1 = 118.33 < 119 = \mu_b$ (breakeven), the owner should select action a_1. $x^* = 116.67$ is optimal order.

e)

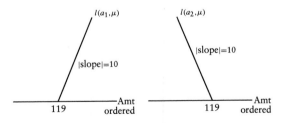

17.31 a) $P(\text{One Defective}) = 0.19$;
$(\text{Savings})P(\text{One Defective}) = \$170$

b) EVSI = 0.675(\$0) + 0.270(\$599) + 0.55(\$1619) = \$251

17.33 The number of cheques processed daily is very close to 800,000.

17.35 a)

	States of Nature				
	S_1	S_2	S_3	S_4	EMV
D_1	−400,000	−600,000	−800,000*	−1,000,000*	−600,000
D_2	−375,000	−590,000	−805,000	−1,020,000	−590,000
D_3	−347,500*	−575,000*	−802,500	−1,030,000	−575,000

$*$ = optimal decision for each state of nature; D_3 is best order.

c) EVPI = $3,500$ is the maximum to pay for perfect information.

17.37 a) $EMV(A_1) = 1,000(0.25) + 1,100(0.35) + 1,300(0.4) = 1,155$

$EMV(A_2) = -500(0.25) + 1,000(0.35) + 2,000(0.4) = 1,025$

$EMV(A_3) = -1,500(0.25) - 500(0.35) + 4,000(0.4) = 1,050$

The optimal action is A_1

b) EMV(PI) = $2,235$; EVPI = $1,080$ is the maximum to pay.

c)

S of N	Priors	Likelihoods	Joints	Posteriors
s_1	0.25	0.05	0.0125	0.034
s_2	0.35	0.10	0.0350	0.095
s_3	0.40	0.80	0.3200	0.871
			$P(\text{Turbo}) = 0.3675$	

$EMV(A_1) = 1,270.8$; $EMV(A_2) = 1,820$; $EMV(A_3) = 3,385.5$

The optimal action with the new information is A_3.

Chapter Eighteen

18.1 a) Nominal   **b)** Ordinal

c) Ordinal

18.3 a) Ratio   **b)** Nominal

c) Ordinal if only names listed; ratio if asset values listed.

d) Nominal   **e)** Ordinal

18.7 Critical region for $\alpha = 0.05$, $n_A = 10$, $n_B = 10$ is $r \le 6$. Since $r = 11$, accept the hypothesis that both samples are from the same population.

18.9 H_0 : Price changes are random H_a : Price changes are not random.
Critical region for $\alpha = 0.05$, $n_I = 14$, $n_N = 9$ is $r \le 7$. Since $r = 7$, reject the null.

18.13 $H_0 : \pi = 1/2$ vs. $H_a : \pi \neq 1/2$
At $\alpha = 0.05$, with $n = 9$ (due to a tie), the critical region is $x \ge 8$. Since $x = 6$, accept H_0.

18.15 a)

Group	White males	Women	Minorities
E_i	700	200	100
O_i	800	150	50

H_0 : White males = 70%; Women = 20%; Minorities = 10%.
H_a : The frequencies are different from these.
$\chi_c^2 = 51.79$. With $\alpha = 0.01$, $\chi_2^2 = 9.21$; reject H_0.

b) $P(\chi_2^2 \ge 51.79) \le 0.005$

18.17 $H_0 : E_1 = E_2 = E_3 = E_4 = 50$ vs.
H_a : frequencies do not all equal 50
$\chi_c^2 = 23$. With $\alpha = 0.05$, $\chi_3^2 = 7.81$; reject H_0.

18.19 H_0 : frequency = 25 in each interval,
H_a : frequencies differ
$\chi_{(0.005,19)}^2 = 38.6$, $\chi_c^2 = 1,188/25 = 47.52$. Reject H_0. Assumption of normality is dubious.

18.21 a)

	7--3		3--11		11--7			
	E	O	E	O	E	O		
Males	10	15	7.5	5	12.5	10		30
Females	10	5	7.5	10	12.5	15		30
	20		15		25			60

H_0 : Errors are independent of shift and sex.
H_a : Errors are not independent of shift and sex.

b) $\chi_c^2 = 7.67$. With $\alpha = 0.05$, $\chi_2^2 = 5.99$; reject H_0.

c) $0.01 \le P(\chi_2^2 \ge 7.67) \le 0.025$

18.23 a) H_0 : The degree of infestation and type of spray are independent, H_a : They are not independent.
$\chi_c^2 = 8$. An $\alpha = 0.05$ would be reasonable.

b) With $\alpha = 0.01$, $\chi_1^2 = 6.63$; H_0 would be rejected.

18.25

	White		Black			
	E	O	E	O		
I	23.2	14	16.8	26	40	
II	11.6	14	8.4	6	20	$\chi_c^2 = 14.61$
III	23.2	30	16.8	10	40	
	58		42		100	

$P(\chi_2 \ge 14.61) \le 0.005$; since the p-value is small, H_0 would be rejected for most α-levels.

18.27 a) $D = \text{Max} \mid F_i - S_i \mid = 0.07$. For $\alpha = 0.05$, $1.35/\sqrt{92} = 0.142$, accept H_0.

b) $H_0 : E_1 = E_2 = E_3 = E_4 = 23$ H_a : The frequencies are not all equal. $\chi_c^2 = 3.48$
For $\alpha = 0.05$, $\chi_3^2 = 7.81$; accept H_0.

18.29 $r_s = 1 - \dfrac{6(18)}{120} = 0.1$, $\tau = \dfrac{0}{10} = 0$

18.31 $r_s = 1 - \dfrac{6(12)}{720} = 0.90$, $\tau = \dfrac{26}{36} = 0.722$

18.33 a) $\tau = \dfrac{19}{45} = 0.422$

b) $r_s = 1 - \dfrac{6(56)}{990} = 0.661$

18.35 a) H_0 : No correlation between test scores.
H_a : Correlation is not equal to zero.

$$r_s = 1 - \dfrac{6(40)}{990} = 0.76 \qquad \tau = \dfrac{25}{45} = 0.556$$

b) $t_c = 0.76 \dfrac{\sqrt{8}}{\sqrt{0.422}} = 3.31$, $t_{(0.025,8)} = \pm 2.306$, reject H_0.

18.37 Using successive residuals as pairs, $n = 13$ and $\Sigma d_i = 618$,
$$r_s = 1 - \dfrac{6(618)}{13^3 - 13} = 1 - \left(\dfrac{3{,}648}{2{,}184}\right) = -0.67$$

Chapter Nineteen

19.1 a) $y = 2.5x + 8$ **b)** $y = -3x$
c) $y = -3x + 1$ **d)** $y = -1.5x + 7$
e) $y = \frac{1}{3}x + \frac{4}{3}$ **f)** $y = 2x - 4$

19.3 a) slope $= 3$, x-intercept $= \frac{7}{3}$, y-intercept $= -7$

b) slope $= -\frac{2}{4} = -\frac{1}{2}$, x-intercept $= \frac{16}{2} = 8$, y-intercept $= \frac{16}{4} = 4$

c) slope $= -\frac{1}{2} \div \frac{1}{4} = -2$, x-intercept $= 2$, y-intercept $= 4$

d) slope $= -3 \div (-2) = \frac{3}{2}$, x-intercept $= \frac{4}{3}$, y-intercept $= \frac{4}{-2} = -2$

e) slope $= \frac{1}{4}$, x-intercept $= -2$, y-intercept $= \frac{2}{4} = \frac{1}{2}$

19.5 a) $x = -1$, $y = 1$ **b)** $x = -\frac{2}{6} = -\frac{1}{3}$, $y = -\frac{10}{3}$

19.7 a)

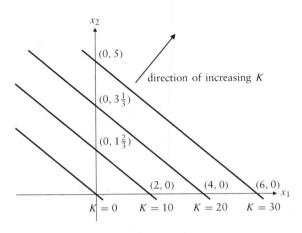

b)

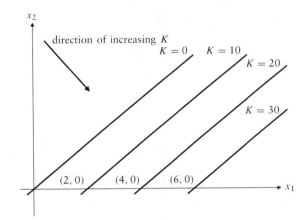

c)

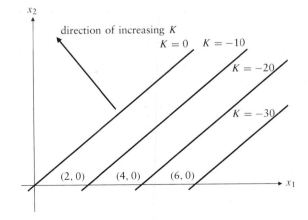

d)

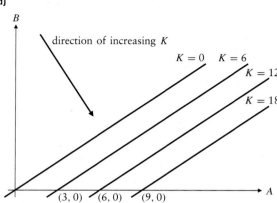

d)

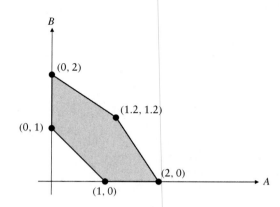

19.9 a)

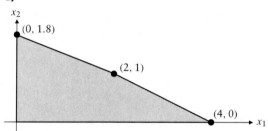

19.11 a) D   **b)** G   **c)** A   **d)** C

19.13 a)

b)

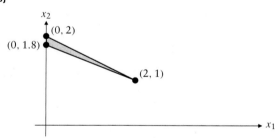

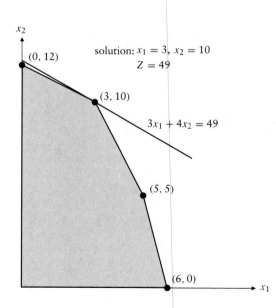

Solution: $x_1 = 3$, $x_2 = 10$, $z = 49$

c)

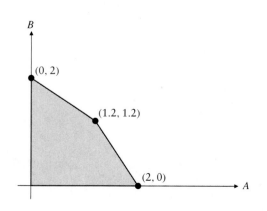

b)

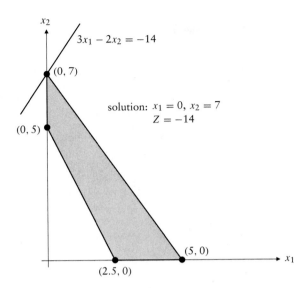

$3x_1 - 2x_2 = -14$

$(0, 7)$

solution: $x_1 = 0$, $x_2 = 7$
$Z = -14$

$(0, 5)$

$(5, 0)$

$(2.5, 0)$

Solution: $x_1 = 0$, $x_2 = 7$, $z = -14$

c)

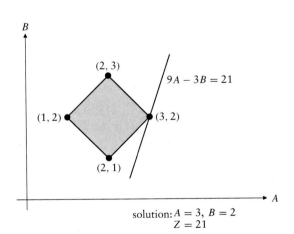

$(2, 3)$

$9A - 3B = 21$

$(1, 2)$

$(3, 2)$

$(2, 1)$

solution: $A = 3$, $B = 2$
$Z = 21$

Solution: $A = 3$, $B = 2$, $z = 21$

d)

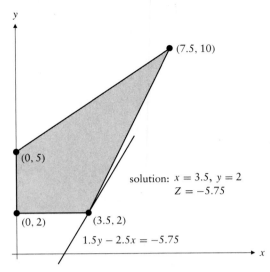

$(7.5, 10)$

$(0, 5)$

solution: $x = 3.5$, $y = 2$
$Z = -5.75$

$(0, 2)$

$(3.5, 2)$

$1.5y - 2.5x = -5.75$

Solution: $x = 3.5$, $y = 2$, $z = -5.75$

19.15 a) shadow price $= \dfrac{253.60 - 253.33}{100.1 - 100} = 2.7$
N.B. The shadow price is really $\frac{8}{3}$, since the answer
253.33 is a rounded version of $253\frac{1}{3}$.

b) Type of constraint: ≥ 0, type of problem: max
Therefore the shadow price ≤ 0.

19.17 a) optimal solution: $x_1 = 6$, $x_2 = 8$
$z = 92 + 6(25 - 6) = 206$

b) optimal solution: $x_1 = 6$, $x_2 = 8$
$z = 92 + 8(1.75 - 7) = 50$

c) $100 > 96$, so the problem cannot be solved without further analysis.

d) optimal $z = 92 + 1(16 - 32) = 76$. The optimal
values of x_1 and x_2 cannot be found without further
analysis.

19.19 a) optimal solution: $x_1 = 0$, $x_2 = 100$
$z = 300 + 100(10 - 3) = 1,000$

b) optimal solution: $x_1 = 0$, $x_2 = 100$
$z = 300 + 0(45 - 40) = 300$

19.21 Let TV stand for the number of TV spots, and
M stand for the number of magazine ads.

a) Net increase per TV spot $= 30,000(.10) - 2,000 = 1,000$
Net increase per magazine ad $= 100,000(.10) - 5,000 = 5,000$

b) $\max Z = 1{,}000\text{TV} + 5{,}000\text{M}$

$$\text{s.t.}\quad 2{,}000\text{TV} + 5{,}000\text{M} \le 100{,}000$$

$$5{,}000\text{M} \le 70{,}000$$

$$2{,}000\text{TV} \le 50{,}000$$

$$\text{TV} \ge 0,\ \text{M} \ge 0.$$

c)

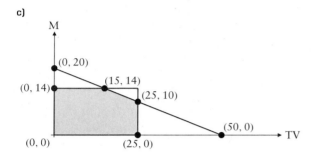

$$\text{at}\quad (0, 0),\ z = 0$$

$$(0, 14),\ z = 70{,}000$$

$$(15, 14),\ z = 85{,}000\quad\text{(optimal)}$$

$$(25, 10),\ z = 75{,}000$$

$$(25, 0),\ z = 25{,}000$$

The optimal advertising campaign comprises 15 TV spots and 14 magazine ads.

19.23 Let S stand for the number of standard widgets, and D stand for the number of deluxe widgets.

a) $\max Z = 10\text{S} + 5\text{D}$

$$\text{s.t.}\quad \text{S} + \text{D} \le 12$$

$$5\text{S} + 8\text{D} \le 80$$

$$5 \ge 0,\ \text{D} \ge 0.$$

b)

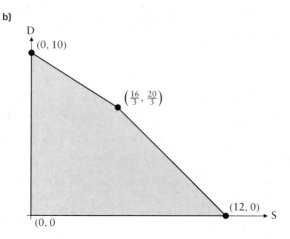

$$\text{at}\quad (0, 0),\ z = 0$$

$$(0, 10),\ z = 50$$

$$\left(\frac{16}{3}, \frac{20}{3}\right),\ z = \frac{260}{3}$$

$$(12, 0),\ z = 120\quad\text{(optimal)}$$

The optimal production plan is to produce 12 standard models, and no deluxe models.

19.25 a) optimal solution: $x_1 = 0$, $x_2 = 100$, $x_3 = 450$ $z = 2{,}450$

b) The coefficient of x_1 would have to be at least 29 in order to have x_1 enter the solution.
The coefficient of x_2 would have to drop to -10 before the optimal value of x_2 would be 0.

c) $c_2 = 5$ is within the allowable range.
Therefore: optimal solution: $x_1 = 0$, $x_2 = 100$, $x_3 = 450$
$z = 2{,}450 + 100(5 - 2) = 2{,}750$

d) $b_1 = 125$ is within the allowable range
Therefore: optimal z-value $= 2{,}450 + 12(125 - 100) = 2{,}750$

e) The printout does not provide enough information to answer the question.

f) $b_3 = 250$ is within the allowable range.
Therefore: optimal z-value $= 2{,}450 + 0(250 - 25) = 2{,}450$

g) $b_2 = 150$ is within the allowable range.
Therefore optimal z-value $= 2{,}450 + 5(150 - 250) = 1{,}950$

19.27 a) Produce 40 units of A, no units of B, and 20 units of C.

b) The resources from departments X and Y are fully utilized, and there is slack in department Z.

c) An additional person-hour in department X would increase the profit by $1.214, and an additional person-hour in department Y would increase the profit by $4.357. An additional person-hour in department Z has no value.

d) Since $22 > 21.071$, $c_2 = 22$ is outside the allowable range. The optimal solution therefore has a different product-mix. There is not, however, enough information in the printout to determine the new product-mix.

19.29 a)

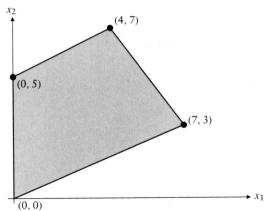

at $(0, 0)$, $z = 0$

  $(0, 5)$, $z = -10$

  $(4, 7)$, $z = -2$

  $(7, 3)$, $z = 15$ (optimal)

Solution: $x_1 = 7$, $x_2 = 3$, $z = 15$

b)

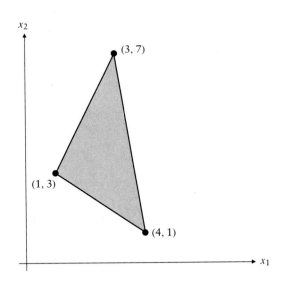

at $(1, 3)$, $z = 13$ (optimal)

  $(3, 7)$, $z = 33$

  $(4, 1)$, $z = 19$

Solution: $x_1 = 1$, $x_2 = 3$, $z = 13$

c)

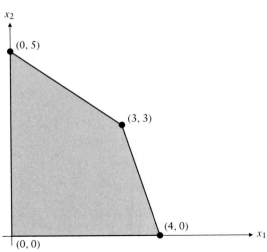

Let $z = x_1 - x_2$.

at $(0, 0)$, $z = 0$

  $(0, 5)$, $z = -5$ (minimum)

  $(3, 3)$, $z = 0$

  $(4, 0)$, $z = 4$ (maximum)

Since the minimum is -5 and the maximum is 4, therefore $-5 \le x_1 - x_2 \le 4$ on the feasible region.

19.31 Let COLT stand for the number of pairs of Colts manufactured, PUMA stand for the number of pairs of Pumas manufactured, and BULLET stand for the number of pairs of Bullets manufactured.
The profit on each pair of Colts is
$55 - 20 - (0.30 + 0.20 + 0.10)(25 + 10) = 14$
The profit on each pair of Pumas is
$75 - 25 - (0.35 + 0.30 + 0.15)(25 + 10) = 19$
The profit on each pair of Bullets is
$85 - 30 - (0.40 + 0.35 + 0.20)(25 + 10) = 21.75$
max $z = 14$ COLT $+ 19$ PUMA $+ 21.75$ BULLET

s.t. 0.30 COLT $+ 0.35$ PUMA $+ 0.40$ BULLET ≤ 100

  0.20 COLT $+ 0.30$ PUMA $+ 0.35$ BULLET ≤ 50

  0.10 COLT $+ 0.15$ PUMA $+ 0.20$ BULLET ≤ 30

  COLT ≥ 0, PUMA ≥ 0, BULLET ≥ 0

19.33 Let C1 stand for the number of grams of cereal products used to make Mix 1, C2 stand for the number of grams of cereal products used to make Mix 2, and C3 stand for the number of grams of cereal products used to make Mix 3. Define P1, P2, P3, A1, A2, A3, CN1, CN2, and CN3 in the obvious analogous way.

Let M1 be the number of 300 g containers of Mix 1, M2 be the number of 300 g containers of Mix 2, and M3 be the number of 300 g containers of Mix 3.

Note that $M1 = \dfrac{C1 + P1 + A1 + CN1}{300}$, and similar expressions hold for M2 and M3.

$\max z = 30\,M1 + 25\,M2 + 35\,M3$

$$-0.015\,C1 - 0.015\,C2$$
$$-0.015\,C3 - 0.020\,P1$$
$$-0.020\,P2 - 0.020\,P3$$
$$-0.025\,A1 - 0.025\,A2$$
$$-0.025\,A3 - 0.020\,CN1$$
$$-0.020\,CN2 - 0.020\,CN3$$

s.t.
$$C1 + C2 + C3 \leq 500{,}000$$
$$P1 + P2 + P3 \leq 110{,}000$$
$$A1 + A2 + A3 \leq 100{,}000$$
$$CN1 + CN2 + CN3 \leq 150{,}000$$

$$C1 \leq 150\,M1$$
$$C2 \leq 200\,M2$$
$$C3 \leq 200\,M3$$

$$P2 \leq 25\,M2$$
$$P3 \leq 50\,M3$$

$$A3 \leq 25\,M3$$

$$C1 + P1 + A1 + CN1 = 300\,M1$$
$$C2 + P2 + A2 + CN2 = 300\,M2$$
$$C3 + P3 + A3 + CN3 = 300\,M3$$

$$P1 \geq 50\,M1$$

$$A1 \geq 50\,M1$$
$$A2 \geq 75\,M2$$

$$CN1 \geq 25\,M1$$
$$CN2 \geq 50\,M2$$

ALL VARIABLES ≥ 0

The constraints have been written in an order appropriate for the LINP option of CMMS.

In order to run this on LINP, the constraints must be rewritten so that all the variables are on the left. This means that the right-hand sides of all but the first 4 constraints will be 0.

For LINP, the variable names must be abbreviated to 3 characters. The following abbreviations have been made:

> MIX becomes M
> CEREAL becomes C
> PEANUT becomes P
> ALMOND becomes A
> COCONUT becomes CN

LINP does not allow four decimal places in the objective-function coefficients, so the objective function was multiplied by 10. This has no effect on the optimal solution, but care must be taken in the sensitivity analysis of the objective function coefficients.

Relevant portions of the printout appear below.

a) $M1 = 141.667$, $M2 = 0$, and $M3 = 2{,}725$. Therefore, 2,725 containers of Mix 3 should be produced, no Mix 2 should be produced, and the rest should all be Mix 1. The optimal profit is $84{,}424.992 \div 10 = \$8{,}442.50$.

b) A 300 g container of Mix 1 contains

0 g of cereal products

$\dfrac{7{,}083.335}{42{,}500}(300) = 50$ g of whole peanuts

$\dfrac{31{,}875.002}{42{,}500}(300) = 225$ g of flaked almonds

$\dfrac{3{,}541.667}{42{,}500}(300) = 25$ g of shredded coconut.

A 300 g container of Mix 3 contains

$\dfrac{500{,}000}{817{,}500}(300) = 183.5$ g of cereal products

$\dfrac{102{,}916.664}{817{,}500}(300) = 37.8$ g of whole peanuts

$\dfrac{68{,}125}{817{,}500}(300) = 25$ g of flaked almonds

$\dfrac{146{,}458.328}{817{,}500}(300) = 53.7$ g of shredded coconut

c) Remember: The coefficients in the objective function have been multiplied by 10. The question is the analysis of what happens if the objective-function coefficient of M1 is changed from 30 to 32.

Since $32 < 35$, the current values of the decision variables prevail, and the new optimal profit is

$$8{,}442.50 + \frac{(141.667)(32-30)}{10} = \$8{,}470.83$$

d) The upper limit for the coefficient of M2 is 29.375.
This translates ($\div 10$) to a price of $2.94 before it would be reasonable to produce any Mix 2.

e) The shadow price of cereal products is 0.104, higher than any of the other ingredients. Montreal Cereal Products would be most interested in getting more cereal products.

f) $200{,}000 < 490{,}000$, so $b_4 = 200{,}000$ is within the allowable range.
Therefore: new optimal profit =
$$8{,}442.50 + \frac{(.099)(200{,}000 - 150{,}000)}{10} = \$8{,}937.50$$

RESULTS

VARIABLE	VARIABLE VALUE	ORIGINAL COEFFICIENT	COEFFICIENT SENSITIVITY
M1	141.667	30	0
M2	0	25	0
M3	2725	35	0
C1	0	.015	.025
C2	0	.015	.05
C3	500000	.015	0
P1	7083.335	.02	0
P2	0	.02	.05
P3	102916.664	.02	0
A1	31875.002	.025	0
A2	0	.025	0
A3	68125	.025	0
CN1	3541.667	.02	0
CN2	0	.02	0
CN3	146458.328	.02	0

CONSTRAINT NUMBER	ORIGINAL RIGHT-HAND VALUE	SLACK OR SURPLUS	SHADOW PRICE
1	500000	0	.104
2	110000	0	.099
3	100000	0	.069
4	150000	0	.099

SENSITIVITY ANALYSIS
OBJECTIVE FUNCTION COEFFICIENTS

VARIABLE	LOWER LIMIT	ORIGINAL COEFFICIENT	UPPER LIMIT
M1	26.111	30	35
M2	NO LIMIT	25	29.375
M3	30	35	70

RIGHT-HAND-SIDE VALUES

CONSTRAINT NUMBER	LOWER LIMIT	ORIGINAL VALUE	UPPER LIMIT
1	300000	500000	680000
2	50000	110000	150000
3	69090.906	100000	279999.937
4	90000	150000	490000

Appendix B

[All graphs in these solutions can be drawn using Lotus 123]

B.1 17, 23, and 29 are prime numbers, and are all odd.
20 is even and $(2)(2)(5) = 20$
24 is even and $(2)(2)(2)(3) = 24$
30 is even and $(2)(3)(5) = 30$

B.3 a) i) $|-2| = 2$

ii) $|5| = 5$, $|-3-5| = |-8| = 8$

iii) $|-9| = 9$, $|9| = 9$

b) i) $(1/3)(1/3)(1/3) = 1/27 = 0.037037\ldots$

ii) $5^{-2} = (1/5)^2 = (1/5)(1/5) = 1/25 = 0.04$

iii) $16^{1/2} = \sqrt{16} = 4$

iv) $125^{(1/3)} = \sqrt[3]{125} = 5$

v) $(1/4)^{-0.5} = (4)^{0.5} = \sqrt{4} = 2$

B.5 a) 2.1761   **b)** 3.1761   **c)** 4.1761

Each one is 1.0000 larger than the previous one.

B.7 a) 5.0106   **b)** 7.3132   **c)** 9.6158

Each one is 2.3026 [$= \ln(10)$] larger than the previous one.

B.9 The logarithms differ by a constant in each case. In B.5 the constant is $\log_{10}(10) = 1$. In B.7 the constant is $\ln(1) = 2.3026$.

B.11 a) $\ln[(e^2)(e^{-1/2})(e^{1.5})] = 3$
Antilog of 3 is $e^3 = 30.085$ (using a calculator)

b) $\ln[(700)(e^{4.6})(e^{-1})] = 10.15108$

Antilog of 10.15108 is $e^{10.15108} = 25618.764$

B.13 a) $\displaystyle\sum_{j=2}^{4} x_{1j}$ **b)** $\displaystyle\sum_{i=1}^{4}\sum_{j=1}^{3} y_{ij}$

B.15 a) $a_0 + a_1 x + a_2 x^2 + a_3 x^3 + a_4 x^4$

b) $3 - 2x + (1/3)x^2 + 0.01x^3 + (1/2)x^4$

B.17 a) Graph of $y = \frac{1}{2}x - 100$ for $0 \le x \le 500$

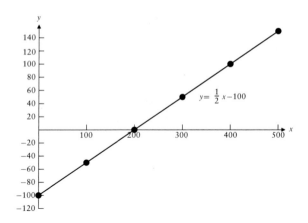

b) Graph of $y = -5x$ for $-5 \le x \le 5$

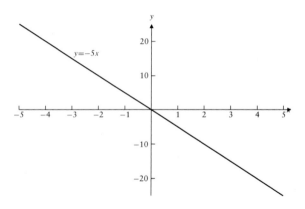

c) Graph of $y \le \frac{1}{2}x - 100$ for $0 \le x \le 500$

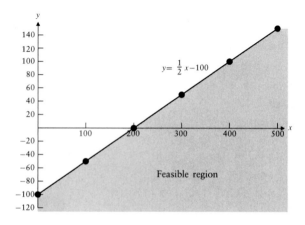

Graph of $y \le -5x$ for $0 \le x \le 5$

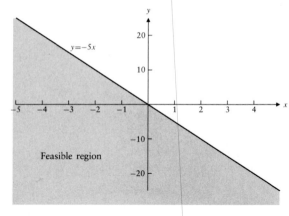

B.19 a) Function is: $y = 0.06x + 0.07(12{,}000 - x)$
Graph of this equation for $0 \le x \le 12{,}000$ is:

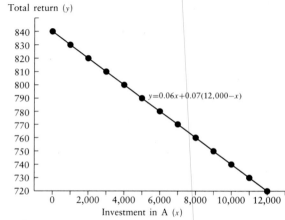

b) Let $x = A$:

$$800 = 0.06A + 0.07(12{,}000 - A)$$

$$A = \$4{,}000 \text{ and thus } B = \$8{,}000$$

B.21 The feasible region is shown on the graph below.

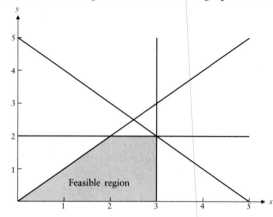

B.23 $f(0) = 0^2 - 12(0) + 40 = \quad 40$
$f(3) = 3^2 - 12(3) + 40 = \quad 13$
$f(5) = 5^2 - 12(5) + 40 = \quad 5$
$f(7) = 7^2 - 12(7) + 40 = \quad 5$
$f(10) = 10^2 - 12(10) + 40 = 20$
$f(15) = 15^2 - 12(15) + 40 = 85$

Graph of $y = x^2 - 12x + 40$ is given below.

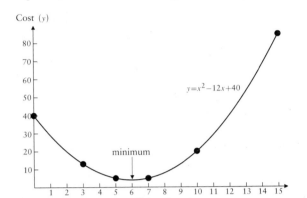

B.25 Graph of TR and TC functions for $0 < Q < 140$ is given below. There are two breakeven points: $Q = 40$ and $Q = 200$, but $Q = 200$ is not in the range between $0 < Q < 140$. Solving mathematically:

$$50,000 + 200Q - Q^2 = 4Q^2 - 1,000Q + 90,000$$

$$5Q^2 - 1,200Q + 40,000 = 0$$

$$(5Q - 1,000)(Q - 40) = 0$$

$$Q = 40$$

Solving for TC or TR yields $56,400 as the breakeven point. [These two functions also show that $Q = 133.3$ is the optimal Q---the maximum profit is the largest

difference between TR and TC]. A graph of TR and TC is given below.

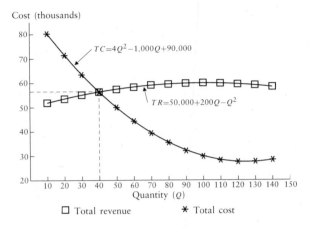

B.27 Graph below is for $AC = 432/Q + 3Q + 10$ for $0 \leq Q \leq 20$. From the graph, $Q = 12$ is seen to minimize average cost. This value can be solved for using calculus.

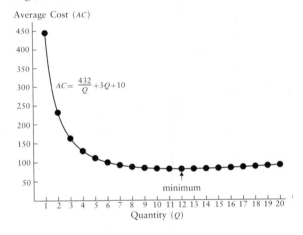

Selected References

Extensive tables of the normal, t, chi-square and F-distributions are found in

Pearson, E.S. and H.O. Hartley. *Biometric Tables for Statisticians*. New York: John Wiley and Sons, 1968.

Binomial probabilities for n = 50 to n = 100 are found in

Romig, H.G. 50--100 *Binomial Tables*. New York: John Wiley and Sons, 1953.

Poisson probability tables are found in

Molina, E. G. *Poisson's Exponential Binomial Limit*. New York: D. Van Nostrand, 1943.

A more detailed treatment of mathematical probability distributions is found in

Hogg, R.V. and A.T. Craig. *Introduction to Mathematical Statistics*. New York: Macmillan, 4th ed., 1978.

Classic texts on analysis of variance and experimental design are

Cochran, W.G. and G.M. Cox. *Experimental Designs*. 2nd ed. New York: Wiley, 1957.

Snedecor, G.W. and W.G. Cochran. *Statistical Methods*. 7th ed. Ames, IA: Iowa University Press, 1980.

Several noteworthy quality control texts are

Deming, W. Edwards. *Out of the Crisis*. New York: John Wiley and Sons, 1986.

Ford Motor Company. *Continuing Process Control and Process Capability*. Internal Training Manual. Ford Motor Company: Dearborn, 1987.

Shewhart, Walter A. *Economic Control of Quality of Manufactured Product*. New York: Van Nostrand, 1931.

Texts on uses or misuses of statistical analysis are

Huff, D. *How to Lie with Statistics*. New York: Norton, 1954.

Jaffe, A.J. and H. F. Spirer. *Misused Statistics: Straight Talk for Twisted Numbers*. New York: Marcel Decker, 1987.

Several textbooks on econometrics and forecasting methods are

Bowerman, B. L. and R. T. O'Connell. *Time Series Forecasting*. 2nd ed. Boston: Druxbury Press, 1987.

Kmenta, J. *Elements of Econometrics*. 2nd ed. New York: Macmillan, 1986.

Murphy, James L. *Introductory Econometrics*. Homewood, IL: Richard D. Irwin, 1973.

A readable text on nonparametric statistics is

Siegel, S. and N.J. Castellan. *Nonparametric Statistics for the Behavioral Sciences.* 2nd ed. New York: McGraw-Hill, 1988.

Other textbooks that give complementary treatment of many of the topics in this book are

Brightman, Harvey and H. Schneider. *Statistics for Business Problem Solving.* Cincinnati: South-Western Publishing Co., 1992.

Cryer, Jonathan D. and R.B. Miller. *Statistics for Business: Data Analysis for Modelling.* Boston: PWS--KENT Publishing, 1991.

Griffiths, William E., C. R. Hill and G.G. Judge. *Learning and Practicing Econometrics.* New York: John Wiley and Sons, 1993.

Harnett, Donald L. and A.K. Soni. *Statistical Methods.* 4th ed. Reading, MA: Addison-Wesley Publishing, 1991.

Roberts, Harry V. *Data Analysis for Managers: with MINITAB.* Redwood City, Calif: The Scientific Press, 1991.

INDEX